OFFICIAL
RUGBY UNION
CLUB DIRECTORY
1995-96

COURAGE

CLUBS CHAMPIONSHIP

OFFICIAL

RUGBY UNION
CLUB DIRECTORY
1995-96

Edited by Tony Williams

Tony Williams Publications

Copyright: Tony Williams Publications

Published in Great Britain by Tony Williams
Publications, 24a Queen Square, North Curry,
Taunton, Somerset TA3 6LE

The publishers wish to confirm that the views
expressed in articles and reviews in this directory
are not necessarily those of the R.F.U., Courage
Ltd or Michael Humphreys & Partners Ltd.

Typeset by Interface (South West) Ltd 01392 444045

Printed in Great Britain by
Hillman Printers (Frome) Ltd.,
Handlemaker Road, Marston Trading Estate,
Frome, Somerset BA11 4RW
Telephone 01373 473526

Trade Sales & Distribution: Little Red Witch
Books 01823 490080

ISBN 1-869833-37-6

Cover Photograph supplied by Colorsport.
*Leicester are understandably thrilled about
winning the Courage Championship.*

Editorial

by Tony Williams

What a year it has been for Rugby Union!

We have enjoyed a spectacular World Cup Competition which underlined the gap between the Europeans and the giant's of the Southern hemisphere.

At last Bath have been relieved of the Courage Championship by their most consistent rivals Leicester and of course we read daily of how Rugby Union will be changed out of all recognition by the introduction of massive payments either from Australian TV corporations or even the individual national unions.

Hopefully our own Rugby Union administrators will rise to the occasion and offer our leading players worthwhile rewards without breaking up the structure of the English game.

It is imperative that players and supporters retain their club and national spirit. A collection of world wide stars playing in the same way as the Old Kerry Packer cricket circus, would attract very little support however technically skilled the players became.

There is nothing to fear in professionalism if all Rugby Union footballers become 'players' who are allowed to receive payment if their clubs wish to reward them. All clubs will set out their own 'house rules' according to their financial status and players will find their level of club depending on their ambition, their ability, their availability to train, and their desire for extra financial rewards.

The massive, highly successful Courage Championship will remain the base from which all ambitious young players will develop. Practically every town in England proudly boasts a Rugby Union Club and the vast majority are taking steps to improve standards of play, of financial strength and of social and playing facilities.

We hope this Directory again supported by magnificent statistics from Steve McCormack and Unisys, research from Bill Mitchell and lovely photos from Joe McCabe and this year Gordon Burney, will mirror the magnificent development of English Club Rugby.

Yes, Rugby Union is changing but we can learn from the experiences of other sports.

So let's make an effort to help it change for the best.

A WELCOME FROM THE RFU

by W J Bishop OBE

President
The Rugby Football Union

I am particularly pleased to write a forward for the Courage Clubs Directory as I was involved in the formation of the Leagues whilst serving as Chairman of the RFU Competition Sub-Committee during the period which led up to the first matches in 1987.

That also led to a long and valued association with Courage and the appointment of Michael Humphreys and Partners Ltd as National Administrators. A lot of people were involved but I would like to record how much I enjoyed working with Mike Reynolds of Courage and Mike Humphreys and Teresa Cash of MH&P during my spell as Chairman.

The Courage Leagues have been a huge success and have played a major part in providing a competitive structure for English rugby – a structure which has been a major factor in the success of the National Team.

I would like to thank all those people throughout the country whose dedicated work has made the worlds largest league structure function so efficiently – without you all it would not be possible.

On behalf of the RFU I would like to thank Courage for their continued support, and wish everyone involved at all levels enjoyment in their tasks and best wishes for Season 1995/96.

W J Bishop

A WELCOME FROM COURAGE

by John Nicolson

**Marketing Director,
Courage Ltd**

Courage is justifiably proud of its record as one of the UK's premier sports sponsors, with a long tradition of supporting sport at every level.

The Courage Clubs Championship is very definitely one of the jewels in the Courage sports sponsorship crown, involving as it does over 90,000 players and 1,190 clubs.

Courage has sponsored England's club league competition since its inception in 1987, and it constitutes the largest sponsorship deal in the sport's history spanning ten years and a financial investment of £11 million.

It is widely recognised that the Courage Clubs Championship has added purpose and competitive edge to club rugby at every level. Few could question the benefits the National team have reaped with three Grand Slam victories in five years and a place in the final and semi final of successive World Cups.

While the Leagues continue to gain momentum and strength this Directory keeps pace by increasing in size and content. Over the years this publication continues to be the prime source of information and method of communication amongst the clubs and administrators of the game. Please pass the Directory around your club so that as many of your members as possible can benefit from the information – or, even better, encourage them to buy their own copy.

Best wishes for the 1995/96 season.

John R. Nicolson.

Courage Ltd Business Unit Addresses

BROOKLANDS
Brooklands Business Park, Vickers Drive South, Weybridge, Surrey. KT13 0YU
Tel: 0193 235 0088
Fax: 0193 233 6268
Business Unit Director John McAlister
General Sales Manager Steve Cannan

CHELMSFORD
Montrose Road, Dukes Park Estate, Springfield, Chlemsford. CM2 6TE
Tel: 0124 546 0888
Fax: 0124 5462558
Business Unit Director Les Bailey
General Sales Manager Mike Crawshaw

EAST ANGLIA
Unit C & D, Frenbury Estate, Hellesdon Park Road, Norwich. NR6 5DP
Tel: 0160 348 2328
Fax: 0160 348 2329
Business Unit Director John Drake
General Sales Manager Steve Parker

EAST MIDLANDS
Lodge Way, Harlestone Road, Northampton. NN5 7UU
Tel: 0160 475 2452
Fax: 0160 458 0411
Business Unit Director Patrick Ryan
General Sales Manager Ian Webb

ELLAND
Huddersfield Road, Elland, Nr. Halifax. HX5 9JP
Tel: 0142 237 5555
Fax: 0142 237 3347
Business Unit Director Colin Lund
General Sales Manager David Marchbank-Smith

LEWES
Daveys Lane, Brook Road, Lewes, E. Sussex. BN7 2BQ
Tel: 0127 347 3116
Fax: 0127 347 3353
Business Unit Director Steve Goodyear
General Sales Manager Dave Brown

LONDON CENTRAL
Wyke Road, Bow Lane, London. E3 2PC
Tel: 0181 986 9833
Fax: 0181 986 0702
Business Unit Director Keith Hogg
General Sales Manager Dan Townsend

LONDON NORTH
Brantwood Road, Tottenham, London. N17 0EE
Tel: 0181 808 1106
Fax: 0181 808 4938
Business Unit Director Don Steen
General Sales Manager Ken Nicol

LONDON SOUTH
Unit 19, Merton Industrial Park, Jubilee Way, Merton, London. SW19 3XZ
Tel: 0181 540 8282
Fax: 0181 542 0047
Business Unit Director John Randle
General Sales Manager Murray Roberts

MAIDSTONE
Medway House, Bircholt Road, Parkwood, Maidstone, Kent. ME15 9XJ
Tel: 0162 267 1311
Fax: 0162 267 7494
Business Unit Director Mark Gerken
General Sales Manager Matt Scott

MANCHESTER
Monsall Road, Newton Heath, Manchester. M10 8PA
Tel: 0161 205 2345
Fax: 0161 205 8634
Business Unit Director Nick Cullen
General Sales Manager Steve Turner

NEWARK
The Brewery, Northgate, Newark-on-Trent, Notts. NG24 1HD
Tel: 0163 661 2688
Fax: 0163 661 2802
Business Unit Director Mike Langford
General Sales Manager Nick Rust

NORTH EAST
Eastern Avenue, Team Valley Trading Estate, Gateshead, Tyne & Wear. NE11 0UU
Tel: 0191 487 8897
Fax: 0191 482 5037
Business Unit Director Neil Fraser
General Sales Manager Trevor North

PRESTON
Unit 147, Brierley Road, Walton Summit, Bamber Bridge, Preston. PR5 8AH
Tel: 0177 269 7755
Fax: 0177 2697797
Business Unit Director Stephen Paul
General Sales Manager Mike Thomas

SOLENT
Reliant Close, Chandlers Ford Ind. Estate, Chandlers Ford, Hants. SO53 4ND
Tel: 0170 326 0144
Fax: 0170 326 0766
Business Unit Director Simon Jackson
General Sales Manager Max Bracher

SOUTH WEST
North Road, Lee Mill Industrial Estate, Ivybridge, Devon. PC21 9PB
Tel: 0175 269 0680
Fax: 0175 289 4725
Business Unit Director Paul Hoffman
General Sales Manager Roger Fergus

TADCASTER
The Brewery, Tadcaster, North Yorks. LS24 9SA
Tel: 0193 783 2091
Fax: 0193 753 0362
Business Unit Director John O'Brien
General Sales Manager John Thorn

THAMES VALLEY
Imperial Way, Basingstoke Road, Reading, Berks. RG2 0RS
Tel: 0173 486 9696
Fax: 0173 487 6202
Business Unit Director Keith Quinn
General Sales Manager Ian Squires

WEST
St. Brendan's Way, Bristol. BS11 9EZ
Tel: 0117 982 5321
Fax: 0117 982 6539
Business Unit Director Mark Todd
General Sales Manager Tony Bird

WEST MIDLANDS
30, First Avenue, Pensnett Trading Estate, Kingswinford, Brierley Hill, West Mids. GY6 7NA
Tel: 0138 440 0001
Fax: 0138 429 1061
Business Unit Director Steve Hollender
General Sales Manager John Barclay

WINSFORD
Road 1, Winsford Industrial Estate, Winsford, Cheshire. CW7 3PQ
Tel: 0160 686 3366
Fax: 0160 655 7634
Business Unit Director Stephen Paul
General Sales Manager Mike Charlton

PRINCIPAL FIXTURES 1995-96

AUGUST 1995
Sat 19th   Kelso Sevens
Sat 26th   Selkirk Sevens
Sun 27th   South East Transvaal v Wales (Witbank)
SEPTEMBER 1995
Sat 2nd   SOUTH AFRICA v WALES (Johannesburg)
            Scottish Premier League 1 to 4 (1)(Sco)
            Scottish Tennents 1556 Cup (1)(Sco)
            Heineken Leagues Divs 1 to 5 (1)(Wal)
Sat 9th   Courage Leagues 1 to 4 (1)(Eng)
            Pilkington Cup 1st Round (Eng)
            Pilkington Shield 1st Round (Eng)
            Scottish Premier League 1 to 4 (2)(Sco)
            Scottish Tennents 1556 Cup (2)(Sco)
            Heineken Leagues Divs 1 to 5 (2)(Wal)
Wed 13th   Scottish Premier League 1 to 4 (3)(Sco)
Sat 16th   Courage Leagues 1 to 4 (2)(Eng)
            Courage Leagues Other Divs (1)(Eng)
            Scottish Premier League 1 to 4 (4)(Sco)
            Scottish National Leagues 1 to 7 (1)(Sco)
            Heineken Leagues Divs 1 to 5 (3)(Wal)
            Insurance Corporation League 1 to 4 (1)(Ire)
Sat 23rd   Courage Leagues 1 to 4 (3)(Eng)
            Courage Leagues Other Divs (2)(Eng)
            Scottish Premier League 1 to 4 (5)(Sco)
            Scottish National Leagues 1 to 7 (2)(Sco)
            Heineken Leagues Divs 1 to 5 (4)(Wal)
            Swalec Cup 1st Round (Wal)
            Insurance Corporation League 1 to 4 (2)(Ire)
Sat 30th   Courage Leagues 1 to 4 (4)(Eng)
            Courage Leagues Other Divs (3)(Eng)
            Scottish Premier League 1 to 4 (6)(Sco)
            Scottish National Leagues 1 to 7 (3)(Sco)
            Heineken Leagues Divs 1 to 5 (5)(Wal)
            Insurance Corporation League 1 to 4 (3)(Ire)
OCTOBER 1995
Tue 3rd   Newport v Barbarians (Newport)
Sat 7th   Courage Leagues 1 & 2 (5)(Eng)
            Pilkington Cup 2nd Round (Eng)
            Pilkington Shield 2nd Round (Eng)
            Scottish Premier League 1 to 4 (7)(Sco)
            Scottish National Leagues 1 to 7 (8)(Sco)
            Heineken Leagues Divs 1 to 5 (6)(Wal)
            Insurance Corporation League 1 to 4 (4)(Ire)
Sat 14th   Courage Leagues 1 & 2 (6)(Eng)
            Courage Leagues 3 & 4 (5)(Eng)
            Courage Leagues Other Divs (4)(Eng)
            Scottish Premier League 1 to 4 (8)(Sco)
            Scottish National Leagues 1 to 7 (4)(Sco)
            Scottish National Leagues 1 to 7 (5)(Sco)
            Heineken Leagues Divs 2 to 5 (7)(Wal)
            Insurance Corporation League 1 to 4 (5)(Ire)
Sun 15th   Insurance Corporation League Div 1 (5)(Ire)
            Old Wesley v Lansdowne
Sat 21st   Wales 'A' v Fiji (Bridgend)
            Courage Leagues 1 & 2 (7)(Eng)
            Courage Leagues 3 & 4 (6)(Eng)
            Courage Leagues Other Divs (5)(Eng)
            Scottish Premier League 1 to 4 (9)(Sco)
            Scottish National Leagues 1 to 7 (6)(Sco)
            Heineken Leagues Div 1 (7)(Wal)
            Heineken Leagues Divs 3 & 4 (8)(Wal)
            Swalec Cup 2nd Round (Wal)
            Insurance Corporation League 1 to 4 (6)(Ire)
Wed 25th   Neath v Fiji (Neath)
Sat 28th   Cardiff v Fiji (Cardiff)
            Courage Leagues 1 & 2 (8)(Eng)
            Courage Leagues 3 & 4 (7)(Eng)
            Courage Leagues Other Divs (6)(Eng)
            Scottish Premier League 1 to 4 (10)(Eng)
            Scottish National Leagues 1 to 7 (7)(Sco)
            Heineken Leagues Divs 1, 2 & 5 (8)(Wal)
            Heineken League Divs 3 & 4 (9)(Wal)
Mon 30th   Combined Scottish Districts Under 21 v
            New Zealand Rugby News Under 21 (TBA)
NOVEMBER 1995
Wed 1st   Treorchy v Fiji (Treorchy)
            Scotland Under 21 v Rugby News New Zealand Under
            21 (TBA)
Sat 4th   Pontypridd v Fiji (Pontypridd)
            Courage Leagues 1 & 2 (9)(Eng)

Pilkington Cup 3rd Round (Eng)
Pilkington Shield 3rd Round (Eng)
Scottish Premier League 1 to 4 (11)(Sco)
Scottish National Leagues 1 to 7 (8)(Sco)
Heineken Leagues Divs 1, 2 & 5 (9)(Wal)
Heineken Leagues Divs 3 & 4 (10)(Wal)
Tue 7th   Llanelli v Fiji (Llanelli)
Wed 8th   Edinburgh v Western Samoa (Inverleith)
Sat 11th   WALES v FIJI (Cardiff Arms Park)
            Courage Leagues 1 & 2 (10)(Eng)
            Courage Leagues 3 & 4 (8)(Eng)
            Courage Leagues Other Divs (7)(Eng)
            Scottish Premier League 1 to 4 (12)(Sco)
            Scottish National Leagues 1 to 7 (9)(Sco)
Sun 12th   Scotland 'A' v Western Samoa (Hawick)
Mon 13th   Glasgow v Western Province (Scotstoun, Glasgow)
Tue 14th   North & Midlands v Western Samoa (McDiarmid Park,
            Perth)
            Connacht v Fiji (Galway)
Fri 17th   South of Scotland v Western Province (Gala)
Sat 18th   ENGLAND v SOUTH AFRICA (Twickenham)
            (sponsored by Save & Prosper)
            SCOTLAND v WESTERN SAMOA (Murrayfield)
            IRELAND v FIJI (Dublin)
            CIS Divisional match (Eng):
            Midland v London (Northampton)
            CIS County Championship matches (Eng)
            Heineken Leagues Divs 1 & 2 (10)(Wal)
            Swalec Cup 3rd Round (Wal)
Sun 19th   CIS Divisional match (Eng):
            South West v North (Bridgwater)
            Scottish Premier League 1 to 4 (13)(Sco)
            Scottish Tennents 1556 Cup (3)(Sco)
Tue 21st   Oxford University v Western Samoa (Oxford)
Sat 25th   CIS Divisional matches (Eng):
            North v London (Wakefield – TBC)
            South West v Midland (Gloucester)
            CIS County Championship matches (Eng)
            Cambridge University v Western Samoa (Cambr'ge)
            Scottish Premier League 1 to 4 (14)(Sco)
            Scottish National Leagues 1 to 7 (10)(Sco)
            Heineken Leagues Divs 1 to 4 (11)(Wal)
            Heineken League Div 5 (10)(Wal)
            Irish Interprovincial matches:
            Exiles v Connacht (TBA)
            Ulster v Munster (Belfast)
Wed 29th   London Division v Western Samoa (Twickenham)
DECEMBER 1995
Sat 2nd   Midland Division v Western Samoa (Leicester)
            CIS Divisional match (Eng):
            London v South West (Wasps, Sudbury – TBC)
            CIS County Championship matches (Eng)
            Pilkington Shield 4th Round (Eng)
            Scottish National Leagues 1 to 7 (11)(Sco)
            Heineken Leagues Divs 1 to 4 (12)(Wal)
            Heineken League Div 5 (11)(Wal)
            Irish Interprovincial matches:
            Connacht v Ulster (Galway)
            Exiles v Leinster (TBA)
Sun 3rd   Scottish Exiles v South of Scotland (London)
Tue 5th   Northern Division v Western Samoa (Hudd'sfield)
Wed 6th   Scottish Exiles v Edinburgh (London)
            North & Midlands v Glasgow (Kirkcaldy)
Sat 9th   South West Division v Western Samoa (Glou'ster)
            CIS Divisional match (Eng):
            Midland v North (TBA)
            CIS County Championship matches (Eng)
            Scottish Regional Leagues (1)(Sco)
            Scottish National Leagues 1 to 7 (12)(Sco)
            Heineken Leagues Divs 1 to 4 (13)(Wal)
            Heineken League Div 5 (12)(Wal)
            Irish Interprovincial matches:
            Leinster v Connacht (Dublin)
            Munster v Exiles (TBA)
Sun 10th   Glasgow v Scottish Exiles (Burnbrea, Glasgow)
            South of Scotland v North & Midlands (Kelso)
Tue 12th   Oxford v Cambridge (Twickenham)
            (for The Bowring Bowl)
            Oxford v Cambridge Under 21s (Stoop Memorial
            Ground, Twickenham, for The Bowring Plate)
            England 'A' v Western Samoa (TBA)

PRINCIPAL FIXTURES 1995-96

Sat 16th	ENGLAND v WESTERN SAMOA (Twicklenham)
	(sponsored by Save & Prosper)
	Sun Alliance Colts County Championship
	(Final at Twickenham – 12.15)
	CIS Divisional Championship matches
	CIS County Championship matches
	Scottish Regional Leagues (2)(Sco)
	Scottish National Leagues 1 to 7 (13)(Sco)
	Swalec Cup 4th Round (Wal)
	Irish Interprovincial matches:
	Munster v Leinster (TBA)
	Ulster v Exiles (Belfast)
Sun 17th	North & Midlands v Scottish Exiles (Rubilaw, Aberdeen)
	Edinburgh v South of Scotland (in Edinburgh)
Fri 22nd	Scotland Schools v France Schools (Goldenacre)
Sat 23rd	Pilkington Cup 4th Round (Eng)
	Pilkington Shield 5th Round (Eng)
	Scottish Regional Leagues (3)(Sco)
	Heineken Leagues Divs 1 & 2 (14)(Wal)
	Irish Interprovincial matches:
	Connacht v Munster
	Leinster v Ulster (Dublin)
Sun 24th	South of Scotland v Glasgow (Selkirk)
	Edinburgh v North & Midlands (in Edinburgh)
Wed 27th	Leicester v Barbarians (Leicester)
Sat 30th	Courage Leagues 1 & 2 (11)(Eng)
	Scottish Regional Leagues (4)(Sco)
	Heineken Leagues Divs 1 & 2 (15)(Wal)
Sun 31st	Glasgow v Edinburgh (Old Anniesland, Glasgow)

JANUARY 1996

Sat 6th	Italy v Scotland 'A' (Italy)
	Italy Under 21 v Scotland Under 21 (Italy)
	Courage Leagues 1 & 2 (12)(Eng)
	Courage Leagues 3 & 4 (9)(Eng)
	Courage Leagues Other Divs (8)(Eng)
	Scottish Regional Leagues (5)(Sco)
	Scottish National Leagues 1 to 7 (14)(Sco)
	Heineken Leagues Divs 1 & 2 (16)(Wal)
	Heineken Leagues Divs 3 & 4 (14)(Wal)
	Heineken League Div 5 (13)(Wal)
	Wales Schools v Scotland Schools (Wales)
Sat 13th	Courage Leagues 3 & 4 (10)(Eng)
	Courage Leagues Other Divs (9)(Eng)
	Scottish Regional Leagues (6)(Sco)
	Scottish National Leagues 1 to 7 (15)(Sco)
	Heineken Leagues Divs 1 & 2 (17)(Wal)
	Heineken Leagues Divs 3 & 4 (15)(Wal)
	Heineken League Div 5 (14)(Wal)
Fri 19th	France 'A' v England 'A' (Paris)
	France Students v England Students (Paris)
	Ireland 'A' v Scotland 'A' (Dublin)
	Ireland Under 21 v Scotland Under 21 (Dublin)
Sat 20th	FRANCE v ENGLAND (Paris)
	IRELAND v SCOTLAND (Dublin)
	Swalec Cup 5th Round (Wal)
	Heineken League Div 5 (15)(Wal)
Sat 27th	Pilkington Cup 5th Round (Eng)
	Pilkington Shield 6th Round (Eng)
	Scottish Regional Leagues (7)(Sco)
	Scottish National Leagues 1 to 7 (16)(Sco)
	Heineken Leagues 3 to 5 (16)(Wal)
	Heineken League Div
	Provincial Cups Round 1 (Ire)

FEBRUARY 1996

Fri 2nd	England Students v Wales Students (TBA)
	Scotland 'A' v France 'A' (Myreside, Edinburgh)
	Scotland Under 21 v France Under 21 (Myreside)
	Wales 'A' v France 'A' (Cardiff)
Sat 3rd	ENGLAND v WALES (Twickenham)
	(sponsored by Save & Prosper)
	SCOTLAND v FRANCE (Murrayfield)
	Provincial Cups Round 2 (Ire)
Sat 10th	Courage Leagues 1 & 2 (13)(Eng)
	Courage Leagues 3 & 4 (11)(Eng)
	Courage Leagues Other Divs (10)(Eng)
	Scottish National Leagues 1 to 7 (17)(Sco)
	Heineken Leagues 3 to 5 (17)(Wal)
Sun 11th	Scotland Students v New South Wales Students (in Scotland)
Fri 16th	Wales 'A' v Scotland 'A' (Cardiff)
	Wales Under 21 v Scotland Under 21 (Cardiff)
	Wales Students v Scotland Students (Glamorgan

	Wanderers)
Sat 17th	FRANCE v IRELAND (Paris)
	WALES v SCOTLAND (Cardiff)
	Courage Leagues 1 & 2 (14)(Eng)
	Courage Leagues 3 & 4 (12)(Eng)
	Courage Leagues Other Divs (11)(Eng)
	Wales Youth v Italian Youth (Aberavon)
Sat 24th	Pilkington Cup Quarter-finals (Eng)
	Pilkington Shield Quarter-finals (Eng)
	Courage Leagues 3 & 4 (13)(Eng)
	Courage Leagues Other Divs (12)(Eng)
	Scottish Tennents 1556 Cup (4)
	Swalec Cup 6th Round (Wal)
	Wales Youth v Ireland Youth (TBA)(or 2nd March)

MARCH 1996

Fri 1st	Scotland Students v England Students (Ed'burgh)
	Ireland 'A' v Wales 'A' (Dublin)
	Ireland Under 21 v Wales Under 21 (Dublin)
	Ireland Students v Wales Students (Dublin)
Sat 2nd	IRELAND v WALES (Dublin)
	SCOTLAND v ENGLAND (Calcutta Cup, Murrayfield)
Wed 6th	East Midlands v Barbarians (Northampton)
Sat 9th	Italy Colts v England Colts (Italy)
	CIS County Championship Semi-finals (Eng)
	Scottish National Leagues 1 to 7 (18)(Sco)
	Heineken Leagues Divs 1 to 5 (18)(Wal)
	French Juniors v Welsh Youth (Fra)
Fri 15th	England 'A' v Ireland 'A' (TBA)
	England Students v Ireland Students (TBA)
	Wales Under 21 v France Under 21 (Cardiff)
	Wales Students v France Students (Cardiff)
Sat 16th	ENGLAND v IRELAND (Twickenham)
	(sponsored by Save & Prosper)
	WALES v FRANCE (Cardiff)
	Scottish Tennents 1556 Cup (5)(Sco)
Wed 20th	British Universities Sports Association Final (Twickenham)
Fri 22nd	England 16 GP v Wales Intermediate Group (Lon)
Sat 23rd	Pilkington Cup Semi-finals (Eng)
	Pilkington Shield Semi-finals (Eng)
	Courage Leagues 3 & 4 (14)(Eng)
	Swalec Cup Quarter-finals (Wal)
	Schools Day (Twickenham):
	The Daily Mail Schools Under 15 Final
	The Daily Mail Schools Under 18 Final
	England 16 Group v Wales 16 Group
	Insurance Corporation League 1 to 4 (7)(Ire)
	Welsh Youth v England Colts (Swansea)
Wed 27th	Scotland Schools v England Schools (Hawick)
Sat 30th	Courage Leagues 1 & 2 (15)(Eng)
	Courage Leagues 3 & 4 (15)(Eng)
	Courage Leagues Other Divs (13)(Eng)
	Royal Navy v Army (Twickenham)
	(Willis Corroon Trophy)
	Combined Services Under 21 v England Students
	Under 21 (Twickenham)
	Heineken Leagues Divs 1 to 5 (19)(Wal)
	Insurance Corporation League 1 to 4 (8)(Ire)
Sat 30th	Hong Kong Sevens
Sun 31st	Hong Kong Sevens
	FIRA Juniors World Championship (Italy)
	– until Su, April 8th

APRIL 1996

Sat 6th	Cardiff v Barbarians (Cardiff)
	Courage Leagues 1 to 4 (16)(Eng)
	Heineken Leagues Divs 1 to 5 (20)(Wal)
	Insurance Corporation League 1 to 4 (9)(Ire)
	France UNSS v England 18 Group (Fra)
	Ireland Schools v Scotland Schools (Cork)
Wed 10th	Royal Navy v Royal Air Force (Twickenham)
	England v Ireland (18 Group)(Hull Ionians)
Sat 13th	Courage Leagues 1 to 4 (17)(Eng)
	Swalec Cup Semi-finals (Wal)
	Insurance Corporation League 1 to 4 (10)(Ire)
	England Colts v Scotland Colts (Coventry)
	Ireland Under 18 v Scotland Under 18 (Ireland)
Wed 17th	Army v Royal Air Force (Twickenham)
Sat 20th	CIS Insurance County Championship
	CIS Insurance Under 21 County Championship
	(Finals at Twickenham)
	Heineken Leagues Divs 1 to 5 (21)(Wal)

PRINCIPAL FIXTURES 1995-96

	Insurance Corporation League 1 to 4 (11)(Ire)
	England Colts v France Colts (Chester)
	Scotland Under 19 v Wales Under 19 (Ayr)
	Scotland Under 18 v Wales Under 18 (Ayr)
Sun 21st	Scottish Tennents 1556 Cup (6)(Sco)
	Insurance Corporation League Div 2 (11)(Ire)
	Wanderers v Dolphin
Sat 27th	Courage Leagues 1 to 4 (18)(Eng)
	Heineken Leagues Divs 1 to 5 (Wal)
	Provincial Cups – Semi-finals (Ire)
Sun 28th	Scottish Tennents 1556 Cup (7)(Sco)

MAY 1996

Sat 4th	Pilkington Cup Final (Twickenham)
	Pilkington Shield Final (Twickenham)
	SWALEC Cup Final (Cardiff Arms Park)
	Provincial Cups – Finals (Ire)
Sun 5th	Scottish Tennents 1556 Cup semi-finals (Sco)
Sat 11th	Middlesex Seven-a-Side Finals (Twickenham)
	Scottish Tennents 1556 Cup Final (Murrayfield)
	May/June Scotland tour to New Zealand

FUTURE FIVE NATIONS DATES

1996-97	1997-98	1998-99
18.1.97	17.1.98	16.1.99
Ire v Fra	Fra v Eng	Ire v Fra
Sco v Wal	Ire v Sco	Sco v Wal
1.2.97	7.2.98	6.2.99
Eng v Sco	Eng v Wal	Eng v Sco
Wal v Ire	Sco v Fra	Wal v Ire
15.2.97	21.2.98	20.2.99
Fra v Wal	Fra v Ire	Fra v Wal
Ire v Eng	Wal v Sco	Ire v Eng
1.3.97	7.3.98	6.3.98
Eng v Fra	Ire v Wal	Eng v Fra
Sco v Ire	Sco v Eng	Sco v Ire
15.3.97	21.3.98	20.3.99
Fra v Sco	Eng v Ire	Fra v Sco
Wal v Eng	Wal v Fra	Wal v Eng

FUTURE TOURS (Provisional)

1996-97	Argentina to England and Wales
	Australia to Scotland and Ireland (Oct/Nov)
1997-98	New Zealand to England and Wales
1998-99	South Africa to Scotland and Ireland

Matt Dawson Northampton 1994-95 Season

11

REVIEW OF THE SEASON

by Bill Mitchell

IF IT was hard to believe at the end of the 1993-94 season that the Courage Leagues were only seven years old, imagine how credulity is strained a year later after eight completed seasons. But a few things have altered, one of them being the change of champions from the habitual Bath to the original title winners, Leicester, and many will say with some justification that the latter would not have happened but for the World Cup and the demands of national team managers, who deprived them of all three Scottish internationals for the vital closing games and the Pilkington Cup Final, which also saw Simon Geoghegan away on Irish duty, while England demands also meant restricted appearances by the likes of Mike Catt, Jon Callard, Jeremy Guscott, Phil de Glanville, Steve Ojomoh, Victor Ubogu, Graham Dawe, Ben Clarke and uncapped prop John Mallett.

When those absences at vital times are considered, Bath can be said to have done superbly well, particularly in the way that they lifted themselves to thrash Wasps in the Pilkington Cup Final after finally conceding not only the title but also their unbeaten home record to Sale the week before. Their final achievement in 1995 was a testimony not only to their strength in depth that enabled them to sustain a league challenge even when depleted, but also to their resilience.

However, in eulogising Bath one must not forget that Leicester also had to make sacrifices on England's behalf, which involved the regular absences of the Underwood brothers, Graham Rowntree, Martin Johnson, Neil Back and the redoubtable Dean Richards, who led the team to its title success. Perhaps Bath were due to be dethroned anyway and if this was to happen Leicester were their most likely successors. This finally became a probability on 15th April, when the West Country club went to Welford Road, where the hosts went one better than the drawn match (20-20) on October 22nd at the Recreation Ground at a time when England demands were only a future threat. So the first ever Courage League champions returned worthily to top spot.

Sale in finishing fourth with that win at Bath had an outstanding season on their return to the top ranks, but Wasps, despite having an array of talent led by Rob Andrew, Damien Hopley and the giant Canadian Norm Hadley, ended with a bare cupboard after being comprehensively destroyed in the Pilkington Cup Final by Bath. A third place in the league will have provided small consolation. However, that talent includes some promising players – especially among the forwards – and they may not have to wait long for something tangible to emerge.

For the rest of the clubs it was mostly a struggle against relegation with only one to descend, but in the final games of the season it could have been any one from Harlequins, West Hartlepool and Northampton with Quins surviving after a visit to Gloucester, while they had by then just saved themselves. Orrell lost at Wasps and the Saints' win in the North East was not enough to earn them safety. Survival brought an end to the career of a great West Hartlepool club man, lock John Dixon, whose dedication to the game brought him few rewards except the knowledge that without him and people like him the game would not survive. There is room for prima donnas and foot soldiers, both are indispensable and, if I were a club coach, I know whom I would rate highest in terms of reliability.

The two other teams – Orrell and injury hit Bristol – were never at any time in positions of comfort, but at least they could approach their ultimate matches in a relaxed frame of mind as their results confirmed. Orrell lost at Wasps (53-25) and Bristol never seemed likely to do neighbours Bath any favours at Leicester (a 17-3 win for the home club).

So Northampton paid the price for poor results early in the campaign and a dearth of tries – a miserable 16 in the end. They are succeeded by Saracens, who performed brilliantly to finish six points clear of nearest rivals Wakefield in League Two, and must now hope that they will be allowed to retain the excellent players who brought them that success and not see them go to more charismatic clubs.

With only one promotion spot available attention in that competiton was soon on the relegation battle with Coventry doomed for one of the places early on. On the last day of the campaign only the top two clubs and Wakefield were safe, but wins for the two exile clubs along with Moseley and Nottingham meant that Fylde had to win at home to Wakefield and hope that one of the others, especially Waterloo, lost. The latter did so (11-14 at home to threatened Nottingham), but Fylde were narrow home victims of Wakefield and sadly down they went.

The League Three replacements buck the recent trend where famous names are being consigned to the ranks of 'also-rans' and younger 'upstart' clubs are climbing over them, because the top two places in their competition were filled by Bedford and Blackheath – and they do not come more famous than those two, unless the name of Richmond is added and they for a long time looked likely candidates for League Four! There was no real challenge to Bedford and 'Club' and the only question as the season closed was where they would finish. In the end Bedford's narrow home victory (21- 20) over Richmond, who had already escaped relegation by the skin of their teeth, kept hem ahead of the South East London side, whose 28-0 ultimate win at Exeter merely rubbed salt in the West Country team's relegation wounds. It was nice to see the admirable Mick Skinner helping out at Blackheath, his spiritual home since he moved South from his native Newcastle.

Clifton, only promoted as League Four champions the previous season, made a swift return as the other demoted club leaving the middle order sides – Rugby, Rosslyn Park, Morley, Otley and Harrogate – to concentrate on ways to do better next season.

It was League Four which really provided the most meritorious promoted sides. The competition was won by Rotherham who won all but one of their 18 games to ascend for a second successive season. Their No.8 Richard Selkirk finally did miss a pair of matches – not through injury but to attend his brother's wedding in the Caribbean – but his appearances record will be hard to beat.

Reading were five points adrift of the Yorkshire club in second place, but both had confirmed their improved status long before the season had ended, Reading gaining promotion for a third successive season. Both sides won their County Cups into the bargain. The main interest at the end of the campaign was concerned with the relegation battle and it was always likely that Broughton Park and Askeans would go down, although Plymouth Albion only escaped by a single point. As with League Three the remaining clubs could afford to relax at a fairly early stage, although the fourth place earned by Havant could well mean that Hampshire will at long last have a club with the potential to achieve better things.

Both Fifth Leagues had excellent champions with Walsall in the North coming through to frustrate the ambitions of Kendal and Wade Dooley's Preston Grasshoppers. The Midlanders only dropped three points all season, but at the foot of the table two other clubs from the region went down, Barker's Butts after a gallant fight, when they crucially lost their last game narrowly at home to Wharfedale and allowed Nuneaton (11-6 winners at Stoke) to escape. Hereford in contrast had a poor season and will need time in the Midlands Divisional set-up to regroup.

Five South in contrast provided thrills at the top as long term leaders Lydney needed only to win at Henley in their final match to leave London Welsh with another season of frustration. But the Oxfordshire club in a high scoring game came out on top (33-30) and the Exiles managed a nail biting 19-13 victory at Metropolitan Police to take the honours – and a place in League Four next season.

Two London and the East clubs filled the bottom two places in this league and revert to junior status after brave fights. Basingstoke and Sudbury always had a chance of survival but a heavy 40-9 home defeat at the hands of Barking destroyed the Suffolk team in their final match and the Hampshire club's only consolation was victory in their county cup when they won their final as the visiting team.

Replacing them will be three unfashionable but ambitious clubs and Cheltenham, who shrugged off the deduction of two points to earn promotion from South West One with a late victory over enterprising Newbury. They go into Five South along with Camberley, who had a fine season.

Into Five North go Sandal, who have Rotherham as a role model for clubs from North One, and Worcester, who have a superb backroom team and excellent youth policy and will not be satisfied with a single promotion season. A club with unlimited ambitions they were worthy winners of the Junior Club of the Year award in the Whitbread/Rugby World annual awards ceremony.

Elsewhere, it is always nice to sing the praises of those clubs who have won all their matches before returning to more serious matters and one of our featured teams last season, Luctonians, immediately press their claims after winning Midlands West Two with a perfect record. In the same division Erdington (North Midlands Two) and Rugby Welsh (Staffs & Warwicks Four) also won all matches, while up North the same feat was recorded by Macclesfield (North Two), Sedgley Park (North West One), Windermere (Cumbria and Lancashire North), Aspull (Cheshire and Lancashire South), Congleton (Cheshire), Newton-le-Willows (Lancashire South), Barnard Castle (Durham and Northumberland Three), Wheatley Hills (Yorkshire One) and finally Wibsey (Yorkshire Two).

Down in the South West Launceston well justified their feature status of last year by winning all their games in the Western Counties league a success repeated in both Cornwall leagues by St Austell (One) and Redruth Albany (Two). Cainscross did the same in Gloucestershire Three as did Wellington in Somerset One, Swindon (Berks, Dorset and Wilts One) and Chinnor (Bucks and Oxon One). London Division also had its heroes starting with Wimbledon in Three South West and augmented in Hampshire with successes for Jersey (One) and Andover (Two). Tring did the same in Hertfordshire, as did Sevenoaks (Kent One), Quintin (Middlesex Four), Kew Occasionals (Surrey Four) and BA Winspan (Sussex Two). A splended effort from one and all!

The excellent performances in recent seasons by various England sides including the top team with three Grand Slams in five campaigns owes a huge debt of gratitude to the existence of the Courage Leagues and the way even the smallest minnows have had to become more professional or go under and that word 'professional' is one we can no longer ignore.

Meanwhile, once again, I must stick my neck out, although advice from a gentleman in West Hartlepool would suggest that it would be foolish, but to 'chicken out' could amount to cowardice on my part. When I make a forecast I am all too delighted when I find that most of the dire ones are wrong and, perhaps, those for whom I predict poor results are actually stimulated into special efforts to prove me and other self styled experts completely wrong.

Anyway, here goes!

League One Champions: Bath. Relegation: Orrell and West Hartlepool.

League Two Champions: Northampton. Promotion: Wakefield. Relegation: London Irish and Bedford.

League Three Champions: Richmond. Promotion: Rugby. Relegation: Otley and Morley.

League Four Champions: Liverpool St Helens. Promotion: Clifton. Relegation: Redruth and Plymouth Albion.

League Five North Champions: Kendal.

League Five South Champions: Lydney.

It is an invidious exercise and congratulations go in advance to all clubs who contrive to make me look foolish!

I just wish all could be winners and no-one losers, so an all incorrect forecast would cause me to shed no tears.

RFU AWARDS

The following were awarded at the RFU Awards Dinner at the
London Hilton on Park Lane
11th May 1995

PLAYER OF THE SEASON
Martin Bayfield
(Northampton)

YOUNG PLAYER OF THE SEASON
Nick Greenstock
(Wasps)

TRY OF THE SEASON
Mick Watson
West Hartlepool v Bath, Courage League
*(The Award is based on the quality of the rugby in scoring the try
rather than the significance of the try)*

UNSUNG HERO
Kevin Murphy
(Honorary England Team Physiotherapist)

The nominations and winners for these Awards
were selected by a panel appointed by the RFU.

The panel was:

Chairman, Rugby Union Writers Club – Tony Roche (Today)
RFU National Promotions Officer – Alan Black
Hon. Asst. England Manager & U21 Manager – John Elliott
Hon. Asst. Coach, England – Les Cusworth

INDEX

Steve McCormack who has brilliantly compiled the vast majority of club and league statistics in this Directory is available to help club statisticians or the media. Please contact him the the publishers:
Tony Williams Publications North Curry, Taunton, Somerset TA3 6DV.
Tel: 01823 490684 or Fax: 01823 490281

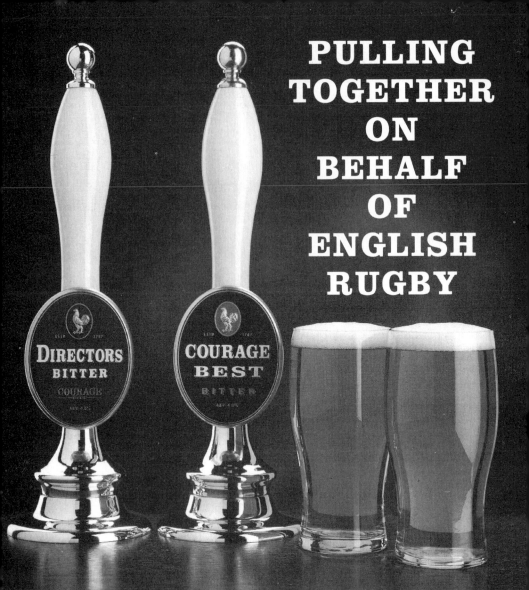

PULLING TOGETHER ON BEHALF OF ENGLISH RUGBY

**Proud Sponsors of
The Courage Clubs Championship
and the England Squad**

COURAGE
CLUBS CHAMPIONSHIP

A TRIBUTE TO BATH F.C.

from Directory Statistician
STEVE McCORMACK

BATH at HOME

	PLD	W	D	L	FOR T	C	P	D	AGAINST T	C	P	D
1987-88	5	4	–	1	11	3	9	2	6	4	6	1
1988-89	6	6	–	–	21	9	13	2	3	2	15	–
1989-90	5	5	–	–	35	26	1	–	3	3	8	–
1990-91	6	5	–	1	23	13	12	1	6	5	8	–
1991-92	6	6	–	–	18	9	18	1	3	2	10	2
1992-93	6	6	–	–	27	17	18	1	3	2	9	2
1993-94	9	9	–	–	27	18	25	1	6	4	11	–
1994-95	9	6	2	1	20	17	27	–	10	3	19	3
TOTAL	52	47	2	3	182	112	123	8	40	25	86	8

BATH AWAY

		W	D	L	FOR T	C	P	D	AGAINST T	C	P	D
1987-88	6	2	1	3	16	13	6	2	11	4	14	3
1988-89	5	4	–	1	22	8	4	–	3	2	2	–
1989-90	6	3	0	3	9	3	7	–	5	3	12	–
1990-91	6	6	–	–	16	10	12	1	2	1	12	–
1991-92	6	4	1	1	16	9	15	1	7	5	10	2
1992-93	6	5	–	1	15	6	14	–	4	2	5	2
1993-94	9	8	0	1	19	9	22	1	7	3	21	2
1994-95	9	6	1	2	16	9	19	1	9	3	21	3
TOTAL	53	38	3	12	129	67	99	6	48	23	102	12

MOST APPEARANCES IN EACH POSITION

Winger
Tony Swift (90)
Phil Blackett (10)

Full Back
Jon Callard (42)
Jon Webb (29)
Audley Lumsden (17)

Winger
Adebayo Adebayo (32)
Jim Fallon (17)

Centre
Jeremy Guscott (65)
Mike Catt (16)
John Bamsey (10)

Centre
Phil de Glanville (59)
Simon Halliday (24)
Istyn Lewis (8)

Stand-Off
Stuart Barnes (72)
Mike Catt (14)
Ritchie Butland (7)

Scrum Half
Richard Hill (74)
Ian Sanders (21)
Steve Knight (6)

Prop
Gareth Chilcott (59)
David Hilton (15)
Chris Clark (7)

Hooker
Graham Dawe (93)
Graham Adams (6)
J Deane (3)

Prop
Victor Ubogo (57)
Robert Lee (37)
John Mallett (14)

Lock
Nigel Redman (78)
Andy Reid (24)
Damian Cronin (20)

Lock
Martin Haag (53)
John Morrison (21)
Sean o'Leary (5)

Flanker
Andy Robinson (89)
Neil Maslem (8)
Eric Peters (3)

No 8
Ben Clarke (46)
Dave Eggerton (33)
Steve Ojomoh (14)

Flanker
John Hall (70)
Steve Ojomoh (19)
Paul Simpson (6)

COMPLETE CHAMPIONSHIP RESULTS
1987-95

		87-88	88-89	89-90	90-91	91-92	92-93	93-94	94-95	W	D	L	W	D	L
Bedford	H			W76-0						1	0	0			
	A												1	0	0
Bristol	H	W15-9	W16-9			W9-4		W9-0	W18-9	5	0	0			
	A			W14-13	W10-3		W31-8	W18-10	W10-9	5	0	0	10	0	0
Coventry	H									0	1	0			
	A	D9-9											0	1	0
Gloucester	H		W19-9			W29-9		W46-17	D19-19	3	1	0			
	A	W16-9		L6-13	W17-15		W20-0	W16-6	W15-0	5	0	1	8	1	1
Harlequins	H	W12-9		W32-12	W23-3		W22-6	W32-13	W22-11	6	0	0			
	A		W26-9			D18-18		W14-12	W25-19	3	1	0	9	1	0
Leicester	H			W26-15		W37-6		W14-6	D20-20	3	1	0			
	A	L13-24	L12-15		W9-3		W13-3	L6-9	L21-31	2	0	4	5	1	4
Liverpool	H				W46-3					1	0	0			
	A		W21-7							1	0	0	2	0	0
London Irish	H						W42-19	W28-8		2	0	0			
	A					W24-21		W32-31		2	0	0	4	0	0
London Scot	H						W40-10			1	0	0			
	A												1	0	0
Moseley	H	W14-0		W27-9	W11-6					3	0	0			
	A		W38-0							1	0	0	4	0	0
Newcastle G	H							W46-3		1	0	0			
	A							W29-5		1	0	0	2	0	0
Northampton	H					W15-6		W32-9	W26-6	3	0	0			
	A				W16-10		L8-11	W30-9	W32-16	3	0	1	6	0	1
Nottingham	H		W22-16			W25-15				2	0	0			
	A	L15-25		L9-12	W22-9					1	0	2	3	0	2
Orrell	H	W23-18	W36-12		W17-9		W39-3	W13-7	W32-13	6	0	0			
	A			W9-6		L9-12		W18-15	D6-6	2	1	1	8	1	1
Rosslyn Pk	H			W34-6	W45-21					2	0	0			
	A		W19-6			W21-13				2	0	0	4	0	0
Rugby	H						W61-7			1	0	0			
	A				W32-0					1	0	0	2	0	0
Sale	H								L13-18	0	0	1			
	A	W46-19							W29-3	2	0	0	2	0	1
Saracens	H					W32-12				1	0	0			
	A			L7-9	W49-6		W19-13			2	0	1	3	0	1
Wasps	H		W16-6			L15-16	W22-17	W24-8	W12-9	4	0	1			
	A	L15-19		W18-9		W24-12		W19-13	L10-11	3	0	2	7	0	3
Waterloo	H	L10-17	W38-9							1	0	1			
	A												1	0	1
W Hartlepool	H							W53-17		1	0	0			
	A						W38-10		W20-18	2	0	0	3	0	0

BATH STATISTICS 1987-1995

TOP POINTS SCORERS

	PTS	T	C	P	D	APPS
Stuart Barnes	467	21	65	71	9	72
Jon Callard	384	16	41	76	–	25
Jon Webb	275	7	41	54	–	29
Tony Swift	184	43	–	–	–	90
Jeremy Guscott	133	27	8	–	1	65
Adebayo Adebayo	69	15	–	–	–	39
John Hall	60	14	–	–	–	70
Mike Catt	58	7	4	4	1	30
Ben Clarke	58	12	–	–	–	47
Phil de Glanville	56	12	–	–	–	59
David Egerton	54	13	–	–	–	38
Richard Hill	48	11	–	–	–	74

TOP APPEARANCE MAKERS

	87-88	88-89	89-90	90-91	91-92	92-93	93-94	94-95	Total
Graham Dawe	9	10	10	12	11	12	17	12	93
Tony Swift	8	7	11	12	12	12	13	15	90
Andy Robinson	8	9	11	12	12	10	14	13	89
Nigel Redman	8	7	6	8	11	11	12	15	78
Richard Hill	10	8	10	11	12	11	12+1	–	74
Stuart Barnes	4	9	10	11	12	11	15	–	72
John Hall	4	8	6	11	–	11	17	13	70
Jeremy Guscott	10	8	9	11	7	10	2	8	65
Gareth Chilcott	8	10	7	6	10	10	8	–	59
Phil de Glanville	–	–	–	5	11	12	15	16	59
Victor Ubogu	–	–	5+1	9+1	10	11	14	8	57
Martin Haag	–	1	1	11	11	1	14	14	53

MOST CHAMPIONSHIP WINNERS MEDALS
(FULL APPEARANCES)

5   G Dawe, T Swift, A Robinson, N Redman, R Hill, S Barnes, J Guscott, G Chilcott, M Haag, D Egerton (10)

4   J Hall, V Ubogu, P de Glanville, S Ojomoh, A Reid, J Bamsey, N Maslem (7)

3   R Lee, J Callard, J Webb, A Adebayo, I Lewis, B Clarke, J Mallett (7)

BATH IN COURAGE LEAGUE

MOST TRIES FOR BATH

HOME		AWAY	
14 v BEDFORD	1989-90	8 v SALE	
9 v RUGBY	1992-93	8 v MOSELEY	
8 v WATERLOO	1988-89	8 v SARACENS	
7 v LIVERPOOL St HELENS	1990-91	5 v RUGBY	
7 v ROSSLYN PARK	1990-91	5 v W HARTLEPOOL	
7 v W HARTLEPOOL	1994-95		

Scored tries in 49 out of 53 away matches.
Only 2 sides Orrell & Leicester have stopped them (twice each).
Stopped the other side scoring a try 19 times in 53 matches .
Only 9 times have the home team scored more than 1 try against Bath, and 4 of these were in the first season.
Lost 4 times at Leicester and twice each at both Nottingham and Wasps.
Best away run: 10 consecutive wins over 1993-94 and 1994-95 seasons.
Worst away run – lost first 3 away matches in 1987-88 and drew the next. Twice since lost 2 consecutive.

Most tries against away from home.

4 v London Irish	1993-94	3 v W Hartlepool	1994-95
3 v Leicester	1987-88		

Most points against – individual total

59	John Liley (Leicester)	39	Jez Harris (Leicester)
53	Rob Andrew (Wasps)	30	Paul Grayson (Northampton)
46	Tim Smith (Gloucester)	26	Mark Tainton (Bristol)
39	Simon Langford (Orrell)	26	Simon Hodgkinson (Nottingham)

Most tries against Bath in a match

2	Mark Bailey (Wasps)	2	Graham Stanton (Sale)
2	Ian Wynn (Orrell)	2	Paul Cook (Nottingham)

Most conversions against Bath in a match

2	David Pears (Harlequins)	2	Simon Langford (Orrell)

Most penalties against Bath in a match

5	Simon Langford (Orrell)	4	Simon Hodgkinson (Nottingham)
5	Guy Gregory (Nottingham)	4	Kent Bray (Harlequins)
5	John Liley (Leicester)	4	Brian Mullen (London Irish)
5	Jez Harris (Leicester)		

Most drop goals against Bath in a season

3	Jez Harris (Leicester)	2	Gareth Hughes (Saracens)
2	Martyn Kimber (Gloucester)		

Had a run of 25 consecutive home wins.
Went 30 matches unbeaten at home.
Failed to score a try in just 4 home matches – two of these v Bristol.
Only conceded more than 1 try at home in just 8 matches.
21 times stopped the opposition scoring tries in 52 home matches.
3 times out scored in terms of tries at home.
5 players who have played all 8 seasons: A Swift, G Dawe, A Robinson, J Guscott, N Redman.
Total Number of players used 80
Tony Swift an ever present – 4 times.

Unisys and the Courage Clubs Championship

As a major worldwide information services company we are active in many different ways in the community in which we work.

UNISYS

As part of our extensive sports programme we are pleased to support the Courage Clubs Championship Directory.

FINAL UNISYS COMPUTER RUGBY UNION STATISTICS 1994-95

These statistics have been collected during the Season for players in all clubs playing first class rugby. They include representative matches, County and Divisional matches, and also include the Varsity Match and Barbarian fixtures.

UNISYS TOP POINTS SCORERS

		Total	Tries	Cons	Pens	DG
1.	Richard Mills (Walsall)	369	4	74	66	1
2.	Andy Finnie (Bedford)	338		43	79	5
3.	Paul Thatcher (Weston Super Mare)	336	5	58	64	1
4.	Chris Mann (Stourbridge)	330	5	55	65	
5.	Phil Belshaw (Reading)	326	2	53	70	
6.	Alex Howarth (Wharfedale)	317	14	47	51	
7.	Rob Andrew (Wasps)	316	5	48	57	8
8.	Simon Hogg (Clifton)	305	1	36	64	12
9.	Simon Blake (Redruth)	301	5	36	66	2
10.	Nick Churchman (Tabard)	299	4	33	68	3
11.	Andy Higgin (Liverpool St Helens)	292	9	41	53	2
12.	Mike Jackson (Wakefield)	285	3	27	72	
13.	Mark Tainton (Bristol)	283	1	31	69	3
14.	Simon Mason (Newcastle Gosforth)	275	2	38	60	3
14.	Jez Harris (Leicester)	275		25	59	16
16.	Kevin Plant (Rotherham)	273	3	45	53	3
17.	Jon Callard (Bath)	271	5	33	60	
18.	Jim Quantrill (Rugby)	270	3	39	59	
19.	Peter Rutledge (Otley)	256	11	27	49	
20.	Jamie Grayshon (Morley)	255	2	22	61	6

UNISYS TOP TRY SCORERS

1.	Jon Rowe (Walsall)	30
2.	Malcolm Walker (Walsall)	20
3.	Colin Charvis (London Welsh)	19
4.	Adam Jewitt (Havant)	18
4.	Chris Greenhall (North Walsham)	18
4.	Chris Tate (Barking)	18

UNISYS TOP KICKERS (Tries excluded)

1.	Richard Mills (Walsall)	349
2.	Andy Finnie (Bedford)	338
3.	Phil Belshaw (Reading)	316
4.	Paul Thatcher (Weston Super Mare)	311
5.	Chris Mann (Stourbridge)	305

UNISYS TOP DROP KICKERS

1.	Jez Harris (Leicester)	16
2.	Simon Hogg (Clifton)	12
3.	Martyn Kimber (Gloucester)	8
3.	Rob Andrew (Wasps)	8
5.	Richard Larkin (Askeans)	7

THE COURAGE CLUBS CHAMPIONSHIP REGULATIONS 1995-96

1 **Description**

The Competition shall be called "The English Clubs Rugby Union Championship" (hereinafter referred to as "the Competition") and shall be open to Clubs in membership with the Rugby Football Union (hereinafter called "the RFU"). All matches in the Competition shall be played under the Laws of Rugby Union Football and shall comply with the Rules and Regulations of the RFU.

2 **Organising Committee**

The Competition will be organised by the Competition Sub-Committee of the RFU (hereinafter referred to as "the Committee") whose decision shall be binding and final on any matter not provided for in and on the interpretation of these Regulations.

3 **Delegation of Administration**

   a) The Committee appoints the RFU National Clubs Association Committee as the Organising Committee of National Leagues 1, 2, 3 and 4 (see Appendix 1).

   b) The Committee appoints the RFU Divisions as the organising Committees of all Leagues within their Divisions.

   c) The Committee will be the organising Committee of National Leagues 5 North and South.

   d) The Committee (in respect of National Leagues 5 North and South), the RFU National Clubs Association and the RFU Divisions shall, subject to Regulation 18(a) of these Regulations, deal with all disputes, transgressions and complaints as laid down by Regulation 19.

4 **Structure**

   a) **National**

There shall be four National Leagues 1, 2, 3 and 4, comprising 10 Clubs each, unless agreed otherwise by the Committee.

   b) **Areas**

     (i) The Northern and Midland RFU Divisions shall combine to provide one National League 5 North and the London and South East and South West RFU Divisions shall combine to provide one National League 5 South each comprised of thirteen Clubs, unless agreed otherwise by the Committee.

     (ii) Promotion from the National Leagues 5 North and South shall be to National League 4.

   c) **RFU Divisions**

     (i) Each of the RFU Divisions shall have a first League.

     (ii) Promotion from the Northern Division League 1 and the Midland Division League 1 shall be to the National League 5 North and from the London and South East Division League 1 and the South West Division League 1 shall be to the National League 5 South.

     (iii) The Divisional League structure below Division League 1 in each Division shall be such as shall, with the approval of the Committee, be determined by that Division.

     (iv) Leagues shall be comprised of 13 Clubs, except that the lowest two Leagues may, with the consent of the appropriate Divisional Committee, consist of more or less, unless agreed otherwise by the Committee.

   d) **General**

     (i) Not more than two lower Leagues may support a higher League.

     (ii) Only Club first XVs may enter the Competition.

     (iii) A Club may only play in any National League 5 or Divisional League according to its RFU Constituent Body allocation.

5 **Club Positions**

The position of a Club in a League shall be established by awarding two points for a win and one point for a draw. In the case of equality, positions shall be determined on the basis of match points scored. A Club with a larger difference between match points for and match points against shall be placed higher in a League than a Club with a smaller difference between match points for and match points against. Should two Clubs have the same number of competition points and the same match points difference, the Club having scored more match points shall be placed higher in the League than the Club having a lesser number of match points for. In the event of the match points for still being unable to establish the position of two Clubs, and if the winning of the Competition or promotion or relegation is involved, the Club who has won the highest number of its League matches shall be placed higher. If this does not establish the position then the Club who has won the most matches, excluding its first League match of the season, then its second League match, until it can be established which is the highest placed Club.

6 **Promotion and Relegation**
   a) Where one League supports one League, the top two Clubs from the lower League at the end of the season shall be promoted to the higher League.
   b) Where two Leagues support one League, the top Club in each of the supporting Leagues at the end of the season shall be promoted to the higher League.
   c) After promotion has taken place in accordance with Clauses (a) and (b) above, the requisite number of Clubs shall be relegated (upon the basis prescribed in Clause (d) below) from each League at the end of the season so that the following season there are 10 Clubs in National Leagues 1, 2, 3 and 4, and 13 Clubs in all other Leagues (or such other number of Clubs as there are to be in the lowest two Leagues in each of the RFU Divisions in accordance with Regulation 4(c)(iv) above).
   d) Except in the cases of relegation from National League 1 to National League 2, from National League 2 to National League 3 and from National League 3 to National League 4 Clubs shall be relegated on a geographical/Divisional/Constituent Body basis as appropriate.

   Note: Given this, and the provisions of Clause (c) above, it is accordingly not possible (except in the cases of relegation from National Leagues 1, 2, 3 and 4 where two Clubs will be relegated from each League) to determine how many Clubs are to be relegated from any particular League until it has first been determined at the end of the season (i) how many Clubs are to be relegated from each (in turn) of the Leagues (both National Leagues and Divisional Leagues) higher than that League and (ii) to which League or Leagues the Clubs from those higher Leagues are to be relegated.

   e) Notwithstanding the foregoing provisions of this Regulation or the provisions of Regulation 4 above, the Committee may, as it shall in its absolute discretion think fit, at any time (i) disapply, suspend, amend and/or vary the foregoing provisions of this Regulation and/or of Regulation 4 as to promotion and relegation and/or as to the number of Clubs comprising any League or Leagues, and/or (ii) transfer any Club from the League in which it would have been placed by virtue of the application of Clauses (a) to (d) of this Regulation to such other League (whether higher or lower) as the Committee shall think fit. Any action taken or decision made by the Committee under the powers conferred on it by the foregoing provisions of this Clause (e) shall be final and binding.

7 **Fixtures**
   a) All League matches shall be played on fixed Saturdays as set out in the Structured Season. (Pages 45-52)
   b) All League matches in National Leagues 1, 2, 3 and 4 shall be played on a home and away basis.
   c) All League fixture lists shall be prepared by the Organising Committee of the League concerned and submitted to the Clubs comprising the League by the 31st May in each year. A copy shall be sent to the Secretary of the RFU by the same date.
   d) Every Club in all League fixtures shall play its bona fide first XV.

8 **Eligibility**
   a) **Clubs**
      (i) Any Club in membership with the RFU may enter the Competition subject to the approval of the Committee and of the appropriate RFU Division according to its RFU Constituent Body allocation.
      (ii) Any Club applying to join the Competition shall only be permitted to do so by being placed in the bottom League in its RFU Division.

(iii) The Committee shall have the power to impose conditions upon the membership or continued participation of any Club or Clubs in the Competition. Any Club or Clubs failing to comply with such conditions shall not be entitled to enter the Competition or to continue to participate in it.

b) **Players**

(i) A Club in a Competition match may only play or select as a replacement, players who hold EFFECTIVE registration for that Club, in accordance with the RFU Registration of Players Regulations.

(ii) A Club may only play or select as a replacement in a Competition match one player who holds EFFECTIVE registration under Regulation 9(b)(ii) of the RFU Registration of Players Regulations.

(iii) A Club may not play or select as a replacement in a match in the Competition any player who has at any time received any material benefit (as defined in Regulation 1.3 of the IRFB Regulations Relating to Amateurism) for playing any form of Rugby Football.

(iv) A Club may not in any one match in the Competition play or select as a replacement more than 2 players who shall have at any time after 7 May 1995 played or attended as a replacement for either of the two highest Senior National Representative Teams of any Home Union other than the RFU provided however that this regulation shall not apply to

(i) any players who shall have played or attended as a replacement for such Teams of Ireland, Scotland and Wales and who shall at the time of the relevant match in the Competition have EFFECTIVE registration with London Irish, London Scottish and London Welsh respectively and whom London Irish, London Scottish and London Welsh respectively wish to play or select as a replacement; or

(ii) any players who had EFFECTIVE registration with any club on 7 May 1995.

Note: After 1 September 1996 only one such player will be allowed under this regulation.

Penalty: A Club shall be deducted two championship points on each occasion that it has been represented by an ineligible player or replacement or been in breach of Regulation 8(b)(i), 8(b)(ii), 8(b)(iii) or 8(b)(iv).

(Warning: The computerised registration list is the only evidence which will be accepted to substantiate a player's EFFECTIVE registration — see Registration Regulation 8).

9   **Players in Representative Matches**

Where a representative match involving any Senior National Representative team or Second Senior Representative Team of any of the Home Unions or the CIS Insurance County Championship Semi-finals or Final is played on a date fixed for a League match, any Club which is affected by three or more players or replacements taking part in such representative match may require the League match to be rearranged for a later date. Such rearranged match will be fixed by the Organising Committee of the League concerned.

10   **Replacements**

a) In all matches in the Competition replacements are permitted in accordance with the RFU Regulations relating to the use of replacements.

b) In the interest of safety every team in the Competition shall have available a replacement or other player on the field capable of playing in the front row of the scrum should a replacement be required whether due to injury or consequent upon a player being ordered off and note (xii) to Law 6(A) applying. If on the first occasion a front row player requires to be replaced his team cannot provide a replacement or other player capable of playing in the front row of the scrum so that uncontested scrums result, his team shall be deemed to have lost the match. Any match points scored by either side shall be disregarded in computing the difference between match points for and against.

11   **Unplayed, Postponed and Abandoned Matches**

a) If weather conditions prevent a match being played or a match is abandoned because of such conditions with less than sixty minutes having been played, the match shall be played or replayed on a date directed by the Organising Committee of the League concerned. If a match is abandoned because of weather conditions when sixty or more minutes have been played, then the score at the moment of abandonment shall stand and be deemed the final score in the match. The referee's decision as to the necessity for abandonment and the number of minutes played at the moment of abandonment shall be final.

b) If the referee finds it necessary to abandon a match for any reason other than weather conditions, then, irrespective of the number of minutes played, the result of that match may be determined by the Organising Committee of the League concerned or that Committee may order the match to be replayed.

c) If a match is abandoned under Clauses (a) or (b) above, the home Club shall supply the secretary of the Organising Committee of the League concerned with the match card duly signed by the referee and stating the exact time of the match abandonment, the existing match score at the time and the reason for the abandonment.

d) In the event of a Competition match not being played the Organising Committee of the League concerned may at its absolute discretion award the Competition points to either side, divide the Competition points equally between the sides or decide that no Competition points shall be awarded. The Organising Committee of the League concerned shall not have the power to award match points.

e) Any Club which is suspended by its County Constituent Body from playing Rugby Union Football for disciplinary reasons will not be permitted to rearrange any League fixtures failing to be played within the period of the suspension. The effects thereof on the non-offending Clubs in the League concerned shall be dealt with by the Organising Committee of the League concerned under Clause (f) below.

f) In the event of a Competition match not being played for whatever reason, whether or not Championship points are awarded to a Club under this Regulation, if that Club be a contender for promotion or relegation at the end of the season, the difference between the match points for and against of all Clubs (other than the offending Club) in the League shall be adjusted to exclude all match points scored in matches played against the offending Club before establishing the final position of each Club in the League in accordance with Regulation 5.

g) In the event of a Club failing to fulfil its League fixtures for reasons unacceptable to the Organising Committee of the League concerned, or if a Club voluntarily withdraws from a League, or if a Club is expelled or suspended from a League or from membership of the Competition, the results of all matches played by it shall be deleted. The final League table positions shall be established under Regulation 5 from all matches played between the remaining Clubs in such League.

12 Completion of Match Result Card

Each Club shall complete a match result card in accordance with the instructions set out in the Administrative Instructions applicable to such Club's League. The Organising Committees are empowered to impose monetary fines for failure to comply with such instructions and non-payment of fines by the due dates may lead to a deduction of two competition points for each such offence.

Providing false information on players or replacements taking part in a match shall be a serious offence.

Penalty: A Club shall be deducted eight championship points on each occasion false information has been provided. This will be in addition to any points which may have been deducted if the players or replacements were ineligible.

13 Referees and Touch Judges

a) The referee for each match shall be appointed or provided by the Referees' Society to which the home Club pay a Referees' Society subscription, subject to any appointments made by the RFU.

b) In all matches in National Leagues 1, 2, 3, 4 and 5 North and 5 South two qualified touch judges shall be appointed by the RFU and the RFU Regulation relating to Law 6 shall apply.

c) In all other matches each Club shall provide a competent touch judge who should not be a replacement. In an emergency a replacement may act as a touch judge with the agreement of the referee.

d) If the referee appointed or provided under Regulation 13(a) has not arrived at the agreed kick-off time or if the referee is unable to officiate for the whole of the match for any reason and a replacement referee is available, the captains of the two Clubs concerned may agree that the replacement referee can officiate and the result shall count in the Competition. Such agreement shall thereafter be binding upon the Clubs. If there is no agreement then the match shall not count in the Competition and it must be replayed in accordance with the provisions of Regulation 11(a)

14 Kick-Offs and Delayed Arrivals

All Saturday matches shall start at the home Club's usual kick-off time but shall not normally be later than 3.00pm. An earlier or later kick-off time may be arranged by mutual agreement between the two Clubs concerned. Any delay may be reported by the non-offending Club to the Organising Committee of the League concerned and may lead to the match being awarded to the non-offending Club.

15 Clash of Colours/Identification of Players

a) In the event of Clubs having similar or clashing colours the home Club will be responsible for changing its colours, subject to the satisfaction of the appointed referee.

b) The jerseys of teams competing in the Competition should all be numbered or lettered to ensure the correct identification of all players and replacements during a match.

16 Grounds

a) A home Club is responsible for correctly and clearly marking its pitch and it must make proper provision to ensure that (with the exception of the touch judges) all spectators, replacements and officials are kept at a reasonable distance from the field of play.

b) When a late decision as to the fitness of the ground for the playing of a match is necessary, it shall be made by the respective captains of the Clubs involved but if the captains are not able to agree, the decision shall be made by the appointed referee.

c) A late decision is defined as one made within 3 hours of the scheduled kick-off time.

17 Finance

a) Monies provided for the 1993-94 Competition and all Competitions thereafter (until otherwise agreed by Courage) shall belong to the Clubs in the Leagues for whom the monies have been provided and shall be distributed in such shares as the Committee shall decide provided always that the Committee may as it shall see fit appropriate for the benefit of Clubs whether or not participating in the Competition and Schools in membership of the ERFSU or distribute for such charitable purposes as the Committee may select not more than 15% of the said monies.

b) Any proposal involving an offer of sponsorship, financial assistance or gift for a League or combination of Leagues must be submitted to the RFU for approval.

c) Gate receipts at a match shall belong to the home Club.

d) The home Club shall be responsible for all match expenses.

e) The away Club shall be responsible for its own travelling and accommodation expenses.

f) Such membership/registration fee may be charged to each participating Club as may from time to time be determined by the Organising Committee of the League concerned with the approval of the Committee.

g) Clubs failing to register claims by the 28th February will not be eligible for payment of sponsorship monies.

18 Disciplinary Powers

a) Without prejudice to the powers of the RFU or the delegation of powers to Constituent Bodies under Rule 12.4, the Committee shall have the power to expel or suspend any Club from membership of the Competition or impose such other penalty as is considered appropriate on any Club for a breach of these Regulations.

b) The Committee shall have the right to delegate disciplinary powers (other than the power to expel or suspend from membership of the Competition) for any breach of these Regulations to an Organising Committee of a League or National League subject to the rights of appeal as hereinafter provided.

c) Specifically an Organising Committee of a League shall have power to discipline any Club participating in such League for breach of any of the Regulations of the Competition by way of loss of match or Competition points, transference of points, review of result or monetary fine, and any such Club may be liable to be placed at the bottom of the League concerned and such Club's results deleted from such League table.

19 Complaints and Appeals

a) Any complaint shall be referred to the Secretary of the League concerned by telephone within 48 hours of knowledge of the occurrence giving rise to the complaint and thereafter submitted in writing within a further 48 hours. The complaining Club shall also send a copy of such complaint in writing within such 48 hours to the other party to the complaint if applicable. The Secretary on receipt of the written complaint shall require the other party to the complaint if applicable to answer the complaint within (7) days of the receipt of the written complaint by the Secretary and the Secretary shall give a ruling within 7 days. If either party to the complaint is dissatisfied with such ruling there shall be a right of appeal to the Organising Committee of the League concerned as set out in Regulation 3 to be given in writing within 7 days of receipt of the Secretary's decision.

b) (i) If either the complaining Club, or the other party to the complaint, or the Club against whom the complaint is made, requires an oral hearing, whether or not a ruling has been given by the Secretary, it shall be requested in writing and the Organising Committee responsible for the League concerned shall, within 72 hours of receiving notice of such request, appoint a time, date and place for the hearing of such complaint. A league Secretary who has given a ruling shall not be entitled to take any part in the review of a ruling he has given other than to explain the reasons for his ruling.

(ii) Where a complaint is heard before the Organising Committee of a league it shall be the obligation of the complaining Club (or other person making the complaint) to establish that upon the balance of probabilities the complaint is justified. If the Organising Committee considers that the complaint is not justified it may dismiss it without hearing the representations of the Club or person against whom the complaint is made. The Organising Committee cannot find a complaint proved without giving the person or Club against whom the complaint is made an opportunity to make representations or call relevant evidence.

c) Any party aggrieved at the decision of the Organising Committee may, within seven days of receipt of the decision, appeal in writing to the Secretary of the RFU restating the grounds on which the original appeal was made. The Club shall not be entitled to introduce any further grounds of objection not previously stated to the Organising Committee, nor to lodge a second objection arising from the circumstances on which the objection is based.

The Secretary of the RFU shall refer the objection to the Competition Sub-Committee of the RFU whose decision shall be final and binding. It shall be the sole discretion of the Competition Sub-Committee whether or not to grant a personal hearing.

d) (i) Any party to an appeal (whether made under Regulation 19(b) or 19(c)) shall provide such information or evidence and within such time as the Organising Committee or the Appeal Committee (as the case may be) shall require.

(ii) Upon a party to an appeal failing to provide such information within the time required, the Organising Committee or the Appeal Committee (as the case may be) shall be entitled to refuse to hear that party when considering the appeal.

e) The Club and/or appellant may be required to pay the cost of the Appeal when a personal hearing is requested and granted.

20 Medical Safety

Whenever possible, the home team should ensure a doctor or other medically qualified person is in attendance throughout the match.

21 Terms and Conditions of Participation

All Clubs participating in the Competition shall at all times comply with each and every of the obligations and requirements entered into by the RFU with third parties, including but not limited to, the sponsors of the Competition under the terms and conditions of the sponsorship agreement. Details of any such obligations and requirements shall be notified by the RFU to participating Clubs as applicable.

22 Copyright

The copyright in the fixture lists of the Competition shall vest in the RFU and must not be reproduced in whole or in part except with the written consent of the RFU.

RFU REGISTRATION OF PLAYERS

Regulations and Operating Procedures – Season 1995/96

These Regulations and Operating Procedures apply to all players making an application to be registered with a Club in membership of the Rugby Football Union on or after **6th May 1995**. All existing RFU player registrations and eligibility dates remain valid.

1   **Definitions – for the purpose of RFU Registration Regulations and Operating Procedures –**

   a)   **Home Union Player** is a player who has, or is currently entitled to hold, as his only or main passport either a passport of the United Kingdom of Great Britain and Northern Ireland or a passport of the Republic of Ireland or a passport issued in the Channel Islands or the Isle of Man.

   b)   **Overseas Player** is any player who is unable to satisfy provisions of 1(a) above.

   c)   **Registrar** is a person appointed annually by the RFU Competition Sub-Committee for each Division/National Clubs Association/National Leagues 5 (North and South) responsible for the administration of computerised registration of players. The Registrars for season 1995/96 are as set out in Appendix 1.

   d)   **Registration Date** is the date on which a properly completed Registration Form is received by the Registrar when the Player's name will be added to a Club's computerised registration list, (subject to Regulation 3(b) of these Regulations).

   e)   **EFFECTIVE Date** is the date when a player's Registration Application becomes EFFECTIVE in accordance with the Registration Regulations.

2   All players competing in the Courage Clubs Championship, the Pilkington Cup and the Pilkington Shield, MUST BE REGISTERED ON THE OFFICIAL REGISTRATION FORM, EDITION 6, DATED APRIL 1995. No other forms will be accepted. Pads of these forms are available from Michael Humphreys & Partners. The first pad in each season will be supplied free of charge. Thereafter pads will only be supplied upon payment of £25 for each pad – cheques to be made payable to 'SPIRE'.

3   (a)   The Registration Application Form when fully completed must be submitted to the Registrar as appropriate – see Regulation 1(c).

   (b)   In Leagues below National League 5 North and South forms may only be submitted to the Registrar by post.

   (c)   In National Leagues 1, 2, 3, 4 and 5 North and South Registration Forms may be submitted either by post or by FAX. If the original Registration Form is received by the Registrar no later than first post on the seventh day after the receipt of the FAX (and only in such case) the registration date shall be deemed to be the date of the FAX.

   (d)   All relevant sections of the Registration Form MUST be completed and personally signed by the player and either the Club Secretary or other official appointed by the Club to have responsibility for maintaining the Club's register of players.

   (e)   All registration applications MUST be accompanied by a stamped self addressed envelope – see Regulation 8(b).

   (f)   Registration Forms from 'overseas' players MUST be accompanied by the completed International Rugby Football Board form endorsed by their own Union and, where that player is claiming possession of a British Passport as his only or main passport, a copy of documentary evidence supporting his claim.

   (g)   No Club playing in National Leagues 1, 2, 3, 4 and 5 North and South may register more than **50 players** at any one time – see Transitional Regulation 9(a)(iv).

   (h)   A Club shall not submit a Registration Form on behalf of any player under the age of 18 years.

   (i)   Any incomplete forms will be returned to the sender and the registration will not be recorded until these have been resubmitted containing all the information required. Applications carrying false information or per-pro signatures are unacceptable and will invalidate any Effective Registration thereby obtained. It may also may render the Club, player and/or official liable to disciplinary action under RFU Rule 5.12, in addition to any statutory penalties that may be imposed under any RFU Competition Regulation.

4   On receipt of the Registration Form, the Registrar will calculate the EFFECTIVE date of registration for the RFU Club Competitions referred to in 1(e) above and enter this date into the computer records.

5   At any point in time a player may only be registered with **two** Clubs affiliated to the RFU, only **one** of which can be EFFECTIVE.

6   Registration Procedure
   a)   A Club wishing to register a player from another Club will submit the **white** and **pink** copies of the Registration Application Form to the Registrar responsible for the Player's new Club.
   b)   On receipt of the correctly completed Form the Registrar will enter the details into the computer and identify an Effective Date for the Player. The Club submitting the application will be notified – see Regulation 3(e) and 8.
   c)   The **pink** copy will be sent to the Registrar for the Player's old club within 7 days. He will then amend his records.
   d)   The yellow copy must be retained by the Club for record purposes.

7   Should Officials of the player's current Club have objections to the player moving under RFU Regulations concerning unpaid subscriptions or RFU Rule 5.12 or any of the IRFB Regulations Relating to Amateurism, these objections must be submitted in writing to the Secretary of the RFU stating all the grounds upon which the objection is made. The Club shall not be entitled to introduce any further grounds of objection not so stated nor to lodge a second objection arising from the circumstances upon which an objection is based.

8   (a)   On or before **1st September** the Registrar will post to each Club a complete list of registered players. This list will show Registration Date, Competition Eligibility Date and movement of players and will be updated on receipt of each new Registration Application Form.
     (b)   A copy of this current list will only be forwarded to the Club if a stamped-addressed envelope has been enclosed with the new Registration Form.
           THE CLUBS'S COMPUTERISED REGISTRATION LIST IS THE ONLY EVIDENCE THAT WILL BE ACCEPTED TO SUBSTANTIATE A PLAYER'S EFFECTIVE REGISTRATION.

9   **Registration Regulations**
   a)   **Registration of Home Union Players**
        The Registration Date is as defined in Regulation 1(d), but the registration becomes EFFECTIVE as follows:-
        (i)   7 days (exclusive of the period 1st May to 31st August) – for a player who is not registered with any other Club in membership of the RFU and who has not played, during the twelve calendar months immediately preceding his Registration Application, for any Club (other than a student Club or school) in membership of any other National Union and has played in any competition organised by that or any other National Union.
              A player in this section (i) whose Registration Application is with a Club in National Leagues 1, 2, 3, 4 and 5 North and South shall have EFFECTIVE registration on the Registration Date.
              A Player in this section (i) may also within 7 days of his Registration Date request that the Registrar cancel his application and such a request must be received in writing by the Registrar within the 7 day period.
        (ii) 60 days – (exclusive of the period 1st May to 31st August) after the Registration Date – for players (other than (i) above) who are moving between Clubs, both of which are playing in a League BELOW the first Divisional League (ie, North Division 1, Midland Division 1, South West Division 1 and London & South East Division 1).
              A player in this section (ii) retains EFFECTIVE registration and may play in RFU competition matches for his current Club throughout the 60 day period of waiting for EFFECTIVE registration with his new Club.
              A player in this section (ii) may also within 60 days of his Registration Date request that the Registrar cancel his application – such a request must be received in writing by the Registrar within the 60 day period.
        (iii) 120 days – (exclusive of the period 1st May to 31st August) after the Registration Date – for players other than those qualifying in (i) and (ii) above.
              A player in this section (iii) may continue to play in RFU competition matches for his current Club throughout the 120 day period of waiting for EFFECTIVE registration with his new Club.
              A player in this section (iii) may also within 120 days of his Registration Date, request that the Registrar cancel his application and such a request must be received in writing by the Registrar within the 120 day period.
   Transitional Regulation (Applicable only to National Leagues 5 North and South)
        (iv) A player in section (iii) above whose registration is cancelled by his Club under the 50 player maximum registration requirement (see Regulation 3g) will qualify for EFFECTIVE registration

30

with his new Club after 60 days (exclusive of the period 1st May to 31 August) providing the Registrar receives his application and enters it on the Club's computerised registration list on or before 30th September 1995. After this date deregistration procedure will apply.

b) **Registration of 'Overseas' Players**

(i) A Registration Application cannot be made until the player arrives in the Four Home Unions and he submits, duly completed by him and endorsed by his own Union, the IRFB form of statutory declaration giving clearance for him to play outside his own Union.

(ii) The Registration Date is as defined in Regulation 1(d), but the registration becomes EFFECTIVE 180 days (exclusive of the period 1st May to 31st August) after the Registration Date. Any absence from the Home Unions during this waiting period will count towards the 60 days stipulated in (b)(iv).

(iii) When a registered player has maintained EFFECTIVE registration for a consecutive period of 730 days (2 years), he ceases to be subject to the restriction in 8(b)(ii)of the Courage Clubs Championship Regulations and 2(b)(ii) of the Pilkington Cup and Pilkington Shield Regulations.

(iv) The registration of an overseas player will cease to be EFFECTIVE if the player is absent from the Four Home Unions at any time for a total of 60 days or more in any calendar year.

(v) A player who loses his EFFECTIVE registration under 9(b)(iv) has to re-apply and is subject to 9(b)(i) and (ii).

(vi) A player, if moving Clubs, is subject to the restrictions in 9(a)(ii) and (iii) which may run concurrently with the restriction in 9(b)(ii).

(vii) It is the responsibility of a Club to inform the Registrar if a player is absent from the Home Unions for a total of 60 days or more in any calendar year.

c) **Registration – General**

(i) Any player, however qualified, who is an employee of a Club, or of a Company which is substantially involved in any activity which is related to a Club, may not be registered with that Club unless authorised by the RFU Amateur Status Sub-Committee.

(ii) The registration or qualifying period of any player who is ineligible to play for any other reason under the Rules and Regulations of the RFU, is suspended for the period of that ineligibility but the right to withdraw a registration is not affected.

(iii) The EFFECTIVE registration for any player, who plays in a match in a Club Competition of any other National Union during the period 1st September to 30th April inclusive, shall be discontinued. A player whose registration is discontinued under this Clause may not re-register until he is residing in the Home Unions and must requalify under 9(a)(ii) or 9(a)(iii) if a Home Union player or 9(b)(ii) if an Overseas player.

(iv) A Player who is registered with a Club which withdraws from all RFU Competitions in the season and who wishes during that season to play for another Club in an RFU Competition, must register with that Club in accordance with these Regulations. If the Club withdrawing does not re-enter any RFU Competition for the following season, the player shall be entitled to EFFECTIVE Registration under paragraph 9(a)(i).

(v) A player with EFFECTIVE Registration may request to be deregistered, or a Club may request for a player to be deregistered. On receipt of such a request, which must be in writing, the Registrar will transfer the player's current Club registration to a lapsed registration file. After 120 days, the player shall no longer be registered.

A Player thus deregistered by a <u>Club</u> in National Leagues 1, 2, 3, 4, 5 North and 5 South may play for that Club during the deregistration period provided that the player remains as one of the 50 registered players allowed in that Club under Regulation 3(g).

(vi) A player whose registration has been deleted under clause 9(c)(v) may reapply for RFU registration and such registration will be EFFECTIVE on the Registration Date subject to the provision of Clause 9(a)(i).

(vii) A player who is under the age of 22 years on 1st September 1995 may request, in writing, to return to the Club which held his initial RFU registration ("his original Club"). His registration with his original Club will be EFFECTIVE immediately upon receipt of his written request by the Registrar, provided that no subsequent registration of that player shall become EFFECTIVE until the period of 120 days shall have elapsed from the date of the player's registration with and upon his returning to his original Club.

(viii) A Club may not register any player who has at any time received any material benefit (as defined in Regulation 1.3 of the IRFB Regulations Relating to Amateurism) for playing any form of Rugby Football.

10 Any dispute on the application of these Regulations and Operating Procedures by the Registrar must be referred in writing to that Registrar stating all the grounds on which the objection is made.

ERRORS AND OMISSIONS ON THE PART OF THE OBJECTING CLUB WILL NOT BE ACCEPTED AS A REASON FOR AN OBJECTION.

If the dispute is not resolved within 7 days, from receipt of the complaint by the Registrar, the Club or player may submit the complaint in writing to the Secretary of the RFU restating the grounds upon which the objection is made. The Club shall not be entitled to introduce any further grounds of objection not previously stated to the Registrar, nor to lodge a second objection arising from the circumstances upon which an objection is based.

The Secretary of the RFU shall refer the objection to the Competition Sub-Committee of the RFU whose decision shall be final and binding.

It shall be at the sole discretion of the Competition Sub-Committee whether or not to grant a personal hearing. The Club and/or player may be required to pay the cost of any such hearing.

11 The Competition Sub-Committee of the RFU shall have absolute and unfettered discretion to decide on any matter not provided for in and on the interpretation of these Regulations and Operating Procedures and their decision shall be final and binding.

Appendix 1

REGISTRARS – SEASON 1995-96

National Clubs Association

DAE Evans
22 Brooks Road, Sutton Coldfield,
West Midlands B71 1HP
Tel: 0121 354 8183 Fax: 0121 321 3221

London & South East Division

C Pool, Courage Registration
PO Box 178, Tewin Wood
Herts AL6 0XX
Tel 01438 798023

South West Division

M Gee
c/o The First Eleven Sports Agency,
PO Box 11, Reading, Berkshire RG6 3DT
Tel: 01734 311244

National Leagues 5 (North and South)

MJ Wilson
c/o Michael Humphreys & Partners Ltd,
68 South Lambeth Road, Vauxhall,
London SW8 1RL
Tel: 0171 820 9911
Fax: 0171 820 9259

Midland Division

DI Robins
c/o Russells News Agency, PO Box 183,
Leicester LE3 8BZ
Tel: 0116 2332200

Northern Division

R Archer
Brookfield House, Scotland Head, Winlaton,
Tyne & Wear NE21 6PL
Tel: 0191 414 3532

Appendix 2.

INTERNATIONAL RUGBY FOOTBALL BOARD

APPLICATION FOR CLEARANCE TO PLAY OR COACH IN ANOTHER UNION

HOME UNION . . . .

1.   NAME . . . .
                (SURNAME)   (FORENAMES)

2.   OCCUPATION . . . .

3.   NAME OF CLUB OR OTHER RUGBY ORGANISATION . . . .

     . . . .

4.   State the highest level at which you have played in your Union
     e.g. International/Other Representative (State level): Club or other Rugby playing
     organisation (state level)

     . . . .

5.   In what country or countries do you intend playing or coaching Rugby?

     . . . .

     Date of Departure from Home Union . . . .

     Anticipated date of return to Home Union . . . .

6.   Will you, a relative, or any other person, receive now, or at any time in the future, any
     payment, benefit or other material reward consequent upon your playing, coaching, or other
     involvement in Rugby Football in the countries listed in 5, or in any other country?   **YES/NO**

7.   Will travel fares be provided for you, a relative, or any other person, as a consequence of your
     arrangement with a Rugby Club, Union, or any other Rugby playing organisation to play or
     coach for them?   **YES/NO**

8.   Will a car or other motor vehicle be provided for you, a relative, or any other person, as a
     consequence of your arrangement with a Rugby Club, Union, or any other Rugby playing
     organisation to play or coach for them?   **YES/NO**

9. Will free or subsidised accommodation be provided for you, a relative, or any oter person,
     entirely as a consequence of your arrangement with a Rugby Club, Union, or any other Rugby
     playing organisation to play to coach for them?   **YES/NO**

10.   If the answer is **YES** to any of the enquiries made at items 6, 7, 8 or 9, full details of the
     arrangement contemplated must be attached.

CONDITIONS OF EMPLOYMENT

Where applicants are being employed please supply the following information:-
– air travel (paid for)
– accommodation (paid for)
– Motor vehicle supplied   (indicate business use only or business use and personal use)
– petrol supplied
– salary received
– job description
– term of employment and hours to be worked
– rugby player or coach
– any special condition?

STATUTORY DECLARATION

I . . . .
(Applicants full name – Forenames first)

of . . . .
solemnly and sincerely declare that I have read, understood and will abide by the Regulations
Relating to Amateurism, attached to this form, as approved by the International Rugby Football
Board and that the above information is correct in all particulars, and make this solemn
declaration conscientiously believing the same to be true.
I understand that on return to my Home Union. I will be required to submit a similar application
to my Home Union before I can be premitted to play or coach there.

. . . .
(Applicant's Signature)

Declared before me at . . . .

this . . . . day of . . . . 19 . . . .

. . . .
(Justice of the Peace, Solicitor or other person, authorised to take a Statutory Declaration)

DECLARATION ON BEHALF OF UNION

The applicant is in good standing with his Club and his Union. He is in no financial debt to his Club
or this Union. He is under no playing suspension order within the jurisdiction of this Union. At the time
of this approval, the player or coach is no longer participating within this Union.

For . . . . Union

. . . . Secretary . . . . Date . . . . . .
NOTE
Should this Declaration be signed by an official of a Union other than the Secretary of the
National Union, it **must** be sent for approval of the Secretary of the National Union.
Original: To be retained by Home Union
Copy: One to the other person concerned another to be sent to the Secretary of the Visited Union

(Union Stamp or Seal over)

Appendix 3.

RUGBY FOOTBALL UNION
ATTENTION ALL PLAYERS!
PLAYER REGISTRATION FOR ALL RUGBY FOOTBALL UNION COMPETITIONS

To play in the Courage Leagues, Pilkington Cup and Pilkington Shield you **must** be registered with the club you are representing. Every club has a computer list of its eligable players. Speak to your club registration officer if you are not on this list and think you should be.

You must be over the age of 18 years to be registered

If you have never been registered with another club and you have or are entitled to have a British Passport as your only or main passport you will be eligible within seven days of the form being received by your club's Registrar.

If you have registered with another club or are not entitled to have a British Passport you will have to serve a waiting period according to the current regulations.

Once correctly registered you will remain on the club's list until either:-
a) You change club.
b) You request to be de-registered.
c) Your club request that you should be de-registered.

This is only a guide. For full details consult your club secretary or other official for a complete set of the current regulations.

RFU Player Registration Guidance Notes (Sheet 1)

(To be read in conjunction with the full Player registration Regulations, which take precedence)

START → | Is the Player a Home Unions player as determined by Reg 1(a)? | NO → | See sheet 3, Regulation 9(b), 'Overseas Players

YES ↓

| Has the Player submitted a Registration Application on the official Reg. Form (Regs 2 & 3)? | NO → | Cannot play or be a replacement for a Club in the Courage Leagues, Pilkington Cup/Shield Competitions

YES ↓

| Has the Form (White & Pink Copies) been sent to the Registrar of YOUR League? Retain Yellow Copy for your records (Reg 6) | NO → | Cannot play or be a replacement for a Club in the Courage Leagues, Pilkington Cup/Shield Competitions

YES ↓

| Have you received a current list from your registrar showing the player(s) eligibility date(s)? (Reg. 8) | NO → | Cannot play until Player is on the list Showing date of Effective Registration. (see Regs 1(e), 4 & 5)

YES ↓

| MAY PLAY on or after the date shown for Effective Registration

RFU Player Registration Guidance Notes (Sheet 2)

START
↓

Immediately preceeding his Registration Application, has the Player played during the last 12 calendar months for any club (other than a Student Club or School) in Membership of ANY OTHER National Union in any competition organised by that or any other National Union? Reg. 9(a)(i)	← NO	Is the Player Registered with another Club in membership of the RFU?	←	Return to START or see sheet 1 or sheet 3 ('Overseas')

YES ↓ (under middle column)   NO ↑ (under right column)

Is the Player moving TO or FROM a Club in Nationals 1, 2, 3, 4, 5 N and S or a Division 1 Club? Reg. 9(a)(iii)	→	Is the player moving between any Club BELOW Division 1 Leagues?

YES ↓   YES ↓

YES → MUST WAIT 120 Days (exclusive of period 1st May to 31st Aug) for Registration to become Effective. Reg. 9(a)(iii)	MUST WAIT 60 DAYS (exclusive of period 1st May to 31st Aug) for Registration to become Effective. Reg. 9(a)(ii)

NO ↓

Registration becomes Effective 7 DAYS after receipt by Registrar of a completed Application Form, (exclusive of period 1st May to 31st Aug) Reg. 9(a)(i) Nationals 1, 2, 3, 4, 5 North and South shall have Effective Registration on the Registration Date

'OVERSEAS' Players as defined in Reg. 1(b) should refer to sheet 3 for a guide to Reg. 9(b)

RFU Players Registration Guidance Notes
(OVERSEAS PLAYERS) (Sheet 3)

START

Is the Player from a Union outside the Four Home Unions?	NO →	See Reg. 9(a) and sheet 2 of these guidance notes.
YES ↓		
Is the Player currently living in one of the Four Home Unions?	NO →	Cannot submit a Registration Application until he is.
YES ↓		
Has the player submitted a completed IRFB Form of Statutory Declaration endorsed by his own Union giving him clearance to play? (see appendix 2)	NO →	Cannot submit a Registration Application until he does.
YES ↓		
Has the Player submitted a Player Registration Form? (Reg. 3)	NO →	Cannot commence Registration Qualification until he does.
YES ↓		
MUST WAIT 180 DAYS (exclusive of 1st May to 31st Aug) for Registration to become Effective. Reg 9 (b)(ii)	NO →	Cannot commence Registration Qualification until he does.

Organising Committee for National Leagues 1, 2, 3 and 4

The Committee shall comprise:

a) The Officers (Chairman, Treasurer, Secretary)

b) Four representatives elected from within their membership by the Members comprising National League 1 of the Courage Clubs Championship.

c) Two representatives from each of the four geographical Divisions of the RFU elected from within their membership by those Members within each of the respective Divisions

The members for 1995/96 are:

J A Allen
60 Dorchester Road,
Leicester LE3 0UF
Tel: 0116 2858407 (H)
      0116 2471234 (B)
Fax: 0116 2471434

B Baister (Honorary Treasurer)
The Cedars, 3 Kidderton Close
Brindley, Nantwich,
Cheshire CW5 8JU
Tel: 01270 524465 (H)
      01928 511234 (B)
Fax: 01270 524465

J Baxter
Exwick Barton, Exwick,
Exeter, Devon
Tel: 01392 73496

A Bragg
Ashgates, Church House,
13-15 Regent Street
Nottingham NG1 5BS
Tel: 01949 20580 (H)
      0115 9415193 (B)
Fax: 0115 9412047

D A E Evans (Secretary)
22 Brooks Road, Wylde Green,
Sutton Coldfield,
West Midlands B72 1HP
Tel: 0121 3548183
Fax: 0121 3213221

R Fawden,
100 Swain's Lane, Highgate,
London N6 6PL.
Tel: 0181 340 2199 (H)
      0181 348 4254 (B)
Fax: 0181 348 5051

R Foster,
27 Carrs Lane, Sandal, Wakefield,
West Yorkshire WF2 6HJ.
Tel: 01924 250116 (H)

F M Gibbon (Chairman),
5 Church Row, Wolviston,
Billingham, Cleveland TS22 5LD.
Tel: 01740 644308 (H)
      01642 602221 (B)
Fax: 01642 341035

G Morey
27 Carter Walk, Penn
Buckinghamshire HP10 8ER
Tel: 01494 814607 (H)
Fax: 01494 815144

J Partridge
c/o Rugby Lions FC, Webb Ellis Road,
Rugby, Warwickshire CV22 7AN
Tel: 01788 813082 (H)
      01788 540333 (B)

B W Redwood
205 Stoke Lane, Westbury-on-Trym,
Bristol BS9 3RX
Tel: 0117 9684342 (H)
      0117 9424273 (B)

T Richmond
Inglenook, Carlinghow Hill
Batley, West Yorkshire WF17 0AG
Tel: 01294 472705 (H)
      01274 480741 (B)
Fax: 01274 487437

D Seabrook,
29 St. Lukes Drive, Orrell,
Nr. Wigan, Lancs. WM5 7AU
Tel: 01695 622648 (H)

C Sewell
6 Font Close, Titchfield Common,
Fareham, Hampshire PO14 4QH
Tel: 01489 583417 (H)
      01705 563904 (B)

P Walker,
13 Wickham Road, Lower Earley
Reading RG6 3TE
Tel: 01734 666302 (H)
      01932 249257 (B)
Fax: 01932 250953

NATIONAL MEDIA CONTACTS

DAILY EXPRESS
Ludgate House, 245 Blackfriars Road,
London SE1 9UX
Tel: 0171 928 8000

DAILY MAIL
Northcliffe House, 2 Derry Street,
London W8 5TT
Tel: 0171 938 6000

DAILY MIRROR
1 Canada Square, Canary Wharf,
London E14 5AB
Tel: 0171 293 3000

THE DAILY TELEGRAPH
1 Canada Square, Canary Wharf,
London E14 5DT
Tel: 0171 538 5000

THE EUROPEAN
Orbit House, 5 New Fetters Lane,
London EC4A 1AR
Tel: 0171 377 4903

EVENING STANDARD
Northcliffe House, 2 Derry Street,
London W8 5TT
Tel: 0171 938 6000

THE GUARDIAN
119 Farringdon Road,
London EC1R 3ER
Tel: 0171 278 2332

THE INDEPENDENT
1 Canada Square, Canary Wharf,
London E14 5DL
Tel: 0171 293 2000

THE DAILY STAR
Ludgate House, 245 Blackfriars Road
London SE1 9UX
Tel: 0171 928 8000

THE SUN
PO Box 481, Virginia Street
London E1 9BD
Tel: 0171 782 4000

THE TIMES
1 Pennington Street, London E1 9XN
Tel: 0171 782 5000

TODAY
1 Virginia Street, London E1 9BS
Tel: 0171 782 4600

MAIL ON SUNDAY
Northcliffe House, 2 Derry Street,
London W8 5TT
Tel: 0171 938 6000

NEWS OF THE WORLD
1 Virginia Street, London E1 9XR
Tel 0171 782 4000

PRESS ASSOCIATION
PA Sport, London House,
Central Park, New Lane,
Leeds LS11 5DZ
Tel: 0113 2344411

NATIONAL MEDIA CONTACTS

THE OBSERVER
119 Farringdon Road,
London EC1R 3ER
Tel: 0171 278 2332

SUNDAY EXPRESS
Ludgate House, 245 Blackfriars Road,
London SE1 9UX
Tel: 0171 928 8000

SUNDAY MIRROR
1 Canada Square, Canary Wharf,
London E14 5AB
Tel: 0171 510 3000

SUNDAY TELEGRAPH
1 Canada Square, Canary Wharf,
London E14 5DT
Tel: 0171 538 5000

SUNDAY TIMES
1, Pennington Street, London E1 9XW
Tel: 0171 782 5000

THE PEOPLE
1 Canada Square, Canary Wharf,
London E14 5AP
Tel: 0171 510 3000

INDEPENDENT ON SUNDAY
1 Canada Square, Canary Wharf,
London E14 5DL
Tel: 0171 293 2000

ITN NEWS
200 Grays Inn Road, London WC1X 8XZ
Tel: 0171 833 3000

BBC TV NEWS
Television Centre, Wood Lane,
London W12 7RJ
Tel: 0181 576 1914

BBC BREAKFAST NEWS
Room 7039, Television Centre
London W12 7RJ
Tel: 0181 576 7501 / 6

SKY NEWS & SKY SPORT
6 Centaurs Business Park, Grant Way,
Isleworth, Middlesex TW7 5QD
Tel: 0171 705 3000

GMTV
The London Television Centre,
Upper Ground, London SE1 9TT
Tel: 0171 827 7000

CHANNEL FOUR NEWS
200 Grays Inn Road,
London WC1X 8XZ
Tel: 0171 833 3000

I.R.N.
200 Grays Inn Road,
London WC1X 8XZ
Tel: 0171 833 3000

RADIO FIVE LIVE
Broadcasting House, London W1 1AA
Tel: 0171 580 4468

THE COURAGE CLUBS
CHAMPIONSHIP GENERAL CONTACTS

NATIONAL ADMINISTRATION OFFICE

Michael Humphreys & Partners Ltd.,
68 South Lambeth Road,
Vauxhall,
London SW8 1RL.
Tel: 0171 820 9911
Fax: 0171 820 9259

Administration Director: Sue Wheeler
Administration Executives: Katie Bullivant
                                     Theo Chapman

Michael Humphreys & Partners (MH&P) is responsible to the Rugby Football Union for the administration of fixtures, results and league tables for all National Leagues.

MH&P also represents the RFU in liaison with the Committee of each RFU Division of the Championship. The Company is responsible for ensuring that all necessary fixtures have been made and that all promotions and relegations are arranged.

Media Relations Director: Susan McMahon
Media Relations Manager: Sara Jones
Media Relations Executive: Julian Yeomans

MH&P is responsible to the RFU for the overall promotion and media relations with regard to the Courage Clubs Championship. All information regarding fixtures, results and tables for the National Leagues is co-ordinated from MH&P. MH&P will also hold the results and the tables for all other leagues in the Championship. All media information regarding the overall Championship is released from MH&P and all enquiries should be directed to MH&P for any regional information not available from the regional contact.

THE RUGBY FOOTBALL UNION

Roger Godfrey,
The Administrative Secretary,
The Rugby Football Union,
Rugby Road, Twickenham,
Middlesex TW1 1DZ
Tel: 0181 892 8161

RFU COMPETITION SUB-COMMITTEE

The Committee will act as a final arbiter in case of all disputes.

Chairman:
Mike Wilson
6 New Road,
Easton-on-the-Hill
Stamford
Lincs. PE9 3NN
Tel: 01780 64019 (H)
Fax: 01780 64676

THE NATIONAL LEAGUES

LEAGUE 1
PAGE 71

LEAGUE 2
PAGE 149

LEAGUE 3
PAGE 205

LEAGUE 4
PAGE 259

NATIONAL LEAGUES STRUCTURE

and immediate supporting leagues

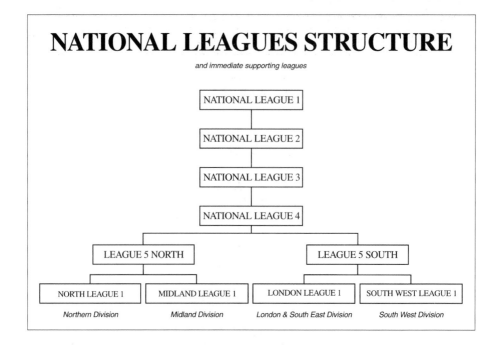

ADMINISTRATIVE INSTRUCTION — NATIONAL LEAGUES 1-4
COURAGE CLUBS CHAMPIONSHIP POSTPONED MATCHES

Matches which have to be postponed should be re-scheduled for the following Saturday. The only exceptions can be when:

a)   One or other side is involved in another National Club Competition (i.e. Pilkington Cup).

b)   On or within two days of the re-scheduled date one or other side has three or more players involved in an RFU Divisional match or a Senior England or A International or the full national representative team of another Home Union.

> NB County Cup and County rugby, Services and Student rugby do not take precedence over Courage Clubs Championship matches in National Leagues 1-4.

If any of the above exceptions apply then the match should be played on the first Saturday when they do not. The RFU National Administration Office will advise Clubs regarding rearranged dates.

Where the next or next available Saturday presents another major difficulty to either side then an appeal may be made within two days of the original match date for an alternative date. This appeal must be made to the Secretary of the Organising Committee. The decision of the Organising Committee is final.

Further to the above, the NCA has laid down guidelines for National League Clubs to follow in the case of possible postponements.

– Every effort must be made to play each match.

– In the event of postponement the decision must be left to the latest possible moment.

– The latest possible moment is normally judged by the departure time of the visiting team.

– Ground costs, sponsorship and media considerations should take second place to playing the match.

– If, prior to the day of a match it is considered that the pitch may be unplayable on the day of the match, a referee experienced at the relevant playing standard should be consulted on the fitness of the pitch before any decision is made. (The RFU will help identify a referee if requested.) On match day, if a decision is to be taken prior to the arrival of the visiting team then the match referee should be consulted.

COURAGE NATIONAL LEAGUES 1995-96

LEAGUE 1

BATH
BRISTOL
GLOUCESTER
HARLEQUINS
LEICESTER
ORRELL
SALE
SARACENS
WASPS
WEST HARTLEPOOL

LEAGUE 2

BEDFORD
BLACKHEATH
LONDON IRISH
LONDON SCOTTISH
MOSELEY
NEWCASTLE GOSFORTH
NORTHAMPTON
NOTTINGHAM
WAKEFIELD
WATERLOO

LEAGUE 3

COVENTRY
FYLDE
HARROGATE
MORLEY
OTLEY
READING
RICHMOND
ROSSLYN PARK
ROTHERHAM
RUGBY

LEAGUE 4

ASPATRIA
CLIFTON
EXETER
HAVANT
LEEDS
LIVERPOOL ST HELENS
LONDON WELSH
PLYMOUTH ALBION
REDRUTH
WALSALL

THE COURAGE CLUBS CHAMPIONSHIP 1994-95

NATIONAL LEAGUES: RFU SENIOR CLUBS ASSOCIATION (EXECUTIVE COMMITTEE)

CHAIRMAN

Frank Gibbon
5 Church Row, Wolviston,
Billingham, Cleveland TS22 5LD.
Tel: 01740 644308 (H)
    01642 602221 (B)
Fax: 01642 341035

HON. SECRETARY

Alwynne Evans,
22 Brooks Road, Wylde Green, Sutton Coldfield,
West Midlands B72 1HP.
Tel: 0121 354 8183 (H)
Fax: 021 321 3221

HON. TREASURER

Brian Baister
The Cedars, 3 Kidderton Close
Brindley, Nantwich, Cheshire CW5 8JU
Tel: 01270 524465 (H)
    01928 511234 (B)
Fax: 01270 524465

MEMBERS

J A Allen
60 Dorchester Road, Leicester LE3 0UF
Tel: 0116 2858407 (H)
    0116 2471234 (B)
Fax: 0116 2471434

J Baxter
Exwick Barton, Exwick, Exeter, Devon
Tel: 01392 73496

A Bragg
Ashgates, Church House, 13-15 Regent Street
Nottingham NG1 5BS
Tel: 01949 20580 (H)
    0115 9415193 (B)
Fax: 0115 9412047

R Fawden,
100 Swain's Lane, Highgate, London N6 6PL.
Tel: 0181 340 2199 (H)
    0181 348 4254 (B)
Fax: 0181 348 5051

R Foster,
27 Carrs Lane, Sandal, Wakefield,
West Yorkshire WF2 6HJ.
Tel: 01924 250116 (H)

G Morey
27 Carter Walk, Penn Buckinghamshire HP10 8ER
Tel: 01494 814607 (H)
Fax: 01494 815144

J Partridge
c/o Rugby Lions FC, Webb Ellis Road,
Rugby, Warwickshire CV22 7AN
Tel: 01788 813082 (H)
    01788 540333 (B)

B W Redwood
205 Stoke Lane, Westbury-on-Trym, Bristol BS9 3RX
Tel: 0117 9684342 (H)
    0117 9424273 (B)

T Richmond
Inglenook, Carlinghow Hill
Batley, West Yorkshire WF17 0AG
Tel: 01294 472705 (H)
    01274 480741 (B)
Fax: 01274 487437

D Seabrook
29 St. Lukes Drive, Orrell,
Nr. Wigan, Lancs. WM5 7AU
Tel: 01695 622648 (H)

C Sewell
6 Font Close, Titchfield Common,
Fareham, Hampshire PO14 4QH
Tel: 01489 583417 (H)
    01705 563904 (B)

P Walker
13 Wickham Road, Lower Earley
Reading RG6 3TE
Tel: 01734 666302 (H)
    01932 249257 (B)
Fax: 01932 250953

COURAGE CLUBS CHAMPIONSHIP

NATIONAL LEAGUE FIXTURES – 1995-96 LEAGUE ONE

September 9th (Week 2)

Gloucester	v	Sale
Leicester	v	Saracens
Orrell	v	Harlequins
Wasps	v	Bristol
West Hartlepool	v	Bath

September 16th (Week 3)

Bath	v	Gloucester
Bristol	v	West Hartlepool
Harlequins	v	Wasps
Sale	v	Leicester
Saracens	v	Orrell

September 23rd (Week 4)

Bristol	v	Harlequins
Leicester	v	Bath
Orrell	v	Sale
Wasps	v	Saracens
West Hartlepool	v	Gloucester

September 30th (Week X1)

Bath	v	Orrell
Gloucester	v	Leicester
Harlequins	v	West Hartlepool
Sale	v	Wasps
Saracens	v	Bristol

October 7th (Week 5)

Bristol	v	Sale
Harlequins	v	Saracens
Orrell	v	Gloucester
Wasps	v	Bath
West Hartlepool	v	Leicester

October 14th (Week 6)

Bath	v	Bristol
Gloucester	v	Wasps
Leicester	v	Orrell
Sale	v	Harlequins
Saracens	v	West Hartlepool

October 21st (Week 7)

Bristol	v	Gloucester
Harlequins	v	Bath
Orrell	v	West Hartlepool
Saracens	v	Sale
Wasps	v	Leicester

October 28th (Week 8)

Bath	v	Saracens
Gloucester	v	Harlequins
Leicester	v	Bristol
Orrell	v	Wasps
West Hartlepool	v	Sale

November 4th (Week 9)

Bristol	v	Orrell
Harlequins	v	Leicester
Sale	v	Bath
Saracens	v	Gloucester
Wasps	v	West Hartlepool

November 11th (Week 10)

Bath	v	West Hartlepool
Bristol	v	Wasps
Harlequins	v	Orrell
Sale	v	Gloucester
Saracens	v	Leicester

December 30th (Week X4)

Gloucester	v	Bath
Leicester	v	Sale
Orrell	v	Saracens
Wasps	v	Harlequins
West Hartlepool	v	Bristol

January 6th (Week 17)

Bath	v	Leicester
Gloucester	v	West Hartlepool
Harlequins	v	Bristol
Sale	v	Orrell
Saracens	v	Wasps

February 10th (Week 22)

Bristol	v	Saracens
Leicester	v	Gloucester
Orrell	v	Bath
Wasps	v	Sale
West Hartlepool	v	Harlequins

COURAGE CLUBS CHAMPIONSHIP

February 17th (Week 23)

Bath	v	Wasps
Gloucester	v	Orrell
Leicester	v	West Hartlepool
Sale	v	Bristol
Saracens	v	Harlequins

March 30th (Week X7)

Bristol	v	Bath
Harlequins	v	Sale
Orrell	v	Leicester
Wasps	v	Gloucester
West Hartlepool	v	Saracens

April 6th (Week 29)

Bath	v	Harlequins
Gloucester	v	Bristol
Leicester	v	Wasps
Sale	v	Saracens
West Hartlepool	v	Orrell

April 13th (Week 30)

Bristol	v	Leicester
Harlequins	v	Gloucester
Sale	v	West Hartlepool
Saracens	v	Bath
Wasps	v	Orrell

April 27th (Week 32)

Bath	v	Sale
Gloucester	v	Saracens
Leicester	v	Harlequins
Orrell	v	Bristol
West Hartlepool	v	Wasps

Quins Chris Sheesby tackled by Aadel Kardooni Leicester

COURAGE CLUBS CHAMPIONSHIP

NATIONAL LEAGUE FIXTURES – 1995-96 LEAGUE TWO

September 9th (Week 2)

London Irish v Northampton
Moseley v Newcastle Gosforth
Nottingham v Blackheath
Wakefield v Bedford
Waterloo v London Scottish

September 16th (Week 3)

Bedford v Waterloo
Blackheath v Wakefield
London Scottish v London Irish
Newcastle Gosforth v Nottingham
Northampton v Moseley

September 23rd (Week 4)

Bedford v Blackheath
Moseley v London Scottish
Nottingham v Northampton
Wakefield v Newcastle Gosforth
Waterloo v London Irish

September 30th (Week X1)

Blackheath v Waterloo
London Irish v Moseley
London Scottish v Nottingham
Newcastle Gosforth v Bedford
Northampton v Wakefield

October 7th (Week 5)

Bedford v Northampton
Blackheath v Newcastle Gosforth
Nottingham v London Irish
Wakefield v London Scottish
Waterloo v Moseley

October 14th (Week 6)

London Irish v Wakefield
London Scottish v Bedford
Moseley v Nottingham
Newcastle Gosforth v Waterloo
Northampton v Blackheath

October 21st (Week 7)

Bedford v London Irish
Blackheath v London Scottish
Newcastle Gosforth v Northampton
Nottingham v Waterloo
Wakefield v Moseley

October 28th (Week 8)

London Irish v Blackheath
London Scottish v Newcastle Gosforth
Moseley v Bedford
Nottingham v Wakefield
Waterloo v Northampton

November 4th (Week 9)

Bedford v Nottingham
Blackheath v Moseley
Newcastle Gosforth v London Irish
Northampton v London Scottish
Wakefield v Waterloo

November 11th (Week 10)

Bedford v Wakefield
Blackheath v Nottingham
London Scottish v Waterloo
Newcastle Gosforth v Moseley
Northampton v London Irish

December 30th (Week X4)

London Irish v London Scottish
Moseley v Northampton
Nottingham v Newcastle Gosforth
Wakefield v Blackheath
Waterloo v Bedford

January 6th (Week 17)

Blackheath v Bedford
London Irish v Waterloo
London Scottish v Moseley
Newcastle Gosforth v Wakefield
Northampton v Nottingham

February 10th (Week 22)

Bedford v Newcastle Gosforth
Moseley v London Irish
Nottingham v London Scottish
Wakefield v Northampton
Waterloo v Blackheath

COURAGE CLUBS CHAMPIONSHIP

February 17th (Week 23)

London Irish	v	Nottingham
London Scottish	v	Wakefield
Moseley	v	Waterloo
Newcastle Gosforth	v	Blackheath
Northampton	v	Bedford

March 30th (Week X7)

Bedford	v	London Scottish
Blackheath	v	Northampton
Nottingham	v	Moseley
Wakefield	v	London Irish
Waterloo	v	Newcastle Gosforth

April 6th (Week 29)

London Irish	v	Bedford
London Scottish	v	Blackheath
Moseley	v	Wakefield
Northampton	v	Newcastle Gosforth
Waterloo	v	Nottingham

April 13th (Week 30)

Bedford	v	Moseley
Blackheath	v	London Irish
Newcastle Gosforth	v	London Scottish
Northampton	v	Waterloo
Wakefield	v	Nottingham

April 27th (Week 32)

London Irish	v	Newcastle Gosforth
London Scottish	v	Northampton
Moseley	v	Blackheath
Nottingham	v	Bedford
Waterloo	v	Wakefield

Bedford captain, Steve Harris, scores against Richmond, not needing the assistance of, left to right, Mark Upex, Matt Deans and ubiquitous and popular Singh Basra

Photograph courtesy of Bedfordshire on Sunday

COURAGE CLUBS CHAMPIONSHIP

NATIONAL LEAGUE FIXTURES – 1995-96 LEAGUE THREE

September 9th (Week 2)

Harrogate	v	Coventry
Otley	v	Reading
Richmond	v	Morley
Rosslyn Park	v	Rotherham
Rugby	v	Fylde

September 16th (Week 3)

Coventry	v	Rugby
Fylde	v	Rotherham
Morley	v	Otley
Reading	v	Harrogate
Rosslyn Park	v	Richmond

September 23rd (Week 4)

Coventry	v	Reading
Harrogate	v	Morley
Otley	v	Rosslyn Park
Richmond	v	Fylde
Rugby	v	Rotherham

September 30th (Week X1)

Fylde	v	Otley
Morley	v	Coventry
Reading	v	Rugby
Rosslyn Park	v	Harrogate
Rotherham	v	Richmond

October 14th (Week 6)

Coventry	v	Rosslyn Park
Harrogate	v	Fylde
Otley	v	Rotherham
Reading	v	Morley
Rugby	v	Richmond

October 21st (Week 7)

Fylde	v	Coventry
Morley	v	Rugby
Richmond	v	Otley
Rosslyn Park	v	Reading
Rotherham	v	Harrogate

October 28th (Week 8)

Coventry	v	Rotherham
Harrogate	v	Richmond
Morley	v	Rosslyn Park
Otley	v	Rugby
Reading	v	Fylde

November 11th (Week 10)

Coventry	v	Richmond
Fylde	v	Morley
Harrogate	v	Otley
Rotherham	v	Reading
Rugby	v	Rosslyn Park

January 6th (Week 17)

Morley	v	Rotherham
Otley	v	Coventry
Reading	v	Richmond
Rosslyn Park	v	Fylde
Rugby	v	Harrogate

January 13th (Week 18)

Coventry	v	Morley
Harrogate	v	Rosslyn Park
Otley	v	Fylde
Richmond	v	Rotherham
Rugby	v	Reading

February 10th (Week 22)

Fylde	v	Harrogate
Morley	v	Reading
Richmond	v	Rugby
Rosslyn Park	v	Coventry
Rotherham	v	Otley

February 17th (Week 23)

Coventry	v	Fylde
Harrogate	v	Rotherham
Otley	v	Richmond
Reading	v	Rosslyn Park
Rugby	v	Morley

February 24th (Week 24)

Fylde	v	Reading
Richmond	v	Harrogate
Rosslyn Park	v	Morley
Rotherham	v	Coventry
Rugby	v	Otley

COURAGE CLUBS CHAMPIONSHIP

March 23rd (Week 28)

Morley	v	Fylde
Otley	v	Harrogate
Reading	v	Rotherham
Richmond	v	Coventry
Rosslyn Park	v	Rugby

March 30th (Week X7)

Coventry	v	Otley
Fylde	v	Rosslyn Park
Harrogate	v	Rugby
Richmond	v	Reading
Rotherham	v	Morley

April 6th (Week 29)

Coventry	v	Harrogate
Fylde	v	Rugby
Morley	v	Richmond
Reading	v	Otley
Rotherham	v	Rosslyn Park

April 13th (Week 30)

Harrogate	v	Reading
Otley	v	Morley
Richmond	v	Rosslyn Park
Rotherham	v	Fylde
Rugby	v	Coventry

April 27th (Week 32)

Fylde	v	Richmond
Morley	v	Harrogate
Reading	v	Coventry
Rosslyn Park	v	Otley
Rotherham	v	Rugby

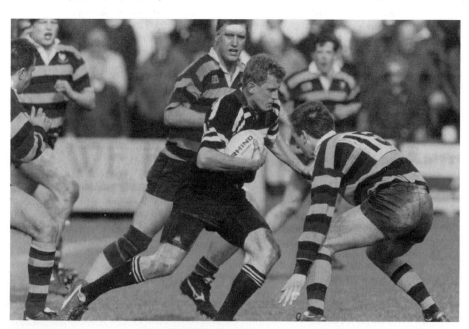

Otley centre Jonathan Flint speeds past Harrogate's Ian Hassall to score at Cross Green in the Courage League Three match which Otley won 33-14.

Photograph courtesy of Gordon Bunney

COURAGE CLUBS CHAMPIONSHIP

NATIONAL LEAGUE FIXTURES – 1995-96 LEAGUE FOUR

September 9th (Week 2)

Clifton	v	London Welsh
Leeds	v	Liverpool St Helens
Plymouth Albion	v	Havant
Redruth	v	Aspatria
Walsall	v	Exeter

September 16th (Week 3)

Aspatria	v	Clifton
Exeter	v	Leeds
Havant	v	Redruth
Liverpool St Helens	v	Plymouth Albion
London Welsh	v	Walsall

September 23th (Week 4)

Aspatria	v	Havant
Clifton	v	Walsall
Leeds	v	London Welsh
Plymouth Albion	v	Exeter
Redruth	v	Liverpool St Helens

September 30th (Week X1)

Exeter	v	Redruth
Havant	v	Clifton
Liverpool St Helens	v	Aspatria
London Welsh	v	Plymouth Albion
Walsall	v	Leeds

Ocotber 14th (Week 6)

Aspatria	v	Exeter
Clifton	v	Leeds
Havant	v	Liverpool St Helens
Plymouth Albion	v	Walsall
Redruth	v	London Welsh

October 21st (Week 7)

Exeter	v	Havant
Leeds	v	Plymouth Albion
Liverpool St Helens	v	Clifton
London Welsh	v	Aspatria
Walsall	v	Redruth

October 28th (Week 8)

Aspatria	v	Walsall
Havant	v	London Welsh
Liverpool St Helens	v	Exeter
Plymouth Albion	v	Clifton
Redruth	v	Leeds

November 11th (Week 10)

Clifton	v	Exeter
Leeds	v	Aspatria
London Welsh	v	Liverpool St Helens
Plymouth Albion	v	Redruth
Walsall	v	Havant

January 6th (Week 17)

Aspatria	v	Plymouth Albion
Clifton	v	Redruth
Havant	v	Leeds
Liverpool St Helens	v	Walsall
London Welsh	v	Exeter

January 13th (Week 18)

Aspatria	v	Redruth
Exeter	v	Walsall
Havant	v	Plymouth Albion
Liverpool St Helens	v	Leeds
London Welsh	v	Clifton

February 10th (Week 22)

Clifton	v	Aspatria
Leeds	v	Exeter
Plymouth Albion	v	Liverpool St Helens
Redruth	v	Havant
Walsall	v	London Welsh

February 17th (Week 23)

Exeter	v	Plymouth Albion
Havant	v	Aspatria
Liverpool St Helens	v	Redruth
London Welsh	v	Leeds
Walsall	v	Clifton

February 24th (Week 24)

Aspatria	v	Liverpool St Helens
Clifton	v	Havant
Leeds	v	Walsall
Plymouth Albion	v	London Welsh
Redruth	v	Exeter

COURAGE CLUBS CHAMPIONSHIP

March 23rd (Week 28)

Exeter	v	Aspatria
Leeds	v	Clifton
Liverpool St Helens	v	Havant
London Welsh	v	Redruth
Walsall	v	Plymouth Albion

March 30th (Week X7)

Aspatria	v	London Welsh
Clifton	v	Liverpool St Helens
Havant	v	Exeter
Plymouth Albion	v	Leeds
Redruth	v	Walsall

April 6th (Week 29)

Clifton	v	Plymouth Albion
Exeter	v	Liverpool St Helens
Leeds	v	Redruth
London Welsh	v	Havant
Walsall	v	Aspatria

April 13th (Week 30)

Aspatria	v	Leeds
Exeter	v	Clifton
Havant	v	Walsall
Liverpool St Helens	v	London Welsh
Redruth	v	Plymouth Albion

April 27th (Week 32)

Exeter	v	London Welsh
Leeds	v	Havant
Plymouth Albion	v	Aspatria
Redruth	v	Clifton
Walsall	v	Liverpool St Helens

Long-serving Leeds prop Adam Machell is determined to keep possession against Reading in Courage League Four.

Pgotograph courtesy of Gordon Bunney

COURAGE CLUBS CHAMPIONSHIP

NATIONAL LEAGUE FIXTURES – 1995-96 LEAGUE FIVE NORTH

September 16th (Week 3)
Worcester v Stoke-on-Trent
Preston Grasshoppers v Lichfield
Broughton Park v Sheffield
Sandal v Birmingham/Solihull
Winnington Park v Nuneaton
Stourbridge v Kendal

September 23rd (Week 4)
Kendal v Worcester
Nuneaton v Stourbridge
Birmingham/Solihull v Winnington Park
Sheffield v Sandal
Lichfield v Broughton Park
Wharfedale v Preston Grasshoppers

September 30th (Week X1)
Worcester v Nuneaton
Stoke-on-Trent v Kendal
Broughton Park v Wharfedale
Sandal v Lichfield
Winnington Park v Sheffield
Stourbridge v Birmingham/Solihull

October 14th (Week 6)
Nuneaton v Stoke-on-Trent
Birmingham/Solihull v Worcester
Sheffield v Stourbridge
Lichfield v Winnington Park
Wharfedale v Sandal
Preston Grasshoppers v Broughton Park

October 21st (Week 7)
Worcester v Sheffield
Stoke-on-Trent v Birmingham/Solihull
Kendal v Nuneaton
Sandal v Preston Grasshoppers
Winnington Park v Wharfedale
Stourbridge v Lichfield

October 28th (Week 8)
Birmingham/Solihull v Kendal
Sheffield v Stoke-on-Trent
Lichfield v Worcester
Wharfedale v Stourbridge
Preston Grasshoppers v Winnington Park
Broughton Park v Sandal

November 11th (Week 10)
Worcester v Wharfedale
Stoke-on-Trent v Lichfield
Kendal v Sheffield
Nuneaton v Birmingham/Solihull
Winnington Park v Broughton Park
Stourbridge v Preston Grasshoppers

January 6th (Week 17)
Sheffield v Nuneaton
Lichfield v Kendal
Wharfedale v Stoke-on-Trent
Preston Grasshoppers v Worcester
Broughton Park v Stourbridge
Sandal v Winnington Park

January 13th (Week 18)
Worcester v Broughton Park
Stoke-on-Trent v Preston Grasshoppers
Kendal v Wharfedale
Nuneaton v Lichfield
Birmingham/Solihull v Sheffield
Stourbridge v Sandal

February 10th (Week 22)
Lichfield v Birmingham/Solihull
Wharfedale v Nuneaton
Preston Grasshoppers v Kendal
Broughton Park v Stoke-on-Trent
Sandal v Worcester
Winnington Park v Stourbridge

February 17th (Week 23)
Worcester v Winnington Park
Stoke-on-Trent v Sandal
Kendal v Broughton Park
Nuneaton v Preston Grasshoppers
Birmingham/Solihull v Wharfedale
Sheffield v Lichfield

February 24th (Week 24)
Wharfedale v Sheffield
Preston Grasshoppers v Birmingham/Solihull
Broughton Park v Nuneaton
Sandal v Kendal
Winnington Park v Stoke-on-Trent
Stourbridge v Worcester

March 30th (Week X7)
Stoke-on-Trent v Stourbridge
Kendal v Winnington Park
Nuneaton v Sandal
Birmingham/Solihull v Broughton Park
Sheffield v Preston Grasshoppers
Lichfield v Wharfedale

COURAGE CLUBS CHAMPIONSHIP

NATIONAL LEAGUE FIXTURES – 1995-96 LEAGUE FIVE SOUTH

September 16th (Week 3)
High Wycombe v Lydney
Henley v Metropolitan Police
North Walsham v Camberley
Weston-super-Mare v Barking
Cheltenham v Askeans
Camborne v Berry Hill

September 23rd (Week 4)
Berry Hill v High Wycombe
Askeans v Camborne
Barking v Cheltenham
Camberley v Weston-super-Mare
Metropolitan Police v North Walsham
Tabard v Henley

September 30th (Week X1)
High Wycombe v Askeans
Lydney v Berry Hill
North Walsham v Tabard
Weston-super-Mare v Metropolitan Police
Cheltenham v Camberley
Camborne v Barking

October 14th (Week 6)
Askeans v Lydney
Barking v High Wycombe
Camberley v Camborne
Metropolitan Police v Cheltenham
Tabard v Weston-super-Mare
Henley v North Walsham

October 21st (Week 7)
High Wycombe v Camberley
Lydney v Barking
Berry Hill v Askeans
Weston-super-Mare v Henley
Cheltenham v Tabard
Camborne v Metropolitan Police

October 28th (Week 8)
Barking v Berry Hill
Camberley v Lydney
Metropolitan Police v High Wycombe
Tabard v Camborne
Henley v Cheltenham
North Walsham v Weston-super-Mare

November 11th (Week 10)
High Wycombe v Tabard
Lydney v Metropolitan Police
Berry Hill v Camberley
Askeans v Barking
Cheltenham v North Walsham
Camborne v Henley

January 6th (Week 17)
Camberley v Askeans
Metropolitan Police v Berry Hill
Tabard v Lydney
Henley v High Wycombe
North Walsham v Camborne
Weston-super-Mare v Cheltenham

January 13th (Week 18)
High Wycombe v North Walsham
Lydney v Henley
Berry Hill v Tabard
Askeans v Metropolitan Police
Barking v Camberley
Camborne v Weston-super-Mare

February 10th (Week 22)
Metropolitan Police v Barking
Tabard v Askeans
Henley v Berry Hill
North Walsham v Lydney
Weston-super-Mare v High Wycombe
Cheltenham v Camborne

February 17th (Week 23)
High Wycombe v Cheltenham
Lydney v Weston-super-Mare
Berry Hill v North Walsham
Askeans v Henley
Barking v Tabard
Camberley v Metropolitan Police

February 24th (Week 24)
Tabard v Camberley
Henley v Barking
North Walsham v Askeans
Weston-super-Mare v Berry Hill
Cheltenham v Lydney
Camborne v High Wycombe

March 30th (Week X7)
Lydney v Camborne
Berry Hill v Cheltenham
Askeans v Weston-super-Mare
Barking v North Walsham
Camberley v Henley
Metropolitan Police v Tabard

NATIONAL LEAGUE ONE

SEASON 1994-95

NATIONAL LEAGUE ONE STATISTICS 1994/95

PLAYING RECORD AND POINTS BREAKDOWN

	P	W	D	L	Pts	HOME				AWAY			
						W	D	L	Pts	W	D	L	Pts
Leicester	18	15	1	2	31	9	0	0	18	6	1	2	13
Bath	18	12	3	3	27	6	2	1	14	6	1	2	13
Wasps	18	13	0	5	26	8	0	1	16	5	0	4	10
Sale	18	7	2	9	16	4	1	4	9	3	1	5	7
Orrell	18	6	3	9	15	4	2	3	10	2	1	6	5
Bristol	18	7	0	11	14	5	0	4	10	2	0	7	4
Gloucester	18	6	1	11	13	5	0	4	10	1	1	7	3
Harlequins	18	6	1	11	13	2	1	6	5	4	0	5	8
W. Hartlepool	18	6	1	11	13	5	0	4	10	1	1	7	3
Northampton	18	6	0	12	12	4	0	5	8	2	0	7	4

RESULTS

		1	2	3	4	5	6	7	8	9	10
1	Bath		18-9	19-19	22-11	20-20	26-6	32-13	13-18	12-9	53-17
2	Bristol	9-10		21-17	19-14	31-22	13-24	20-9	44-22	24-25	12-17
3	Gloucester	10-15	19-17		17-28	9-3	14-13	9-6	8-20	16-21	48-12
4	Harlequins	19-25	9-10	10-14		13-40	10-9	6-8	15-15	26-57	20-10
5	Leicester	31-21	17-3	16-6	22-8		28-15	29-19	37-20	21-6	33-16
6	Northampton	16-32	15-18	9-6	16-23	18-20		15-3	9-22	19-13	25-14
7	Orrell	6-6	20-16	43-14	10-28	0-6	13-10		22-19	10-16	22-22
8	Sale	3-19	21-9	16-14	19-20	10-20	41-6	8-8		12-17	22-7
9	Wasps	11-10	27-15	45-8	25-7	18-23	27-21	53-25	52-22		33-22
10	West Hartlepool	18-20	47-11	27-21	10-8	6-12	12-21	17- 19	23-13	20-17	

WEEK BY WEEK POSITIONS

	10/9	17/9	24/9	1/10	8/10	15/10	22/10	29/10	5/11	7/1	14/1	11/2	4/3	25/3	8/4	15/4	22/4	29/4
Bath	3	2	1	1	1	2	2	2	1	1	1	1	1	2	1	2	2	2
Bristol	8	4	4	3	3	3	4	4	4	4	4	4	5	6	5	5	6	6
Gloucester	10	5	6	8	8	7	8	6	5	6	7	6	6	7	7	7	7	7
Harlequins	5	7	9	6	4	6	7	8	8	8	9	9	9	9	8	8	9	8
Leicester	2	3	2	2	2	1	1	1	2	2	2	2	2	1	2	1	1	1
Northampton	9	9	10	10	10	10	9	10	10	10	10	10	10	10	10	10	10	10
Orrell	4	6	7	5	7	5	5	5	6	5	6	7	7	5	6	6	4	5
Sale	6	8	5	7	6	8	6	7	7	7	5	5	4	4	4	4	5	4
Wasps	1	1	3	4	5	4	3	3	3	3	3	3	3	3	3	3	3	3
West Hartlepool	7	10	8	9	9	9	10	9	9	9	8	8	8	8	9	9	8	9

NATIONAL LEAGUE ONE 1994-95
POINTS SCORING RECORDS

	Tries	by Forward	by Back	Tries in no matches	No tries against	Players used	Replace- ments	Ever presents
Leicester	27	7	20	15	8	31	7	1
Bath	36	10	26	16	6	33	5	0
Wasps	58	20	38	15	3	31	4	1
Sale	39	14	25	16	4	27	2	2
Orrell	23	0	23	13	5	31	11	1
Bristol	21	8	13	12	3	32	3	2
Gloucester	25	8	17	14	4	32	2	1
Harlequins	27	8	19	15	1	39	10	2
West Hartlepool	35	10	25	16	1	33	4	2
Northampton	16	7	9	10	3	33	9	1
	307	92	215					

FOR

	PTS	T	C	P	D	HOME PTS	T	C	P	D	AWAY PTS	T	C	P	D
Leicester	400	27	17	64	13	234	17	10	37	6	166	10	7	27	7
Bath	373	36	26	46	1	215	20	17	27	—	158	16	9	19	1
Wasps	470	58	30	37	3	291	36	21	21	2	179	22	9	16	1
Sale	327	39	24	24	4	152	17	11	13	2	175	22	13	11	2
Orrell	256	23	9	38	3	146	14	8	18	2	110	9	1	20	1
Bristol	301	21	11	56	2	193	17	9	28	2	108	4	2	28	—
Gloucester	269	25	15	32	6	150	14	10	19	1	119	11	5	13	5
Harlewuins	275	27	10	37	3	128	10	3	24	—	147	17	7	13	3
West Hartlepool	312	35	19	33	—	175	23	9	14	—	137	12	10	19	—
Northampton	267	16	11	52	3	142	6	5	32	2	125	10	6	20	1
	3250	307	172	419	38		174	103	233	17		133	69	186	21

AGAINST

	PTS	T	C	P	D	HOME PTS	T	C	P	D	AWAY PTS	T	C	P	D
Leicester	239	15	10	44	4	114	8	4	20	2	125	7	6	24	2
Bath	245	19	6	40	6	122	10	3	19	3	123	9	3	21	3
Wasps	313	24	14	53	2	153	12	6	26	1	164	12	8	27	1
Sale	343	32	15	46	5	120	12	3	15	3	223	20	12	31	2
Orrell	326	30	19	44	2	137	11	8	22	—	189	19	11	22	2
Bristol	353	32	17	49	4	160	16	10	17	3	193	16	7	32	1
Gloucester	336	37	17	37	2	135	13	5	19	1	201	24	12	18	1
Harlequins	348	38	25	32	4	188	23	14	13	2	160	15	11	19	2
West Hartlepool	412	45	29	38	5	144	14	7	16	4	268	31	22	22	1
Northampton	335	35	20	36	4	151	14	9	19	2	184	21	11	17	2
	3250	307	172	419	38		133	69	186	21		174	103	233	17

NATIONAL LEAGUE ONE 1994-95
Most Tries, Penalties, Grop Goals, Conversions

LEADING TRY SCORERS

8	Paul Holford	Gloucester
7	Ian Wynn	Orrell
7	Phil Hopley	Wasps
6	Derek Eves	Bristol
6	Nick Greenstock	Wasps
6	Damion Hopley	Wasps
5	Paul Hodder	West Hartlepool
5	Gareth Stocks	Sale
5	Jim Mallinder	Sale
5	Graham Childs	Wasps
5	Steve Hackney	Leicester
5	Adebayo Adebayo	Bath
5	Lawrence Dallaglio	Wasps
4	Simon Morris	Gloucester
4	Charlie Vyvyan	Sale
4	Chris Yates	Sale
4	Peter Mesnah	Harlequins
4	Gavin Sharp	Bristol
4	Tony Underwood	Leicester
4	John Ufton	Wasps
4	Tony Swift	Bath
3	Tim Smith	Gloucester
3	Tony Elwine	West Hartlepool
3	Alan Brown	West Hartlepool
3	Mike Watson	West Hartlepool
3	Steve Cook	West Hartlepool
3	Simon Verbickas	Sale
3	Jos Baxendale	Sale
3	Dylan O'Grady	Sale
3	Neil Ashurst	Sale
3	Mark Appleson	Sale
3	Gavin Thompson	Harlequins
3	Chris Sheasby	Harlequins
3	David John	Bristol
3	Rory Underwood	Leicester
3	Matt Greenwood	Wasps
3	Richard Kinsey	Wasps
3	Phil Horrocks	Orrell
3	James Naylor	Orrell
3	Dewi Morris	Orrell
3	John Liley	Leicester
3	Matt Dawson	Northampton
3	Grant Seeley	Northampton
3	Phil de Granville	Bath
3	Audley Lumsden	Bath
3	Simon Geoghegan	Bath

PENALTIES

56	Mark Tainton	Bristol
52	Paul Grayson	Northampton
40	Jez Harris	Leicester
39	Jon Callard	Bath
28	Paul Challinor	Harlequins
26	Rob Andrew	Wasps
24	John Liley	Leicester
19	Mark Mapletoft	Gloucester
19	Tim Stimpson	West Hartlepool
14	Paul Turner	Sale
14	Kevan Oliphant	West Hartlepool
13	Simon Langford	Orrell
13	Gerry Ainscough	Orrell
12	Lee Osborne	Gloucester
11	Guy Gregory	Wasps
10	Rob Liley	Sale

DROP GOALS

13	Jez Harris	Leicester
6	Martyn Kimber	Gloucester
3	Rob Andrew	Wasps
3	Paul Turner	Sale
2	Paul Challinor	Harlequins
2	Paul Grayson	Northampton
2	Mark Tainton	Bristol
2	Paul Hamer	Orrell
1	Jim Staples	Harlequins
1	Mike Catt	Bath
1	Steve Taberner	Orrell
1	Jim Mallinder	Sale
1	Adam Hepher	Northampton

CONVERSIONS

19	Rob Andrew	Wasps
18	Paul Turner	Sale
14	Jon Callard	Bath
13	Tim Stimpson	West Hartlepool
11	Mark Tainton	Bristol
11	Paul Grayson	Northampton
11	Jez Harris	Leicester
9	Mark Mapletoft	Gloucester
8	Ritchie Butland	Bath
6	John Liley	Leicester
6	Simon Langford	Orrell
6	Gerry Ainscough	Orrell
6	Rob Liley	Sale
6	Kevan Oliphant	West Hartlepool
4	Mike Catt	Bath
4	Lee Osborne	Gloucester
4	Paul Challinor	Harlequins

NATIONAL LEAGUE ONE 1994-95

INDIVIDUAL TOP POINT SCORERS

		PTS	T	C	P	D
Mark Tainton	Bristol	196	—	11	56	2
Paul Grayson	Northampton	189	1	11	52	2
Jez Harris	Leicester	181	—	11	40	13
Jon Callard	Bath	150	1	14	39	—
Rob Andrew	Wasps	135	2	19	26	3
Paul Challinor	Harlequins	103	1	4	28	2
John Liley	Leicester	99	3	6	24	—
Tim Stimpson	West Hartlepool	93	2	13	19	—
Paul Turner	Sale	92	1	18	14	3
Mark Mapletoft	Gloucester	85	2	9	19	—
Simon Langford	Orrell	61	2	6	13	—
Gerry Ainsworth	Orrell	61	2	6	13	—
Kevan Oliphant	West Hartlepool	54	—	6	14	—
Lee Osborne	Gloucester	44	—	4	12	—
Guy Gregory	Wasps	43	—	5	11	—
Rob Liley	Sale	42	—	6	10	—
Paul Holford	Gloucester	40	8	—	—	—
Ian Wynn	Orrell	35	7	—	—	—
Phil Hopley	Wasps	35	7	—	—	—
Ritchie Butlans	Bath	33	1	8	4	—
Mike Catt	Bath	30	2	4	3	1
Derek Eves	Bristol	30	6	—	—	—
Nick Greenstock	Wasps	30	6	—	—	—
Damian Hopley	Wasps	30	6	—	—	—
Jim Mallinder	Sale	28	5	—	—	1
Will Greenwood	Harlequins	27	2	1	5	—

Rob Andrew (Wasps & England)

Photo: Joe McCabe

NATIONAL LEAGUE ONE

STATISTICS
1987-95

NATIONAL LEAGUE ONE TABLES

1987-88

	P	W	D	L	F	A	Pts
Leicester	10	9	0	1	225	133	37
Wasps	11	8	1	2	218	136	36
Harlequins	11	6	1	4	261	128	30
Bath	11	6	1	4	197	156	30
Gloucester	10	6	1	3	206	121	29
Orrell	11	5	1	5	192	153	27
Moseley	11	5	0	6	167	170	26
Nottingham	11	4	1	6	146	170	24
Bristol	10	4	1	5	171	145	23
Waterloo	10	4	0	6	123	208	22
Coventry	11	3	1	7	133	246	21
Sale	11	0	0	11	95	374	0

1988-89

	P	W	D	L	F	A	Pts
Bath	11	10	0	1	263	98	20
Gloucester	11	7	1	3	215	112	15
Wasps	11	7	1	3	206	138	15
Nottingham	11	6	1	4	142	122	13
Orrell	11	6	1	4	148	157	13
Leicester	11	6	1	4	189	199	13
Bristol	11	6	0	5	188	117	12
Harlequins	11	5	0	6	194	184	10
Rosslyn Park	11	5	0	6	172	208	10
Moseley	11	3	0	8	113	242	6
Waterloo	11	1	1	9	120	235	3
Liverpool St. H.	11	1	0	10	116	254	2

1989-90

	P	W	D	L	F	A	Pts
Wasps	11	9	0	2	250	106	18
Gloucester	11	8	1	2	214	139	17
Bath	11	8	0	3	258	104	16
Saracens	11	7	1	3	168	167	15
Leicester	11	6	0	5	248	184	12
Nottingham	11	6	0	5	187	148	12
Harlequins	11	6	0	5	218	180	12
Orrell	11	5	0	6	221	132	10
Bristol	11	4	0	7	136	144	8
Rosslyn Park	11	4	0	7	164	243	8
Moseley	11	2	0	9	138	258	4
Bedford	11	0	0	11	70	467	0

1990-91

	P	W	D	L	F	A	Pts
Bath	12	11	0	1	280	104	22
Wasps	12	9	1	2	252	151	19
Harlequins	12	8	0	4	267	162	16
Leicester	12	8	0	4	244	140	16
Orrell	12	7	0	5	247	105	14
Gloucester	12	6	0	6	207	163	12
Rosslyn Park	12	6	0	6	216	174	12
Nottingham	12	6	0	6	138	194	12
Northampton	12	5	1	6	149	254	11
Saracens	12	5	0	7	151	228	10
Bristol	12	4	1	7	135	219	9
Moseley	12	1	1	10	113	244	3
Liverpool St. H.	12	0	0	12	88	349	0

1991-92

	P	W	D	L	F	A	PD	Pts
Bath	12	10	1	1	277	126	151	20
Orrell	12	10	0	2	204	95	109	20
Northampton	12	9	1	2	209	136	73	19
Gloucester	12	7	1	4	193	168	11	15
Saracens	12	7	1	4	176	165	11	15
Leicester	12	6	1	5	262	216	46	13
Wasps	12	6	0	6	177	180	-3	12
Harlequins	12	5	1	6	213	207	6	11
London Irish	12	3	3	6	147	237	-90	9
Bristol	12	4	0	8	192	174	18	8
Rugby	12	2	3	7	124	252	-128	7
Nottingham	12	2	1	9	133	204	-71	5
Rosslyn Park	12	0	1	11	111	258	-147	1

1992-93

	P	W	D	L	F	A	PD	Pts
Bath	12	11	0	1	355	97	258	22
Wasps	12	11	0	1	186	118	118	68
Leicester	12	9	0	3	220	116	104	18
Northampton	12	8	0	4	215	150	65	16
Gloucester	12	6	0	6	173	151	22	12
Bristol	12	6	0	6	148	169	-21	12
London Irish	12	6	0	6	175	223	-48	12
Harlequins	12	5	1	6	197	187	10	11
Orrell	12	5	0	7	175	183	-8	10
London Scottish	12	3	1	8	192	248	-56	7
Saracens	12	3	0	9	137	180	-43	6
West Hartlepool	12	3	0	9	149	236	-87	6
Rugby	12	1	0	11	104	368	-264	2

NATIONAL LEAGUE ONE RESULTS

1987-88

		1	2	3	4	5	6	7	8	9	10	11	12
1	Bath		15-9			21-9		14.0		23-18			10-17
2	Bristol				16-21			21-10			37-3	12-12	N/P
3	Coventry	9-9	25-3			12-15			15-20	11-24	24-19		15-10
4	Gloucester	9-16		39-3				18-16	17-9		61-7	13-24	
5	Harlequins		28-22		9-9		9-12		34-8	6-12	66-0		37-4
6	Leicester	24-13	15-10	32-16	N/P						42-15	12-9	39-15
7	Moseley			26-3		11-32	3-21			28-10		19-12	27-3
8	Nottingham	25-15	3-16				13-22	21-12		12-12			
9	Orrell		13-25		9-13		30-6				19-0		30-6
10	Sale	17-46						15-19	0-17			6-14	
11	Wasps	19-15		49-6		17-16			17-9	23-15			
12	Waterloo				16-6			10-9			29-13	13-22	

1988-89

		1	2	3	4	5	6	7	8	9	10	11	12
1	Bath		16-9	19-9					22-16	36-12		16-6	38-9
2	Bristol			18-6			50-14	18-10		15-6			14-3
3	Gloucester		10-11			28-0		37-9	13-6			19-3	
4	Harlequins	9-26		26-11			15-6	38-15					23-24
5	Leicester	15-12	13-12		21-31				15-27	28-15	15-6		
6	Liverpool St. Helens	7-21		9-31		12-23			15-22		12-32		
7	Moseley	0-38				22-13	18-15			10-12	7-13		13-6
8	Nottingham		10-6		12-0	12-12		13-9				9-15	
9	Orrell			6-16	16-15		20-4		12-6			9-9	15-12
10	Rosslyn Park	6-19	18-16	8-26	12-16				9-18	19-13			
11	Wasps		21-9		23-15		16-10	39-10			39-16		
12	Waterloo			15-15		22-34	6-12			9-18	14-24	0-29	

1989-90

		1	2	3	4	5	6	7	8	9	10	11	12
1	Bath		76-0			32-12	26-15	27-9			34-6		
2	Bedford			6-16		8-71		0-24		7-25		3-22	9-44
3	Bristol	13-14			6-13		11-13		13-9		6-15		21-22
4	Gloucester	13-6	37-6			24-9				16-10	41-12	21-21	
5	Harlequins			13-7			15-12		22-27	15-9	19-15		12-9
6	Leicester		60-3		16-26			38-20	15-6		34-6		
7	Moseley			10-16	12-16	22-21			6-22				0-42
8	Nottingham	12-9	47-16		12-3					9-25	6-11	25-12	
9	Orrell	6-9		12-15			33-10	25-13			64-14		
10	Rosslyn Park		45-12				9-23	18-6				13-15	6-14
11	Saracens	9-7		17-12		15-9	33-13			12-6			
12	Wasps	9-18			29-4		29-12		16-12	12-6		24-6	

1990-91

	1	2	3	4	5	6	7	8	9	10	11	12	13
1 Bath				23-3		46-3	11-6			17-9	45-21		15-16
2 Bristol	3-10		15-12		10-6				6-22	3-36		25-6	
3 Gloucester	15-17			38-19			30-12		22-6	9-16		21-16	
4 Harlequins		38-16				41-12	33-6	21-6			18-6		12-18
5 Leicester	3-9		18-6	12-15					25-9	15-12	29-6		
6 Liverpool St. Helens		6-7	7-26		7-28			13-23	12-13			3-17	
7 Moseley		9-9		19-43	20-12			10-16			9-19	,9-22	
8 Northampton	10-16	12-9	6-7	18-28					22-15			15-6	
9 Nottingham	9-22			6-19			12-7			16-12		3-28	12-10
10 Orrell				12-9		38-0	16-0	60-0			12-3		12-14
11 Rosslyn Park		16-13	17-12		17-15	39-9		48-0	9-15				
12 Saracens	6-49			7-39			21-6				19-12	13-11	6-15
13 Wasps		46-19	14-9		12-22	51-4		21-21			13-10		

1991-92

	1	2	3	4	5	6	7	8	9	10	11	12	13
1 Bath		9-4	29-9		37-6		15-6	25-15				32-12	
2 Bristol				16-0		14-19	9-15			22-4	48-4		10-33
3 Gloucester		29-15			21-3	22-15	10-17			12-9			15-11
4 Harlequins	18-18		21-18		20-13			23-6	7-10			21-37	
5 Leicester		25-9				36-13	19-22			51-16	22-22		31-12
6 London Irish	21-26			3-39				7-21	12-12	6-6			18-13
7 Northampton				25-14		12-12		12-3	20-12	29-0			28-15
8 Nottingham		0-32	3-14		14-27	9-12	18-9		34-9				
9 Orrell	10-9	23-9	18-12		21-9		20-6				23-0		
10 Rosslyn Park	13-21		12-24					4-22		7-15	6-10		7-15
11 Rugby	0-32		16-19	29-20				9-9	3-21		6-22		
12 Saracens		13-4	12-12		9-20	27-9	9-14	13-12					
13 Wasps	12-24			20-6				11-7	13-12		17-10	6-12	

1992-93

	1	2	3	4	5	6	7	8	9	10	11	12	13
1 Bath				22-6		42-19	40-6		39-3	61-7		22-11	
2 Bristol	8-13		9-22		15-0				23-11		12-7		19-11
3 Gloucester	0-20			25-5					8-13	21-12	19-5		6-21
4 Harlequins		16-0				47-24	22-22	7-12		35-14		13-15	
5 Leicester	3-13		22-21	23-0					9-0	30-3			21-8
6 London Irish		9-7	6-18		14-30			12-3		10-9			25-13
7 London Scottish		8-11	8-3		11-28	28-21		21-34					10-15
8 Northampton	11-8	16-6	6-21		12-13						21-17		55-9
9 Orrell				18-16		8-12	13-10	9-10		66-0		10-11	
10 Rugby		21-32			5-28	0-14	20-45	7-13				3-34	
11 Saracens	13-19			3-18			41-17		6-9	14-9		9-13	
12 Wasps		7-6	14-9		14-13	18-9	10-6	20-12					
13 West Hartlepool	10-38			9-12					39-15	5-6	3-10	6-19	

NATIONAL LEAGUE ONE STATISTICS 1993/94

PLAYING RECORD AND POINTS BREAKDOWN

	P	W	D	L	F	A	Pts	P	W	D	L	F	A	P	W	D	L	F	A
								HOME						AWAY					
Bath	18	17	0	1	431	181	34	9	9	0	0	249	71	9	8	0	1	182	110
Leicester	18	14	0	4	425	210	28	9	8	0	1	262	74	9	6	0	3	163	136
Wasps	18	10	1	7	362	340	21	9	6	0	3	218	145	9	4	1	4	144	195
Bristol	18	10	0	8	331	276	20	9	6	0	3	200	140	9	4	0	5	131	136
Northampton	18	9	0	9	305	342	18	9	6	0	3	174	126	9	3	0	6	141	201
Harlequins	18	8	0	10	333	287	16	9	5	0	4	170	144	9	3	0	6	163	143
Orrell	18	8	0	10	327	302	16	9	6	0	3	193	124	9	2	0	7	134	178
Gloucester	18	6	2	10	247	356	14	9	4	1	4	132	150	9	2	1	6	115	206
London Irish	18	4	0	14	217	391	8	9	1	0	8	123	188	9	3	0	6	94	203
Newcastle Gosforth	18	2	1	15	190	453	5	9	1	1	7	92	178	9	1	0	8	98	305

RESULTS

		1	2	3	4	5	6	7	8	9	10
1	Bath		9-0	46-17	32-13	14-6	28-8	46-3	37-9	13-7	24-8
2	Bristol	10-18		16-12	20-16	40-22	21-8	26-0	22-31	30-17	15-16
3	Gloucester	6-16	6-24		24-20	14-23	9-10	15-9	19-14	30-25	9-9
4	Harlequins	12-14	15-20	38-20		13-25	30-15	12-6	15-7	13-20	22-17
5	Leicester	9-6	21-9	28-8	3-10		38-3	66-5	36-9	23-18	38-6
6	London Irish	31-32	0-16	12-15	7-33	10-22		17-19	13-16	19-6	14-10
7	Newcastle Gosforth	5-29	13-22	12-12	3-22	13-22	9-13		8-28	13-12	16-18
8	Northampton	9-30	22-19	19-3	15-14	19-10	23-12	43-23		9-13	15-17
9	Orrell	15-18	16-13	6-10	21-20	0-18	24-3	42-12	27-6		42-24
10	Wasps	13-19	34-8	29-18	18-15	13-15	21-22	38-21	24-11	28-16	

WEEK BY WEEK POSITIONS

	18/9	25/9	2/10	9/10	13/11	20/11	4/12	11/12	8/1	15/1	29/1	12/2	12/3	26/3	9/4	23/4	30/4
Bath	1	1	1	1	1	1	1	1	1	1	1	1	1	1	1	1	1
Bristol	2	3	6	7	5	7	6	7	6	6	5	7	6	5	4	4	4
Gloucester	5	8	9	9	9	9	8	8	8	5	7	8	7	8	8	8	8
Quins	7	7	5	3	2	3	4	4	4	4	4	4	4	4	6	6	6
Leicester	3	4	2	2	3	2	2	2	2	2	2	2	2	2	2	2	2
London Irish	9	10	8	8	8	8	9	9	9	9	9	9	9	9	9	9	9
Newcastle Gosforth	5	9	10	10	10	10	10	10	10	10	10	10	10	10	10	10	10
Northampton	10	5	3	4	6	6	7	5	7	8	6	5	5	6	5	5	5
Orrell	8	6	7	6	4	4	5	6	5	7	8	6	8	7	7	7	7
Wasps	4	2	4	5	7	5	3	3	3	3	3	3	3	3	3	3	3

COURAGE CHAMPIONSHIP STATISTICS 1987–1995

LEAGUE ONE

	CHAMPIONS	RUNNERS-UP	RELEGATED
1987-88	Leicester	Wasps	Coventry Sale
1988-89	Bath	Gloucester	Waterloo Liverpool St Helens
1989-90	Wasps	Gloucester	Bedford
1990-91	Bath	Wasps	Moseley Liverpool St Helens
1991-92	Bath	Orrell	Nottingham Rosslyn Park
1992-93	Bath	Wasps	Saracens London Scottish W. Hartlepool Rugby
1993-94	Bath	Leicester	London Irish Newcastle Gosforth
1994-95	Leicester	Bath	Northampton

TEAM RECORDS

Highest score: Bath 76 Bedford 0. 13-1-90
Highest aggregate: 83 Harlequins 26 Wasps 57. 17-9-94
Highest score by a losing side: London Irish 31 Bath 32. 30-4-94
Highest Scoring draw: 22-22 Leicester v Rugby 25-4-92, Orrell v W. Hartlepool 7-1-95
Most consecutive wins: 17 Bath 1993-94 through 1994-95
Most consecutive defeats: 12 Liverpool St Helens 1990-91, Newcastle Gosforth 1993-94
Most points for in a season: 469 Wasps 1994-95
Most points against in a season: 483 Newcastle Gosforth 1993-94
Least points for in a season: 70 Bedford 1989-90
Least points against in a season: 95 Orrell 1991-92
Most tries for in a season: 58 Wasps 1994-95
Most tries against in a season: 83 Bedford 1989-90
Least tries for in a season: 8 Waterloo 1988-89
Least tries against in a season: 6 Bath 1988-89, Wasps 1992-93
Most conversions for in a season: 30 Wasps 1994-95
Most conversions against in a season: 42 Bedford 1989-90
Most penalties for in a season: 64 Leicester 1994-95
Most penalties against in a season: 53 Gloucester 1993-94, Wasps 1994-95
Least penalties for in a season: 7 Bedford 1989-90
Least penalties against in a season: 11 Harlequins 1987-88
Most drop goals for in a season: 13 Leicester 1994-95
Most drop goals against in a season: 8 Wasps 1993-94

INDIVIDUAL RECORDS

Most points in a season: 202 Jez Harris Leicester 1993-94
Most tries in a season: 11 Andrew Harriman Harlequins 1987-88, Darren O'Leary Harlequins 1993-94
Most conversions in a season: 29 Stuart Barnes Bath 1989-90
Most penalities in a season: 56 Mark Tainton Bristol 1994-95
Most drop goals in a season: 13 Jez Harris Leicester 1994-95
Most points in a match: 31 John Liley Leicester v Rosslyn Park 21- 3-92
Most tries in a match: 4 Gary Hartley Nottingham v Bedford 18-11-89, Tony Swift Bath v Bedford 13-1-90,
Jeremy Guscott Bath v Bedford 13-1-90. Paul Hamer Orrell v Rugby 13-3-93,
Tony Underwood Leicester v Newcastle Gosforth 12-3-94
Most conversions in a match: 10 Stuart Barnes Bath v Bedford 13-1-90
Most penalities in a match: 7 David Pears Harlequins v Rosslyn Park 7-12-91,
Jez Harris Leicester v Bristol 11-12-93 & v Gloucester 29-1-94, Rob Andrew Wasps v Orrell 11-12-93,
Mark Tainton Bristol v Leicester 5-11-94
Most drop goals in a match: 3 John Steele Northampton v Wasps 23-3-91, Jez Harris Leicester v Wasps 23-11-91

SEASON BY SEASON LEADING SCORERS

	POINTS		TRIES
1987-88	126 Dusty Hare (Leicester)	11	Andrew Harriman (Harlequins)
1988-89	103 Rob Andrew (Wasps)	10	Jeremy Guscott (Bath)
1989-90	126 John Liley (Leicester)	10	Tony Swift (Bath)
1990-91	126 Rob Andrew (Wasps)	9	Rory Underwood (Leicester) Andrew Harriman (Harlequins)
1991-92	129 John Liley (Leicester)	9	Rory Underwood (Leicester)
1992-93	122 Jon Webb (Bath)	7	Stuart Barnes (Bath)
1993-94	202 Jez Harris (Leicester)	11	Daren O'Leary (Harlequins)
1994-95	196 Mark Tainton (Bristol)	8	Paul Holford (Gloucester)

100 POINTS IN A COURAGE SEASON DIVISION ONE

PTS	PLAYER	CLUB	SEASON	T	C	P	D
202	Jez Harris	Leicester	1993-94	2	18	41	11
196	Mark Tainton	Bristol	1994-95	—	11	56	2
189	Paul Grayson	Northampton	1994-95	1	11	52	2
181	Jez Harris	Leicester	1994-95	—	11	40	13
178	Jon Callard	Bath	1993-94	4	25	36	—
161	Mark Tainton	Bristol	1993-94	—	19	40	1
159	Rob Andrew	Wasps	1993-94	2	16	38	1
150	Jon Callard	Bath	1994-95	1	14	39	—
143	Kent Bray	Harlequins	1993-94	1	12	38	—
135	Rob Andrew	Wasps	1994-95	2	19	26	3
132	Paul Grayson	Northampton	1993-94	2	10	33	1
129	John Liley	Leicester	1991-92	4	19	25	—
126	Dusty Hare	Leicester	1987-88	—	15	31	1
126	John Liley	Leicester	1989-90	7	16	22	—
126	Rob Andrew	Wasps	1990-91	4	16	26	—
122	Jon Webb	Bath	1992-93	3	19	23	—
120	David Pears	Harlequins	1990-91	1	16	23	5
114	David Pears	Harlequins	1989-90	2	14	24	2
111	Michael Corcoran	London Irish	1992-93	2	4	31	—
110	John Liley	Leicester	1990-91	2	18	22	—
110	John Steele	Northampton	1991-92	—	10	28	2
109	Martin Strett	Orrell	1990-91	1	21	20	1
107	David Pears	Harlequins	1991-92	4	15	21	—
106	John Liley	Leicester	1992-93	2	15	22	—
104	Martin Strett	Orrell	1989-90	4	4	20	—
104	Martin Strett	Orrell	1991-92	1	8	26	2
103	Rob Andrew	Wasps	1988-89	2	13	21	2
103	Stuart Barnes	Bath	1989-90	6	29	7	—
103	Paul Challinor	Harlequins	1994-95	1	4	28	2
101	Steve Pilgrim	Wasps	1991-92	2	6	27	—

MOST POINTS IN A COURAGE DIVISION ONE MATCH

31	John Liley	Leicester v Rosslyn Park	21-3-92
28	Martin Strett	Orrell v Rosslyn Park	28-4-90
27	David Pears	Harlequins v Bedford	14-10-89
26	John Liley	Leicester v Bedford	23-9-89
26	Stuart Barnes	Bath v West Hartlepool	27-3-93
26	Paul Grayson	Northampton v Bristol	2-10-93
26	Mark Tainton	Bristol v Leicester	5-12-94
24	Dusty Hare	Leicester v Rosslyn Park	19-11-88
24	Stuart Barnes	Bath v Bedford	13-1-90
24	Rob Andrew	Wasps v Bristol	27-4-91
23	Jamie Salmon	Harlequins v Waterloo	27-2-88
23	Rob Andrew	Wasps v Rosslyn Park	22-10-88
23	David Pears	Harlequins v Saracens	20-10-90
23	Rob Andrew	Wasps v Orrell	11-12-93
23	Jez Harris	Leicester v Gloucester	29-1-94
22	Dusty Hare	Leicester v Sale	26-3-88
22	John Graves	Rosslyn Park v Bedford	31-3-90
22	Stuart Thresher	Harlequins v London Irish	31-10-92
22	Jon Callard	Bath v Northampton	18-9-93
22	Michael Corcoran	London Irish v Wasps	26-3-94
22	Rob Andrew	Wasps v Sale	15-10-94
22	Jez Harris	Leicester v Sale	29-10-94
21	Ian Aitchison	Waterloo v Sale	2-1-88
21	David Pears	Harlequins v Rosslyn Park	7-12-91
21	Ben Rudling	Saracens v Harlequins	21-3-92
21	Jon Webb	Bath v Rugby	9-1-93
21	Jez Harris	Leicester v Bristol	11-12-93
21	Jez Harris	Leicester v Northampton	8-1-94
20	Dusty Hare	Leicester v Waterloo	4-4-88
20	Stuart Thresher	Harlequins v Sale	23-4-88
20	Tim Smith	Gloucester v Harlequins	12-3-90
20	John Liley	Leicester v London Irish	19-9-92
20	Mark Appleson	London Scottish v Rugby	31-10-92
20	Paul Hamer	Orrell v Rugby	13-3-93
20	Tony Underwood	Leicester v Newcastle Gosforth	12-3-94
20	Rob Andrew	Wasps v Gloucester	10-9-94
20	Jez Harris	Leicester v Harlequins	15-10-94
20	Paul Grayson	Northampton v W. Hartlepool	5-11-94

MOST TRIES IN A COURAGE DIVISION ONE MATCH

4	Gary Hartley	Nottingham v Bedford	18-11-89
4	Tony Swift	Bath v Bedford	13-1-90
4	Jeremy Guscott	Bath v Bedford	13-1-90
4	Paul Hamer	Orrell v Rugby	13-3-93
4	Tony Underwood	Leicester v Newcastle Gosforth	12-3-94
3	Peter Shillingford	Moseley v Wasps	5-2-88
3	Mark Charles	Leicester v Sale	26-3-88
3	Andrew Harriman	Harlequins v Nottingham	1-4-88
3	Simon Smith	Wasps v Coventry	13-4-88
3	Andrew Harriman	Harlequins v Sale	23-4-88
3	Jeremy Guscott	Bath v Moseley	12-11-88
3	Mark Bailey	Wasps v Moseley	19-11-88
3	John Liley	Leicester v Bedford	23-9-89
3	Mike Wedderburn	Harlequins v Bedford	14-10-89
3	Mark Bailey	Wasps v Gloucester	14-10-89
3	Derek Morgan	Gloucester v Rosslyn Park	11-11-89
3	Jon Callard	Bath v Bedford	13-1-90
3	Chris Gerard	Leicester v Moseley	31-3-90
3	Paul Manley	Orrell v Rosslyn Park	28-4-90
3	Dewi Morris	Orrell v Liverpool St Helens	13-10-90
3	Dewi Morris	Orrell v Northampton	27-10-90
3	Rory Underwood	Leicester v Northampton	21-1-91
3	Andrew Harriman	Harlequins v Bristol	30-3-91
3	Will Carling	Harlequins v Bristol	30-3-91
3	Graham Childs	Wasps v Liverpool St Helens	20-4-91
3	Rob Andrew	Wasps v Bristol	27-4-91
3	Rory Underwood	Leicester v Moseley	27-4-91
3	Steve Hackney	Leicester v London Irish	4-1-92
3	Tony Swift	Bath v Leicester	11-1-92
3	Rory Underwood	Leicester v Rosslyn Park	21-3-92
3	Mike Lloyd	Bristol v Rugby	28-3-92
3	Martin Pepper	Nottingham v Rosslyn Park	4-4-92
3	Chris Oti	Wasps v Bristol	25-4-92
3	Stuart Barnes	Bath v Hartlepool	27-3-93
3	Derek Eves	Bristol v Rugby	22-3-93
3	Ian Wynn	Orrell v Wasps	30-4-94
3	Simon Morris	Gloucester v W. Hartlepool	17-9-94
3	Damian Hopley	Wasps v Sale	15-10-94

MOST LEAGUE APPEARANCES – DIVISION ONE PLAYERS

94	Andy Mullins	Prop	Harlequins
93	Graham Dawe	Hooker	Bath
91	Ian Smith	Flanker	Gloucester
90	Simon Langford	Full Back/Centre	Orrell
90	John Buckton	Centre	Saracens
90	John Dixon	Second Row	West Hartlepool
90	Tony Swift	Winger	Bath
89	Andy Robinson	Flanker	Bath
87	Steve Bates	Scrum Half	Wasps
87	John Wells	Flanker	Leicester
87	Phil Lancaster	Prop	West Hartlepool
86	Derek Eves	Flanker	Bristol
85	John Stabler	Stand Off	West Hartlepool
84	Richard Andrews	Prop	Saracens
83	David Southern	Prop	Orrell
82	Simon Mitchell	Hooker	West Hartlepool
81	Tim Smith	Full Back	Gloucester
80	Abdel Kardooni	Scrum Half	Leicester
79	Olwen Evans	Winger	West Hartlepool
78	Nigel Redman	Second Row	Bath
78	Steve Taberner	Full Back	Orrell
77	Paul Hull	Full Back	Bristol
76	Kevan Oliphant	Full Back	West Hartlepool
76	Ralph Knibbs	Centre	Bristol
75	Dave Cooke	Winger	West Hartlepool
75	Andy Blackmore	Second Row	Bristol
74	Dave Baldwin	Second Row	Sale
74	Richard Hill	Scrum Half	Bath
73	David Manley	Flanker	Orrell
72	Martin Whitcombe	Prop	Sale
72	Stuart Barnes	Stand Off	Bath
71	Rob Andrews	Stand Off	Wasps
71	Jim Mallinder	Full Back	Sale

NATIONAL LEAGUE ONE

MEMBER CLUBS
1995-96

League Registrar:
DAE Evans
22 Brrooks Road
Sutton Coldfield
West Midlands B71 1HP
Tel: 0121 354 8183
Fax: 0121 321 3221

Tony Swift playing his last game for Bath goes past Nick Greenstock of Wasps to score a try at Twickenham in the Pilkington Cup Final.

BATH F.C.

NICKNAME: **FOUNDED:** 1865

CLUB OFFICIALS

President
Brendan Perry
Chairman
Richard Mawditt
Club Secretary
John W Quin
7 Bennett St., Bath BA1 2QJ
Tel: (H&W) 01225 443252
Fixtures Secretary
Tom Martland
22 Gainsborough Gardens, Bath
BA1 4AJ. Tel (H) 01225 317801 (W)
01225 443253
Press Officer
Ken Johnstone
Tel (H&W) 01225 723579

Review of the Season

ALTHOUGH they had to cede the top spot in the League to Leicester Bath can still look back on their season with satisfaction, since a week after their final disappointment – a 13-18 home defeat by Sale – they were back on familiar ground (Twickenham) and impressively demolished Wasps by a 36-16 scoreline, a feat which was made even more superb by the fact that World Cup and injury absences meant that they fielded a weakened (on paper) team.

But for that triumph they might have looked upon the season as a failure but is second place in a competition failure? And which club could even have finished that high when World Cup demands from team managers left them unable to field any Scotland squad player after 1st April with Ireland's Simon Geoghegan being unavailable for the Pilkingon Cup final owing to his country's warm-up game against Italy?

England squad members were only allowed limited appearances during the league run-in campaign, when they lost a vital match narrowly at Leicester, so in every respect their achievements were almost miraculous.

They start the new season under the captaincy of England centre Phil de Glanville, who also led them at Twickenham against Wasps after retiring skipper John Hall, who now joins the backroom staff along with Richard Hill, who had to cry off with injury. Without so many calls on their staff they will again be fancied to land the league title.

Any side with such players as Callard, Catt, Adebayo, Ubogu, Reed, Ojomoh, Ben Clarke, Hilton, Dawe and Peters among others on their strength must be worth a good bet, but that superb wing Tony Swift, who has finally retired, will be missed.

Colours: Blue, white and black   **Change Colours:** White shirts with thin blue/black hoops

BATH F.C.

COURAGE LEAGUE
MATCH DETAILS 1994-95

No	Date	Opponents	Ven	Result		Scorers
1	Sep 10	Bristol	H	W	18-9	Lumsdon (T) (PT) Callard (C 2P)
2	Sep 17	Northampton	A	W	32-16	Swift (2T) Adebayo (T) Callard (C 5P)
3	Sep24	Orrell	H	W	32-13	Sleightholme (T) Adams (T) DeGlanville (T) Clarke (T) Catt (3C 2P)
4	Oct 1	Gloucester	A	W	15-10	Robinson (T) Sanders (T) Catt (C P)
5	Oct 8	Wasps	H	W	12-9	Catt (4P)
6	Oct 15	West Hartlepool	A	W	20-18	Hall (2T) Callard (2C DG P)
7	Oct 22	Leicester	H	D	20-20	Swift (T) Catt (T) Callard (2C 2P)
8	Oct 29	Harlequins	H	W	22-11	Geoghegan (T) Callard (C 5P)
9	Nov 5	Sale	A	W	19-3	DeGlanville (T) Adebayo (T) Callard (3P)
10	Jan 7	Bristol	A	W	10-9	Geoghegan (T) Callard (P C)
11	Jan 14	Northampton	H	W	26-6	Swift (T) Geoghegan (T) Callard (2C 4P)
12	Feb 11	Orrell	A	D	6-6	Callard (2P)
13	Mar 4	Gloucester	H	D	19-19	Callard (T C 4P)
14	Mar 25	Wasps	A	L	10-11	Callard (C P) Butland (T)
15	Apr 8	West Hartlepool	H	W	53-17	Adebayo (2T) Lumsden (2T) Adams (T) DeGlanville (T) Ubogu (T) Butland (6C 2P)
16	Apr 15	Leicester	A	L	21-31	Adebayo (T) Catt (T) Callard (3P 1C)
17	Apr 22	Harlequins	A	W	25-19	Guscott (T) Yates (T) Sleightholme (T) Butland (2C 2P)
18	Apr 29	Sale	H	L	13-18	Callard (2P 1C) Pen Try

Courage League Records 1994-95

League Debuts: Hayden Long, Jon Sleightholme, Simon Johnson, Simon Geoghegan, Ritchie Butland, Ed Pearce, Marcus Olson
Tries on Debut: Sleightholme, Geoghegan
No Ever Presents – only division one side not to have one
Most appearances: 16 Philip De Glanville
One of 3 teams to score tries in 16 out of 18 League games

● Players used: 33

● Stopped the opposition scoring tries in 6 matches – second only to Leicester

● Converted 72% of their tries – highest % in the League

● Went 3 matches without a win – their worst ever run

● Lost 3 out of last 5

● Lost at home to Sale – only their 3rd ever home defeat – previous defeats Waterloo and Wasps

● John Callard passes Jon Webb on Bath's all time points list

	Pts	T	C	P	D	Apps	Aver
Stuart Barnes	467	21	65	71	9	72	6.49
Jon Callard	384	16	41	76	-	45	8.53
Jon Webb	275	7	41	54	-	29	9.48

● Callard now holds the record for the most penalties in Match, Season and Career with 5, 39 and 76 respectively.

● Bath suffered their worst defeats in League matches home and away v Sale and Leicester respectively

● Tony Swift retires as the top try scorer in the Division:

	Tries	Apps	Strike Rate
Tony Swift	43	90	2.09
Jeremy Guscott	27	65	2.41

BATH F.C.

MATCH BY MATCH PLAYERS BY POSITION

Callard	Swift	Lumsden	DeGlanville	Adebayo	Catt	Sanders	Hilton	Dawe	Ubogu	Reed	Redman	Robinson	Hall	Clarke B	Mallett	Ojomoh	Olsen	Guscott	Sleightholme	Geoghegan	Haag	Rayner	Clark C
16	15	14	12	11	10	9	1	2	3	4	5	6	7	8									
16	15	12	14	11	10	9	1	2		4	5			7*	8	3	6						
	15	12	14		10	9	1			5		6	7		3	8				11		4	
	15	16	14		10	9		2	1	5		6		8	3	7				11		4	12
16	15		14	11	10	9	1	2			5	6	7	8	3*					4		12	R54
16	15		14	11	10		1	2		5	4		7	8		6	9	12					3
16	15		14	11	10	9	1	2	3	5	4	6	8	7				12					
16	15		14		10	9		2	1	5			7	8	3	6		12		11	4		
16			14	11	10	9		2	1		5		7		3	6		12	15		4		
16	15		14		10			2			5	6*	7	8	3		9	12		11	4		1
16	15		14			1				5	6	7		3	8	9	12		11	4			
16			14		10	1	2			5	6			8	9			11	15	4	3		
16	15		14	11	12	9		2	3	5	6		8		7					4		1	
16			14		12	9				5	6		8	3				15	11	4			
	15	16	14	12		9			3		5	7	8					11		4			
16	15		14	11	12	9		1		5		7	8	3	6					4			
	15	16		14	9					5	7	8		3	6		12	11		4			
16	15		14		9	2				5	7	6	8				12	11		4			

Also Played: Beddow R38 match2, R70 match 7; Long No 16 match 3; Adams No 2 matches 3, 11, 14, 15, 16, 17, R34 match 18; Butland No 10 matches 11, 13, 14, 15, 16, 17, 18; Lewis No 12 match 12; Peters No 8 match 9, No 7 matches 12, 14; Johnson No 9 match 6, R29 match 13; Crumpton No 3 match 18; Yates No 1 match 14, 15, 17, 18

PROGRAMME DETAILS

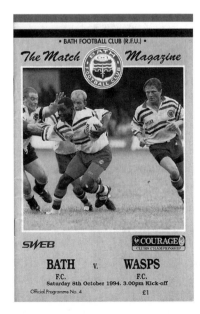

PRICE: £1.00

PAGES: 40
Colour throughout with at least 12 original pages in each issue. Attractive different cover photo for each issue. Excellent programme.

EDITOR:
Ken Johnstone
01225 723579

ADVERTISING RATES:
Please phone Editor

BATH F.C.

COURAGE LEAGUE STATISTICS

compiled by Steve McCormack

Season	Div	P	W	D	L	F	T	C	P	D	A	T	C	P	D	Most Points	Most Tries
1987-88	1	11	6	1	4	197	28	14	15	4	156	17	8	20	4	40 Phil Cue	4 Tony Swift
1988-89	1	11	10	0	1	263	43	17	17	2	98	6	4	22	0	83 Stuart Barnes	10 Jeremy Guscott
1989-90	1	11	8	0	3	258	44	29	8	0	104	8	6	20	0	103 Stuart Barnes	10 Tony Swift
1990-91	1	12	11	0	1	280	39	23	24	2	104	8	6	20	0	98 Stuart Barnes	6 Tony Swift
1991-92	1	12	10	1	1	277	34	18	33	2	126	10	7	20	4	95 Stuart Barnes	8 Tony Swift
1992-93	1	12	11	0	1	355	42	23	32	1	97	7	4	14	4	122 Jon Webb	7 Stuart Barnes
1993-94	1	18	17	0	1	431	46	27	47	2	181	13	7	32	2	178 Jon Callard	5 Mike Catt. Ben Clarke
1994-95	1	18	12	3	3	373	36	26	46	1	245	19	6	40	6	150 Jon Callard	5 Adebayo Adebayo
TOTALS		105	85	5	15	2434	312	177	222	14	1111	88	48	188	20		

BIGGEST WIN	**Home:** 76-0 v Bedford 13.1.90 CL1	**Away:** 49-6 v Saracens 27.4.91 CL1
BIGGEST DEFEAT	**Home:** 13-18 v Sale 29.4.95 CL1	**Away:** 21-31 v Leicester 15.4.95 CL1
MOST TRIES in a match	**For:** 14 v Bedford 13.1.90	**Against:** 4 v London Irish 30.4.94
MOST CONSECUTIVE	**Wins:** 15	**Defeats:** None
MOST APPEARANCES	**Forward:** 93 Graham Dawe	**Back:** 90 Tony Swift
MOST CONSECUTIVE APPEARANCES	50 Tony Swift 9.9.89-25.9.93	
CONSECUTIVE SCORING MATCHES	**Tries:** 4 Tony Swift, Jeremy Guscott	
	Points: 10 Jon Callard	

	IN A SEASON	IN A CAREER	IN A MATCH
MOST POINTS	178 Jon Callard 1993-94 CL1	467 Stuart Barnes 1987-94	26 Stuart Barnes v W Harrtlepool 27.3.93 Away CL1
MOST TRIES	10 Jeremy Guscott 1988-89 CL1 & Tony Swift 1989-90 CL1	43 Tony Swift 1987-95	4 Jeremy Guscott & Tony Swift v Bedford 13.1.90 Home CL1
MOST CONVERSIONS	29 Stuart Barnes 1989-90 CL1	65 Stuart Barnes 1987-94	10 Stuart Barnes v Bedford 13.1.90 Home CL1
MOST PENALTIES	39 Jon Callard 1994-95 CL1	76 Jon Callard 1989-95	5 Jon Webb v Northampton 7.12.91 Home CL1 v Harlequins 19.9.92 Home CL1 v Gloucester 13.2.93 Away CL1 Jon Callard v Newcastle Gos 13.11.93 Home CL1 v Northampton 17.9.94 Away CL1 v Harlequins 29.10.94 Home CL1
MOST DROP GOALS	2 Stuart Barnes 1987-88 1988-89 1990-91 CL1	9 Stuart Barnes 1987-94	1 on 14 occasions by 6 players Stuart Barnes 9 Phil Cue 1 Jonathan Palmer 1 Jeremy Guscott 1 Ed Raynor 1 Mike Catt 1

BATH F.C.

Name	Ht	Wt	Birthdate	Birthplace	Clubs	App	Pts	T	C	P	DG
BACKS											
Jon Callard	5.10	12.7	1.6.66	Leicester	Bath	45	384	16	41	76	-
England A				Teacher							
Hayden Long					Bath	1	-	-	-	-	-
Audley Lumsden	6.0	13.7	6.6.67	London	Bath	30+1	46	10	-	-	-
				Teacher							
Tony Swift	5.10	13.7	24.5.59	Preston	Fylde						
				Accountant	Bath	90	184	43	-	-	-
Adebayo Adebayo	5.9	11.12	30.10.70	Ibadan (NLF)	Bath	39	69	15	-	-	-
England U21 B											
Jon Sleightholme	5.11	13.6	5.8.72	Wakefield	Wakefield	38	127	27	-	-	-
England A U21					Bath	8	10	2	-	-	-
Simon Geoghegan	6.1	13.3	1.9.68	Barnet	London Irish	52	67	15	-	-	-
Ireland U25 B					Bath	5	15	3			
Phil de Glanville	6.0	13.6	1.10.68	Loughborough	Bath	59	56	12	-	-	-
England U21 B A				Marketing							
Jeremy Guscott	6.1	13.2	7.7.65	Bath	Bath	65	133	27	8	-	1
England				Public Relations							
Iestyn Lewis	6.0	13.0	1.11.71		Bath	9	4	1	-	-	-
Wales U21 Students											
Ed Rayner					Bath	2	17	-	1	4	1
Mike Catt	5.10	13.0	17.9.71	Port Elizabeth	Bath	30	58	7	4	4	1
England A U21				Public Relations							
Ritchie Butland					Harlequins						
					Bath	7	33	1	8	4	-
Ian Sanders	5.9	10.0		Cornwall	Bath	21+3	5	1	-	-	-
England U21 U18 U16				Police Officer							
Simon Johnson					Bath	1+1	-	-	-	-	-
Marcus Olson					Llandovery						
					Bath	3+1	-	-	-	-	-
FORWARDS											
Dave Hilton	5.10	16.4	4.5.71		Bristol	16	-	-	-	-	-
					Bath	15	5	1	-	-	-
Victor Ubogu	5.9	16.0	8.9.64	La77	Richmond						
England A B				PR Director	Bath	57	46	10	-	-	-
John Mallett	6.0	16.0	28.5.70		Bath	18+2	4	1	-	-	-
England U18 Emerging				Manager							
Chris Clark'	6.1	15.6			Swansea				-	-	-
England A U21				Accountant	Bath	7+1	-	-	-	-	-
Kevin Yates					Bath	5	5	1	-	-	-
Darren Crompton	6.1	17.0			Bath	3	-	-	-	-	-
England U21 U18 U16											
Graham Dawe	5.11	13.3	4.9.59	Plymouth	Bath	93	13	3	-	-	-
England				Farmer							
Gareth Adams	5.11	13.3	12.9.70	Wakefield	Bath	8+3	10	2	-	-	-
				Student							
Andy Reed	6.7	16.12	4.5.69	Lostwithiel	Plymouth						
Scotland				Marketing	Bath	24	-	-	-	-	-
Nigel Redman	6.4	17.2	16.8.64	Cardiff	Bath	78	31	7	-	-	-
England				Engineer							
Martin Haag	6.5	16.7	28.7.65	Chelmsford	Bath	53+2	18	4	-	-	-
Wales U21 Students				Insurance							
Andy Robinson	5.9	13.12	3.4.64	Taunton	Bath	89	35	8	-	-	-
England				Schoolmaster							
John Hall	6.3	16.4	15.3.62	Bath	Bath	70	60	14	-	-	-
England											
Ben Clarke	6.5	17.0	15.4.68	Bishops Stortford	Saracens	22	35	8	-	-	-
				Public Relations	Bath	47	58	12	-	-	-
Steve Ojomoh	6.2	16.7	22.3.70	Benin City	Bath	33	5	1	-	-	-
England				Student							
Eric Peters	6.5	16.4	28.1.69		Saracens	-	-	-	-	-	-
Scotland					Bath	4					
Ed Pearce					Bath	1	-	-	-	-	-

BATH F.C.

The Recreation Ground, Bath BA2 6PW

Telephone: ~~01225 465328~~
Fax: 01225 443253

(handwritten: 10588)

(handwritten: (01225) 460588)

Total Capacity: 8,500
Seated: 2,500
Standing: 6,000
Simple Directions to Ground: City Centre
Nearest Railway Station: Bath Spa
Car Parking: Limited
Season Tickets: Adults £50 OAPs £40 Children £25
Match Prices: Adults £3
Membership: £15
Training Nights: Mondays & Wednesdays

ALL TIME TOP TEN COURAGE LEAGUE RECORDS

APPEARANCES		POINTS	
93	Graham Dawe	467	Stuart Barnes
90	Tony Swift	384	Jon Callard
89	Andy Robinson	275	Jon Webb
78	Nigel Redman	184	Tony Swift
74	Richard Hill	133	Jeremy Guscott
72	Stuart Barnes	69	Adebayo Adebayo
70	John Hall	60	John Hall
65	Jeremy Guscott	58	Mike Catt
59	Gareth Chilcott	58	Ben Clarke
59	Philip de Glanville	56	Philip de Glanville

MOST POINTS 467 STUART BARNES

Season	Apps	Points	Tries	Cons	Pens	D G
1987-88	4	32	1	2	6	2
1988-89	9	83	-	13	17	2
1989-90	10	103	6	29	7	-
1990-91	11	64	4	9	6	2
1991-92	12	95	3	10	20	1
1992-93	11	69	7	2	9	1
1993-94	15	21	-	-	6	1
Total	72	467	21	65	71	9

MOST TRIES 43 TONY SWIFT

Season	Appearances	Tries
1987-88	8	4
1988-89	7	3
1989-90	11	10
1990-91	12	6
1991-92	12	8
1992-93	12	4
1993-94	13	4
1994-95	15	4
Total	90	43

MOST APPEARANCES 93 GRAHAM DAWE

Season	Appearances
1987-88	9
1988-89	10
1989-90	10
1990-91	12
1991-92	11
1992-93	12
1993-94	17
1994-95	12
Total	93

BRISTOL F.C.

NICKNAME: **FOUNDED:** 1888

CLUB OFFICIALS

President
Arthur Holmes
Chairman
Bill Redwood
Club Secretary
T Wynne Jones
31 Bromley Heath Road, Downend,
Bristol BS16 6HY
Tel: (H) 0117 956 9161
Fixtures Secretary
Keith Gerrish
52 West Town Lane, Brislington,
Bristol BS4 5DB
Tel: (H) 0117 977 7009
Press Officer
David Tyler
Tel: 0117 951 4448

Review of the Season

There was a time in their recent campaign that people saw BRISTOL as potential candidates for relegation and for the most part they had to fight for survival during a campaign when they were not always lucky in their efforts to avoid injuries, which sometimes made a talented squad look weak.

In the end they arrived at their last game at Leicester, which resulted in a 17-3 loss to the champions, with enough points in hand to breathe easily enough but they will need to perform better from the start in the new campaign to avoid many more traumas.

A vital match in their survival was on 8th April when Gloucester came to the Memorial Ground with both sides needing the points to insure against the drop and Bristol won a splendid game 21-17, but in the Pilkington Cup where a good run was needed they followed an overwhelming 41-10 home victory over Nottingham with defeat by a 12-8 margin at home to Leicester in dreadful conditions.

The loss of Simon Shaw too early in the season was a big blow, but skipper Derek Eves once again inspired everyone around him and he received fine support in the pack from hooker Mark Regan, tighthead David Hinkins, lock Bob Armstrong and Craig Barrow and Ian Patten in the backrow. The star backs were inevitably Paul Hull at fullback and scrum-half Kyran Bracken, both of whom played for England although Hull was infortunate to be left out of the World Cup party and Bracken was latterly handicapped by injury.

Fly-half Mark Tainton had by the end of the season broken all meaningful club kicking records and his consistency with the boot will be vital in the club's quest for better times.

Colours: Blue and white   **Change Colours**: Red and white

BRISTOL F.C.

COURAGE LEAGUE
MATCH DETAILS 1994-95

No	Date	Opponents	Ven	Result		Scorers
1	Sep 10	Bath	A	L	9-18	Tainton (3P)
2	Sep 17	Sale	H	W	44-22	Regan (T) Hull (T) Eves (T) Sharp (T) John (T) Tainton (2C 5P)
3	Sep 24	Harlequins	H	W	19-14	Eves (T) Tainton (C 2P)
4	Oct 1	Northampton	A	W	18-15	Tainton (6P)
5	Oct 8	Orrell	H	W	20-9	Eves (2T) Denney (T) Tainton (C P)
6	Oct 15	Gloucester	A	L	17-19	Eves (T) Tainton (4P)
7	Oct 22	Wasps	H	L	24-25	Patten (T) Williams (T) Tainton (1C 4P)
8	Oct 29	West Hartlepool	A	L	11-47	G Sharp (T) Tainton (2P)
9	Nov 5	Leicester	H	W	31-22	G Sharp (T) Tainton (C 7P 1DG)
10	Jan 7	Bath	H	L	9-10	Tainton (P3)
11	Jan 14	Sale	A	L	9-21	Tainton (P3)
12	Feb 11	Harlequins	A	W	10-9	Wring (T) Tainton (C P)
13	Mar 4	Northampton	H	L	13-24	Sharp (T) Tainton (1C 2P)
14	Mar 25	Orrell	A	L	16-20	Denney (T) Tainton (3P 1C)
15	Apr 8	Glcouester	H	W	21-17	John (2T) Tainton (1D 2P 1C)
16	Apr 15	Wasps	A	L	15-27	Tainton (5P)
17	Apr 22	West Hartlepool	H	L	12-17	Chudleigh (T) Eves (T) Tainton (1C)
18	Apr 19	Leicester	A	L	3-13	Tainton (P)

Courage League Records 1994-95

League Debuts: Gavin Sharp, Mark Chudleigh, Neil Matthews, Andy Williams, Dave Bennett, Chris Moore, Nick Smith, Altan Ozdemir, Mark Fountaine, Gareth Archer
Try on Debut: Williams
2 Ever Presents: Mark Tainton, Dave Hinkins
Most appearances: 86 Derek Eves

● Tainton was leading scorer for the 4th consecutive season, beating the record on 3 he shared with Jonathon Webb

● Derek Eves passes Ralph Knibbs' record of most appearances – Eves finishes the season with 86. He also extended his record of consecutive appearances to 81 until he missed the away trip to Orrell when he was on England Sevens duty in Hohg Kong.

● Knibbs also lost his record of appearances for a back – Paul Hull finished the season on 77 just one ahead of Knibbs.

● Mark Tainton re-writes Bristol's points scoring records. In the home match v Leicester he finished with 26 points, beating the previous record of 19 he had set earlier in the season v Sale. The 7 penalties v Leicester beat his own record of 6 that he had set a month earlier v Northampton

● Tainton scored in all 18 matches and extended his record of scoring in consecutive matches to 26

● Bristol suffered their biggest away defeat when going down 11-47 to West Hartlepool

● Tainton beat his own record for points in a season

	Pts	T	C	P	D	Apps	Ave
1993-94	161	-	19	40	1	18	8.94
1994-95	196	-	11	56	2	18	10.89

● Tainton has yet to score a try in his 496 points in 59 games.

BRISTOL F.C.

MATCH BY MATCH PLAYERS BY POSITION

Hull	John	Denney	Wring	Sharpe G	Tainton	Bracken	Sharp A	Regan	Hinkins	Shaw	Blackmore	Armstrong	Eves	Patten	Williams	Newell	Chudleigh	Ozdemir	Barrow	Matthews	Knibbs	Fontaine	Smith N
A	B	C	D	E	F	G	H	I	J	K	L	M	N	O									
A	B	C	D	E	F	G	H	I	J	K	L	M	N	O									
A	B	C	D	E	F		H	I	J	K	L	M	O	N			G						
A	B	C	D	E	F		H	I	J	K	L		O	M			G		N				
A	B	C		E	F		H	I	J	K	L		O	N			G		M	D			
A	B		D	E	F	G	H	I	J	K	L		N	O						M	C		
A			D	B	F	G	H	I	J		L		O	N*	E					M	C		
A			D	B	F	G		I	J		L		N		E				K		C		H
A	E		D	B	F	G	H	I	J	K	L	M	N	O							C		
	B		D*	E	F	G	H	I	J	K	L	M	N	O		R40					C		
A	E		B		F		H*	I	J	K	L	M	O	N			G		D		C		
A		D	B		F				J		L	M	N	O	E		G		H				C
A		D		B	F	G		I	J			M	N	L	E				H	O			C
A		D		B	F			I	J			M	O		E		G		H	N		L	C
A	B	D			F			I	J	K			O	N	E		G		H	M		L	C
A	B	D			F			I	J	K			O	N	E		G		H	M		L	C
A	B	D			F			I	J	K			O	N	E		G		H	M		L	C
A	B	D		E	F			I	J			M	O	N			G		H			L	C

Also Played: Pearson M match 8; Moore O match 8; Bennett A match 10; Lathrobe R52 match 11, I match 12, R61 match 14; Adams K matches 12, 13, 15; Archer K match 18; Stiff R40 match 4, K match 7; Griffin R78 match 7

PROGRAMME DETAILS

PRICE: £1.00

PAGES: 40
Colour throughout.
At least 16 pages of original copy in last edition.
Colour throughout with attractive cover.
Excellent production.

EDITOR:
John Harding

ADVERTISING RATES:
Please apply to Commercial Manager

BRISTOL
FOOTBALL CLUB
—— RFU ——
v
GLOUCESTER
(F.C.)

CLUBS CHAMPIONSHIP

Saturday
8th April
1995

Kick off 3.00pm

1994/95

£1.00

Official Sponsors
HIGGS AND HILL HOMES

Official Programme 17

BRISTOL F.C.

COURAGE LEAGUE STATISTICS
compiled by Steve McCormack

Season	Div	P	W	D	L	F	T	C	P	D	A	T	C	P	D	Most Points	Most Tries
1987-88	1	10	4	1	5	171	22	16	16	1	145	17	13	16	1	58 Jon Webb	3 Andy Dun
1988-89	1	11	6	0	5	188	24	10	21	3	117	13	4	16	3	50 Jon Webb	2 by 8 players
1989-90	1	11	4	0	7	136	14	4	24	0	144	19	7	18	0	47 Jon Webb	2 Paul Hull. John Davis
1990-91	1	12	4	1	7	135	16	7	17	2	219	32	20	16	1	35 Simon Hogg	4 Julian Horrobin
1991-92	1	12	4	0	8	192	29	14	13	3	174	23	8	19	3	29 Mark Tainton	5 Pete Stiff
1992-93	1	12	6	0	6	148	13	7	23	0	169	18	11	15	4	68 Mark Tainton	3 Derek Eves
1993-94	1	18	10	0	8	331	33	20	40	2	276	23	13	44	1	161 Mark Tainton	8 Alistair Saveriamutto
1994-95	1	18	7	0	11	301	21	11	56	2	353	32	17	49	41	196 Mark Tainton	6 Derek Eves
TOTALS		104	45	2	57	1602	172	89	210	13	1597	177	93	193	17		

BIGGEST WIN — **Home:** 50-14 v Liverpool St H 22.4.89 CL1 — **Away:** 32-0 v Nottingham 16.11.91 CL1 & 32-21 v Rugby 27.3.93 CL1

BIGGEST DEFEAT — **Home:** 3-36 v Orrell 17.11.90 CL1 — **Away:** 11-47 v West Hartlepool 29.10.94

MOST TRIES in a match — **For:** 10 v Rugby 28.3.92 — **Against:** 8 v Wasps 27.4.91

MOST CONSECUTIVE — **Wins:** 4 — **Defeats:** 7

MOST APPEARANCES — **Forward:** 86 Derek Eves — **Back:** 77 Paul Hull

MOST CONSECUTIVE APPEARANCES 81 Derek Eves 11.3.88-4.3.95

CONSECUTIVE SCORING MATCHES — **Tries:** 3 Alastair Saverimutto — **Points:** 26 Mark Tainton

	IN A SEASON	IN A CAREER	IN A MATCH
MOST POINTS	196 Mark Tainton 1994-95 CL1	496 Mark Tainton 1987-95	26 Mark Tainton v Leicester 5.11.94 Home CL1
MOST TRIES	8 Alistair Saverimutto 1993-94 CL1	17 Derek Eves 1987-95	3 Mike Lloyd v Rugby 28.3.92 Home CL1. Derek Eves v Rugby 27.3.93 Home CL1
MOST CONVERSIONS	19 Mark Tainton 1993-94 CL1	47 Mark Tainton 1987-95	5 Jonathan Webb v Sale 24.10.87 Home CL1
MOST PENALTIES	56 Mark Tainton 1994-95 CL1	130 Mark Tainton 1957-95	7 Mark Tainton v Leicester 5.11.94 Home CL1
MOST DROP GOALS	3 Simon Hogg 1988-89 CL1	5 Simon Hogg 1987-93	2 Simon Hogg v Leicester 9.3.91 Home CL1

BRISTOL F.C.

Name	Ht	Wt	Birthdate	Birthplace	Clubs	App	Pts	T	C	P	DG
BACKS											
Paul Hull	5.9	11.8	17.5.68	London	Bristol	77	94	16	3	5	-
England A U21				RAF							
Dave Bennett	6.2	13.7	13.5.72		Newcastle G	25	4	1	-	-	-
				Farmer	Bristol	1	-	-	-	-	-
David John	6.5	13.3	23.9.65	Mechanic	Bristol	36	25	5	-	-	-
Gavin Sharp	5.9	13.8	4.1.70	RAF	Bristol	15	20	4	-	-	-
Andy Williams	6.2	14.0	25.12.70		Bristol	8	5	1	-	-	-
				Policeman							
Ralph Knibbs	6.1	13.0	3.8.64		Bristol	176	48	9	-	-	3
England				Personnel							
Mark Denney	5.11	14.8	25.1.75								
				Student	Bristol	13	15	3	-	-	-
Dean Wring	6.0	16.0			Bristol	37	29	5	-	2	-
				Technician							
Neil Matthews	5.10	13.0	11.4.70	Gloucester	Gloucester						
England U21					Bristol	3	-	-	-	-	-
Neil Smith			14.7.72		Bristol	6	-	-	-	-	-
				Manager							
Mark Tainton	5.8	12.0	10.3.69		Bristol	59	496	-	47	130	4
				Sales Engineer							
Kyran Bracken	5.10	13.0	22.11.71	Dublin	Bristol	31	15	3	-	-	-
England U21 A											
Mark Newall	5.7	11.8	22.1.68		Bristol	5+3	-	-	-	-	-
				Schoolmaster							
Mark Chudleigh	5.8	12.0	31.7.74		Bristol	8	5	1	-	-	-
				Student							
FORWARDS											
Alan Sharp	5.9	13.9	7.10.68		Bristol	49	-	-	-	-	-
				Salesman							
David Hinkins	6.1	17.0	20.10.66		Bristol	67	-	-	-	-	-
				Teacher							
Pete Smith	6.0	17.2	28.4.61		Bristol	14	4	1	-	-	-
				Engineer							
Altam Odizer	5.8	16.0	3.9.74		Bristol	7	-	-	-	-	-
				Brewer							
Mark Regan	5.11	14.0	28.1.72		Bristol	38	5	1	-	-	-
				Engineer							
Andy Lathrope	5.10	12.8	6.2.66		Bristol	12+7	-	-	-	-	-
				Telecom Engineer							
Simon Shaw	6.9	20.0	1.9.73		Bristol	31	-	-	-	-	-
				Student							
Andy Blackmore	6.7	17.8	1.11.65		Bristol	75	9	2	-	-	-
				Salesman							
Peter Stiff	6.4	18.0	1.4.58		Bristol	27+2	28	7	-	-	-
				Printer							
Phil Adams	6.5	17.0	2.2.63		Bristol	28	-	-	-	-	-
				Builder							
Mark Fountaine	6.6	16.5	7.6.67		Bristol	5	-	-	-	-	-
				Schoolmaster							
Gareth Archer					Newcastle G	18+1	10	2	-	-	-
				Army	Bristol	1	-	-	-	-	-
Bob Armstrong	6.3	17.8	17.8.67		Bristol	27+1	-	-	-	-	-
				Marine							
Derek Eves	8.10	14.8	7.1.66		Bristol	86	80	17	-	-	-
				Salesman							
Ian Patten	6.5	14.8	31.8.70		Bristol	31	15	3	-	-	-
				Bank Clerk							
Craig Barrow	6.6	14.7	26.2.69		Bristol	48	14	3	-	-	-
England Students				Teacher							
Joel Pearson	6.0	15.7	8.3.70		Bristol	7	-	-	-	-	-
				Financial Consultant							
Chris Moore	6.5	16.0	7.11.68		Bristol	1	-	-	-	-	-
				RAF							

BRISTOL F.C.

Memorial Ground, Filton Avenue, Horfield, Bristol BS7 0AQ
Telephone: 0117 951 4448
Fax: 0117 941 4226

Total Capacity: 8,700
Seated: 1,200
Standing: 7,500
Simple Directions to Ground: M4 to Junction 19, M32 to Junction 2, join B4469 towards Horfield. Ground signposted left at second set of traffic lights after 'Brunel Ford'
Nearest Railway Station: Bristol Parkway
Car Parking: 300
Season Tickets:
Match Prices: Stand - Adults £6.00, OAP £4.00, Juvenile £2.00; Enclosure - Adults £5.00, OAP £4.00, Juvenile £2.00; Ground - Adults £4.00, OAP £3.00, Juvenile £1.00
Membership: Stand - Adults £88.13, OAP/Students/Juvenile £49.94; Enclosure - Adults £58.75, OAP/Students/Juvenile £41.13; Ground - Adults £47.00, OAP/Students/Juvenile £29.38
Training Nights: Tuesday & Thursdays

ALL TIME TOP TEN COURAGE LEAGUE RECORDS

APPEARANCES		POINTS	
86	Derek Eves	496	Mark Tainton
77	Paul Hull	155	Jonathan Webb
76	Ralph Knibbs	115	Simon Hogg
75	Andy Blackmore	94	Paul Hull
67	Dave Hinkins	80	Derek Eves
59	Mark Tainton	32	Paul Collings
51	Alan Sharp	48	Ralph Knibbs
49	David Palmer	40	Alastair Saverimutto
48	Craig Barrow	40	Julian Davies
45	Paul Collings	32	Huw Duggan

MOST POINTS
496 Mark Tainton

Season	Apps	Points	Tries	Cons	Pens	D G
1987-88	4	11	-	1	3	-
1988-89	1	-	-	-	-	-
1989-90	2	25	-	2	7	-
1990-91	1	6	-	-	2	-
1991-92	5	29	-	7	4	1
1992-93	10	68	-	7	18	-
1993-94	18	161	-	19	40	1
1994-95	18	196	-	11	56	2
Total	59	496	-	47	130	4

MOST TRIES
17 Derek Eves

Season	Appearances	Tries
1987-88	1	-
1988-89	3	-
1989-90	11	-
1990-91	12	2
1991-92	12	3
1992-93	12	3
1993-94	18	3
1994-95	17	6
Total	86	17

MOST APPEARANCES
86 Derek Eves

Season	Appearances
1987-88	1
1988-89	3
1989-90	11
1990-91	12
1991-92	12
1992-93	12
1993-94	18
1994-95	17
Total	86

GLOUCESTER R.F.C.

NICKNAME: "CHERRY AND WHITES"   **FOUNDED:** 1873

CLUB OFFICIALS

President
S T Day
Chairman
Allan Brinn
Club Secretary
A D Wadley
Byeways, Belmont Avenue,
Hucclecote, Gloucester GL3 3SF
Tel: (H) 01452 617202 (W) 01452 381087
Fixtures Secretary
Mike Nicholls
90 Kingsholm Road, Gloucester GL1 3BB
Tel: (H) 01452 301879 (W) 0121 772 6644
Press Officer
Allan Brinn
Tel: (H) 01452 522029 (W) 01452 303722

Exciting Developments at Kingsholm

After a couple of mediocre seasons we started 1994/5 with hopes of making an impact in Division One, after a successful pre-season Tour to South Africa.

Unfortunately we failed to find any consistency and although achieving some good results we lost a number of matches by narrow margins. A few of these results going our way would have changed the outlook dramatically. However these criteria could be applied to a number of 1st Division Clubs.

In spite of this we had some encouraging representation at International level with Ian Smith (Scotland) and Richard West (England) going to the World Cup and David Sims and Paul Holford touring Australia with England 'A'. We were also delighted that our young forward Phil Greening captained England Colts.

Although we do not have an official Player of the Year, several players enhanced their reputations throughout a difficult season. A straw poll conducted amongst our supporters, however, would almost certainly come out with the name of David Sims. He was magnificent all season and has been acknowledged by the players who have elected him Captain for the 1995/6 season.

With thoughts already turning to next season, there are some exciting developments in the quest to make us a force in the 1st Division again.

The appointment of Mike Coley as our Chief Executive/Marketing Manager and the involvement of former Internationals Mike Teague, John Fidler and Peter Kingston on the playing side will form a team that we hope will transform the fortunes of the club. We have ambitious plans for ground development which we hope will run in tandem with the re-emergence of success on the playing field.

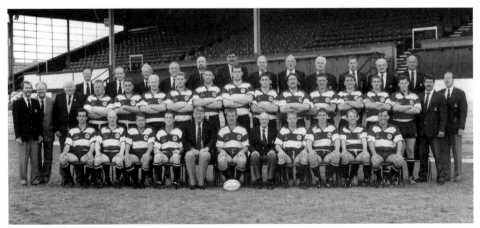

Back: Jim Holder, Mervyn Elway, Cecil Pope, Mike Nicholls, Terry Close, John Fidler, John Beaman, Reg Collins, Allan Townsend, Bob Clewes, Tom Day, David Foyle. Centre: Andy Mitchell, Doug Wadley (Treasurer/Secretary), Roy Morris, Adey Powles, Tony Windo, Pete Glanville, Mark Nicholls, Dave Sims, Richard West, Simon Devereux, Mike Teague, Martin Roberts, Simon Morris, Paul Holford, Paul Ashmead, Viv Wooley (Coach), Eric Stevens (Team Secretary). Front: Martin Kimber, Bruce Fenley, Pete Jones, Tim Smith, Allan Brinn (Chairman), Andy Deacon (Captain), Mervyn Hughes (President), Lee Osborne, Ian Smith, Don Caskie, John Hawker
Colours: Cherry, white, black   **Change Colours:** Black

GLOUCESTER R.F.C.

COURAGE LEAGUE
MATCH DETAILS 1994-95

No	Date	Opponents	Ven	Result		Scorers
1	Sep 10	Wasps	A	L	8-45	Morris (T) Mapletoft (P)
2	Sep 17	West Hartlepool	H	W	48-12	Morris (3T) Holford (2T) T Smith (T) Mapletoft (T) Mapletoft (1P 5C)
3	Sep 24	Leicester	A	L	6-16	Mapletoft (P) Kimber (DG)
4	Oct 1	Bath	H	L	10-15	T Smith (T) Mapletoft (CP)
5	Oct 8	Sale	A	L	14-16	T Smith (T) Kimber (DG) Mapletoft (2P)
6	Oct 15	Bristol	H	W	19-17	Sims (T) Mapletoft (4P 1C)
7	Oct 22	Northampton	A	L	6-9	Mapletoft (2P)
8	Oct 29	Orrell	H	W	9-6	Mapletoft (2P) Kimber (DG)
9	Nov 5	Harlequins	A	W	14-10	Holford (2T) Osborne (2C)
10	Jan 7	Wasps	H	L	16-21	Mapletoft (1T 1C 3P)
11	Jan 14	West Hartlepool	A	L	21-22	Teague (T) Ashmead (T) Mapletoft (C 2P) Kimber (DG)
12	Feb 11	Leicester	H	W	9-3	Osborne (3P)
13	Mar 4	Bath	A	D	19-19	Holford (T) Kimber (2DG) Osborne (C 2P)
14	Mar 25	Sale	H	L	8-20	Holford (T) Osborne (P)
15	Apr 8	Bristol	A	L	17-21	Holford (2T) Teague (1T) Osborne (1C)
16	Apr 15	Northampton	H	W	14-13	Sims (T) T Smith (3P)
17	Apr 22	Orrell	A	L	14-43	Ashmead (T) Osborne (3P)
18	Apr 29	Harlequins	H	L	17-28	Cornwell (2T) Osborne (1P 2C)

Courage League Records 1994-95

League Debuts: Mark Mapletoft, Martyn Kimber, Chris Raymond, Lee Osborne, Adrian Powles, Mark Cornwell, Robin Saltmarsh, Rob Fidler, Paul Greening
32 Players used
Only Ever Present Paul Holford
Most appearances: 91 Ian Smith

● Mark Mapletoft equals Tim Smith's record for points in a season – 85

	Pts	T	C	P	D	App	Ave	Season
Tim Smith	85	1	12	19	-	10	8.50	1988-89
Mark Mapletoft	85	2	9	19	-	11	7.72	1994-95

● Mapletoft's 85 points sees him move into second place on Gloucester's all time points scoring list

● Simon Morris becomes the second player after Derek Morgan to score a hat trick of tries in a league match

● Martin Kimber aets a record for most drop goals in a season for Gloucester. Kimber's 6 easily beat the previous record of 3 set by Damian Cummings.

● Paul Holford breaks the record for most tries in a league season for Gloucester with 8. The previous record of 6 was held by Jim Breeze, Mike Hamlin and Derek Morgan

● Holford's 8 came in 18 league matches. He has now played in 38 of Gloucester's last 40 games since making his debut v Northampton in March 1993 Holford and Morris move into 2nd and 4th on Gloucester's all time try list

	Tries	App	Strike Rate
Derek Morgan	15	36	2.40
Marcus Hannaford	12	64	5.33
Paul Holford	12	38	3.16
Simon Morris	11	38	3.45

● Tim Smith passes 500 points – he ends the season on 514 from 81 appearances averaging 6.35 per game – since league rugby began he has scored 30% of Gloucester's points

● Lock Dave Sims breaks Mike Hamlin's record of 40 consecutive appearances. Sims managed 47 before missing the away match at Bristol in April

● Their defeat by Harlequins on the last day of the season was their biggest home league defeat

● The 7 tries they conceded at Wasps were the most they have conceded in a league match – previous was 6 v Bath in October 1993

GLOUCESTER R.F.C.

MATCH BY MATCH PLAYERS BY POSITION

Mapletoft	Holford	Morris	Maslen	Powles	Smith T	Fenley	Jones	Hawker	Deacon	Sims	West	Glanville	Smith I	Caskie	Devereux	Kimber	Raymond	Ashmead	Windo	Kearsey	Teague	Osborne	Cornwell
15	14	13	12		10	9	1	2	3	4	5	6	7		R57								
15	14	13	12		11	9	1	2	3	4	5	6	7			10	8						
15	14	13	12		11	9	1	2	3	5	4	6	7			10	8						
15	14	13	12		11	9	1	2	3	4	5	6*	7			10	8	R60					
15	14	13	12		11	9			3	4	5		7			10	8		1	2	6		
15	14	13	12			9	1		3	4	5		7			10	8			2	6	11	
15	14	13	12			9	1		3	4	5		7			10	8			2	6	11	
15	14	13	12			9		2	3	4			7		5	10		6	1		8	11	
15	14	13	12*			9		2	3	5			7		4	10		6	1		8	11	
15	14	12				9		2	3	4	5			13	6	10		7			8	11	
15*	14	12	R64	1		9		2	3	4	5		7	13		10		6			8	11	
	14	11		1	15	9		2	3	4	5	6	7	12		10					8	13	
	14	11		1	15	9		2	3	4	5	6	7	13		10					8	12	
	14	11			15	9	3	2		4	5	6		13	4	10			1		8	12	
	14		1		15	9		2	3		5	6		13		10					8	11	4
	14		1		15	9		2	3	4	5	6		13				7			8	10	
	14		1		15	9		2	3	4		6		12		10		7				13	5
	14				15				3			6		13	4	10		7	1		8	11	5

Also Played: Nicholls No 8 match 1, R40 match 14; Nicholson No 11 match 1; Roberts No 12 matches 15, 16, 18; Stanley No 7 matches 14, 15; Saltmarsh No 11 matches 16, 17; Fidler No 8 match 11; Hannaford No 9 match 18; Greening No 2 match 18; Morgan R17 match 9

PROGRAMME DETAILS

PRICE: £1.00

PAGES: 32
Very attractive cover. Spot colour throughout. Twelve pages of original copy and excellent presentation of the line-ups.

EDITOR: Peter Arnold
Tel: 01452 380481

ADVERTISING RATES: From £300

GLOUCESTER R.F.C.

COURAGE LEAGUE STATISTICS

compiled by Steve McCormack

Season	Div	P	W	D	L	F	T	C	P	D	A	T	C	P	D	Most Points	Most Tries
1987-88	1	10	6	1	3	206	32	18	14		**121**	9	2	23	4	Nick Marment	6 Jim Breeze
1988-89	1	11	7	1	3	215	31	14	21	0	**112**	14	7	13	1	85 Tim Smith	6 Mike Hamlin
1989-90	1	11	8	1	2	214	32	10	21	1	**139**	16	9	19	0	75 Tim Smith	6 Derek Morgan
1990-91	1	12	6	0	6	207	29	17	19	0	**163**	19	9	22	1	75 Tim Smith	3 Ian Smith Derek Morgan Paul Ashmead Chris Dee
1991-92	1	12	7	1	4	193	19	12	29	2	**168**	16	10	26	2	81 Tim Smith	5 Simon Morris
1992-93	1	12	6	0	6	173	17	8	24	0	**151**	12	5	25	2	71 Tim Smith	3 Tim Smith Derek Morgan
1993-94	1	18	6	2	10	247	21	11	36	4	**356**	29	23	53	2	82 Tim Smith	3 Tim Smith Derek Morgan
1994-95	1	18	6	1	11	269	25	15	32	6	**336**	37	17	37	2	85 Mark Mapletoft	8 Paul Holford
TOTALS		104	52	7	45	1724	206	105	196	13	**1546**	152	82	218	14		

BIGGEST WIN
Home: 61-7 v Sale 16.4.88 CL1
Away: 31-9 v Liverpool St H 22.10.88 CL1

BIGGEST DEFEAT
Home: 17-28 v Harlequins 29.4.95 CL1
Away: 17-46 v Bath 2.10.93 CL1

MOST TRIES in a match
For: 11 v Sale 16.4.88 CL1
Against: 7 v Wasps 10.9.94 CL1

MOST CONSECUTIVE
Wins: 5
Defeats 4

MOST APPEARANCES
Forward: 91 Ian Smith
Back: 81 Tim Smith

MOST CONSECUTIVE APPEARANCES
47 Dave Sims 11.4.92-25.3.95

CONSECUTIVE SCORING MATCHES
Tries: 3 Jim Breeze, Tim Smith, Mike Hamlin
Points: 15 Tim Smith

	IN A SEASON	IN A CAREER	IN A MATCH
MOST POINTS	85 Tim Smith 1988-89 CL1 Mark Mapletoft 1994-95 CL1	514 Tim Smith 1987-95	20 Tim Smith v Harlequins 12.3.90 Home CL1
MOST TRIES	8 Paul Holford 1994-95 CL1	15 Derek Morgan 1988-93	3 Derek Morgan v Rosslyn Park 11.11.89 Home CL1 Simon Morris v
MOST CONVERSIONS	12 Tim Smith 1988-89 CL1 1990-91 CL1	53 Tim Smith 1987-95	6 Paul Mansell v Sale 16.4.88 Home CL1
MOST PENALTIES	21 Tim Smith 1991-92 CL1 + 1993-94 CL1	121 Tim Smith 1987-95	6 Tim Smith v Harlequins 12.3.90 Home CL1
MOST DROP GOALS	6 Martyn Kimber 1994-95 CL1	6 Martyn Kimber 1994-95	2 Martyn Kimber v Bath 4.3.95 Away CL1

GLOUCESTER F.C.

Name	Ht	Wt	Birthdate	Birthplace	Clubs	App	Pts	T	C	P	DG
BACKS											
Mark Mapletoft	5.7	13.0	25.12.71	Mansfield	Rugby	41	201	6	14	45	3
				Sales Manager	Gloucester	11	85	2	9	19	-
Tim Smith	5.11	13.0	10.5.62	Gloucester	Gloucester	81	514	9	53	121	1
				Scaffolder							
Paul Holford	5.11	12.12	2.12.69	Gloucester	Gloucester	38	60	12	-	-	-
England Emerging				Bricklayer							
Lee Osborne	5.11	12.0	7.3.70	Cinderford	Berry Hill						
				Planner	Gloucester	13	42	-	6	10	-
Robin Saltmarsh	5.11	14.0	1.8.72	Barnstaple	Bristol						
				Student	Gloucester	2	-	-	-	-	-
Simon Morris	6.0	12.10	3.5.69	Gloucester	Lydney						
				Policeman	Gloucester	38	55	11	-	-	-
Ben Maslen	6.0	14.0	23.3.72	Brighton	Cheltenham						
				Accountant	Gloucester	11+1	-	-	-	-	-
Don Caskie	5.7	12.0	12.12.66	Almondsbury	London Scottish						
				Sales Manager	Gloucester	69	17	4	-	-	-
Martin Roberts	6.3	15.0	26.1.68	Gloucester	Cheltenham						
				Builder	Gloucester	12+1	56	1	6	13	-
Mark Nicholson	5.10	13.0	5.10.68	Plymouth	Exeter						
				Teacher	Gloucester	14+1	5	1	-	-	-
Martyn Kimber	6.0	13.10	20.9.68	Aukland	Stroud	-	1	-	-	-	-
				Engineer	Gloucester	16	18	-	-	-	6
Bruce Fenley	5.8	12.0	7.9.68	Cheltenham	Moseley	35+3	-	-	-	-	-
				Surveyor	Gloucester	30	10	2	-	-	-
Marcus Hannaford					Gloucester	64	49	12	-	-	-
FORWARDS											
Peter Jones	5.10	15.0	28.12.63	Arbroath	Longlevens						
				Engineer	Gloucester	48	4	1	-	-	-
Andy Deacon	6.1	16.0	31.7.65	Gloucester	Longlevens						
				Drayman	Gloucester	38	10	2	-	-	-
Adrian Powles	5.11	17.0	14.3.67	Cowsford	Berry Hill						
				Htg Engineer	Gloucester	7+1	-	-	-	-	-
Tony Windo	6.0	16.0	30.4.69	Gloucester	Longlevens						
				Technician	Gloucester	24	5	1	-	-	-
John Hawker	5.10	13.10	17.5.63	Gloucester	Matson						
				Computer Prog	Gloucester	45	8	2	-	-	-
Dave Kearsley	6.0	13.10	18.4.67	Gloucester	Cheltenham						
				Fireman	Gloucester	14+3	5	1	-	-	-
Dave Sims	6.6	17.0	22.11.69	Gloucester	Longlevens						
England A U21				Manager	Gloucester	66	18	4	-	-	-
Richard West	6.8	17.0	20.3.71	Hereford	Moseley						
England (1)				Teacher	Gloucester	41	10	2	-	-	-
Simon Devereux	6.3	16.10	20.10.68	Gloucester	Spartans						
				Prod Eng	Gloucester	16+1					
Mark Cornwell	6.7	16.10	22.2.73	Gloucester	Old Richians						
				Salesman	Gloucester	3	10	2	-	-	-
Peter Glanville	6.2	15.3	10.6.71	Gloucester	Longlevens						
				Manager	Gloucester	23	-	-	-	-	-
Ian Smith	6.0	13.10	16.3.63	Gloucester	Longlevens						
Scotland (11)				Civil Eng	Gloucester	91	25	6	-	-	-
Mark Nicholls	6.4	15.12	7.7.71	Gloucester	Longlevens						
				Solicitor	Gloucester	5+1	-	-	-	-	-
Chris Raymond	6.5	17.0	1.3.68	Cheltenham	Moseley	42+2	5	1	-	-	-
				Teacher	Gloucester	6					
Paul Ashmead	6.0	14.0	3.1.66	Gloucester	Longlevens						
				Technician	Gloucester	43+1	42	10	-	-	-
Mike Teague	6.4	15.6	8.10.60	Gloucester	Gloucester	38	34	8	-	-	-
England (29)				Builder	Moseley	22	10	2	-	-	-
Andrew Stanley	6.0	14.0	15.9.62	Gloucester	Gordon League	7	-	-	-	-	-
				Lecturer	Gloucester	7	-	-	-	-	-
Rob Fidler	6.4	15.3	21.9.74	Gloucester	Gloucester	1	-	-	-	-	-
England U18 U16				Student							

GLOUCESTER R.F.C.

Kingsholm, Kingsholm Road, Gloucester GL1 3AX

Telephone: 01452 381087
Fax: 01452 383321

Total Capacity: 12,000
Seated: 1,250
Standing: 10,750
Simple Directions to Ground: M5 jcn 11 towards Glos, first r/about right towards Glos/Wales, next r/about left, next r/about straight over, ground 300 yards on right.
Nearest Railway Station: Gloucester
Car Parking: 250
Season Tickets: Adults G'stand £90.00, Ground £45.00; Children/OAPs G/stand £45.00, Ground £22.50
Match Prices: Adults £8.50, Children/OAPs £5.00
Membership: Seniors N/A Juniors N/A
Training Nights: Tuesday and Thursday

ALL TIME TOP TEN COURAGE LEAGUE RECORDS

APPEARANCES		POINTS	
91	Ian Smith	514	Tim Smith
81	Tim Smith	85	Mark Mapletoft
69	Don Caskie	82	Nick Marment
66	Dave Sims	63	Derek Morgan
64	Marcus Hannaford	61	Mike Hamlin
59+1	Damian Cummins	56	Martin Roberts
48	Peter Jones	55	Simon Morris
48	Nick Scrivens	49	Marcus Hannaford
48	Mike Hamlin	44	Jim Breeze
45	John Hawker	42	Lee Osborne & Paul Ashmead

MOST POINTS
514 Tim Smith

Season	Apps	Points	Tries	Cons	Pens	D G
1987-88	4	21	-	3	5	1
1988-89	10	85	1	12	19	-
1989-90	8	75	2	5	19	-
1990-91	11	75	- 12	17	-	-
1991-92	9	81	-	9	21	-
1992-93	11	71	3	4	16	-
1993-94	16	82	-	8	21	1
1994-95	12	24	3	-	3	-
Total	81	514	9	53	121	1

MOST TRIES
15 Derek Morgan

Season	Appearances	Tries
1987-88	8	3
1988-89	1	-
1989-90	10	6
1990-91	8	3
1991-92	2	-
1992-93	7	3
Total	36	15

MOST APPEARANCES
91 Ian Smith

Season	Appearances
1987-88	10
1988-89	10
1989-90	11
1990-91	11
1991-92	8
1992-93	12
1993-94	17
1994-95	12
Total	91

HARLEQUIN F.C.

NICKNAME: QUINS   **FOUNDED:** 1866

18   66

CLUB OFFICIALS

President
David Brooks
Chairman
Roger Looker
Club Secretary
Geoff Morey
Stoop Memorial Ground, Craneford
Way, Twickenham TW2 7SQ
Tel: (H) 0181 892 0822
Fixtures Secretary
Graeme Murray
25 Barham Road, Wimbledon, London
SW20 0ES
Tel: (H) 0181 946 1976 (W) 0171 736
1155
Press Officer
Alex Saward
Tel: (H) 0171 377 1151

Review of the Season

On paper HARLEQUINS – an elite club by tradition – should be challenging the best but if their last league match at Gloucester had not been won they and not Northampton would have been faced with League Two fare in the coming season and, to be honest, few outside their own Stoop Memorial Ground would have been in mourning.

They won that match handsomely (28-17) and did stay up but it had been too close for comfort and a club which boasts an array of talent should have done better. With the likes of Will Carling, Brian Moore, Jason Leonard, Andy Mullins and Ireland's Jim Staples plus Paul Challinor, Rory Jenkins and Chris Sheasby (to mention just a few) they have the basis for a side to take on all comers, or would they be better off if they were to stick to their own developed talent and allow their more famous players to move elsewhere?

Their superb reputation as a cup team was almost confirmed again as they disposed of Saracens (9-5 at home), London Irish (40-15 away), and Wakefield (13-8 at home) before holders Bath appeared at the Stoop and dismissed them by a convincing 31-13 score. But cups bring in cash and not survival in the league. The new season could be interesting.

Colours: As 1994/95   **Change Colours**: As 1994/95

HARLEQUIN F.C.

COURAGE LEAGUE
MATCH DETAILS 1994-95

No	Date	Opponents	Ven	Result	Scorers
1	Sep 10	Sale	A	W 20-19	O'Leary (T) Sheasby (T) Carling (T) Bray (1C 1P)
2	Sep 17	Wasps	H	L 26-57	Moore (T) Challinor (T) Shearsby (T) Challinor (1C 3P)
3	Sep 24	Bristol	A	L 14-19	Keyter (T) Challinor (2P 1DG)
4	Oct 1	West Hartlepool	H	W 20-10	Cassell (T) Challinor (5P)
5	Oct 8	Northampton	A	W 23-16	Thompson (2T) Cassell (1T) Challinor (C P) Greenwood (P)
6	Oct 15	Leicester	H	L 13-40	Thompson (T) Greenwood (1C 2P)
7	Oct 22	Orrell	H	L 6-8	Greenwood (2P)
8	Oct 29	Bath	A	L 11-22	Greenwood (T) Challinor (1P 1DG)
9	Nov 5	Gloucester	H	L 10-14	Pinnock (T) Bray (1P 1C)
10	Jan 7	Sale	H	D 15-15	Challinor (5P)
11	Jan 14	Wasps	A	L 7-25	Mensah (T) Staples (C)
12	Feb 11	Bristol	H	L 9-10	Challinor (3P)
13	Mar 4	West Hartlepool	A	L 8-10	Mensah (T) Challinor (P)
14	Mar 25	Northampton	H	W 10-9	Kitchin (T) Staples (T)
15	Apr 8	Leicester	A	L 8-22	Wright (T) Challinor (P)
16	Apr 15	Orrell	A	W 28-10	Mensah (T) Staples (T) Thresher (T) Challinor (3P 2C)
17	Apr 22	Bath	H	L 19-25	Sheasby (1T) Greenwood (1T) Challinor (3P)
18	Apr 29	Gloucester	A	W 28-17	Henderson (T) Mensah (T) Pen Try Staples (3P 2C)

Courage League Records 1994-95

League Debuts: Peter Mesnah, Rob Kitchen, Bill Davison, Chris Wright, Rory Jenkins, Justin Cassell, Will Greenwood, Nick Collins, D Currie, Andy Pinnock, Jim Staples, Spencer Bromley, Laurence Boyle, Crawford Henderson, Mike Watson, Simon Mitchell
Used 39 Players – more than any other side in the division
2 Ever Presents: Rob Kitchen, Chris Sheasby
Most appearances: 94 Andy Mullins

- Had a better away record than home, 4 wins to 2, scoring 17 of their 27 tries away from home

- Only once managed to keep a clean sheet in terms of tries, v Northampton, 38 tries against, 2nd worst record in the division

- Went 8 matches without a win

- Never fielded the same team in consecutive games

- Conceded a record 9 tries in their worst ever defeat, 26-57 v Wasps – 6 was previously the highest number of tries against and 37 in terms of points

- Converted only 37% of the tries they scored – worst in the division

- Peter Mensah leading scorer in his first season with the club

- Paul Challinor becomes the 3rd Quins player to pass 200 league points and moves into 2nd place in the all time list

	Pts	T	C	P	D	App	Ave
David Pears	346	7	46	69	7	32	10.81
Paul Challinor	221	8	9	50	5	47	4.10
Stuart Thresher	212	10	32	35	-	42+1	5.04

HARLEQUIN F.C.

MATCH BY MATCH PLAYERS BY POSITION

Bray	O'Leary	Carling	Mensah	Thompson	Challinor	Kitchin	Leonard	Moore	Thresher	Snow	Davison	Coker	Pepper	Sheasby	Glenister	Mullins	Staples	Wright	Keyter	Kenkins	Cassell	Greenwood	Alexander
15	14	13	12*	11	10	9	1	2		4	5	6	7	8	12								
R48	14	13*	12	11	10	9	1	2		4	5	6	7	8	15	3							
		14	12*	13	10	9	1	2		4	5		7			3		R13	11	6	8		
			11	13	10	9	1	2		4	5			8		3			14	6	7	15	12
		13		11	10*	9	1	2		4		6		8				R39	14	6	7	15	12
		13		11		9	1	2*		4	5			8					14	6	7	10	12,
		13**		11		9	1			4	5	6	7	8	R**			10	14*		R*	15	12
		11		13	10*	9	3		R	4	5	6**	7	9								15	12
10	14	13		12		9	1	2	5	4	R22	6	7*	8								15	
	11	13			10*	9		2	5	4			7	8		3	15	R77	6				
			11*			9				5		6		8	R67	3	15	10	13	7			
			12	13	10	9			5	4				8		3	15				7	11	
			13	12	10	9	1	2	5	4		6		8		3					7	15	
		13	14		10	9	1	2	5	4				8		3	15				7	12	
	11		13		10	9				4				8		3		15			7		
		12	13		10	9	1	2	5	4				8		3	15				7		
			13		10	9			5	4				8		3	15				7	12	11
		13	12		10	9	1	2	5	4				8		3	15				7		

Also Played: Hobley No 3 match 1; Madderson No 15 match 3; Collins No 3 matches 5, 6; Osman No 12 matches 11, 15; Currie No 15 match 6; Simmonds R33 match 6; Hamilton-Smith No 2 matches 7, 8, 11, 12, 17; Brown No 1 matches 8, 10, 11, 12, 15, 17, No 3 match 9; Pinnock No 14 match 8, No 11 match 9; Watson No 6 matches 14, 15, 16, 17, 18; Mitchell No 2 match 15; Henderson No 14, matches 13, 15, 16, 17, 18; Boyle No 12 match 10; Russell No 6 match 12, No 5 match 16; Desmond No 4 match 11; Luxton R45 match 8

PROGRAMME DETAILS

PRICE: £1.00

PAGES: 40
On excellent paper with colour on the outer third.
Attractive cover and ten pages of original copy.
No photos but smart presentation.

EDITOR:
Mike Coley

ADVERTISING RATES:
Full page colour £1,085, page colour £865, full page b/w
£565, page b/w £295, page b/w £175

HARLEQUIN F.C.

COURAGE LEAGUE STATISTICS
compiled by Steve McCormack

Season	Div	P	W	D	L	F	T	C	P	D	A	T	C	P	D	Most Points	Most Tries
1987-88	1	11	6	1	4	261	38	26	18	1	128	19	5	11	3	58 Stuart Thresher	11 Andrew Harriman
1988089	1	11	5	0	6	194	25	17	18	2	184	23	16	20	0	71 Stuart Thresher	4 Jon Eagle & Mickey Skinner
1989-90	1	11	6	0	5	218	26	15	26	2	180	22	10	21	3	114 David Peaars	5 Craig Luxton
1990-91	1	12	8	0	4	267	32	20	28	5	162	17	8	24	2	120 David Pears	9 Andrew Harriman
1991-92	1	12	5	1	6	213	27	15	23	2	207	28	16	18	3	109 David Pears	4 David Pears
1992-93	1	12	5	1	6	197	23	11	19	1	187	17	9	26	2	57 Stuart Thresher	3 Will Carling Stuart Thresher Paul Challinor Rob Glenister
1993-94	1	18	8	0	10	333	30	15	50	1	287	34	18	27	0	143 Kent Bray	11 Daren O'Leary
1994-95	1	18	6	1	11	275	27	10	37	3	348	38	25	32	4	103 Paul Challinor	4 Peter Mensah
TOTALS		105	50	4	51	1958	228	129	219	17	1683	198	107	179	17		

BIGGEST WIN — **Home:** 66-0 v Sale 23.4.87 CL1   **Away:** 71-8 v Bedford 14.10.89 CL1

BIGGEST DEFEAT — **Home:** 26-57 v Wasps 17.9.94 CL1   **Away:** 19-38 v Gloucester 27.4.91 CL1

MOST TRIES in a match — **For**: 12 v Sale 23.4.87 v Bedford 14.10.89   **Against:** 9 v Wasps 17.9.94 CL1

MOST CONSECUTIVE — **Wins:** 4   **Defeats:** 4

MOST APPEARANCES — **Forward:** 94 Andy Mullins   **Back:** 63 Will Carling

MOST CONSECUTIVE APPEARANCES — 42 Andy Mullins 16.11.91-30.4.94

CONSECUTIVE SCORING MATCHES — **Tries:** 3 Andrew Harriman

Points: 10 David Pears (twice)

	IN A SEASON	IN A CAREER	IN A MATCH
MOST POINTS	143 Kent Bray 1993-94 CL1	346 David Pears 1989-94	27 David Pears v Bedford 14.10.89 Away CL1
MOST TRIES	11 Andrew Harriman 1987-88 CL1 Daren O'Leary 1993-94 CL1	22 Andrew Harriman 1987-93	3 Andrew Harriman v Nottingham 1.4.88 Home CL1 v Sale 23.4.88 Home CL1 v Bristol 30.3.91 Home CL1 Mike Wedderburn v Bedford 14.10.89 Awa CL1 Will Carling v Bristol 30.3.91 Home CL1
MOST CONVERSIONS	16 David Pears 1990-91 CL1	45 David Pears 1989-94	8 David pears v Rosslyn Park 7.12.91 Away CL1
MOST PENALTIES	38 Kent Bray 1993-94 CL1	69 David Pears 1989-94	7 David Pears v Rosslyn Park 7.12.91 Away CL1
MOST DROP GOALS	5 David Pears 1990-91 CL1	7 David Pears 1989-94	2 David Pears v Rosslyn Park 13.10.92 Home CL1 v Leicester 23.3.91 Away CL1

HARLEQUINS F.C.

Name	Ht	Wt	Birthdate	Birthplace	Clubs	App	Pts	T	C	P	DG
BACKS											
Kent Bray	6.0	13.5	21.5.66	Brisbane	Harlequins	27+2	164	2	14	40	1
Will Greenwood	6.2	14.0	20.10.72	Blackburn	Waterloo	4	5	1	-	-	-
				Merchant Banker	Harlequins	10	27	2	1	5	-
Jim Staples	6.2	13.9	20.10.65	London	London Irish	58	55	13	-	-	1
Ireland (18)				Bank Employee	Harlequins	7	25	2	3	2	1
Daren O'Leary	6.0	13.0	27.6.73	Haroldwood	Saracens	10	15	3	-	-	-
England U16 U18 U21				Student	Harlequins	26	60	12	-	-	-
Gavin Thompson	6.0	14.0	20.8.69	Croydon	Rosslyn Park						
England A				Underwriter	Harlequins	58	60	14	-	-	-
Jason Keyter	5.11	13.2	20.12.73	Port Elizabeth	Harlequins	12	25	5	-	-	-
England U16				Sales Executive							
Spencer Bromley	6.1	14.10	12.12.69	Manchester	Rugby	21+1	10	2	-	-	-
England U21					Harlequins	8	-	-	-	-	-
Crawford Henderson	6.1	14.0	11.2.69	London	London Scottish	7	-	-	-	-	-
					Harlequins	5	5	1	-	-	-
Rob Glenister	5.10	13.7	14.12.65	Barnet	Bedford						
				Sales Manager	Harlequins	47+6	83	18	2	-	-
Peter Mensah	6.0	13.8	10.11.66	Ghana	Old Mill Hillians						
England A				Futures Broker	Harlequins	11	20	4	-	-	-
Will Carling	5.11	14.2	12.12.65	Bradford on Avon	Harlequins	63	70	16	-	-	-
England (60)				Director							
Laurence Boyle	5.10	13.1	29.1.70	Warwick	Moseley	19	22	3	2	1	1
England U21					Leicester	9+1	14	3	-	-	-
Jeff Alexander	6.2	14.0	28.11.70	Kensington	Harlequins	22	21	3	2	1	-
England U21											
Paul Challinor	6.0	13.2	5.12.69	Wolverhampton	Harlequins	47	221	8	9	50	5
England U21				Accounts Manager							
Chris Wright	5.6	11.7	8.2.68	Heswel	Orrell	24	24	6	-	-	-
				Financial Adviser	Wasps	5+7	-	-	-	-	-
					Harlequins	3+3	5	1	-	-	-
Rob Kitchen	5.9	12.5	25.7.71	Chertsey	Bristol	10+4	19	4	-	-	-
				Bond Broker	Harlequins	18	5	1	-	-	-
Craig Luxton	5.10	12.0	11.3.64	Opotin (NZ)	Harlequins	28+3	24	6	-	-	-
FORWARDS											
Jason Leonard	5.10	17.2	14.8.68	Barking	Saracens	19	4	1	-	-	-
England (43)				Carpenter	Harlequins	47	4	1	-	-	-
Martin Hobley	6.1	17.3	19.1.69	Witney	Harlequins	17+3	-	-	-	-	-
Andy Mullins	5.11	16.0	12.12.64	Blackheath	Harlequins	94	4	1	-	-	-
England (1)				Broker							
Simon Brown	5.10	16.0	31.10.12	Oxford	Harlequins	11+1	-	-	-	-	-
Brian Moore	5.9	14.3	11.1.62	Birmingham	Nottingham	26	4	1	-	-	-
England (63)				Solicitor	Harlequins	45	9	2	-	-	-
Simon Mitchell	5.9	15.5	23.11.65	Saltburn	W. Hartlepool	82+1	32	7	-	-	-
					Harlequins	1	-	-	-	-	-
Alex Snow	6.7	17.0	29.4.69	Chelsea	Heriots						
England U21				Equity Broker	Harlequins	36	10	2	-	-	-
Bill Davison	6.6	16.6	8.4.69	Zambia	Rosslyn Park	23	10	2	-	-	-
					Harlequins	9	-	-	-	-	-
Peter Thresher	6.7	16.9	9.6.70	Farnborough	Harlequins	12+2	5	1	-	-	-
Troy Coker	6.6	18.11	30.5.63	Brisbane	Harlequins	32	9	2	-	-	-
Australia				General Manager							
Martin Pepper	5.11	15.7	14.12.69	Beverley	Harlequins	16	-	-	-	-	-
England A B U21				Teacher	Nottingham	22	21	5	-	-	-
Chris Sheasby	6.3	16.0	30.11.66	Windsor	Harlequins	45+2	29	6	-	-	-
England A				Maths Master							
Rob Jenkins	6.2	15.12	29.6.70	Leicester	London Irish	15	5	1	-	-	-
England A U18				Solicitor	Harlequins	13	-	-	-	-	-
Mark Russell	6.4	17.6	16.12.65	Nairobi	Harlequins	37	9	2	-	-	-
England A				Unit Broker							
Mike Watson	6.7	17.4	2.7.65	Sunderland	W. Hartlepool	27	25	5	-	-	-
England A					Harlequins	5	-	-	-	-	-

Also available: Backs: Andy Pinnock (2 apps, 5pts, 1 try), David Currie (1 app), Chris Madderson (7 apps). Forwards: Neil Collins (3 apps), J Hamilton-Smith (6 apps), Ian Desmond (2 apps).

95

HARLEQUIN F.C.

Stoop Memorial Ground, Craneford Way, Twickenham TW2 7SQ

Telephone: 0181 892 0822
Fax: 0181 744 2764

Total Capacity: 8,500
Seated: 2,100
Standing: 6,400
Simple Directions to Ground: See 1994/95
Nearest Railway Station: Twickenham
Car Parking: 500
Season Tickets: -
Match Prices: Adults: League £8.00 Friendly £3.00, Children/OAPs League £3.00 Friendly £2.00
Membership: Seniors £25 Juniors £15
Training Nights: Tuesday & Thursday

ALL TIME TOP TEN COURAGE LEAGUE RECORDS

APPEARANCES		POINTS	
94	Andy Mullins	346	David Pears
63	Will Carling	221	Paul Challinor
58	Gavin Thompson	212	Stuart Thresher
50	Richard Langhorn	164	Kent Bray
47+6	Rob Glenister	89	Andy Harriman
47	Paul Challinor	83	Rob Glenister
47	Jason Leonard	72	Jamie Salmon
45	Brian Moore	70	Will Carling
45	Chris Sheasby	60	Gavin Thompson
44	Mickey Skinner	60	Daren O'Leary

MOST POINTS: 346 David Pears

Season	Apps	Points	Tries	Cons	Pens	D G
1989-90	11	114	2	14	24	2
1990-91	10	120	1	16	23	5
1991-92	9	109	4	15	21	-
1992-93	1	3	-	-	1	-
1993-94	1	-	-	-	-	-
Total	32	346	7	45	69	7

MOST TRIES: 22 Andrew Harriman

Season	Appearances	Tries
1987-88	5	11
1988-89	5	1
1989-90	2	-
1990-91	10	9
1991-92	4	-
1992-93	7	1
Total	33	22

MOST APPEARANCES: 94 Andy Mullins

Season	Appearances
1987-88	11
1988-89	10
1989-90	9
1990-91	10
1991-92	12
1992-93	12
1993-94	18
1994-95	12
Total	94

LEICESTER F.C.

NICKNAME: Tigers   **FOUNDED:** 1880

CLUB OFFICIALS

President
D J Wheeler
Chairman
D W G Tom
Club Secretary
J A Allen
60 Dorchester Road, Leicester LE3 0UF
Tel: (W) 0116 2471234
Fixtures Secretary
J W Berry
Hall Lane, Kinoulton, Notts
Tel: (W) 01949 81428

Review of the Season

If anyone were ever to take a bet on someone to dethrone Bath as champions LEICESTER's Tigers would have been an obvious choice and a pre-New Year draw at the Rec suggested that if the champions were to slip up the logical successors were in place – and so it proved.

Leicester despite that draw trailed Bath into April and remained as challengers until the 15th of that month when the vital match took place at Welford Road, where three Jez Harris dropped-goals and a nap hand of penalties by John Liley kept them just ahead until a desperate attempt by the visitors to run the ball from defence foundered and in went Rory Underwood to score their only try and clinch a league lead, which was not to be relinquished over the remaining two matches, and it saw Leicester end up with a four point winning margin – and the title.

In the Pilkington Cup wins over Blackheath (56-11 at home), Bristol (12-8 away) and Sale (14-12 away) meant a semi-final at home to Wasps, who won the day thanks to the unerring boot of Rob Andrew, but that was a minor disappointment in an excellent campaign.

Great praise is also due to the team for the way they made light of the demands of England, which meant restricted appearances in April from the Underwood brothers, Graham Rowntree, Neil Back and skipper Dean Richards, who also played on when he was frequently suffering from niggling injuries.

It was fortunate that John Liley and Jez Harris (fullback and fly-half respectively) were always there when needed and did the business. All the others who were called to the Tigers' colours also did brilliantly in a real team effort.

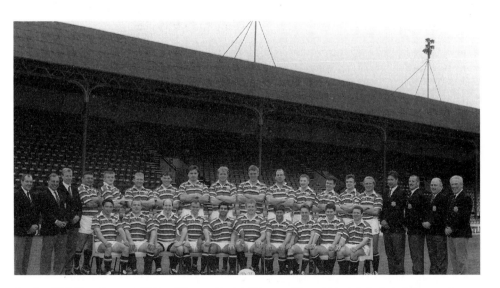

Standing: J Hill (Team Secretary), AO Ross (Director of Rugby), M Dowson (Fitness Adviser), D Garforth, G Rowntree, D Jelley, JM Wells, MD Poole, P Grant, T Smith, C Tarbuck, R Robinson, S Potter, W Drake-Lee, N Back, PW Dodge (Coach), IR Smith (Coach), JA Allen (Hon Sec), JT Thomas (President) Seated: R Underwood, R Cockerill, JG Liley, ST Hackney, A Kardooni, D Richards (capt), J Harris, J Hamilton, W Kilford, D Edwards.   *Photo: Peter Hallas*
Colours: Scarlet green and white hoops   **Change Colours**: Red with white and green band

LEICESTER F.C.

COURAGE LEAGUE
MATCH DETAILS 1994-95

No	Date	Opponents	Ven	Result	Scorers
1	Sep 10	Northampton	H	W 28-15	Hackney (T) T Underwood (T) Harris (6P)
2	Sep 17	Orrell	A	W 6-0	Harris (2P)
3	Sep 24	Gloucester	H	W 16-6	Johnson (T) Liley (C 3P)
4	Oct 1	Wasps	A	W 23-18	T Underwood (T) Harris (5P DG)
5	Oct 8	West Hartlepool	H	W 33-16	Murphy (2T) Liley (T) M Johnson (T) Liley (2C 3P)
6	Oct 15	Harlequins	A	W 40-13	Hackney (2T) Kardoon (T) Liley (T) Harris (4C 3P DG)
7	Oct 22	Bath	A	D 20-20	Hamilton (T) Harris (5P)
8	Oct 29	Sale	H	W 37-20	Hackney (2T) T Underwood (1T) Harris (2C 5P DG)
9	Nov 5	Bristol	A	L 22-31	Tarbuck (T) Harris (C 4P DG)
10	Jan 7	Northampton	A	W 20-8	Wigley (T) (Pen Try) Harris (2C P DG)
11	Jan 14	Orrell	H	W 29-14	Kilford (T) Tarbuck (T) Harris (2C 5P)
12	Feb 11	Gloucester	A	L 3-9	Harris (P)
13	Mar 4	Wasps	H	W 21-6	R Underwood (2T) Liley (C 3P)
14	Mar 25	West Hartlepool	A	W 12-6	Harris (DG 3P)
15	Apr 8	Harlequins	H	W 22-8	T Underwood (T) Harris (DG) Liley (C 4P)
16	Apr 15	Bath	H	W 31-21	R Underwood (T) Harris (3DG) Liley (1C 5P)
17	Apr 22	Sale	A	W 20-10	Liley (T 3P) Harris (2DG)
18	Apr 29	Bristol	H	W 17-3	Potter (T) Liley (3P) Harris (DG)

Courage League Records 1994-95

League Debuts: Diccon Edwards, Andy McAdam, Rob Field. J Murphy, M Grant made debuts as replacements
Tries on Debut: 2 Murphy
Only Ever Present: Darren Garforth – Garforth has missed only 2 league games since making his debut in November 1991 v Gloucester – 58 out of 60
Most appearances: 87 John Wells

● 100% home record – played 9 won 9

● Stopped the opposition scoring tries in 8 out of their 18 league games – the best record in the Division

● Conceded just 15 tries – best in the Division, but 2 more than Bath's record of the previous season

● Only 34% of their points came from tries, 2nd lowest in the Division – only Northampton were below them

● 48% of their points came from penalties – 2nd only to Northampton

● Of the players scoring tries only 3 were forwards

● Jez Harris dropped 13 goals to beat his record of 11 from last season – he now has 35 in 61 appearances

● John Liley becomes the second man after Rob Andrew to score 600 First Division points

	Pts	T	C	P	D	App	Ave
John Liley	607	18	79	124	63	9.63	

● Rory Underwood passes 30 Division One tries – the second man after Tony Swift of Bath to achieve this feat

	Tries	Apps	Strike Rate
Rory Underwood	31	67	2.16
Tony Underwood	23	42	1.83

● Abdel Kardooni passes Ian Bates' record of most appearances by a back for Leicester in league rugby – Bates' record was 66 and Kardooni ended the season on 80

LEICESTER F.C.

MATCH BY MATCH PLAYERS BY POSITION

Kilford	Hackney	Edwards	Potter	Underwood T	Harris	Kardooni	Rowntree	Cockerill	Garforth	Johnson M	Poole	Wells	Drake-Lee	Richards	McAdam	Back	Liley	Underwood R	Tarbuck	Johnson C	Robinson	Jelley	Smith
O	N	M	L	K	J	I	A	B	C	D	E	F	G	H									
O	N	M	L		J	I	A	B	C	D	E	F			H	K	G						
		M	L	N		I	A		C	D	E	F		G		H	O	K		B			
		M	L	N	J	I	A	B	C	D	E	F	G	H			O	K					
	N	M	L	N		I	A		C	D	E*	F		H		G	O	K		B			
	N*	M**	L	N	J	I	A	B	C	D			F		G				R	H				E
		M	L		J	I	A	B	C	D			F		G		H	O	N					E
	N	L*	M	N	J	I			C	D			F		H		G	O			B	A		
	N	M	L		J	I		B	C	D			F		H			O	K		G	A		E
O		M			J		A	B	C	D	E				M	G			F	L			
O	N	L	M		J	I	A	B	C	D	E				K	G		H					
	N	M	L		J	I	A		C	D		F		G	K	H	O			B			E
		L		N	J	I	A	B	C	D	E			H		G	O	K	F		M		
		M	L		J	I	A	B	C	D	E	F	G		K		O	N	H				
	N	M	L	K	J			B	C		E	F*				G	O		H	A			
		L		N	J	I	A	B	C	D	E	F		H		G	O	K			M		
	N		L		J	I	A	B	C	D	E	F	H*				O	K	F		M		
K	N		L		J	I		B	C		E	F	H	G			O				M		A

Also Played: Murphy R30 match 5; Wingham R75 match 6, N match 11; Malone J matches 3, 5; Field E match 8; Hamilton N matches 7, 10, I match 15; Evans N match 10; Wigley K match 10; Grewcork R match 8, R37 match 10; P Grant D matches 15, 18, R match 17; M Grant R match 15

PROGRAMME DETAILS

PRICE: £1.00

PAGES: 44
Colour throughout on good paper.
A really well presented and colourful interesting publication
with colour photos and plenty of original reading

EDITOR:
Stuart Farmer

ADVERTISING RATES:
£900 full page, £500 half page

TIGERS

OFFICIAL SPONSOR — TETLEY BITTER
OFFICIAL PROGRAMME £1 — THE PILKINGTON CUP
TIGERS v BLACKHEATH
SATURDAY DECEMBER 17th 1994 – K.O. 2.30pm

LEICESTER F.C.

LEICESTER F.C.

COURAGE LEAGUE STATISTICS
compiled by Steve McCormack

Season	Div	P	W	D	L	F	T	C	P	D	A	T	C	P	D	Most Points	Most Tries
1987-88	1	10	9	0	1	225	21	15	31	6	133	14	10	17	2	126 Dusty Hare	5 Barry Evans
1988-89	1	11	6	1	4	189	19	10	29	2	199	25	12	21	4	97 Dusty Hare	3 Rory Underwood Barry Evans Dean Richards
1989-90	1	11	6	0	5	248	36	16	22	2	184	24	14	17	3	126 John Liley	7 John Liley
1990-91	1	12	8	0	4	244	29	19	25	5	140	12	7	21	5	110 John Liley	9 Rory Underwood
1991-92	1	12	6	1	5	262	33	20	26	4	216	26	11	28	2	129 John Liley	9 Rory Underwood
1992-93	1	12	9	0	3	220	21	17	23	4	116	13	3	14	1	106 John Liley	3 Tony Underwood Nigel Richardson
1993-94	1	18	14	0	4	425	41	23	47	11	210	18	9	32	2	202 Jez Harris	8 Tony Underwood
1994-95	1	18	15	1	2	400	27	17	64	13	239	15	10	44	4	181 Jez Harris	5 Steve Hackney
TOTALS		104	73	3	28	2213	227	137	267	47	1437	147	76	194	23		

BIGGEST WIN		**Home:** 66-5 v Newcastle Gosforth 12.3.94 CL1	**Away:** 43-19 v Moseley 27.4.91 CL1
BIGGEST DEFEAT		**Home:** 21-31 Harlequins 26.11.89 CL1	**Away:** 6-37 v Bath 11.1.92 CL1
MOST TRIES in a match		**For:** 11 v Bedford 23.9.89 CL1	**Against:** 7 v Bath 11.1.92 CL1
MOST CONSECUTIVE		**Wins:** 9	**Defeats:** 2
MOST APPEARANCES		**Forward:** 87 John Wells	**Back:** 67 Rory Underwood
MOST CONSECUTIVE APPEARANCES		32 Darry Garforth 28.3.9-23.4.94	
CONSECUTIVE SCORING MATCHES		**Tries:** 3 Rory Underwood, Neil Back	
		Points: 24 John Liley	

	IN A SEASON	IN A CAREER	IN A MATCH
MOST POINTS	202 Jez Harris 1993-94 CL1	607 John Liley 1988-95	31 John Liley v Rosslyn Park 21.3.92 Home CL1
MOST TRIES	9 Rory Underwood 1990-91 + 1991-92 CL1	31 Rory Underwood 1987-95	4 Tony Underwood v Newcastle Gosforth 12.3.94 Home CL1
MOST CONVERSIONS	19 John Liley 1991-92 CL1	79 John Liley 1988-95	7 John Liley v Rosslyn Park 21.3.92 Home CL1
MOST PENALTIES	41 Jez Harris 1993-94 CL1	124 John Liley 1988-95	7 Jez Harris v Bristol 11.12.93 Home CL1 v Gloucester 29.1.94 Home CL1
MOST DROP GOALS	13 Jez Harris 1994-95 CL1	35 Jez Harris 1987-95	3 Jez Harris v Wasps 23.11.91 Home CL1 v Bath 15.4.95 Home CL1

LEICESTER F.C.

Name	Ht	Wt	Birthdate	Birthplace	Clubs	App	Pts	T	C	P	DG
BACKS											
Wayne Kilford	5.11	13.0	25.9.68	Malvern	Nottingham	20	23	1	2	5	-
England U21				Sales Engineer	Leicester	20	18	3	-	1	-
John Liley	5.11	12.10	21.8.67	Wakefield	Wakefield	5	22	2	4	2	-
England B				Accountant	Leicester	63	607	18	79	124	-
Steve Hackney	5.11	14.0	13.6.68	Stockton	Nottingham	25	8	2	-	-	-
England A				Marketing Exec	Leicester	42	71	15	-	-	-
Rory Underwood	5.9	14.0	19.6.63	Middlesboro	Leicester	67	129	31	-	-	-
England (79)				RAF							
Tony Underwood	5.9	13.7	17.2.69	Ipoh (Mal)	Leicester	42	107	23	-	-	-
England (20)				Equity Broker							
Andy McAdam	6.1	13.5	29.3.71	Coventry	Leicester	4					
England U16				Bank Officer							
Jaime Hamilton	5.9	12.6	1.7.70	Guildford	Leicester	4+14	5	1	-	-	-
				Sales Rep							
Barry Evans	6.0	13.7	10.10.62	Hinckley	Coventry						
England (2)				Account Manager	Leicester	28	44	11	-	-	-
Dillon Edwards	5.8	13.4	13.3.73	London	Wakefield	23	10	2	-	-	-
Wales A, England U21				Graduate Trainee	Leicester	15	-	-	-	-	-
Stuart Potter	5.11	13.8	11.11.67	Lichfield	Nottingham	30	20	5	-	-	-
England A				Insurance Broker	Leicester	43	30	6	-	-	-
Richie Robinson	6.1	14.0	5.7.67	Kendal	Leicester	7	5	-	-	-	-
				Accountant							
David Wigley	6.0	12.7	16.12.68		Leicester	3	5	1	-	-	-
Jez Harris	5.7	12.7	22.2.65	Kettering	Leicester	61	448	4	35	85	35
England A				Boat Builder							
Niall Malone	5.11	13.5	30.4.71	Coventry	Leicester	3+2	-	-	-	-	-
Ireland (2)				Telesalesman							
Abdel Karooni	5.8	12.12	17.5.68	Tehran	Wasps	1					
England A				Broker	Leicester	80	44	10	-	-	-
FORWARDS											
Graham Rowntree	6.0	16.10	18.4.71	Stockton	Leicester	45	5	1	-	-	-
England 3 'A' U21 U18 U16				Insurance Broker							
Darren Garforth	5.10	16.10	9.4.66	Coventry	Leicester	58	-	-	-	-	-
England A				Technician							
Derek Jelley	6.0	16.7	4.3.72	Nuneaton	Leicester	7	-	-	-	-	-
				Con Engineer							
Richard Cockerill	5.8	14.10	16.12.70	Rugby	Leicester	42	10	2	-	-	-
England A				Antique Restorer							
Chris Johnson	5.11	16.0	23.5.73	Oldham	Leicester	6	5	1	-	-	-
England Students				Student							
Martin Johnson	6.7	17.12	9.3.70	Solihull	Leicester	49	10	2	-	-	-
England (18)				Bank Official							
Matt Poole	6.7	17.7	6.2.69	Leicester	Leicester	58	15	3	-	-	-
England U21				Equipment Manager							
Tom Smith	6.7	17.10	27.12.64	Leicester	Bedford	10	-	-	-	-	-
				Development Officer	Leicester	39	13	3	-	-	-
Rob Field	6.6	17.10	22.6.71	Coventry	Coventry	19+1	5	1	-	-	-
				Student	Leicester	1	-	-	-	-	-
Paul Grant	6.6	16.0	3.8.69	Boston	Leicester	2+1					
				Farmer							
John Wells	6.1	14.0	12.5.63	Driffield	Leicester	87	29	7	-	-	-
England A B				Policeman							
Bill Drake-Lee	6.0	15.0	9.8.70	Kettering	Leicester	10	-	-	-	-	-
				Surveyor							
Neil Back	5.10	14.0	16.1.69	Coventry	Nottingham	7+1	8	2	-	-	-
England (5) U21				Pensions Supervisor	Leicester	53	39	8	-	-	-
Dean Richards	6.4	17.8	11.7.63	Nuneaton	Leicester	66	46	11	-	-	-
England (45)				Police Officer							
Chris Tarbuck	6.4	15.7	20.8.68	Harlow	Saracens	44	12	3	-	-	-
				Marketing	Leicester	11	15	3	-	-	-

LEICESTER F.C.

The Club House, Aylestone Road, Leicester LE2 7LF
Telephone: 0116 254 1607
Fax: 0116 285 4766

Total Capacity: 16,320
Seated: 12,200
Standing: 4,120
Simple Directions to Ground: From M1 - Junction 21 - along A46 towards Leicester at traffic lights turn right (at Post House) 1 mile T junction turn left 2 mile on entering a one way system. Ground on right.
Nearest Railway Station: Leicester
Car Parking: 20
Season Tickets: Adults £47.00, Children/OAPs £27.00
Match Prices: Adults £7.00 Children/OAPs £5.00
Membership: Seniors £10.00 Juniors £8.00
Training Nights: Tuesday & Thursday

ALL TIME TOP TEN COURAGE LEAGUE RECORDS

APPEARANCES		POINTS	
87	John Wells	607	John Liley
80	Adbel Kardooni	448	Jez Harris
67	Rory Underwood	223	Dusty Hare
66	Ian Bates	129	Rory Underwood
66	Dean Richards	107	Tony Underwood
63+2	John Liley	71	Steve Hackney
61	Jez Harris	46	Dean Richards
58	Matt Poole	44	Adbel Kardooni
58	Darren Garforth	39	Neil Back
54	Steve Redfern	32	Les Cusworth

MOST POINTS: 607 John Liley

Season	Apps	Points	Tries	Cons	Pens	D G
1988-89	+1	9	-	-	3	-
1989-90	11	126	7	16	22	-
1990=91	11	110	2	18	22	-
1991-92	11	129	4	19	25	-
1992-93	11	106	2	15	22	-
1993-94	6	28	-	5	6	-
1994-95	13+1	99	3	6	24	-
Total	63+2	607	18	79	124	-

MOST TRIES: 31 Rory Underwood

Season	Appearances	Tries
198788	5	1
1988-89	7	3
1989-90	8	4
1990-91	12	9
1991-92	8	9
1992-93	10	2
1993-94	9	-
1994-95	8	3
Total	67	31

MOST APPEARANCES: 87 John Wells

Season	Appearances
1987-88	9
1988-89	7
1989-90	9
1990-91	12
1991-92	10
1992-93	10
1993-94	15
1994-95	15
Total	87

ORRELL R.U.F.C.

NICKNAME: **FOUNDED:** 1927

CLUB OFFICIALS

President
Bob Gaskell
Chairman
Ron Pimblett
Club Secretary
John Arrowsmith
1 Fisher Drive, Orrell WN5 8QX
Tel: 01942 216879
Fixtures Secretary
Barry Cooper
Crab Tree Lane, 81 Burscough
Tel: (H) 01704 893239
Press Officer
Barry Cooper
Tel: (H) 01704 893239

Review of the Season

One of the minor miracles of modern rugby is that the forecast demise of ORRELL has never happened which delights the ordinary fan and frustrates those who see glamour and charisma as the most important ingredients of the cynical modern game.

Although fifth place in the top league was finally achieved it was not done without a few anxious moments but by the time that the last day of the season arrived they had sufficient in hand to view a visit to Wasps as a festive occasion rather than a desperate fight for survival and a 53-25 defeat can realistically be seen in that context.

The Pilkington Cup was a disappointment with a home win over West Hartlepool being followed by a gallant but unavailing home battle against holders and subsequent winners Bath but the 25-19 margin told everyone that the visitors had to fight hard for success.

In the new season the team will have to carry on without the help of a great club personality in Simon Langford and their team is made up of some talented players, whose names are not too well known in the South, but the likes of fullback Taberner (the captain), Naylor, fly-half Gerry Ainscough (back again), props Winstanley and Cundick, Scottish hooker Scott, Jackson, Brierley and No8 Bibby will not be brushed aside by anyone.

Back: John Russell, Dave Jackson, Steve Bibby, Howard Parr, Chris Brierly, Dave Cleary, Paul Manley, Matt Farr. Middle: Sammy Southern (Chairman of Rugby), Phil Moss (Coach), John Arrowsmith (Club Secretary), Phil Horrocks, Jim Naylor, Phil Winstanley, Ian Wynn, Steve Taberner, Paul Hamer, Jason Cundick, Sarah Booth (Physio), Mike Slemen (Strategist). Seated: Terry Blackburn (1stXV Manager), Paul Johnson, Alan Peacock, Bob Gaskell (President), Dewi Morris (capt), Ron Pimblett (Chairman), Gerry Ainscough, Austin Healey, Andy Clerk (Fitness Coach). On Grass: Dave Topping, Simon Langford, Tony Redmond, Martin Scott
Colours: Amber/black   **Change Colours**: Red/amber/black

ORRELL R.U.F.C.

COURAGE LEAGUE
MATCH DETAILS 1994-95

No	Date	Opponents	Ven	Result		Scorers
1	Sep 10	West Hartlepool	A	W	19-17	Wynn (T) Langford (P) Ainscough (C 3P)
2	Sep 17	Leicester	H	L	0-6	
3	Sep 24	Bath	A	L	13-32	Wynn (2T) Winstanley (P)
4	Oct 1st	Sale	H	W	22-19	Naylor (T) Langford (1C 5P)
5	Oct 8	Bristol	A	L	9-20	Langford (3P)
6	Oct 15	Northampton	H	W	13-10	Brock (T) Wynn (T) Langford (P)
7	Oct 22	Harlequins	A	W	8-6	Morris (T) Langford (P)
8	Oct 29	Gloucester	A	L	6-9	Langford (2P)
9	Nov 5	Wasps	H	L	10-16	Manley (T) Hamer (C) Hamer (DG)
10	Jan 7	West Hartlepool	H	D	22-22	Hamer (T DG) Langford (C 4P)
11	Jan 14	Leicester	A	L	19-29	Morris (T) Naylor (T) Langford (3P)
12	Feb 11	Bath	H	D	6-6	Langford (2P)
13	Mar 4	Sale	A	D	8-8	Wynn (T) Langford (P)
14	Mar 25	Bristol	H	W	20-16	Ainscough (5P) Horrocks (T)
15	Apr 8	Northampton	A	L	3-15	Taberner (P)
16	Apr 15	Harlequins	H	L	10-28	Horrocks (T) Ainscough (P C)
17	Apr 22	Glcouester	H	W	43-14	Wynn (2T) Ainscough (2T 4C) Horrocks (T) Taberner (T) Morris (T)
18	Apr 23	Wasps	A	L	25-53	Langford (T P) Naylor (T) Ainscough (4P)

Courage League Records 1994-95

League Debuts: Austin Healey, Tony Redmond, John Russell, Jason Cundick, Ian Bruce, Martin Scott, John Huxley, Graeme Smith
Try on Debut: Ian Bruce
Sent off on Debut: Martin Scott
Only Ever Present: Steve Bibby
Most appearances: 90 Simon Langford

● Lowest points scorers in the Division

● 4th best defensive record

● Had just 10 players scoring tries

● No forward scored a try

● Mid season drew 3 out of 4 matches

● Suffered worst home defeat going down 10-28 to Harlequins in April and 2 weeks later suffered their worst away defeat at Wasps 25-53

● Conceded 8 tries in the defeat at Wasps having previously not conceded more than 5 in a match

● Simon Langford passes Sammy Southerns record of 83 league appearances and ends the season on 90

● Dewi Morris retires from first class rugby as Orrell's leading try scorer

	TRIES	APPS	STRIKE RATE
Dewi Morris	24	62	2.58
Phil Halsall	19	59	3.10
Nigel Heslop	18	46	2.55

● Gerry Ainscough passes Martin Street's record of points for Orrell in league rugby

	Pts	T	C	P	D	App	Aver
Gerry Ainscough	337	12	34	71	2	66	5.10
Martin Street	323	6	43	67	4	40	8.07

ORRELL R.U.F.C.

MATCH BY MATCH PLAYERS BY POSITION

Langford	Naylor	Johnson	Wynn	Healey	Ainscough	Morris	Winstanley	Redmond	Russell	Cooper	Brierley	Cleary	Manley	Bibby	Cundick	Scott	Taberner	Farr	Huxley	Topping	Cusani	Hayter	Bruce
15	14	13	12	11	10	9	1	2	3	4	5	6	7	8									
15	14	12	13	11	10	9	R66	2	1	4	5	7*	6	8	3								
15	14	12	13	11	10	9	1	2		5	4		8	7	3								
15	14	12	13	11	10	9*	1	2		4	5	7	6	8				R31					
15	14	12	13	11	10			2	1	4		6*	8	7						9		R55	
15		12	13	11		9	1	2		4	5	7	6	8	3								14
15	14	12	13	11		9	1	2		4	5	8	6	7	3								
15	14	12		11		9	1	2		4	5	8	6	7	3			13					
	14	13	12	11		9*		2	1	4	5	7	6	8	3		15	R34					
15	14	12	13	11		9	1	2		5	4	7		8	3							6*	
15	14	12	13	11		9	1		3	4	8					2^{50}			6	5			
15	14	12	13	11	10		1			4	12**	6**		8	3*	2			7	5			
15	14	12	13	11	R43	9*	1			4	R73	6		8	3	2			6	5			
	14	12	13		10		1			4	5		6	8	3	2	15		6	9			
11	12	13	14		10	9	1			4	5		8	7	3	2	15		6				
	14	12*	13	R40	10		1			5	R46	6+		8	3	2	15		6	9	4		
	14	13	12		10	9	1			5				8	3	2	15		7	6			
12	14	13			10		1			5				8	3	2	15		7	9			

Also Played: Glynn No 5 match 5; Rimmer No 3 matches 4, 5; Parr No 6 matches 3, 18; **R28 match 10; Jackson R75 match 15 No 4 matches 17 & 18; Southern R19 match 12, R61 match 10, R match 18; Smith No 11 match 18; Horrocks No 11 match 14, 16, 17; Hamer No 10 matches 6, 7, 8, 9, 10, 11, 13; Huxley. 7 matches 11, 12, 13, 14, No 6 matches 15, 17, 18.

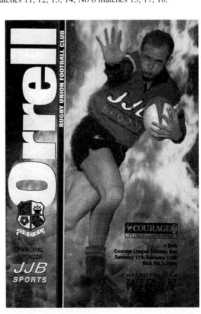

PROGRAMME DETAILS

PAGES: 40
Attractive cover and layout with full colour and good paper.
Twelve pages of original copy per issue

EDITOR:
Kevin Bailey

ADVERTISING RATES:
£500 full page, £250 page, £150 page

ORRELL R.U.F.C.

COURAGE LEAGUE STATISTICS
compiled by Steve McCormack

Season	Div	P	W	D	L	F	T	C	P	D	A	T	C	P	D	Most Points	Most Tries
1987-88	1	11	5	1	5	192	24	12	24	0	153	17	5	23	2	72 Gerry Ainscough	6 Gerry Ainscough
1988-89	1	11	6	1	4	148	13	9	24	2	157	14	7	27	2	54 Gerry Ainscough	3 Nigel Heslop
1989-90	1	11	5	0	6	221	28	17	25	0	132	9	3	28	2	1989-90	104 Martin Strett
1990-91	1	12	7	0	5	247	34	21	21	2	105	12	6	14	1	109 Martin Strett	7 Phil Halsall & Dewi Morris
1991-92	1	12	10	0	2	204	26	8	26	2	95	8	3	17	2	104 Martin Strett	7 Dewi Morris
1992-93	1	12	5	o	7	175	20	6	21	0	183	19	11	22	0	63 Gerry Ainscough	6 Dewi Morris
1993-94	1	18	8	0	10	327	36	24	33	0	302	25	16	43	4	84 Simon Langford	8 James Naylor
1994-95	1	18	6	3	9	256	23	9	38	3	326	30	19	44	2	81 Simon Langford	7 Ian Wynn
TOTALS	-	105	52	5	48	1770	204	106	212	9	1453	134	72	218	15		

BIGGEST WIN — **Home:** 66-0 v Rugby 13.3.93 CL1   **Away:** 36-3 v Bristol 17.11.90 CL1

BIGGEST DEFEAT — **Home:** 10-28 v Harlequins 15.4.95 CL1   **Away:** 25-53 v Wasps 29.4.95 CL1

MOST TRIES in a match — **For**: 11 v Rugby 13.3.93 CL1 v Northampton 27.10.90 Home CL1 v Rosslyn Park 28.4.90 Home CL1   **Against:** 8 v Wasps 29.4.95 Home CL1

MOST CONSECUTIVE — **Wins:** 5   **Defeats:** 4

MOST APPEARANCES — **Forward:** 83+3 David Southern   **Back:** 90 Simon Langford

MOST CONSECUTIVE APPEARANCES — 39 David Southern 26.9.87-17.11.90

CONSECUTIVE SCORING MATCHES — **Tries:** 3 Gerry Ainscough, Martin Strett, Phil Halsall   **Points:** 17 Martin Strett

	IN A SEASON	IN A CAREER	IN A MATCH
MOST POINTS	109 Martin Strett 1990-91 CL1	337 Gerry Ainscough 1987-95	28 Martin Strett v Rosslyn Park 28.4.90 Home CL1
MOST TRIES	8 James Naylor 1993-94 CL1	24 Dewi Morris 1990-95	4 Paul Hamer v Rugby 13.3.93 Home CL1
MOST CONVERSIONS	21 Martin Strett 1990-91 CL1	43 Martin Strett 1988-93	8 Martin Strett v Rosslyn Park 28.4.90 Home CL1
MOST PENALTIES	26 Martin Strett 1991-92 CL1	71 Gerry Ainscough 1987-95	6 Martin Strett v Gloucester 28.3.92 Home CL1
MOST DROP GOALS	2 Martin Strett 1991-92 CL1 Paul Hamer 1994-95 CL1	4 Martin Strett 1988-93	1 on 9 occasions by 4 players. Martin Strett 4 Gerry Ainscough 2 Paul Hamer 2 Steven Taberner

ORRELL F.C.

Name	Ht	Wt	Birthdate	Birthplace	Clubs	App	Pts	T	C	P	DG
BACKS											
Simon Langford	6.1	14.7	18.12.60	Wigan	Orrell	90+1	279	3	27	70	-
England B				Director							
Steve Taberner	5.10	12.7	15.9.62	Orrell	Orrell	78	60	13	-	-	1
				Teacher							
James Naylor	5.11	14.0	6.2.74	Halifax	Old Crosslevians						
England A U21 U18				Student	Orrell	34	55	11	-	-	-
Austin Healey	5.9	13.0	26.10.73	Wallasey	Waterloo	20	18	3	-	-	1
England U21				Student	Orrell	15+1	5	1	-	-	-
Phil Horrocks	6.2	15.7	24.9.69	Wigan	Orrell	6	15	3	-	-	-
				Engineer							
Ian Bruce			14.9.72		Orrell	1	5	1	-	-	-
Graeme Smith	6.2	13.6	31.12.75	Paisley	Orrell	1	-	-	-	-	-
				Student							
Paul Johnson	6.0	13.10	19.5.62	Huddersfield	Leeds	6	10	2	-	-	-
				Director	Orrell	27	10	2	-	-	-
Ian Wynn	6.2	14.0	19.8.68	St Helens	Orrell	44+1	55	11	-	-	-
				Draughtsman							
Matt Farr	5.11	15.0	16.8.64	Cheshire	Winnington Park						
				Meat Inspector	Orrell	8+2	-	-	-	-	-
Paul Hamer	5.10	12.4	12.11.66	St Helens	Sale	14	29	3	1	5	-
				Print Manager	Orrell	31+1	58	10	1	-	2
Gerry Ainscough	6.0	12.4	7.8.64	Billinge	Leicester	6	8	2	-	-	-
England B				Engineer	Orrell	66+1	337	12	34	71	2
Dewi Morris	6.0	14.0	9.2.64	Crickhollow	Liverpool St H	20	8	2	-	-	-
England (26) B				Sales Manager	Orrell	62	106	24	-	-	-
Dave Topping	5.7	11.7	14.1.74	Billinge	Orrell	7	-	-	-	-	-
				Student							
FORWARDS											
Phil Winstanley	6.0	16.0	16.9.68	Orrell	Orrell	21+2	12	2	-	1	-
				Legal Executive							
John Russell	5.10	16.2		Manchester	Broughton Park	33	5	1	-	-	-
				Builder	Orrell	5	-	-	-	-	-
Jason Cundick	6.4	16.6		Cheshire	Winnington Park						
				Teacher	Orrell	14	-	-	-	-	-
Andy Rimmer	5.11	17.7			Orrell	4	-	-	-	-	-
Tony Redmond	5.11	14.10	14.1.71	Orrell	Orrell	10	-	-	-	-	-
				Student							
Martin Scott	6.0	15.10	5.7.67	Falkirk	Edinburgh Ac						
				Civil Servant	Orrell	8	-	-	-	-	-
Clive Cooper	6.5	16.0	7.11.65	Longton	Liverpool St H	10	-	-	-	-	-
				Postman	Orrell	27+1	-	-	-	-	-
Chris Brierley	6.4	18.0	31.7.62	Colchester	Sale	2	-	-	-	-	-
				Policeman	Orrell	40+3	-	-	-	-	-
Chas Cusani	6.6	16.7	22.10.65	Wigan	Orrell	53	12	3	-	-	-
				Catering Manager							
Mickey Glynn	6.3	15.7	22.1.65	Wigan	Orrell	13	-	-	-	-	-
				Builder							
David Cleary	6.3	15.5	15.9.61	Wigan	Orrell	61	48	11	-	-	-
				Builder							
Paul Manley	6.1	15.7	26.1.68		Burnage						
				Student	Orrell	73	29	7	-	-	-
Steven Bibby	6.5	18.0	7.7.69	Wigan	Orrell	36+3	14	3	-	-	-
				Mechanic							
Howard Parr	6.4	16.6	1.11.72	York	Orrell	4+2	-	-	-	-	-
				Student							
Stuart Hayter	5.10	13.2	5.7.65		London W						
				Sales Engineer	Orrell	16+2	5	1	-	-	-
Jeff Huxley	6.3	16.7	28.6.63	Orrell	Orrell						
				Policeman							
Adam Jackson	6.7	16.6	28.1.73	Blackpool	Orrell	4+1	-	-	-	-	-
				Student							
David Southern	5.10	15.5	29.12.52	Wigan	Orrell	83+3	-	-	-	-	-
England B				Transport Manager							

ORRELL R.U.F.C.

Edgehall Road, Orrell WN5 8TL
Telephone: 01695 623193
Fax: 01695 632116

Total Capacity: 4,950
Seated: 250
Standing: 4,700
Simple Directions to Ground: M6 motorway Jnc 26 and turn left at T/L at end of slip road. Turn left at T/L at Stag Inn 400 yds. Turn left at T/L 400 yds. Turn left at T/L - Edgehall Road (2 miles from M6)
Nearest Railway Station: Orrell
Car Parking: 300
Season Tickets:
Match Prices: Adults £6.00 Children/OAPs £3.00
Membership: Seniors £47.00 Juniors £15.00
Training Nights: 1st & V Tuesday/Thursday

ALL TIME TOP TEN COURAGE LEAGUE RECORDS

APPEARANCES		POINTS	
90	Simon Langford	337	Gerry Ainscough
83+3	David Southern	323	Martin Strett
78	Steve Taberner	279	Simon Langford
73	David Manley	106	Dewi Morris
66	Gerry Ainscough	78	Phil Halsall
65	Martin Hynes	72	Nigel Heslop
65	Neil Hitchin	60	Steve Taberner
62	Dewi Morris	58	Paul Hamer
61	Dave Cleary	55	James Naylor
59	Phil Halsall	55	Ian Lynn

MOST POINTS: 337 Gerry Ainscough

Season	Apps	Points	Tries	Cons	Pens	D G
1987-88	10	72	6	6	12	
1988-89	9	54	-	3	15	1
1989-90	2	-	-	-	-	-
1990-91	10	22	4	-	1	1
1992-93	12	63	-	6	17	-
1993-94	12+1	65	-	13	13	-
1994-95	11+1	61	2	6	13	-
Total	66+2	337	12	34	71	2

MOST TRIES: 24 Dewi Morris

Season	Appearances	Tries
1990-91	11	7
1991-92	12	7
1992-93	11	3
1993-94	14	4
1994-95	14	3
Total	62	24

MOST APPEARANCES: 90 Simon Langford

Season	Appearances
1987-88	9
1988-89	10
1989-90	9
1990-91	10
1991-92	12
1992-93	12
1993-94	13
1994-95	13
Total	90

SALE F.C.

NICKNAME: **FOUNDED:** 1861

CLUB OFFICIALS

President
John Gardiner
Chairman
Tom Barker
Club Secretary
Laura Murrell
Sale FC, Heywood Road, Sale, Cheshire M33 3WB
Tel (H) 0161 926 8164 (W) 0161 905 6318
Fixtures Secretary
Tony Dolan
9 Greenway Road, Timperley, Altrincham, Cheshire WA15 6BD
Tel (H) 0161 282 7643 (W) 0161 7795 0711
Press Officer
Christine Kenrick
Tel (H) 0161 962 1365 (W) 0161 200 2019

Review of the Season

By tradition SALE is one of England's elite clubs, but all that means nothing nowadays with the pecking order constantly changing and famous outfits languishing in oblivion in many cases.

Sale did at one time look in danger of following the same route, but they realised that time never stands still and met the challenge with fourth place in the recent campaign after promotion the previous season proving that they are back where they belong. That high ranking was confirmed by a superb final game performance and victory (18-13) at Fortress Bath, where most people leave with only humiliation to show for their efforts.

The cup was less successful as they had to bow out narrowly to visitors Leicester (12-14) after a resounding earlier victory at home to Harrogate (33-0), but the future looks bright particularly if Welsh fly-half and coach Paul Turner can in his latter seasons continue to inspire as he has done so far. He has some talented players to back him including fullback Mallender, Appleson, Baxendell, Bob Liley and scrum-half Saverimutto amongst the backs and a lively pack with two props called Smith, hooker Diamond, Fowler, Baldwin, Ashurst and No8 Charlie Vyvyan, who has made a fine come-back after injuries threatened to end his career.

This lack of fame amongst the playing staff, which may not last too long, has helped stability and extra demands on their time have so far not been a handicap. If that situation changes fans can feel assured that contingency plans to add depth to their talent are already operating.

Colours: Royal blue/white hoops & blue shorts   **Change Colours**: Red/black hoops & red shorts

SALE F.C.

COURAGE LEAGUE
MATCH DETAILS 1994-95

No	Date	Opponents	Ven	Result		Scorers
1	Sep 10	Harlequins	H	L	19-20	Stocks (T) Vyvyan (T) Ashurst (T) Turner (2C)
2	Sep 10	Bristol	A	L	22-44	Mallindor (T) Turner (1C 4P 1DG)
3	Sep 24	Northampton	H	W	41-6	Appleson (2T) O'Grady (2T) Mallindor (T 1DG) Turners (5C 1DG)
4	Oct 1	Orrell	A	L	19-22	Vyvyan (T) Ashurst (T) O'Grady (T) Turner (2C)
5	Oct 8	Gloucester	H	W	16-14	Verbickas (2T) Turner (2P)
6	Oct 15	Wasps	A	L	22-52	Stocks (T) Baxendale (T) Baldwin (T) Liley (1P 2C)
7	Oct 22	West Hartlepool	H	W	26-14	Warr (T) Vyvyan (T) Verbickas (T) Turner (2C 1P)
8	Oct 29	Leicester	A	L	20-37	Baxendale (T) Vyvyan (T) Turner (C2 1P 1DG)
9	Nov 5	Bath	H	L	19-3	Liley (P)
10	Jan 7	Harlequins	A	D	15-15	Fowler (T) Baxendale (T) Turner (1C 1P)
11	Jan 14	Bristol	H	W	21-9	Mallindor (T) Stocks (T) Turner (1C 3P)
12	Feb 11	Northampton	A	W	22-9	Yates (2T) Ashurst (T) Turner (2C 1P)
13	Mar 4	Orrell	A	D	8-8	Yates (T) Turner (P)
14	Mar 25	Gloucester	A	W	20-8	Mallindor (T) Fowler (T) Turner (T)
15	Apr 8	Wasps	H	L	12-17	Liley (4P)
16	Apr 15	West Hartlepool	A	L	17-23	Yates (2T) Mallinder (T) Liley (C)
17	Apr 22	Leicester	H	L	10-20	Stocks (T) Liley (1P 1C)
18	Apr 29	Bath	A	W	18-13	Baldwin (T) Appleson (T) Liley 2P 1C)

Courage League Records 1994-95

League Debuts: Chris Saverimutto, Neil Ashurst, Charlie Vyvyan, Mark Appleson, Rob Liley, Chris Yates, John Fowler, Arthur Morris
Tries on Debut: Ashurst, Vyvyan, Appleson, Fowler
2 Ever Presents: Baxendale & Diamond – 4 players missed just 1 game
Most appearances: 74 Dave Baldwin

● Used just 27 players – lowest in the Division by 4

● 2nd highest try scorers – 39

● Scored tries in 16 out of 18 games

● Dis double over Northampton and Gloucester

● Dave Baldwin passes Martin Whitcombe's record of 61 appearances by a back. Mallinder finishes on 71

● Paul; Turner passes 200 league points and ends the season just short of 300

● Mallinder captained this side for most of the season in the absence of club captain Mike Kenrick

● Became only the 3rd side to win a match at the Recreation Ground, Bath

● Mallinder extends his club record of tries to 25

	TRIES	APPS	STRIKE RATE
Jim Mallinder	25	71	2.84
Simon Verbickas	19	20	1.05

SALE F.C.

MATCH BY MATCH PLAYERS BY POSITION

Mallinder	Verbickas	Baxendell	Stocks	Young	Turner	Saverimutto	Whitcombe	Diamond	Smith A	Baldwin	O'Grady	Erskine	Ashurst	Vyvyan	Appleson	Smith P	Kenrick	Greenwood	Wheeler	Liley	Warr	Yates	Fowler
15	14	12	12	11	10	9	1	2	3	4	5	6	7	8									
15	14	13	12	11	10	9	1	2	3	4	5	6	7	8									
15	14	13	12		10	9		2	3		5	4	7	8	11	1		6					
15	14	13	12		10	9		2	3	4	5		7	8	11	1	6						
15	14	13	12		10	9		2	3	4	6	5	7		11		8	1					
15	14	13	12			9		2	3	5		4	7	8	11		6			1	10		
15	14	13	12		10			2	3	4		5	7	8	11	1	6			9			
15	14	13	12		10			2		4	5		8	7	11	1	6	3		9			
	14	13	12		10			2	3	4		5	7	8	11	1	6		15	9			
15		13	12		10	9		2	3	5	6		7	8	11	1						14	4
15		13	12		10			2	3	4		6	7	8	14	1						11	5
15		13	12		10	9		2	3	4		6	7	8	11	1						14	5
15		13	12		10			2	3	5		6	7	8	14	1					9	11	4
14		12	11		10	9		2	3	5		6		8	13	1			15				4
14		13	12		10	9		2	3	5		6	7	8		1			15			11	4
14		13	12		10	9		2	3			6	7	8		1			15			11	4
14		13	12		10	9		2	3	5		6	7	8		1			15			11	4
15		13				9		2	3	5	R40	6	7*	8	14	1			10			11	4

Also Played: Parker No 5 match 16; Birt No 12 match 18; Morris No 7 match 14

PROGRAMME DETAILS

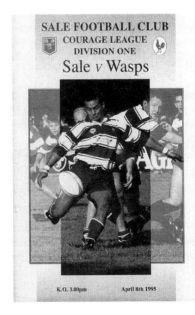

SALE FOOTBALL CLUB
COURAGE LEAGUE DIVISION ONE
Sale *v* Wasps
K.O. 3.00pm   April 8th 1995

PAGES: 44

Attractive publication an excellent paper with at least a dozen pages of original copy. Different shades of blue throughout with smart cover.

EDITOR: Jen Elwood

ADVERTISING RATES:
Full page £500 b/w, half page £275 b/w

SALE F.C.

COURAGE LEAGUE STATISTICS
compiled by Steve McCormack

Season	Div	P	W	D	L	F	T	C	P	D	A	T	C	P	D	Most Points	Most Tries
1987-88	1	11	0	0	11	95	9	4	16	1	375	60	40	15	3	49 Graham Jenion	3 Howard Fitton
1988-89	2	11	6	0	5	195	18	9	32	3	152	16	8	23	1	102 David Pears	3 David Pears
1989-90	2	11	4	0	7	153	16	7	25	0	182	23	12	22	0	29 Graham Jenion	4 Phil Stansfield
1990-91	2	12	5	1	6	224	32	15	18	4	156	23	11	8	6	82 Richard Booth	5 Jeff Powell
1991-92	2	12	6	0	6	204	23	11	28	2	209	25	11	27	2	79 Matthew Alexander	5 Jim Mallinder
1992-93	2	12	7	1	4	237	26	13	22	5	102	5	4	20	3	63 Phil Jee	7 Mark Warr
1993-94	2	18	13	2	3	438	57	30	28	3	160	9	5	32	3	144 Paul Turner	16 Simon Verbickas
1994-94	1	18	7	2	9	327	39	24	24	4	343	32	15	46	5	92 Paul Turner	5 Gareth Stocks & Jim Mallinder
TOTALS		105	48	6	51	1873	220	113	193	22	1679	193	106	193	23		

BIGGEST WIN **Home:** 88-9 v Otley 12.2.94 CL2 **Away:** 38-11 v Liverpool St H 14.12.91 CL2

BIGGEST DEFEAT **Home:** 17-46 v Bath 28.4.88 CL1 **Away:** 6-66 v Harlequins 23.4.88 CL1

MOST TRIES in a match **For**: 14 v Otley 12.2.94 CL2 **Against:** 12 v Harlequins 23.4.88 CL1

MOST CONSECUTIVE **Wins:** 7 **Defeats:** 11

MOST APPEARANCES **Forward:** 74 Dave Baldwin **Back:** 71 Jim Mallinder

MOST CONSECUTIVE APPEARANCES 39 Phil Stansfield 22.10.88-14.3.92

CONSECUTIVE SCORING MATCHES **Tries:** 8 Simon Verbickas

Points: 14 Richard Booth

	IN A SEASON	IN A CAREER	IN A MATCH
MOST POINTS	144 Paul Turner 1993-94 CL2	290 Paul Turner 1992-95	25 Simon Verbickas v Otley 12.2.94 Home CL2
MOST TRIES	16 Simon Verbickas 1993-94 CL2	25 Jim Mallinder 1988-95	5 Simon Verbickas v Otley 12.2.94 Home CL2
MOST CONVERSIONS	29 Paul Turner 1993-94 CL2	55 Paul Turner 1992-95	9 Paul Turner v Otley 12.2.94 Home CL2
MOST PENALTIES	26 David Pears 1988-89 CL2	46 Paul Turner 1992-95	5 David Pears v Headingly 19.11.88 Home CL2
MOST DROP GOALS	3 David Shufflebottom 1990-91 CL2 Paul Turner 1993-94 CL2 1994-95 CL1	9 Paual Turner 1992-95	2 David Pears v Bedford 22.2.89 Home CL2 Paul Turner v Morley 3.10.92 Home CL2 v Wakefield 9.4.94 Away CL2

SALE F.C.

Name	Ht	Wt	Birthdate	Birthplace	Clubs	App	Pts	T	C	P	DG
BACKS											
Jim Mallinder	6.3	15.0	16.3.66	Halifax	Roundhay						
				Teacher	Sale	71	119	25	-	-	2
Rob Liley	6.1	13.0	3.4.70	Wakefield	Wakefield	23	214	2	23	51	2
England U21				Insurance Inspector	Sale	7	42	-	6	10	-
Simon Verbickas	6.1	13.7	22.4.75	Manchester	Broughton Park	1	2	-	1	-	-
				Sales Rep	Sale	20	95	19	-	-	-
Kevn Young	5.10	13.7	13.1.61	Yorkshire	Headingley						
				Quality Manager	Sale	44	57	12	-	-	-
Mark Appleson	5.10	13.7	26.2.68	Yorkshire	London Scottish						
				Teacher	Sale	13	15	3	-	-	-
Chris Yates	6.1	15.8	13.5.71	Otahuhu	Sale	8	20	4	-	-	-
				Bailiff							
Jos Baxdendell	6.0	13.0	13.5.71	Macclesfield	Sheffield						
				Surveyor	Sale	26	15	3	-	-	-
Gareth Stocks	5.10	13.13	17.12.69	Rochdale	Sale	35	35	7	-	-	-
England A				Finance Controlle							
Matt Birt	6.2	15.0	23.11.69	Taunton	Macclesfield						
				Surveyor	Sale	20	15	3	-	-	-
Paul Turner	5.10	11.8	16.2.59	Newport	Newbridge						
Wales (3)				Marketing	Sale	40	290	3	55	46	9
Chris Saverimutto	5.8	12.7	8.8.71		Waterloo						
					Sale	14	-	-	-	-	-
Mark Warr	5.9	12.10	24.2.68	Wallasey	Barkers Butt						
				Social Worker	Sale	28	50	10	-	-	-
FORWARDS											
Martin Whitcombe	6.1	16.8	14.9.62	Yorkshire	Sale	72	28	6	-	-	-
Andrew Smith	6.1	17.4	28.3.69	Nantwich	Sale	42	-	-	-	-	-
				Builder							
Paul Smith	6.0	17.0	28.3.69	Nantwich	Sale	31	-	-	-	-	-
				Builder							
Nick Wheeler	6.0	17.7	13.12.59	Liverpool	Sale	39	-	-	-	-	-
				Insurance							
Steve Diamond	5.10	14.0	3.2.68	Manchester	Sale	58	15	3	-	-	-
				Printer							
Dave Baldwin	6.5	18.0	3.9.65	Ilkley	Wakefield	11	-	-	-	-	-
England A				Print Manager	Sale	74	33	7	-	-	-
Dylan O'Grady	6.3	16.7	19.11.71	Manchester	Sale	19	20	4	-	-	-
				Transport							
John Fowler	6.8	17.8	6.2.68	Kent	Richmond						
				Accountant	Newcastle G						
					Sale	9	10	2	-	-	-
Guy Parker	6.6	16.0	28.1.63	Lancashire	Morley						
				Sales	Sale	25	-	-	-	-	-
Dave Erskine	6.5	16.8	14.10.69	London	Sale	41	35	7	-	-	-
				Insurance Inspector							
Neil Ashurst	6.2	16.0	12.5.69	St Helens	Orrell						
England B U21				Plasterer	Sale	17	15	3	-	-	-
Charlie Vyvyan	6.6	17.4	1.9.65	Wimbledon	Richmond						
				Surveyor	Sale	17	20	4	-	-	-
Mike Kenrick	6.3	15.8	3.1.64	Manchester	Sale	70	48	11	-	-	-
				Recruitment							
Andy Morris	6.0	15.0	1.9.71	Blackburn	Sale	1	-	-	-	-	-
England U21				Corporate Finance	Notts	5	-	-	-	-	-
Howard Greenwood	6.1	14.10	6.9.66	Leeds	Sale	2	-	-	-	-	-
				Recruitment							

SALE F.C.

Heywood Road, Sale, Cheshire M33 3WB

Telephone: 0161 973 6348
Fax: 0161 969 4124

Total Capacity: 4,000
Seated: 750
Standing: 3,250
Simple Directions to Ground: Junction 19 M6, approx 8 miles along A556/A56, turn right Marsland Road, Heywood Road on right after half mile.
Nearest Railway Station: Brooklands - Metro
Car Parking: 100
Season Tickets: Adults: £7.00 League Children/OAPs: £4.00 League
Match Prices: Adults: £3.00 Children/OAPs: £3.00
Membership: Seniors: £30.00 Juniors: £15.00
Training Nights: Tuesday & Thursday

ALL TIME TOP TEN COURAGE LEAGUE RECORDS

APPEARANCES		POINTS	
74	Dave Baldwin	290	Paul Turner
72	Martin Whitcombe	132	Phil Jee
71	Jim Mallinder	127	Richard Booth
70	Mike Kenrick	119	Jim Mallinder
63	Andy McFarlane	105	Graham Jenion
61+1	Phil Stansfield	102	David Pears
58	Steve Diamond	95	Simon Verbickas
44	Kevin Young	79	Matthew Alexander
42	Andrew Smith	57	Kevin Young
42	Jeff Powell	55	Jeff Powell

MOST POINTS: 290 Paul Turner

Season	Apps	Points	Tries	Cons	Pens	D G
1992-93	7	54	1	8	8	3
1993-94	17	144	1	29	24	3
1994-95	16	92	1	18	14	3
Total	40	290	3	55	46	9

MOST TRIES: 25 Jim Mallinder

Season	Appearances	Tries
1989-90	8	2
1990-91	9	5
1991-92	10	5
1992-93	11	2
1993-94	16	6
1994-95	17	5
Total	71	25

MOST APPEARANCES: 74 Dave Baldwin

Season	Appearances
1988-89	3
1989-90	10
1990-91	7
1991-92	11
1992-93	11
1993-94	17
1994-95	15
Total	74

SARACENS

NICKNAME: SARRIES   **FOUNDED:** 1876

CLUB OFFICIALS

President
James Wyness
Club Secretary
B. D. W. Richards
36 Stone Hall Road, Winchmore Hill,
London N21 1LP
Tel (H) 0181 245 7917
Fixtures Secretary
D. H. J. Grammer
75 Roundwood Lane, Harpenden,
Herts AL5 3EX
Tel: (H) 01582 762356
Press Officer
Bill Edwards
Tel (H) 0181 449 6313 (W) 0181 449 3770

A Champion Achievement

In the end Saracens took Courage League Two by storm to win the championship at a canter, through an impressive team discipline and commitment, instilled by coach Mark Evans.

Skipper and scrum-half Brian Davies showed unquestionable dedication in travelling to training and matches from South Wales where he now lives and works. It was his third season at the helm and he led his side to triumph in style.

The team possessed outstanding collective fitness and organisation and always seemed able to step up a gear under pressure. There was strength throughout and they were equally at home in forward control or a more expansive game. It was a season where our two back row stars Anthony Diprose and Richard Hill stole much of the plaudits and indeed Diprose was absolutely magnificent in every match.

There was an almost ever-present front row of Stuart Wilson, Gregg Botterman and Richard Andrews who were a solid and mobile unit. Botterman's season was capped by a dream call-up. Having played for Emerging England, he replaced the injured Graham Dawe on the England bench for the Five Nations match against Scotland.

By the time we played Wakefield for the second time they were the only team at that stage to have beaten us. They knew they had to win to keep alive their promotion ambitions and in a real mudbath produced a thrilling contest. Trailing 3-0 after the visitors broke away to win a penalty, Tunningley levelled and then it was the courageous Green who plunged over for a match- winning score. But Saracens had to show all their powers of defensive resilience to survive for a final 10-3 win.

It was a team effort right through the club. Behind the squad was an efficient management and coaching team. Sponsors, Pinnacle Insurance, could not have been more active benefactors and the supporters travelled the country to cheer on the team, thanks to the Supporters Club running coaches to away matches.

Now, the prize next season is the mighty challenge of League One rugby which everyone can look forward to with relish.   *Bill Edwards*

Top: Barry Crawley, John Green, Richard Hill, Mark Burrow, Anthony Diprose, Kathy Barrett (Physio), Peter Harries. Centre: Mark Evans (Coach), Mike Scott (Team Manager), Tom Ellis, Charles Olney, Andy Tunningley, John Buckton, Gary Clark, Dan Dooley, Bruce Millar (Chair of Playing), Mike Williams (Coach). Front: Gavin Reynolds, Paul Butler, Andy Lee, Richard Andrews (Vice Captain), Brian Davies (Captain), Mark Langley, Gregg Botterman, Martin Gregory, Nikki Townley (Masseuse)
Colours: Black shirt, black shorts, red socks   **Change Colours**: Black, red, white hoops, black shorts, red socks

SARACENS F.C.

COURAGE LEAGUE
MATCH DETAILS 1994-95

No	Date	Opponents	Ven	Result		Scorers
1	Sep 10	Moseley	A	W	11-9	Harries (T) Lee (DG) Tunningley (P)
2	Sep 17	L/Irish	H	W	35-22	Green (T) Diprose (T) Harries (T) Lee (DG) Tunningley (T 3C 2P)
3	Sep 24	Wakefield	A	L	8-17	Diprose (T) Lee (DG)
4	Oct 1	Waterloo	H	W	27-5	Green (T) Lee (T) Crawley (T) Tunningley (3C 2P)
5	Oct 8	Nottingham	A	W	17-9	Butler (T) Lee (DG) Tunningley (3P)
6	Oct 15	Fylde	H	W	18-7	Tunningley (6P)
7	Oct 22	Newcastle/G	A	W	17-11	Green (T) Tunningley (4P)
8	Oct 29	Coventry	A	W	33-6	Buckton (2T) Butler (T) Harries (T) Tunningley (2C 3P)
9	Nov 5	L.Scottish	H	W	27-17	Tunningley (T C 3P) Harries (T) Lee (2DG)
10	Jan 7	Moseley	H	W	17-15	Wilson (T) Hill (T) Gregory (T) Tunningley (C)
11	Jan 14	L/Irish	A	W	16-6	Harries (T) Buckton (T) Tunningley (2P)
12	Feb 11	Wakefield	H	W	10-3	Green (T) Tunningley (C P)
13	Mar 4	Waterloo	A	W	23-16	Diprose (T) Penalty (T) Tunningley (2C 3P)
14	Mar 25	Nottingham	H	W	32-7	Botterman (T) Clark (T) Butler (T) Green (T) Lee (3P) Tunningley (1P)
15	Apr 8	Fylde	A	W	37-15	Green (T) Harries (T) Hill (T) Diprose (T) Gregory (T) Tunningley (3C 2P)
16	Apr 15	Newcastle/G	H	D	16-16	Clark (2T) Tunningley (2P)
17	Apr 22	Coventry	H	W	38-0	Dooley (T) Langley (T) Hill (T) Green (T) Tunningley (T) Butler (T) Tunningley (4C)
29	Apr 29	L/Scottish	A	L	7-22	Pen Try Tunningley (1C)

Courage League Records 1994-95

League Debuts: D Horsley, Danny Zaltman, Tom Ellis, Dan Phillips, Richard Thompson, Sean O'Leary, Ian Wright, G Reynolds, G Truelove, G Andrews
Players used: 33
2 Ever Presents Andy Tunningley, Richard Andrews
Most appearances: 90 John Buckton

- Unbeaten at home – 8 wins, 1 draw

- Most tries in the Division – 43

- The forwards outscored the backs 23-30 in tries

- Scored tries in 17 out of 18 games – failed in home match v Fylde

- Had just 28 penalties scored against

- Andy Tunningley beat his own record for points in a season

Season	Pts	T	C	P	D	App	Ave
1993-94	149	5	14	31	1	17	8.76
1994-95	162	3	21	35	0	18	9.00

- Tunningley passed Ben Rudling's record of points and penalties

	Pts	T	C	P	D	App	Ave
Andy Tunningley	365	9	45	76	1	51	7.16
Ben Rudling	214	4	21	45	7	35	6.11

- Andy Lee equals record of 2 drop goals in a match and breaks Ben Rudling's season and career record with 6 and 10 respectively

	Tries	Apps	Strike Rate
Dave McLagen	17	27	1.59
John Buckton	17	90	5.30

- John Buckton equals Dave McLagen's record of 17 tries

SARACENS F.C.

MATCH BY MATCH PLAYERS BY POSITION

Tunningley	Harries	Buckton	Dooley	Butler	Lee	Davies	Andrews	Botterman	Wilson	Langley	Burrow	Green	Hill	Diprose	Gregory	Ravenscroft	Crawley	Clark	Ellis	Phillips	Zaltzman	Atkinson	Olney
15	14	13		11	10	9	1	2	3	4	5	6		8		12	7						
15	11	13			10	9	1	2	3	4	5	6		8	14	12	7						
15	11	13	12		10	9	1	2	3		5	4	7	6	14		8						
15	11		13		10	9	1	2	3		5	4	7	6	14	12	8						
15	14	13		11	10	9	1	2	3		5	4	7	6		12	8						
15	14	13		11	10	9	1	2	3		5	4	7	6		12	8						
15	14	13		11	10	9	1	2	3			4	7	6		12	8				5		
15	14	13		11	10	9	1	2	3		5	4	7	6		12	8	R					
15	14	13		11	10	9	1	2	3			6	7	8		12		4	R	R	5		
15		13		11	10	9	1	2	3	4		5	7	6	14		8	R				12	
15	11	13	12		10	9	1	2	3	4		5	7	6	14		8	R					
15	14		12	11	10	9	1	2	3	4	5	6	7	8									
15		13	12	11	10	9	1		3	4	5	6	7	8	14			R					2
15		13	12	11	10	9	1	2	3	4		6			14		8			7			
15	11	13	12		10	9	1	2	3	4	5	6	7	8	14								
15		13	12	11			1	2			4			8		6	9	7					R
15		13	12	11	10	9	3			4	5	6	7		14		8						2
15				11	10	9	3	2		4	5		7	8		6	R					12	

Also Played: Horsley R match 2; Thompson No 13 match 12; Cooke R match 13; Horsley No 5 match 14; Hughes No 10 match 16; Kemp No 14 match 16; Wright No 3 match 16; O'Leary No 5 match 16; Reynolds No 1 match 17; Reynolds No 1 match 18; Thompson No 13 match 18; Truelove No 14 match 18

PROGRAMME DETAILS

PAGES: 36
No colour other than cover. Eight pages of interesting copy

ADVERTISING RATES:
Full Page b/w £500 page b/w £300

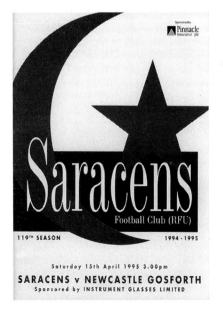

Sponsored by Pinnacle Insurance plc

Saracens Football Club (RFU)

119TH SEASON   1994-1995

Saturday 15th April 1995 3.00pm
SARACENS v NEWCASTLE GOSFORTH
Sponsored by INSTRUMENT GLASSES LIMITED

SARACENS F.C.

COURAGE LEAGUE STATISTICS
compiled by Steve McCormack

Season	Div	P	W	D	L	F	T	C	P	D	A	T	C	P	D	Most Points	Most Tries
1987-88	2	11	7	2	2	228	38	17	13	1	86	11	6	8	2	46 Nick Holmes	10 Dave McLagen
1988-89	2	11	11	0	0	288	37	19	33	1	80	9	4	11	1	138 Andy Kennedy	7 Dave McLagen
1989-90	1	11	7	1	3	168	25	16	11	1	167	26	9	14	1	50 Andy Kennedy	4 Ben Clarke
1990-91	1	12	5	0	7	151	20	10	14	3	228	32	20	18	2	36 Ben Rudling	4 Ben Clarke
1991-92	1	12	7	1	4	176	18	10	22	6	165	17	8	27	0	91 Ben Rudling	4 Martin Gregory
1992-93	1	12	3	0	9	137	13	6	16	4	180	15	9	28	1	43 Ben Rudling	3 Darren O'Leary & Barry Crawley
1993-94	2	18	11	1	6	299	30	16	34	5	238	16	10	41	5	149 Andy Tunningley	5 Richard Hill & Andy Tunningley
1994-95	2	18	15	1	2	389	43	21	38	6	213	20	13	28	1	162 Andy Tunningley	7 John Green
TOTALS		105	66	6	33	1836	224	115	181	27	1357	146	79	175	13		

BIGGEST WIN — **Home:** 50-10 v Bedford 19.11.88 CL2 — **Away:** 48-12 v Blackheath 23.3.88 CL2

BIGGEST DEFEAT — **Home:** 6-49 v Bath 27.4.91 — **Away:** 3-52 v Sale 18.9.93 CL2

MOST TRIES in a match — **For:** 9 v Gosforth 22.4.89 CL2 — **Against:** 9

MOST CONSECUTIVE — **Wins:** 17 — **Defeats:** 7

MOST APPEARANCES — **Forward:** 84+1 Richard Andrews — **Back:** 90 John Buckton

MOST CONSECUTIVE APPEARANCES 68 Brian Davies

CONSECUTIVE SCORING MATCHES — **Tries:** 6 Dave McLagen

Points: 19 Andy Tunningley

	IN A SEASON	IN A CAREER	IN A MATCH
MOST POINTS	162 Andy Tunningley 1994-95 CL2	365 Andy Tunningley 1990-95	24 Andy Kennedy v Northampton 12.11.88 Away CL2
MOST TRIES	10 Dave McLagen 1987-88 CL2	17 Dave McLagen 1987-90 & John Buckton 1987-95	3 Laurie Smith v Gosforth 22.4.89 Away CL2
MOST CONVERSIONS	21 Andy Tunningley 1994-95 CL2	45 Andy Tunningley 1990-95	5 Nick Holmes v Blackheath 23.3.88 Away CL2 v London Scot 23.4.88 Home CL2 Andy Kennedy v Bedford 19.11.88 Home CL2 v Moseley 28.10.89 Home CL1
MOST PENALTIES	35 Andy Tunningley 1994-95 CL2	76 Andy Tunningley 1990-95	6 Andy Tunningley v Fylde 15.10.94 Home CL2
MOST DROP GOALS	6 Andy Lee 1994-95 CL2	10 Andy Lee 1989-95	2 Andy Lee v Wasps 22.2.92 Away CL1 v London Scot 5.11.94 Home CL2 Ben Rudling v London Irish 11.4.92 Home CL1 Gareth Hughes v Bath 24.4.93 Home CL1

SARACENS F.C.

Name	Ht	Wt	Birthdate	Birthplace	Clubs	App	Pts	T	C	P	DG
BACKS											
Andy Tunningley	6.2	13.6	29.3.67	Harrogate	Sandal						
				Actuarial Consultant	Saracens	51	365	9	45	76	1
Peter Harries	6.2	13.4	10.9.70	Romford	Pontypridd						
England U16				Teacher	Saracens	16	45	9	-	-	-
Paul Butler	5.10	12.7	28.5.65	Wolverhampton	Saracens	29	33	1	-	-	-
				Bank Manager							
Martin Gregory	6.0	14.0	3.8.62	Dagenham	Southend						
				Director	Saracens	34	38	9	-	-	-
Malcolm Kemp	6.3	13.6	26.2.72	London	Saracens	13	5	1	-	-	-
				Student							
George Truelove	6.3	14.6	22.9.75	Newcastle	Saracens	1	-	-	-	-	-
England U 18				Student							
John Buckton	6.2	14.0	22.12.61	Hull	Saracens	90	73	17	-	-	-
England (3)				Sales Manager							
Steve Ravenscroft			2.11.70	Bradford	Bradford & Bingley						
England U16 U18				Solicitor	Saracens	34	10	2	-	-	-
Andy Atkinson	6.1	13.12	25.6.64	Nairobi	Wakefield						
				Policeman	Saracens	3	-	-	-	-	-
Richard Thompson					Saracens	2	-	-	-	-	-
				Teacher							
Andy Lee	5.10	13.6	10.11.68	Wanstead	Saracens	31	81	4	4	8	10
England U21				Student							
Gareth Hughes	6.1	12.10	25.7.66	Wales	Blackheath						
				Teacher	Saracens	13	21	-	-	1	6
Brian Davies	5.10	11.10	22.1.66	Nairobi	Southend						
				Systems Analyst	Saracens	70	35	8	-	-	-
Tom Ellis	5.10	12.12	5.10.71	Kings Lynn	Wasps						
				Medical Rep	Saracens	1+3					
FORWARDS											
Richard Andrews	5.8	15.10	25.3.64	Stevenage	Bacavians						
				Design Engineer	Saracens	84+1	5	1	-	-	-
Stuart Wilson	5.11	15.7	27.3.64	London	Cheshunt						
				Plasterer	Saracens	50	10	2	-	-	-
Chris Wright	6.4	16.2	15.7.64	Wheathampstead	Saracens	1	-	-	-	-	-
				Policeman							
Gavin Reynolds					Saracens	1	-	-	-	-	-
Greg Botterman	5.11	15.0	3.3.68	Hertford	Bacavians						
				Director	Saracens	51+2	5	1	-	-	-
Charles Olney	5.10	16.0	11.8.71	Taunton	Wellington						
				Accountant	Saracens	2+1	-	-	-	-	-
Mark Burrow	6.6	17.10	9.7.69	Chelmsford	Saracens	29	-	-	-	-	-
				Student							
Mark Langley	6.4	17.10	9.6.67	Cardiff	Swansea						
					Saracens	52	10	2	-	-	-
Sean O'Leary	6.8	17.4	25.9.64	Plymouth	Wasps/Bath						
				Doctor	Saracens	1	-	-	-	-	-
Dave Horsley					Saracens	1+1	-	-	-	-	-
John Green	6.4	17.5	17.3.67	Romford	Bridgend						
				Teacher	Saracens	33	45	9	-	-	-
Tony Diprose	6.5	17.5	22.9.72	Orsett	Saracens	37+1	20	4	-	-	-
England A U21 U16				Student							
Richard Hill	6.3	15.10	23.5.73	Salisbury	Salisbury						
England A U21 U18 U16				Student	Saracens	25	40	8	-	-	-
Barry Crawley	6.3	15.7	24.11.64	Essex	Southend						
				Accountant	Saracens	37+2	33	7	-	-	-
Gary Clark	6.3	17.0	3.6.65	Coventry	Saracens	6+4					
					Teacher						
Danny Zaltman	6.6	17.8	22.12.75	Hendon	Brentwood						
				Student	Saracens	2+1	-	-	-	-	-
Dan Phillips	6.3	15.3	29.12.70	Edmonton	Saracens	2+1	-	-	-	-	-
				Policeman							

SARACEN F.C.

Bramley Road Sports Ground, Chaseside, Southgate, London N14 4AB

Telephone: 0181 449 3770 - 0181 449 8662
Fax: 0181 449 9101

Total Capacity:
Seated:
Standing:
Simple Directions to Ground: M25 exit 24 (Potters Bar) follow A111 to Cockfosters Ground 300 yds on left after 1st roundabout (2m)
Nearest Railway Station: Tube Cockfosters
Car Parking: 400
Season Tickets: £70.00 ground only
Match Prices:
Membership: Seniors £35.00 Colts £15
Training Nights: Monday Tuesday Wednesday Thursday

ALL TIME TOP TEN COURAGE LEAGUE RECORDS

APPEARANCES		POINTS	
90	John Buckton	365	Andy Tunningley
84+1	Richard Andrews	214	Ben Rudling
70	Brian Davies	188	Andy Kennedy
62	L Adamson	81	Andy Lee
52	M Langley	76	Dave McLagen
51+2	Greg Butterman	73	John Buckton
51	Andy Tunningley	57	Nick Holmes
50	Scott Wilson	56	Floyd Steadman
46	Sean Robinson	55	Sean Robinson
44	Chris Tarbuck	51	Laurie Smith

MOST POINTS: 51 Andy Tunningley

Season	Apps	Points	Tries	Cons	Pens	D G
1990-91	6	30	1	4	6	-
1991-92	4	5	-	1	1	-
1992-93	6	19	-	5	3	-
1993-94	17	149	5	14	31	1
1994-95	18	162	3	21	35	-
Total	51	365	9	45	76	1

MOST TRIES: 17 Dave McLagen

Season	Appearances	Tries
1987-88	10	10
1988-89	10	7
1989-90	7+1	-
Total	27+1	17

MOST APPEARANCES: 90 John Buckton

Season	Appearances
1987-88	8
1988-89	8
1989-90	10
1990-91	12
1991-92	12
1992-93	8
1993-94	17
1994-95	15
Total	90

WASPS F.C.

NICKNAME: WASPS   **FOUNDED:** 1867

CLUB OFFICIALS

President
Bill Treadwell
Chairman
Sir Patrick Lowry
Club Secretary
Ivor A Montlake
Nash House, 25 Mount Sion, Tunbridge
Wells, Kent TN1 1TZ
Tel (H&W) 01892 511348
Fixtures Secretary
Don Willis
Woodland Gardens, Isleworth,
Middlesex TW7 6LN
Tel (H&W) 0181 560 7594
Press Officer
John M Gasson
Tel (H) 01234 838 735 (W) 0171 409 3455

Review of the Season

Most Clubs would be overjoyed if they ended the season by coming Third in the League and runners up in the Pilkington Cup Final at Twickenham. (Incidentally, Bath won deservedly in a cracking game, for those who failed to discover what happened due to a virtual press blackout.)

Wasps, however, are not overjoyed, for they know they are capable of doing better than that. There was a silver lining in that they consciously pioneered a new running style, which took everyone by surprise, but has proved, not only to be pretty effective, but to have given spectators and especially the players themselves immense pleasure and delight.

Wasps had four players on England's Tour to South Africa in 1994 – Rob Andrew, Captain Dean Ryan, Steve Bates and Lawrence Dallaglio. The first three, on their return, having seen how the South African provincial teams ripped England's defences open by swift handling, scientifically backed up by forwards who could handle and, above all, make decisions, convened with Wasps coach Rob Smith.

They took the decision to adopt this style – which is very high risk – and to persevere for at least two seasons, for they recognised it takes time to gain the self and mutual confidence necessary to achieve the level required. They accepted they would lose games they might otherwise have won and that they could well end up mid-table or even lower. In some ways in the circumstances coming third and reaching the Cup Final is perhaps not such an under-achievement after all.

Wasps are committed to building on this and will continue in the same way for 1995/96, knowing they are now half-way there, and having learnt so much, not least that against the very best sides, it is necessary to vary their approach from time to time – a lesson that near the end of the season led to successive victories over Bath and Leicester in eight days.

But, above all, the players love the freedom of this style (especially nine tries v Harlequins at Stoop!) – and by Heavens, so do the spectators. They haven't overlooked that Leicester scored 20 League tries, and Wasps got 58 (the record) as well as also setting a new League Points Record of 470.

Last season, Wasps suggested that four of their young U21 players were to be watched. It can be reported as follows – **Nick Greenstock** – Rugby Union Young Player of the Year, also capped in the season at England U21, Students, Emerging Players and 'A' levels, plus Barbarians and then called out to South Africa to cover the injured Kyran Bracken in the World Cup Quarter Final;

Peter Scrivener, capped as captain of England U21 and England Students and **Jon Ufton**, also capped for England U21 and played full back in 22 of Wasps 23 League and Cup Games. New names? – Watch for prop Will Green!

Finally, we must congratulate our World Cup heroes, Rob Andrew M.B.E., Damian Hopley and Nick Popplewell for giving us so much pleasure during that amazing event, even if the final outcome was so disappointing. It is interesting to note that New Zealand have adopted Wasps' style and it seems to work rather well - might even catch on?

Colours: Black with gold wasp on left breast   **Change Colours**: Black and gold hoops

WASPS F.C.

COURAGE LEAGUE
MATCH DETAILS 1994-95

No	Date	Opponents	Ven	Result		Scorers
1	Sep 10	Gloucester	H	W	45-8	Andrew (2T) Ufton (T) Childs (T) Hopley (T) Greenwood (T) Dallaglio (T) Andrew (2C 2P)
2	Sep 17	Harlequins	A	W	57-26	Hunter (2T) Greenstock (2T) Childs (T) Hopley (T) Dallaglio (T) Wilkins (T) Ryan (T) Andrew (3C 1P DG)
3	Sep 24	West Hartlepool	A	L	15-20	Greenwood (T) Dunston (T) Gregory (1C 1P)
4	Oct 1	Leicester	H	L	18-23	Andrew (5P 1DG)
5	Oct 8	Bath	A	L	9-12	Andrew (3P)
6	Oct 15	Sale	H	W	52-22	D Hopley (3T) P Hopley (T) Childs (T) Kinsey (T) Andrew (5C 3P DG)
7	Oct 22	Bristol	A	W	25-24	Ufton (T) Pilgrim (T) Pen Try Andrew (2C 2P)
8	Oct 29	Northampton	H	W	27-21	D Hopley (T) P Hopley (T) Delaney (T) Dallaglio (T) Andrew (2C 1P)
9	Nov 5	Orrell	A	W	16-10	D Hopley (T) Gregory (1C 3P)
10	Jan 7	Gloucester	A	W	21-16	P Hopley (T) Bates (T) Dallaglio (T) Andrew (2P)
11	Jan 14	Harlequins	H	W	25-7	Greenstock (2T) Ufton (T) Gregory (2P 2C)
12	Feb 11	West Hartlepool	H	W	33-22	Braithwaite (2T) Delaney (T) Dallaglio (T) Childs (T) Braithwaite (3C) Ufton (1C)
13	Mar 4	Leicester	A	L	6-21	Andrew (2P)
14	Mar 25	Bath	H	W	11-10	Greenwood (T) Andrew (2P)
15	Apr 8	Sale	A	W	17-12	P Hopley (2T) Gomersall (1T) Ufton (C)
16	Apr 15	Bristol	H	W	27-15	P Hopley (T) Kinsey (T) Gregory (5P 1C)
17	Apr 22	Northampton	A	L	13-19	James (T) Andrew (C 2P)
18	Apr 29	Orrell	H	W	53-25	Ufton (2T) P Hopley (T) Greenstock (T) Dunn (T) White (T) Greenwood (T) Kinsey (T) Andrew (5C P)

Courage League Records 1994-95

League Debuts: Jon Ufton, Norman Hadley, Andy Gomersall, Nick Popplewell, Sean Rosier
Try on Debut: Ufton, Gomersall (on full debut after two appearances as replacement), James
31 Players used
Only Ever Present: Matt Greenwood
Most appearances: 87 Steve Bates

● Won 8 out of 9 at home – only defeat v Leicester

● Failed to score a try v Leicester at home or away and Bath away

● Scored 58 tries, a divisional record, 19 more than any other team in the division

● 21 different players scored tries

● 62% of their points came from tries, the highest in the division and only 24% from penalties, 2nd lowest in the division

● Wasps achieve their biggest home and away wins – 53-25 and 57-26 v Orrell and Harlequins respectively

● Rob Andrew becomes the first man to score 600 first division points

	Pts	T	C	P	D	App	Ave
Rob Andrew	681	16	77	145	8	71	9.59

● Andrew and Phil Hopley join Mark Bailey in third place on Wasps Courage League try list

WASPS F.C.

MATCH BY MATCH PLAYERS BY POSITION

Ufton	Hunter	Childs	Hopley D	Greenstock	Andrew	Bates	Holmes	Dunn	Dunston	Greenwood	Hadley	Dallaglio	Wilkins	Ryan	Gomershall	Gregory	Hopley P	Popplewell	Pilgrim	Kinsey	White	Molloy	Probyn
15	14	13	12	11	10	9	1	2	3	4	5	6	7	8									
15	14	13	12	11	10	9	1	2	3	4	5	6	7	8									
15	14	13	12*			9	1	2	3	4	5	6	7	8	12	10			11				
15	14	13			10	9	1	2	3	6	5		8						11	4	7		
15	14	13			10	9		2		4	5	7	8	6					11			1	3
15		13	12		10	9			3	6	5	8	7				14		11	4		1	
15		13	12		10	9				4	5	6	8	7			14		11			1	3
15		13	12		10	9			3	4	5	6	7	8			14		11			1	
15		12	13			9				4	5	6	7	8		10	14		11			1	3
15	14	12		13	10	9			3		5		6	7			11	1		4			
15	14	13	12	11		9					5		6	7	8		10	1		4			3
15	14	12		13		9			3		5		6	7				1		4			
15	14	12	13	11	10	9		2		4	5	6	7	8								1	3
15		12	13		10	9		2	3	4	5	6		8			14	1			7		
15		12	13			9				4	5	6		8	9		14	1			7		3
	14	12	13					2	3	6	5			8	9	10	11	1	15	4	7		
15	11		13		10	9	1		3	6			8				14			4	7		
15		12	13	11	10	9		2	3	4	5	6		8			14			R68	7*	1	

Also Played: Thompson No 13 match 4, No 12 match 5; Scrivens No 8 matches 10, 12; Rosier No 11 matches 12, 14, 15*; Shortland No 5 match 17; Braithwaite No 10 matches 12, 15; James No 12 match 17

PROGRAMME DETAILS

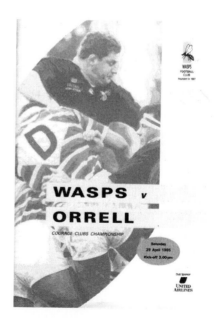

PAGES: 32
Plenty of reading. Colour only on the cover. Good paper.
Action photos included.

EDITOR: Kevin O'Shea

ADVERTISING RATES:
£720 per page b/w

WASPS F.C.

COURAGE LEAGUE STATISTICS

compiled by Steve McCormack

Season	Div	P	W	D	L	F	T	C	P	D	A	T	C	P	D	Most Points	Most Tries
1987-88	1	11	8	1	2	218	29	12	25	1	136	14	7	21	1	57 Nick Stringer	5 Mark Bailey. Simon Smith
1988-89	1	11	7	1	3	206	24	15	24	2	138	13	7	20	4	103 Rob Andrew	4 Mark Bailey
1989-90	1	11	9	0	2	250	39	17	20	0	106	9	5	19	1	90 Rob Andrew	7 Mark Bailey
1990-91	1	12	9	1	2	252	35	17	26	0	151	12	8	25	4	126 Rob Andrew	7 Chris Oti
1991-92	1	12	6	0	6	177	18	6	29	2	180	17	8	27	0	101 Steve Pilgrim	5 Chris Oti
1992-93	1	12	11	0	1	186	19	8	24	1	118	6	5	25	1	59 Alan Buzza	4 Phil Hopley. Chris Oti
1993-94	1	18	10	1	7	362	33	19	50	3	340	28	13	50	8	159 Rob Andrew	5 Damian Hopley
1994-95	1	18	13	0	5	470	58	30	37	3	313	24	14	53	2	135 Rob Andrew	7 Phil Hopley
TOTALS		105	73	4	28	2121	255	124	235	12	1482	123	67	240	21		

BIGGEST WIN — **Home:** 53-25 v Orrell 29.4.95 CL1 — **Away:** 57-26 v Harlequins 17.9.94 CL1

BIGGEST DEFEAT — **Home:** 12-24 v Bath 14.3.92 CL1 — **Away:** 24-42 v Orrell 30.4.94 CL1

MOST TRIES in a match — **For:** 9 v Coventry 13.4.88 Home CL1, Bedford 12.3.90 Away CL1, v Liverpool HH 20.4.91 Home CL1 — **Against:** 6 v Orrell 30.4.94 CL1

MOST CONSECUTIVE — **Wins:** 9 — **Defeats:** 4

MOST APPEARANCES — **Forward:** 70+1 Jeff Probyn 1987-95 — **Back:** 87 Steve Bates 1987-95

MOST CONSECUTIVE APPEARANCES 36 Richard Kinsey 29.2.92-30.4.94

CONSECUTIVE SCORING MATCHES — **Tries:** 3 Chris Oti, Simon Smith — **Points:** 16 Rob Andrew

	IN A SEASON	IN A CAREER	IN A MATCH
MOST POINTS	159 Rob Andrew 1993-94 CL1	681 Rob Andrew 1987-95	24 Rob Andrew v Bristol 27.4.91 Home CL1
MOST TRIES	7 Mark Bailey 1989-90 CL1 Chris Oti 1990-91 CL1 Phil Hopley 1994- 95 CL1	22 Chris Oti 1988-94	3 Simon Smith v Coventry 13.4.88 Home CL1 Mark Bailey v Moseley 19.11.88 Home CL1 v Gloucester 14.10.89 Home CL1 Graham Childs v Liverpool St H 20.4.91 Home CL1 Rob Andrew v Bristol 27.4.91 Home CL1 Chris Oti v Bristol 25.4.92 Away CL1 Damian Hopley v Sale 15.10.94 Home
MOST CONVERSIONS	19 Rob Andrew 1994-95 CL1	77 Rob Andrew 1987-95	6 Rob Andrew v Liverpool St H 20.4.91 Home CL1 v Bristol 27.4.91 Home CL1
MOST PENALTIES	38 Rob Andrew 1993-94 CL1	145 Rob Andrew 1987-95	7 Rob Andrew v Orrell 11.12.93 Home CL1
MOST DROP GOALS	3 Rob Andrew 1994-95 CL1	8 Rob Andrew 1987-95	1 on 12 occasions by 3 players Rob Andrew 8

WASPS F.C.

Name	Ht	Wt	Birthdate	Birthplace	Clubs	App	Pts	T	C	P	DG
BACKS											
Jon Ufton	6.0	13.10	31.1.74	Dulwich	Wasps	16+1	17	3	1	-	-
England U18 U16				Student							
Steve Pilgrim	5.10	14.0	26.10.67	Sdicup	Wasps	52	168	8	15	35	-
England U21				Sportswear							
Simon Hunter	6.2	15.0	8.7.62	Devon	Harlequins	3	8	2	-	-	-
				Marble Importer	Wasps	19	15	3	-	-	-
Nick Greenstock	6.3	15.0	3.11.73	Dubai	Wasps	9	35	7	-	-	-
England U21				Student							
Phil Hopley	6.2	14.7	6.10.66	London	London Irish						
				Doctor	Wasps	38	87	16	1	2	-
Graham Childs	6.0	13.7	3.4.68	Worthing	Northern						
England B					Wasps	61	55	12	-	-	-
Daman Hopley	6.2	14.11	12.4.70	London	Wasps	29	71	15	-	-	-
England (1) A				Money Broker							
Adrian Thompson	6.0	12.3	30.1.60	Chingford	Harlequins	23	-	-	-	-	-
				Accountant	Wasps	8	-	-	-	-	-
Rob Andrew	5.9	12.7	18.2.63	Richmond	Nottingham						
England (70)				Cht Surveyor	Wasps	71	681	16	77	145	8
Guy Gregory	6.0	13.4	13.1.69	Chalfont	Nottingham	48	331	2	27	70	19
England A					Wasps	5	48	-	6	12	-
Chris Braithwaite	6.0	13.0	26.12.71		Windsor						
				Student	Wasps	5	52	3	5	8	1
Steve Bates	5.10	13.0	4.3.63	Merthyr	Wasps	87	28	6	-	-	-
England (1) A				Teacher							
Andy Gomarsall	5.10	13.8	24.1.74	Durham	Bedford						
England U18 U16				Student	Wasps	2+2	5	1	—	-	-
FORWARDS											
Garry Holmes	5.11	16.0	7.7.65	Hampstead	Wasps	60	5	1	-	-	-
England A											
Ian Dunston	5.10	17.0	11.6.68	Essex	Wasps	30	13	3	-	-	-
Darren Molloy	6.2	11.7	31.8.72	London	Wasps	14	-	-	-	-	-
England U21				Student							
Jeff Probyn	5.10	15.7	27.4.56	London	Richmond						
England (37)				Repo Furniture	Wasps	70	9	2	-	-	-
Nick Popplewell	5.10	18.0	6.4.64	Dublin	Graystone						
Ireland (33)				Money Broker	Wasps	6	-	-	-	-	-
Kevin Dunn	5.10	14.2	5.6.65	Gloucester	Gloucester						
England A B				Builder	Wasps	37	10	2	-	-	-
Paul Delaney	5.8	15.7	7.4.71	London	Wasps	12+5	10	2	-	-	-
Matt Greenwood	6.6	17.5	25.9.64	Leeds	Nottingham	27	4	1	-	-	-
England A U21				Surveyor	Wasps	47	15	3	-	-	-
Norm Hadley	6.7	20.0	2.12.64	Winnipeg	UBC Old Boys						
Canada				Money Broker	Wasps	14	-	-	-	-	-
Richard Kinsey	6.5	18.7	5.2.64	Barnett	Wasps	53+2	15	3	-	-	-
				R.F.U. Y.D.G.							
Steve Shortland	6.7	17.10	12.4.68	Sheffield	Harlequins	5	4	1	-	-	-
England U21				Teacher	Wasps	12	15	3	-	-	-
Lawrence Dallaglio	6.4	15.7	10.5.72	London	Wasps	32+4	35	7	-	-	-
England A U21				Student							
Chris Wilkins	6.3	16.0	3.7.71	Farnborough	Wasps	16	10	2	-	-	-
Dean Ryan	6.6	17.7	22.6.66	Tuxford	Saracens						
England (3) A B				Banking	Wasps	63	41	9	-	-	-
Mike White	6.1	15.8	30.3.66	Poole	Wasps	59	36	8	-	-	-
				Sportswear							

BACKS: Shane Rosier (3 apps), Aaron Jones (1app, 1 try) and FORWARD: Peter Scrivener (3 apps) also played.

WASPS F.C.

Repton Avenue, Sudbury, Nr. Wembley, Middlesex HA0 3DW

Telephone: 0181 902 4220
Fax: 0181 900 2659

Total Capacity: 4,500
Seated: 1,350
Standing: 3,150
Simple Directions to Ground: No change from last year
Nearest Railway Station: Sudbury Town Station on Piccadilly line
Car Parking: 500
Season Tickets: Adults £75.00 OAPs £35
Match Prices:
Membership: Seniors £25.00 Juniors £12.00
Training Nights: Tuesday Wednesday Thursday

ALL TIME TOP TEN COURAGE LEAGUE RECORDS

APPEARANCES		POINTS	
87	Steve Bates	681	Rob Andrew
71	Rob Andrew	168	Steve Pilgrim
70	Jeff probyn	95	Chris Oti
63	Dean Ryan	87	Phil Hopley
61	Graham Childs	72	Mark Bailey
60+1	Gary Holmes	72	Simon Smith
59	Mike White	71	Damian Hopley
53+2	Richard Kinsey	62	Alan Buzza
52	Steve Pilgrim	57	Nick Stringer
48	Fran Clough	55	Graham Childs

MOST POINTS: 681 Rob Andrew

Season	Apps	Points	Tries	Cons	Pens	D G
1987-88	8	39	2	2	8	1
1988-89	10	103	2	13	21	2
1989-90	10	90	4	10	18	-
1990-91	12	126	4	16	26	-
1991-92	1	-	-	-	-	-
1992-93	5	29	-	1	8	1
1993-94	13	159	2	16	38	1
1994-95	12	135	2	19	26	3
Total	71	681	16	77	145	8

MOST TRIES: 22 Chris Oti

Season	Appearances	Tries
1988-89	4	3
1990-91	5	7
1991-92	11	5
1992-93	11	4
1993-94	7	3
Total	38	22

MOST APPEARANCES: 87 Steve Bates

Season	Appearances
1987-88	7
1988-89	10
1989-90	11
1990-91	5
1991-92	11
1992-93	12
1993-94	15
1994-95	16
Total	87

WEST HARTLEPOOL R.F.C.

NICKNAME: "WEST"   **FOUNDED:** 1881

CLUB OFFICIALS

Chairman
Bob Bateman
Club Secretary
Tony Savage
17 Greenbank Court, Hartlepool,
Cleveland TS26 0HH
Tel (H&W) 01429 273187
Fixtures Secretary
Dave Butcher
55 Arncliffe Gardens, Hartlepool,
Cleveland
Tel (H) 01429 236886
(W) 01325 300616
Press Officer
Steve Smith
Tel (H) 01429 272160
(W) 01191 265112

Review of the Season

When WEST HARTLEPOOL went into their final match at home to Northampton they were in an unexpected position of comparative luxury as defeat would only have meant survival for the visitors if Harlequins lost at Gloucester, whereas wins in their penultimate two matches – at home to high-flying Sale and at struggling Bristol – had been insurance against relegation for the home club.

This was just as well and the irony was that Northampton achieved their away win but still descended because Harlequins won at Kingsholm. Survival was consolation for a nail-biting season, not enhanced by cup success as the Pilkington Cup campaign ended abruptly at the first hurdle – an emphatic 28-7 victory for hosts Orrell.

Backroom problems did not help and the departures of hooker Mitchell and No8 Watson to Harlequins early in the saeson did morale no good, but matters could be better in the new season with the regular availability of Scotland's Rob Wainwright and Derrick Patterson and some more than useful forwards who have been nurtured in their own backyard – Lancaster, Westgarth, Brown and Evans among them. Add in a most promising fullback in Stimpson and the prolific wing Owen Evans and a further struggle is by no means inevitable if they can manage to start well.

The North East has as much right to a good side as London and West Hartlepool are the best flag-wavers in that region, although they will miss lock John Dixon – a most admirable example in dedication to everyone and superb servant to the club.

Back: Dave Rusby, Steve McManners, Ashley Parker, Mike Shelley, Dave Mitchell, John Stabler, Troy Jacques, John Dixon, Kevin Westgarth, Alan Brown, Paul Evans, Tim Herbert, Glyn Evans, Paul Beal, Phil Lancaster. Front: Kevan Oliphant, Tony Elwine, Steve Cook, Steve Jones, Tim Stimson, Paul Hodder (Capt), Owen Evans, Derrick Patterson, Stuart Kneale, Rob Wainwright
Colours: Red, White, Green   **Change Colours**: Blue, White

WEST HARTLEPOOL R.F.C.

COURAGE LEAGUE
MATCH DETAILS 1994-95

No	Date	Opponents	Ven	Result		Scorers
1	Sep 10	Orrell	H	L	17-19	Evans (T) Oliphant (4P)
2	Sep 17	Gloucester	A	L	12-48	Oliphant (4P)
3	Sep 24	Wasps	H	W	20-15	Stabler (T) Emmerson (T) Oliphant (2C 2P)
4	Oct 1	Harlequins	A	L	10-20	Hodder (T) Oliphant (P C)
5	Oct 8	Leicester	A	L	16-33	Stabler (T) Oliphant (1C 3P)
6	Oct 15	Bath	H	L	18-20	Watson (T) Cooke (T) Hodder (T) Stimpson (P)
7	Oct 22	Sale	A	L	7-22	Stimpson (T) Oliphant (C)
8	Oct 29	West Hartlepool	H	W	47-11	Watson (2T) Hodder (T) Evans (T) Brown (T) Elwine (T) Stimpson (T 3C 2P)
9	Nov 5	Northampton	A	L	14-25	Whitaker (T) Hodder (T) Stimpson (2C)
10	Jan 7	Orrell	A	D	22-22	Hodder (T) Stimpson (C 5P)
11	Jan 14	Gloucester	A	W	22-21	Jones (T) Mitchell (T) Elwine (T) Stimpson (2C P)
12	Feb 11	Wasps	A	L	22-33	Herbert (T) Stimpson (1C 5P)
13	Mar 4	Harlequins	H	W	10-8	Brown (T) Jones (T)
14	Mar 25	Leicester	H	L	6-12	Stimpson (2P)
15	Apr 8	Bath	A	L	17-53	Brown (T) Cook (T) Elwine (T) Oliphant (C)
16	Apr 15	Sale	H	W	23-17	Jaques (T) Cook (T) Evans (T) Stimpson (2P 1C)
17	Apr 22	Bristol	A	W	17-12	O Evans (T) Cook (T) Stimson (2C 1P)
18	Apr 29	Northampton	H	L	12-21	Cook (T) Evans (T) Stimpson (C)

Courage League Records 1994-95

League Debuts: Phil New, Stuart Kneale, Matthew Emmerson, Mike Shelley, Derrick Patterson, Rob Wainwright, Kevin Whitaker, Tim Stimpson, Tim Herber, Paul Beal, Chris Murphy, Stephen Jones, Troy Jaques, James Whitaker, Steve Cook made full debut after 3 games as replacement
Players used: 33
2 Ever Presents: Tony Elwine, Paul Hodder
Most appearances: 90 John Dixon

- 4th highest try scorers in the division

- Did double over Bristol

- Owen Evans outscored Dave Cooke 4 tries to 1 to join Cooke as the side's leading all time try scorers

	Tries	App	Strike Rate
Owen Evans	29	79	2.72
Dave Cooke	29	75	2.58

- John Dixon passes Phil Lancaster's record on league appearances. Dixon finishes the season with 90, 3 ahead of Lancaster

- Steve Cook equals Owen Evan's record of scoring tries in 4 consecutive league matches

- John Stabler extended his club scoring record by 10 points with 2 tries, while Kevan Oliphant moved into second place on West Hartlepool's all time list

	Pts	T	C	P	D	App	Ave
John Stabler	579	11	76	118	8	85	6.81
Kevan Oliphant	176	5	16	37	4	76	2.31

WEST HARTLEPOOL R.F.C.

MATCH BY MATCH PLAYERS BY POSITION

Oliphant	Evans	Elwine	Hodder	Cooke D	Stabler	Wrigley	Lancaster	Mitchell S	Beal	Dixon	Westgarth	Mitchell D	Brown	Watson	Cook S	Stimpson	Rusby	Jones	Herbert	Patterson	Shellet	Wainwright	Whittaker K
15	13	12	11	10	9	1		2		4	5	6	7	8									
15	13	12	11	10	9						5	4	7		12	3			8				
15	13	12	11	10				2		4	5	2	7	8			1			9	3		
15	12	13	11	10				2		4	5		7	8			1			9	3	6	
15	13	12	11	10				2		4	5	6	7	8			1			9	3		14*
	13	12	11	10				2		4	5	6	7	8	9	15	1		3				14
11	13	12		10				2		4	5	6	7	8	9	15	1		3				14
	14	13	12	10			1	2		4	5	6		8		15				9	3	7	11
11	12	13			9		1		3	4*	5	6	7			15		14	2	8			10
11	13	12			9		1		3	4		6	7			15		14	2	8			10
	14	13	12				1		3	4		6	7			15		11	2	9	8		10
	14	13	12		9		1		3	4	5	6	7			15		11	2				10
	14	13	12				1		3	4		6	7			15		11	2	9	8		
15	14	13	12				1		3	4	5		7	8		15		11	2				
	14	13	12				1		3	4	5	6	7	8	9			11	2				10
	14	13	12				1		3	4		6	7		9	15		11	2				10
	14	13	12				1		3	4	5		7		9	15		11	2				10

Also Played: Kneale No 2 match 2; New No 3 match 1, No 1 match 2; Emmerson No 6 matches 2, 3, R18 match 4; Evans G No 14 matches 1, 2, 3, 4; Evans P No 8 match 2, No 6 match 15, No 5 match 17, No 8 match 18; Murphy R70 match 10, No 5 match 11; Parker No 10, matches 14,15; Whittaker No 6 match 18

PROGRAMME DETAILS

PRICE: £1.00

PAGES: 28

Good paper with attractive colour. Four pages of colour and any little original copy or reading matter

ADVERTISING RATES: Please contact Commercial Director

WEST HARTLEPOOL R.F.C.

COURAGE LEAGUE STATISTICS

compiled by Steve McCormack

Season	Div	P	W	D	L	F	T	C	P	D	A	T	C	P	D	Most Points	Most Tries
1987-88	3	11	10	0	1	249	33	12	27	4	105	11	5	16	1	83 John Stabler	6 Owen Evans
1988-89	3	11	5	1	5	164	19	11	18	4	133	18	8	14	1	60 John Stabler	8 Dave Cooke
1989-90	3	11	5	2	4	175	20	10	23	2	120	8	4	21	1	65 Gary Armstrong	5 Dave Cooke
1990-91	3	12	10	1	1	282	42	24	21	1	90	13	4	10	0	87 John Stabler	9 John Wrigley
1991-92	2	12	11	0	1	244	33	17	26	0	89	12	4	11	0	118 John Stabler	7 John Wrigley
1992-93	1	12	3	0	9	149	14	8	21	0	236	24	13	28	2	89 John Stabler	3 Alan Brown
1993-94	2	18	13	2	3	389	39	25	43	5	271	22	13	36	9	103 John Stabler	7 John Wrigley
1994-95	1	18	6	1	11	312	35	19	33	-	412	45	29	38	5	93 Tim Stimpson	5 Paul Hodder
TOTALS		105	63	7	35	1964	235	126	212	16	1462	153	80	174	19		

BIGGEST WIN — **Home:** 48-20 v Otley 15.1.94 CL2   **Away:** 43-6 v Birmingham 6.2.88 CL3

BIGGEST DEFEAT — **Home:** 10-38 Bath 27.3.93 CL1   **Away:** 9-55 v Northampton 3.4.93 CL1

MOST TRIES in a match — **For:** 8 v Birmingham 6.2.88 CL3; 8 v Broughton Park 9.3.91 CL3   **Against:** 8 v Northampton 3.4.93 CL1

MOST CONSECUTIVE — **Wins:** 9   **Defeats:** 5

MOST APPEARANCES — **Forward:** 89 John Dixon 1987-95   **Back:** 85 John Stabler 1987-95

MOST CONSECUTIVE APPEARANCES — 64 John Stabler 11.7.89-26.3.94

CONSECUTIVE SCORING MATCHES — **Tries:** 4 Owen Evans, Steve Cook   **Points:** 36 John Stabler

	IN A SEASON	IN A CAREER	IN A MATCH
MOST POINTS	118 John Stabler 1991-92 CL3	579 John Stabler 1987-95	23 John Stabler v Broughton Park 9.3.91 Home CL3
MOST TRIES	9 John Wrigley 1990-91 CL3	29 Dave Cooke & Owen Evans 1987-95	3 Owen Evans v Nuneaton 23.4.88 Home CL3 Peter Robinson v Vale of Lune 2.3.91 Away CL3 Jonathan Wrigley v Moseley 14.12.91 Home CL2
MOST CONVERSIONS	19 John Stabler 1990-91 CL3	76 John Stabler 1987-95	6 Jihn Stabler v Broughton Park 9.3.91 Home CL3
MOST PENALTIES	26 John Stabler 1991-92 CL2	118 John Stabler 1987-95	6 John Stabler v Met Police 6.1.88 Away CL3
MOST DROP GOALS	3 John Stabler 1988-89 CL3	8 John Stabler 1987-95	2 Kevan Oliphant v Vale of Lune 7.11.88 Away CL3 John Stabler v Sheffield 19.11.88 Home CL3

WEST HARTLEPOOL F.C.

Name	Ht	Wt	Birthdate	Birthplace	Clubs	App	Pts	T	C	P	DG
BACKS											
Kevan Oliphant	5.8	12.0	11.1.67	Hartlepool	W. Hartlepool	76+1	176	5	16	37	4
Tim Stimpson	6.3	14.3	10.9.73	Wakefield	W. Hartlepool	12	93	2	13	19	-
England A U21 U16											
Glyn Evans	5.11	13.7	19.5.70	Hartlepool	W. Hartlepool	13	5	1	-	-	-
Dave Cooke	5.7	12.7	7.8.59	Middlesborough	W. Hartlepool	75	124	29	-	-	-
Bill Ridley	6.0	12.8	5.1.65	Gateshead	W. Hartlepool	5+1	-	-	-	-	-
Owen Evans	5.10	13.8	22.10.65	Hartlepool	W. Hartlepool	79	126	29	-	-	-
Stephen Jones	6.0	12.9	9.6.75	Hartlepool	W. Hartlepool	9	10	2	-	-	-
Kevin Whitaker	5.10	12.7	28.9.69	Kendal	Heriots						
					W. Hartlepool	12	5	1	-	-	-
Tony Elwing	6.2	15.0	23.11.70	Hartlepool	W. Hartlepool	22	15	3	-	-	-
Paul Hodder	5.10	13.10	13.4.65	Hamilton (NZ)	W. Hartlepool	69+1	65	12	-	2	1
John Stabler	6.2	14.4	5.2.63	Hartlepool	W. Hartlepool	85	529	11	76	118	8
Ashley Parker	6.0	13.0	30.4.71	Hartlepool	W. Hartlepool	6	12	-	-	2	2
Jonathan Wrigley	5.9	12.7	10.12.66	Hartlepool	Hartlepool R						
					W. Hartlepool	53	99	23	-	-	-
Steve Cook	5.8	12.4	16.12.73	St Helens	Liverpool St H						
					W. Hartlepool	6+3	20	4	-	-	-
Derrick Patterson	5.8	12.11	6.7.68	Hawick	Edinburgh Acc						
Scotland (2)					W. Hartlepool	7	-	-	-	-	-
FORWARDS											
Phil Lancaster	6.1	16.4	15.1.64	Hartlepool	W. Hartlepool	87	13	3	-	-	-
Phil New	5.11	16.8	8.4.67	Didcot	Henley						
					W. Hartlepool	2	-	-	-	-	-
David Rusby	6.0	16.10	2.3.71	North Shields	Percy Park						
					W. Hartlepool	3+1	-	-	-	-	-
Mike Shelley	6.1	17.10	13.4.74	Leeds	West Park						
					W. Hartlepool	7	-	-	-	-	-
Paul Beal	5.11	16.1	10.2.68	Redcar	Redcar						
					W. Hartlepool	9	-	-	-	-	-
Simon Mitchell	5.9	15.5	23.11.65	Saltburn	Acklam						
					W. Hartlepool	82	32	7	-	-	-
Stuart Kneale	5.10	13.4	30.4.74	Leeds	Morley						
					W. Hartlepool	1	-	-	-	-	-
Tim Herbert	6.0	16.8	28.9.67	London	W. Hartlepool	9	5	1	-	-	-
John Dixon	6.5	18.7	5.10.61	Middlesborough	Acklam						
					W. Hartlepool	89	14	3	-	-	-
Kevin Westgarth	6.7	17.0	6.5.61	Durham	Tynedale						
					W. Hartlepool	48	-	-	-	-	-
David Mitchell	6.4	15.0	10.10.71	Peterborough	Harrogate	1	-	-	-	-	-
					W. Hartlepool	41+4	5	1	-	-	-
Paul Evans	6.3	15.10	3.1.67	Bridlington	W. Hartlepool	48+2	23	5	-	-	-
Alan Brown	6.2	15.0	20.9.67	Stockton	Stockton						
					W. Hartlepool	67+1	64	14	-	-	-
Matthew Emmerson	5.10	13.4	24.12.72	Stockley	W. Hartlepool	2+1	5	1	-	-	-
Rob Wainwright	6.5	15.4	22.3.65	Perth	Edinburgh Acc						
Scotland (17)					W. Hartlepool	6	-	-	-	-	-
Chris Murphy	6.8	18.4	2.2.76	Hull	W. Hartlepool	1+1	-	-	-	-	-
Troy Jacques	6.5	17.4	11.3.72	Sydney	W. Hartlepool	6	5	1	-	-	-
James Whittaker	6.4	15.8	8.3.14	Lincoln	Tynedale						
					W. Hartlepool	1	-	-	-	-	-
Mike Watson	6.7	17.4	2.7.65	Sunderland	W. Hartlepool	27	25	5	-	-	-

WEST HARTLEPOOL R.F.C.

Brierton Lane, Hartlepool, Cleveland TS25 2DR

Telephone: 01429 272640 (Clubhouse) 01429 233149 (Office)
Fax: 01429 261857

Total Capacity: 6,100
Seated: 600
Standing: 5,500
Simple Directions to Ground: From A1 or A19 take A689 to Hartlepool. Within a mile of first houses turn left into Brierton Lane (opposite Travellers Rest PH). Ground 800 yds on left after Hospital/Nursing Home
Nearest Railway Station: Hartlepool (2 miles)
Car Parking: 200
Season Tickets: Adults £45
Match Prices: Adults £8 (£6 ground only) Children/OAPs £3
Membership: Seniors £18 Juniors £7
Training Nights: Tuesdays & Thursdays (Seniors) Mondays & Wednesdays (WLTS) Sunday (Junior & Minis)

ALL TIME TOP TEN COURAGE LEAGUE RECORDS

APPEARANCES		POINTS	
90	John Dixon	579	John Stabler
87	Phil Lancaster	176	Kevan Oliphant
85	John Stabler	126	Owen Evans
82+1	Simon Mitchell	124	Dave Cooke
79	Owen Evans	99	John Wrigley
76	Kevan Oliphant	96	Glyn Armstrong
75	Dave Cooke	93	Tim Stimpson
70	Paul Whitelock	72	Peter Robinson
69+1	Paul Hodder	65	Paul Hodder
67	Alan Brown	64	Alan Brown

MOST POINTS:
579 John Stabler

Season	Apps	Points	Tries	Cons	Pens	D G
1987-88	7	83	1	5	22	1
1988-89	8	60	-	9	11	3
1989-90	11	27	-	3	6	1
1990-91	11	89	3	19	12	1
1991-92	12	118	2	16	26	-
1992-93	12	89	2	8	21	-
1993-94	15	103	1	16	20	2
1994-95	9	10	2	-	-	-
Total	85	579	11	76	118	8

NATIONAL LEAGUE TWO

SEASON 1994-95

NATIONAL LEAGUE TWO STATISTICS 1994/95

PLAYING RECORD AND POINTS BREAKDOWN

	P	W	D	L	Pts	HOME W	HOME D	HOME L	HOME Pts	AWAY W	AWAY D	AWAY L	AWAY Pts
Saracens	18	15	1	2	31	8	1	0	17	7	0	2	14
Wakefield	18	12	1	5	25	7	0	2	14	5	1	3	11
Newcastle	18	8	2	8	18	5	1	3	11	3	1	5	7
London South	18	9	0	9	18	6	0	3	12	3	0	6	6
London Irish	18	9	0	9	18	7	0	2	14	2	0	7	4
Moseley	18	8	1	9	17	5	0	4	10	3	1	5	7
Nottingham	18	8	1	9	17	5	1	3	11	3	0	6	6
Waterloo	18	8	0	10	16	4	0	5	8	4	0	5	8
Fylde	18	8	0	10	16	4	0	5	8	4	0	5	8
Coventry	18	2	0	16	4	2	0	7	4	0	0	9	0

RESULTS

		1	2	3	4	5	6	7	8	9	10
1	Coventry		17-21	36-30	5-19	11-22	19-15	6-19	16-33	14-15	17-22
2	Fylde	22-8		27-12	10-31	10-6	6-12	33-14	15-37	8-11	12-16
3	London Irish	25-8	23-12		25-13	47-19	32-22	24-22	6-16	3-33	23-3
4	London Scottish	30-0	28-3	15-27		29-24	24-13	17-18	22-7	24-21	13-25
5	Moseley	19-8	6-8	42-16	24-15		6-3	19-12	9-11	11-16	9-25
6	Newcastle Gosforth	38-22	45-14	19-15	10-18	37-10		27-6	11-17	15-15	33-16
7	Nottingham	23-7	9-10	22-11	23-8	9-9	18-33		9-17	29-25	28-11
8	Saracens	38-0	18-7	35-22	27-17	17-15	16-16	32-7		10-3	27-5
9	Wakefield	19-14	24-13	25-3	42-19	17-22	9-21	22-17	17-8		21-12
10	Waterloo	26-5	12-19	22-19	17-9	12-27	18-13	11-14	16-23	18-19	

WEEK BY WEEK POSITIONS

	10/9	17/9	24/9	1/10	8/10	15/10	22/10	29/10	5/11	7/1	14/1	11/2	4/3	25/3	8/4	15/4	22/4	29/4
Coventry	6	9	9	9	9	9	10	10	10	10	10	10	10	10	10	10	10	10
Fylde	1	8	10	10	10	10	9	8	9	9	9	9	9	7	8	8	7	9
London Irish	2	5	7	5	6	4	5	5	4	2	5	3	4	3	5	5	5	5
London Scot	9	10	6	4	5	5	6	4	6	6	7	7	6	5	4	4	4	4
Moseley	7	4	2	8	4	6	8	9	8	8	8	8	8	9	7	7	8	6
Newcastle G	8	3	5	3	3	3	3	3	5	5	4	2	3	4	3	3	3	3
Nottingham	10	6	8	7	8	8	7	7	7	7	6	6	7	8	9	9	9	7
Saracens	4	2	3	1	1	1	1	1	1	1	1	1	1	1	1	1	1	1
Wakefield	5	7	4	6	7	7	4	6	3	3	2	4	2	2	2	2	2	2
Waterloo	3	1	1	2	2	2	2	2	2	4	3	5	5	6	6	6	6	8

NATIONAL LEAGUE TWO 1994-95 POINTS SCORING RECORDS

	Tries	by Forward	by Back	Tries in no matches	No tries against	Players used	Replace-ments	Ever presents
Sarecens	43	23	20	17	5	33	12	2
Wakefield	29	5	24	15	5	27	6	2
Newcastle Gosforth	37	17	20	14	6	28	5	4
London Scottish	30	6	24	12	3	42	10	1
London Irish	36	13	23	15	4	33	11	—
Moseley	20	9	11	12	3	34	10	—
Nottingham	24	10	14	13	2	31	5	3
Waterloo	20	6	14	13	3	33	4	1
Fylde	25	5	20	14	6	30	13	3
Coventry	16	3	13	15	—	37	6	—

FOR

	PTS	T	C	P	D	HOME PTS	T	C	P	D	AWAY PTS	T	C	P	D
Saracens	389	43	21	38	6	220	25	13	20	3	169	18	8	18	3
Wakefield	354	29	16	58	1	196	16	10	32	—	158	13	6	26	1
Newcastle Gosforth	373	37	22	46	2	225	24	12	25	2	148	13	10	21	—
London Scottish	351	30	18	44	11	192	17	9	24	9	149	13	9	20	2
London Irish	363	36	18	46	3	208	20	12	26	2	155	16	6	20	1
Moseley	299	20	14	54	3	145	8	6	28	3	154	12	8	28	—
Nottingham	299	24	13	50	1	170	14	8	28	—	129	10	5	21	2
Waterloo	287	20	8	52	5	152	9	4	30	3	135	11	4	22	2
Fylde	250	25	13	28	5	143	16	9	14	1	107	9	4	14	4
Coventry	213	16	5	35	6	141	9	3	25	5	72	7	2	10	1
	3178	280	148	452	42										

AGAINST

	PTS	T	C	P	D	HOME PTS	T	C	P	D	AWAY PTS	T	C	P	D
Saracens	213	20	13	28	1	92	11	8	7	—	121	9	5	21	1
Wakefield	261	18	9	47	4	129	10	5	22	1	132	8	4	25	3
Newcastle Gosforth	281	20	8	51	4	133	10	4	25	—	148	10	4	26	4
London Scottish	321	28	17	45	4	138	11	7	21	2	173	17	10	24	2
London Irish	381	31	17	52	12	148	13	7	21	2	233	18	10	31	10
Moseley	303	33	15	32	4	114	11	4	16	1	189	22	11	16	3
Nottingham	322	26	12	51	5	131	10	6	21	2	191	16	6	30	3
Waterloo	331	33	14	42	4	148	15	5	18	3	183	18	9	24	1
Fylde	329	28	15	53	—	147	15	6	20	—	182	13	9	33	—
Coventry	436	43	28	50	5	196	16	10	28	4	240	27	18	22	1
	3178	280	148	452	42										

NATIONAL LEAGUE TWO 1994-95
Most Tries, Penalties, Grop Goals, Conversions

LEADING TRY SCORERS

8	Tony Penn	Newcastle Gosforth
7	John Green	Saracens
7	Richard Thompson	Wakefield
6	Peter Harries	Saracens
6	Rob Henderson	London Irish
5	Greg Anderton	Fylde
5	MarkDouglas	Coventry
5	Steve Gough	Fylde
5	Brendan Hanavan	Fylde
5	Martin Corry	Newcastle Gosforth
5	Ray Hennessy	London Irish
5	Ian Barclay	Fylde
4	Neil Ryan	Waterloo
4	Tony Diprose	Saracens
4	Paul Butler	Saracens
4	Steve Wright	Waterloo
4	Dave Millard	London Scottish
4	Fraser Harrold	London Scottish
4	Andy Smallwood	Nottingham
4	Ross Wilkinson	Newcastle Gosforth
4	B Shepherd	Coventry

DROP GOALS

6	Andy Lee	Saracens
5	Ian Barclay	Fylde
4	John Steele	London Scottish
4	Murray Walker	London Scottish
3	Neil Ryan	Waterloo
3	Simon Hodgkinson	Moseley
2	Kevin Troup	London Scottish
2	Richard Angell	Coventry
2	Mark Lakey	Coventry
2	Owen Cobbe	London Irish

CONVERSIONS

21	Simon Mason	Newcastle Gosforth
21	Andy Tunningley	Saracens
16	Michael Corcoran	London Irish
16	Mike Jackson	Wakefield
12	Simon Hodgkinson	Moseley
11	Andy Parker	Fylde
8	Steve Swindells	Waterloo
6	Ian Stent	Nottingham
6	Matt Gallagher	Nottingham
6	John Steele	London Scottish
4	Murray Walker	London Scottish
3	Richard Angell	Coventry
3	C Russell	London Scottish

PENALTIES

57	Mike Jackson	Wakefield
48	Steve Swindells	Waterloo
45	Simon Mason	Newcastle Gosforth
41	Simon Hodgkinson	Moseley
38	Michael Corcoran	London Irish
35	Andy Tunningley	Saracens
26	Richard Angell	Coventry
25	Ian Stent	Nottingham
25	Matt Gallagher	Nottingham
18	John Steele	London Scottish
13	Murry Walker	London Scottish
8	C Russell	London Scottish
6	Owen Cobbe	London Irish
4	Fraser Harrold	London Scottish

NATIONAL LEAGUE TWO 1994-95

INDIVIDUAL TOP POINT SCORERS

		PTS	T	C	P	D
Mike Jackson	Wakefield	213	2	16	57	—
Simon Mason	Newcastle Gosforth	193	1	21	45	—
Michael Corcoran	London Irish	164	3	16	38	1
Andy Tunningley	Saracens	162	3	21	35	—
Steve Swindells	Waterloo	160	—	8	48	—
Simon Hodgkinson	Moseley	156	—	12	41	3
Ian Stent	Nottingham	97	2	6	25	—
Matt Gallagher	Nottingham	92	1	6	25	—
Andy Parker	Fylde	91	—	11	23	—
Richard Angell	Coventry	90	—	3	26	2
John Steele	London Scottish	78	—	6	18	4
Murray Walker	London Scottish	74	3	4	13	4
Alistair Kerr	Moseley	53	2	2	13	—
Ian Barclay	Fylde	43	4	1	2	5
Tony Penn	Newcastle Gosforth	40	8	—	—	—
Steve Gough	Fylde	36	5	1	3	—
Neil Ryan	Waterloo	35	4	—	2	3
John Green	Saracens	35	7	—	—	—
Richard Thompson	Wakefield	35	7	—	—	—
Fraser Harrold	London Scottish	34	4	1	4	—
Andy Lee	Saracens	32	1	—	1	6
Peter Harries	Saracens	30	6	—	—	—
Rob Henderson	London Irish	30	6	—	—	—
C Russell	London Scottish	30	—	3	8	—

Wakefield's top try scorer Richard Thompson breaks through Paul Bell's tackle in the Courage League Two match at College Grove which Wakefield won 25-3

Photo: Gordon Bunney

NATIONAL LEAGUE TWO

STATISTICS 1987-95

NATIONAL LEAGUE TWO RESULTS

1987-88

		1	2	3	4	5	6	7	8	9	10	11	12
1	Bedford		6-0	16-25		33-25		21-9	6-6	17-16		15-3	
2	Blackheath					·			22-7	19-12	3-4		12-48
3	Gosforth		26-8				14-22		12-14	N/P	12-10		
4	Headingley	7-13	21-9	26-7						38-3		12-12	3-12
5	Liverpool St. Helens		15-0	15-10	6-6		14-0	10-3				3-13	
6	London Irish	12-12	16-12		12-32			3-6			17-15		9-27
7	London Scottish		18-9	13-8	6-22					50-3			
8	London Welsh				10-18	10-27	6-13	24-24					
9	Northampton					9-13	15-13		14-16		3-16	0-22	
10	Richmond	28-25			14-13	3-13		9-6	26-22				3-22
11	Rosslyn Park		14-8	14-3			20-3	15-6	16-15		20-12		
12	Saracens	33-4		7-7		10-13		34-0	7-23	22-6		6-6	

1988-89

		1	2	3	4	5	6	7	8	9	10	11	12
1	Bedford		19-99				15-21	9-6	18-6		15-3		
2	Blackheath	12-13			34-10	21-3					31-3	12-6	12-24
3	Coventry		18-12		19-12	7-18				22-10		7-3	
4	Gosforth	16-17				29-14		16-14	34-26		16-4		9-27
5	Headingley	7-7					48-9	22-10	24-0		9-12		3-7
6	London Irish		21-22	6-29	35-7				24-19	18-10		18-18	
7	London Scottish		6-3				16-21			3-3		16-17	
8	London Welsh		15-15	14-21				29-10		0-22		9-16	
9	Northampton	42-3	15-7		13-12	19-7						15-12	4-32
10	Richmond			12-3			18-18	12-32	14-3	15-12			10-27
11	Sale	15-15			23-15	15-24					50-9		10-12
12	Saracens	50-10		13-6			20-3	19-9	37-4				

1989-90

		1	2	3	4	5	6	7	8	9	10	11	12
1	Blackheath		16-21				28-18	9-10	9-37		0-21		
2	Coventry					13-13	18-25		15-13	21-18	18-10		22-12
3	Gosforth	12-12	0-16				6-27	15-22			22-18		
4	Headingley	31-12	30-22	17-10				15-3			3-9		
5	Liverpool St. Helens	16-3		16-11	10-4			13-13			22-15		10-3
6	London Irish				25-19	12-23			27-19	12-36			24-33
7	Northampton		24-18				33-21		6-4	12-6	41-25		
8	Plymouth Albion			28-13	9-20	20-3				11-12	21-16		33-28
9	Richmond	15-15		36-3	86-8	6-17					16-7		
10	Rugby			49-9	31-8	6-11	23-10			16-28			28-6
11	Sale	14-18	24-22				19-27	3-16	15-11		20-13		
12	Waterloo	10-19		25-7	9-6			6-12		13-23		12-9	

1990-91

		1	2	3	4	5	6	7	8	9	10	11	12	13
1	Bedford			7-9	16-10	18-19	21-16		10-9			10-10		
2	Blackheath	12-16					13-19	9-19		12-9		14-12	12-7	
3	Coventry		16-4		11-3	20-4			21-9		9-13			26-15
4	Headingley		16-15			9-10		7-18	31-6		11-20			16-13
5	London Irish		21-18					24-16	19-18		29-17		15-9	39-0
6	London Scottish			9-12	30-7	13-17			32-0		27-19			22-16
7	Newcastle/Gosforth	22-7		10-9			12-13			38-3		7-6	6-13	
8	Plymouth		13-3					12-3		19-13	6-28		15-9	13-21
9	Richmond	28-17		0-13	17-6	18-18	15-40					10-9		
10	Rugby	28-3	18-7					25-8		28-9			14-6	16-13
11	Sale			23-16	42-0	36-24	25-10		20-9		18-26			
12	Wakefield	27-0		32-10	17-9		21-9			20-3		13-10		
13	Waterloo	13-13	3-15					12-10		25-9		17-13	6-14	

1991-92

		1	2	3	4	5	6	7	8	9	10	11	12	13
1	Bedford		52-10					8-9	9-4			6-25	25-4	6-30
2	Blackheath			21-13	9-6		3-9	31-6		16-20			6-34	
3	Coventry	19-13				15-32			6-30		19-12	21-20		18-24
4	Liverpoool St. H.	6-22		0-19		4-41	6-49			11-38				0-32
5	London Scottish	38-0	36-16						16-11		40-13	31-4		7-6
6	Morley	19-12		12-16		12-13				12-13	9-13			13-21
7	Moseley			12-22	33-3	18-25	19-3			15-10	47-15			
8	Newcastle-Gosforth		39-0		76-4		60-12	20-26	54-21				37-6	
9	Plymouth Alb.	24-9		10-13	25-10	9-10	10-12				10-15			
10	Sale	16,6	10-14						19-15			37-3	3-17	13-15
11	Wakefield		20-6		34-25			14-9	8-18	22-7			24-18	
12	Waterloo			10-6	40-12	22-15	16-9	18-17		12-3				
13	West Hartlepool		21-8					27-4	13-7	21-4		7-0	27-9	

1992-93

		1	2	3	4	5	6	7	8	9	10	11	12	13
1	Bedford			30-15	24-12	25-10			15-9	22-16		9-9		
2	Blackheath	16-12						9-12	5-46		18-14	3-20	9-9	
3	Coventry		38-15		37-10	41-3	19-22			13-18				6-32
4	Fylde		9-9				15-15	5-32			9-22		7-27	14-15
5	Morley		8-23		10-10		6-13	13-36		6-28				12-27
6	Moseley	9-9	23-6					19-16			32-10		3-14	9-12
7	Newcastle/Gosforth	19-13		26-3					28-6		14-3	7-3	17-20	
8	Nottingham			16-10	19-8	78-0	9-5			17-12				14-9
9	Richmond		13-23		29-6		28-21	9-21					11-6	12-16
10	Rosslyn Park	13-16		32-10		43-24		6-18	24-18		18-8			
11	Sale			24-0	51-3	34-0	6-13		25-8	21-10				
12	Wakefield	27-3		8-0		16-15			22-9		20-15	6-12		
13	Waterloo	28-8	27-6					3-13			12-9	25-24	22-11	

NATIONAL LEAGUE TWO TABLES

1987-88

	P	W	D	L	F	A	Pts
Rosslyn Park	11	8	2	1	155	83	18
Liverpool St. H.	11	8	1	2	154	97	17
Saracens	11	7	2	2	228	86	16
Headingley	11	6	2	3	202	104	14
Bedford	11	6	2	3	152	139	14
Richmond	11	6	0	5	140	156	12
London Scottish	11	4	1	6	141	158	9
London Irish	11	4	1	6	120	177	9
London Welsh	11	3	2	6	153	185	8
Gosforth	10	2	1	7	99	129	5
Blackheath	11	2	0	9	102	187	4
Northampton	10	1	0	9	81	226	2

1988-89

	P	W	D	L	F	A	Pts
Saracens	11	11	0	0	288	80	22
Bedford	11	6	2	3	141	187	14
Northampton	11	5	2	4	195	152	12
Sale	11	6	0	5	150	143	12
Coventry	11	6	0	5	150	143	12
London Irish	11	5	2	4	194	222	12
Headingley	11	5	1	5	179	136	11
Blackheath	11	4	1	6	181	144	9
Richmond	11	4	1	6	112	216	9
Gosforth	11	4	0	7	176	246	8
London Scottish	11	3	1	7	146	160	7
London Welsh	11	1	1	9	125	235	3

1989-90

	P	W	D	L	F	A	Pts
Northampton	11	9	1	1	192	135	19
Liverpool St. H.	11	8	2	1	154	106	18
Richmond	11	7	1	3	282	135	15
Coventry	11	6	1	4	206	185	13
London Irish	11	6	0	5	228	247	12
Rugby	11	5	0	6	238	172	10
Plymouth Albion	11	5	0	6	206	164	10
Headingley	11	5	0	6	161	226	10
Sale	11	4	0	7	153	182	8
Blackheath	11	3	2	6	141	205	8
Waterloo	11	3	0	8	147	193	6
Gosforth	11	1	1	9	108	266	3

1990-91

	P	W	D	L	F	A	Pts
Rugby	12	10	0	2	252	146	20
London Irish	12	9	1	2	239	192	19
Wakefield	12	8	0	4	188	109	16
Coventry	12	8	0	4	172	129	16
London Scottish	12	7	0	5	240	178	14
Gosforth	12	6	0	6	169	140	12
Sale	12	5	1	6	224	156	11
Bedford	12	4	2	6	138	203	10
Waterloo	12	4	0	8	134	169	8
Blackheath	12	4	0	8	134	169	8
Plymouth Albion	12	4	0	8	129	210	8
Richmond	12	3	1	8	134	245	7
Headingley	12	3	0	9	125	215	6

1991-92

	P	W	D	L	F	A	PD	Pts
London Scottish	12	11	0	1	304	130	174	22
West Hartlepool	12	11	0	1	244	89	155	22
Waterloo	12	8	0	4	206	184	22	16
Newcastle Gosf'th	12	7	0	5	371	231	140	14
Wakefield	12	7	0	5	187	194	-7	14
Coventry	12	7	0	5	187	196	-9	14
Moseley	12	6	0	6	215	196	19	12
Sale	12	6	0	6	204	209	-5	12
Morley	12	4	0	8	171	202	-31	8
Bedford	12	4	0	8	168	204	-36	8
Blackheath	12	4	0	8	140	266	-126	8
Plymouth	12	3	0	9	153	209	-56	6
Liverpool St. H.	12	0	0	12	87	418	-331	0

1992-93

	P	W	D	L	F	A	PD	Pts
Newcastle Gosf'th	12	10	0	2	241	106	135	20
Waterloo	12	10	0	2	228	138	90	20
Wakefield	12	8	1	3	186	123	63	17
Nottingham	12	8	0	4	249	154	104	16
Sale	12	7	1	4	237	102	135	15
Moseley	12	6	2	4	184	150	34	14
Bedford	12	6	2	4	186	183	3	14
Rosslyn Park	12	5	0	7	209	199	10	10
Richmond	12	5	0	7	204	196	8	10
Blackheath	12	4	2	6	142	231	-89	10
Coventry	12	3	0	9	192	236	-44	6
Fylde	12	0	3	9	108	290	-182	3
Morley	12	0	1	11	107	374	-267	1

NATIONAL LEAGUE TWO STATISTICS 1993/94

PLAYING RECORD AND POINTS BREAKDOWN

	P	W	D	L	F	A	Pts	P	W	D	L	F	A	P	W	D	L	F	A
										HOME						AWAY			
Sale	18	13	2	3	438	160	28	9	0	0	0	292	79	9	0	0	0	146	81
W. Hartlepool	18	13	2	3	389	271	28	9	6	2	1	202	48	9	7	0	2	187	123
Saracens	18	11	1	6	299	238	23	9	7	0	2	138	78	9	4	1	4	161	160
Wakefield	18	8	3	7	347	240	19	9	5	1	3	200	127	9	3	2	4	147	113
Moseley	18	9	1	8	266	220	19	9	6	1	2	146	112	9	3	0	6	120	108
Nottingham	18	8	1	9	254	326	17	9	5	0	4	150	179	9	3	1	5	104	147
Waterloo	18	6	2	10	231	346	14	9	3	1	5	134	157	9	3	1	5	97	189
London Scottish	18	6	0	12	232	325	12	9	4	0	5	121	170	9	2	0	7	111	155
Rugby	18	5	1	12	186	302	11	9	5	0	4	87	130	9	0	1	8	99	172
Otley	18	4	1	13	235	449	9	9	2	1	6	84	140	9	2	0	7	151	309

RESULTS

		1	2	3	4	5	6	7	8	9	10
1	L. Scottish		16-8	21-14	3-11	22-11	3-12	12-37	11-37	9-18	24-22
2	Moseley	27-12		17-0	30-22	13-11	9-3	15-16	20-11	6-6	9-31
3	Nottingham	23-18	6-25		25-30	17-16	9-30	18-9	16-13	27-21	9-17
4	Otley	13-6	12-26	12-18		3-3	9-5	9-11	0-22	15-21	11-28
5	Rugby	7-5	6-3	16-14	19-10		8-21	6-30	16-12	3-8	6-27
6	Sale	28-12	13-16	41-7	88-9	16-3		52-3	11-11	15-6	28-12
7	Saracens	6-11	14-10	13-3	31-19	6-3	3-8		20-10	37-0	8-14
8	Wakefield	17-11	13-12	6-6	26-14	48-16	19-28	14-23		47-6	10-11
9	Waterloo	13-17	12-5	8-19	39-16	19-17	10-28	2-12	6-18		15-25
10	W. Hartlepool	21-19	16-15	13-23	48-20	28-19	11-11	22-20	13-13	30-11	

WEEK BY WEEK POSITIONS

	23/9	2/10	9/10	13/11	20/11	4/12	11/12	8/1	15/1	29/1	12/2	12/3	26/3	9/4	23/4	30/4
L. Scottish	7	8	7	8	7	8	9	9	10	10	10	10	10	10	9	8
Moseley	3	5	6	5	8	5	5	6	7	5	5	5	5	5	5	5
Nottingham	9	9	10	10	10	10	10	10	8	9	6	6	6	6	6	6
Otley	4	3	4	6	6	6	7	8	9	8	9	9	9	9	10	10
Rugby	8	6	8	9	9	9	8	5	6	7	7	8	8	8	8	9
Sale	1	2	2	3	2	2	2	3	2	2	2	2	2	2	1	1
Saracens	5	4	3	2	3	3	3	2	3	3	3	3	3	3	3	3
Wakefield	6	7	5	4	4	4	4	4	4	4	4	4	4	4	4	4
Waterloo	10	10	9	7	5	7	6	7	5	6	8	7	7	7	7	7
W Hartlepool	2	1	1	1	1	1	1	1	1	1	1	1	1	1	2	2

COURAGE CHAMPIONSHIP STATISTICS 1987–1995

LEAGUE TWO

	CHAMPIONS	RUNNERS-UP	RELEGATED
1987-88	Rosslyn Park	Liverpoool St Helens	None
1988-89	Saracens	Bedford	London Welsh London Scottish
1989-90	Northampton	Liverpool St Helens	None
1990-91	Rugby	London Irish	Richmond Headingley
1991-92	London Scottish	West Hartlepool	Plymouth Albion Liverpool St Helens
1992-93	Newcastle Gosforth	Waterloo	Bedford Rosslyn Park Richmond Blackheath Coventry Fylde Morley
1993-94	Sale	West Hartlepool	Rugby Otley
1994-95	Saracens	Wakefield	Fylde Coventry

TEAM RECORDS

Highest score: Sale 88 Otley 9. 12-2-94
Highest aggregate: 97 points as above
Highest score by a losing side: 30 Coventry 36 London Irish 30. 8-10-94
Highest scoring draw: 24-24 London Scottish v London Welsh. 13-4-88
Most consecutive wins: 15 Saracens 1987-88 through 1988-89
Most consecutive defeats: 13 Coventry 1994-95
Most points for in a season: 438 Sale 1993-94
Most points against in a season: 449 Otley 1993-94
Least points for in a season: 81 Northampton 1987-88
Least points against in a season: 80 Saracens 1989-90
Most tries for in a season: 57 Newcastle Gosforth 1992-93, Sale 1993-94
Most tries against in a season: 65 Liverpool St. Helens 1991-92
Least tries for in a season: 7 Morley 1992-93
Least tries against in a season: 5 Sale 1992-93
Most conversions for in a season: 31 Newcastle Gosforth 1992-93
Most conversions against in a season: 37 Liverpool St. Helens 1991-92
Most penalties for in a season: 58 Wakefield 1994-95
Most penalties against in a season: 53 Fylde 1994-95
Least penalties for in a season: 6 Newcastle Gosforth 1987-88
Least penalties against in a season: 8 Saracens 1987-88, Sale 1990-91
Most drop goals for in a season: 11 London Scottish 1994-95
Most drop goals against in a season: 12 London Irish 1994-95

INDIVIDUAL RECORDS

Most points in a season: 213 Mike Jackson (Wakefield) 1994-95
Most tries in a season: 16 Simon Verbickas (Sale) 1993-94
Most conversions in a season: 31 David Johnson (Newcastle Gosforth) 1991-92
Most penalities in a season: 57 Mike Jackson (Wakefield) 1994-95
Most drop goals in a season: 9 Guy Gregory (Nottingham) 1992-93
Most points in a match: 28 David Johnson Newcastle Gosforth v Morley 11-1-92, v Liverpool St Helens 29-2-92
Most tries in a match: 5 Simon Verbickas (Sale) v Otley 12-2-94
Most conversions in a match: 9 David Johnson Newcastle Gosforth v Liverpool St Helens 29-2-92, Paul Turner Sale v Otley 12-2-94
Most penalities in a match: 6 on 19 occasions by 13 players – most 3 Michael Corcoran (London Irish)
Most drop goals in a match: 3 Martin Livesey Richmond v Northampton 19-11-88
Murray Walker London Scottish v West Hartlepool 23-4-94

SEASON BY SEASON LEADING SCORES

	POINTS		TRIES
1987-88	75 Andy Finnie (Bedford)	10	Dave McLagan (Saracens)
1988-89	138 Aany Kennedy (Saracens)	7	Dave McLagan (Saracens)
1989-90	107 Ian Aitchison (London Irish)	7	Jim Fallon (Richmond)
1990-91	117 Brian Mullen (London Irish)	9	Lindsay Renwick (London Scottish)
1991-92	147 David Johnson (Newcastle Gosforth)	11	Nick Grecian (London Scottish)
1992-93	136 David Johnson (Newcastle Gosforth)	7	Jon Sleightholme (Wakefield)
1993-94	172 Guy Gregory (Nottingham)	16	Simon Verbickas (Sale)
1994-95	213 Mike Jackson (Wakefield)	8	Tony Penn (Newcastle Gosforth)

100 POINTS IN A COURAGE SEASON DIVISION TWO

PTS	PLAYER	CLUB	SEASON	T	C	P	D
213	Mike Jackson	Wakefield	1994-95	2	16	57	—
193	Simon Mason	Newcastle Gosforth	1994-95	1	21	45	2
171	Guy Gregory	Nottingham	1993-94	1	11	43	5
164	Michael Corcoran	London Irish	1994-95	3	16	38	1
162	Andy Tunningley	Saracens	1994-95	3	21	35	—
160	Steve Swindells	Waterloo	1994-95	—	8	48	—
156	Simon Hodgkinson	Moseley	1994-95	—	12	41	3
149	Andy Tunningley	Saracens	1993-94	5	14	31	1
147	David Johnson	Newcastle Gosforth	1991-92	1	31	26	3
144	Paul Turner	Sale	1993-94	1	29	24	3
138	Andy Kennedy	Saracens	1988-89	5	14	30	—
137	Steve Swindells	Waterloo	1993-94	2	5	39	—
136	David Johnson	Newcastle Gosforth	1992-93	1	16	30	3
126	Paul Grayson	Waterloo	1992-93	1	8	29	6
124	Nick Grecian	London Scottish	1991-92	11	13	18	—
120	Martin Livesey	Richmond	1989-90	3	24	20	—
119	Peter Rutledge	Otley	1993-94	3	10	28	—
118	John Stabler	West Hartlepool	1991-92	2	16	26	—
117	Brian Mullen	London Irish	1990-91	1	16	22	5
115	Mark Mapletoft	Rugby	1993-94	5	9	22	2
111	Ian Aitchison	London Irish	1989-90	—	18	22	3
106	Guy Gregory	Nottingham	1992-93	1	10	18	9
105	John Steele	Northampton	1989-90	2	11	22	3
103	John Stabler	West Hartlepool	1993-94	1	16	20	2
102	David Pears	Sale	1988-89	3	3	26	2
101	Robert Liley	Wakefield	1992-93	1	9	24	2
100	Chris Howard	Rugby	1989-90	3	17	16	1
100	Brian Mullen	London Irish	1988-89	—	8	25	3

MOST POINTS IN A COURAGE DIVISION TWO MATCH

28	David Johnson	Newcastle Gosforth v Morley	11-1-92
28	David Johnson	Newcastle Gosforth v Liverpool St Helens	29-2-93
27	Simon Hodgkinson	Moseley v London Irish	8-4-95
26	Andy Mitchell	London Scottish v Northampton	3-10-87
25	Chris Howard	Rugby v Newcastle Gosforth	11-11-89
25	Andy Finnie	Bedford v Coventry	27-3-93
25	Guy Gregory	Nottingham v Otley	11-9-93
25	Simon Verbickas	Sale v Otley	12-2-94
24	Simon Irving	Headingley v London Scottish	12-11-88
24	Andy Kennedy	Saracens v Northampton	12-11-88
24	Nick Grecian	London Scottish v Blackheath	16-11-91
23	Simon Hodgkinson	Nottingham v Blcakheath	26-9-92
23	David Johnson	Newcastle Gosforth v Nottingham	10-10-92
23	Guy Gregory	Nottingham v Morley	24-10-92
23	Gary Abraham	Rosslyn Park v Morley	27-3-93
23	Rob Liley	Wakefield v Rugby	11-9-93
23	Paul Turner	Sale v Otley	12-2-94
22	Gary Clark	Gosforth v London Welsh	12-11-88
22	Andy Kennedy	Saracens v Bedford	19-11-88
22	Rob Liley	Wakefield v Liverpool St Helens	28-3-92
22	Ian Aitchison	Waterloo v Blackheath	25-4-92
22	John Graves	Rosslyn Park v Coventry	13-2-93
22	Andy Tunningley	Saracens v London Scottish	11-12-93
22	Simon Mason	Newcastle Gosforth v Nottingham	15-10-94
22	Mike Jackson	Wakefield v London Scottish	8-4-95
22	Michael Corcoran	London Irish v Newcastle Gosforth	29-4-95
21	Andy Kennedy	Saracens v London Welsh	22-10-88
21	Marc Thomas	Coventry v Morley	19-9-92
21	Paul Turner	Sale v Fylde	19-9-92
21	Steve Swindells	Waterloo v Nottingham	30-4-94
20	Nick Preston	Richmond v Headingley	6-2-88
20	Nick Holmes	Saracens v Blackheath	23-3-88
20	Andy Kennedy	Saracens v Blackheath	26-11-88
20	Gavin Hastings	London Scottish v Coventry	27-4-89
20	John Steele	Northampton v Coventry	10-3-90
20	Martin Livesey	Richmond v Headingley	28-4-90
20	Andy Atkinson	Wakefield v Coventry	17-11-90
20	Mark Slade	Plymouth v Bedford	14-12-91
20	Ian Aitchison	Waterloo v Liverpool St Helens	21-12-91
20	Jon Eagle	Blackheath v Moseley	28-3-92
20	Paul Grayson	Waterloo v Sale	13-3-93

MOST TRIES IN A COURAGE DIVISION TWO MATCH

5	Simon Verbickas	Sale v Otley	12-2-94
3	Jerry Macklin	London Scottish v Northampton	3-10-87
3	Orsen Bluitt	Northampton v Bedford	21-11-87
3	John Roberts	Headingley v Northampton	16-4-88
3	Pete Rowland	Coventry v London Irish	10-9-88
3	Dave Kennell	Headingley v Gosforth	14-1-89
3	Laurie Smith	Saracens v Gosforth	22-4-89
3	Nick Saunders	Plymouth Albion v Blackheath	14-10-89
3	Graham Robbins	Coventry v Waterloo	13-1-90
3	Rob Saunders	London Irish v Rugby	13-10-90
3	Jon Wrigley	West Hartlepool v Moseley	14-12-91
3	Peter Walton	Newcastle Gosforth v Blackheath	14-12-91
3	Jon Sleightholme	Wakefield v Blackheath	4-1-92
3	Gary Clark	Newcastle Gosforth v Liverpool St Helens	29-2-92
3	Richard Arnold	Newcastle Gosforth v Liverpool St Helens	29-2-92
3	Dave Spillar	Moseley v Sale	4-4-92
3	Richard Gee	Coventry v Morley	19-9-92
3	Malcolm Walker	Nottingham v Morley	24-10-92
3	Mark Warr	Sale v Otley	12-2-94

MOST LEAGUE APPEARANCES – DIVISION TWO PLAYERS

102	Dave Scully	Scrum Half	Wakefield
89	Richard Byrom	Winger	Nottingham
87	Chris Gray	Second Row	Nottingham
86	Ross Wilkinson	Centre	Newcastle Gosforth
86	Mark Linnett	Prop	Moseley
84	Andy Finnie	Stand Off	Bedford
83	Terry Garnett	Hooker	Wakefield
76	Martin Freer	Prop	Nottingham
76	Neil Frankland	Hooker/Flanker	Newcastle Gosforth
75	Frank Packman	Centre	Northampton
75	Gary Pearce	Prop	Northampton
74	Ian Skingsley	Back Row	Bedford
74	Harvey Thorneycroft	Winger	Northampton
72	Paul Burnell	Prop	London Scottish
71	Peter Hackett	Hooker	Waterloo
71	Steve Peters	Prop	Waterloo
71	Nick Grecian	Winger	London Scottish
70	Mark Upex	Second Row	Bedford
70	Mark Howe	Hooker	Bedford
69	Paul Stewart	Second Row	Wakefield
69	David Hindmarch	Second Row	Nottingham
68	Nigel Wilkinson	Second Row	Waterloo
68	Nick Allott	Second Row	Waterloo
65	Lindsay Renwick	Winger	London Scottish
64	Mike Harris	Back Row	Blackheath
64	Dave Millard	Scrum Half	London Scottish
64	Steve Townend	Stand Off	Wakefield
63	Gary Rees	Flanker	Nottingham
62	Brian Barley	Centre	Wakefield
58	Steve Douglas	Scrum Half	Newcastle Gosforth
58	Jim Staples	Full Back	London Irish
58	John Steele	Stand Off	Northampton
57	Paul Collins	Flanker	London Irish
57	David Johnson	Stand Off	Newcastle Gosforth
57	Peter Wood	Second Row	Wakefield
57	Tim Rodber	Flanker	Nothampton
56	Clifton Jones	Winger	Nottingham

NATIONAL LEAGUE TWO

MEMBER CLUBS
1995-96

League Registrar:
DAE Evans
22 Brrooks Road
Sutton Coldfield
West Midlands B71 1HP
Tel: 0121 354 8183
Fax: 0121 321 3221

Morley's Yorkshire Under 21 full back Peter Massey strides away from Richmond fly half Adrian Boyd in the Courage League Three match which Morley won 31-24   Photo: Gordon Bunney

BEDFORD R.U.F.C.

NICKNAME: Blues   **FOUNDED:** 1886

CLUB OFFICIALS
President
G B Willey
Chairman
I M Bullerwell
Club Secretary
A D Mills
1 Newbury House, Kimbolton Road,
Bedford MK40 2PD
Tel: (H) 01234 212524 (W) 01234 364351
Fixtures Secretary
J R Saunders
College Farm, Oakley, Beds
Tel: (H&W) 01234 822328
Press Officer
Howard Travis
Tel: (H) 01234 771675 (W) 01234
275392

Supporters Deserve Success

The Blues made no secret of their intention to win the Division III title. In a nail biting climax against Richmond on the last Saturday of the season, Paul Alston's side achieved their aim in front of an enthusiastic 4500 crowd at Goldington Road when the trophy was presented by former player Dudley Wood.

The achievement was the greater for recognising that Bedford's front five never really dominated any side and were often 'up against it'. Instead, coach Mike Rafter based the style of play around an abrasive and mobile back row, a three quarter line which on its day was outstanding, and the phenomenal kicking of Andy 'Albert' Finnie.

Youthful promise was exhibited throughout the season with Matt Deans, John Farr, Marcus Cook and Ben Whetstone, all excelling under the guidance of older hands, Fran Clough and Paul Alston, whilst Rob Subbiani has become the darling of the crowd with his exhilarating pace and style.

Rafter in his third year at Bedford said "There is great potential at Bedford both on and off the field, it's a good place to play rugby", but in one respect it is first class already – support! Few first division clubs could boast Bedford's tremendous away support, and Division II status must be retained if only for them. Only three games were lost at home in the entire season, in no small part due to the spirit and size of our crowds.

High points of last season include a narrow defeat to NZ provincial champions Canterbury, featuring hitherto unknown Andrew Mehrtens. Ian Skingsley's championship winning season with the Midlands and Paul Alston and Rob Subbiani's selection for the Barbarians Easter tour.

This season holds much promise for the supporter not least the visit of Western Province from South Africa, Northampton from just over the country border and Martin Bayfield on his bike from just half a mile away. Roll on September!

Back: Giles Witheat, Ben Whetstone, Mark Sharp, Mark Howe, Mark Redrup, Matt Roach, John Farr, Singh Basra. Middle: Richard Greed (Coach), Matthew Oliver, Peter Garrett, Steve Harris, Mark Upex, Ian Skingsley, Marcus Cook, Matt Deans, Graham Radford (Team Sec) Front: Phillip Duffell (Physio), Dick Tilley (Coach), Andy Finnie, Bruce Willey (President), Paul Alston (Capt), Ian Bullerwell (Chairman), Pob Subbiani, Mike Rafter (Head Coach), Neil Beytell   Photo: Charles Wooding
Colours: Oxford & Cambridge blue hoops   **Change Colours**: Navy blue, light blue and cerise hoop

BEDFORD R.U.F.C.

COURAGE LEAGUE
MATCH DETAILS 1994-95

No	Date	Opponents	Ven	Result		Scorers
1	Sep 9	Rugby	A	L	9-25	Finnie (3P)
2	Sep 17	Clifton	H	W	19-5	Farr (1T) Finie (1C 4P)
3	Sep 24	Richmond	A	W	16-14	Farr (1T) Finnie (1C 3P)
4	Oct 1	Morley	H	W	45-8	Finnie (3C 3P) Subbiani (T) Clough (T) Goldsmith (T) Whetstone (T) Farrett (T) Howe (T)
5	Oct 15	Rosslyn Park	A	W	31-13	Finnie (2C 3P 1DG) Deans (T) Skingsley (T) Howe (T)
6	Oct 22	Blackheath	H	W	12-3	Finnie (4P)
7	Oct 29	Exeter	A	W	19-3	Cook (1T) Finnie (1C 4P)
8	Nov 12	Harrogate	H	W	39-13	Finnie (2C 5P) Turner (2T) Whetstone (T) Alston (T)
9	Jan 7	Otley	A	L	6-12	Finnie (2P)
10	Jan 14	Clifton	A	W	21-18	Whetstone (1DG) Finnie (4P 2DG)
11	Feb 25	Morley	A	L	9-28	Finnie (3P)
12	Mar 11	Rosslyn Park	H	W	31-5	Finnie (2C 4P) Subbiani (2T) Simons (T)
13	Mar 25	Blackheath	A	D	12-12	Finnie (1C) Whetstone (T) Alston (T)
14	Apr 1	Exeter	H	W	23-10	Finnie (2C 3P) Simons (T) Pen Try
15	Apr 8	Otley	H	W	32-11	Finnie (C 5P) Cook (T) Whetstone (T) Harris (T)
16	Apr 12	Rugby	H	L	17-35	Finnie (4D) Simons (T)
17	Apr 15	Harrogate	A	W	59-15	Redrup (T) Witheat (T) Finnie (5C 3P) Deans (2T) Skingsley (T) Cook (T) Whetstone (T) Upex (T)
18	Apr 29	Richmond	H	W	21-20	Finnie (3C) Cook (T) Whetstone (T) Harris (T)

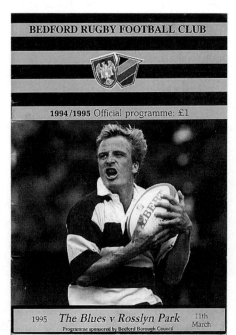

BEDFORD RUGBY FOOTBALL CLUB

1994/1995 Official programme: £1

1995 *The Blues v Rosslyn Park* 11th March
Programme sponsored by Bedford Borough Council

PROGRAMME DETAILS
Price: £1.00
Pages: 36
Ten original pages in each issue. Attached colour cover with the rest black and white. Two good action photos and quality paper.

Advertising Rates: Full page £450.00

CLUB & GROUND DETAILS
Goldington Road, Bedford TK40 3NE
Telephone: 01234 347511/354619

Total Capacity: 7,500
Seated: 800
Standing: 6,700
Simple Directions to Ground: Near Junction of A428 Bedford to Cambridge road and B660 Bedford to Kimbolton road.
Nearest Railway Station: Bedford Midland Road A428
Car Parking: 110
Season Tickets: Adults £60.00 Children/OAPs
Match Prices: Adults £75.00 Children/OAPs
Membership: Seniors £50.00 Juniors £10.00
Training Nights: Monday & Thursdays, Colts Mondays & Wednesdays

BEDFORD R.U.F.C.

MATCH BY MATCH PLAYERS BY POSITION

Cook	Whetstone	Turner	Finnie	Garratt	Sharp	Basra	Upex	Deans	Alston	Skingsley	Farr	Harris	Clough	Subbiani	Wyer-Roberts	Simons	Houghton	Allen	Howe	Thame	Chandler	Kemble
15	12	11	10	1	2	3	5	6	7	8										13	14	
15	12	11	10	1	2	3	5	6	7		9	4								13	14	8
	12	11	10	1	2	3	5	6	7		9	4		14						13	15	8
	13	11	10	1		3	5		8	6	9	4	12	14					2		7	
15	13*		10	1		3	5	R	8	6	9	4	12	14				11	2		7	
15	13		10	1		3	5	6	8	7	9	4	12					11	2			
15	13		10*	1		3	5	6	8	7	9	4	12					11	2			
15*	13	11	10	1	2	3	5	6	8	7	9	4		14				12				
15	12		10	1	2	3	4		8	6	9	7	13*		5			11				
	13	11	10	1	2	3	4	7*	8	6	9	5	12	14	R							
	13	11	10			3	4		7	6	9	8	12	15	5	14	1		2			
	12	11	10			3	5		7	6	9	8*	13	14	4	15	1		2			
15	12		10		2	3	4		7		9	6	13	14	5		1	11				
15	12		10		2	3	5	6	7*		9	4	13	14	R		1	11				
15	12		10		2	3	5	6	7	8	9	4	13	14			1	11				
15	12		10	1	2	3	4	6	7	8	9		13	14*	5			11				
15	12		10		2	3	4	6		8	9	5	13				1					
15	12		10	1	2	3	5	6	8		9	4										

Also Played: Skench No 9 match 1; J Cooley R matches 5, 8, 16; M Redrup No 14, matches 17, 18; M Wrigh No 4 match 1; I Gaylord R match 7; G Witheat No 11 matches 17, 18; A Goldsmith No 15 match 4, No 14 matches 6, 7; N Beytell R match 9; M Roach No 7 matches 17, 18; C Glanvill No 14 match 9, No 15 match 10; R Thompson R match 12; M Oliver No 12 match 18; M Rennell No 8 matches 13, 14

Courage League Records 1994-95

League Debuts: Jon Cooley, Jon Gaylord, Neil Beytell, Jason Simons, Ross Thompson, Mark Redrup, Giles Witheat, Matt Roach, Mathew Oliver, Fran Clough, Andrew Goldsmith, Mathew Wrigh, John Farr

Try on Debut: John Farr, Fran Clough, Andrew Goldsmith

Players used: 32

Ever Presents 3 Andy Finnie, Mark Upex, Singh Basra

Most appearances: 84 Andy Finnie

- Andy Finnie scored 228 (54%) of Bedford's 421 points last season

- Since League rugby started Bedford have scored 1624 points of which Finnie has contributed 782 (48%). After Finnie on Bedford's points list is Ben Whetstone – over 700 points behind on 73

- Finnie's 228 points was a National Divisions record beating the 222 points scored by Simon Hogg for Clifton in Division Four in 1993-94

- The previous best in Division Three was Finnie's own 172 last season

- Finnie beat his own record of 45 penalties in a Division Three season with his 56 putting him joint second for most penalties in a Courage League season

Mike Jackson (Wakefield)	57
Mark Tainton (Bristol)	56
Andy Finnie (Bedford)	56
Paul Grayson (Northampton)	52

- Finnie started the season in 5th place on the all time scoring list and by the end of the season was the all time top scorer, 15 points ahead of Rotherham's Kevin Plant

- Ian Skingsley passes Marc Howe's record of appearances for a forward, ending the season on 74 to Howe's 70

- Ben Whetstone passes Vince Turner to become leading try scorer for Bedford

	Tries	Apps	Strike Rate
Ben Whetstone	14	42	3.0
Vince Turner	13	39	3.0

BEDFORD R.U.F.C.

COURAGE LEAGUE STATISTICS
compiled by Steve McCormack

Season	Div	P	W	D	L	F	T	C	P	D	A	T	C	P	D	Most Points	Most Tries
1987-88	2	11	6	2	3	168	18	12	22	2	164	17	9	23	3	75 Andy Finnie	3 Steve Harris. Steve Batty. Brian Gabriel
1988-89	2	11	6	2	3	141	13	7	21	4	187	23	13	20	3	56 Andy Finnie	2 Steve Harris & Gary Colleran
1989-90	1	11	0	0	11	70	9	5	7	1	467	83	42	15	2	13 Richard Creed	3 Mark Howe
1990-91	2	12	4	2	6	138	16	7	16	4	203	27	10	22	3	78 Andy Finnie	3 Tim Young
1991-92	2	12	4	0	8	168	20	11	19	3	204	24	15	25	1	92 Andy Finnie	5 Mark Rennell
1992-93	2	12	6	2	4	186	13	8	32	3	183	15	9	24	6	75 Andy Finnie	3 Mark Rennell
1993-94	3	18	12	0	6	332	29	14	50	3	260	27	13	32	1	172 Andy Finnie	8 Vince Turner
1994-95	3	18	13	1	4	421	38	24	56	5	250	27	14	28	1	228 Andy Finnie	6 Ben Whetstone
TOTAL		105	51	9	45	1624	156	88	223	25	1918	243	125	189	20		

BIGGEST WIN — **Home:** 52-10 v Blackheath 14.3.92 CL2 — **Away:** 59-15 v Harrogate 15.4.95 CL3

BIGGEST DEFEAT — **Home:** 8-71 v Harlequins 14.10.89 CL1 — **Away:** 0-76 v Bath 13.1.90 CL1

MOST TRIES in a match — **For**: 9 v Blackheath 14.3.92 CL2 — **Against:** 14 v Bath 13.1.90 CL1

MOST CONSECUTIVE — **Wins:** 7 — **Defeats:** 4

MOST APPEARANCES — **Forward:** 74 Ian Skingsley — **Back:** 84 Andy Finnie

MOST CONSECUTIVE APPEARANCES — 46 Paul Alston 19.9.92 to 12.4.95

CONSECUTIVE SCORING MATCHES — **Tries:** 5 Vince Turner — **Points:** 27 Andy Finnie

	IN A SEASON	IN A CAREER	IN A MATCH
MOST POINTS	228 Andy Finnie 1994-95 CL3	782 Andy Finnie 1987-95	25 Andy Finnie v Coventry 27.3.93 Home CL2
MOST TRIES	8 Vince Turner 1993-94 CL3	14 Ben Whetstone 1992-95	2 on 14 occasions most 3 Vince Turner
MOST CONVERSIONS	24 Andy Finnie 1994-95 CL3	71 Andy Finnie 1987-95	5 Steve Batty v Liverpool St Helens 30.4.88 Home CL2 Andy Finnie v Blackheath 14.3.92 CL2 v Harrogate 15.4.95 Away CL3
MOST PENALTIES	56 Andy Finnie 1994-95 CL3	189 Andy Finnie 1987-95	7 Andy Finnie v Coventry 27.4.94 Home CL3
MOST DROP GOALS	4 Andy Finnie 1990-91 CL2 1994-95 CL3	20 Andy Finnie 1987- 95	2 Andy Finnie v Coventry 27.3.94 Home CL2 v Clifton 14.1.95 Away CL3

BLACKHEATH F.C.

NICKNAME: The Club   **FOUNDED:** 1858

CLUB OFFICIALS
President
Martin Turner
Chairman
Frank McCarthy
Club Secretary
Barry Shaw
86 Crown Woods Way, Eltham,
London SE9 2NN
Tel: (H) 0181 850 7976 (W) 0171 494
1455
Fixtures Secretary
Jim Collett
8 Vanbrugh Field, Blackheath SE3
Tel: (H) 0181 858 7571 (W) 0181 539
3348
Press Officer
Chris Benstead
Tel: CB 01474 704575

Review of the Season

When this directory first came out – and for a second season also –
BLACKHEATH was almost the only senior club which steadfastly refused to
provide anything other than perfunctory information, but that has all changed as has
their total commitment to the Courage Leagues with the result that they are back in
League Two after a brief break amongst the 'also-rans' and those who value
tradition will rejoice in that.

In a generally satisfactory season 'Club' were the second of two clubs
promoted from League Three – a point behind champions Bedford and four clear of
their nearest challengers Rugby – with a dozen victories and only four defeats.

Their Pilkington Cup campaign was also satisfying with a 24-12 win at
Rosslyn Park being followed by a 31-0 thrashing in the next round for visitors
Redruth. A trip to Leicester ended in a 56-11 defeat, but it was all a vast
improvement on previous efforts.

What is needed now is for the consistent players from League Three to repeat
their performances on a tougher stage and those who excelled in this respect were
centre Smith, half-backs Howard (a most reliable kicker) and Friday, hooker
Ridgway, lock Furneaux and an excellent back row in Harris, Booth and Walton.
All are relatively unknown, but they give 100 per cent in the cause.

W.L.M.

Chris Friday

0181 288

6152.

Fax 0181 249 0607

Photo: Tom Morris

Colours: Red and black hoops, blue collar   **Change Colours:** Red and black hoop on a light blue background

BLACKHEATH F.C.

COURAGE LEAGUE
MATCH DETAILS 1994-95

No	Date	Opponents	Ven	Result		Scorers
1	Sep 10	Rosslyn Park	A	W	19-14	Howard (1C 4P) Smith (T)
2	Sep 17	Rugby	H	W	15-11	Howard (4P 1D)
3	Sep 24	Exeter	H	W	21-7	Howard (1C 3P) Friday (T) Harris (T)
4	Oct 1	Harrogate	A	L	8-13	Booth (T) Howard (1P)
5	Oct 15	Otley	H	W	23-3	Howard (1C 1P) Burns (C 2P T) M Griffiths (T)
6	Oct 22	Bedford	A	L	3-12	Howard (1P)
7	Oct 29	Clifton	H	W	27-0	Howard (1C 4P 1D) M Griffiths (T) Hanslip (T)
8	Nov 12	Richmond	A	W	8-5	Howard (1P) M Griffiths (T)
9	Jan 7	Morley	H	W	18-9	Howard (6P)
10	Jan 14	Rugby	A	L	6-15	Howard (2P)
11	Feb 11	Rosslyn Park	H	W	9-3	Burns (3P)
12	Feb 25	Harrogate	H	W	24-0	Howard (3C 1P) Ridgway (T) Shadbolt (T) Hanslip (T)
13	Mar 4	Otley	A	W	15-0	M Griffiths (T) McIntyre (T) Friday (T)
14	Mar 25	Bedford	H	D	12-12	Howard (1C) Booth (T) Shadbolt (T)
15	Apr 1	Clifton	A	W	25-12	Burns (T 1C 1P) Harris (T) Walton (T) Ridgway (T)
16	Apr 8	Morley	A	D	29-29	Howard (1C 4P) M Griffiths (T) Friday (T) Booth (T)
17	Apr 15	Richmond	H	L	9-45	Howard (3P)
18	Apr 29	Exeter	A	W	28-0	Howard (T 2C 3P) Ridgway (T) Friday (T)

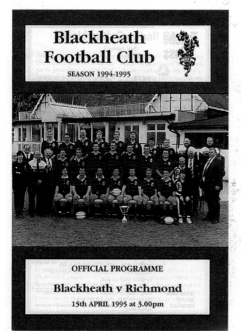

Blackheath
Football Club
SEASON 1994-1995

OFFICIAL PROGRAMME
Blackheath v Richmond
15th APRIL 1995 at 3.00pm

PROGRAMME DETAILS

Pages: 32
Neat and tidt production on good paper. Not very much reading but amusing Player Profile pages. Smart cover.
Editor & price not known.
Advertising Rates: Please phone Club

CLUB & GROUND DETAILS
The Rectory Field, Charlton Road, Blackheath, London SE3
Telephone: 0181 8581578

Nearest Railway Station: Blackheath or Westcombe Park

BLACKHEATH F.C.

MATCH BY MATCH PLAYERS BY POSITION

Douglas	M Griffiths	Coyne	Smith	Mitchell	Howard	Friday	Stewart	Ridgway	Essenhigh	Sampson	Furneaux	Booth	Harris	Begley	Walton	Burns	Hanslip	Griffiths D	McIntyre	Codling	Shadbolt	Jervis
15	14	13	12	11	10	9	1	2	3	4	5	7	6									
15	14	13	12	11	10	9	1	2	3		5	7	8	4	6							
15	14	13	12	11	10	9	1	2	3		5	7	8	4	6							
15		13	12	11	10	9	1	2	3		5*	7	8	4	6							
	14	13		11	10	9	1	2	3	4		7	8	5	6	15						
	14	13	12		10	9	1	2	3		5	7	8	4	6	15	11					
	14	13	12		10	9	1	2	3	4	5	7	8		6	15	11					
	14	13	12		10	9	1	2	3	4	5	7	8		6	15	11					
			12		10	9	1	2	3		5*	7			8	15		14	13	4		11
		13	12		10	9	1	2	3	4		7		5	8	15		14				11
	11					9	3	2		4		7			8	15		14	13	5	1	12
	14		12		10	9	3	2			5	7	8		6	15	11		13	4	1	
	14		12		10	9	3	2			5	7	6		8	15	11		13	4	1	
	14		12		10	9	3	2			5	7	6		8	15	11		13	4	1	
			12		10	9		2			5*	7	6		8	15	11	14	13	4	1	
	14*		12		10	9	3	2		4		7	6		8	15	11		13	5	1	
			12		10	9	3	2		4		7	6		8	15	11	14	13	5	1	
			12		10	9	3	2	R	4		7	6		8**		11	14	13	5	1*	

Also Played: S Slack No 8 match 1; J Taylor R match 4; S Graves No 12 match 5; S Barham No 6 match 9; J Osenton R matches 9, 15, No 6 match 10; L White No 6 match 11, R2 match 18; A Reading No 10 matches 11, 15, R match 16; A Reading No 10 matches 11, 15, R match 16; J Tierney No 3 match 15; A Jowett No 15 match 18

Courage League Records 1994-95

League Debuts: Paul Essenhigh, Mark Hanslip, Damian Griffiths, Simon Jervis, Alex Codling, James Osenton, Paul Shadbolt, Leon White, Ashley Reading, Andy Jowett

Tries on Debut: M Hanslip

Players used: 31

Ever Presents 3 – Mike Friday, Colin Ridgway, Toby Booth

Most appearances: 64 Mike Harris

- Sam Howard re-writes Blackheath's scoring record. He become the first man to score over 100 points in a season beating the previous record of 97 set by Grant Eagle two seasons ago. He also sets seasonal records for conversions and penalties, 11 and 38. The previous records were 10 by Colin Parker (87-88 and 89-90) and 26 by Grant Eagle (92-93)

	Pts	T	C	P	D	App	Ave
Sam Howard	147	1	11	38	2	16	9.18
Grant Eagle	97	1	4	26	2	11	8.81

- Mike Friday scored 4 tries and took his League tally to 13 passing Pat Jones' record of most tries which was 11

- Mike Harris passed Pat Jones' record for most appearances

- Sam Howard broke Grant Eagle's record of scoring in 9 consecutive matches, extending the record to 11

- Howard also equalled Eagle's record of 6 penalties in a match

- Blackheath easily had the best defensive record in the Division. The 190 points against was 60 better than anyone else. Conceded less tries than anyone else, just 18 – 5 fewer than the next best

BLACKHEATH F.C.

COURAGE LEAGUE STATISTICS

compiled by Steve McCormack

Season	Div	P	W	D	L	F	T	C	P	D	A	T	C	P	D	Most Points	Most Tries
1987-88	2	11	2	0	9	102	14	5	11	1	187	27	11	17	2	30 Nick Colyer	2 Pat Jones Giles Marshall Martin Holcombe
1988-89	2	11	4	1	6	181	19	12	19	8	144	17	5	22	0	70 Colin Parker	3 Peter Vaughan Mickey Scott
1989-90	2	11	3	2	6	141	15	12	15	4	205	25	12	27	0	57 Colin Parker	3 Jon King
1990-91	2	12	4	0	8	134	12	4	22	4	169	18	8	25	2	48 Colin Parker	3 Pat Jones
1991-92	2	12	4	0	8	140	12	4	25	3	266	37	20	26	0	61 Neil Munn	2 Andy Mercer
1992-93	2	12	4	2	6	142	9	5	27	2	231	23	13	26	4	97 Grant Eagle	5 Joe mcIntyre
1993-94	3	18	11	0	7	305	36	13	30	3	222	18	12	34	2	78 Stuart Burns	9 Mike Friday
1994-95	3	18	12	2	4	299	27	13	44	2	190	18	11	25	1	147 Sam Howard	5 Matt Griffiths
Total		105	44	7	54	1444	144	68	193	27	1614	183	92	202	11		

BIGGEST WIN **Home:** 31-10 v Gosforth 24.9.88 CL2 **Away:** 28-0 v Exeter 29.4.95 CL3

BIGGEST DEFEAT **Home:** 5-46 v Nottingham 26.9.92 CL2 **Away:** 10-52 v Bedford 14.4.94 CL3

MOST TRIES in a match **For:** 6 v Gosforth 24.9.88 CL2 v Havant 8.1.94 CL3 **Against:** 9 v Bedford 14.4.94 CL3

MOST CONSECUTIVE **Wins:** 4 **Defeats:** 6

MOST APPEARANCES **Forward:** 64 Mike Harris **Back:** 55 Pat Jones

MOST CONSECUTIVE APPEARANCES 36 Toby Booth, Mike Friday 1993-95

CONSECUTIVE SCORING MATCHES **Tries:** 3 Peter Mitchell

Points: 11 Sam Howard

	IN A SEASON	IN A CAREER	IN A MATCH
MOST POINTS	147 Sam Howard 1994-95 CL3	175 Colin Parker 1987-91	20 Grant Eagle v Moseley 28.3.92 Home CL2
MOST TRIES	9 Mike Friday 1993-94 CL3	13 Mike Friday 1993-95	3 Mike Friday v Morley 6.11.93 Home CL3
MOST CONVERSIONS	11 Sam Howard 1994-95 CL3	23 Colin Parker 1987-91	3 Colin Parker v Richmond 12.11.88 Home CL2 v London Irish 28.4.90 Home CL2 Paul Mycroft v Morley 6.11.93 Home CL3 Sam Howard v Harrogate 25.2.95 Home CL3
MOST PENALTIES	38 Sam Howard 1994-95 CL3	38 Colin Parker 1987-91 Sam Howard 1993-95	6 Grant Eagle v Moseley 28.3.92 Home CL2 v Rosslyn Park 9.1.93 Home CL2 Sam Howard v Morley 7.1.95. Home CL3
MOST DROP GOALS	8 Jon King 1988-89 CL2	16 Jon King 1987-91	2 Jon KIng v Coventry 19.11.88 Away CL2 v London Irish 22-4 89 Away CL2 v London Irish 28.4.90 Home CL2

LONDON IRISH R.F.C.

NICKNAME: THE IRISH   **FOUNDED:** 1898

CLUB OFFICIALS
President
Ronnie Johnston
Chairman
Duncan Leopold
Club Secretary
Kieran McCarthy
c/o London Irish R.F.C., The Avenue,
Sunbury on Thames, Middx TW16 5EQ
Tel: (H) 0181 9404999 (W) 01932 783034
Fixtures Secretary
Bill Gingles
Flat 609, Keyes House, Dolphin
Square, London SW1V 3LX
Tel: (H) 0171 7988507 (W) 0171 4805516
Press Officer
Mike Flatley
Tel: (H) 0181 3983878 (W) 0181 7463334

Review of the Season

Reflections on the Club's performance in the Courage League Second Division during the year are, in the main, reassuring. The year has been all about consolidation and bringing on new players. We faced the loss of a number of key players at the start of the season but recovered composure and started to play some exciting rugby. Several performances in the league justified the view that we are on the right road. London Irish finished in fifth position of Division Two, showing a 50% success rate and forming a platform from which we can launch ourselves into next season when we should be stronger, more settled and can look forward to the introduction of a number of top flight players. An intensive pre-season training regime has been planned for the summer, augmented by a short tour to Limerick and Cork during the last week-end in August, all forming part of the vital preparation to set a serious challenge for a top position in the Second Division for 1995/96.

We entered the Pilkington Cup at fourth round stage with an away fixture against Basingstoke which was won by 18 points to 3. The Fifth round draw resulted in a home fixture against near neighbours Harlequins. This was always going to be a formidable task for the team and the Quins won through to the Sixth round on a score line of 40 points to 15.

We have had another year of unqualified success with the under-age groups; U21, U19, Youth and Mini. The Club is mindful that its future lies within this Division and it is the Playing Committee's priority to harness this talent in order to ensure a fluid passage to the adult playing level.

Back: B Walsh, A Higgins, I Jaimeson, R Hennessy, M Corcoran, J Sharkey, P Neary, G Halpin, M Leonard. Front: N Donovan, R Kellam, L Condon, K Street, A Verling, O Cobbe, S Burns, R Saunders, R Henderson
Colours: Green shirts, white shorts, green socks   **Change Colours:** White shirts, white shorts, green socks

LONDON IRISH R.F.C.

COURAGE LEAGUE
MATCH DETAILS 1994-95

No	Date	Opponents	Ven	Result	Scorers
1	Sep 10	London Scottish	H	W 25-13	Walsh (T) Corcoran (1C 6P)
2	Sep 17	Saracens	A	L 22-35	Corcoran (2C 1P) Saunders (T) Halpin (T) Short (T)
3	Sep 24	Waterloo	A	L 19-22	Higgins (T) Corcoran (T 3P)
4	Oct 1	Fylde	H	W 23-12	Henderson (T) Pen Try Corcoran (2C 3P)
5	Oct 8	Coventry	A	L 30-36	Henderson (T) Hennessey (T) Corcoran (1C 6P)
6	Oct 15	Moseley	H	W 47-19	Henderson (T) Corcoran (T 3C P) O'Sullivan (T) Jameson (T) Cobbe (DG) Hennessey (2T)
7	Oct 22	Warrington	H	L 3-25	Corcoran (P)
8	Oct 29	Nottingham	H	W 24-22	Henderson (2T) O'Sullivan (T) Corcoran (1C 4P)
9	Nov 5	Newcastle Gos	A	W 15-9	Averling (T) Henderson (T C P)
10	Jan 7	London Scottish	A	W 27-15	Street (T) Bishop (T) Cobbe (C 4P DG)
11	Jan 14	Saracens	H	L 6-16	Cobbe (2P)
12	Feb 11	Waterloo	H	W 23-3	Henderson (T) Bird (2T) Cathcart (1C 2P)
13	Mar 4	Fylde	A	L 12-27	Bird (T) McEntegart (T) Corcoran (C)
14	Mar 25	Coventry	H	W 25-8	Irons (T) Hall (T) McEntegart (T) Corcoran (2C 2P)
15	Apr 8	Moseley	A	L 16-42	Hennessey (T) Street (T) Corcoran (2P)
16	Apr 15	Warrington	H	L 3-33	Corcoran (P)
17	Apr 22	Nottingham	A	L 11-22	Neary (T) Corcoran (2P)
18	Apr 29	Newcastle Gos	H	W 32-22	Corcoran (2C 5P DG) Hennessey (T) Pen Try

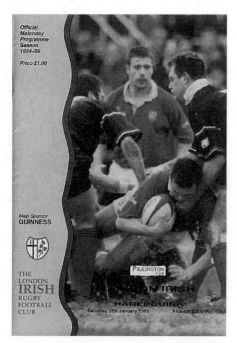

Official Matchday Programme Season 1994-/95

Price £1.00

Main Sponsor GUINNESS

THE LONDON IRISH RUGBY FOOTBALL CLUB

PROGRAMME DETAILS

Price: £1.00
Pages: 60
Colour throughout including some excellent photos. Sixteen original pages in each issue. Attractive cover and good paper throughout.
Editor: Mike Flatley
Tel: (H) 0181 3983878 (W) 0181 7463334
Advertising Rates: Full page £8.00 Half Page £5.00

CLUB & GROUND DETAILS
LONDON IIRISH R.F.C.

The Avenue, Sunbury on Thames, Middlesex TW16 5EQ
Telephone: 01932 783034
Fax: 01932 784462

Total Capacity: 6.000
Seated: 1,400
Standing: 4,600
Simple Directions to Ground: From Junction 1 on M3, take A308 to Kingston – Avenue 2nd turn on right
Nearest Railway Station: Sunbury on Thames
Car Parking: 400 within club grounds
Season Tickets: Adults £5.00
Match Prices: Adults £2.00
Membership: £60.00
Training Nights: Mondays & Wednesdays

LONDON IRISH R.F.C.

MATCH BY MATCH PLAYERS BY POSITION

Hennessey	Corcoran	Henderson	Burns	Street	Cobbe	Donovan	Kellam	Halpin	Jameson	Averling	Walsh	Neary	Bird	Briers	Hall	McEntegart	O'Sullivan	Bishop	Bell	McCormack	Tewington	Coveney	Irons
15	14	13	12	11	10	1	2	3	4	6	8	R											
15	14	13	12		10	1	2	3	4	6	8		7										
15	14	13	12		10	1	2	3	4	6	8		9										
15	14	13	12		10	1	2	3	4	6	8		9										
15	14	13	12	11		1	2	3**	4		8	7		R	6	R2							
15	14	13*			10	1			4		8	6	7	9	5		11	R	12	3			
15	14	13*			10	1			4		8	6	7	9	5		11		12	3			
15	14	13			10				4		8	6	7	9	5		11		12	3			
15	14	13			10				4		8	6	7	9	5		11		12	3			
15		13	14		10	1	2	3	4		8	6	7		5		11		12			9	
15		13	14		10	1	2	3	4		8	6	7		5		11		12			9	
		13			15		2	3				5	8	7	5	14			12	1	9	4	6
15	14											5	8	7	4		11	13	12	1	9		6
15	11		13	10*			2	3			8			R	5	14			12	1	9	4	6
15	14		13				2	3			8	7		9	5		11		12	10	1	4	6
15	11		13		10		2				8	7		R	4	14			12	3	9*	5	6
15	14		12	10			2				8	7	9		4		11	13		3		5	6
15	14	13		11			2	3			8	7	9		4				12		R	5	6

Also Played: Sharkey No 7* match 1, No 4 matches 3,4; Short No 11 matches 2, 3, 4; Saunders No 9 matches 1, 2, No 9* match 5, R match 3; Cathcart No 10 matches 5, 12, 13, 18; Mahon R matches 7, 18; Higgins No 5 matches 1, 2, 3, 4, 5; Nolan No 11 match 12; Holden No 7 match 14; Spores No 2 matches 6, 7, 8, 9, 13; Fitzpatrick No 1 matches 8, 9, 16, 17, No 3 match 13, No 12 match 18;

Courage League Records 1994-95

League Debuts: Ian Jameson, Barry Walsh, Cameron Short, Eugene McEntegart, Justin Bishop, Danny Spokes, Justin Fitzpatrick, Tim Ewington, Pat Coveney, Philip Irons, Vincent Holden
Players used: 33
Ever Presents: none

- Scored tries in 15 matches

- Second best home record and second worst away record

- Michael Corcoran extends his club points scoring record and in the process passes 300 and 400 League points Corcoran leads the Exiles points scoring list for the 4th consecutive season and beats his record for points in a season which was 111 in 1992-93

Season	Pts	T	C	P	D	App	Ave
1992-93	111	2	4	31	-	11	10.09
1994-95	164	3	16	38	1	15	10.93

- Corcoran passes Brian Mullen's record of conversions ending the season with 28, 1 ahead of Mullen

- Rob Henderson equals the club record for most tries in a season – the other two players to score 6 tries were Shaun Brown and Rob Saunders

- In the match v Moseley in October they recorded their biggest home win and also broke their record for most tries in a match with 7.

- It was also a season in which they had the biggest away win and defeat v London Scottish and Coventry respectively

LONDON IRISH R.F.C.

COURAGE LEAGUE STATISTICS
Compiled by Steve McCormack

Season	Div	P	W	D	L	F	T	C	P	D	A	T	C	P	D	Most Points	Most Tries
1987-88	2	11	4	1	6	120	15	6	14	2	177	22	10	20	3	27 Paul Bell	4 Harry Harbison
1988-89	2	11	5	2	4	194	20	9	26	6	222	25	13	29	3	100 Brian Mullen	5 Simon Geoghegan
1989-90	2	11	6	0	5	228	25	19	27	3	247	33	20	21	4	111 Ian Aitcheson	6 Shaun Brown
1990-91	2	12	9	1	2	239	30	16	22	7	192	21	12	26	2	117 Brian Mullen	6 Rob Saunders
1991-92	1	12	3	3	6	147	11	8	25	4	237	31	13	26	3	71 Michael Corcoran	4 Michael Corcoran
1992-93	1	12	6	0	6	175	9	5	33	7	223	25	16	20	2	111 Michael Corcoran	3 Simon Geoghegan
1993-94	1	18	4	0	14	217	19	7	34	2	391	40	22	43	6	75 Michael Corcoran	4 Michael Geoghegan
1994-95	2	18	9	0	9	363	36	18	46	3	381	31	17	52	12	164 Michael Corcoran	6 Rob Henderson
TOTALS		105	46	7	52	1683	165	88	227	34	2000	228	123	237	35		

BIGGEST WIN	**Home:** 47-19 v Moseley 15.10.94 CL2	**Away:** 27-6 v Gosforth 18.11.90 CL2, 27-15 v London Scottish 7.1.95 CL2
BIGGEST DEFEAT	**Home:** 3-39 v Harlequins 21.12.91 CL1	**Away:** 30-36 v Coventry 8.10.94 CL2
MOST TRIES in a match	**For**: 7 v Moseley 15.10.94 CL2	**Against:** 7 v Headingley 12.11.88 CL2
MOST CONSECUTIVE	**Wins:** 4	**Defeats:** 7
MOST APPEARANCES	**Forward:** 57 Paul Collins	**Back:** 58 Jim Staples
MOST CONSECUTIVE APPEARANCES	25 Neil Donovan	
CONSECUTIVE SCORING MATCHES	**Tries:** 4 Rob Saunders	**Points:** 16 Michael Corcoran

	IN A SEASON	IN A CAREER	IN A MATCH
MOST POINTS	164 Michael Corcoran 1994-95 CL2	429 Michael Corcoran 1989-95	22 Michael Corcoran v Wasps 26.3.94 Away CL1 v Newcastle Gosforth 29.4.95 Hime CL2
MOST TRIES	6 Shaun Brown 1989-90 CL2 & Rob Saunders 1990-91 & Rob Henderson 1994-95 CL2	15 Simon Geoghegan 1988-94	3 Rob Saunders v Rugby 13.10.90 Home CL2
MOST CONVERSIONS	16 Ian Aitchison 1989-90 CL2 & Brian Mullen 1990-91 CL2 & Michael Corcoran 1994-95 CL2	28 Michael Corcoran 1989-94	4 Brian Mullen v Gosforth 19.11.88 Home Cl2
MOST PENALTIES	38 Michael Corcoran 1994-95 CL2	102 Michael Corcoran 1989-95	6 Michael Corcoran v London Scottish 27.3.93 Away CL1 v London Scottish 10.9.94 Home CL2 v Coventry 8.10.94 Away CL2
MOST DROP GOALS	6 Paul Burke 1992-93 CL1	10 Brian Mullen 1988-92	2 Ralph Kuhn v London Scottish 14.1.89 Away Cl2 Brian Mullen v Richmond 8.4.89 Away CL2 Ian Aitchison v Plymouth 13.1.90 Home CL2 Paul Burke v Bristol 24.1.92 Home CL2

LONDON SCOTTISH F.C.

NICKNAME: Scottish   **FOUNDED:** 1878

CLUB OFFICIALS

President
A C W Boyle
Club Secretary
John J Smith
London Scottish F.C., Richmond
Athletic Ground, Richmond, Surrey
TW9 2SS
Tel: (H) 01784 459463 (W) 0181 332 2473
Fixtures Secretary
A Rhodes
19 St Peter Street, Winchester, Hants,
SO23 8BU
Tel: (H) 01489 782617 (W) 01962 844440
Press Officer
John J Smith
Tel: (H) 01784 459463 (W) 0181 332 2473

Review of the Season

After the great escape of the previous season LONDON SCOTTISH – on paper at least – would seem to have had fewer worries in season 1994-95, but like their Irish exile rivals they needed victory in their final match not only to confirm themselves in fourth place in League Two but also to insure themselves against relegation. A resounding 22-7 home win over runaway champions Saracens achieved just that, so the final verdict must be that the season was good especially as there was usually a long injury list to create problems.

Cup success was lacking as the Fourth Round draw brought them a visit from Bath and a 31-6 thrashing, but if they can field their strongest side in most of their matches in the coming season their prospects should be good.

Talent is not in short supply with excellent centres in Eriksson and Fraser Harrold, John Steele at fly-half (a consistently fine kicker), scrum-half David Millard still one of the best, Paul Burnell an inspiring captain and Nesbit a fine back-five prospect.

With ordinary luck they should do well and challenge for a return to League One.

Colours: Blue shirts white shorts   **Change Colours**: White

LONDON SCOTTISH F.C.

COURAGE LEAGUE
MATCH DETAILS 1994-95

No	Date	Opponents	Ven	Result		Scorers
1	Sep 10	London Irish	A	L	13-25	Troup (T) Walker M (1C 2P)
2	Sep 17	Waterloo	H	L	13-25	Millard (T) Wichary (T) Walker M (P)
3	Sep 24	Fylde	A	W	31-10	Troup (2T) Signorini (T) Russell (2C 4P)
4	Oct 1	Coventry	H	W	30-0	Wichary (2C 1P) Russell (1C 1P) Walker M (2T) Morrison (T) Troup (1DG)
5	Oct 8	Moseley	A	L	15-24	Walker M (T C P) Johnston (T)
6	Oct 15	Wakefield	H	W	24-21	Walker M (C 3P DG) Millard (2T)
7	Oct 22	Nottingham	A	L	8-23	Watson (T) Wichary (DG)
8	Oct 29	Newcastle Gos	H	W	24-13	Walker M (P 2DG) Eriksson (2T) Troup (DG) Wichary (1C)
9	Nov 5	Saracens	A	L	17-27	Harrow (2T) Walker M (C P) Wichary (C)
10	Jan 7	London Irish	H	L	15-27	Walker M (4P 1DG)
11	Jan 14	Waterloo	A	L	9-17	Russell (3P)
12	Feb 11	Fylde	H	W	28-3	Steele (2C 3P) Harrold (T) Holmes (T) Clarke (T)
13	Mar 4	Coventry	A	W	19-5	Ferguson (T) Steele (1C 3P DG)
14	Mar 25	Moseley	H	L	29-34	Walker A (T) Harrold (T) Steele (2C 4P 1DG)
15	Apr 4	Newcastle Gos	A	W	18-10	Sly (T) Eriksson (T) Steele (1C 2P)
16	Apr 8	Wakefield	A	L	19-42	Harrold (1C 4P) Jackson (T)
17	Apr 15	Nottingham	H	L	17-18	Clarke (T) Steele (3P 1DG)
18	Apr 29	Saracens	H	W	22-7	Millard (T) Ferguson (T) Steele (3P 1DG)

London Scottish Football Club

Founded 1878

Saturday, 25th March, 95
London Scottish v Moseley

PROGRAMME DETAILS

Pages: 24
Very little original copy (four pages and teams). No colour.
Disappointing cover and paper.

Advertising Rates: £500 per page

CLUB & GROUND DETAILS
Richmond Athletic Ground, Richmond, Surrey TW9 2SS
Telephone: 0181 332 2473
Fax: 0181 332 6775

Total Capacity: 6,200
Seated: 1,200
Standing: 5,000
Simple Directions to Ground: On the A316 100 yards from Richmond Circus
Nearest Railway Station: Richmond BR/Underground
Car Parking: 200
Season Tickets: Adults £5.00 Children/OAPs £3.00
Match Prices: Adults £2.00 Children/OAPs £2.00
Membership: Seniors £45.00 Juniors £15.00
Training Nights: Monday & Wednesday

LONDON SCOTTISH F.C.

MATCH BY MATCH PLAYERS BY POSITION

Wichary	Watson	Eriksson	Millard	Walker M	Troup	Burnell	Scott	Dixon	Morrison	Nesbit	Pearson	Leckie	Harrold	Wiseman	Jackson	Robinson T	Holmes	Ferguson	Steele	McGiven	Walker A	McClellan	Robinson N.
15	14	12	11	10	9	3	5	6	7	8												2	
15	14	13	12	10	9	3	4		7	5	11	8			1							2	
15		13		10	9	3	4		7	5		8	12								14		
15	12*	12		10	9	3	4	6**	7	5	14		13								8	R	
		12	15	10	9	3		6	7	5	14	8	13								11	2	
12	14	15		10	9	3		6	7	5		8	13	1									
15	14	12	9	10		3		6		8			13	1								2	
15		12		10	9	3	4	6	7	5	11	8	13	1								2	
15		12		10	9	3	4**		7	5	11	8	13	1	6	R*							
	14			10	9	3	4	6	8	5	11		12					7					15
	14	13	9	10		3	4	6	8	5	11		12					7					15
		12	9				4		8	5			13	1	6	13	7	14	10	2			15
		12	9				4			5			13	1*	6	13	7**	14	10	2	8		15
	11	12	9			3	4			5			13	1*	6		7	14	10	2	8		15
		12	9				4			5			13	3	6		7	14	10	2	8		15
		12				3	5			8			10	1	6*		7	14		2			15
		12	9			3	5	7	4				13	1			8	14	10	2			15
		12	9				5			8			13		3		7	14	10				15

Also Played: Corbett No 13 match 10; Main No 2 matches 10, 11, 18; Clarke No 11 matches 12, 13, 17, 19; Sanderson No 1 match 15, R matches 13, 14; Allan No 11 match 16; Withers-Green No 9 match 16; Signorini No 1 matches 3, 4, 5, 10, 11; Sly No 13 matches 1, 16, No 11 match 15; Stewart No 1 match 1; Johnston No 4 matches 1, 5, 16, 18; No 5 match 7, R matches 4, 13**; Rowlands No 6 matches 2, 17, 18; No 7 match 7, R match 16; Russell No 11 matches 3, 4**, No 15 match 11; Gilchrest No 2 matches 3, 4, 6, 9; Gray No 6 match 3; Dingwall No 12 match 6*; Bell No 11 matches 6, 7, No 14 matches 8, 9; Mackay No 4 match 6, R match 9**; Dorr-Ewing No 4 match 7, R match 18

Courage League Records 1994-95

League Debuts: Tony Robinson, Patrick Bell, Grant Corbett, John Steele, Johnnie Clarke, Dave McGavin, S Anderson, M Allan, Evan Ferguson, 5 Holmes, N Robinson, D Rowlands

Players used; 42

Ever Present: A Nesbit

Most appearances: 72 Paul Burnell

● Murray Walker breaks Richard Cramb's record of 8 drop goals finishing the season on 9. Walker, after 2 seasons with the club is now second on the all time list behind Nick Grecian

	Pts	T	C	P	D	App	Ave
Nick Grecian	335	23	41	52	1	71	4.72
Murray Walker	155	5	8	29	9	28	5.54

● Ex Northampton stand-off John Steele made a prolific start to his Scottish career averaging 13 points a match

Pts	T	C	P	D	App	Ave
78	-	6	18	4	6	13.00

● Scrum half Dave Millard moves into third place on the all-time list behind Nick Grecian and Lindsay Renwick

	Tries	Apps	Strike Rate
Lindsay Renwick	23	64	2.78
Nick Grecian	23	21+1	3.09
Dave Millard	16	64+1	4.00

● Ex Havant winger Johnnie Clarke scored try on debut.

LONDON SCOTTISH F.C.

COURAGE LEAGUE STATISTICS
compiled by Steve McCormack

Season	Div	P	W	D	L	F	T	C	P	D	A	T	C	P	D	Most Points	Most Tries
1987-88	2	11	4	1	6	141	18	9	16	1	158	20	9	18	2	38 Andy Mitchell	4 Lindsey Renwick
1988-89	2	11	3	1	7	146	15	7	23	1	160	15	8	26	2	49 Gavin Hastings	3 Nick Grecian
1989-90	3	11	11	0	0	258	40	22	14	4	92	7	2	20	-	64 Gavin Hastings	4 Tim Exeter
1990-91	2	12	7	0	5	240	37	19	15	3	178	19	12	24	2	89 Nick Grecian	9 Lindsey Renwick
1991-92	2	12	11	0	1	304	45	23	25	1	130	14	4	21	1	124 Nick Grecian	11 Nick Grecian
1992-93	1	12	3	1	8	192	23	10	17	2	248	31	15	21	-	40 Nick Grecian	4 Lindsey Renwick
1993-94	2	18	6	0	12	232	17	9	36	7	325	30	17	40	7	81 Murray Walker	3 Ronnie Eriksson
1994-95	2	18	9	0	9	351	30	18	44	11	321	28	17	45	4	78 John Steele	4 Dave Millard Fraser Harrold
TOTAL		108	54	3	48	1864	225	117	190	30	1612	164	84	215	18		

BIGGEST WIN   **Home:** 50-3 v Northampton 3.10.87 CL2   **Away:** 45-20, Rugby 31.10.91 CL1

BIGGEST DEFEAT   **Home:** 11-37 v Wakefield 26.3.94 CL2   **Away:** 19-42 v Wakefield 8.4.95 CL2

MOST TRIES in a match   **For**: 7 on 3 0   **Against:** 6 on 3 0

MOST CONSECUTIVE   **Wins:** 12   **Defeats:** 6

MOST APPEARANCES   **Forward:** 72 Paul Burnell   **Back:** 71 Nick Grecian

MOST CONSECUTIVE APPEARANCES   53 Nick Grecian 10.9.88-21.11.92

CONSECUTIVE SCORING MATCHES   **Tries:** 6 Nick Grecian

Points: 12 Nick Grecian

	IN A SEASON	IN A CAREER	IN A MATCH
MOST POINTS	124 Nick Grecian 1991-92 CL2	335 Nick Grecian 1988-94	26 Andy Mitchell v Northampton 3.10.87 Home CL2
MOST TRIES	11 Nick Grecian 1991-92 CL2	23 Lindsey Renwick 1982-94 Nick Grecian 1988-94	3 Jerry Macklin v Northampton 3.10.87 Home CL2
MOST CONVERSIONS	16 Nick Grecian 1990-91 CL2	41 Nick Grecian 1988-94	5 Andy Mitchell v Northampton 3.10.87 Home CL2 Gavin Hastings v Vale of Lune 23.9.89 Home CL3 Mark Appleson v Rugby 31.10.92 Away CL1
MOST PENALTIES	18 Nick Grecian 1991-92 CL2	52 Nick Grecian 1988-94	4 on 10 occasions by 7 players. Most Gavin Hastings and Murray Walker (2)
MOST DROP GOALS	5 Murray Walker 1993-94 CL2	9 Murray Walker 1993-95	3 Murray Walker v Hartlepool 23.4.94 Home CL2

MOSELEY F.C.

NICKNAME: MOSE   **FOUNDED:** 1873

CLUB OFFICIALS

President
D A E Evans
Chairman
K P Birrell
Club Secretary
Peter G Veitch
c/o Moseley F.C. (RU), The Reddings,
Reddings Road, Moseley, Birmingham
B13 8LW
Tel: (H) 01527 832660 (W) 0121 427 1213
Fixtures Secretary
P G Walters
168 Green Lanes, Wylde Green, Sutton
Coldfield, Birmingham B43 5LX
Tel: (H) 0121 355 1283 (W) 0121 354 8116
Press Officer
Barrie Corless
Tel: (H) 01564 779158 (W) 0121 442 2095

Review of the Season

MOSELEY had reason to thank their lucky stars that their final League Two match of the season – and survival – was at Coventry, who had already long since been relegated and were by then looking to ways of improving in 1995-96 in lower company. Moseley won at Coundon Road (22-11) and must now plan for fewer traumas in the new campaign, with a situation of more defeats than victories not being repeated.

The club once ended a long run of cup successes for Bath, but there was no repetition of such heady days. A visit from Northampton stopped any illusions (16-6), so they must now look at their staff and hope that their most consistent players continue to keep their heads above water and that talented fullback Dossett returns to full fitness.

They had to thank Simon Hodgkinson for his consistent kicking as usual even though he is now a veteran. He has been well supported by centres Kerr and Bonney and Becconsall is a fine scrum-half prospect. The most consistent members of the pack have been tighthead Webber, locks Watson and Bright and the back-row men Robinson and Poll.

It should not take much to bring success to The Reddings and this well supported club will look for more consistency from their staff to bring that about plus a touch, perhaps, of Barrie Corless magic.

The squad that defeated Coventry in the last Courage League game of the season that raised Moseley from 8th place to 5th in Division Two. Back: Jag Johal, Robin Poll, Neil Martin, Gary Watson, Martin Bright, Mark Young, Jan Bonney, Liam Corbett, Alistair Kerr, Bob Robinson, Nathan Webber, derek Nutt (Coach). Front: Doug Payne, Stuart Caley, Charlie Mulraine, Ken Birrell (Chairman), Simon Hodgkinson (Capt), Alwynne Evans (President), Eral Anderson, Andy Houston, Rowan Fuller
Colours: Red and black hoops   **Change Colours:** White hoops

MOSELEY F.C.

COURAGE LEAGUE
MATCH DETAILS 1994-95

No	Date	Opponents	Ven	Result		Scorers
1	Sep 10	Saracens	H	L	9-11	Kerr (3P)
2	Sep 17	Wakefield	A	W	22-7	Robinson (T) Hodgkinson (1C 5P)
3	Sep 24	Nottingham	H	W	19-12	Linnett (T) Hodgkinson (1C 3P 1DG)
4	Oct 1	Newcastle Gos	A	L	10-37	Poll (T) Hodgkinson (1C 1P)
5	Oct 8	London Scottish	H	W	24-15	Bright (2T) Hodgkinson (1C 4P)
6	Oct 10	London Irish	A	L	19-47	Mulraine (T) Hodgkinson (1C 4P)
7	Oct 22	Waterloo	H	L	9-25	Hodgkinson (3P)
8	Oct 29	Fylde	A	L	6-10	Hodgkinson (2P)
9	Nov 5	Coventry	H	W	19-8	Dossett (T) Kerr (1P) Hodgkinson (1C 3P)
10	Jan 7	Saracens	A	L	15-17	Anderson (T) Kerr (1T 1C 1P)
11	Jan 14	Wakefield	H	L	11-16	Anderson (T) Kerr (2P)
12	Feb 11	Nottingham	A	D	9-9	Hodgkinson (3P)
13	Mar 18	Newcastle Gos	H	W	6-3	Kerr (2P)
14	Mar 23	London Scottish	A	L	24-29	Payne (T) Hanson (T) Kerr (1C 4P)
15	Apr 8	London Irish	H	W	42-16	Matthews (T) Payne (T) Becconsall (T) Hodgkinson (3C 5P 2DG)
16	Apr 15	Waterloo	A	W	27-12	Kerr (T) Owen (2T) Houston (T) Hodgkinson (2C 1P)
17	Apr 22	Fylde	H	L	6-8	Hodgkinson (2P)
18	Apr 29	Coventry	A	W	22-11	Robinson (T) Hodgkinson (1C 5P)

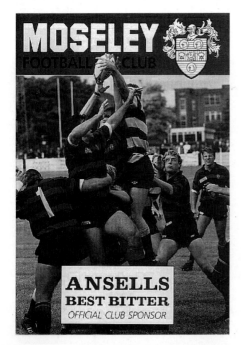

PROGRAMME DETAILS

Pages: 48
Sixteen pages of original copy in each issue. No photos other than the excellent cover. Colour only on the cover.

Advertising Rates: Please apply to Commercial Manaager: David Coleman 0121 449 2149

CLUB & GROUND DETAILS

The Reddings, Reddings Road, Moseley,
Birmingham B13 8LW
Telephone: 0121 449 2149
Fax: 0121 442 4147

Total Capacity:
Standing: 5,000
Simple Directions to Ground: A38 South Birmingham to Edgbaston Road, turn at traffic lights to Egsbaston Cricket Ground on left. To Island right into Russell Road, left into Moorcroft Road, left into Reddings Road.
Nearest Railway Station: Birmingham New Street
Car Parking: Some space available in Ground
Season Tickets: Adults £65.00 Children/OAPs £30.00
Match Prices: Adults £6.00 Children/OAPs £3.00
Membership: Seniors £33.00 Juniors £12.00
Training Nights: Tuesday & Thursday

MOSELEY F.C.

MATCH BY MATCH PLAYERS BY POSITION

Dossett	Payne	Kerr	Bonney	Hodgkinson	Becconsall	Linnett	Ball	Webber	Watson	Robinson	Poll	Bright	Proctor	Anderson	Mulraine	Hill	Fuller	Hanson	Owen	Martin	Cox	Purdy	Houston
15	14	13	12	10	9	1	2	3	4	7	8							11					
15	14	13	12	10	9	1	2	3	4	7	8	5	6					11					
15	14	13	12	10	9*	1	2	3	4	7	8							11					
15		13	12	10		1	2	3	4	7	8	5		11	9			14					
15		13	11	10				3	4	7	8	5	6	14	9	12	1						
15		13	11	10				3	4	7	8		6	14	9	13	1						
	11		12	10					4	7	8	5	6	14	9	13	1						
	11		12	10				3	4	7	8	5	6	14	9	13	1						
15	11	13	12	10*			2	3	4	7	8	5	6	14	9	R	1						
15	11	13	12	10	9			3	4	7	6	5		14			1		8				
15	11	13	12		9			3	4	7		5		14			1		8	6			
15	11	13	12	10				3	4	7	6	5		14	9		1		8	2			
		13	12	10	9	1		3	4	7	6	5						11	8	2	15	R	
	14	13	12		9*	1		3	4	7	6	5		R				11	8	2	15		10
	11	13	R	10*	9	1		3	R**		6	5		14				8	7**	2	15		12
		13	12	10		1		3		7	6	5		14	9				8	2	15		12
	11	13		10		1		3		7	6	4		14	9				8	2			12
	11	15	13	10				3	4	7	6	5		14	9		1		8				12

Also Played: Massey R match 3; Smith R match 8; Wilkinson No 14 match 13, No 11 match 16; Lloyd No 5 matches 1, 3; Howells No 5 match 6; Caley No 2 matches 10, 11, 18; Mathews No 4 matches 15, 16, No 5 match 17; Hart No 6 mathews 1, 34; Corbett No 3 match 7; Birch No 10 match 11; Johal R matches 17, 18; Hampton No 2 matches 5, 6, 7, 8

Courage League Records 1994-95

League Debuts: Doug Payne, Nathan Webber, Bob Robinson, Charles Mulraine, Nigel Hill, Rowan Fuller, Matthew Howells, Stuart Caley, Simon Owen, Matt Birch, Dave Wilkinson, Robert Matthews

Players used: 34

Ever Presents None 3 played 17 Webber, Robinson, Poll

Most appearances: 86 Mark Linnett

● Simon Hodgkinson re-writes Moseley's points scoring records. He broke his own record for points in a season

	Pts	T	C	P	D	App	Ave
1993-94	83	-	7	23	-	13	6.38
1994-95	156	-	12	41	3	16	9.75

● Hodgkinson broke his own record of 23 penalties in a season. He broke Mark Hardcastle's record of 2 drop goals in a season and equalled Alistair Kerr's career record of 3

● Carl Arntzen started the season as the club's leading scorer in League rugby. By the end of the season both Hodgkinson and Kerr had passed him

	Pts	T	C	P	D	App	Ave
Simon Hodgkinson	239	-	19	64	3	29	8.24
Alistair Kerr	192	2	25	41	3	48	4.0
Carl Arntzen	176	2	21	41	1	34	5.18

● Hodgkinson also smashed the record for most points in a match – he scored 27 v London Irish, 3c 5p, 2d, to beat the previous record of 15, a record he had set earlier in the season of 17. 3 times he equalised the record of 5 penalties in a match, a record he also shared with Simon Pennington. His 2 drop goals in the match v London Irish saw him equal Alistair Kerr's record of 2 set 3 years earlier

MOSELEY F.C.

COURAGE LEAGUE STATISTICS
compiled by Steve McCormack

Season	Div	P	W	D	L	F	T	C	P	D	A	T	C	P	D	Most Points	Most Tries
1987-88	1	11	5	0	6	167	25	8	17	0	170	22	14	17	1	48 John Goodwin	8 Peter Shillingford
1988-89	1	11	3	0	8	113	13	8	14	1	242	34	20	20	2	46 Carl Arntzen	4 Peter Shillingford
1989-90	1	11	2	0	9	138	20	8	14	0	258	37	28	17	1	52 Carl Arntzen	6 Simon Robson
1990-91	1	12	1	1	10	113	12	7	15	2	244	34	18	21	3	68 Carl Arntzen	2 Carl Arntzen Graham Smith Laurence Boyle
1991-92	2	12	6	0	6	215	31	14	18	3	196	25	9	25	1	62 Alastair Kerr	6 Dave Spiller
1992-93	2	12	6	2	4	184	19	7	22	3	150	8	23	5		40 Bob Massey	3 Nick Parry Bob Massey
1993-94	2	18	9	1	8	266	23	14	40	1	220	21	10	32	1	83 Simon Hodgkinson	5 Mark Linnett
1994-94	2	18	8	1	9	299	20	14	54	3	303	33	15	32	4	156 Simon Hodgkinson	2 by 6 players
TOTAL		105	40	5	60	1495	163	80	194	13	1783	216	122	187	18		

BIGGEST WIN **Home:** 47-15 v Sale 4.4.92 CL2 **Away:** 26-20 v Newcastle Gos 25.4.92 CL2

BIGGEST DEFEAT **Home:** 19-43 v Leicester 27.4.91 CL1 **Away:** 19-47 v London Irish 15.10.94 CL2

MOST TRIES in a match **For**: 9 v Sale 4.4.92 CL2 **Against:** 8 v Bath 12.11.88 Home CL1 Wasps 16.11.69 Home CL1

MOST CONSECUTIVE **Wins:** 3 **Defeats:** 7

MOST APPEARANCES **Forward:** 86 Mark Linnett **Back:** 48 Alastair Kerr

MOST CONSECUTIVE APPEARANCES 32 Mark Linnett 3.11.92-1.10.94

CONSECUTIVE SCORING MATCHES **Tries:** 3 Peter Shillingford & Simon Purdy
Points: 11 Carl Arntzen

	IN A SEASON	IN A CAREER	IN A MATCH
MOST POINTS	156 Simon Hodgkinson 1994-95 CL2	222 Simon Hodgkinson 1993-95	27 Simon Hodgkinson v London Irish 8.4.95 Home CL2
MOST TRIES	8 Peter Shillingford 1987-88 CL1	20 Peter Shillingford 1987-94	3 Peter Shillingford v Wasps 5.2.88 Home CL1 Dave Spillar v Sale 4.4.92 Home CL2
MOST CONVERSIONS	13 Alastair Kerr 1991-92 CL2	25 Alastair Kerr 1991-95	4 Alastair Kerr v Sale 4.4.92 Home CL2
MOST PENALTIES	41 Simon Hodgkinson 1994-95 CL2	25 Alastair Kerr 1991-95	5 Simon Pennington v Morley 16.11.91 Home CL2 Simon Hodgkinson v Saracens 8.1.94 Home CL2 v Wakefield 17.9.94 Away CL2 v London Irish 8.4.95 Home CL2 v Coventry 29.4.95 Away CL2
MOST DROP GOALS	3 Simon Hodgkinson 1994-95 CL2	3 Alastair Kerr 1991-95 Simon Hodgkinson 1993-95	2 Alastair Kerr v Plymouth 21.12.92 Home CL2

NEWCASTLE GOSFORTH R.F.C.

NICKNAME: **FOUNDED:** 1877

CLUB OFFICIALS
President
Godfrey Clark
Chairman
Ken Lockerbie
Club Secretary
Trevor K Hogg NGRFC
Kingston Park, Brunton Road,
Kenton Bank Foot,
Newcastle upon Tyne NE13 8AF
Tel: (W) 0191 214 0422
Fixtures Secretary
Tom Hall
10 Elmfield Grove, Gosforth,
Newcastle upon Tyne NE3 4XA
Tel: (H) 0191 285 6565 (W) 0191 281 5711
Press Officer
Kingsley Hyland
Tel: (H) 0191 285 4997 (W) 0191 201 2387

Review of the Season

Newcastle consolidated well after relegation the previous season and finished a highly creditable third ending the season as the second highest try scorers in the Division. More pleasing was the fact that they conceded just 20 tries, again the second best record in the Division.

Full back Simon Mason, in his first season with the club following his move from Liverpool St Helens, made a valuable contribution. Mason ended the season with 193 points, smashing David Johnson's record of 147.

Newcastle had a very unsettled half back pairing using three players in each position. The side was unable to get any consistency.

Captain Richard Arnold had the unfortunate distinction of being the first man to be sent off twice in a Courage League season.

Winger Tony Penn continued his hot streak and has now scored 10 tries in his last 20 matches.

Newcastle have lost a number of key players in the close season and need to replace them quickly if they are to build on last season's success.

Back: Tetlow, Corrie, Fowler, Archer, Frankland, Knight. Middle: Brown, Black, Dungait, Balfour, Fraser, Chandler, Hetherington, Parker, Willcox, Cassidy, Douglas, Old, Laing, Reed. Front: Van-Zandvliet, Penn, Wilkinson, Arnold (Capt), Clark, Merritt, Mason
Colours: Black green and white hoops, white shorts, green socks   **Change Colours:** Red and white hoops

NEWCASTLE GOSFORTH R.F.C.

COURAGE LEAGUE
MATCH DETAILS 1994-95

No	Date	Opponents	Ven	Result	Scorers
1	Sep 10	Waterloo	A	L 13-18	Curry (T) Mason (1C 2P)
2	Sep 17	Fylde	H	W 45-14	Wilkinson (2T) Mason (4C 4P) Chandler (T) Archer (T) Arnold (T)
3	Sep 24	Coventry	A	L 15-19	Wilkinson (T) Merritt (T) Mason (C P)
4	Oct 1	Moseley	H	W 37-10	Long (T) Mason (3C 2P) Wilkinson (T) Penn (T) Archer (T) Casado (T)
5	Oct 8	Wakefield	A	W 21-9	Penn (T) Archer (T) Mason (1C 3P)
6	Oct 15	Nottingham	H	W 27-6	Curry (T) Mason (T C 5P)
7	Oct 22	Saracens	H	L 11-17	Hetherington (T) Mason (2P)
8	Oct 29	London Scottish	A	L 13-24	Penn (T) Mason (1C 2P)
9	Nov 5	London Irish	H	L 9-15	Mason (2P 1DG)
10	Jan 4	Waterloo	H	W 33-16	Douglas (T) Mason (2C 3P) Penn (T) Hetherington (T) Arnold (T)
11	Jan 14	Fylde	A	W 12-6	Mason (4P)
12	Feb 18	Coventry	H	W 38-22	Douglas (T) Van Zandvlieet (T) Mason (1C 2P) Tetlow (T) Penn (T) Hetherington (T) Arnold (T)
13	Mar 18	Moseley	A	L 3-6	Mason (P)
14	Mar 25	Wakefield	H	D 15-15	Mason (4P 1DG)
15	Apr 2	London Scottish	H	L 10-18	Penn (T) Mason (1C 1P)
16	Apr 8	Nottingham	A	W 33-18	Mason (3C 4P) Curry (T) Metcalfe (T) Cramb (T)
17	Apr 15	Saracens	A	D 16-16	Curry (T) Mason (1C 3P)
18	Apr 29	London Irish	A	L 22-32	Penn (2T) Curry (T) Mason (2C 1P)

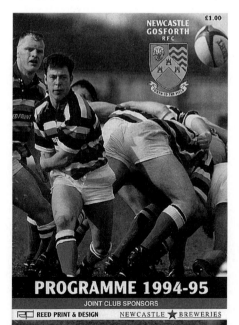

PROGRAMME DETAILS

Price: £1.00
Pages: 36
Excellent quality paper. Two full page colour photos. Ten pages of original copy per issue with an attractive and colourful cover. Half the pages contain colour and good features are included
Editor:
Advertising Rates: Full page colour £500, full page b/w £400, half page b/w/ £300, third page b/w £275

CLUB & GROUND DETAILS

Kingston Park, Brunton Road, Kenton Bank Foot, Newcastle upon Tyne NE13 8AF
Telephone: 0191 214 0422
Fax: 0191 214 0422

Total Capacity: 9,999
Seated: 365
Standing: 9,634
Simple Directions to Ground: From south follow signs to airport on A1 taking the western by-pass turn off at Kingston Park
Nearest Railway Station: Newcastle Central
Car Parking: 450
Season Tickets: Adults £65.00 Children/OAPs £45.00
Match Prices: Adults £6.00 Children/OAPs £4.00
Membership: Seniors £45 Juniors £8
Training Nights: Tuesday & Thursday

NEWCASTLE GOSFORTH R.F.C.

MATCH BY MATCH PLAYERS BY POSITION

Mason	Wilcox	Wilkinson	Tetlow	Penn	Chandler	Merritt	Robson	Hetherington	Van Zandvliet	Archer	Cramb	Curry	Frankland	Arnold	Casado	Long	Gibbs	Cassidy	Metcalfe	Hoole	Douglas	Mitchell	Clark P
15	14	13	12	11	10	9		2	3	4		6	7	8									
15	10	12		11	13	9		2	3	4		6		8	14	1	5	7					
15	10	13		11	12	9		2	3			6			14	1	5	7	4				
15	10	13		11	12			2	3			6		8*	14	1	5	7	4	R	9		
15	10	13		11	12			2	3	4		8			14	1	5*	7		6	9	R	
15	10	13	12	11				2	3	4		6	7	8SO	14	1		5			9		
15	10	13		11	12			2	3	4		8			14	1	7	5		6	9		
15	10	13		11	12			2	3	4		8			14	1	7	5		6	9		
15	10	13	12	11				2	3			6	5		14	1		7		8	9	4	
15		13	12	11				2	3	4		6		8	14	1	7	5			9		10
15		13	12	11				2	3	4		6		8	14	1	7	5			9		10
15		13	14	11	12			2	3	5		6		8		1	7		4		9		10
15		13		11	12			2	3			6		8	14	1	7	5			9	4	10
15		13	12	11			R	2	3		10	6		8	14	1	7	5			9*	4	
15		13		11	12	9		2	3		10	6		8	14	1	7	5				4	
15		13	11	14	12	9		2	3		10	6		8		1	7	5				4	
15		13	12	14		9		2	3		10	6		8	11	1		5				4	
15		13	R	14	12	9		2	3		10	6		8SO	11	1	7	5				4	

Also Played: Whitfield No 7 match 17; Fraser No 1 match 1; Fowler No 5 match 1; Clark R match 2, No 8 match 3

Courage League Records 1994-95

League Debuts: Simon Mason, Richard Cramb, George Robson, I Whitfield
Players used: 28 – second lowest in Division
Ever Presents 3 Simon Mason, Tony Penn
Sent Off: Captain Richard Arnold, twice
Most appearances: 86 Ross Wilkinson

● Second highest try socrers in the Division

● Stopped opposition scoring tries in 6 matches – best record in the Division

● Simon Mason beat David Johnson's record for most points in a season

	Pts	T	C	P	D	App	Ave
Simon Mason	193	1	22	45	2	18	10.72
David Johnson	147	1	31	26	1	12	12.25

● Mason also broke Johnson's record of 30 penalties in a season from 1992-93

● Winger Tony Penn broke the record for most tries in a season by a back – the previous record was 6 held by 3 players

NEWCASTLE R.F.C.

COURAGE LEAGUE STATISTICS
compiled by Steve McCormack

Season	Div	P	W	D	L	F	T	C	P	D	A	T	C	P	D	Most Points	Most Tries
1987-88	2	10	2	1	7	124	14	4	16	4	145	21	5	16	1	56 David Johnson	4 David Walker
1988-89	2	11	4	0	7	176	21	13	21	1	248	41	14	12	6	57 Peter Clark	3 David Walker
1989-90	2	11	1	1	9	108	11	5	17	1	266	39	25	20	0	62 Graham Spearman	1 by 11 players
1990-91	2	12	6	0	6	169	20	10	21	2	140	16	8	15	5	66 David Johnson	5 Steve Douglas
1991-92	2	12	7	0	5	371	57	31	26	1	140	16	8	15	5	147 David Johnson	10 Peter Walton
1992-93	2	12	10	0	2	241	22	16	30	3	106	7	4	20	1	136 David Johnson	6 Ross Wilkinson
1993-94	1	18	2	1	15	190	17	6	27	4	483	54	27	51	2	79 David Johnson	4 Ross Wilkinson
1994-95	2	18	8	2	8	373	37	22	46	2	281	20	8	52	4	193 Simon Mason	8 Tony Penn
Total		104	40	5	59	1752	199	107	204	18	1809	214	96	205	24		

BIGGEST WIN	**Home:** 76-4 v Liverpool St H 29.2.92 CL2	**Away:** 36-13 v Morley 21.11.92 CL2
BIGGEST DEFEAT	**Home:** 9-47 v Saracens 22.4.89 CL2	**Away:** 5-66 v Leicester 12.3.94 CL1
MOST TRIES in a match	**For**: 13 v Liverpool St H 29.2.92	**Against:** 10 v Leicester 12.3.94
MOST CONSECUTIVE	**Wins:** 6	**Defeats:** 12
MOST APPEARANCES	**Forward:** Neil Frankland	**Back:** Ross Wilkinson
MOST CONSECUTIVE APPEARANCES	44 Neil Frankland 13.1.90-2.10.93	
CONSECUTIVE SCORING MATCHES	**Tries:** 3	
	Points: 18 Simon Mason	

	IN A SEASON	IN A CAREER	IN A MATCH
MOST POINTS	193 Simon Mason 1994-95 CL2	484 David Johnson 1987-94	28 David Johnson v Morley 11.1.92 Home CL2 v Liverpool St H 24.2.92 Home CL2
MOST TRIES	10 Peter Walton 1991-92 CL2	20 Ross Wilkinson 1987-95	3
MOST CONVERSIONS	31 David Johnson 1991-92 CL2	65 David Johnson 1987-94	9 David Johnson v Liverpool St H 29.2.92 Home CL2
MOST PENALTIES	45 Simon Mason 1994-95 CL2	105 David Johnson 1987-94	6 David Johnson v Morley 11.1.92 Home CL2
MOST DROP GOALS	4 David Johnson 1987-88 CL2	10 David Johnson 1987-94	2 David Johnson v Bedford 5.12.87 Away CL2

NORTHAMPTON F.C.

NICKNAME: SAINTS   **FOUNDED:** 1880

CLUB OFFICIALS

President
Roger Horwood
Chairman
Murray Holmes
Club Secretary
Roger Horwood
c/o Trinity Pavilion, Abbey Street, St
James, Northampton NN5 5LN
Fixtures Secretary
Bob Taylor
c/o Trinity Pavilion, Abbey Street, St
James, Northampton NN5 5LN
Press Officer
Ian McGeechan

Review of the Season

Long after the half-way stage of the recently completed season NORTHAMPTON seemed to be doomed but they staged a brave recovery with four wins in their last six matches and a most unlucky defeat at Gloucester (14-13) so they must count themselves most unfortunate to descend, a courageous success by Harlequins in their final match at Gloucester sealing their fate.

The fact that they also had a good cup run to the last eight showed that they were a better side than their ill luck suggested as they went past Moseley (16-6 at home) and Richmond (27-6 also at home) before a gallant effort at ultimate winners Bath (26-6) ended all that.

At full strength the Saints have a potentially fine side and the chances are that their star players, whose appearances were latterly restricted by World Cup commitments, will not defect, so a League Two outfit which can call on Nick Beal, Harvey Thornycroft, Paul Grayson, Martin Bayfield, Peter Walton and Tim Rodber plus some very talented young players should be back in the top flight sooner rather than later.

Back: M Volland, R McNaughton, D Elkington. Middle: P Pask (Physio), P Larkin (Coach), G Wright (Coach), A Pountney, M Hynes, J Phillips, M Bayfield, G Webster, G Seely, S Foale, M Allen, R Horwood (Hon Sec), D Hurlston (Team Sec), B Ingram (Team Sec). Front: A Clarke, P Grayson, I McGeechan (Director of Rugby), T Rodber (Captain), R Taylor: President) N Beal, H Thorneycroft, G Pearce

Colours: Black/green/gold hoops   **Change Colours:** White with black/green/gold hoops

NORTHAMPTON F.C.

COURAGE LEAGUE
MATCH DETAILS 1994-95

No	Date	Opponents	Ven	Result		Scorers
1	Sep 10	Leicester	A	L	15-28	Grayson (5P)
2	Sep 17	Bath	H	L	16-32	Grayson (1T 1C 3P)
3	Sep 24	Sale	A	L	6-14	Grayson (2P)
4	Oct 1	Northampton	H	L	15-18	Grayson (5P)
5	Oct 8	Northampton	H	L	16-23	Hunter (T) Grayson (1C 2P 1DG)
6	Oct 15	Northampton	A	L	10-13	Dawson (T) Grayson (C P)
7	Oct 22	Gloucester	H	W	9-6	Grayson (3P)
8	Oct 29	Wasps	A	L	21-27	Rodber (T) Pountney (T) Grayson (C 3P)
9	Nov 5	West Hartlepool	H	W	25-14	Cassell (T) Grayson (C 6P)
10	Jan 7	Leicester	H	L	18-20	Rodber (T) Seeley (T) Grayson (C 2P)
11	Jan 14	Bath	A	L	6-26	Grayson (2P)
12	Feb 11	Sale	H	L	9-22	Grayson (3P)
13	Mar 4	Bristol	A	W	24-13	Hunter (T) Dawson (T) Grayson (2C) Thorneycroft (T) Allen (T)
14	Mar 25	Harlequins	A	L	9-10	Grayson (3P)
15	Apr 8	Orrell	H	W	15-3	Grayson (1DG 4P)
16	Apr 15	Gloucester	A	L	13-14	Dawson (T)
17	Apr 22	Wasps	H	W	19-13	Seely (T) Grayson (4P 1C)
18	Apr 29	West Hartlepool	A	W	21-12	Seely (T) Allen (T) Grayson (C 2P) Hepher (DG)

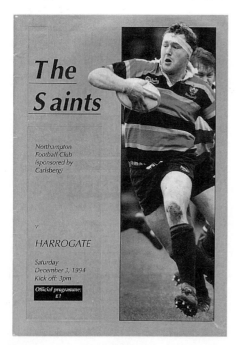

The Saints

Northampton
Football Club
(sponsored by
Carlsberg)

v

HARROGATE

Saturday
December 3, 1994
Kick off: 3pm
Official programme:
£1

PROGRAMME DETAILS

Price: £1.00
Pages: 36
Good quality paper with at least 14 original pages per issue.
Interesting features with colour used on cover, for some
advertisements and the attractive cover.
Editor: Brian Barron
Advertising Rates: Please contact Byline Publishing 01604
29483

CLUB & GROUND DETAILS

Franklins Gardens, Weedon Road, Northampton NN5 5BG
Telephone: Rugby Admin 01604 755149 Commercial 01604
751543
Fax: Rugby Admin 01604 588408 Commercial 01604
750061

Total Capacity: 8,500
Seated: 2,500
Standing: 6,000
Simple Directions to Ground: From M1, Junction 15A or
16 follow A45 to Northampton and Saints signs
Nearest Railway Station: Castle Station Nipton
Car Parking: 500
Season Tickets: Adults £90 Children/OAPs £36
Match Prices: League Adults £7 Ground £4 Other Adults £5
Ground £3
Membership:
Training Nights: Tuesday & Thursday

NORTHAMPTON F.C.

MATCH BY MATCH PLAYERS BY POSITION

Hunter	Moir	Beal	MacNaughton	Thorneycroft	Grayson	Taylor	Volland	Roworth	Allen C	Bayfield	Allen M	Walton	Pountney	Rodber	Parkman	Lewis	Seeley	Hynes	Clarke	Phillips	Elkington	Foale	Dawson
15	14	13	12	11	10	9	1	2	3	4	5	6	7	8									
15	11		12	14	10	9	1	2	3	4	5	6	7	8	13								
	11	13	12	14	10	9		3			5	6	7	8			1	2	4				
15		13	12	11	10			2	3		5	6*	R71	7	14		1		4		9	8	
15		13	12	11	10			2	3		5		7	8	14		1		4		6	9	
15**		13	12	11	10	R**		2	3*	4			R*	7		1	5				6	9	
		13		11	10						5	12	7	6		3	8	1	2	4			9
		13		11	10						5	12	7	6		3	8	1	2	4			9
		13		11	10						5	12	R	6		3	8	1	2	4	R**	**	9
	14	15		11	10	9					5	12		8	13	3	6	1	2	4			
	11	15		14	10	9	R					12	7		13	3	8	1	2*	5	R**		
	14	15		11	10							12	7		13	3	8	1	2	4	5	9	
15		14		11	10					5	13		6	12		3	8	1	2	4*			9
15		14		11	10	1				5	12	6	8	13		3		2	4				9
15		14		11	10	1				5	12	6	7		13			2	4	R			
15		14		11	10			1		5	12	6	7	8	13			2	4			9*	
15		14	13	11	10	1					12	6	7			8		2	4			9	5
	14		13	11	15	1					12		7			8		2	4			9	

Also Played: Edwards No 5 matches 1, 2; Gallagher No 9 match 15, R match 16; Judd No 5 matches 3, 7, 8, 9; Wright No 7 match 6; Cassell No 7 matches 9, 10, 13, No 7** match 14, No 7* match 15, No 6 match 12; Morgan No 14 matches 6, 7, 8, No 14 match 9; Hepher No 10 match 18; Webster No 4 match 11, No 5 match 18, R match 13; Pearce No 3 matches 15, 16, 17, 18

Courage League Records 1994-95

League Debuts: Budge Pountney, Martin Hynes, Mark Lewis, Grant Segley, Matt Allen, Justyn Cassell, Andy Gallagher, Alastair Hepher, John Wright
Try on Debut: Cassell
Players used: 33
Ever Presents 2 Grayson, Thorneycroft
Most appearances: 75 Gary Pearce & Frank Packman

- Had only 2 wins in first 12 games including 6 straight losses to start the season
- Did double over West Hartlepool
- Failed to score tries in 8 of their 18 games
- Scored just 16 tries – easily he lowest in the Division
- Paul Grayson contributed 73% of Northampton's points – 189 out of 267
- Grayson broke his own record for points in a season, previously 132

	Pts	T	C	P	D	App	Ave
1993-94	132	2	10	33	1	13	10.15
1994-95	189	1	11	52	2	18	10.50
	321	3	21	85	3	31	10.35

- Northampton's leading points scorer John Steele scored 425 points in 58 games at an average of 7.33 per game
- Tim Rodber actually made more League appearances than last season, 13 to 12, as did England team mate Bayfield, 14 to 10
- Tim Rodber equalled Paul Alston's record of tries by a forward in the League. They both have 9

	Tries	Apps	Strike Rate
Paul Alston	9	41	4.55
Tim Rodber	9	57	6.33

NORTHAMPTON F.C.

COURAGE LEAGUE STATISTICS

compiled by Steve McCormack

Season	Div	P	W	D	L	F	T	C	P	D	A	T	C	P	D	Most Points	Most Tries
1987-88	2	10	1	0	9	81	10	7	9	0	226	33	20	16	2	27 Phil Larkin	4 Paul Alson
1988-89	2	11	5	2	4	165	28	10	10	1	131	12	7	17	6	43 John Steele	6 Frank Packman
1989-90	2	11	9	1	1	192	23	11	22	4	135	12	6	22	3	105 John Steele	4 Frank Packman & John Thame
1990-91	1	12	5	1	6	149	15	10	20	3	254	38	18	19	3	83 John Steele	3 Wayne Shelford
1991-92	1	12	9	1	2	209	22	11	30	3	136	11	7	23	3	110 John Steele	5 Harvey Thorneycroft
1992-93	1	12	8	0	4	215	24	16	20	1	150	11	4	27	2	52 John Steele	6 Harvey Thorneycroft
1993-94	1	18	9	0	9	305	23	14	50	4	342	34	17	40	6	Paul Grayson	2 by 7 players
1994-95	1	18	6	0	12	267	16	11	52	3	335	35	20	36	4	189 Paul Grayson	3 Grant Segley & Matt Dawson
TOTAL		104	52	5	47	1583	161	90	213	19	1709	186	99	200	29		

BIGGEST WIN — **Home:** 55-9 v West Hartlepool 3.4.93 CL1   **Away:** 34-22 v London Scottish 24.4.93 CL1

BIGGEST DEFEAT — **Home:** 3-50 v London Scottish 3.10.87 CL1   **Away:** 0-60 v Orrell 27.10.90 CL1

MOST TRIES in a match — **For:** 8 v Rugby 28.4.90 CL1 v West Hartlepool 3.4.93 CL1   **Against:** 11 v Orrell 27.10.CL1

MOST CONSECUTIVE — **Wins:** 7   **Defeats:** 6

MOST APPEARANCES — **Forward:** 75 Gary Pearce   **Back:** 75 Frank Packman

MOST CONSECUTIVE APPEARANCES — 31 Frank Packman

CONSECUTIVE SCORING MATCHES — **Tries:** 4 Ian Hunter   **Points:** 18 Paul Grayson

	IN A SEASON	IN A CAREER	IN A MATCH
MOST POINTS	189 Paul Grayson 1994-95 CL1	425 John Steele 1988-94	26 Paul Grayson v Bristol 2.10.93 Away CL1
MOST TRIES	6 Frank Packman 1988-89 CL2	Harvey Thorneycroft 1992-93 CL1	19 Frank Packman 1987-95
MOST CONVERSIONS	11 John Steele 1989-90 CL2 Paul Grayson 1994-95 CL1	40 John Steele 1988-94	6 Nick Beal v West Hartlepool 3.4.93 Home CL1
MOST PENALTIES	52 Paul Grayson 1994-95 CL1	95 John Steele 1988-94	6 paul Grayson v West Hartlepool 5.11.94 Home CL1
MOST DROP GOALS	3 John Steele 1989-90 CL2 1990-91 CL1	11 John Steele 1988- 94	3 John Steele v Wsps 23.9.91 Away CL1

NOTTINGHAM R.F.C.

NICKNAME: Green & Whites   **FOUNDED:** 1877

CLUB OFFICIALS
President
John Drapkin
Chairman
Alan Bragg
Club Secretary
Mrs A E Gill
Barn End, Hill Road, Orston,
Nottingham NG13 9ND
Tel: (H) 01949 851197
Fixtures Secretary
George Reay
43 Mapperley Orchard, Arnold,
Nottingham NG5 8AH
Tel: (H) 0115 926 2612
Press Officer
Andi Starr
Tel: (H) 960 9411 Mobile 0850 835827

Review of the Season

Not so long ago NOTTINGHAM were firmly established in the top flight, but relegation to League Two combined with moves to other clubs and retirements have hit them badly and in a season of constant struggle, which included a 41-10 disaster at Bristol in their only Pilkington Cup outing, it needed a 14-11 success at fellow strugglers Waterloo in their last game to preserve their status for at least another season.

Some players are now veterans, notably Chris Gray their former Scotland lock, and they were not helped by injuries to key backs, although the pack looks promising with consistent performances having come from the front-row of Freer, hooker and captain West and tighthead Jackson. No8 Bradley also performed well, but new talent is needed elsewhere with the scrum-half position a problem unless Gabriel can recover previous form, although Smallwood on the left wing could be a lethal try-scorer.

The remaining backs need to find some confidence and if they do fans can expect good results from fullback Gallagher and the centres Byrom, Musto and Furley, but the new season might still be tough and survival rather than promotion might be their main aim.

Back: Paul Stone (Coach), Taff Purnell (Baggage Manager), Richard Byrom, Matt Gallagher, Ben Ryan, Nick Carroll, Nigel Malik, Nick Berry, David Hindmarch, David Wright, Steve Cairns, Ian Stent, David Moss-Bowpitt (Coach). Front: Richard Bygrave, Andy Smallwood, Buster Musto, Gary Rees, Dorian West (Capt), Andy Furley, Andy Jackson, Martin Freer, Alan Royer
Colours: Green and White   **Change Colours**: Yellow hoops

NOTTINGHAM F.C.

COURAGE LEAGUE
MATCH DETAILS 1994-95

No	Date	Opponents	Ven	Result		Scorers
1	Sep 10	Fylde	A	W	14-33	Bygraves (T) Gallagher (3P)
2	Sep 17	Coventry	H	W	23-7	Musto (T) Furley (T) Gallagher (2C 3P)
3	Sep 24	Moseley	A	L	12-19	Gallagher (4P)
4	Oct 1	Wakefield	H	W	29-25	Bradley (T) Smallwood (T) Gallagher (2C 5P)
5	Oct 8	Saracens	H	L	9-17	Gallagher (3P)
6	Oct 15	Newcastle Gos	A	L	6-27	Stent (2P)
7	Oct 22	London Scottish	H	W	23-8	Stent (1T 2C 3P) Penalty Try
8	Oct 29	London Irish	A	L	22-24	West (T) Stent (1C 5P
9	Nov 5	Waterloo	H	W	28-11	Furley (2T) Pen Try, Stent (2C 3P)
10	Jan 7	Fylde	H	L	9-10	Stent (3P)
11	Jan 14	Coventry	A	W	19-6	West (T) Carroll (DG) Gallagher (1C 3P)
12	Feb 11	Moseley	H	D	9-9	Gallagher (3P)
13	Mar 4	Wakefield	A	L	17-22	Smallwood (T) Passmore (T) Pen Try, Gabriel (1C)
14	Mar 25	Saracens	A	L	7-32	Musto (T) Gallagher (C)
15	Apr 8	Newcastle Gos	H	L	18-33	Smallwood (T) Gallagher (P) Gabriel (T) Bees (T)
16	Apr 15	London Scottish	A	W	18-17	Gallagher (T) West (T) Stent (1C 2P)
17	Apr 22	London Irish	H	W	22-11	Gray (T) Stent (T 4P)
18	Apr 29	Waterloo	A	W	14-11	Smallwood (T) Stent (3)

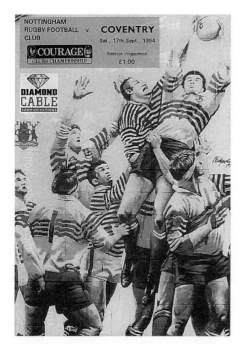

PROGRAMME DETAILS

Price: £1.00
Pages: 36
At least ten new pages in each issue printed on good paper with an original cover design
Editor: Alan Hodgkinson
Advertising Rates: Full page colour £400, Full page b/w £275, Half page £150

CLUB & GROUND DETAILS

Ireland Avenue, Dovecote Lane, Beeston, Nottingham NG9 1JD
Telephone: 0115 9254238/9224920
Fax: 0115 9254238

Total Capacity: 4,950
Seated: 450
Standing: 4,500
Simple Directions to Ground: Off Queens Road, Beeston (main Nottingham to Long Eaton Road)
Nearest Railway Station: Beeston
Car Parking: 175
Season Tickets: Adults £50 Children/OAPs £25
Match Prices: Adults £2 Children/OAPs £1
Membership: Seniors £30 Juniors £15
Training Nights: Mondy & Thursday - Senior; Sunday am - Mini/Junior

NOTTINGHAM R.F.C.

MATCH BY MATCH PLAYERS BY POSITION

Gallagher	Byrom	Musto	Furley	Bygrave	Carroll	Freer	West	Jackson	Gray	Langley	Malik	Rees	Bradley	Smallwood	Roberts	Hindmarch	Davies	Sussoms	Stent	Webster	Brennan	Gabriel	Passmore
15	14	13	12	11	10	1	2	3	4	5	6	7	8										
15	14	13	12		10	1	2	3	4		6	7	8	11	9	5							
15	14	13	12		10	1	2	3	4		6	7	8	11	9	5							
15	14	13	12		10	1	2	3	4			7	8	11	9	5	6						
15*	14	13	12		10	1	2	3	4			7	8	11	9	5		6					
15	14	12	13			1	2	3	4		8	7		11	9	5	6		10				
15	14	13	12			1	2	3	4	5	8	7		11	9		6		10				
15	14	13	12			1	2	3	4		8	7		11*	9	5	6		10				
	15	12	14			1	2	3	4	5			8	11	9		6		10	13	7		
15	14	12			10	1	2	3	4	5			8	11			6			13	7	9	
15	14	12			10	1	2	3	4	5			8	11						13	7	9	6
10	14	12	13			1	2	3	4*	5	R		8	11							7	9	6
15	14	10	13			1	2	3	4R			7		11				5		12	8	9	6
10	14					1	2	3	4				6	11				5		13		9	
15	14		13			1	2	3	4				6	11				5	10			9	
	15		13	14		1	2		4				6					5	10			9	
15	14		13			1	2		4				8	11				5	10			9	6

Also Played: Royer No 9 match 1, R match 9; Hartley No 15 matches 13, 15; Parsonage R match 14, No 8 matches 15, 16, 17; Tomlinson No 12, matches 15, 16, 17, 18; Downey R match 16 No 3, matches 17, 18; Jones No 1 match 17; Beese No 7 matches 15, 16, 17, 18

Courage League Records 1994-95

League Debuts: Nick Carroll, Bob Sussame, Ian Stent, John Brennan, Andy Passmore, Richard Tomlinson, Gareth Beese
Tries on Debut: G Beese
Players used: 31
Ever Presents 3 Richard Byrom, Dorian West, Martin Freer
Most appearances: 89 Richard Byrom

● Dorian West ends the season on 40 consecutive League appearances, one behind Guy Gregory's club record

● Andy Smallwood ends the season in second place on Nottingham's try scoring list

	Tries	Apps	Strike Rate
Richard Byrom	11	89	8.09
Andy Smallwood	9	31	3.44

● Dorian West and Mark Bradley now jointly hold the record for Nottingham in League rugby, 6. Bradley previously held the record, 5, with Martin Pepper

NOTTINGHAM R.F.C

COURAGE LEAGUE STATISTICS
compiled by Steve McCormack

Season	Div	P	W	D	L	F	T	C	P	D	A	T	C	P	D	Most Points	Most Tries
1987-88	1	11	4	1	6	146	14	6	22	4	170	22	11	18	2	86 Simon Hodgkinson	5 Clifton Jones,
1988-89	1	11	6	1	4	142	10	6	24	6	122	7	5	26	2	98 Simon Hodgkinson	2 Lee Johnson
1989-90	1	11	6	0	5	187	22	15	19	4	148	21	8	15	1	82 Simon Hodgkinson	5 Gary Hartley
1990-91	1	12	6	0	6	138	12	9	22	2	194	24	12	22	2	80 Simon Hodgkinson	3 Richard Byrom
1991-92	1	12	2	1	9	133	11	7	22	3	204	24	12	27	1	48 Guy Gregory	4 Martin Pepper
1992-93	2	12	8	0	4	249	22	14	28	9	145	13	4	21	3	106 Guy Gregory	3 Richard Byrom
1993-94	2	18	8	1	9	254	17	11	44	5	326	31	18	38	7	171 Guy Gregory	5 Andy Smallwood
1994-5	2	18	8	1	9	299	24	13	50	1	322	26	12	51	5	97 Ian Stent	4 Andy Smallwood
TOTALS		105	48	5	52	1548	132	81	231	34	1631	168	83	218	23		

BIGGEST WIN — **Home:** 78-0 v Morley 24.10.92 CL1 — **Away:** 46-5 v Blackheath 26.9.92 CL2

BIGGEST DEFEAT — **Home:** 18-33 v Newcastle Gosforth 8.4.95 CL2 — **Away:** 7-41 v Sale 23.4.94 CL2

MOST TRIES in a match — **For**: 12 v Morley 24.10.92 CL1 — **Against:** 6 v Sale 23.4.94 CL2

MOST CONSECUTIVE — **Wins:** 5 — **Defeats:** 6

MOST APPEARANCES — **Forward:** 87 Chris Gray — **Back:** 89 Richard Byrom

MOST CONSECUTIVE APPEARANCES — 41 Guy Gregory 23.11.91-30.4.94

CONSECUTIVE SCORING MATCHES — **Tries:** 4 Andy Smallwood — **Points:** 20 Guy Gregory

	IN A SEASON	IN A CAREER	IN A MATCH
MOST POINTS	171 Guy Gregory 1993-94 CL2	416 Simon Hodgkinson 1987-93	25 Guy Gregory v Otley 11.9.93 Home CL2
MOST TRIES	5 Clifton Jones 1987-88 CL1 Gary Hartley 1989-90 CL1 Andy Smallwood 1993-94 CL2	11 Richard Byrom 1987-95	4 Gary Hartley v Morley 24.10.92 Home CL2
MOST CONVERSIONS	13 Simon Hodgkinson 1989-90 CL1	35 Simon Hodgkinson 1987-93	9 Guy Gregory v Morley 24.10.92 Home CL2
MOST PENALTIES	43 Guy Gregory 1993-94 CL2	100 Simon Hodgkinson 1987-93	6 Guy Gregory v Saracens 12.3.94 CL2
MOST DROP GOALS	9 Guy Gregory 1992-93 CL2	19 Guy Gregory 1991-94	2 Andy Sutton v Harlequins 31.3.90 Away CL1 Guy Gregory v Rosslyn Park 4.4.92 Home Cl1 v Rosslyn Park 21.1.92 Away CL2 v Fylde 9.1.93 Home CL2 v Bedford 13.2.93 Away CL2

WAKEFIELD R.F.C.

NICKNAME: Field   **FOUNDED:** 1901

CLUB OFFICIALS
President
Alan Birkinshaw
Chairman
Nigel Foster
Club Secretary
Jim Coulson
39 Melbourne Road, St Johns,
Wakefield WF1 2RL
Tel: (H) 01274 872710 (W) 01924 374801
Fixtures Secretary
Bill Halstead
84 Whitcliffe Road, Cleckheaton BD19 3DR
Tel: (H) 01274 872710
Press Officer
Jim Coulson
Tel: (H) 01274 872710 (W) 01924 374801

Review of the Season

Our ultimate ambition is to play First Division rugby. Yet in a season which started indifferently but finished magnificently, we were thwarted once again by a change in regulations. In any other season, Second position (7 pts clear of Third) would have seen us challenging the elite this season for league points instead of friendly matches. Until the last Saturday of the season we were the only side to beat Saracens and gave them a real battle in horrendous conditions at Southgate, losing only 10-3. We had a superb Pilkington Cup starting in magnificent fashion by beating Gloucester 19-9 at home in the "shock" of the round. Fate decreed we travel to Lydney in the next round - eventually! The Friday night meet of 4.00 pm was met by only 1 player, with Yorkshire in the grip of a blizzard. The last player didn't arrive until 8.30 pm, nearly 6 hours after setting off. An excellent win at Lydney followed but our quarter final at Harlequins was a repeat of our heavy defeat of a couple of seasons earlier. This time we had our chances, but Lady Luck didn't shine and we bowed out 13-8.

The second half of the season has given us real hope that, at last, this season we can finally climb to the summit and achieve First Division status. New recruits Alistair Bailey, Andy Hodgkinson, Marcus Kelly, Mike McCarthy, Shaun McMain, Richard Petyt, Roger Robert, Chris Rushforth, Ian Shuttleworth, Ben Wheeler and Steve Wigley strengthened our squad with youth and experience. Wime some new recruits to add, we could see the emergence of Yorkshire's First Division club. The omens are good, the playing strength is good (2nd XV - North East Merit table winner - 4 times in 5 years, Colts had their best ever season). We are on the launching pad, and ready for lift off. Can we make it? Watch this space!

Photo: Gordon Bunney

Colours: Black and gold quarters   **Change Colours**: All red

WAKEFIELD R.F.C.

COURAGE LEAGUE
MATCH DETAILS 1994-95

No	Date	Opponents	Ven	Result	Scorers
1	Sep 10	Coventry	A	W 15-14	Morley (2T) Jackson (1C 1P)
2	Sep 17	Moseley	H	L 17-22	Morley (T) Jackson (4P)
3	Sep 24	Saracens	H	W 17-8	Thompson (2T) Jackson (2C 1P)
4	Oct 1	Nottingham	A	L 25-29	Maynard (T) Jackson (1C 6P)
5	Oct 8	Newcastle Gos	H	L 9-21	Jackson (3P)
6	Oct 15	London Scottish	A	L 21-24	Jackson (1C 2P) Thompson (T) Stewart (T) Scully (P)
7	Oct 22	London Irish	H	W 25-3	Garnett (T) Jackson (1C 6P)
8	Oct 29	Waterloo	A	W 19-18	Maynard (T) Petyt (T DG) Jackson (2P)
9	Nov 5	Fylde	H	W 24-13	Scully (T) Metcalfe (T) Jackson (1C 4P)
10	Jan 7	Coventry	H	W 19-14	White (T) Jackson (1C 4P)
11	Jan 14	Moseley	A	W 16-11	Thompson (T) Jackson (1C 3P)
12	Feb 11	Saracens	A	L 3-10	Jackson (P)
13	Mar 4	Nottingham	H	W 22-17	Whine (T) Jackson (1C 5P)
14	Mar 25	Newcastle Gos	A	D 15-15	Jackson (5P)
15	Apr 8	London Scottish	H	W 42-19	White (T) Jackson (2T 3C 2P) Thompsosn (T) Scully (T) Falkingham (T)
16	Apr 13	London Irish	A	W 33-3	Jackson (2C 3P) Thompson (2T) Maynard (T) Garnett (T)
17	Apr 22	Waterloo	H	W 21-12	Holloway (2T) Jackson (1C 3P)
18	Apr 29	Fylde	A	W 11-8	Falkingham (T) Jackson (2P)

PROGRAMME DETAILS

Price: £1.00
Pages: 32
With inner eight pages of original copy each game. The remainder of the programme is mostly advertisements with colour throughout. The cover could be more attractive.

Advertising Rates: £100-£600

CLUB & GROUND DETAILS

College Grove, Eastmoor Road, Wakefield WF1 3RR
Telephone: 01924 374801
Fax: 01924 374801

Total Capacity: 2,450
Seated: 450
Standing: 2,000
Simple Directions to Ground: As before
Nearest Railway Station: Wakefield
Car Parking: 300
Season Tickets: Adults £55.00 Ladies £25.00 Children/OAPs £25 Ladies £17.50
Match Prices: Adults £5 + £1 Stand Children/OAPs £3 + £1 Stand
Membership: Seniors £25.00 Juniors £10.00
Training Nights: Mondays & Thursdays - Colts Wednesday

WAKEFIELD R.F.C.

MATCH BY MATCH PLAYERS BY POSITION

Jackson	Thompson	Metcalfe	Maynard	Morley	Scowling	Scully	Szabo	Garnett	McMain	Croft	Falkingham	Stewart	Griffiths	Sowerby	Cawthorne	White	Green	Yates	Day	Petyt	Bailey	Crushworth	Lathem
15	14	13	12	11	10	9	1	2	3	4	5	6	7	8									
15	14	13	12	11		10	1	2	3	4	5	6	7	8	9								
15	14		13	11		10	1	2	3	4		5	7		9	12	8						
15	14	12	13*	11		10	1	2	3	4		5	7		9	R	8						
15	14	12	13	11		10	1	2	3	4		5	7*		9		8	6					
15	14	12	13	11	10	9	3	2		4		5	7	8			6		1				
15	14	12		11	10	9	3	2		4		5	7	8	13		6		1				
15	14		12	11		9	3*	2		4		5	7	8	13		6		1	10			R
15		13	12	11		9		2		4		5	7	8	14		6	3		10			1
15	11	12	13			9		2		4		5	7	8	14		6	3		10			1
15	11	12	13			9		2		4		5		8	14		6	7	3	10			1
15	11	12	13			9		2		4		5		8	14		6	7	3	10			1
15	11	12	13		10	9	3	2^SO		4		5		8	14		6	7					1
15	11	12	13				3	2		4		5		8	9	14	6	7		10*			1
15	11	12	13			9		2			5			8	14		6	7	3	10	4		1
15	11	12	13		10	9		2		4				8	14		6	7	3	5	R		1
15	11	12	13			9		2		4*				8				7	3	5	6		1
15	11	12	13		10	9		2	5**	4	R**			8	14		6	7	3*				1

Also Played: Kelly R match 14; Shuttleworth No 10 match 17, Burman R1 match 18; Holloway No 14 match 17; Price No 6 matches 3, 4, R match 5

Courage League Records 1994-95

League Debuts: Shaun McMain, Kern Yates, Richard Petyt, Andy Bailey, Chris Rushworth, Ian Shuttleworth, Tom Holloway
Tries on Debut: Richard Petyt
Players Used: 27 – lowest in Division
Ever Presents 2 Mike Jackson, Terry Garnett
Most appearances: 102 Dave Scully
Player sent off: Terry Garnett

● Mike Jackson broke Ray Adamson's 7 year record of most points in a season as well as Guy Gregory's Divisional record

	Pts	T	C	P	D	App	Ave
Mike Jackson	213	2	16	56	-	18	11.83
Ray Adamson	105	1	19	21	-	8	13.13

● Jackson also passes Andy Atkinson's league record for career points

	Pts	T	C	P	D	App	Ave
Mike Jackson	303	2	25	81	-	31	9.77
Andy Atkinson	223	11	30	39	-	37+2	6.03

● Dave Scully becomes the second player to reach 100 League appearances in the National Divisions The first by 1 week was another scrum half, Andy Maunder from Exeter. Scully extended his try scoring record to 30

	Tries	Apps	Strike Rate
Dave Scully	30	102	3.40
Jon Sleightholme	27	38	1.40
Mike Harrison	22	47	2.14
Richard Thompson	19	55	2.89

● Only 5 of Wakefield's 29 tries were scored by forwards

WAKEFIELD R.F.C.

COURAGE LEAGUE STATISTICS
compiled by Steve McCormack

Season	Div	P	W	D	L	F	T	C	P	D	A	T	C	P	D	Most Points	Most Tries
1987-88	3	11	10	0	1	308	45	25	26	0	90	8	5	13	3	105 Ray Adamson	8 Simon Cowling
1988-89	3	11	9	0	2	282	46	25	16	0	114	12	6	15	3	69 Andy Atkinson	8 Dave Scully
1989-90	3	11	7	1	3	210	34	16	13	1	126	15	6	16	2	31 Ray Adamson	7 Mike Harrison Mike Murtagh
1990-91	2	12	8	0	4	188	25	11	21	1	109	8	4	21	2	89 Andy Atkinson	4 Raz Bowers Dave Scully
1991-92	2	12	7	0	5	187	30	14	13	0	194	27	16	14	4	32 Rob Liley Jon Sleightholme	8 Jon Sleightholme
1992-93	2	12	8	1	3	186	17	10	24	3	123	10	5	15	6	101 Rob Liley	7 Jon Sleightholme
1993-94	2	18	8	3	7	347	34	18	47	0	240	21	9	35	4	90 Mike Jackson	12 Jon Sleightholme
1994-95	2	18	12	1	5	354	29	16	58	1	261	18	9	47	4	213 Mike Jackson	7 Richard Thompson
TOTAL		105	69	6	30	2062	260	135	218	6	1257	119	60	176	28		

BIGGEST WIN   **Home:** 70-0 v Metropolitan Police 24.9.88 CL3   **Away:** 50-3 v Birmingham 31.10.87 CL3

BIGGEST DEFEAT   **Home:** 19-28 v Sale 9.4.94 CL2   **Away:** 3-37 v Sale 7.12.91 CL2

MOST TRIES in a match   **For**: 14 v Metropolitan Police 24.9.88   **Against:** 6 v Sale 7.12.91

MOST CONSECUTIVE   **Wins:** 10   **Defeats:** 3

MOST APPEARANCES   **Forward:** 83 Terry Garnett   **Back:** 102 Dave Scully

MOST CONSECUTIVE APPEARANCES   49 Dave Scully

CONSECUTIVE SCORING MATCHES   **Tries:** 3

   Points: 21 Robert Liley

	IN A SEASON	IN A CAREER	IN A MATCH
MOST POINTS	213 Mike Jackson 1994-95 CL2	303 Mike Jackson 1993-95	23 Robert Liley v Rugby 11.9.93 Home CL2
MOST TRIES	12 Jon Sleightholme 1993-94 CL2	30 Dave Scully 1987-95	3 on 8 occasions by 6 players Simon Cowling 2. Mike Harrison 2. Andy Holloway. Andy Atkinson. Mike Murtagh. Jon Sleightholme
MOST CONVERSIONS	19 Ray Adamson 1987-88 CL3	36 Ray Adamson 1987-90	7 Ray Adamson v Birmingham 31.10.87 Away CL3
MOST PENALTIES	57 Mike Jackson 1994-95 CL2	81 Mike Jackson 1993-94	6 Ray Adamson v Vale of Lune 27.2.88 Home CL3. Mike Jackson v Nottingham 1.10.94 Away CL2 v London Irish 22.10.94 Home CL2
MOST DROP GOALS	2 Robert Liley 1992-93 CL2	2 Steve Townend 1987-93 Robert Liley 1991-93	1 on 6 occasions by 4 players Steven Townend 2. Robert Liley 2. Richard Petyt 1. Brian Barley

WATERLOO F.C.

NICKNAME: **FOUNDED:** 1882

CLUB OFFICIALS

President
John Kay
Chairman
Ray Wilson
Club Secretary
Keith Alderson
66 St Michaels Road, Blundell Sands,
Liverpool L23 7UW
Tel: (H) 0151 924 1168 (W) 0151 933 8088
Fixtures Secretary
John Rimmer
2 Chapel Meadow, Longton, Preston
PR4 5NR
Tel: (H) 01772 614277 (W) 01772
885000
Press Officer
Ian H Fazey
Tel: 0151 928 3441

Review of the Season

When WATERLOO took the field at home against Nottingham both needed both the points at stake to avoid relegation and the visitors won a desperately close final game – 14-11. So, Waterloo could only escape if Fylde failed to gain a point at home against second placed Wakefield, who had nothing to gain from a victory.

As luck would have it Wakefield did win and League Two rugby continues at Blundellsands for another season, but there will have to be some very hard thinking by the Waterloo management about playing staff problems and other matters if another season of nail-biting is to be avoided.

Even the Pilkington Cup provided little cheer as a narrow (21-19) win at rising stars Rotherham was followed by an embarrassing 54- 13 defeat by subsequent finalists Wasps at home.

Apart from their consistent scrum-half Wright, Waterloo had no ever present player during the league campaign, which started well enough with six wins in the first seven matches and only two successes thereafter. Fullback Swindells, the most successful kicker, missed only one game and flanker Peter Buckton was absent on only three league occasions, but in other positions injuries and loss of form caused too much chopping and changing with utility back Craig and tighthead Peters being regulars once they became available on a permanent basis.

So, the missing ingredient is consistency and a scoring record which was superior in the programme only to the two relegated clubs. There is plenty of planning to do by a club, which quite recently knocked Bath out of the Pilkington Cup.

Colours: Myrtle, scarlet and white hoops   **Change Colours:** White with myrtle and scarlet 'V' hoops

WATERLOO F.C.

COURAGE LEAGUE
MATCH DETAILS 1994-95

No	Date	Opponents	Ven	Result	Scorers
1	Sep 10	Newcastle Gos	H	W 18-13	Swindells (6P)
2	Sep 17	London Scottish	A	W 25-13	White (T) Ryan (1DG) Swindells (1C 5P)
3	Sep 24	London Irish	H	W 22-19	Thompson (2P) Northey (T) Beeley (T) Ryan (2DG)
4	Oct 1	Saracens	A	L 5-27	Ryan (T)
5	Oct 8	Fylde	A	W 16-12	Brennand (T) Ryan (T) Swindells (2P)
6	Oct 15	Coventry	H	W 26-5	Buckton (2T) Swindells (2C 4P)
7	Oct 22	Moseley	A	W 25-9	Swindells (2C 2P) Wright (T) Bibby (T) Craig (T)
8	Oct 29	Wakefield	H	L 18-19	Swindells (5P) Aitcheson (1DG)
9	Nov 5	Nottingham	A	L 11-28	Brennand (T) Swindells (2P)
10	Jan 7	Newcastle Gos	A	L 16-33	Ryan (T) Wright (T) Swindells (2P)
11	Jan 14	London Scottish	H	W 17-9	Greenhalgh (T) Ryan (2P) Swindells (2P)
12	Feb 11	London Irish	R	L 3-23	Swindells (P)
13	Mar 4	Saracens	H	L 16-23	Wright (T) Swindells (1C 3P)
14	Mar 25	Fylde	H	L 12-19	Swindells (4P)
15	Apr 8	Coventry	A	W 22-17	Allott (T) Ryan (DG) Swindells (1C 4P)
16	Apr 15	Moseley	H	L 12-27	Wright (T) Buckton (T) Swindells (1C)
17	Apr 22	Wakefield	A	L 12-21	Swindells (4P)
18	Apr 29	Nottingham	H	L 11-14	Ryan (T) Swindells (2P)

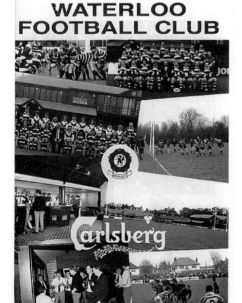

PROGRAMME DETAILS

Pages: 32
With an attractive cover, on good paper. Colour throughout but very little original reading matter.

Advertising Rates: Full page £500 half page £250

CLUB & GROUND DETAILS

The Pavilion, St Anthony's Road, Blundell Sands, Liverpool L23 8TW
Telephone: 0151 924 4552

Total Capacity: 8,900
Seated: 100
Standing: 8,000
Simple Directions to Ground: End of M57, follow signs for Crosby, Waterloo F.C. sign-posted to ground.
Nearest Railway Station: Blundell Sands and Crosby
Car Parking: 100
Season Tickets:
Match Prices: Adults £6.00 Ground £5.00 Children/APs £3.00 Ground £2.50
Membership: Seniors £28.00 Juniors £19.00
Training Nights: Tuesdays and Thursdays

WATERLOO F.C.

MATCH BY MATCH PLAYERS BY POSITION

Swindells	Brennand	Aitcheson	Northey	Greenhalgh	Ryan	Wright	Beckett	Hayton	Turner	Fletcher	Way	Blyth	Buckton	White	Meredith	Thompson	Bibby	Allott	Beeley	McCraig	Peters	Ireland	Handley
15	14	13	12	11	10	9	1	2	3	4	5	6	7	8									
15	11		13	12	10	9	1	2	3	4	5	6	7	8	14								
	14		12	11	10	9	1	2	3		5	6		6			15	13	4	8			
15	14		12		10	9	1	2	3		5	6	7*	8			11	13	4				
15	14		12	11	10	9	1	2	3	4	5	6						13	8				
15		10		11		9	1	2		4	5	6	7*				12	13	8	14	3		
15	14	10				9	1	2		4	5	6					13	12	8	11	3	7	
15	14	10				9	1	2	3	4	5	6					13	12	8	11		7	
15	14	10				9	1	2			5	8	7				13	12	4	11	3	6	
15				11	10	9	1				4	8	7				12	5		13	3	6	
15*				11	10	9	1		2		4	8	7				15		5	13	3	6	
14	13				10	9	1		2			6	7	4	11	15			8	12	3		
11	12					9	1		2			6	7	4	14		12	5	8	13	3		10
11					10	9			2				7	4			12	5	8	13	7		15
11					10	9					4		7	6			13	5	8	13	3		15
11	12				10	9			2		5		7	6			13	4	8		3		15
15	12				10	9			2				7	4				5	8	13	3		
15					10	9	1		2			6	7	4	11			5		13	3		12

Also Played: Woolfenden R matches 4, 6; Fraser No 14 matches 10, 11; Wilkinson No 5 match 12; Cooper No 6 match 17, No 8 match 18; P Ashcroft No 7 match 5; Donovan No 2 matches 10, 15; V Ashcroft No 6 match 14; O'Grady No 1 matches 14, 15, 16, 17; Lomas R match 11, No 14 matches 14, 15, No 11, match 17; Harman No 14 matches 16, 17, 18

Courage League Records 1994-95

League Debuts: John Brennand, Ben Kay, Chris Thompson, Carl Bibby, Terry Donovan, Chris Lomas, Robert Harman
Players used: 33
Ever Present: Simon Wright

● Steve Swindells breaks his own record for points in a season

	Pts	T	C	P	D	App	Ave
1994-95	160	-	8	48	-	17	9.41
1993-94	137	2	5	39	-	17	8.06

● Swindells ends the season on 309 points, just 3 behind Ian Aitchison, the Club's leading scorer

	Pts	T	C	P	D	App	Ave
Ian Aitchison	312	3	22	76	9	43	7.26
Steve Swindells	309	3	15	88	-	44	7.02

● Steve Peters joins Paul Hackett as the Club's leading appearance maker in the League with 71

WATERLOO F.C.

COURAGE LEAGUE STATISTICS
compiled by Steve McCormack

Season	Div	P	W	D	L	F	T	C	P	D	A	T	C	P	D	Most Points	Most Tries
1987-88	1	10	4	0	6	123	13	4	14	7	208	23	13	27	3	66 Ian Aitchison	4 Peter Cooley
1988-89	1	11	1	1	9	120	8	5	25	1	235	31	15	23	4	77 Ian Aitchison	4 Peter Cooley
1989-90	2	11	3	0	8	147	16	7	21	2	193	29	16	15	0	43 Richard Angell	5 Peter Cooley
1990-91	2	12	4	0	8	154	15	8	24	2	206	30	13	16	4	57 Ian Aitchison	8 Steve Bracegirdle
1991-92	2	12	8	0	4	206	21	13	31	1	184	27	14	15	1	92 Ian Aitchison	4 Gary Meredith
1992-93	2	12	10	0	2	228	17	10	33	8	138	7	2	32	1	126 Paul Graxson	3 Austin Healey
1993-94	2	18	6	2	10	231	13	8	47	3	346	35	24	40	1	137 Steve Swindells	2 Gary Meredith. Steve Swindells. John Ashcroft
1994-95	2	18	8	0	10	287	20	8	52	5	331	33	14	42	4	160 Steve Swindells	4 Neil Ryan & Steve Wright
TOTALS		104	36	3	47	1496	123	63	247	29	1841	215	111	210	18		

BIGGEST WIN — **Home:** 40-12 v Liverpool St H 21.12.91 CL2   **Away:** 34-6 v Blackheath 25.4.92 CL2

BIGGEST DEFEAT — **Home:** 22-34 v Leicester 12.11.88 CL1   **Away:** 6-47 v Wakefield 4.12.93 CL2

MOST TRIES in a match — **For**: 5 v Liverpool St H 221.12.91 CL2   **Against:** 8 v Bath 8.4.89 CL1

MOST CONSECUTIVE — **Wins:** 7   **Defeats:** 11

MOST APPEARANCES — **Forward:** 71 Peter Hackett, Steve Peters   **Back:** 46 Jeff Tickle

MOST CONSECUTIVE APPEARANCES — 39 Shaun Gallagher

CONSECUTIVE SCORING MATCHES — **Tries:** 4 Steve Bracegirdle   **Points:** 14 Steve Swindells

	IN A SEASON	IN A CAREER	IN A MATCH
MOST POINTS	160 Steve Swindells 1994-95 CL2	312 Ian Aitchison 1987-95	22 Ian Aitchison v Blackheath 25.4.92 Away CL2
MOST TRIES	8 Steve Bracegirdle 1990-91 CL2	14 Steve Bracegirdle 1990-93	2 on 7 occasions by 6 players - Steve Bracegirdle only man twice
MOST CONVERSIONS	10 Ian Aitchison 1991-92 CL2	22 Ian Aitchison 1987-95	4 Ian Aitchison v Liverpool St H 21.12.91 Home CL2
MOST PENALTIES	48 Steve Swindells 1994-95 CL2	88 Steve Swindells 1992-95	6 Ian Aitchison v Blackheath 25.4.92 Away CL2 Steve Swindells v Otley 12.3.94 Away CL2 v Newcastle Gos 10.9.94 Home CL2
MOST DROP GOALS	6 Paul Grayson 1992-93 CL2	9 Ian Aitchison 1987-95	2 Ian Aitchison v Gloucester 31.10.87 Home CL1 v Sale 2.1.88 Home CL1 Ian Croper v Sale 9.3.91 Home CL2 Paul Grayson v Sale 13.3.93 Home CL2 Neil Ryan v London Irish 24.9.94 Home CL2

NATIONAL LEAGUE THREEE

SEASON 1994-95

Former England captain and current Otley scrum half Nigel Melville fires the ball to his backs watched by Harrogate's Richard Marcroft in the courage League Three match which Otley won 33-14

Photo: Gordon Bunney

NATIONAL LEAGUE THREE STATISTICS 1994/95

PLAYING RECORD AND POINTS BREAKDOWN

	P	W	D	L	Pts	HOME				AWAY			
						W	D	L	Pts	W	D	L	Pts
Bedford	18	13	1	4	27	8	0	1	16	5	1	3	11
Blackheath	18	12	2	4	26	7	1	1	15	5	1	3	11
Rugby	18	11	0	7	22	8	0	1	16	3	0	6	6
Rosslyn Park	18	10	0	8	20	5	0	4	10	5	0	4	10
Morley	18	9	2	7	20	5	1	3	11	4	1	4	9
Otley	18	9	0	9	18	7	0	2	14	2	0	7	4
Harrogate	18	7	2	9	16	4	1	4	9	3	1	5	7
Richmond	18	6	1	11	13	4	0	5	8	2	1	6	5
Clifton	18	5	1	12	11	3	1	5	7	2	0	7	4
Exeter	18	3	1	14	7	1	1	7	3	2	0	7	4

RESULTS

		1	2	3	4	5	6	7	8	9	10
1	Bedford		12-3	19-5	23-10	39-13	45-8	32-11	21-20	31-5	17-35
2	Blacjheath	12-12		27-0	21-7	24-0	18-9	23-3	9-45	9-3	15-11
3	Clifton	18-21	12-25		29-15	17-17	7-18	19-13	18-6	12-21	19-37
4	Exeter	3-19	0-28	6-15		13-14	12-12	18-11	3-14	9-11	11-15
5	Harrogate	15-59	13-8	27-13	17-3		23-3	20-37	8-8	35-50	8-27
6	Morley	28-9	29-29	3-25	6-13	21-8		14-38	31-24	18-13	13-3
7	Otley	12-6	0-15	14-3	16-3	33-14	6-9		19-6	10-3	33-7
8	Richmond	14-16	5-8	21-14	41-5	12-18	17-38	15-14		11-14	19-10
9	Rosslyn Park	13-31	14-19	25-8	10-11	25-12	9-12	13-5	23-21		35-8
10	Rugby	25-9	15-6	29-8	17-11	12-13	27-5	38-3	21-20	18-26	

WEEK BY WEEK POSITIONS

	10/9	17/9	24/9	1/10	15/10	22/10	29/10	12/11	7/1	14/1	11/2	25/2	4/3	25/3	1/4	8/4	15/4	29/4
Bedford	10	6	6	2	1	1	1	1	1	1	1	2	2	2	2	2	1	1
Blackheath	5	2	1	5	3	5	2	3	3	3	3	1	1	1	1	1	2	2
Clifton	3	8	8	7	6	6	7	7	7	7	8	8	9	9	9	9	9	9
Exeter	2	5	7	8	8	8	9	9	10	10	10	10	10	10	10	10	10	10
Harrogate	4	1	4	4	4	2	4	4	4	4	4	4	4	5	7	7	7	7
Morley	9	10	10	10	10	9	8	8	8	8	7	6	5	4	6	6	6	5
Otley	8	4	3	1	5	4	3	2	2	2	2	3	3	3	3	3	4	6
Richmond	7	9	9	9	9	10	10	10	9	9	9	9	8	8	8	8	8	8
Rosslyn Park	6	7	5	6	7	7	6	6	5	6	6	5	7	7	5	4	5	4
Rugby	1	3	2	3	2	3	5	5	6	5	5	7	6	6	4	5	3	3

NATIONAL LEAGUE THREE 1994-95 POINTS SCORING RECORDS

	Tries	by Forward	by Back	Tries in no matches	No tries against	Players used	Replacements	Ever presents
Bedford	38	16	22	13	3	32	10	4
Blackheath	27	11	16	12	8	31	6	3
Rugby	40	11	29	15	4	26	3	1
Rosslyn Park	38	18	20	15	6	41	16	1
Morley	23	3	20	11	6	27	5	5
Otley	24	6	18	13	7	31	4	1
Harrogate	27	6	21	16	4	32	15	2
Richmond	31	8	23	14	3	39	2	—
Clifton	25	7	18	15	5	33	12	—
Exeter	11	1	10	9	1	35	7	—

FOR

	PTS	T	C	P	D	HOME PTS	T	C	P	D	AWAY PTS	T	C	P	D
Bedford	421	38	24	56	5	239	23	14	31	1	182	15	10	25	4
Blackheath	299	27	13	44	2	158	11	8	27	2	141	16	5	17	—
Rugby	355	40	22	35	2	202	21	11	23	2	153	19	11	12	—
Rosslyn Park	313	38	18	24	5	167	19	9	13	5	146	19	9	11	—
Morley	277	23	12	41	5	163	13	7	25	3	114	10	5	16	2
Otley	278	24	13	42	2	143	12	7	22	1	135	12	6	20	1
Harrogate	275	27	16	34	2	166	17	9	21	—	109	10	7	13	2
Richmond	319	31	19	41	1	155	15	7	22	—	164	16	12	19	1
Clifton	242	25	12	26	5	151	13	7	21	3	91	12	5	5	2
Exeter	153	11	4	26	4	75	4	2	15	2	78	7	2	11	2
	2932	284	153	369	33	1619	138	81	220	19	1313	136	72	149	14

AGAINST

	PTS	T	C	P	D	HOME PTS	T	C	P	D	AWAY PTS	T	C	P	D
Bedford	250	27	14	28	1	110	12	7	12	—	140	15	7	16	1
Blackheath	190	18	11	25	1	90	9	6	11	—	100	9	5	14	1
Rugby	271	26	12	35	4	101	10	6	11	2	170	16	6	24	2
Rosslyn Park	280	22	10	46	4	127	10	4	21	2	153	12	6	25	2
Morley	326	33	19	39	2	164	18	9	18	—	164	15	10	21	2
Otley	258	23	10	35	6	66	6	3	8	2	192	17	7	27	4
Harrogate	404	45	25	39	4	208	27	14	14	1	196	18	11	25	3
Richmond	290	27	16	39	2	137	14	8	16	1	153	13	8	23	1
Clifton	344	33	19	40	7	173	16	9	21	4	173	17	10	19	3
Exeter	319	30	17	43	2	139	14	6	17	2	180	16	11	26	—
	2932	284	153	369	33	1313	136	72	149	14	1619	148	81	220	19

NATIONAL LEAGUE THREE 1994-95
Most Tries, Penalties, Grop Goals, Conversions

LEADING TRY SCORERS

8	David Bishop	Rugby
7	Rob Bell	Harrogate
7	Tony Clark	Morley
7	Eddie Saunders	Rugby
6	Scott Benton	Morley
6	Peter Rutledge	Otley
6	Ben Whetstone	Bedford
5	Matt Griffiths	Blackheath
5	Mike Palmer	Rugby
5	Craig Reed	Harrogate
5	Tim Smither	Rosslyn Park
4	Andy Cuthbert	Richmond
4	Mark Wyatt	Clifton
4	Matt Brain	Clifton
4	Adam Gillolly	Rugby
4	Marcus Cook	Bedford
4	Matt Friday	Blackheath
3	Jon Phillips	Clifton
3	Trevor Davies	Clifton
3	Mark Beresford	Vlifton
3	John Gardner	Rugby
3	Mark Chatterton	Exeter
3	Glyn Melville	Otley
3	Dan Perrett	Rosslyn Park
3	Rob Subbiani	Bedford
3	Jason Simons	Bedford
3	Matt Deans	Bedford
3	Toby Booth	Blackheath
3	Mark Hanslip	Blackheath
3	Colin Ridgway	Blackheath

PENALTIES

56	Andy Finnie	Bedford
39	Jaime Grayshon	Morley
38	Sam Howard	Blackheath
37	Peter Rutledge	Otley
30	John Gregory	Richmond
27	Jim Quantrill	Rugby
26	Simon Hogg	Clifton
26	Dan Clappison	Harrogate
11	Jason Hoad	Richmond
9	Matt Giffen	Rosslyn Park
9	Andy Green	Exeter
8	Denzil Evans	Rugby
6	Andy Holder	Rosslyn Park
6	Ian Stewart	Exeter
6	Guy Easterby	Harrogate
6	Stuart Burns	Blackheath
6	Andy Parton	Rosslyn Park

DROP GOALS

5	Simon Hogg	Clifton
5	Jamie Grayshon	Morley
4	Andy Finnie	Bedford
3	Andy Maddock	Rosslyn Park
2	Ian Stewart	Exeter
2	Dan Clappison	Harrogate
2	Andrew Holder	Rosslyn Park
2	Sam Howard	Blackheath
1	Jim McLeod	Rugby
1	David Bishop	Rugby
1	Jeff Tutchings	Exeter
1	Andy Green	Exeter
1	Simon Hawkins	Otley
1	Jonathan Flint	Otley
1	John Gregory	Richmond
1	Ben Whetstone	Bedford

CONVERSIONS

24	Andy Finnie	Bedford
19	John Gregory	Richmond
19	Jim Quantrill	Rugby
13	Peter Rutledge	Otley
12	Jaime Grayshon	Morley
12	Dan Clappison	Harrogate
11	Sam Howard	Blackheath
9	Simon Hogg	Clifton
6	Matt Giffin	Rosslyn Park
5	Andy King	Rosslyn Park
4	Andy Holder	Rosslyn Park
3	Denzil Evans	Rugby
3	Andy Parton	Rosslyn Park
3	Mark Beresford	Clifton
3	Guy Easterby	Harrogate
3	Ian Stewart	Exeter

NATIONAL LEAGUE THREE 1994-95

INDIVIDUAL TOP POINT SCORERS

		PTS	T	C	P	D
Andy Finnie	Bedford	228	—	24	56	4
Peter Rutledge	Otley	167	6	13	37	—
Jaime Grayson	Morley	166	2	12	39	5
Sam Howard	Blackheath	147	1	11	38	2
John Gregory	Richmond	133	1	19	30	—
Jim Quantrill	Rugby	131	2	20	27	—
Simon Hogg	Clifton	116	1	9	26	5
Dan Clappison	Harrogate	110	1	12	26	2
Matt Giffin	Rosslyn Park	51	3	6	8	—
David Bishop	Rugby	43	8	—	—	1
Andy Holder	Rosslyn Park	37	1	4	6	2
Ian Stewart	Exeter	35	1	3	6	2
Eddie Saunders	Rugby	35	7	—	—	—
Tony Clark	Morley	35	7	—	—	—
Rob Bell	Harrogate	35	7	—	—	—

Bedfordshire Times player of the season, Andy Finnie, being given advice on how to kick from coach Mike Rafter!!

Andy Finnie, or "Albert" as he's affectionately known, was a member of the Bedford Colts side in 1982-3, when he made his debut against Old Paulines. Also making his debut that day was his present captain, Paul Alston. He has been a regular ever since having played over 300 games and scored 2494 points. His kicking from hand is peerless and he has saved many a difficult situation with a raking touch finder.

Andy has not only been an extremely loyal servant to Bedford but has also proved to be a great ambassador for the town and club. Three games were won with the last kick of the match including, a touch-line conversion deep in injury time away to Richmond. He was voted 'Player of the season' by the readers of The Bedfordshire Times.

Photograph courtesy of Charles Wooding

NATIONAL LEAGUE THREE

STATISTICS 1987-95

NATIONAL LEAGUE THREE RESULTS

1987-88

		1	2	3	4	5	6	7	8	9	10	11	12
1	Birmingham					3-22		3-3	3-46	, 15-42	3-50	6-43	
2	Exeter	32-0				4-3			9-18	12-12		19-29	6-18
3	Fylde	68-7	48-13								12-14	3-23	12-17
4	Maldston	18-3	23-9	16-18			15-0	9-3			14-16		
5	Metropolitan Police		9-23		9-6		26-12		25-18			6-7	6-22
6	Morley	23-3	10-10	12-38						7-12		7-38	
7	Nuneaton		9-11	13-18		7-12	21-6		9-7				
8	Plymouth Albion			33-17	45-11		24-0			43-7		16- 12	
9	Sheffield	34-0		13-12	10-3	13-6		15-9			8-3		
10	Vale of Lune		27-3			13-6	25-19	6-3	13-16				12-21
11	Wakefield				27-9			33-3		41-0	32-12		16-12
12	West Hartlepool				12-10		23-3	37-14	19-10	25-10			

1988-89

		1	2	3	4	5	6	7	8	9	10	11	12
1	Askeans		6-20			21-10		12-28				10-23	10-10
2	Exeter					14-6	12-25	6-21		19-12	12-26		
3	Fylde	13-6	16-14		34-7				12-17	9-24			18-13
4	Maidstone	12-15	0-21			10-27	11-28					6-23	
5	Metropolitan Police		17-15				32-13		6-36		13-7		10-25
6	Nuneaton	12-19	24-10					3-21	15-18		16-6		22-18
7	Plymouth Albion		43-6		20-6	57-3				34-13		21-12	20-12
8	Rugby	41-3	23-3		44-3			10-26			28-9	14-13	
9	Sheffield	17-27			28-3	10-6	25-16		6-22		9-9		
10	Vale of Lune	29-12		6-0	12-7			6-20				4-19	
11	Wakefield		29-18	10-6		70-0	42-4			25-22			
12	West Hartleypool		16-3		37-9				3-15	12-4	9-6	9- 16	

1989-90

		1	2	3	4	5	6	7	8	9	10	11	12
1	Askeans		19-11			29-26		12-19	20-9	16-26	25-21		
2	Exeter	30-3		22-17		15-7			9-7			18-13	15-15
3	Fylde				12-26		18-13	17-14			19-18	15-11	
4	London	31-6	16-7			18-14		36-0			34-3		
5	London Welsh		29-9				3-22	9-10		20-0			17-15
6	Lydney	7-20	16-6		16-20				18-13	7-9		7-9	
7	Nuneaton		27-14					19-15	11-18	16-14		7-9	
8	Roundbay			27-21	3-30	22-6				22-10	20-0		12-15
9	Sheffield		7-3	33-18	24-28							12-27	13- 10
10	Vale of Lune		25-10			9-0	21-20	24-10		7-28			6-16
11	Wakefield	40-14			4-10	24-10			26-3		37-20		10-10
12	West Hartlepool	25-6		10-12	3-9		28-6	28-4					

1990-91

		1	2	3	4	5	6	7	8	9	10	11	12	13
1	Askeans		29-6	9-10		19-7			9-9	22-10		9-9		
2	Broughton Park				10-4		9-12	3-0	11-15		13-11		6-7	
3	Clifton		25-6		28-3			9-4	9-15	17-22		18-16		
4	Exeter	13-7					9-3	28-3			13-3		14-12	18- 18
5	Fylde		6-14	25-6	11-11				16-6	20-3		29-12		
6	Lydney	31-6		10-10		4-20					12-10		9-14	3-19
7	Metropolitan Police	3-21				6-20	13-15				17- 12		24-18	8-12
8	Morley				22-6		19-7	11-17			30-3		33-3	10- 9
9	Nuneaton		16-6		6-13		35-3	23-12	10-17			14-23		
10	Roundhay	23-4		34-7		7-7				10-6			22-13	9-21
11	Sheffield		13-21		16-28		24-16	16-23	18-23		23- 3			
12	Vale of Lune	16-6		14-7		9-18				18-27		9- 13		0-32
13	West Hartleypool	w/o	47-4	36-16		18-4				39-8		29-10		

1991-92

		1	2	3	4	5	6	7	8	9	10	11	12	13
1	Askeans				3-12			36-0		12-8	10-8	6-17	9-6	
2	Broughton Park	42-15		20-15		9-10			27-3		3-20			22-7
3	Clifton	48-7			21-3		42-3		26-9	16-10		29-9		
4	Exeter		13-0	16-10			9-16	26-13	25-18					15-15
5	Fylde	34-4						17-0		16-13	9-9	12-13	29-12	
6	Headingley	0-25	19-13	11-38		6-12			10-9					18-3
7	Lydney		3-17		21-15		9-16		22-4			7-18		13-19
8	Nuneaton	16-16		12-15		9-18				33-8	9-15		25-25	
9	Otley		23-16		3-9		19-12	34-4			119-9	15-10		
10	Redruth				10-16		13-6	15-6		21-16		6-9	13- 3	
11	Richmond		20-18	16-15	16-16		28-13		43-6					57-3
12	Roundhay		9-9		13-31		25-12	28-3				3-50		18-5
13	Sheffield	12-6		16-23		4-22			13-9	22-10	17-15			

1992-93

		1	2	3	4	5	6	7	8	9	10	11	12
1	Askeans		23-16	6-18	6-24				8-6				8-45
2	Aspatria			24-8		16-21	13-12	10			42-20		15-32
3	Broughton Park				19-33	3-22	10-30			10-21	31-3		
4	Clifton	10-10		35-24		13-13					24-8		35-6
5	Exeter	P					21-18	28-33		16-11	15-8	20-9	
6	Havant	10-3			17-6			35-11	9-6	20-16		3-3	
7	Leeds	24-23	34-15		43-32				16-10	0-16		10-17	
8	Liverpool St. Helens		77-5	21-3	21-8	19-26							13-3
9	Otley	61-6	47-8		14-9				20-7			19-19	21-7
10	Plymouth Albion	20-23					3-35	22-27	6-12	16-28	13-20		
11	Redruth	23-13	24-6	10-5	13-5				26-11				11-20
12	Sheffield			12-5		15-6	8-9	12-0			48-11		

NATIONAL LEAGUE THREE TABLES

1987-88

	P	W	D	L	F	A	Pts
Wakefield	11	10	0	1	308	90	20
West Hartlepool	11	10	0	1	249	105	20
Plymouth A.	11	8	0	3	276	125	16
Sheffield	11	7	1	3	134	161	15
Vale of Lune	11	7	0	4	183	149	14
Fylde	11	6	0	5	269	170	142
Met. Police	11	5	0	6	130	128	10
Maidstone	11	4	0	7	134	162	8
Exeter	11	3	2	6	128	197	8
Nuneaton	11	2	1	8	94	157	5
Morley	11	1	1	9	109	235	3
Birmingham	11	0	1	10	46	381	1

1990-91

	P	W	D	L	F	A	Pts
West Hartlepool	12	10	1	1	282	90	21
Morley	12	9	1	2	210	118	19
Fylde	12	7	2	3	183	115	16
Exeter	12	7	2	3	160	139	16
Clifton	12	6	1	5	172	186	13
Askeans	12	4	2	6	141	137	10
Nuneaton	12	5	0	7	180	200	10
Broughton Park	12	5	0	7	109	185	10
Roundhay	12	4	1	7	147	166	9
Sheffield	12	4	1	7	193	222	9
Lydney	12	4	1	7	125	188	9
Met. Police	12	4	0	8	130	188	8
Vale of Lune	12	3	0	9	123	221	6

1998-89

	P	W	D	L	F	A	Pts
Plymouth A.	11	11	0	0	311	89	22
Rugby	11	10	0	1	268	99	20
Wakefield	11	9	0	2	282	114	18
West Hartlepool	11	5	1	5	164	133	11
Nuneaton	11	5	0	6	178	214	10
Sheffield	11	4	1	6	170	182	9
Vale of Lune	11	4	1	6	120	145	9
Askeans	11	4	1	6	141	215	9
Exeter	11	4	0	7	142	180	8
Fylde	11	4	0	7	136	181	8
Met. Police	11	4	0	7	130	275	8
Maidstone	11	0	0	11	74	289	0

1991-92

	P	W	D	L	F	A	PD	Pts
Richmond	12	10	1	1	296	124	172	21
Fylde	12	9	1	2	198	109	89	19
Clifton	12	9	0	3	298	132	166	18
Exeter	12	8	2	2	203	138	65	18
Redruth	12	6	1	5	155	123	32	13
Broughton Park	12	5	1	69	196	157	39	11
Askeans	12	5	1	6	149	203	-54	11
Sheffield	12	5	1	6	146	228	-82	11
Otley	12	5	0	7	177	190	-13	10
Roundhay	12	3	2	7	161	240	-79	8
Headingley	12	4	0	8	139	220	-81	8
Nuneaton	12	1	2	9	153	237	-84	4
Lydney	12	2	0	10	91	261	-170	4

1989-90

	P	W	D	L	F	A	Pts
Lon. Scottish	11	11	0	0	258	92	22
Wakefield	11	7	1	3	310	126	15
West Hartlepool	11	5	2	4	175	110	12
Sheffield	11	6	0	5	176	174	12
Askeans	11	6	0	5	170	235	12
Exeter	11	5	1	5	149	153	11
Roundhay	11	5	0	6	156	166	10
Fylde	11	5	0	6	169	222	10
Vale of Lune	11	4	0	7	154	219	8
Nuneaton	11	4	0	7	127	196	8
Lydney	11	3	0	8	153	166	6
Lon. Welsh	11	3	0	8	141	179	6

1992-93

	P	W	D	L	F	A	PD	Pts
Otley	11	8	1	2	274	118	156	17
Havant	11	8	1	2	185	93	92	17
Exeter	11	8	1	2	247	169	78	17
Redruth	11	7	2	2	175	125	50	16
Sheffield	11	7	0	4	208	134	74	14
Leeds	11	7	0	4	228	220	8	14
Liverpool St. H.	11	5	0	6	203	130	73	10
Clifton	11	4	2	5	206	175	31	10
Aspatria	11	3	1	7	170	308	-138	7
Askeans	11	3	0	8	132	300	-168	6
Broughton Park	11	2	0	9	136	217	-81	4
Plymouth Albion	11	0	0	11	130	305	-175	0

NATIONAL LEAGUE THREE STATISTICS 1993/94

PLAYING RECORD AND POINTS BREAKDOWN

	P	W	D	L	F	A	Pts	HOME						AWAY					
								P	W	D	L	F	A	P	W	D	L	F	A
Coventry	18	14	0	4	406	259	28	9	8	0	1	255	125	9	6	0	3	151	134
Fylde	18	13	0	5	339	219	26	9	9	0	0	206	72	9	4	0	5	133	147
Bedford	18	12	0	6	332	260	24	9	8	0	1	182	98	9	4	0	5	150	162
Blackheath	18	11	0	7	305	222	22	9	7	0	2	204	94	9	4	0	5	101	128
Rosslyn P	18	10	1	7	372	240	21	9	5	0	4	195	109	9	5	1	3	177	131
Exeter	18	9	1	8	308	271	19	9	7	1	1	180	121	9	2	0	7	128	150
Richmond	18	9	0	9	337	300	18	9	6	0	3	187	128	9	3	0	6	150	172
Morley	18	6	0	12	245	334	12	9	4	0	5	139	128	9	2	0	7	106	206
Havant	18	3	0	15	203	432	6	9	3	0	6	137	195	9	0	0	9	66	237
Redruth	18	2	0	16	178	488	4	9	2	0	7	89	181	9	0	0	9	89	307

RESULTS

		1	2	3	4	5	6	7	8	9	10
1	Bedford		6-0	21-15	18-14	23-12	27-12	25-10	22-3	18-6	28-13
2	Blackheath	34-9		13-14	22-5	11-17	30-14	29-9	31-13	18-6	16-7
3	Coventry	17-10	23-19		39-12	24-18	22-3	35-5	60-13	23-20	22-25
4	Exeter	13-12	16-3	32-27		27-3	25-20	14-15	19-12	21-16	13-13
5	Fylde	20-6	20-8	15-9	15-6		11-3	24-18	54-6	23-10	24-6
6	Havant	14-20	19-27	16-21	0-41	10-22		20-7	36-19	17-16	5-22
7	Morley	18-17	12-13	9-12	10-9	9-11	25-0		35-6	13-27	8-33
8	Redruth	14-33	7-16	3-19	9-20	11-10	15-3	12-14		9-27	9-39
9	Richmond	20-26	22-0	15-22	16-12	29-27	36-3	23-10	20-9		6-19
10	Rosslyn Park	12-17	3-15	10-12	21-9	3-13	46-8	34-18	30-8	36-9	

WEEK BY WEEK POSITIONS

	13/11	20/11	4/12	11/12	18/12	8/1	15/1	22/1	29/1	12/2	26/2	12/3	26/3	9/4	23/4	30/4
Bedford	1	2	1	3	3	6	6	7	7	7	4	3	4	3	3	3
Backheath	5	7	7	7	7	4	5	2	4	3	2	6	3	4	4	4
Coventry	3	3	2	1	1	1	1	1	1	1	1	1	1	1	1	1
Exeter	7	6	6	6	4	7	7	5	5	6	5	4	6	6	7	6
Fylde	4	4	4	4	5	5	2	3	2	4	3	2	2	2	2	2
Havant	9	9	9	9	9	9	9	9	9	9	9	9	9	9	9	9
Morley	8	8	8	8	8	8	8	8	8	8	8	8	8	8	8	8
Redruth	10	10	10	10	10	10	10	10	10	10	10	10	10	10	10	10
Richmond	2	1	3	2	2	3	4	6	6	2	6	5	7	7	6	7
Rosslyn Park	6	5	5	5	6	2	3	4	3	5	7	7	5	5	5	5

COURAGE CHAMPIONSHIP STATISTICS 1987–1995

LEAGUE THREE

	CHAMPIONS	RUNNERS-UP	RELEGATED
1987-88	Wakefield	West Hartlepool	Morley Birmingham
1988-89	Plymouth Albion	Rugby	Maidstone Metropolitan Police
1989-90	London Scottish	Wakefield	London Welsh
1990-91	West Hartlepool	Morley	Metropolitan Police Vale of Lune
1991-92	Richmond	Fylde	Lydney Nuneaton
1992-93	Otley	Havant	Sheffield Leeds Liverpool St Helens Clifton Aspatria Askeans Broughton Park Plymouth
1993-94	Coventry	Fylde	Havant Redruth
1994-95	Bedford	Blackheath	Clifton Exeter

TEAM RECORDS

Highest score: Liverpool St Helens 77 Aspatria 5. 13-3-93
Highest aggregate: 85 Harrogate 35 Rosslyn Park 50. 29-4-95
Highest score by a losing side: Harrogate 35 Rosslyn Park 50. 29-4-95
Highest scoring draw: 29-29 Morley v Blackheath 8-4-95
Most consecutive wins: 11 London Scottish 1989-90
Most consecutive defeats: 11 Maidstone 1988-89
Most points for in a season: 421 Bedford 1994-95
Most points against in a season: 488 Redruth 1993-94
Least points for in a season: 46 Birmingham 1987-88
Least points against in a season: 89 Plymouth 1988-89
Most tries for in a season: 48 Rosslyn Park 1993-94
Most tries against in a season: 71 Birmingham 1987-88
Least tries for in a season: 3 Birmingham 1987-88
Least tries against in a season: 5 Plymouth 1988-89
Most conversions for in a season: 31 Fylde 1987-88
Most conversions against in a season: 34 Birmingham 1987-88
Most penalties for in a season: 56 Bedford 1994-95
Most penalties against in a season: 46 Rosslyn Park 1994-95
Least penalties for in a season: 8 Morley 1987-88
Least penalties against in a season: 10 West Hartlepool 1990-91
Most drop goals for in a season: 7 Lydney 1989-90
Most drop goals against in a season: 7 Clifton 1994-95

INDIVIDUAL RECORDS

Most points in a season: 228 Andy Finnie Bedford 1994-95
Most tries in a season: 12 Brendan Hanavan Fylde 1993-94
Most conversions in a season: 30 Steve Burnage Fylde 1987-88
Most penalities in a season: 56 Andy Finnie Bedford 1994-95
Most drop goals in a season: 6 Andy Higgin Vale of Lune 1989-90, Mike Smith Lydney 1989-90, Andy Rimmer Broughton Park 1990-91
Most points in a match: 28 Steve Burnage Fylde v Birmingham 7-11-87
Most tries in a match: 4 on 8 occasions by 6 players. Most Brendan (3 times)
Most conversions in a match: 9 Steve Burnage Fylde v Birmingham 7-11-87
Most penalities in a match: 7 Andy Finnie Bedford v Coventry 23-4-94
Most drop goals in a match: 4 Andy Rimmer Broughton Park v Sheffield 17-11-90

SEASON BY SEASON LEADING SCORERS

	POINTS		TRIES
1987-88	121 Steve Burnage (Fylde)	10	Brendan Hanavan (Fylde)
1988-89	123 Chris Howard (Rugby)	8	Steve Walklin (Plymouth Albion)
			Dave Scully (Wakefield)
1989-90	102 Andy Higgin (Vale of Lune)	7	Mike Harrison (Wakefield)
			Brendan Hananan (Fylde)
1990-91	108 Mark Rodgers (Sheffield)	9	John Wrigley (West Hartlepool)
1991-92	106 Mike Jackson (Fylde)	8	Matt Brain (Clifton)
1992-93	122 Andy Green (Exeter)	8	Martin Kelly (Broughton Park)
			Mark Sephton (Liverpool)
1993-94	172 Andy Finnie (Bedford)	12	Brendan Hanavan (Fylde)
1994-95	228 Andy Finnie (Bedford)	8	David Bishop (Rugby)

100 POINTS IN A COURAGE SEASON DIVISION THREE

PTS	PLAYER	CLUB	SEASON	T	C	P	D
228	Andy Finnie	Bedford	1994-95	—	24	56	4
172	Andy Finnie	Bedford	1993-94	—	14	45	3
167	Peter Rutledge	Otley	1994-95	6	13	37	—
166	Jamie Grayshon	Morley	1994-95	2	12	39	5
151	Richard Angell	Coventry	1993-94	3	23	29	1
147	Sam Howard	Blackheath	1994-95	1	11	38	2
133	John Gregory	Richmond	1994-95	1	19	30	—
131	Jim Quantrill	Rugby	1994-95	2	20	27	—
125	Andy Green	Exeter	1993-94	3	16	24	2
123	Chris Howard	Rugby	1988-89	7	19	19	—
122	Andy Green	Exeter	1992-93	—	10	31	3
121	Steve Burnage	Fylde	1987-88	4	30	14	1
121	Peter Rutledge	Otley	1992-93	3	14	26	—
117	Jamie Grayshon	Morley	1993-94	—	12	28	3
116	Simon Hogg	Clifton	1994-95	1	9	26	5
110	Dan Clappison	Harrogate	1994-95	1	12	26	2
109	Andy Parker	Fylde	1993-94	3	17	20	—
108	Martin Livesey	Plymouth	1987-88	2	23	17	1
108	Mark Rodgers	Sheffield	1990-91	7	7	22	—
106	Mike Jackson	Fylde	1991-92	1	12	26	—
105	Ray Adamson	Wakefield	1987-88	1	19	21	—
102	Andy Higgin	Vale of Lune	1989-90	—	9	22	
101	Dominic Cundy	Plymouth	1988-89	1	20	—	
100	Simon Hogg	Clifton	1991-92	2	16	19	1

MOST POINTS IN A COURAGE DIVISION THREE MATCH

28	Steve Burnage	Fylde v Birmingham	7-11-87
25	Dominic Cundy	Plymouth Albion v Metropolitan Police	26-11-89
25	Mark Rodgers	Sheffield v Askians	13-3-93
25	Richard Angell	Coventry v Redruth	30-4-94
24	Chris Howard	Rugby v Maidstone	26-11-88
23	John Stabler	West Hartlepool v Broughton Park	9-3-91
22	Andy Atkinson	Wakefield v Metropolitan Police	24-9-88
22	Simon Hogg	Clifton v Lydney	28-3-92
22	Kevin O'Brien	Broughton Park v Askeans	11-4-92
22	Martin Livesey	Richmond v Blackheath	13-11-93
22	Peter Rutledge	Otley v Harrogate	29-10-94
21	John Stabler	West Hartlepool v Sheffield	3-10-87
21	Gareth Hughes	London Welsh v Fylde	13-1-90
21	Peter Rutledge	Otley v Askians	27-3-93
21	Jason Hoad	Richmond v Fylde	5-2-94
21	Andy Finie	Bedford v Coventry	23-4-94
21	Jamie Grayshon	Morley v Richmond	25-3-95
20	Steve Burnage	Fylde v Exeter	3-10-87
20	Ray Adamson	Wakefield v Vale of Lune	27-2-88
20	Robin Goodliffe	Sheffield v London Scottish	14-10-89
20	Andy Green	Exeter v Met Police	10-11-90
20	Mark Sephton	Liverpool St Helens v Aspatria	13-3-93
20	Dean Crompton	Liverpool St Helens v Aspatria	13-3-93
20	Mark Farrar	Otley v Askeans	27-3-93
20	Brendan Hanavan	Richmond v Blackheath	11-4-95
20	P. Gregory	Richmond v Blackheath	11-4-95
20	King	Rosslyn Park v Harrogate	29-4-95

MOST TRIES IN A COURAGE DIVISION THREE MATCH

4	B Hanavan	Fylde v Exeter	3-10-87
4	S Walklin	Plymouth Albion v Birmingham	17-10-87
4	I Russell	Plymouth Albion v Fylde	31-10-87
4	B Hanavan	Fylde v Birmingham	7-11-87
4	D Cottrell	Clifton v Askeans	4-1-92
4	M Sephton	Liverpool St Helens v Aspatria	13-3-93
4	D Crompton	Liverpool St Helens v Aspatria	13-3-93
4	M Farrar	Otley v Askeans	27-3-93
4	B Hanavan	Fylde v Redruth	9-4-94
3	K Norris	Plymouth Albion v Sheffield	12-9-87
3	M Preston	Fylde v Morley	17-10-87
3	S Cowling	Wakefield v Birmingham	31-10-87
3	S Cowling	Wakefield v Nuneaton	5-12-87
3	A Halloway	Wakefield v Morley	12-3-88
3	M Cathery	Exeter v Birmingham	26-3-88
3	O Evans	West Hartlepool v Nuneaton	23-4-88
3	C Howard	Tugby v Vale of Lune	10-9-88
3	M Harrison	Wakefield v Met Police	24-9-88
3	A Atkinson	Wakefield v Met Police	24-9-88
3	S Hughes	Plymouth Albion v Fylde	19-11-88
3	P Gavin	Met Police v Maidstone	14-1-89
3	M Murtagh	Wakefield v Askeans	11-11-89
3	H Hughes	London Welsh v Fylde	13-1-90
3	M Harrison	Wakefield v London Welsh	28-4-90
3	D Cottrell	Clifton v Broughton Park	13-10-90
3	A Green	Exeter v Met Police	10-11-90
3	M Spearman	Clifton v Exeter	17-11-90
3	P Robinson	West Hartlepool v Vale of Lune	2-3-91
3	G Walker	Roundhay v Askeans	6-4-91
3	M Chatterton	Exeter v Headingley	23-11-91
3	A Ireland	Fylde v Askeans	14-12-91
3	J Wrigley	West Hartlepool v	14-12-91
3	P Della-Savina	Richmond v Nuneaton	28-3-92
3	G Melville	Otley v Aspatria	24-10-92
3	C Thornton	Leeds v Exeter	13-3-93
3	H Langley	Exeter v Broughton Park	24-4-93
3	M Kelly	Broughton Park v Exeter	24-4-93
3	M Friday	Blackheath v Morley	6-11-93
3	A Brooks	Rosslyn Park v Havant	12-3-94

NATIONAL LEAGUE THREE

MEMBER CLUBS
1995-96

League Registrar:
DAE Evans
22 Brrooks Road
Sutton Coldfield
West Midlands B71 1HP
Tel: 0121 354 8183
Fax: 0121 321 3221

MOST LEAGUE APPEARANCES – DIVISION THREE PLAYERS

91	Trevor Revan	Prop	Rugby
90	Richard Selkirk	Flanker	Rotherham
90	Tony Clark	Winger	Morley
89	David Bishop	Scrum Half	Rugby
86	Andy Hargreaves	Flanker	Otley
85	Eddie Saunders	Winger	Rugby
85	Paul Scott	Winger	Rotherham
83	Kevin Plant	Stand Off	Rotherham
83	Jamie Grayshon	Stand Off	Morley
82	John Dudley	Second Row	Rotherham
81	Phil Bowman	Second Row	Rugby
81	Stephen Rice	Prop	Otley
79	Steve Towse	Centre/Stand Off	Harrogate
76	Richard Pell	Stand Off	Rugby
75	Dave Barnett	Prop	Rosslyn Park
72	David Wheat	Flanker	Harrogate
72	Ian Hassell	Full Back	Harrogate
72	Mike Barnett	Hooker	Otley
71	Sam Coy	Prop	Rotherham
71	Craig West	Flanker	Rotherham
71	Brendan Hanavan	Winger	Fylde
71	Simon Tipping	Flanker	Otley
69	Glyn Melville	Winger	Otley
69	Ian Carroll	Second Row	Otley
69	Craig Burns	Prop	Fylde
66	Andy Simpson	Prop	Harrogate
66	Paul Essenhigh	Prop	Rosslyn Park
65	John Taylor	Flanker	Fylde
63	Richard Angell	Stand Off	Coventry
62	Andy Parker	Full Back	Fylde
62	Julian Hyde	Second Row	Coventry
61	Guy Easterby	Scrum Half	Harrogate
61	Ian Barclay	Stand Off	Fylde
61	Mark Lakey	Centre	Coventry

COVENTRY F.C.

NICKNAME: COV   **FOUNDED:** 1874

CLUB OFFICIALS
President
P B Jackson
Chairman
G Sugrue
Club Secretary
P B Jackson
147 Chester Road, Castle Bromwich,
Birmingham B36 0AE
Tel: 0121 747 2498
Fixtures Secretary
J Butler
62 Spring Lane, Whittington, Nr
Lichfield, Staffs WS14 9NA
Tel: (H) 01543 432654 (W) 01827 289999
Press Officer
R Wilkinson
Tel: (H) 01203 672151 (W) 01203 661174

Review of the Season

The season could hardly have been more disastrous for COVENTRY, whose future in League Two had been virtually decided long before Christmas, by which time they had also suffered a 45-7 home demolition at the hands of Fylde in the fourth round of the Pilkington Cup.

Of their 18 League Two fixtures only two were won with the rest lost and those successes came in the first five matches of the campaign after which there was a continuous stream of losses, the last one ensuring that Moseley would not join them in League Three next season.

In such circumstances it is difficult to pick out anyone who could be said to have done well, but tighthead Hardwick, who also represented the Midland Division, was an honourable exception with hooker Addleton and loosehead Tregilgas, the captain, also earning plaudits for their brave efforts in a lost cause.

Few others managed to do themselves justice in a dire situation, but lock Hyde clearly has potential and experienced Kevin Hickey, who filled all three back-row positions in the side at various times also strove gallantly.

It is a case of back to the blackboard and most will hope that the better times and a respected side will return to Coundon Road soon. The club which produced such great men as Peter Jackson, Harry Wheatley and so many others deserves as much, although it must be earned.

Photo: Birmingham Post & Mail
Change Colours: Dark blue

Colours: Navy blue/white hoops

COVENTRY F.C.

COURAGE LEAGUE
MATCH DETAILS 1994-95

No	Date	Opponents	Ven	Result	Scorers
1	Sep 10	Wakefield	H	14-15	Douglas (T) Angell (3P)
2	Sep 17	Nottingham	A	7-23	Horrobin (T) Angell (C)
3	Sep 24	Newcastle Gos	W	19-15	Douglas (T) (Angell 1C 4P)
4	Oct 1	London Scottish	L	0-30	
5	Oct 8	London Irish	H	36-30	Powls (T) Lakey (T 2DG) Angell (1C 5P 1DG)
6	Oct 15	Waterloo	A	5-26	Douglas (T)
7	Oct 22	Fylde	H	17-21	Douglas (T) Angell (4P)
8	Oct 29	Saracens	H	16-33	Douglas (T) Angell (P) Quick (1C 2P)
9	Nov 5	Morley	A	8-19	Quick (1P) Shepherd (T)
10	Jan 7	Wakeford	A	14-19	Gulliver (T) Angell (3P)
11	Jan 14	Nottingham	H	6-19	Angell (2P)
12	Feb 11	Newcastle Gos	A	22-38	Handcocks (T) Hart (1C 5P)
13	Mar 4	London Scottish	H	5-19	Caswell (T)
14	Mar 25	London Irish	A	8-25	Shepherd (T) Hart (1DG)
15	Apr 8	Waterloo	H	17-22	Shepherd (T) Angell (3P 1DG)
16	Apr 18	Saracens	A	0-38	
18	Apr 29	Moseley	H	11-22	Gee (T) Hart (1P 1DG)

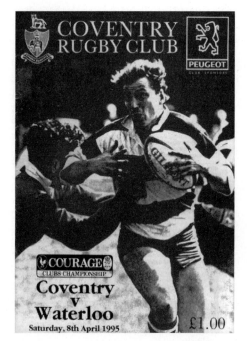

COVENTRY RUGBY CLUB

PEUGEOT

COURAGE CLUBS CHAMPIONSHIP

Coventry
v
Waterloo
Saturday, 8th April 1995

£1.00

PROGRAMME DETAILS
Price: £1.00
Pages: 28

CLUB & GROUND DETAILS
Barker Butts Lane, Coundon, Coventry CV6 1DU
Telephone: 01203 593399/591274
Fax: 01203 601194

Total Capacity: 10,000
Seated: 1,100
Standing: 8,900
Simple Directions to Ground: From ringroad take the A414
to Birmingham, turn right at traffic lights and follow road
across railway line. Coming in on the A45 pick up A414, turn
left at Holy Head Pub, right at traffic lights, Ground on right
hand side.
Nearest Railway Station: Coventry
Car Parking: Nil
Season Tickets: Adults £50.00 Children £20.00 OAPs £25.00
Match Prices: Adults £6.00 Children/OAPs £4.00
Membership: Seniors £10.00 Juniors £10.00
Training Nights: Monday and Thursday

COVENTRY F.C.

MATCH BY MATCH PLAYERS BY POSITION

Gee	Curtis	Lakey	Angell	Douglas	Tregilgas	Addleton	Hardwick	Gissing	Crofts	Horrobin	Hickey	Powls	Chapman	Hyde	Thomas	Gallinson	Hart	Dowson	Barden	Handcocks	Shepherd	Grewcock	Blundell
15	13	12	10	9	1	2	3	4	6	7	8												
15	13	12	10	9	1	2	3	4	6	7	8												
11	10	15	9		1	2	3	4		7		14	12	5	6	8							
11	10*	15	9		1	2	3	4		7		14	12	5	6**	8	13	R					
11	12	10	15		1	2	3	4	6		7	14	13	5		8		9					
15	12	10	9		1	2	3	5	6		7	14	13	4		8			11				
11	12	10	15	9	1	2	3		6		7	14	13	4		8							
	12	13	10	9	1	2	3		6		7	14		4		8			11				
	12		10	9	1	2	3		6		7	14		4		8			11				
		10	15		1	2	3			7	6			4	8		12	9	14	13	11		
		10	15		1	2	3			7	6			4	8		12	9	14	13	11		
15					1	2	3			7		14		4	6		10	9	3		11	8	
	14				1	2				7		15		4	6		13	9	12		11	8	
15	12					2			6	7	R	11		4			10		13	14		5	9
15			10			2	3		6		7			4			12		14	13	11	5	9
15	13		10			2	3		6		7	12		4			10		13	14		5	9
15									6		7			4			10		11	12	14		9
15	12				1	2	3				7			4	6		10		11	13	14	5	9

Also Played: Woodman No 11 matches 1, 2; Carter R** match 4; Miles R matches 9, 11; Kelnan R match 12; Thompason No 12 match 12; Harrison No 10 match 13; Caswell No 3 match 13, No 13 match 12; Morgan No 1 match 14, No 3 match 17; Sharp No 2 match 17; Anderson No 5 match 17; Quick No 15 matches 8, 9; Thomson No 14 matches 1, 2, No 13 matches 3, 9; Mackie No 5 matches 1, 2, 7, 8, 9; Gulliver No 5 matches 10, 11, 12, 13; Lewis No 1 matches 15, 16, 17, No 3 match 14; Smith No 8 matches 14, 15, 16, 17, 18

Courage League Records 1994-95

League Debuts: B Powls, G Allinson, J Hart, C Quick, S Hancoxs, B Shepherd, P Miles, D Grewcock, D Keenan, R Thompson, P Harrison, G Caswell, R Morgan, N Lewis, S Smith, G Sharp, A Andreau

Players used: 37

Ever Presents None – Most 17 Daddleton

Most appearances: 63 Richard Angell

● Richard Angell became the first Coventry player to pass 300 points. Angel, who made his Coventry debut back in September 1990 in the home match v Waterloo, finished the season on 371 points

	Pts	T	C	P	D	App	Ave
1990-95	371	9	43	77	5	63	5.88

● Angell's 63 appearances for the club is also a record – previously it was 51, a record he shared with Mark Lakey

● Mark Lakey extended his club record for drop goals by 2 to 10. In total he has 88 points for the club which puts him 4th on the all time list behind Angell, Steve Thomas and Martin Fairn

● Mark Douglas moves into joint second place on the all time try scoring list. His 5 tries last season put him on 9, the same as Richard Angell, Steve Thomas, Barry Evans and Doug Woodman, which is half as many as the man in front, Kevin Hickey on 18.

	Tries	Apps	Strike Rate
Kevin Hickey	18	59	3.28
Mark Douglas	9	17	1.89
Richard Angell	9	63	7.0
Doug Woodman	9	19	2.11
Barry Evans	9	32	3.56
Steve Thomas	9	36	4.00

COVENTRY F.C.

COURAGE LEAGUE STATISTICS

compiled by Steve McCormack

Season	Div	P	W	D	L	F	T	C	P	D	A	T	C	P	D	Most Points	Most Tries
1987-88	1	11	3	1	7	139	14	10	19	2	246	35	17	23	1	28 Martin Fairn	3 Paul Suckling
1988-89	2	11	6	0	5	150	22	7	12	4	143	16	11	16	3	36 Martin Fairn	4 Dick Travers
1989-90	2	11	6	1	4	206	25	11	24	4	185	23	9	21	4	79 Steve Thomas	6 Steve Thomas
1990-91	2	12	8	0	4	172	23	13	17	1	129	19	10	10	1	37 Richard Angell	4 Richard Angell
1991-92	2	12	7	0	5	187	18	11	29	2	196	22	15	25	1	13 Steve Thomas	4 Kevin Hickey
1992-93	2	12	3	0	9	192	21	15	16	3	236	24	13	26	4	53 Richard Angell	4 Barry Evans
1993-94	3	18	14	0	4	406	47	27	37	2	259	29	12	26	4	151 Richard Angell	9 Doug Woodman
1994-95	2	18	2	0	16	213	16	5	35	6	436	43	28	50	5	90 Richard Angell	5 Mark Douglas
Total		105	49	2	54	2665	186	99	189	24	1830	211	115	197	23		

BIGGEST WIN — **Home:** 60-3 v Redruth 30.4.94 CL3 — **Away:** 29-6 v London Irish 10.9.88 CL2

BIGGEST DEFEAT — **Home:** 16-33 v Saracens 29.10.94 CL2 — **Away:** 6-49 v Wasps 13.4.88 CL1

MOST TRIES in a match — **For:** 9 v Redruth 30.4.94 — **Against:** 9 v Wasps 13.4.88

MOST CONSECUTIVE — **Wins:** 5 — **Defeats:** 13

MOST APPEARANCES — **Forward:** 62 Julian Hyde — **Back:** 63 Richard Angell

MOST CONSECUTIVE APPEARANCES — 35 Richard Angell Warwick Bullock

CONSECUTIVE SCORING MATCHES — **Tries:** 3 Peter Suckling Steve Thomas Brian Shepherd Doug Woodman Mark Douglas

Points: 7 Richard Angell

	IN A SEASON	IN A CAREER	IN A MATCH
MOST POINTS	151 Richard Angell 1993-94 CL3	371 Richard Angell 1990-95	25 Richard Angell v Redruth 30.4.94
MOST TRIES	9 Doug Woodman 1993-94 CL3	18 Kevin Hickey 1988-95	3 Peter Rowlands v London Irish 10.9.89 Away CL2 Graham Robbins v Waterloo 13.1.90 Home CL2 Richard Gee v Morley 19.9.92 Home CL2
MOST CONVERSIONS	23 Richard Angell 1993-94 CL3	43 Richard Angell 1990-95	6 Richard Angell v Redruth 30.4.94 Home CL3
MOST PENALTIES	29 Richard Angell 1993-94 CL3	77 Richard Angell 1990-95	6 Steve Thomas v Sale 23.9.89 Away CL2
MOST DROP GOALS	4 Mark Lakey 1988-89 CL2	10 Mark Lakey 1987-95	2 Mark Lakey v Moseley 3.4.93 Home CL2 v London Irish 8.10.94 Home CL2

FYLDE R.U.F.C.

NICKNAME:　　　　　　　　　　　　　　　　　　　　　　　　　　　　**FOUNDED:** 1919

CLUB OFFICIALS
President
Gordon Aplin T.D.
Chairman
Ray Woolley
Club Secretary
Peter Makin
5 Ribblesdale Place, Preston,
Lancashire PR1 8BZ
Tel: (H) 01253 722713 (W) 01772 259625
Fixtures Secretary
David Taylor
18 St Georges Road, St Annes on Sea,
Lancashire FY8 2AE
Tel: (H) 01995 61322 (W) 01253 781010
Press Officer
A S Brown
Tel: (H) 01253 883100

Review of the Season

Victory in their final match at home to Wakefield would have brought survival for FYLDE, Bill Beaumont's club, and a season of gallant struggles against the odds would have been rewarded, but it was not to be as the Yorkshire side won a narrow victory - a draw would have been enough for the home team - and down went the Lancashire club on points difference with Moseley surviving.

This was all a tragedy and it could be attributed to the fact that amongst the forwards there was too much enforced chopping and changing with only No8 Greatorex an ever-present and the locks O'Neill and Taylor along with tighthead Rigby being reasnably regular in their appearances.

Among the backs Parker at fullback played in every game and was the leading scorer, the two wings Brendan Hanavan (the skipper) and Anderton missed one game between them, the centres Gough and Seed were consistent and so were the half-backs Barclay and O'Toole.

A regular pack is needed by a brave side, which did well enough in cup matches by winning at Coventry in Round Four (a massive 45-7 success) and going out bravely at Sale (55-13).

Fylde RUFC – Lancashire Cup winners 1994-95
Colours: Claret gold and white　　　　　　　　　　　　　　　　　**Change Colours:** Maroon

FYLDE R.U.F.C.

COURAGE LEAGUE
MATCH DETAILS 1994-95

No	Date	Opponents	Ven	Result	Scorers
1	Sep 10	Nottingham	H	33-14	Gough (T) Ashton (T) Parker (2c 2P) Barclay (2T 1DG)
2	Sep 17	Newcastle Gos	A	14-45	Hanavan (T) Parker (3P)
3	Sep 24	London Scottish	H	10-31	Anderton (T) Parker (1C 1P)
4	Oct 1	London Irish	A	12-23	Parker (3P) Barclay (1DG)
5	Oct 8	Waterloo	H	12-16	Parker (4P)
6	Oct 15	Saracens	A	7-18	Hanavan (T) Parker (1C)
7	Oct 22	Coventry	A	21-17	Hanavan (T) Anderton (T) Barclay (DG) Parker (1C 2P)
8	Oct 29	Moseley	H	10-6	Dixon (T) Parker (C P)
9	Nov 5	Wakefield	A	13-24	O'Toole (T) Parker (1C 2P)
10	Jan 7	Nottingham	A	10-9	Gough (1T 1C 1P)
11	Jan 14	Newcastle Gos	H	6-12	Parker (2P)
12	Feb 11	London Scottish	A	3-28	Parker (P)
13	Mar 4	London Irish	H	27-12	Hanavan (T) Barclay (T) Anderton (T) Parker (2C 1P) Ashton (T)
14	Mar 25	Waterloo	A	19-12	Gough (1P T) Barclay (2DG) Anderton (T)
15	Apr 8	Saracens	H	15-37	Gough (T) Barclay (P) Penalty Try Parker (1C)
16	Apr 18	Coventry	H	23-8	Hanavan (T) Gough (T) Barclay (T DG) Parker (1C 1P)
17	Apr 22	Moseley	A	8-6	Gough (T P)
18	Apr 29	Wakefield	H	8-11	Greatorex (T) Barclay (P)

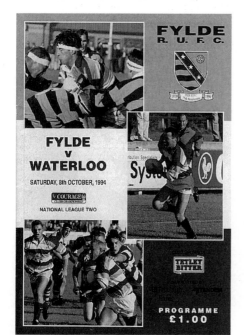

PROGRAMME DETAILS
Price: £1.00
Pages: 32

CLUB & GROUND DETAILS
The Woodlands Memorial Ground, Blackpool Road, Ansdell, Lytham St Annes, Lancashire FY8 4EL
Telephone: 01253 734733

Total Capacity: 5,490
Seated: 490
Standing: 5,000
Simple Directions to Ground: To the end of M55 then follow signs for Lytham St Annes - B5230 then B5261 onto Queensway. The ground is about 3 miles on left opposite Blossoms Pub and R.C. Church.
Nearest Railway Station: Ansdell and Fairhaven
Car Parking:
Season Tickets: N/A
Match Prices: Adults £5.00 Children £1.00 OAPs £3.00
Membership: Seniors £50.00 Juniors £15.00
Training Nights: Monday and Thursday

FYLDE R.U.F.C.

MATCH BY MATCH PLAYERS BY POSITION

Parker	Hanavan	Gough	Seed	Anderton	Barclay	O'Toole	Burns	Dixon	Gregg	O'Neill	Young	Russell	Ashton	Greatorex	McIntyre	Greenwood	Frith	Rigby	Stowe	Taylor	Jones	Liddle	Evans M
15	14	13	12	11	10	9	1	2	3	4	5	6	7	8									
15	14	13	12	11	10	9	1	2	3	4	5	6	7	8									
15	14		13	11	10	9	1	2	3	4	5	6	7	8		12							
15		13		11	10					4	5	6	7	8	2	12	1	3					
15	14	12	13	11	10	9		2		4	5		7	8			1	3	6				
15	14	12	13	11	10	9		2			5	7		8			1	3	6	4			
15	14	13	12	11	10	9		2			5		7	8			1	3	6	4	R		
15	14	10	13	11		9		2			5	6	7	8		12	1	3		4			
15	14	12	13*	11	10	9		2			5	6	7	8		R	1	3		4			
15	14	12*		11	10	9	1	2			5	6	7			13		3	8	4	R		
12	14		13	11	10	9	1	2*			5	6	7			12		3	8	4		R	
15	14			11		9	1			4				8	2			3	6	5	15		13
15	14		13	11	10	9	1		R	4		6	7	8				3*	5			2	12
15	14	12	13	11	10	9	1					6	7	8				3	5			2	
15	14	12	13*	11	10	9	1	2		4			7	8				3	5				R
15	14	12	13*	11	10	9	1	2		4		6	7**	8				3	5				R
15	14	13		11	10	9	1	2		4		6	7	8				3	5				12

Also Played: R Evans R match 2; Collinge No 14 match 4; Frith No 1 match 4, Weightman R match 5; Bellcombe R2 match 9; Jackman No 10 match 13; Tasner No 7 match 12; Hodgson R match 14; Bell R2 matches 15, 17, No 6 match 16

Courage League Records 1994-95

League Debuts: J Gregg, T Stowe, P Jones, A Liddle, M Evans, C Jackman, G Tasker, A Hodgson, A Bell
Players used: 30
Ever Presents: 3 Andy Parker, Greg Anderton, Mark Greatorex
Most appearances: 71 Brendan Hanavan

● Andy Parker finished leading scorer for the second season running. The record is 3 times held by Steve Burnage and Mike Jackson Parker is now 3rd on the all time list behind Burnage and Jackson

	Pts	T	C	P	D	App	Ave
S Burnage	318	6	45	64	4	37	8.59
M Jackson	222	5	21	53	-	53	4.19
A Parker	212	6	28	42	-	62	3.42

● Prolific try scorer Brendan Hanavan set another record by passing Craig Burns' record of 69 appearances and ended the season with 71. Hanavan's main exploits are in the try scoring field where he holds a number of records. He extended his club record to 40, worth 178 points, which puts him 4th on the all time points list for the club. He has topped the club's try scoring list in 5 of his 7 seasons with Fylde.

● Ian Barclay breaks the record for most drop goals in a match, season and career. His 2 drop goals in the match v Waterloo saw him become the first to do this. He beat the record of 2 in a season held by Steve Burnage with his 5 and extended his career total to 7, three more than Burnage.

● Barclay is also the only player to have played for Fylde in all 8 League seasons

FYLDE R.U.F.C.

COURAGE LEAGUE STATISTICS
compiled by Steve McCormack

Season	Div	P	W	D	L	F	T	C	P	D	A	T	C	P	D	Most Points	Most Tries
1987-88	3	11	6	0	5	269	41	30	14	1	164	26	12	11	1	121 Steve Burnage	10 Brendan Hanavan
1988-89	3	11	4	0	7	136	13	6	24	0	181	26	13	14	3	88 Steve Burnage	4 Mark Hesketh
1989-90	3	11	5	0	6	169	19	9	23	2	222	30	15	24	0	91 Steve Burnage	7 Brendan Hanavan
1990-91	3	12	7	2	3	183	25	10	19	2	115	14	7	13	2	62 Mike Jackson	5 Brendan Hanavan
1991-92	3	12	9	1	2	198	21	12	28	2	109	11	4	16	3	106 Mike Jackson	4 Antony Ireland
1992-93	2	12	0	3	9	108	9	3	18	1	290	31	18	30	3	40 Mike Jackson	2 John Nicholson Steve Gough
1993-94	3	18	13	0	5	339	46	20	21	2	219	19	11	31	3	109 Andy Parker	12 Brendan Hanavan
1994-95	2	18	8	0	10	250	25	13	28	5	329	28	15	53	0	91 Andy Parker	5 Brendan Hanavan Steve Gough Greg Anderton
TOTALS		105	52	6	47	1652	199	103	135	15	1629	185	95	192	15		

BIGGEST WIN — **Home:** 68-7 v Birmingham 7.11.87 CL3 — **Away:** 38-12 v Morley 17.10.87 CL3

BIGGEST DEFEAT — **Home:** 15-37 v Saracens 8.4.95 CL2 — **Away:** 3-51 v Sale 19.9.92 CL2

MOST TRIES in a match — **For:** 10 v Birmingham 7.11.87 CL3 v Redruth 9.4.94 Home CL3 — **Against:** 7 v Plymouth 19.11.88 CL3

MOST CONSECUTIVE — **Wins:** 6 — **Defeats:** 5

MOST APPEARANCES — **Forward:** 69 Craig Burns — **Back:** 71 Brendan Hanavan

MOST CONSECUTIVE APPEARANCES 34 Mike Jackson

CONSECUTIVE SCORING MATCHES — **Tries:** 3 Mark Preston Andy Parker Greg Anderton — **Points:** 20 Steve Burnage

	IN A SEASON	IN A CAREER	IN A MATCH
MOST POINTS	121 Steve Burnage 1987-88 CL3	318 Steve Burnage 1987-91	28 Steve Burnage v Birmingham 7.11.87 Home CL3
MOST TRIES	12 Brendan Hanavan 1993-94 CL3	40 Brendan Hanavan 1987-95	4 Brendan Hanavan v Exeter 3.10.87 Home CL3 v Birmingham 7.11.87 Home CL3 v Redruth 9.4.94 Home CL3
MOST CONVERSIONS	30 Steve Burnage 1987-88 CL3	45 Steve Burnage 1987-91	9 Steve Burnage v Birmingham 7.11.87 Home CL3
MOST PENALTIES	26 Mike Jackson 1991-92 CL3	64 Steve Burnage 1987-91	4 Steve Burnage v Rugby 14.1.89 Home CL3 v Lydney 10.3.90 Home CL3 Mike Jackson v Morley 13.10.90 Home CL3 v Exeter 21.12.91 Away CL3 v Richmond 11.1.92 Home CL3 Andy parker v Waterloo 8.10.94 Home CL2
MOST DROP GOALS	5 Ian Barclay 1994-95 CL2	7 Ian Barclay 1987-95	2 Ian Barclay v Waterloo 25.3.95 Away CL2

HARROGATE R.U.F.C.

NICKNAME: FOUNDED: 1871

CLUB OFFICIALS
President
Glyn Smith
Chairman
Allen Tattersfield
Club Secretary
Rodney Spragg
Pear Tree Cottage, Nidd, Harrogate
HG3 3BJ
Tel: (H) 01423 770126 (W) 01423 562634
Fixtures Secretary
G Siswick
22A Hillway, Tranmere Park, Guiseley,
Nr. Leeds LS20 8HB
Tel: (H) 01943 875620 (W) 01132 570413
Press Officer
John Ashman
Tel: (H) 01423 770354

Review of the Season

Although HARROGATE could only finish seventh out of ten in League Three there was seldom any danger of the club being relegated after their excellent promotion achievement of the previous season and they can look back on the campaign with reasonable satisfaction with the added bonus that they reached the Pilkington Cup fourth round thanks to good home wins over Sheffield (46-10) and Lichfield (22-14) before the potential fairy tale ende at high flying Sale (33-0).

In the new season the club should be able to consolidate, although further promotion would be a surprise. Skipper Richard Marcroft will provide inspiration and plenty of points should come from the trusty boots of fly-half Dan Clappison and Scrum-half Guy Easterby with left wing Rob Bell running in enough tries to keep opposition frowns in place.

The club that helped to launch the international careers of Peter Squires and Jeff Young can be proud of the way they are representing the spa town against bigger and more glamorous names.

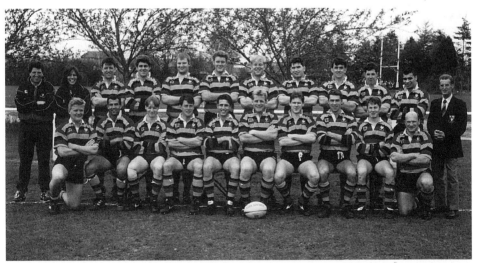

*Back: P Clegg (Coach), W Carswell (Physio), A Simpson, A Caldwell, S Brown, A Ludiman, P Taylor, T Ashton, S Burton,
G Easterby, G Kubu, L Nattress (Groundsman). Front: R Marcroft, J Wade, D Clappison, R Whyley, S Towse, J Hopkinson
(Capt), D Wheat, R Bell, C Reed, S Carbutt*
Colours: Red amber and black shirts and socks, black shorts   **Change Colours**: Red hoops

HARROGATE R.U.F.C.

COURAGE LEAGUE
MATCH DETAILS 1994-95

No	Date	Opponents	Ven	Result	Scorers
1	Sep 10	Richmond	A	18-12	Reed (T) Easterby (T C) Towse (2P)
2	Sep 17	Morley	H	23-3	Bell (T) Simpson (T) Clappison (2C 3P)
3	Sep 24	Rosslyn Park	A	12-25	Clappison (4P)
4	Oct 1	Blackheath	H	13-8	Reed (T) Clappison (1C 2P)
5	Oct 15	Exeter	A	14-13	Bell (T) Clappison (2P 1DG)
6	Oct 22	Rugby	A	13-12	Hassell (T) Clappison (1C 1P 1DG)
7	Oct 29	Otley	H	20-37	Bell (T) Clappison (5P)
8	Nov 12	Bedford	A	13-39	Eatkins (T) Clappison (1C 2P)
9	Jan 9	Coventry	H	27-13	Rood (T) Bell (T) Clappison (1C 1P) Kubu (2T) Yates (C)
10	Jan 14	Morley	A	8-21	Bell (T) Yates (P)
11	Feb 11	Richmond	H	8-8	Hopkinson (T) Easterby (P)
12	Feb 25	Blackheath	A	0-24	
13	Mar 4	Exeter	H	17-3	Bell (T) Easterby (4P)
14	Mar 25	Rugby	H	8-27	Bell (T) Easterby (P)
15	Apr 1	Otley	A	14-33	Simpson (T) Whoat (T) Easterby (2C)
16	Apr 8	Coventry	A	17-17	Towse (T) Hopkinson (T) Clappison (2C 1P)
17	Apr 15	Bedford	H	15-59	Rood (T) Clappison (T C P)
18	Apr 29	Rosslyn Park	H	35-30	Clappison (3C 3P) Reed (T) Easterby (T) Marcroft (T) Caldweed (T)

HARROGATE
RUGBY UNION FOOTBALL CLUB
COURAGE NATIONAL LEAGUE 3 1994-95

H. R. U. F. C.

(FOUNDED 1871)

RUNNERS UP NATIONAL LEAGUE DIVISION 4

1993 - 1994

Official Programme

COUNTY GROUND, CLARO ROAD, HARROGATE

PROGRAMME DETAILS

Pages: 32

Editor: Bob Thompson
Advertising Rates: Please phone Club

CLUB & GROUND DETAILS
County Ground, Claro Road, Harrogate, North Yorkshire HG1 4AG
Telephone: 01423 566966
Fax: 01423 562776

Total Capacity: 4,999
Seated: 499
Standing: 4,500
Simple Directions to Ground: Claro Road is on the north side of the A59 York-Skipton road between the Granby and County Hotels
Nearest Railway Station: Harrogate
Car Parking: 400
Season Tickets: Tickets: Adults £5.00 inc programme and parking Children U16 free OAPs £2.50
Match Prices: Adults £1.00 U16 free OAPs £1
Membership: Seniors £36.00 Juniors £21.00
Training Nights: Monday and Thursdays

HARROGATE R.U.F.C.

MATCH BY MATCH PLAYERS BY POSITION

Hassell	Taylor	Creed	Eatkins	Bell	Towse	Easterby	Simpson	Wade	Hall	Taylor	Castleton	Baker	Wheat	Hopkinson	Clappison	Marcroft	Pride	Ashton	Whyley	Field	Kubu	Scarbutt	Woolley
15	14	13	12	11	10	9	1	2	3	4	5	6	7*	8									
15	14	13	12	11		9	1	2	3	4	5	6	7	8	10								
15		13	14	11	12*	9	1	2	3	4	5		7	8**	10	6	R2						
15		13	14	11	12	9	1	2	3	4			7	8	10	6		5					
15		13	14	11	12	9	1			4			7	8	10	6		5	2	3			
15		13	14	11	12	9	1	2		4			7	8	10	6		5	3				
15		13	14	11		9	1	2	3	4	12		7	8	10	6		5					
15		13	14	11			1		3	4	5	6*	R	8	10	7			2				
		13	12	11		9	1		3	4	5		7*	8	10	R	6		2	14			
15		13	12	11	R	9	1		3			7	5	8		6			2	14*			
15		13	14	11	10	9			3	4			7	8		6		5	2	1*	12	R	
		13		11	10	9			3	4	5*			8		7	6		2		15	1	14
		13		11	10	9		2*	3	5	5			8		7	6		R		14	1	15
15		13		11	10	9	1		3	4			7	8		6	R	5*	2	12			14
15		13		11	10	9	1		3*	R	5		7	8		6			2	12			14
15		13		11	12	9	1				5*		7	8	10	6	12		2	3			14
15		13		11	12	9	1			4	5			8	10	7	12	6*	2	3			14
		13		11	10	9	1			4			7*	15	8	6			2	14			3

Also Played: Rutaan R match 12, No 4 matches 15, 16; Easterby R match 1; Wong R1 match 3; Harris No 12 matches 7, 8; Irvine No 9 match 8; Yates No 15 match 9, No 10 match 10; Ludiman No 5 match 18; Caldwell No 12 match 18; Burrow R match 18; Brown, No 4 match 10; Pearson R match 6, No 12 matches 12, 13

Courage League Records 1994-95

League Debuts: D Clappison, T Ashton, R Harris, S Carbutt, A Ludiman

Players used: 32

Ever Presents 2 Craig Reed, Rob Bell

Most appearances: 79 Steve Towse

- Rob Bell holds the record for most consecutive appearances. Since his debut v Stoke on the opening League fixture of the 1992-93 season Bell has been an ever present with 48 consecutive games. Not far behind him is Craig Atkins who made his debut in 1992-93 v Walsall and has now played 41 consecutive games.

- Dan Clappison replaced Ralph Zoing as the season's leading scorer – Zoing had been top points scorer in each of the previous 7 seasons. Clappison broke Zoing's record of 22 penalties in a season with 26

- Harrogate end the season in disastrous fashion suffering 2 heavy home defeats conceding 50 points in both games v Bedford and Rosslyn Park. The 59-15 defeat against Bedford being their worst ever at home. After starting March in 4th place they ended up 7th

- Jeremy Hopkinson extended his club try scoring record by just 2 to 29 giving him a strike rate of 1 try in every two games

	Tries	Apps	Strike Rate
J Hopkinson	29	58	2.00
S Baker	20	41	2.05
E Atkins	16	54	3.37
R Bell	13	48	3.69
G Easterby	13	61	4.69

HARROGATE R.U.F.C.

COURAGE LEAGUE STATISTICS
compiled by Steve McCormack

Season	Div	P	W	D	L	F	T	C	P	D	A	T	C	P	D	Most Points	Most Tries
1987-88	N1	10	5	0	5	147	17	8	21	-	113	11	6	19	0	28 Ralph Zoing	2 Andy Caldwell Dave Bowe
1988-89	N1	10	7	1	2	204	33	18	12	-	120	11	5	22	0	64 Ralph Zoing	8 Clive Ware
1989-90	N1	10	8	0	2	188	20	12	26	2	82	10	6	9	1	88 Ralph Zoing	4 Clive Ware
1990-91	D4N	12	6	1	5	220	35	16	16	-	204	22	14	27	3	43 Ralph Zoing	9 Jeremy Hopkinson
1991-92	D4N	12	6	0	6	170	20	12	19	3	175	18	8	29	0	45 Ralph Zoing	3 Steve Baker
1992-93	D4N	12	10	1	1	363	46	32	21	2	115	10	4	17	2	131 Ralph Zoing	9 Guy Easterby Steve Baker
1993-94	4	18	14	2	2	479	60	31	30	9	219	20	15	26	1	106 Ralph Zoing	13 Jeremy Hopkinson
1994-95	3	18	7	2	9	275	27	16	34	2	404	45	25	39	4	110 Dan Clappison	7 Rob Bell
TOTALS		102	63	7	32	204	258	145	179	18	1432	147	83	188	11		

BIGGEST WIN   **Home:** 78-12 v Aspatria 30.4.94 CL4   **Away:** 34-6 v West Park 22.10.88 N1 v Kendal 3.10.92 D4N

BIGGEST DEFEAT   **Home:** 15-59 v Bedford 15.4.95 CL3   **Away:** 13-39 v Bedford 12.11.94 CL3

MOST TRIES in a match   **For**: 14 v Aspatria 30.4.94 CL4   **Against:** 9 v Otley 22.9.90 Home D4N

MOST CONSECUTIVE   **Wins:** 5   **Defeats:** 3

MOST APPEARANCES   **Forward:** 77 David Wheat   **Back:** 79 Steve Towse

MOST CONSECUTIVE APPEARANCES   48 Rob Bell

CONSECUTIVE SCORING MATCHES   **Tries:** 6 Clive Ware

     Points: 13 Ralph Zoing

	IN A SEASON	IN A CAREER	IN A MATCH
MOST POINTS	131 Ralph Zoing 1992-93 D4N	505 Ralph Zoing 1987-94	25 Steve Baker v Lichfield 14.11.92 Home D4N
MOST TRIES	13 Jeremy Hopkinson 1991-92 D4N	29 Jeremy Hopkinson 1990-95	5 Steve Baker v Lichfield 14.11.92 Home D4N
MOST CONVERSIONS	28 Ralph Zoing 1992-93 D4N	88 Ralph Zoing 1987-94	9 Ralph Zoing v Towcestrians 13.3.93 Home D4N
MOST PENALTIES	26 Dan Clappison 1994-95 CL3	95 Ralph Zoing 1987-94	7 Ralph Zoing v Halifax 18.11.89 Home N1
MOST DROP GOALS	3 Ralph Zoing 1993-94 D4N	6 Ralph Zoing 1987-94	2 Ralph Zoing v Askeans 20.11.93 Home D4N

MORLEY R.F.C.

NICKNAME: THE MAROONS   **FOUNDED:** 1878

CLUB OFFICIALS
President
John W Mellor
Chairman
Alan S Gray
Club Secretary
David Vinegrad
5 Elmfield Court, Morley, West
Yorkshire LS27 0EP
Tel: (H) 0113 252 9306 (W) 0836 663601
Fixtures Secretary
Brian Falshaw
17 Rein Road, Morley, West Yorkshire
LS27 0HZ
Tel: (H) 0113 253 9507 (W) 0860 383628
Press Officer
Fred Pickstone
Tel: (H) 0113 253 3508

Again Bill Mitchell Got Us Wrong!

Last season was Morley's most successful since being promoted to the Second Division in 1992.

In 1993/4 their young squad struggled to stay in Division Three, but achieved fifth position in 1994/5 with the help of a handful of experienced players.

Leading the team was Tony Clark, with over 400 club appearances, admirably supported by the Yorkshire hooker Gordon Throup – each played in every league match.

Exciting players emerged around veteran Nick Kenyon, loyal clubman Andy Sales, Alistair Yule and Jamie Grayshon whose goal-kicking several times proved vital.

Ever present in League games were England Under 21s scrum-half Scott Benton and centre Jonathon Shepherd, whilst lock Jonathon Stow was unavailable only once. Full back Peter Massey and flanker Ben Wade played for the North under 21s and with Chris Barnes on the wing, Morley provided six of Yorkshire's under 21 Championship winning team.

After the first five League games, "The Maroons" were without a win, but in the remaining fixtures, they remarkably registered nine victories, two draws and defeats only at Blackheath and Rugby Lions. Richmond and Rosslyn Park were accounted for at home and away, only promoted Blackheath and demoted Exeter were not beaten once and victory at Otley in the last match of the season put Morley ahead of their other Yorkshire rivals in Division Three. Successful Rugby Chairman Chris Leathley and coach Alan Price continue in 1995/96. The Club hopes to have widened it's coaching staff well before the start of the season, which is anticipated with increased confidence.

"The Maroons" again disproved Bill Mitchell's forecast of relegation; perhaps he'll not see them in any corner of his Crystal Ball in this edition of The Directory.

Photo: Les Pratt

Colours: Maroon and white quarters, maroon shorts   **Change Colours:** Black

MORLEY R.F.C.

COURAGE LEAGUE
MATCH DETAILS 1994-95

No	Date	Opponents	Ven	Result	Scorers
1	Sep 10	Exeter	H	6-13	Grayshon (2P)
2	Sep 17	Harrogate	A	3-23	Jenkins (P)
3	Sep 24	Otley	H	14-38	Benton (T) Grayshon (3P)
4	Oct 1	Bedford	A	8-45	Clark (T) Grayshon (P)
5	Oct 15	Coventry	H	3-25	Sales (P)
6	Oct 22	Richmond	A	38-17	Shepherd (T) Clark (T) Grayshon (3C 3P DG) Benton (2T)
7	Oct 29	Rugby	H	13-3	Benton (T) Grayshon (1C 2P)
8	Nov 12	Rosslyn Park	A	12-9	Grayshon (4P)
9	Jan 1	Blackheat	A	9-18	Grayshon (3P)
10	Jan 7	Harrogate	H	21-8	Emerson (2T) Grayshon (1C 2P DG)
11	Feb 11	Exeter	A	12-12	Saws (T) Benton (T) Grayshon (1C)
12	Feb 25	Bedford	H	28-9	Clark (3T) Grayshon (T C 2P)
13	Mar 4	Coventry	A	18-7	Shepherd (T) Penalty Try Grayshon (1C 1P DG)
14	Mar 25	Richmond	H	31-24	Clark (T) Grayshon (T 2C 4P) Throup (T)
15	Apr 4	Rugby	A	5-27	Clark (T)
16	Apr 8	Blackheath	H	29-29	Yule (T) Benton (T) Grayshon (2C 3P 2DG)
17	Apr 15	Rosslyn Park	H	18-13	Grayshon (5P 1DG)
18	Apr 29	Otley	A	9-6	Grayshon (3P)

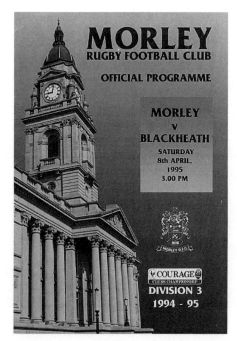

PROGRAMME DETAILS

Pages: 24

CLUB & GROUND DETAILS

Scatcherd Lane, Morley, West Yorkshire LS27 0JJ
Telephone: 0113 253 3487 (Club Office 0113 252 7598)
Fax: 0113 253 4144

Total Capacity: 5,826
Seated: 826
Standing: 5,000
Simple Directions to Ground: From West: Leave M62 at Junction 27. Follow A650 towards Wakefield for 1.2 miles. Turn left into St. Andrews Avenue. Club is 0.3 miles on left. From East: Leave M62 at Junction 28. Follow A650 towards Bradford for 1.7 miles. Turn right into St. Andrews Avenue. Club is 0.3 miles on left.
Nearest Railway Station: Morley Low
Car Parking: 110
Season Tickets:
Match Prices: Adults £4.00 Children/OAPs £2.00
Membership: Seniors £45.00 Juniors £10.00
Training Nights: Monday and Thursday

MORLEY R.F.C.

MATCH BY MATCH PLAYERS BY POSITION

Massey	Rowland	Shepherd	Sales	Clark	Grayshon	Benton	McFarland	Throup	Oxley	Stowe	Fountain	Spence	Bethell	Hill	Chard	Sonia	Emerson	Yule	McSwiney	Kenyon	Irish	Barnes	Wade
15	14	13	12	11	10	9	1	2	3	4	5	6	7	8	R								
15	14	13	12	11		9	1	2	3	4		6	7	8	R1	R2							
15	14	12		11	10	9	1	2	3	4	5	6		8			13	7					
	14	12		11	10	9	1	2	3	4		6		8			13	7					
15	14	12	10	11		9	1	2		4		6		8			13	7	3	5			
14	13	15		11	10	9	1	2		4		6		8			12	7	3	5			
14	13	15		11	10	9	1	2		4		6		8			12	7	3	5			
14	13	15		11	10	9	1	2		4		6		8			12	7	3	5			
14	13	15		11	10	9	1	2		4		6		8			12	7	3	5			
14	13	15		11	10	9	1	2		4		6		8			12	7	3	5			
15	13	14		11	10	9	1	2		4		6		8			12	7	3	5			
15	13	R2		11	10	9	1	2		4		6		8			12	7	3	5		14	R1
15	12	R1		11	10	9	1	2	3	4		6					13	7		5		14	8
15	12	13		11	10	9	1	2		4				8				7	3	5		14	6
15	12	13		11	10	9	1	2	3	4				8				7		5		14	6
15	12			11	10	9	1	2	3	4		6		8			13	7		5		14	
15	12			11	10	9	1	2	3	4		6		8			13	7		5		14	
15	12	14		11	10	9	1	2	3	4				8			13	7	3	5			

Also Played: Jenkins No 10 match 2; Toothin No 5 match 2; Johnson No 15 match 4; Cottom No 5 match 4

Courage League Records 1994-95

League Debuts: 7 3 Shepherd, P Fountain, J Bethell, I Toothill, C Johnson, A Cottom, C Barnes
Players used: 27
Ever Presents 5 J Shepherd, T Clark, S Benton, G Throup, J Stowe

- Jamie Grayshon tops Morley's points scoring chart for the 8th consecutive season. In this he broke his own seasonal record of 117 set last season. In 1994-95 Grayshon scored 166 points and set a seasonal record for penalties and drop goals of 39 and 5 respectively and equalled his own record of 12 conversions

- Winger Tony Clark is just as prolific in the try scoring department. Clark topped the try scoring list for the 6th time, 4th consecutive, in 8 seasons. Clark's 7 tries was his second best effort after last season's 8

- After losing their first 5 games of 1994-95, Morley lost just 2 more out of 13, of which 9 were won and 2 drawn

- Winger Clark became the second Morley player to score a hat trick of tries – in the impressive 28-9 win over the Division's champion team, Bedford

- Grayshon twice broke the record for points in a match. The original record was 17. He first broke the record with 18 points in the big away win over Richmond. In the return fixture later in the season he extended the record to 21 points

MORLEY R.F.C.

COURAGE LEAGUE STATISTICS

compiled by Steve McCormack

Season	Div	P	W	D	L	F	T	C	P	D	A	T	C	P	D	Most Points	Most Tries
1987-88	3	11	1	1	9	199	14	8	8	1	235	33	14	22	3	37 Jamie Grayshon	4 Tony Clark
1988-89	ALN	10	5	0	5	135	12	6	23	2	141	13	7	22	3	94 Jamie Grayshon	6 Tony Clark
1989-90	ALN	10	8	0	2	169	22	9	19	2	115	12	5	16	3	78 Jamie Grayshon	5 Paul White
1990-91	3	12	9	1	2	210	30	15	19	1	118	12	5	18	2	50 Jamie Grayshon	5 Mark Faulkner
1991-92	2	12	4	0	8	171	20	11	20	3	202	30	14	17	1	57 Jamie Grayshon	4 Tony Clark
1992-93	2	12	0	1	11	107	7	3	19	3	374	45	28	28	3	66 Jamie Grayshon	2 Tony Clark
1993-94	3	18	6	0	12	245	25	12	29	3	334	33	23	39	2	117 Jamie Grayshon	8 Tony Clark
1994-95	3	18	9	2	7	277	23	12	41	5	326	33	19	39	2	166 Jamie Grayshon	7 Tony Clark
Total		103	42	5	56	1413	153	76	178	20	1845	211	115	201	19		

BIGGEST WIN	**Home:** 35-6 v Redruth 30.10.93 CL3	**Away:** 49-6 v Liverpool St H 14.3.92 CL2
BIGGEST DEFEAT	**Home:** 7-38 v Wakefield 12.3.88 CL3	**Away:** 0-78 v Nottingham 24.10.92 CL2
MOST TRIES in a match	**For**: 9 v Liverpool St H 14.3.92 CL2	**Against:** 12 Nottingham 24.10.72 CL2
MOST CONSECUTIVE	**Wins:** 8	**Defeats:** 11
MOST APPEARANCES	**Forward:** 60 Gary Demaine	**Back:** 90 Tony Clark
MOST CONSECUTIVE APPEARANCES	49 Gary Demaine	
CONSECUTIVE SCORING MATCHES	**Tries:** 3 Jon Clark 2 Mike Faulkner	
	Points: 13 Jamie Grayshon	

	IN A SEASON	IN A CAREER	IN A MATCH
MOST POINTS	166 Jamie Grayshon 1994-95 CL3	662 Jamie Grayshon 1987-95	21 Jamie Grayshon v Richmond 25.3.95 Home CL3
MOST TRIES	8 Tony Clark 1993-94 CL3	35 Tony Clark 1987-95	3 Paul White v Winnington park 28.4.90 Home ALN Tony Clark v Bedford 25.2.95 Home CL3
MOST CONVERSIONS	12 Jamie Grayshon 1993-94 CL3 1994-95 CL3	63 Jamie Grayshon 1987-95	5 Jamie Grayshon v Liverpool St H 14.3.92 Away CL2
MOST PENALTIES	39 Jamie Grayshon 1994-95 CL3	151 Jamie Grayshon 1987-95	5 Jamie Grayshon v Rosslyn Park 15.4.95 Home CL3
MOST DROP GOALS	5 Jamie Grayshon 1994-95	18 Jamie Grayshon 1987-95	2 Jamie Grayshon v Wakefield 13.2.93 Away CL2 v Richmond 13.11.93 Home CL3

OTLEY R.U.F.C.

NICKNAME: FOUNDED: 1865

CLUB OFFICIALS
President
G Hinchliffe
Chairman
M H E Dracup
Club Secretary
C Wright
c/o Otley RUFC, Cross Green, Otley,
West Yorks LS21 1HE
Tel: (H) 01943 465589
Fixtures Secretary
R Franks
c/o Otley RUFC, Cross Green, Otley,
West Yorks LS21 1HE
Tel: (H) 01943 877086
Press Officer
J C Finch
Tel: (H) 01943 872491

Review of the Season

OTLEY exactly broke even by finishing sixth in League Three and their early exit from the Pilkington Cup (29-28 at Tynedale in a thriller) suggests that they had a fairly humdrum season, but had they been able to play as well in the second half of the season as they had in their first nine matches, which brought seven victories, they might have been challengers for promotion instead of mid-table finishers.

There seemed to be no good reason for the slump, which brought some heavy defeats in its wake. The team which ended the season was similar to the one that sarted off in September 1994 and there were plenty of consistent performers such as fullback Rutledge, the centres Flint and Overend, fly-half Hawkins and his partner Waddington and some hard working forwards such as the props Baldwin and Rigg, front jumper Carroll and back-row man Winterbottom.

The talent is there and the need for consistency is clearly next season's priority if a promotion challenge similar to the early part of last season is to be mounted.

Colours: Black and white hoops   **Change Colours**: Red with black hoops

OTLEY R.U.F.C.

COURAGE LEAGUE
MATCH DETAILS 1994-95

No	Date	Opponents	Ven	Result	Scorers
1	Sep 10	Clifton	A	13-19	Rutledge (T C 2P)
2	Sep 17	Richmond	H	19-6	Rutledge (T C 4P)
3	Sep 24	Morley	A	38-14	Rutledge (3C 4P) Melville (T) Hawkins (T) Waddington (T) Atkinson (T)
4	Oct 1	Rosslyn Park	H	10-3	Overend (T) Henry (T)
5	Oct 15	Blackheath	A	3-23	Colquhoun (P)
6	Oct 22	Exeter	H	16-3	Penalty Try Rutledge (1C 3P)
7	Oct 29	Harrogate	A	37-20	Melville (T) Hawkins (T) Munro (T) Rutledge (2C 6P)
8	Nov 22	Rugby	H	33-7	Waddington (T) Penalty Try Rutledge (T 3C 4P)
9	Jan 7	Bedford	H	12-6	Rutledge (4P)
10	Jan 14	Richmond	A	14-15	Atkinson (T) Rutledge (3P)
11	Feb 14	Clifton	H	14-3	Carroll (T) Hawkins (2P 1DG)
12	Feb 25	Rossly Park	A	5-13	Melville (T)
13	Mar 4	Blackheath	H	0-15	
14	Mar 25	Exeter	A	11-18	Flint (1DG) Rutledge (1T 1P)
15	Apr 1	Harrogate	H	33-14	Flint (T) Overend (T) Howard (T) Rutledge (T 2C 3P)
16	Apr 8	Bedford	A	11-32	Rutledge (T 2P)
17	Apr 15	Rugby	A	3-36	Rutledge (P)
18	Apr 29	Morley	H	6-9	Hawkins (P) Atkinson (P)

NATIONAL LEAGUE 3
SEASON 1994/95

Saturday 29th April 1995
Courage National League 3

OTLEY
V
MORLEY

K.O. 3.00 pm.

OFFICIAL MATCH PROGRAMME
No. 18 Price £1.00

PROGRAMME DETAILS
Price: £1.00
Pages: 40

CLUB & GROUND DETAILS

Cross Green, Otley, West Yorkshire LS21 1HE
Telephone: 01943 850142 (Clubhouse)
01943 461180 (Office)
Fax: 01943 461180

Total Capacity: 7,000
Seated: 850
Standing: 6,150
Simple Directions to Ground: Take Harrogate road from the centre of Otley. The Ground is about 3/4 mile on the left.
Nearest Railway Station: Leeds
Car Parking: 100
Season Tickets: Adults £45.00 OAPs £20.00
Match Prices: Adults £5.00 Children/OAPs £3
Membership: Seniors £25.00
Training Nights: Tuesdays & Thursdays

OTLEY R.U.F.C.

MATCH BY MATCH PLAYERS BY POSITION

Rutledge	Melville	Flint	Overend	Greig	Hawkins	Waddington	Baldwin	Barnett	Carroll	Tipping	Hargreaves	Henry	Atkinson	Rice	Bennett	Winterbottom	Hargreaves	Munro	Scott	Cook	Billington	Burkis
15	14	13	12	11	10	9	1	2	4	6	7	8										
15	14	13	12		10	9	1	2	4		7	5	11	3	6	8						
15	14	13	12		10	9		2	4		7	5	11	3	6	8						
15	14	13	12		10	9			4		7	5	11	3	6	8		2				
	14		13		10	9	1				7		11	2	4	6	8	2	12			
15	14		12		10	9	1		4		7	5	11	3	6	8		2	13			
15	14	13	12		10	9	1		4	6	7	5	11	3		8		2				
15	14	13	12		10	9	1		4		7		11	3	6	8		2				
15	14	13	12	11	10	9		2	4		7	5		3	6	8						
15*	14	13	12		10	9	1	2	4	6	7		14	3	R	8			5			
15*	14	13	12		10	9			4	6	7		14	3	R	8		2	5			
15	14	13			10	9	1			6	7	4	11	3		8		2	5	12		
	15	13			10	9			4	6	7	5	11	3		8		2	14	12		
15	14	10	12			9	1	2	4			5	11	3	7	8					13	6
15	14	13	12	11	10		1	2	4		7	5		3		8						6
15	14		13				1	2	4		7	5		3	6						12	8
	15	13	12			9	1		4		7	5	11	3	6	R		2				8
	15			11	10		1	2	4		7		14	3		8				12	13	6

Also Played: Reid No 3 match 1, R2 match 17; Wilson No 5 matches 1, 18; Demaine No 1 matches 3, 4, 9, 11, 13; Colquhoun No 15 match 5; Scott No 5 matches 5, 8; Melville No 9 matches 15, 16, 19; Kirkby No 11 match 16; Cadman No 10 matches 16, 17

Courage League Records 1994-95

League Debuts: Tony Greig, Simon Hawkins, Andrew Reid, Neil Hargreaves, Alex Bennett, Dan Cook, Mark Billington, Jonathan Burke, Mark Kirkby, Tony Cadman
Players used: 31
Ever Present: Glyn Melville

● Peter Rutledge tops Otley's points scoring chart for the third consecutive season – he also topped the try scoring charts. Last season he became the first Otley player to pass 300 and then 400 points taking him to a career total of 407 – nearly 280 ahead of the next on the list

● Sean Atkinson moves into third place on the club's all time try list behind Glyn Melville and Jon Walker

	Tries	Apps	Strike Rate
G Melville	39	69	1.77
J Walker	27	36	1.33
S Atkinson	15	58	3.86

OTLEY R.U.F.C.

COURAGE LEAGUE STATISTICS
compiled by Steve McCormack

Season	Div	P	W	D	L	F	T	C	P	D	A	T	C	P	D	Most Points	Most Tries
1987-88	N1	10	5	1	4	194	30	13	16	-						34 Ian Colquhoun	8 Glyn Melville
1988-89	N1	10	5	0	5	197	28	17	-							59 Robert Sharp	3 Robert Sharp
1989-90	N1	10	9	0	1	137	19	8	14	1						43 David Lester	3 John Walker & David Lester
1990-91	D4N	12	11	0	1	428	76	35	16	2	89	10	2	13	3	77 David Lester	16 John Walker
1991-92	3	12	5	0	7	177	24	9	19	2	190	24	8	24	2	62 Richard Petyt	4 Mark Farrar
1992-93	3	11	8	1	2	274	32	15	28	-	118	14	6	11	1	121 Peter Rutledge	6 Glyn Melville
1993-94	2	18	4	1	13	235	22	10	28	7	449	53	29	38	4	119 Peter Rutledge	7 Sean Atkinson
1994-95	3	18	9	0	9	278	24	12	42	2	258	23	10	35	6	167 Peter Rutledge	6 Peter Rutledge
Total		101	56	3	42	1920	255	120	180	14							

BIGGEST WIN — **Home:** 61-0 v Askeans 27.3.93 CL3 — **Away:** 50-21 v Harrogate 22.9.90 D4N

BIGGEST DEFEAT — **Home:** 3-29 v Kendal 22.4.89 N1 — **Away:** 9-88 v Sale 12.2.94 CL2

MOST TRIES in a match — **For:** 10 v Hereford 1991 D4N — **Against:** 14 v Sale 12.2.94 CL2

MOST CONSECUTIVE — **Wins:** 9 — **Defeats:** 7

MOST APPEARANCES — **Forward:** 86 Alex Hargreaves — **Back:** 69 Glyn Melville

MOST CONSECUTIVE APPEARANCES 41 Richard Petyt 11.11.91-30.4.94

CONSECUTIVE SCORING MATCHES — **Tries:** 5 Glyn Melville — **Points:** 17 Peter Rutledge

	IN A SEASON	IN A CAREER	IN A MATCH
MOST POINTS	167 Peter Rutledge 1994-95 CL3	407 Peter Rutledge 1992-95	25 Jon Howarth v Lichfield 13.10.90 Away D4N
MOST TRIES	16 John Walker 1990-91 D4N	39 Glyn Melville 1987-95	4 Glyn Melville v Wilton 12.3.88 Home ND1 John Walker v Harrogate 22.9.90 Away D4N Mark Farrar v Askeans 27.3.93 Home CL3
MOST CONVERSIONS	17 Jon Howarth 1990-91 D4N	37 Peter Rutledge 1992-95	7 Ian Colquhoun v Birmingham 27.4.91 Home D4N
MOST PENALTIES	37 Peter Rutledge 1994-95 CL3	91 Peter Rutledge 1992-95	6 Peter Rutledge v Harrogate 29.10.94 Away CL3
MOST DROP GOALS	7 Richard Petyt 1993-94 CL2	9 Richard Petyt 1991-94	2 Richard Petyt v Nottingham 11.9.93 Away CL2

READING R.F.C.

NICKNAME: GREEN MACHINE   **FOUNDED:** 1898

CLUB OFFICIALS

President
John Lucas
Chairman
Bob Needham
Club Secretary
Mike Wickson
21 Lunds Farm Road, Woodley,
Reading RG5 4PZ
Tel: (H) 01734 695999 (W) 01734 475002
Fixtures Secretary
Sefton Hewitt
21 Purfield Drive, Wargrave, Berks
RG10 8AP
Tel: (H) 01734 402909 (W) 01734 722666
Press Officer
Nigel Sutcliffe
Tel: (H) 01734 786035 (W) 01734 575833

Review of the Season

It was another golden season for Reading, who secured their third successive promotion by finishing runners-up in National League 4.

They also won the Berkshire Cup for a record-equalling ninth time, and retained the Southern Merit Table title while the Wanderers took the second team title for the first time.

To put the icing on the cake they reached the Plate final of Middlesex Sevens at Twickenham, losing 15-12 to Orrell after collecting the scalps of Bath and London Scottish.

Once again the inspired coaching and organisation of Director of Rugby Mike Tewkesbury and the calm leadership of skipper John Dixon enabled them to progress further in the Courage Clubs championship structure.

Reading owed a big debt to full-back Phil Belshaw, who was once again in great kicking form as he amassed 205 League points in 17 matches.

The Sonning men showed strength in depth when injury ended the season prematurely for key players fly-half Jason Dance and No 8 Mark Vatcher – and other members of the first team squad suffered knocks.

The season began well for Reading. They won their first six League games and topped the table briefly after champions Rotherham slipped up at Havant.

However the South Yorkshiremen toppled Reading the following week and although "The Green Machine" regained their composure with victories over Liverpool St Helens and Askean, they lost 31-30 at Plymouth during a flu epidemic at the club.

Reading finished the season strongly by taking 13 out of a possible 16 points.

They went down narrowly to Rotherham again, before winger Martin Richmond's try in the sixth minute of injury time in the penultimate game at Liverpool St Helens clinched a 14-14 draw and promotion. Then Reading celebrated by blitzing Askean with eight tries in a 52-34 last day of the season romp.

It was all heady stuff for a club which teetered on the brink of extinction in the early 1980s – and during 1982-3 won only one match.

Colours: Myrtle & white irregular hoops, navy shorts, myrtle socks   **Change Colours:** Navy shirts, white 'V'

READING R.F.C.

COURAGE LEAGUE
MATCH DETAILS 1994-95

No	Date	Opponents	Ven	Result	Scorers
1	Sep 10	Plymouth A	H	27-17	Belshaw (2C 1P) Dixon (T) C Hutson (T) McGeever (T) Armstrong (T)
2	Sep 17	Redruth	A	28-23	R Hutson (2T) Jones (T) Belshaw (2C 3P)
3	Sep 24	Leeds	H	26-19	R Hutson (T)
4	Oct 1	Aspatria	A	15-9	Belshaw (5P)
5	Oct 15	Havant	H	18-13	C Hutson (T) Pen Try, Belshaw (1C 2P)
6	Oct 22	Broughton Park	A	21-9	Rodgers (T) Vatcher (T) Belshaw (1C 3P)
7	Oct 29	Rotherham	A	12-24	Rodgers (1DG) Belshaw (3P)
8	Nov 12	Liverpool St H	H	28-6	Smith (2C 3P) C Hutson (T) Armstrong (T) Kerley (T)
9	Jan 7	Askeans	A	14-12	McCracken (T) Belshaw (3T)
10	Jan 14	Plymouth A	A	30-31	Fanning (T) Phillips (2T) Belshaw (3C 3P)
11	Feb 11	Redruth	H	29-11	Fanning (T) Vatcher (T) Belshaw (3C 1P) Kerley (T) McCracken (T)
12	Feb 25	Leeds	A	23-15	Dixon (T) Jones (T) Belshaw (2C 3P)
13	Mar 4	Aspatria	H	29-25	R Hutson (T) C Hutson (T) Richmond (DG) Belshaw (2C 4P)
14	Mar 25	Havant	A	22-18	Fanning (T) Belshaw (1C 5P)
15	Apr 1	Broughton Park	H	31-12	Belshaw (2C 4P) Phillips (T) Armstrong (T) Perkin (T)
16	Apr 8	Rotherham	H	16-23	Phillips (T) C Hutson (T) Belshaw (2P)
17	Apr 13	Liverpool St H	A	14-4	Richmond (T) Belshaw (3P)
18	Apr 29	Askeans	H	32-24	Belshaw (1T 6C) Dixon (T) Fanning (T) R Hutson (T)

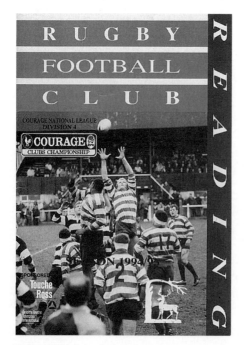

PROGRAMME DETAILS

Pages: 56
Editor: Nigel Sutcliffe
Advertising Rates: £150 per page

CLUB & GROUND DETAILS

Holne Park, Sonning Lane, Reading RG4 0ST
Telephone: 01734 696592
Fax: 01734 272622

Total Capacity: 2,200
Seated: 200
Standing: 2,000
Simple Directions to Ground: (A4) Reading - Maidenhead road, turn left 2 miles out of Reading signpost to Sonning
Nearest Railway Station: Railway
Car Parking: 280
Season Tickets: Adults £25.00 Children Free OAPs £25
Match Prices: Adults (Members only) No charge Children/OAPs No charge
Membership: Seniors £12 per month Juniors £20 p.a.
Training Nights: Tuesday & Thursday

READING R.F.C.

MATCH BY MATCH PLAYERS BY POSITION

Belshaw	Richmond	Dixon	Fanning	Hutson	Rodgers	Phillips	Gutteridge	Jones	Turrell	Hutson	Till	McGeever	Armstrong	Loudwell	Warren	Vatcher	Kerley	Dance	Pratt	Alexander	McCracken	Hill
15	24	13	12*	11	10	9	1	2	3	4	5	6	7	8	R							
15	14	13		11	10	9	1	2	3	4	5	6	7			8						
15	14	13		11	10	9	1	2	3	4	5	6	7		12	8						
15	14	13		11	10	9			3	4	5	6	7		12	8						
15	14	13		10	9	1	2	3	4			6	7		12	8			5	11		
15	14		13	10	9	1	2	3	4			6	7		12	8			5	11		
15	14		13	10	9	1	2	3	4			6	7		12	8			5	11		
	14	13	12				1	2	3	4		6	7			8	9	10	5	11		
15	14		12	10			1		3	4		6	7			8	9		5		11	
15	14		12			9	1		3	4	5	6	7			8		10			11	
15	14	13	12				1		3	4		6				8	9	10	5	11		
15	14	13	12	11	10		1	2	3	8		6	7					9	5			
15	14	13		11	10		1	2	3	8		6	7					9	5			
15	14	13	12	11			1	2	3	4		6	7	8				9	5		10	
15	14	13	12			9	1		3	4		6	7	8					5	11	10	
15	14	13	12			9	1		3	4		6	7	8					5	11	10	
15	14	13	12			9	1		3	4		6	7	8					5	11	10	
15	14	13	12	11			1*	2	3	4		6	7	8				9	5		10	

Also Played: Perrin No 2 matches 11, 15, 16, 17; Nicholson No 7 match 11; Hal R match 19; Palmer No 12 match 2; Smith No 15 match 9, R match 17; Cochlin No 1 match 4; Blackmore No 2 match 4; Atherton No 4 matches 12, 13; Hopkinson No 2 matches 9, 10; Lacey No 13 match 9; Kearns No 13 match 10, No 12 match 13

Courage League Records 1994-95

Players used: 33
Ever Presents 4 – M Richmond, I Turrell, C Hutson, I MacGeever

● Full back Phil Belshaw breaks the Reading record for points in a season for the third consecutive season and the fourth time in all. Belshaw has now topped the points scoring list 6 seasons out of 8

● Twice towards the end of the season Belshaw equalled his own record of 17 points in a match. He also equalled his own record for conversions in a match, 6, and penalties in a match, 5.

● Curtis Hutson equalled the record of tries in a season with 6, this record he shares with Roberts, Mark Alexander and Rodney Hutson

● Reading spent 13 of the 18 weeks in second place, had just one week on top of the table

● Won 8 out of 9 games at home

● Two of their 3 defeats were v Rotherham

READING R.F.C.

COURAGE LEAGUE STATISTICS
compiled by Steve McCormack

Season	Div	P	W	D	L	F	T	C	P	D	A	T	C	P	D	Most Points	Most Tries
1987-88	SW2	10	7	1	2	146	27	8	7	-	75	7	4	13	0	27 Neil Spencer	5 Neil Spencer & Rodney Hutson
1988-89	SW1	10	5	0	5	144	22	10	11	1	146	24	7	11	1	55 Phil Belshaw	3 Jon Deane & Curtis Hutson
1989-90	SW1	10	3	0	7	128	22	8	7	1	207	30	15	18	1	45 Phil Belshaw	3 Gary Williams & Alan Spence
1990-91	SW1	10	7	1	2	208	36	14	11	1	100	12	5	14	0	43 Phil Belshaw	6 Paul Roberts & Curtis Hutson
1991-92	SW1	10	4	0	6	120	15	9	12	2	163	27	8	12	1	36 Martin Radford	4 John Dixon & Rodney Hutson
1992-93	SW1	12	11	0	1	267	32	16	25	-	99	9	3	15	1	104 Phil Belshaw	6 Mark Alexander & Rodney Hutson
1993-94	D5S	12	10	1	1	248	26	8	34	-	61	5	3	10	0	133 Phil Belshaw	5 Ian McGeever
1994-95	4	18	14	1	3	435	44	28	52	1	319	33	17	36	4	204 Phil Belshaw	6 Curtis Hutson
Total		92	61	4	27	1696	224	101	159	6	1170	147	62	129	8		

BIGGEST WIN	**Home:** 59-6 v Salisbury	**Away:** 46-10 v Gordon League
BIGGEST DEFEAT	**Home:** 20-31 v Cinderford	**Away:** 21-36 v Weston Super Mare
MOST TRIES in a match	**For**: 11 v Salisbury	**Against:**
MOST CONSECUTIVE	**Wins:** 18	**Defeats:** 4
MOST APPEARANCES	**Forward:** Kevin Jones	**Back:** Rodney Hutson
MOST CONSECUTIVE APPEARANCES	47 Ian Turrell	
CONSECUTIVE SCORING MATCHES	**Tries:** 3 by 3 players	
	Points: 34 Phil Belshaw	

	IN A SEASON	IN A CAREER	IN A MATCH
MOST POINTS	204 Phil Belshaw 1994-95 D2	602 Phil Belshaw 1988-95	17 Phil Belshaw v Basingstoke 12.2.94 Home D55 v Havant 25.3.95 Away D4 v Askeans 29.4.94 Home D4
MOST TRIES	6 Curtis Hutson 1990-91 & 1994-95 Paul Roberts 1990-91 Mark Alexander 1992-93 Rodney Hutson 1992-93	27 Rodney Hutson 1987-95	3 Curtis Hutson v Torquay Home SW1 Mark Alexander v Penry Away SW1
MOST CONVERSIONS	26 Phil Belshaw 1994-95 D2	85 Phil Belshaw 1988-95	6 Phil Belshaw v Salisbury Home SW1 v Askeans 29.4.95 Home D4
MOST PENALTIES	49 Phil Belshaw 1994-95 D2	132 Phil Belshaw 1988-95	5 Phil Belshaw v Weston-Super-Mare 29.1.94 Away D55 v Basingstoke 12.2.94 Home D55 v Aspatria 1.10.94 Away D4 v Havant 25.3.95 Away D4
MOST DROP GOALS	1 by 4 players on 6 occasions most 3 Simon Rogers	3 Simon Rogers 1987-95	1 on 6 occasions by 4 players 3 Simon Rogers

RICHMOND F.C.

NICKNAME: FOUNDED: 1861

CLUB OFFICIALS
President
David Buchanan
Chairman
Michael Hess
Club Secretary
J Wright
Richmond F.C., The Athletic Ground,
Kew Foot Road, Richmond, Surrey
TW9 2SS
Tel: (H) 0181 392 9671
(W) 0171 225 1881
Fixtures Secretary
Vic Balchin
11 Troutbeck Close, Twyford, Berks
RG10 9DA
Tel: (H) 01734 345765
Press Officer
Vinny Codrington
Tel: (H) 0181 8782174 (W) 0181 3327112

Review of the Season

There was a time last season when RICHMOND were in such dire straits that a starting place in League Four in September 1995 seemed inevitable, but a brave recovery was mounted which meant that their last match defeat at Bedford in a 21-20 thriller merely gave the home team the championship as the visitors were safe. An astonishing 45-9 win at traditional rivals Blackheath at guaranteed that, but eighth place out of ten had been too close for comfort.

As if to prove that their league form was too bad to be true they played well enough in the Pilkington Cup to reach the last sixteen with a home demolition of Camborne (47-22), a 15-13 victory at Havant and a fourth round success against gallant Tabard (24-16) and their departure from the competition at Northampton was by a decisive 27-6 scoreline but was no disgrace.

They will be led by Mike Hutton in the new season and can count on excellent coaching from John Kingston, whose experience as skipper and prop of Cambridge University not so long ago, is invaluable. Add consistent scoring from fly-half John Gregory, his partner Hoad and hooker Andy Cuthbert (the top tries scorer) plus the contributions of several other players of talent and the next campaign should be a totally different proposition.

0850   003684

Colours: Old gold, red and black   **Change Colours**: Black with gold collar hoops

RICHMOND F.C.

COURAGE LEAGUE
MATCH DETAILS 1994-95

No	Date	Opponents	Ven	Result	Scorers
1	Sep 10	Harrogate	H	12-18	Head (4P)
2	Sep 17	Otley	A	6-19	Head (2P)
3	Sep 24	Bedford	H	14-16	Cliff (T) Head (3P)
4	Oct 1	Clifton	A	6-18	Head (2P)
5	Oct 15	Rugby	A	20-21	Lloyd (T) Greenwood (T) Gregory (2C 2P)
6	Oct 22	Morley	H	17-38	Hutton (T) Palmer (T) Gregory (2C 1P)
7	Oct 29	Rosslyn Park	A	21-23	Head (T) Gregory (T C 3P)
8	Nov 12	Blackheath	H	5-8	Cuthbert (T)
9	Jan 7	Exeter	A	14-3	Greenwood (T) Gregory (3P)
10	Jan 14	Otley	H	15-14	Gregory (5P)
11	Feb 11	Harrogate	A	8-8	Elliott (T) Gregory (P)
12	Feb 25	Clifton	H	21-14	Greenwood (T) Thompson (T) Gregory (1C 3P)
13	Mar 4	Rugby	H	19-10	Foster (T) Boyd (T) Gregory (3P)
14	Mar 25	Morley	A	24-31	Cuthbert (T) Gregory (3C 1P) Short (T) Boyd (T)
15	Apr 1	Rosslyn Park	H	11-14	Boyd (T) Gregory (2P)
16	Apr 8	Exeter	H	41-5	Luger (T) Short (T) Boyd (T) Cottler (T) Elliott (2T) Gregory (4C 1P)
17	Apr 15	Blackheath	A	45-9	Hutton (2T) Cuthbert (T) Fitzgerald (2T) Gregory (4C 4P)
18	Apr 29	Bedford	A	20-21	Cuthbert (T) Luger (T) Gregory (2C 2P)

All's well that ends well...

PRESIDENT'S MESSAGE

With just Sevens and the Heavies tour to come, an eventful season is drawing to a close. Inevitably the main focus of the Club's attention has been the fortunes of the 1st XV and, no doubt, much will be written about that elsewhere in this organ. However, it is personally satisfying to note that for once I was correct in my prediction, in the Christmas Newsletter, that we had far too good a team to go down. After a league record of played 6, lost 6 going into the New Year, the boys lost only 3 out of the remaining 10 - and we really should have won those 3! Stirring stuff, and I am delighted for skipper Mike Hutton and the boys, and for John Kingston and the coaching staff.

Elsewhere on the pitch there has been continuing success for Richmond. The coaching and managerial organisation has brought considerable success to the Club, and it is a source of encouragement to all that the Club's 1st XV already is himself a product of our mini and youth rugby. The Under 21, and other senior teams, have certainly had their moments this season as well. Our minis and youth sections continue to be the envy of other clubs. As ever, impressive coaching and managerial organisation has brought considerable success to the Club, and it is a source of encouragement to all that the Club's 1st XV already is in such good heart and on an upward arc. I look back over three very happy years, though there are one or two regrets. When I took over from Graham Tardif I set myself the goal of being a President for the whole Club. Despite attempting to drink vast quantities of beer with all and sundry, this has proved to be difficult to achieve, the main result being a significant expansion of my waistline! The paramount requirement of following the 1st XV effectively precluded anything more than cursory support for the other teams. I was therefore extremely touched and proud at the Annual Dinner this year (at least I think I was - my recall of the evening is somewhat hazy) when Doug Goodwin presented me with a great summer. I shall be handing over to Dave Buchanan - a man with 'Richmond' written on his heart if there ever was one and I know you will all join me in wishing him every good fortune for the next three years. Cheers, Dave succession to Dudley Wood - see separate article! So thank you, all of you. If I don't see you at the A.G.M., have a great summer. I shall be handing over to bankard and heart of all the players. I have been extremely lucky in the support that I have received from each and every one of you, and in particular from Vinny Codrington and our illustrious Chairman, Tony Hallett. Tony, of course, has just great honour to the Club through his appointment as Secretary to the RFU in

So, as I come to the end of my term as your President, it is great to see the Club Steve James

PROGRAMME DETAILS

Pages: 12 (A4)

Editor: Vinny Codrington
Tel: (H) 0181 8782174 (W) 0181 3327112
Advertising Rates: £300.00 half page £500.00 full page

CLUB & GROUND DETAILS

Richmond F.C., The Athletic Ground, Kew Foot Road,
Richmond, Surrey TW9 2SS
Telephone: 0181 9400397
Fax: 0181 3326775

Total Capacity: 2,840
Seated: 840
Standing: 2,000
Simple Directions to Ground: On main A316 past
Richmond Circus roundabout heading towards Twickenham
Nearest Railway Station: Richmond
Car Parking: 500
Season Tickets:
Match Prices: £5.00 adults £2.50 children
Membership: £55.00 seniors £27.00 juniors
Training Nights: Tuesdays & Thursdays

RICHMOND F.C.

MATCH BY MATCH PLAYERS BY POSITION

Head	Dontch	Lloyd	Hutton	Luger	Cliff	Sinclair	Cuthbert	Yeldham	Sage	Carr	Palmer	Fitzgerald	Huning	Gregory	Dellasavina	Foster	Greenwood	Short	Thompson	Elliott	Boyd	Kottler	Smith
15	14	13	12	11	10	1	2	3	4	5	6	8											
15	14	13	12	11	10	1	2	3	4	5	6	8	9										
15	14		12	11	10	1	2	3	4	5	6	8	9	13	7								
15	14	13	12	11	10		2	3	4	5	6	8	9		7	1							
	14		12				2	3	4	5	6	8	9	15	7	1	11						
	14		12			1	2	3	4	5	R	8	9	15	7		11						
10	14		12			1				5	6	8	9	15	7		11						
10	11		12			1	2		4	5*	6			15	7		14	9	8				
10			12			3	2		4	5				15	7	1	14	9					
10			12			3	2		4	5	6			15	7	1	14	9	8	13			
			12	11			2	3	4	5	6			15	7	1	14	9	8	13	11		
			12	11		1	2	3	4	5	6			15	7		14	9	8		11		
			12	11			2	3	4	5	6			15	7	1	14	9	8		11		
			12	11			2	3	4	5	6			15	7	1	14	9	8		11		
		13		11			2	3	4	5	6			15	7	1		9		12	11	14	8
		13		11		3	2		4	5	6			15	7	1		9		12	11	14	8
		13		11			2	3	4	5	6			15	7	1		9		12	11	14	8
		13		11			2	3		5	6			15		1		9		12	11	14	8

Also Played: Rowe No 9 match 1; Kryztofiah No 7 matches 1, 2; Dowse No 13 matches 5, 6; Morris No 10 matches 5, 6; Williams No 6 match 6; Clark No 13 matches 7, 14; Rodgers No 7 match 7; Goodwin No 3 matches 7, 8; Lewis No 4 matches 7, 18, R match 8; Goodburn No 13 match 8; Gavin No 8 match 9; Rollitt No 6 match 9; Lloyd Davies No 3 matches 9, 12, 13; Brown No 11 matches 9, 10; Jones No 7 match 18

Courage League Records 1994-95

League Debuts: D Luger, G Sage, T Palmer, I Krystofiak, M Dowse, B Short, D Williams, S Rodgers, R Favin, L Davies, S Brown, A Boyd, J Kottler, D Smith

Players used: 39

Ever Presents: None, 17 – M Hutton, A Cuthbert, P Carr, M Fitzgerald

	Pts	T	C	P	D	App	Ave
J Gregory	136	1	19	30	1	15	9.06
M Livesey	120	3	24	20	-	11	10.90

● John Gregory broke Martin Livesey's record for points in a season

● Gregory broke the seasonal record for penalties which was 20 and held by Livesey and Jason Hoad

● Paul Greenwood ended the season as leading try scorer 2 ahead of centre Mike Hutton

	Tries	Apps	Strike Rate
P Greenwood	18	42	2.33
M Hutton	16	60	3.75

● John Gregory's prolific season sees him move into second place on Richmond's all time list behind Martin Livesey and just one point ahead of Jason Hoad

	Pts	T	C	P	D	App	Ave
M Livesey	512	5	74	100	14	54	9.48
J Gregory	145	1	19	33	1	20	7.25
J Hoad	144	3	17	32	-	33	4.36

RICHMOND F.C.

COURAGE LEAGUE STATISTICS

compiled by Steve McCormack

Season	Div	P	W	D	L	F	T	C	P	D	A	T	C	P	D	Most Points	Most Tries
1987-88	2	11	6	0	5	140	14	6	20	4	156	22	7	16	2	60 Simon Smith	5 Simon Pennock
1988-89	2	11	4	1	6	112	8	4	21	3	216	24	18	25	3	74 Martin Livesey	3 Paul Seccombe
1989-90	2	11	7	1	3	282	41	29	20	0	135	16	4	19	2	120 Martin Livesey	7 Jim Fallon
1990-91	2	12	3	1	8	134	17	9	14	2	245	25	14	31	8	38 Martin Livesey	6 Mike Hutton
1991-92	3	12	10	1	1	296	39	22	26	6	124	13	9	17	1	95 Martin Livesey	6 Phil Della-Savina
1992-93	2	12	5	0	7	204	19	4	25	2	196	15	8	33	2	95 Martin Livesey	3 David Sole
1993-94	3	18	9	0	9	337	30	26	40	5	300	30	18	37	1	90 Martin Livesey	6 Paul Greenwood
1994-95	3	18	6	1	11	319	31	19	41	1	290	27	16	39	2	136 John Gregory	4 Andy Cuthbert. Adrian Boyd
TOTALS		105	50	5	50	1824	199	119	207	23	1662	172	94	217	21		

BIGGEST WIN   **Home:** 86-8 v Headingley 28.4.90 CL2   **Away:** 50-3 v Roundhay 11.4.92 CL3

BIGGEST DEFEAT   **Home:** 15-40 v London Scot 17.11.90 CL2   **Away:** 9-50 v Sale 10.9.88 CL2

MOST TRIES in a match   **For:** 16 v Headingley 28.4.90   **Against:** 8 v Sale 10.9.88 CL2

MOST CONSECUTIVE   **Wins:** 7   **Defeats:** 9

MOST APPEARANCES   **Forward:**   **Back:**

MOST CONSECUTIVE APPEARANCES

CONSECUTIVE SCORING MATCHES   **Tries:** 3 Jim Fallon, Rick Forde, Mike Hutton

Points: 19 Martin Livesey

	IN A SEASON	IN A CAREER	IN A MATCH
MOST POINTS	136 John Gregory 1994-95 CL3	512 Martin Livesey 1988-894	22 Martin Livesey v Blackheath 13.11.93 Home CL3
MOST TRIES	7 Jim Fallon 1989-90 CL2	18 Paul Greenwood 1991-95	3 Phil Della- savina v Nuneaton 29.3.92 CL3
MOST CONVERSIONS	24 Martin Livesey 1989-90 CL2	74 Martin Livesey 1988-94	7 Martin Livesey v Sheffield 24.4.92 CL3
MOST PENALTIES	30 John Gregory 1994-95 CL3	100 Martin Livesey 1988-94	6 Nick Preston v Bedford 27.3.88 Home CL2 Martin Livesey v London Irish 8.4.89 Home CL@ Jon Clark v Lydney 14.3.92 Home CL3
MOST DROP GOALS	6 Martin Livesey 1991-92 CL3	14 Martin Livesey 1988-94	3 Martin Livesey v Northampton 19.11.88 Home CL2

ROSSLYN PARK F.C.

NICKNAME: The Park   **FOUNDED:** 1879

CLUB OFFICIALS

President
Richard Malthouse
Chairman
Eric Mountjoy
Club Secretary
David E Whittam FRCS
37 Queens Road, Kingston upon
Thames, Surrey KT2 7SL
Tel: (H) 0181 5494209 (W) 0181 9448059
Fixtures Secretary
Don Bell
148 Trentham Street, London SW18 5DJ
Tel: (H) 0181 8705285
Press Officer
Bernard Wiggins
Tel: (H) 01273 844028 (W) 01817 252052

Review of the Season

Same old story for Park – lots of tries, lots of players used and no promotion. Last season saw Park use far too many players to gain any sort of consistancy. Nineteen players made their League debuts – easily the highest in the Division.

After an indifferent start to the season they came back strongly to win five out of their last seven matches to finish fourth.

Park also had the problem of not having a consistent goal kicker with Giffin, Maddock and Holder all having a go at some time.

The last two wins of the season were emphatic successes against Rugby and Harrogate, both of whom were riding high. The only settled part of the side was the front three of Perrett, Barnett and Horrocks-Taylor. They never played the same line-up in consecutive League games. Club stalwart Tony Brocks retired in the final game of the season at Harrogate.

Colours: Red and white hoops   **Change Colours**: Dark blue

ROSSLYN PARK F.C.

COURAGE LEAGUE
MATCH DETAILS 1994-95

No	Date	Opponents	Ven	Result	Scorers
1	Sep 10	Blackheath	H	14-14	Parton (3P) Smithson (T)
2	Sep 17	Exeter	A	11-9	Warren (T) Ring (2P)
3	Sep 24	Harrogate	H	25-12	Campbell (T) Holden (T) Smither (T) Parton (2C 2P)
4	Oct 1	Otley	A	5-10	Holder (T)
5	Oct 13	Bedford	H	13-31	Holder (DG) Parton (1T 1C 1P)
6	Oct 22	Clifton	A	21-2	Jones (T) Giffen (1C 3P) Dower (T)
7	Oct 29	Richmond	H	23-21	Barnett (T) Pickup (T) Lyeth (T) Giffen (1C 2P)
8	Nov 12	Morley	H	9-12	Holder (DG) Giffen (2P)
9	Jan 7	Rugby	A	26-18	Vander (T) Rolls (2T) Maddock (T) Giffen (3C)
10	Jan 14	Exeter	H	10-11	Walshe (T) Giffen (1C 1P)
11	Feb 11	Blackheath	A	3-9	Maddock (P)
12	Feb 25	Otley	H	13-3	Giffen (T) Steed (T) Maddock (DG)
13	Mar 11	Bedford	A	5-31	Vander (T)
14	Mar 25	Clifton	H	25-8	Smither (2T) Holder (2C 1P) Ritchie (T) Maddock (DG)
15	Apr 1	Richmond	A	14-11	Perrett (T) Holder (3P)
16	Apr 8	Rugby	H	35-8	C Lamerton (T) Holder (1T 2C 1P) Vander (T) Perrett (T) Smither (T) Maddock (DG)
17	Apr 15	Morley	A	13-18	Perrett (T) Vander (T) Giffen (P)
18	Apr 29	Harrogate	A	50-35	Barnett (T) King (2T 5C) Duthie (T) Giffen (2T) Brooks (T) Vander (T)

PROGRAMME DETAILS

Price: £1.00
Pages: 32

CLUB & GROUND DETAILS

Rosslyn Park F.C., Priory Lane, Roehampton, London SW15 5JH
Telephone: 0181 8761879
Fax: 0181 8787527

Total Capacity: 4,630
Seated: 630
Standing: 4,000
Simple Directions to Ground: Ground situated at the junction of the upper Richmond Road (South Circular) and Roehampton Lane SW15
Nearest Railway Station: Barnes (Southern Region from Waterloo)
Car Parking: In the ground
Season Tickets:
Match Prices: £1.00
Membership: £58.75
Training Nights: Tuesdays and Thursdays

ROSSLYN PARK F.C.

MATCH BY MATCH PLAYERS BY POSITION

Parton	Holder	Smither	Perrett	Barnett	Horrocks	Millward	Vander	Pickup	Lyeth	Jones	Walshe	Giffen	Flood	Rolls	Ritchie	Munn	Dower	Maddock	Miller	Enson	Fennell	Duthie	Gibson
15	13	9	1	2	3	4	6	R															
15	13	9	1	2		4		6	R	5													
15	13	9*	1	2	3	4		6	12						R								
15	13	9	1	2		4	7	6	12	R													
15	13		1	2	3		R	6	12	4	9	11	R			8							
	10		1	2	3	8			12	4	9	11	14		6	15	5						
			1	2	3			6	12	4	9	11	14	8	15	5							
14	10		1	2	3	8		6	12	4	9	11	13		15	5							
			1	2		8	7	6	12	R	9	11	13	14	15	4	10						
15			1	2		8*	7	6	13	4	9	11	12	14	5	10							R
			1	2	3	8	7		13		9	11	12	14	15	5	10				6		
	15			2	3		7				9	11		8	5		10	13	12	1	6		
	15			2	3	5	7				9	14		R	8*	5	10	13	12	1	6		
	15	14	1	2		12	7				9				8*	5	10	13	12		6		
	15	14	1	2*		8	7				9	11					10	13	12		6		5**
	15	14	1	2		8	7				9	11					10	13	12		6		5
	15		1	2		8	7				9	11	13		5		10		12		6		4
			1*	2			R	7**			15				R			13	12	3	6		5

Also Played: Blake No 14 match 1, No 11 match 18; Furner No 12 matches 1, 2, No 10 matches 5, 7; Sinclair No 11 matches 1, 2, 3, 4; King No 10 matches 1, 2, 18; Hanchett No 5 matches 1, 5*; Hill No 7 matches 1, 2, 3; Brooks No 8 matches 1, 2, 3, 4, 18; Warren No 14 matches 2, 3, 4, 5; Henwood No 3 matches 2, 4, 14, 18; Ashworth No 10 matches 3, 4; Campbell-Lamerton No 5 matches 3, 4, No 5* match 9, No 4 matches 14, 15, 16, 18; Downey No 7 matches 5, 6, 7, 8; Spencer No 13 matches 6, 7; Steed No 14 matches 12, 17, No 11 matches 13, 14; James R2 match 15; Bayliss No 4 match 11, No 4* match 12; Langton R match 18; Springhall No 9 match 18; Cons No 3 matches 9, 10, 15, 16, 17

Courage League Records 1994-95

League Debuts: D Ferner, N Hanchett, A Vander, I Hill, C Henwood, T Jones, P Flood, J Rolls, C Ritchie, A Hunn, G Spencer, T Dower, A Maddock, J Steed, B Fennell, M Duthie, J Cons, S Bayliss, R Springhall
Players used: 41
Ever Presents 1 Dave Barnett

● Andy Holder breaks the record for career drop goals with 6. He previously shared the record of 4 with Mark Jermyn

● Andy Maddock breaks the record for most drop goals in a season. Maddock dropped 3 goals last season to beat Paul Roblin's record of 2 set in 1991-92

● Back row forward Tony Brooks retired as the club's leading try scorre – 16 in 66 appearances. Brooks is one of two players to have played in all 8 seasons for Rosslyn Park, the other is David Barnett

● Barnett ends the season with the record of most appearances for Park, beating the old record of 66 held by Paul Essenhigh. Barnett's final total is 75

● Park had 6 players contribute on the kicking side, which is why Matt Giffen finished leading scorer with just 54 points – only one more than the 53 that John Graves scored in the 1991-92 season to top the club's scoring chart, the season they were relegated from Division One to Division Two

ROSSLYN PARK F.C.

COURAGE LEAGUE STATISTICS
compiled by Steve McCormack

Season	Div	P	W	D	L	F	T	C	P	D	A	T	C	P	D	Most Points	Most Tries
1987-88	2	11	8	2	1	155	20	9	17	2	83	8	3	14	1	73 John Graves	6 Tony Brooks
1988-89	1	11	5	0	6	172	20	13	21	1	208	22	12	30	2	89 John Graves	3 Simon Hunter Richard Crawford Rob Nelson-Williams
1989-90	1	11	4	0	7	164	19	8	21	3	243	40	19	15	-	87 John Graves	4 Mark Jermyn
1990-91	1	12	6	0	6	216	30	12	20	4	174	15	9	27	5	92 John Graves	3 Peter Taylor Guy Leleu Kelwin Wyles
1991-92	1	12	0	1	11	111	12	3	17	2	258	24	18	36	6	53 John Graves	2 Mark Thomas Kelvin Wyles
1992-93	2	12	5	0	7	209	17	5	36	2	199	13	7	34	6	61 John Graves Gary Abraham	3 Paul Essenhigh
1993-94	3	18	10	1	7	372	48	27	25	1	240	28	11	23	3	59 Paul Roblin	9 Sean Rosier
1994-95	3	18	10	0	8	313	38	18	24	5	280	22	10	46	4	54 Matt Giffen	5 Tim Smither Alex Vander
Total		105	48	4	53	1712	204	95	181	20	1685	172	89	225	27		

BIGGEST WIN **Home:** 48-0 v Northampton 27.4.91 Cll **Away:** 50-35 v Harrogate 29.4.95 CL3

BIGGEST DEFEAT **Home:** 13-31 v Bedford 15.10.94 CL3 **Away:** 14-64 v Orrell 28.4.90 CL1

MOST TRIES in a match **For**: 9 v Northampton 27.4.91 Home Cll **Against:** 11 v Orrell 28.4.90 Away CL1

MOST CONSECUTIVE **Wins:** 5 **Defeats:** 8

MOST APPEARANCES **Forward:** 75 David Barnett **Back:** 61 John Graves

MOST CONSECUTIVE APPEARANCES 45 John Graves 19.9.87 - 27-4-91

CONSECUTIVE SCORING MATCHES **Tries:** 3 Sean Rosier, Dan Perrent, Alex Vander

Points: 25 John Graves

	IN A SEASON	IN A CAREER	IN A MATCH
MOST POINTS	92 John Graves 1990-91 CL1	455 John Graves 1987-93	22 John Graves v Coventry 13-2-93 Home CL2
MOST TRIES	9 Sean Rosier 1993-94 CL3	16 Tony Brooks 1987-93	3 Tony Brooks v Havant 12-3-94 Home CL3
MOST CONVERSIONS	13 John Graves 1988-89 CL1	44 John Graves 1987-93	5 Andy King v Harrogate 29-4-95 Away CL3
MOST PENALTIES	21 John Graves 1988-89 CL1	114 John Graves 1987-93	6 Gary Abraham v Morley 27-3-93 Home CL2
MOST DROP GOALS	3 Andy Maddock 1994-95 CL3	6 Andy Holder 1989-95	2 Paul Roblin v Gloucester 4.1.92 Away CL1

ROTHERHAM R.U.F.C.

NICKNAME: **FOUNDED:** 1923

CLUB OFFICIALS

President
Paul Jones
Club Secretary
Keith Oxley
119 Broom Lane, Rotherham S60 3NN
Tel: (H) 01709 542887 (W) 01142 523389
Fixtures Secretary
Andy Fraser
10 Birch Close, Killamarsh, Sheffield
Tel: (H) 01142 482051 (W) 01142 7690245
Press Officer
Steve Cousins
Tel: (W) 01709 540982

Review of the Season

Rotherham kept up their remarkable run in the Courage Leagues with their 5th title in the eight seasons of league rugby. They finished well clear in National Division 4 with 17 wins and a record 576 pts. to move in to the top 30 clubs in the country.

Rotherham made a good start to their league season with a big victory over Askeans at home and followed this with another win on the long away trip to Plymouth. The momentum was maintained in the first half of the season with just one defeat 29-32 at Havant the only slip up. When the league break came they were top of the table with 7 wins to their 8 games. During the first half of the season victories away at Morley and at home to Wharfdale took the club through to the 4th round of the Pilkington Cup for the first time in their history where they lost narrowly 18-21 to Waterloo at home. The resumption of the league programme after Christmas saw a vital win earned at Liverpool St. Helens when a 5 -14 half time deficit was turned in to an 18-14 victory. The return fixtures were all won to stretch the winning sequence to twelve games. Promotion was effectively gained with four games left and a victory at closest rivals Reading sealed the title with two games to go.

The end of the season brought another first for the club when National Division 3 opponents Otley and Harrogate were beaten in the semi-final and final respectively to enable Rotherham to take the Yorkshire Cup for the first time.

Photo: Rotherham Advertiser

Colours: Maroon and sky hoops **Change Colours:** Maroon

ROTHERHAM R.U.F.C.

COURAGE LEAGUE
MATCH DETAILS 1994-95

No	Date	Opponents	Ven	Result		Scorers
1	Sep 10	Askeans	H	W	53-9	Challinor (2T) Scott (1T) Hough (1T) Sorby (1T) Bayston (1T) Coy (1T) Plant (2P 6C)
2	Sep 17	Plymouth A	A	W	23-15	Bayston (1T) Ashwith (1T) Plant (2P 2C) Worral (1P)
3	Sep 24	Redruth	H	W	31-7	Scott (1T) Ashwith (1T) Dudgy (1T) Selkirk (1T) Plant (3P 1C)
4	Oct 1	Leeds	A	W	17-8	Randerson (1T) Plant (4P)
5	Oct 15	Aspatria	H	W	63-11	Dudley (3T) Ashwith (1T) Worrall (1T) Brooksbank (1T) Selkirk (1T) Pen Try Plant (2P 6C) Harper (T) Pen Try
6	Oct 22	Havant	A	L	29-32	Scott (1T) Ashwith (1T) Selkirk (1T) Plant (4P 1C)
7	Oct 29	Reading	H	W	24-12	Hough (1T) Worral (1T) Plant (4P 1C)
8	Nov 12	Broughton Park	H	W	50-0	Scott (1T) Sorby (1T) Dudgy (1T) Challinor (1T) West (1T) Turner (1T) Plant (4P 4C)
9	Jan 7	Liverpool Sth	A	W	18-14	Heaselgrave (2T) Plant (1T 1P)
10	Jan 14	Askeans	A	W	31-17	West (1T) Heaselgrave (1T) Wareham (1T) Plant (4P 2C)
11	Feb 25	Redruth	A	W	19-13	Rodgers (1T) Glynn (4P 1C)
12	Mar 3	Leeds	H	W	34-18	Coy (2T) Bayston (1T) Brackenbury (1T) Plant (4P C)
13	Mar 11	Plymouth A	H	W	35-23	Worrall (1T 2P 2C) Selkirk (2T) Bayston (1T) Harris (1T)
14	Mar 25	Aspatria	A	W	32-11	Harper(1T) Worral (2C) Plant (1P) Scott (1T) West (2T) Selkirk (1T)
15	Apr 1	Havant	H	W	35-10	Bunting (1T) West (3T) Harper (1T) Plant (2C 2P)
16	Apr 8	Reading	A	W	23-16	Scott (2T 2C 2P 1DG)
17	Apr 15	Broughton Park	H	W	34-18	Plant (3C 1P) Harper (1T) Turner (2T) Harris (2T)
18	Apr 29	Liverpool St H	H	W	25-23	Dudley (2T) Khoo (T) Plant 2C 2P)

PROGRAMME DETAILS

Pages: 44
Advertising Rates: Full page £350.00

CLUB & GROUND DETAILS
Rotherham R.U.F.C., Clifton Lane, Rotherham
Telephone: 01709 370763

Total Capacity: 1,520
Seated: 270
Standing: 1250
Simple Directions to Ground: (a) Leave M1 at Junc 33.
Follow Rotherway for half mile to roundabout. Take second
exit signposted Bawtry. Traffic lights straight on up hill to
roundabout. Exit first left. Follow road into town centre.
Ground approx 1 mile on right. (b) Leave M18 at Junc 1
follow signs to Rotherham. After 2 miles approx at 2nd
roundabout (Brecks Hotel) fork right. At next roundabout
(Stag Inn) secon exit. Follow road into town centre. Ground
approx 1 mile on right.
Nearest Railway Station: Rotherham
Car Parking: 30 in ground unlimited
Season Tickets:
Match Prices: Adults £4.00 Children/OAP's £1.50
Membership: Seniors £7.00 Juniors/OAP's £5.00
Training Nights: Mondays and Thursdays

Welcome to R.R.U.F.C.

ROTHERHAM R.U.F.C.

MATCH BY MATCH PLAYERS BY POSITION

P Scott	S Hough	J Sorby	R Askwith	K Plant	S Worrall	S Wilson	T Bayston	S Coy	J Dudley	J Brookbank	A Challinor	C West	R Selkirk	D Pullen	M Pinder	T Khoo	M Randerson	J Harper	T Turner	D Breakwell	S Bunting
14	13	12	11	10	9	1	2	3	4	5	6	7	8				R				
14	13	12	11	10	9	1	2	3	4	5			8	15	7						
14	13		11	10	9	1	2	3	4	5	6		8	12	7	15					
14			11	10		1	2	3	4	5	6		8		7	15	9	13			
14	12		11	10	9	1	2	3	4	5	6	7				15		13			
14	12		11	10	9	1	2	3	4	5	6		8	13	7						
14	13	12		10	9	1	2	3	4	5	6		8	15	7			11			
14		12		10	9		2	3	4	5	6	7	8	15				13			
14				10			2		4	5		7	8			13	R		12	15	1
14				10			2			5		7	8			13			12	15	1
11							2	3	4	5		7	8				14	13	12	15	1
14				10	9		2	3	4	5		7	8				11	13	12	15	1
14	13			10	9		2	3				7	8				11		12	15	1
14				10	9		2	3	4		6	7					11	13	12	15	1
14				10	9		2	3	4		6	7					11	13	12	15	1
14	12			10	9	R	2	3	4		6	7	8				11	13		15	

Also Played: D Walker No 15 match 1, No 12 match 4, No 15 match6; M Wood No 6 match 2; R Heaslegrave No 11 matches 8, 9, 10; R Wareham No 1 match 8, No 3 matches 9, 10; G Glynn R matches 10, 11

Courage League Records 1994-95

League Debuts: M Pinder, T Khoo, J Harper, M Randerson, R Heaslegrave, R Wareham, D Breakwell, G Glynn, R Brackenbury, N Harris
Players used: 31
Ever Present: T Bayston
Most appearances: 90 Richard Selkirk

● Finished the season with 12 straight wins

● Kevin Plant continues his remarkable scoring feats. He ends the season with 202 points, only the 6th man to top 200 points in a National Division season. He now has 767 career points, second only to Bedford's Andy Finnie

	Pts	T	C	P	D	App	Ave
A Finnie	782	3	71	189	20	84	9.31
K Plant	767	10	123	147	12	83	9.24

● Paul Scott scored 8 tries last season to extend his club record to 42. Close on his heels is flanker Richard Selkirk

	Tries	Apps	Strike Rate
Paul Scott	42	85	2.02
Richard Selkirk	39	90	2.30
John Dudley	26	82	3.15
Craig West	18	71	3.94

● Richard Selkirk extended his club record of appearances to 90. He appeared in the first 89 league matches that Rotherham played before missing the match v Reading in April because he was attending his brother's wedding in the Caribbean!

ROTHERHAM R.U.F.C.

COURAGE LEAGUE STATISTICS

compiled by Steve McCormack

Season	Div	P	W	D	L	F	T	C	P	D	A	T	C	P	D	Most Points	Most Tries
1987-88	NE1	10	8	0	2	175	22	9	21	2	52	3	2	9	2	55 Kevin Plant	6 Richard Selkirk
1988-89	NE1	10	10	0	0	273	40	22	21	2	54	3	3	11	1	115 Kevin Plant	12 Paul Scott
189-90	N2	10	9	0	1	214	26	16	24	2	134	15	10	18	0	98 Kevin Plant	6 Paul Scott
1990-91	N1	10	6	1	3	198	28	13	17	3	107	11	6	16	1	81 Kevin Plant	4 John Dudley. Danny Walker. Richard Selkirk
1991-92	N1	10	10	0	0	245	36	19	21	0	123	7	5	10	0	60 Steve Worrall	7 Richard Selkirk
1992-93	D4N	12	10	1	1	259	32	15	21	2	123	13	6	16	0	50 Steve Worrall	8 Andy Challinor
1993-94	D5N	12	10	1	1	335	42	25	23	2	142	12	8	22	0	118 Kevin Plant	8 John Dudley
1994-95	4	18	17	0	1	576	70	38	48	2	267	25	14	34	4	202 Kevin Plant	8 John Dudley. Paul Scott

BIGGEST WIN   **Home:** 76-3 v Durham 19.3.94 D5N   **Away:** 34-3 v Blaydon 14.1.89 NE2, 34-18 v Broughton Park 15.4.95 CL4

BIGGEST DEFEAT   **Home:** 10-18 v Huddersfield 7.4.90 N2   **Away:** 29-32 v Havant 22.10.94 CL4

MOST TRIES in a match   **For**: 11 v Durham 19.3.94 D5N   **Against:**

MOST CONSECUTIVE   **Wins:** 17   **Defeats:** 2

MOST APPEARANCES   **Forward:** 90 Richard Selkirk   **Back:** 85 Paul Scott

MOST CONSECUTIVE APPEARANCES   89 Richard Selkirk 12.9.87 to 1.4.94

CONSECUTIVE SCORING MATCHES   **Tries:** 4 Grant Treece

Points: 14 Kevin Plant (Twice)

	IN A SEASON	IN A CAREER	IN A MATCH
MOST POINTS	202 Kevin Plant 1994-95 CL4	767 Kevin Plant 1987-95	24 Paul Scott v Westoe 8.4.89 Away NE1
MOST TRIES	12 Paul Scott 1988-89 NE1	42 Paul Scott 1987-95	6 Paul Scott v Westoe 8.4.89 Away NE1
MOST CONVERSIONS	33 Kevin Plant 1994-95	123 Kevin Plant 1987-95	9 Kevin Plant v Durham 19.3.94 Home D5N
MOST PENALTIES	41 Kevin Plant 1990-91 N1	147 Kevin Plant 187-95	6 David Francis v Keighley 8.4.89 Home NE1
MOST DROP GOALS	3 Kevin Plant 1990-91 N1	12 Kevin Plant 1987-95	1 on 15 occasions Kevin Plant 12

RUGBY LIONS F.C.

NICKNAME: The Lions **FOUNDED:** 1994

CLUB OFFICIALS

Chairman
Don Willis
Club Secretary
John Partridge
c/o Rugby Lions Football Club, 26
Albert Street, Rugby CV21 2RS
Tel: (H) 01788 813982
Fixtures Secretary
Richard Stocking
5 Cunningham Way, Rugby CV22 7JD
Tel: (H) 01788 816598 (W) 01604
702529
Press Officer
Roger Large
Tel: (H) 01788 816363 (W) 01788
816132

Review of the Season

The Lions finished the season in style, winning seven of the last nine games, including the last three. Included in that run of three at the end of the season was an emphatic win over champions Bedford 35-17. They had a mid-season blip losing four in a row which cost them any chance of promotion.

They used just 26 players, the lowest in the Division and had just 4 players making their League debuts.

In his first season full back Jim Quantrill's kicking proved to be a success while scrum half David Bishop finished as the Division's leading try scorer. Veteran winger Eddie Saunders was one behind on 7. Not surprisingly they finished the season as leading try scorers.

If they can carry forward their end of season form there is no reason why they cannot gain promotion in the new season ahead.

Colours: Orange, black and white shirts, black shorts   **Change Colours:** White shirts, navy shorts, red and white socks

RUGBY LIONS F.C.

COURAGE LEAGUE
MATCH DETAILS 1994-95

No	Date	Opponents	Ven	Result	Scorers
1	Sep 10	Bedford	H	25-9	Bishop (T) Palmer (T) Gardner (T) Quantrill (2C 2P)
2	Sep 17	Blackheath	A	11-15	Saunders (T) Quantrill (2P)
3	Sep 24	Clifton	H	29-8	Bishop (T) Mee (T) Gardner (T) Oram (T) Quantrill (3C 1P)
4	Oct 1	Exeter	A	15-11	Mills (T) Bishop (T) Evans (1C 1P)
5	Oct 15	Richmond	H	21-20	Evans (7P)
6	Oct 22	Harrogate	A	12-13	Bishop (1DG) Quantrill (3P)
7	Oct 29	Morley	A	3-13	Quantrill (P)
8	Nov 2	Otley	A	7-33	Bishop (T) Evans (1C)
9	Nov 7	Rosslyn Park	H	18-26	Saunders (T) Pell (T) Quantrill (1C 2P)
10	Nov 14	Blackheath	H	15-6	Gillooly (T) Bishop (T) Quantrill (1C 1P)
11	Mar 4	Exeter	H	17-11	Quantrill (T 4P)
12	Mar 18	Richmond	A	10-19	Saunders (T) Quantrill (1C 1P)
13	Mar 25	Harrogate	A	27-8	Gillooly (T) Rovan (T) Quantrill (2C 1P) Jenkins (T) Burdett (T)
14	Apr 1	Morley	H	27-5	Quantrill (T P 2C) Palmer (T) Gillooly (T) Smith (T)
15	Apr 5	Rosslyn Park	A	8-35	Mills (T) Quantrill (P)
16	Apr 12	Bedford	A	35-17	Saunders (3T) Bishop (T) Evans (C) Quantrill (3P 2C)
17	Apr 25	Otley	H	38-3	Bullman (T) Bishop (T) Saunders (T) Quantrill (3P 2C) Palmer (2T)
18	Apr 29	Clifton	A	37-19	Palmer (T) Gillooly (T) Bishop (T) Gardner (T) Burdett (T) Quantrill (3C 2P)

THE RUGBY LIONS FOOTBALL CLUB

RUGBY LIONS
v
COVENTRY
Saturday 25th February 1995

THE HOME
OF RUGBY
FOOTBALL

THE LIONS SPONSORS ARE

🌀 RUGBY CEMENT

PROGRAMME DETAILS

Editor: Roger Large
Advertising Rates: Whole Page £250.00 + VAT half page £130.00 + VAT Quarter page ££70.00 + VAT

CLUB & GROUND DETAILS

Rugby Lions F.C., 9 Webb Ellis Road, Rugby CV22 7AW
Telephone: 01788 542433
Fax: 01788 542433

Total Capacity: 4,200
Seated: 200
Standing: 4,000
Simple Directions to Ground: Second turning right, half mile southwest of town centre on A4071, Bilton Road
Nearest Railway Station: Rugby
Car Parking: 100
Season Tickets: £45.00 Adults £10.00 Children £20.00 OAPs
Match Prices: £1.00
Membership: £25.00 Senior £10.00 Junior
Training Nights: Mondays and Thursdays

RUGBY LIONS F.C.

MATCH BY MATCH PLAYERS BY POSITION

Quantrill	Mills	Palmer	Gillooly	Saunders	Pell	Bishop	Mee	Milner	Revan	Smith	Bowman	Gardner	Oram	Darragh	Jenkins	Elliott	Watson	Evans	Burdett	Underhill	McLeod	Kirby	Jellis
15	14	13	12	11	10	9	1	2	3	4	5	6	7	8									
15	14	13	12	11	10	9	1	2	3	4	5		7	8	6	R							
15	14	13	12	11*	10	9	1	2	3	4	5	6	7	8			R						
	11	13	12		10	9	1	2	3	4	5	6	7	8			14	15					
	11	13	12		10	9	1	2	3	4	5	6	7	8			14	15					
15	11	12	13	14		9	1		3	4	5	6	7	8		10			2				
15	11	13	12	14	10		1		3	4	5	6	7	8		9			2				
15	11	13	12		10	9	1		3	4	5		7	8			14		2				
15	11	12	13	14	10	9	1		3	4			7	8	6				2	5			
15	11		12	14		9	1			4	5	6	7			8			2		10	3	
15	11	12	13	14	10			1		4	6	8			7	9			2	5		3	
15	11	12	13	14	10	9		1		4	5	6			7				2	8		3	
15	11	13	12	14		9	2*	1	2	5	7					8			12		10	3	6
15	11	13	12	14		9		1		4	5		7			8			2		10	3	6
15	11	13	12	14		9		1		4	5		7			8			2		10	3	6
15		13	12	14		9		1		4	5		7			8	11		2		10	3	6
15		13	12	14		9		1		4	5		7			8	11		2		10	3	6
15		13	12	14		9		1		4	5		7*	R		8	11	10	2			3	6

Also Played: Allott No 13 match 10; Gubbins No 6 match 8

Courage League Records 1994-95

League Debuts: 4 R Elliott, D Evans, M Allott, R Kirby
Players used: 26
Ever Presents: 1 A Gillooly, 3 played 17
Most appearances: 89 David Bishop

● Jim Quantrill breaks Chris Howard's seven year record for most points in a season. In 1988-89 Howard scored 123 points whilst last season saw Quantrill eclipse that figure with 129

	Pts	T	C	P	D	App	Ave
Jim Quantrill	129	2	19	27	-	16	8.06
Chris Howard	123	7	19	19	-	11	11.18

● Quantrill's 19 conversions and 27 penalties were both seasonal records for Rugby

● Scrum half David Bishop topped the try scoring list for the third time with his 8 tries, second only to his 9 of 1990-91 He now has a career total of 27, second only to winger Eddie Saunders

	Tries	Apps	Strike Rate
Eddie Saunders	42	85	2.02
Dave Bishop	27	89	3.29

● Denzil Evans breaks the club record of 6 penalties in a match – the previous record was shared by Chris Howard and Russell Hensley. Evans kicked 7 penalties v Richmond in October. This also equalled Andy Finnie's Division 3 record

● Second row forward Steve Smith passed Mark Fleetwood's record of consecutive appearances. Fleetwood's record was 35 which Smith broke in the game at Exeter in October. His run was ended when he was forced to miss the return fixture with Exeter, 43 games in total.

RUGBY LIONS F.C.

COURAGE LEAGUE STATISTICS

compiled by Steve McCormack

Season	Div	P	W	D	L	F	T	C	P	D	A	T	C	P	D	Most Points	Most Tries
1987-88	4N	10	9	0	1	184	25	15	17	1	100	9	2	18	2	69 Chris Howard	7 Eddie Saunders
1988-89	3	11	10	0	1	268	41	19	19	3	99	8	5	19	0	123 Chris Howard	7 Eddie Saunders. Chris Howard
1989-90	2	11	5	0	6	238	34	21	18	2	172	24	11	17	1	100 Chris Howard	7 Eddie Saunders
1990-91	2	12	10	0	2	252	39	18	16	6	146	20	9	13	3	68 Stuart Vaudin	9 David Bishop
1991-92	1	12	2	3	7	124	11	4	23	1	252	36	15	26	0	60 Mark Mapletoft	2 Eddie Saunders. David Bishop
1992-93	1	12	1	0	11	104	10	6	11	3	368	50	26	19	3	26 Mark Mapletoft	3 Eddie Saunders
1993-94	2	18	5	1	12	186	15	9	25	6	302	29	17	39	2	115 Mark Mapletoft	5 Mark Mapletoft
1994-95	3	18	11	0	7	355	40	22	35	2	271	26	12	35	4	131 Jim Quantrill	8 David Bishop
TOTALS		104	53	4	47	1711	215	114	162	24	1610	202	97	186	15		

BIGGEST WIN   **Home:** 49-9 v Gosforth 11.11.89 CL2   **Away:** 37-19 v Clifton 29.4.95 CL3

BIGGEST DEFEAT   **Home:** 20-45 v London Scottish 31.10.92 CL1   **Away:** 0-66 v Orrell 13.3.93 CL1

MOST TRIES in a match   **For:** 8 v Askeans 8.10.88 CL3   **Against:** 11 v Orrell 13.3.93

MOST CONSECUTIVE   **Wins:** 8   **Defeats:** 9

MOST APPEARANCES   **Forward:** 91 Trevor Revan   **Back:** 89 David Bishop

MOST CONSECUTIVE APPEARANCES 42 Steve Smith 11.4.92 to 14.1.95

CONSECUTIVE SCORING MATCHES   **Tries:** 5 Eddie Saunders

Points: 19 Chris Howard

	IN A SEASON	IN A CAREER	IN A MATCH
MOST POINTS	131 Jim Quantrill 1994-95 CL3	306 Chris Howard 1987-91	25 Chris Howard v Gosforth 1.11.89 Home CL2
MOST TRIES	9 David Bishop 1990-91 CL2	42 Eddie saunders 1987-91	3 Chris Howard v Vale of Lune 10.9.88 Home CL3
MOST CONVERSIONS	20 Jim Quantrill 1994-95 CL3	52 Chris Howard 1987-91	6 Chris Howard v Gosforth 11.11.89 Home CL2
MOST PENALTIES	27 Jim Quantrill 1994-95 CL3	52 Chris Howard 1987-91	7 Denzil Evans v Richmond 15.10.94 Home CL3
MOST DROP GOALS	4 Richard Pell 1987-88 D4N	13 Richard Pell 1987-95	1 on 24 occasions Richard Pell 13

NATIONAL LEAGUE FOUR NORTH & SOUTH 1987-93
NATIONAL LEAGUE FOUR 1993-95

NATIONAL LEAGUE 4 NORTH TABLES

1987-88

	P	W	D	L	F	A	Pts
Rugby	10	9	0	1	184	100	18
Durham	10	8	0	2	165	100	16
Roundhay	10	6	2	2	131	67	14
Preston G'hprs	10	5	1	4	178	149	11
Northern	10	5	1	4	121	137	11
Broughton Park	10	5	0	5	152	106	10
Stourbridge	10	5	0	9	132	134	10
Lichfield	10	4	0	6	150	165	8
Birkenhead Park	10	4	0	6	117	179	8
Derby	10	2	0	8	136	197	4
Solihull	10	0	0	10	59	219	0

1990-91

	P	W	D	L	F	A	Pts
Otley	12	11	0	1	424	89	22
Lichfield	12	8	1	3	177	152	17
Preston G'hprs	12	8	0	4	192	109	16
Winnington Park	12	7	1	4	167	148	15
Kendal	12	6	2	4	191	132	14
Harrogate	12	6	1	5	220	204	13
Northern	12	5	3	4	148	169	13
Stourbridge	12	5	1	6	134	161	11
Walsall	12	5	0	7	149	176	10
Durham City	12	4	1	7	109	185	9
Hereford	12	3	2	7	122	208	8
Stoke	12	2	1	9	126	278	5
Birm. Solihull	12	1	1	10	116	265	3

1988-89

	P	W	D	L	F	A	Pts
Roundhay	10	8	1	1	235	81	17
Broughton Park	10	8	0	2	179	92	16
Stourbridge	10	6	0	4	118	79	12
Northern	10	5	0	5	188	155	10
Winnington Park	10	5	0	5	188	155	10
Preston G'hprs	10	5	0	5	161	141	10
Durham City	10	5	0	5	172	157	10
Morley	10	5	0	5	135	141	10
Lichfield	10	4	1	5	112	113	9
Stoke on Trent	10	3	0	7	88	138	9
Birmingham	10	0	0	10	29	171	0

1991-92

	P	W	D	L	F	A	PD	Pts
Aspatria	12	11	0	1	253	100	153	22
Hereford	12	10	1	1	223	133	90	21
Kendal	12	8	1	3	157	123	34	17
Preston G'Hprs	12	8	0	4	195	123	72	16
Lichfield	12	6	1	5	174	177	-3	13
Stourbridge	12	6	0	6	163	137	26	12
Harrogate	12	6	0	6	170	175	-5	12
Winnington Park	12	4	1	7	159	173	-14	9
Towcestrians	12	4	0	8	123	153	-30	8
Durham City	12	4	0	8	133	215	-82	8
Walsall	12	3	1	8	139	187	-48	7
Vale of Lune	12	3	1	8	119	185	-66	7
Northern	12	2	0	10	105	232	-127	4

1989-90

	P	W	D	L	F	A	Pts
Broughton Park	10	8	0	2	246	111	16
Morley	10	8	0	2	169	115	16
Stourbridge	10	7	0	3	146	133	14
Durham City	10	6	0	4	195	169	12
Kendal	10	6	0	4	130	136	12
Preston G'hprs	10	5	0	5	122	109	10
Lichfield	10	5	0	5	110	121	10
Northern	10	4	0	6	139	144	8
Winnington Park	10	4	0	6	142	152	8
Walsall	10	2	0	8	143	183	4
Stoke	10	0	0	10	88	257	0

1992-93

	P	W	D	L	F	A	PD	Pts
Harrogate	12	10	1	1	363	115	248	21
Rotherham	12	10	1	1	259	123	136	21
Preston G'hprs	12	8	0	4	144	140	4	16
Stoke on Trent	12	7	0	5	193	168	25	14
Lichfield	12	6	1	5	221	224	-3	13
Kendal	12	6	0	6	182	189	-7	12
Walsall	12	6	0	6	165	179	-14	12
Durham City	12	6	0	6	179	219	-40	12
Stourbridge	12	5	1	6	161	144	17	11
Winnington Park	12	5	1	6	167	165	2	11
Hereford	12	2	2	8	147	216	-69	6
Nuneaton	12	2	0	10	138	269	-131	4
Towcestrians	12	1	1	10	118	286	-168	3

NATIONAL LEAGUE 4 SOUTH TABLES

1987-88

	P	W	D	L	F	A	Pts
Askeans	10	8	1	1	141	83	17
Sidcup	10	7	2	1	130	72	16
Lydney	10	7	0	3	173	99	14
Camborne	10	5	2	3	113	119	12
Havant	10	5	0	5	116	102	10
Stroud	10	5	0	5	112	114	10
Southend	10	5	0	5	63	108	10
Sudbury	10	3	2	5	125	106	8
Salisbury	10	3	1	6	84	94	7
Cheltenham	10	3	0	7	95	152	6
Streatham/Croydon	10	0	0	10	70	173	0

1990-91

	P	W	D	L	F	A	Pts
Redruth	12	12	0	0	225	79	24
Basingstoke	12	9	0	3	187	104	18
Lon. Welsh	12	7	0	5	235	165	14
Camborne	12	6	0	6	204	179	12
Weston S-Mare	12	6	0	6	192	182	12
North Walsham	12	5	2	5	170	180	12
Sudbury	12	6	0	6	160	172	12
Havant	12	5	0	7	157	173	10
Southend	12	5	0	7	152	194	10
Ealing	12	5	0	7	174	218	10
Maidstone	12	4	1	7	122	164	9
Maidenhead	12	4	1	7	130	208	9
Cheltenham	12	2	0	10	150	240	4

1988-89

	P	W	D	L	F	A	Pts
Lydney	10	8	1	1	240	98	17
Havant	10	8	1	1	177	92	17
Camborn	10	6	1	3	198	126	13
Redruth	10	6	1	3	136	81	13
Sudbury	10	5	1	4	141	89	11
Cheltenham	10	4	2	4	122	151	10
Salisbury	10	4	1	5	113	139	9
Southend	10	4	0	6	116	168	8
Ealing	10	3	0	7	144	188	6
Stroud	10	3	0	7	119	180	6
Sidcup	10	0	0	10	74	168	0

1991-92

	P	W	D	L	F	A	PD	Pts
Havant	12	11	0	1	301	91	210	22
Basingstoke	12	11	0	1	218	88	130	22
Lon. Welsh	12	9	0	3	292	160	132	18
Sudbury	12	8	0	4	235	150	85	16
High Wycombe	12	8	0	4	196	139	57	16
Camborne	12	7	0	5	166	195	-29	14
North Walsham	12	5	0	7	153	152	1	10
Maidstone	12	5	0	7	147	180	-33	10
Weston S-Mare	12	4	0	8	175	215	-40	8
Met. Police	12	3	0	9	149	195	-46	6
Southend	12	3	0	9	134	240	-106	6
Sidcup	12	3	0	9	103	290	-187	6
Ealing	12	0	1	11	112	286	-174	2

1989-90

	P	W	D	L	F	A	Pts
Met. Police	10	9	0	1	255	74	18
Clifton	10	8	1	1	240	122	17
Redruth	10	7	0	3	151	84	14
Camborne	10	6	1	3	164	113	13
Havant	10	5	1	4	132	126	11
Sudbury	10	5	0	5	162	138	10
Southend	10	4	2	4	124	125	10
Basingstoke	10	3	1	6	138	144	7
Cheltenham	10	2	0	8	107	201	4
Maidstone	10	2	0	8	64	237	4
Salisbury	10	1	0	9	74	247	2

1992-93

	P	W	D	L	F	A	PD	Pts
Sudbury	12	11	1	0	337	130	207	23
London Welsh	10	10	0	2	353	170	183	20
Lydney	12	8	0	4	187	170	17	16
Cambourne	12	7	1	4	180	168	12	15
Basingstoke	12	7	0	5	192	145	47	14
Southend	12	6	1	5	196	189	7	13
Berry Hill	12	4	3	5	187	216	-29	11
High Wycombe	12	5	0	7	196	160	36	10
Met Police	12	4	1	7	201	207	-6	9
Weston-S-Mare	12	4	1	7	154	226	-72	9
North Walsham	12	4	0	8	125	209	-84	8
Maidstone	12	2	0	10	122	306	-184	4
Thurrock	12	2	0	10	147	295	-148	2

NATIONAL LEAGUE FOUR NORTH
RESULTS

1990-91

		1	2	3	4	5	6	7	8	9	10	11	12	13
1	Birmingham		3-16		9-9	6-42		15-9				13-17	15-22	
2	Durham			23-2	6-3	15-15		6-12				3-16	10-11	
3	Harrogate	30-12					14-14		21-50	25-15	48-12	6-16		
4	Hereford				29-6		10-34	3-12		13-9	21-9	15-24		
5	Kendal			7-13			6-13		3-16	12-6	19-0	7-4		
6	Lichfield	18-13	25-8						7-37	11-16	27-17	24-7		
7	Northern				4-18	18-3	16-16	6-9					17-10	18-12
8	Otley	51-15	29-3		50-0			43-6					36-0	36-0
9	Preston Grasshoppers	21-12	13-0					14-19	16-4		36-3	23-0		
10	Stoke	12-3	25-3					13-13	11-40			6-10	9-23	
11	Stourbridge	18-0	12-16					10-10	7-32				20-13	6-9
12	Walsall		0-12		22-7	12-13	12-13			9-20				15-13
13	Winnington		22-6	9-9	21-17	13-4					0-3	35-9		

1991-92

		1	2	3	4	5	6	7	8	9	10	11	12	13
1	Aspatria		21-12				2-15		16-0	3-0	23-0	24-9		
2	Durham City	15-26					13-9		24-15	3-22	12-18	9-21		
3	Harrogate		9-6		12-19	13-22	18-0						26-14	13-7
4	Hereford	21-18	31-0				33-4				33-10		9-6	4-3
5	Kendal	3-13	18-6		9-9		14-4						10-4	18-10
6	Litchfield			25-24	13-23	6-38	9-16						21-14	19-12
7	Northern	13-41	10-11						10-24	6-26	13-6	7-9		
8	Preston G'hoppers			16-13	42-14	13-14	0-10						13-6	28-3
9	Stourbridge			32-8	10-12	21-3	9-17		3-24		10-23			
10	Towcestrians			3-7	6-15	18-6	0-21		4-9					22-10
11	Vale of Lune			10-15		6-12	9-9		6-11	8-15	15-13			
12	Walsall	9-26	6-16					19-15		10-14	12-10	18-6		
13	Winnington Park	3-13	29-18					22-7		20-0		19-10	21-21	

1992-93

		1	2	3	4	5	6	7	8	9	10	11	12	13
1	Durham		7-33	31-10	19-6				10-28				6-7	35-17
2	Harrrogate					54-6	25-16	36-3		19-13	20-5	71-7		
3	Hereford		12-29	11-7		14-15		0-8			19-19	38-10		
4	Kendal		6-34			6-20		19-12		36-17	6-9	25-13		
5	Lichfield	54-11					42-6	15-12		12-16	14-12	13-13		
6	Nuneaton	18-17		22-13	13-36				10-28				16-9	5-36
7	Preston Grasshoppers	8-10					13-3		10-6	9-7	17-16	28-7		
8	Rotherham		6-6	20-7	30-16	34-12							36-11	16-5
9	Stoke	20-11		14-5			15-14		13-15				32-6	20-9
10	Stourbridge	10-12					17-16		12-14	14-6		27-0	9-11	
11	Towcestrians	27-17					11-6		11-26	19-32	9-12	10-12		
12	Walsall		14-21	29-6	3-10	2-10		12-14						26-8
13	Winnington Park		20-15	12-12	8-9		17-8	9-10			15-0			

NATIONAL LEAGUE FOUR SOUTH RESULTS

1990-91

		1	2	3	4	5	6	7	8	9	10	11	12	13
1	Basingstoke			10-0	32-10				15-6		0-4		10-12	27-19
2	Camborne	12-5				17-12	18-25	30-12		26-6		19-6		
3	Cheltenham		25-18		12-25				6-15		3-7		25-10	18-35
4	Ealing	12-6		29-9			9-17	22-6		13-14		12-16		
5	London Welsh	12-13		31-7	18-26				6-16	32-10		26-12		
6	Maidenhead		6-20			22-6	6-28			9-18		9-8		10-9
7	North Walsham	8-12		23-17	39-11				16-16		6-16		13-7	
8	Redruth		24-6			26-7	18-16					20-6	25-0	23-4
9	Southend	3-27		19-12	0-7			27-12	16-12	9-17				
10	Sudburm		11-6			20-9	12-17	16-19				24-20		22-9
11	Weston-S-Mare		24-10			7-12	18-7	21-8		21-18		6-18		

1991-92

		1	2	3	4	5	6	7	8	9	10	11	12	13
1	Basingstoke		22-13		16-7		9-7			18-6	38-6	11-3		
2	Camborne			18-15		10-8		19-9	21-14				3-17	14-11
3	Ealing	8-28				12-8	12-15			10-28	10-13	10-12		
4	Havant		34-9	42-3				42-12	19-6				16-9	25-10
5	High Wycombe	13-7			7-10		23-14			25-12	33-9	25-22		
6	London Welsh		35-15		6-9			18-15	29-18				34-12	36-19
7	Maidstone	0-7		21-18		9-12				12-10	20-10	31-17		
8	Met. Police	0-15		40-7		3-14		7-3		3-13	10-15			
9	North Walsham		6-17		7-9		3-21				30-3	6-0		23-9
10	Sidcup		9-17		3-32		6-49				10-3		4-27	15-21
11	Southend		12-10		3-56		13-26	19-15					7-21	15-20
12	Sudbury	6-22		25-0		25-12		13-15	30-13	25-9				
13	Weston-S-Mare	19-25		28-7		6-16		7-0	10-17			15-22		

1992-93

		1	2	3	4	5	6	7	8	9	10	11	12	13
1	Basingstoke		25-16		12-5			19-8	10-6			9-16		37-6
2	Berry Hill			16-16			14-22	18-6	18-7			9-9		18-18
3	Camborne	12-8				6-32	13-8			17-12	11-5		34-11	
4	High Wycombe		7-10	8-10				22-5	29-17			20-22		27-5
5	London Welsh	36-16	44-3		13-8					42-12	46-21		45-14	
6	Lydney	20-18			19-18	6-5				11-3	20-26		15-14	
7	Maidstone			11-10		23-35	8-28		5-38	,5-36			16-13	
8	Metropolitan Police			19-3		27-32		7-13			16-16	10-49		14-16
9	North Walsham	3-16	8-29		10-8			14-11	10-13			8-20		
10	Southend	11-6	31-25		12-6			37-10	15-16			11-6		
11	Sudbury			22-10		18-6	20-17				24-11		58-11	41-14
12	Thurock	6-16	23-6		25-28			34-14	6-27	11-18				
13	Weston-S-Mare			16-38		10-17	24-8			6-10	3-0		23-0	

NATIONAL LEAGUE FOUR STATISTICS 1993/94

PLAYING RECORD AND POINTS BREAKDOWN

	P	W	D	L	F	A	Pts	HOME						AWAY					
								P	W	D	L	F	A	P	W	D	L	F	A
Clifton	18	16	2	0	477	205	34	9	8	1	0	283	96	9	8	1	0	194	109
Harrogate	18	14	2	2	479	211	30	9	8	1	0	292	100	9	6	1	2	187	111
Liverpool St Helens	18	11	1	6	396	275	23	9	7	1	1	238	134	9	4	0	5	158	141
Plymouth	18	9	0	9	286	416	18	9	6	0	3	167	141	9	3	0	6	119	275
Aspatria	18	8	0	10	295	372	16	9	6	0	3	180	126	9	2	0	7	115	246
Leeds	18	7	0	11	243	318	14	9	6	0	3	158	110	9	1	0	8	85	208
Askeans	18	6	1	11	268	358	13	9	5	0	4	133	147	9	1	1	7	135	211
Broughton P	18	6	0	12	243	356	12	9	4	0	5	121	160	9	2	0	7	122	196
Sheffield	18	5	1	12	287	310	11	9	4	0	5	188	148	9	1	1	7	99	162
Sudbury	18	4	1	13	240	393	9	9	2	1	6	128	164	9	2	0	7	112	229

RESULTS

		1	2	3	4	5	6	7	8	9	10
1	Askeans		26-12	11-19	3-40	12-16	11-3	5-20	28-16	9-6	28-15
2	Aspatria	23-20		16-18	12-21	9-20	11-8	16-10	46-21	19-9	28-0
3	Broughton Park	27-16	8-3		12-15	0-31	27-7	5-31	9-15	17-16	16-26
4	Clifton	37-13	33-11	18-8		6-6	33-6	35-21	47-10	33-11	41-10
5	Harrogate	22-7	78-29	33-6	15-15		28-10	21-7	53-22	12-6	20-6
6	Leeds	9-19	35-15		13-22	29-20		17-9	3-1	24-3	14-3
7	L'pool St Helens	30-23	19-12	33-21	16-20	24-10	33-10		38-8	18-8	27-12
8	Plymouth Albion	13-10	9-13	39-13	13-17	15-29	30-17	13- 12		11-9	28-21
9	Sheffield	32-9	20-22	16-11	9-18	9-28	27-10		45-3		17-19
10	Sudbury	18-18	18-6	20-18	16-26	7-27	8-14	16-20	6-13	19-22	

WEEK BY WEEK POSITIONS

	13/11	20/11	4/12	11/12	8/1	22/1	29/1	12/2	26/2	12/3	26/3	9/4	23/4	30/4
Askeans	5	7	4	6	5	7	8	9	9	9	8	7	7	7
Aspatria	10	10	10	10	8	6	6	8	5	5	4	5	5	5
Broughton	7	8	8	8	9	9	7	5	7	7	7	8	9	8
Clifton	1	1	1	1	1	1	1	1	1	1	1	1	1	1
Harrogate	3	2	2	2	2	2	2	2	2	2	2	2	2	2
Leeds	6	4	5	7	7	8	9	7	6	6	6	6	6	6
L'pool St Helens	2	3	3	3	3	3	3	3	3	3	3	3	3	3
Plymouth	8	5	6	4	4	4	4	4	4	4	5	4	4	4
Sheffield	4	6	7	5	6	5	5	6	8	8	9	9	8	9
Sudbury	9	9	9	9	10	10	10	10	10	10	10	10	10	10

NATIONAL LEAGUE FOUR STATISTICS 1994/95

PLAYING RECORD AND POINTS BREAKDOWN

	P	W	D	L	Pts	HOME				AWAY			
						W	D	L	Pts	W	D	L	Pts
Rotherham	18	17	0	1	34	9	0	0	18	8	0	1	16
Reading	18	14	1	3	29	8	0	1	16	6	1	2	13
Liverpool St. H	18	10	3	5	23	7	1	1	15	3	2	4	8
Havant	18	10	2	6	22	8	0	1	16	2	2	5	6
Leeds	18	8	0	10	16	5	0	4	10	3	0	6	6
Aspatria	18	7	1	10	15	5	1	3	11	2	7	4	4
Redruth	18	6	2	10	14	4	2	3	10	2	0	7	4
Plymouth	18	4	2	12	10	4	2	3	10	0	0	9	0
Askeans	18	4	1	13	9	3	0	6	6	1	1	7	3
Broughton P	18	4	0	14	8	2	0	7	4	2	0	7	4

RESULTS

		1	2	3	4	5	6	7	8	9	10
1	Askeans		21-23	5-23	34-25	15-14	6-9	15-8	12-14	12-19	17-31
2	Aspatria	8-8		15-0	19-18	11-22	16-6	26-8	9-15	32-19	11-32
3	Broughton Park	16-24	18-9		12-15	0-11	12-25	19-9	9-21	8-14	18-34
4	Havant	50-13	24-8	37-22		10-3	17-7	27-25	18-22	23-16	32-29
5	Leeds	35-10	12-3	60-8	6-18		20-26	30-25	18-23	19-0	8-17
6	Liverpool St Helens	14-3	42-5	30-3	22-12	35-10		24-5	14-14	49-21	14-18
7	Plymouth	29-6	23-11	21-24	17-17	13-17	17-17		31-30	24-8	15-27
8	Reading	52-34	29-25	31-17	18-15	26-19	28-6	27-17		29-11	16-23
9	Redruth	28-16	18-23	24-14	22-22	20-17	11-11	25-14	23-28		13-19
10	Rotherham	53-9	63-11	50-0	35-10	34-18	25-23	35-23	24-12	31-7	

WEEK BY WEEK POSITIONS

	10/9	17/9	24/9	1/10	15/10	22/10	29/10	12/11	7/1	14/1	11/2	25/2	4/3	25/3	1/4	8/4	15/4	29/4
Askeans	10	10	10	10	10	10	10	10	10	10	10	10	10	10	10	10	9	9
Aspatria	8	8	8	9	9	9	8	7	6	7	6	6	6	6	6	6	7	6
Broughton Park	9	6	5	5	5	5	7	8	8	8	8	9	9	8	9	9	10	10
Havant	5	3	3	2	4	3	4	3	3	3	3	4	4	4	4	4	4	4
Leeds	3	5	6	7	8	7	6	5	5	5	5	5	5	5	5	5	5	5
Liverpool St. H	2	2	2	4	3	4	3	4	4	4	4	3	3	3	3	3	3	3
Plymouth	7	9	9	6	7	8	9	9	9	9	9	8	8	9	8	8	8	8
Reading	4	4	4	3	2	1	2	2	2	2	2	2	2	2	2	2	2	2
Redruth	6	7	7	8	6	6	5	6	7	6	7	7	7	7	7	7	6	7
Rotherham	1	1	1	1	1	2	1	1	1	1	1	1	1	1	1	1	1	1

NATIONAL LEAGUE FOUR 1994-95 POINTS SCORING RECORDS

	Tries	by Forward	by Back	Tries in no matches	No tries against	Players used	Replace-ments	Ever presents
Rotherham	70	38	22	18	4	31	8	2
Reading	44	19	25	16	4	33	3	4
Liverpool St Helens	44	10	34	15	4	35	11	1
Havant	51	25	26	18	3	35	2	2
Leeds	36	12	24	15	4	35	10	3
Aspatria	32	13	19	18	3	34	17	—
Redruth	30	11	19	17	1	32	13	1
Plymouth	35	14	21	16	1	31	7	1
Askeans	19	1	18	10	1	30	6	1
Broughton Park	20	5	15	11	2	30	11	4

FOR

	PTS	T	C	P	D	HOME PTS	T	C	P	D	AWAY PTS	T	C	P	D
Rotherham	576	70	38	48	2	350	45	25	24	1	226	25	13	24	1
Reading	435	44	28	52	1	256	31	19	21	—	179	13	9	31	1
Liverpool	374	44	26	30	4	244	33	20	13	—	130	11	6	17	4
Havant	390	51	21	27	4	238	31	13	18	1	152	20	8	9	3
Leeds	335	36	19	35	4	208	23	12	23	—	127	13	7	12	4
Aspatria	265	32	6	29	2	147	18	3	17	—	118	14	3	12	2
Redruth	309	30	18	39	2	184	18	11	24	—	125	12	7	15	2
Plymouth	324	35	16	35	4	190	20	9	20	4	134	15	7	15	—
Askeans	257	19	12	40	6	137	8	5	25	4	120	11	7	15	2
Broughton Park	217	20	9	32	1	112	9	2	21	—	105	11	7	11	1
	3482	381	193	367	30	2066	236	119	206	10	1416	145	74	161	20

AGAINST

	PTS	T	C	P	D	HOME PTS	T	C	P	D	AWAY PTS	T	C	P	D
Rotherham	267	25	14	33	5	123	10	8	15	4	144	15	6	18	1
Reading	319	33	17	37	3	161	18	10	14	3	158	15	7	22	—
Liverpool	243	27	15	26	—	91	12	5	7	—	152	15	10	19	—
Havant	330	32	16	44	2	145	16	7	17	—	185	16	9	27	2
Leeds	297	30	15	34	3	127	13	7	15	1	164	17	8	19	2
Aspatria	378	39	18	48	1	128	15	4	15	—	250	24	14	33	1
Redruth	387	44	16	39	6	160	15	8	19	4	227	29	8	20	2
Plymouth	381	42	21	38	5	153	14	10	18	3	228	28	11	20	2
Askeans	451	56	33	32	3	166	16	7	21	3	285	40	26	11	—
Broughton Park	435	53	28	36	2	162	16	8	20	2	273	37	20	16	—
	3482	381	193	367	30	1416	145	74	161	20	2066	236	119	206	10

NATIONAL LEAGUE FOUR 1994-95
Most Tries, Penalties, Grop Goals, Conversions

LEADING TRY SCORERS

10	Nick Roach	Havant
9	Adam Jewitt	Havant
8	Jim Bates	Havant
8	Martin Kelly	Broughton Park
7	Craig Marriot	Aspatria
7	Mark Richardson	Aspatria
7	Paul Scott	Rotherham
7	John Dudley	Rotherham
7	Craig West	Rotherham
7	Mark Sephton	Liverpool St Helens
6	Chris Thornton	Leeds
6	Phil Griffin	Leeds
6	Curtis Hutson	Reading
6	Richard Selkirk	Rotherham
6	Steve Walklin	Plymouth
6	Les Oman	Plymouth
5	Kevin Davies	Liverpool St Helens
5	Rodney Hutson	Reading
5	John Russell	Askeans
5	S Bartliffe	Leeds
4	Lee Fanning	Reading
4	Colin Phillips	Reading
4	Ian Williams	Liverpool St Helens
4	Nick Walker	Liverpool St Helens
4	Andy Higgin	Liverpool St Helens
4	Nick Jongs	Liverpool St Helens
4	Tom Bayston	Rotherham
4	Russ Askwith	Rotherham
4	Harper	Rotherham
4	Simon Blake	Redruth
4	Ian Harrison	Plymouth
4	Ralph Bennett	Leeds
4	Stuart Lancaster	Leeds
4	Howard Evans	Askeans
4	Robbie Graham	Askeans

PENALTIES

49	Phil Belshaw	Reading
41	Kevin Plant	Rotherham
39	Simon Blake	Redruth

38	Richard Larkin	Askeans
32	Andy Rimmer	Broughton Park
29	Martin Thompson	Plymouth
27	Andy Higgin	Liverpool St Helens
21	Mike Scott	Aspatria
15	Ralph Bennett	Leeds
14	Pete Russell	Havant
10	Dan Eddie	Leeds
9	Rob Ashworth	Havant
7	Stuart Langley	Leeds

DROP GOALS

6	Richard Larkin	Askeans
2	Mike Scott	Aspatria
2	Brian Wellens	Liverpool St Helens
2	Andy Higgin	Liverpool St Helens
2	Simon Blake	Redruth
2	Richard Thompson	Plymouth
2	Martin Thompson	Plymouth
2	J Firkin	Havant
2	Pete Russell	Havant
1	Simon Rodgers	Reading
1	Kevin Plant	Rotherham
1	Steve Worrell	Rotherham
1	Jon Eagle	Leeds
1	Kevin Bowling	Leeds
1	Chris Spowart	Leeds
1	Dan Eddie	Leeds
1	Andy Rimmer	Broughton Park

CONVERSIONS

33	Kevin Plant
26	Phil Belshaw
24	Andy Higgin
18	Simon Blake
16	Pete Russell
13	Martin Thompson
11	Richard Larkin
9	Andy Rimmer
9	Ralph Bennett
6	Staurt Langley
6	Mike Scott

LEADING POINTS SCORES

		PTS	T	C	P	D
Phil Belshaw	Reading	204	1	26	49	—
Kevin Plant	Rotherham	202	2	33	41	1
Simon Blake	Redruth	179	4	18	39	2
Richard Larkin	Askeans	159	1	11	38	6
Andy Higgin	Liverpool St Helens	155	4	24	27	2
Martin Thompson	Plymouth	129	2	13	29	2
Andy Rimmer	Broughton Park	117	—	9	32	1
Pete Russell	Havant	95	3	16	14	2
Mike Scott	Aspatria	95	1	6	21	1
Ralph Bennett	Leeds	83	4	9	15	—
Nick Roach	Havant	50	10	—	—	—
Les Oman	Plymouth	45	6	—	5	—
Adam Jewitt	Havant	45	9	—	—	—
Stuart Langley	Leeds	43	2	6	7	—
Rob Ashworth	Havant	40	1	4	9	—
Jim Bates	Havant	40	8	—	—	—
Martin Kelly	Broughton Park	40	8	—	—	—
Dan Eddie	Leeds	37	—	2	10	1

COURAGE CHAMPIONSHIP STATISTICS 1987–1995

LEAGUE FOUR

	CHAMPIONS	RUNNERS-UP	RELEGATED
1993-94	Clifton	Harrogate	Sheffield Sudbury
1994-95	Rotherham	Reading	Askeans Broughton Park

TEAM RECORDS

Highest score: Harrogate 78 Aspatria 21. 30-4-94
Highest aggregate: 99 points as above
Highest score by a losing side: 34 Reading 52 Askeans 34. 29-4-95
Highest scoring draw: 22-22 Redruth v Havant 14-1-95
Most consecutive wins: 12 Rotherham 1994-95
Most consecutive defeats: 11 Askeans 1994-95
Most points for in a season: 576 Rotherham 1994-95
Most points against in a season: 451 Askeans 1994-95
Least points for in a season: 217 Broughton park 1994-95
Least points against in a season: 205 Clifton 1993-94
Most tries for in a season: 70 Rotherham 1994-95
Most tries against in a season: 56 Askeans 1994-95
Least tries for in a season: 19 Sudbury 1993-94, Askeans 1994-95
Least tries against in a season: 17 Clifton 1993-94
Most conversions for in a season: 38 Rotherham 1994-95
Most conversions against in a season: 33 Askeans 1994-95
Most penalties for in a season: 52 Reading 1994-95
Most penalties against in a season: 48 Aspatria 1994-95
Least penalties for in a season: 26 Leeds 1993-94
Least penalties against in a season: 26 Harrogate 1993-94, Liverpool St Helens 1994-95
Most drop goals for in a season: 14 Clifton 1993-94
Most drop goals against ina season: 8 Leeds, Askeans 1993-94

INDIVIDUAL RECORDS

Most points in a season: 222 Simon Hogg Clifton 1993-94
Most tries in a season: 16 Jon Phillips Clifton 1993-94
Most conversions in a season: 33 Kevin Plant Rotherham 1994-95
Most penalities in a season: 49 Phil Belshaw Reading 1994-95
Most drop goals in a season: 14 Simon Hogg Clifton 1993-94
Most points in a match: 23 Ralph Zoing Harrogate v Plymouth 23-3-94
Most tries in a match: 3 on 11 occasions by 10 players
Most conversions in a match: 6 Ralph Zoing Harrogate v Plymouth 23-3-94,
Kevin Plant Rotherham v Askeans 10-9-94, v Aspatria 15-10-94, Phil Belshaw Reading v Askeans 29-4-95
Most penalities in a match: 7 Kevin O'Brien Broughton Park v Liverpool St Helens 22-1-94
Most drop goals in a match: 2 Simon Hogg Clifton v Leeds 30-10-93, v Sheffield 4-12-93,
Ralph Zoing Harrogate v Askeans 20-11-93, Dan Eddie Leeds v Broughton Park 19-2-94,
Richard Larkin Askeans v Aspatria 9-4-94, Mike Scott Aspatria v Redruth 7-1-95

SEASON BY SEASON LEADING SCORERS

	POINTS	TRIES
1993-94	222 Simon Hogg (Clifton)	16 Jon Phillips (Clifton)
1994-95	204 Phil Belshaw (Reading)	10 Nick Roach (Havant)

100 POINTS IN A COURAGE SEASON DIVISION FOUR

PTS	PLAYER	CLUB	SEASON	T	C	P	D
222	Simon Hogg	Clifton	1993-94	3	24	39	14
204	Phil Belshaw	Reading	1994-95	1	26	49	—
202	Kevin Plant	Rotherham	1994-95	2	33	41	1
179	Simon Blake	Redruth	1994-95	4	18	39	2
159	Richard Larkin	Askeans	1994-95	1	11	38	6
155	Andy Higgin	Liverpool St Helens	1994-95	4	24	27	2
150	Mark Rodgers	Sheffield	1993-94	3	12	37	—
140	Simon Mason	Liverpool St Helens	1993-94	2	—	30	1
129	Mike Scott	Aspatria	1993-94	1	1	33	1
129	Martin Thompson	Plymouth	1994-95	2	13	29	2
117	Richard Larkin	Askeans	1993-94	—	9	29	4
117	Andy Rimmer	Broughton Park	1994-95	—	9	32	1
106	Ralph Zoing	Harrogate	1993-94	1	16	20	3

MOST POINTS IN A COURAGE DIVISION FOUR MATCH

23	R Zoing	Harrogate v Plymouth	23-3-94
22	M Rogers	Sheffield v Leeds	13-11-93
22	A Higgin	Liverpool St Helens v Aspatria	1-4-95
21	K O'Brien	Broughton Park v Liverpool St Helens	22-1-94
21	R Larkin	Askeans v Aspatria	9-4-94
21	R Larkin	Askeans v Aspatria	29-10-94
20	D Breakwell	Leeds v Aspatria	23-10-93
20	A Higgin	Liverpool St Helens v Broughton Park	10-9-94
20	A Higgin	Liverpool St Helens v Leeds	15-10-94
20	S Blake	Redruth v Plymouth	22-10-94
20	K Plant	Rotherham v Broughton Park	12-11-94
19	R Larkin	Askeans v Broughton Park	25-2-95
19	R Larkin	Askeans v Havant	15-4-95
18	S Hogg	Clifton v Sheffield	4-12-93
18	J Cowling	Sudbury v Askeans	8-1-94
18	S Hogg	Clifton v Aspatria	12-2-94
18	S Mason	Liverpool St Helens v Leeds	12-3-94
18	K Plant	Rotherham v Askeans	10-9-94
18	A Rimmer	Broughton Park v Aspatria	17-9-94
18	K Plant	Rotherham v Aspatria	15-10-94

MOST TRIES IN A COURAGE DIVISION FOUR MATCH

3	J Phillips	Clifton v Leeds	30-10-93
3	J Phillips	Clifton v Sudbury	20-11,93
3	M Wyatt	Clifton v Sudbury	20-11-93
3	J Hopkinson	Harrogate v Broughton Park	11-12-93
3	R Bailey	Plymouth v Broughton Park	12-3-94
3	M Richardson	Aspatria v Plymouth	23-4-94
3	E Atkins	Harrogate v Aspatria	30-4-94
3	P Taylor	Harrogate v Aspatria	30-4-94
3	J Dudley	Rotherham v Aspatria	15-10-94
3	C West	Rotherham v Havant	1-4-95
3	S Lancaster	Leeds v Broughton Park	29-4-95

MOST LEAGUE APPEARANCES – DIVISION FOUR PLAYERS

102	Andy Maunder	Scrum Half	Exeter
95	Harry Langley	Second Row	Exeter
86	Jeff Tutchings	Centre	Exeter
82	Mark Wyatt	No 8	Clifton
79	Rob Harding	Second Row	Walsall
77	Andy Green	Stand Off	Exeter
75	Richard Mills	Stand Off	Walsall
73	Richard Gibbins	Prop	Exeter
73	Ian Stewart	Full Back	Exeter
71	Tony Cook	Second Row	Redruth
70	Stu Whitworth	Centre	Redruth
68	Glyn Williams	Flanker	Redruth
63	Geraint Tillot	Flanker	Walsall
61	Mike Cathery	Flanker	Exeter
60	Graeme Peacock	Second Row	London Welsh
59	Simon Blake	Winger/Stand Off	Redruth
59	Paul Westgate	Flanker	Exeter
58	Wayne Hone	Flanker	Clifton
57	Andy Knowles	Winger	Redruth
57	Paul Cox	Prop	Clifton
57	Gary Taylor	Prop	Walsall
56	Kevin Thomas	Full Back	Redruth

NATIONAL LEAGUE FOUR

MEMBER CLUBS
1995-96

League Registrar:
DAE Evans
22 Brrooks Road
Sutton Coldfield
West Midlands B71 1HP
Tel: 0121 354 8183
Fax: 0121 321 3221

Player of the Year Kevin Bowling sets up another attack for Leeds v Havant, 17th September 1994

ASPATRIA R.U.F.C.

NICKNAME: BLACK/REDS   **FOUNDED:** 1875

CLUB OFFICIALS

President
N Lazonby
Chairman
D Miller
Club Secretary
J M Hanley
7 King Street, Aspatria, Cumbria CA5 3AD
Tel: (H) 016973 20328 (W) 01946 815111
Fixtures Secretary
P Gray
Ingledene, Queen Street, Aspatria,
Cumbria CA5 3AP
Tel: (H) 016973 21760 (W) 016973 31234
Press Officer
J M Hanley
Tel: (H) 016973 20328 (W) 01946 815111

Review of the Season

A final league position of sixth meant that for most of the season after a poor start ASPATRIA were in no danger of relegation. The first four games were lost but a 16-6 home win over Liverpool St Helens started a revival which ended with five more wins from the next six matches and victory in the final match - 32-19 at home to Redruth - was icing on the cake in terms of league form.

But all that was eclipsed by a Pilkington Cup run which toook them to the last sixteen after superb performances against Leeds (23-0 at home), Scunthorpe (14-9 at home) and Bedord (an excellent 32-6 home success). A visit to Exeter in the next round saw their demise – 18-6 – but it made the season for the club.

It will also have provided encouragement for the new season and the playing strength looks good enough led by top scorer Mike Scott at fly-half and well supported efforts over the season from Marriott, Hetherington and Southward among the backs plus excellent forward backing from prop Sewall, flankers Vaughan and Urquhart and No8 Richardson among others.

The new season is full of promise if a good start is achieved.

Colours: Black/red hoop shirts   **Change Colours**: Red shirts hoops

ASPATRIA R.U.F.C.

COURAGE LEAGUE
MATCH DETAILS 1994-95

No	Date	Opponents	Ven	Result		Scorers
1	Sep 10	Leeds	H	L	11-12	Marriott (T) Hunter (2P)
2	Sep 17	Broughton	A	L	9-18	Scott (3P)
3	Sep 24	Havant	A	L	8-24	Marriott (T) Scott (1P)
4	Oct 1	Reading	H	L	9-15	Hunter (2P) Scott (1P)
5	Oct 15	Rotherham	A	L	11-63	Richardson (T) Scott (2P)
6	Oct 22	Liverpool St H	H	W	16-6	Scott (1C 3P) Stephenson (T)
7	Oct 29	Askeans	A	W	23-21	Scott (1C 2P) Murray (T) Richardson (T) Pen Try
8	Nov 12	Plymouth	H	W	26-8	Scott (2P) N Brown (T) Marriott (2T) Doggart (T)
9	Jan 7	Redruth	A	W	23-18	Scott (1C 2D(Richardson (2T) Marriott (T)
10	Jan 14	Leeds	A	L	3-12	Scott (1P)
11	Feb 11	Broughton P	H	W	15-0	Richardson (T) Southward (T) Murray (T)
12	Feb 25	Havant	H	W	19-18	Scott (1C 4P) Urquhart (T)
13	Mar 4	Reading	A	L	25-29	Scott (1T 1C 1P) Marriott (2T) Richardson (T)
14	Mar 25	Rotherham	H	L	11-32	Scott (2P) Urquhart (T)
15	Apr 1	Liverool St H	A	L	5-42	Barton (T)
16	Apr 8	Askeans	H	D	8-8	Davison (T) Scott (1P)
17	Apr 15	Plymouth	A	L	11-23	Scott (2P) Hetherington (T)
18	Apr 29	Redruth	H	W	32-19	Scott (1C) Petch (T) Barton (T) Miller (2T) Southward (T) Richardson (T)

PROGRAMME DETAILS

Advertising Rates: £100 full page

CLUB & GROUND DETAILS

Bower Park, Station Road, Aspatria, Cumbria
Telephone: 016973 20420

Total Capacity: Unlimited
Seated: 250
Standing: Unlimited
Simple Directions to Ground:
Nearest Railway Station: Aspatria Station
Car Parking: 300

Match Prices: Adults £3.00 Children/OAPs £1.00
Membership: Seniors £25.00 Juniors £5.00
Training Nights: Tuesday and Thursday

ASPATRIA R.U.F.C.

MATCH BY MATCH PLAYERS BY POSITION

Hunter	Davidson	Stephenson	Cusack	Marriott	Hetherington	Hazlewood	Irvings	Barton	Sewall	Clematson	Atkinson	Maughan	Urquhart	Hancock	Richardson	Scott	Southward	Brown N	Murray	Miller	Petch	Tomlinson	Tinnion
15	14	13	12	11	10	9	1	2	3	4	5	6	7	8									
	14	12	15	11		9	1		3		4		6	7		8	10	13					
15				11	13	9	1	2	3	4		6			8	10	12		14				
15		14		11	13				3			7	6	5	8	10	12	2		11	R		
		12	14	15			1		3	r		6	5	4		10	13			11	R		
		12	14	15			1		3		5	7			8	10	3	2	11			4	6
		12	14	15			1		3	R	R	6	5		8	10	13	2	11		R		
15			11	13				3	5		4		6		8	10		2	14	12	R		
			11	13						4	5	6			8	10	12	2	14	15	9		15
	14		11	13			1		3	5	4	6	7		8	10	12	2		15	9		
15	14		11	13			1		3	4	5	7	6		8	10	12	2		9	R		
			11	13					3	5		7	6		8	10	12	2		15	9	4	
	14		11	13				2	3	5		6			8	10	12		15	9	4		
	14		11	13			1		3			5	6		8	10	12	2		15	9	4	
R	13		11	10	9	1	2	3	4			7	6		8	10	12			11	5		
	14			13				2	1	5		6			8	10	12			11	10	4	

Also Played: C Irving No 2 match 2, No 6 match 3, R match t; F Storey No 5 match 2, No 4 matches 4, 6, 8; A Day No 5 match 3; C Campbell No 9 matches 4, 5, 6, R match 18; B Kyffin No 10 match 5, R match 6, No 14 match 14; D Benson No 7 matches 5, 15, 16, 18; R Hill R match 9; M Brown No 8 match 4, R matches 14, 15, 16; Tom Borthwick R match 13; J McClung No 1 matches 4, 5, 14, 15, No 3 matches 10, 18; G Doggart No 9 matches 7, 8, 9, 11, 18

Courage League Records 1994-95

● George Doggert and Jimmy Miller continued their battle to be the club's leading try scorer. Miller started the season one in front, Doggert caught him in November v Plymouth and both men had 25 tries. In the last game of the season Miller notched up 2 more tries in the game v Redruth to lead Doggert 27 to 25. Miller's 27 tries have come in all 8 League seasons while Diggert's have come in 6 seasons

● 5 straight defeats saw Aspatria have their worst ever start to a season and with a defeat in their last game of 1993-94 set a club record of 6 straight defeats

ASPATRIA R.U.F.C.

COURAGE LEAGUE STATISTICS
compiled by Steve McCormack

Season	Div	P	W	D	L	F	T	C	P	D	A	T	C	P	D	Most Points	Most Tries
1987-88	N2	10	8	0	2	263	39	25	19	-	60	6	1	11	-	108 David Pears	13 George Doggert
1988-89	N1	10	7	1	2	206	21	8	24	7	100					99 Andrew Harrison	4 David Murray Malcolm Brown
1989-90	N1	10	6	2	2	182	19	10	19	2	119					63 Jimmy Miller	5 Jimmy Miller
1990-91	N1	10	8	0	2	178	20	12	22	4	93					59 Andrew Harrison	5 Jimmy Miller
1991-92	D4N	12	11	0	1	253	36	19	23	-	100					55 Andrew Harrison	7 Jimmy Miller
1992-93	3	11	3	1	7	170	16	9	23	1	308	43	21	16	1	84 Andrew Harrison	2 by 4 players
1993-94	4	18	8	0	10	303	27	14	43	1	372	42	21	36	4	129 Mike Scott	7 Mark Richardson
1994-95	4	18	7	1	10	265	32	6	29	2	378	39	18	48	1	95 Mike Scott	7 Mark Richardson Craig Marriott
Totals		99	58	5	36	1820	210	103	202	17	1530						

BIGGEST WIN	**Home:** 52-3 v Huddersfield 31.10.87 N2	**Away:** 37-3 v Wilmslow 17.10.87 N2
BIGGEST DEFEAT	**Home:** 15-34 v Sheffield 10.10.92 CL3	**Away:** 5-78 v Harrogate 30-4-94 CL4
MOST TRIES in a match	**For:** 8 three times	**Against:** 14 v Harrogate 30-4-94 CL4
MOST CONSECUTIVE	**Wins:** 17	**Defeats:** 6
MOST APPEARANCES	**Forward:**	**Back:**
MOST CONSECUTIVE APPEARANCES		
CONSECUTIVE SCORING MATCHES	**Tries:** 7 George Doggert	
	Points: 13 Andrew Harrison & Mike Scott	

	IN A SEASON	IN A CAREER	IN A MATCH
MOST POINTS	129 Mike Scott 1993-94 CL4	340 Andrew Harrison 1987-92	27 Jimmy Miller v Hull Ionians 11.11.89 Away N1
MOST TRIES	13 George Doggert 1987-88 N2	27 Jimmy Miller 1987-95	3 George Doggert v New Brighton 10.10.87 Home N2 v Devonport 2.1.88 Home N2 v Northern 4.1.92 Away 4N Stuart Urquhart v Birkenhead Park 28.4.90 Home N1 Jimmy Miller v Durham 14.12.91 Away 4N Mark Richardson v Plymouth 23.4.94 Home CL4
MOST CONVERSIONS	11 Andrew Harrison 1991-92 Mike Scott 1993-94 CL4	43 Andrew Harrison 1987-92	7 David Pears v New Brighton 10.10.87 Home N2 v Huddersfield 31.10.87 Home N2
MOST PENALTIES	33 Mike Scott 1993-94 CL4	77 Andrew Harrison 1987-92	7 Jimmy Miller v Hull Ionians 11.11.89 Away N1
MOST DROP GOALS	3 Andrew Harrison 1988-89	7 Tom Borthwick 1987-95	2 Andrew Harrison v Wigton 19.11.88 Away N1 Mike Scott v Redruth 7.1.95 Away CL4

CLIFTON R.F.C.

NICKNAME: THE CLUB   **FOUNDED:** 1872

CLUB OFFICIALS

President
Grant Watson
Chairman
Norman Golding
Club Secretary
Peter Cumberlidge
48 Worrall Road, Clifton, Bristol BS8 4EU
Tel: (H) 0117 973 5048
Fixtures Secretary
Brian "Ben" Jordan
17 Royal Close, Henbury,
Bristol BS10 7XF
Tel: (H) 0117 950 4723
Press Officer
Brian "Ben" Jordan
Tel: (H) 0117 950 4723

Review of the Season

There is a saying that 'What goes up must come down', but CLIFTON will not like to be given that information as they tackle the task of repeating the efforts of two seasons ago and hope to regain the promotion they won so conciuvincingly on that occasion.

After a good start their form fell apart and on the last day of the campaign they needed a monumental win at home to Rugby to escape with Richmond being totally demolished at Bedford. Neither event happened and they play in League Four in the new season.

In the Pilkington Cup it was also undistinguished fare with a narrow 20-19 win at Ruislip being followed by defeat at Basingstoke (239-26).

Perhaps, the time has come for one or two loyal veterans to stand down, although Simon Hogg at fly-half still managed to play in 35 of the club's matches and was top scorer with 305 points, other consistent men being the wings Trevor Davis and John Phillips.

There is plenty of useful talent available but the likes of Mark Wyatt, Chris Blake, Wayne Hone and Matt Brain – good though they are – cannot go on for ever.

Back: Grant Watson (President), John Phillips, Mike Skinner (Team Manager), Lee Ashford, Mark Beresford, Matt Todds, Mark Wyatt, Lee Waddon. Simon Swales, Richard Clifton (Committed Supporter), Fred Cannon (Vice President), Derek Farley (Vice President), Alan Kendall (Membership Secretary), Brian Jordan (Fixture Secretary). Middle: Bob Miller (Assistant Coach), Adam Burns, Paul Crocker, Norman Goulding (Chairman), Wayne Hone (Captain), Dean Dewdney, Paul Futter, Peter Polledri (Coach). Front: Charles Newth, Paul Jeffery, Peter Naivalura, Matt Brain, Simon Hogg, Kevin Bogira, Paul Cox

Photo: Keith Fowler

Colours: Lavender and black hoops   **Change Colours:** Under review hoops

CLIFTON R.F.C.

COURAGE LEAGUE
MATCH DETAILS 1994-95

No	Date	Opponents	Ven	Result		Scorers
1	Sep 10	Otley	H	W	19-13	Hogg (1C 2P 2D) Phillips (T)
2	Sep 17	Bedford	A	L	5-19	Phillips (T)
3	Sep 24	Rugby	A	L	8-29	Hogg (1D) Beresford (T)
4	Oct 1	Richmond	H	W	18-6	Hogg (1C 1P 1D) Phillips (T) Cottrell (T)
5	Oct 15	Morley	A	W	25-3	Hogg (2C 2P) Brain (T) Jeffrey (T) Wyatt (T)
6	Oct 22	Rosslyn Park	H	L	12-21	Hogg (4P)
7	Oct 29	Blackheath	A	L	0-27,	
8	Nov 12	Exeter	H	W	29-15	Hogg (2C 5P) Beresford (T) Brain (T)
9	Jan 7	Harrogate	A	L	13-27	Hogg (1D) Davies (T) Heywood (T)
10	Jan 14	Bedford	H	L	18-21	Hogg (1C 2P) Davies (T) Waddon (T)
11	Feb 11	Otley	A	L	3-14	Hogg (1D)
12	Feb 25	Richmond	A	L	14-21	Beresford (2C) Wyatt (T) Haivalurua (T)
13	Mar 4	Morley	H	L	7-18	Beresford (1C) Brain (T)
14	Mar 25	Rosslyn Park	A	L	8-25	Davies (T) Hogg (1P)
15	Apr 1	Blackheath	H	L	12-25	Brain (T) Hogg (1C) Naivalurua (T)
16	Apr 8	Harrogate	H	D	17-17	Hogg (4P) Beresford (T)
17	Apr 15	Exeter	A	W	15-6	Hogg (1T 1C 1P) Wyatt (T)
18	Apr 29	Rugby	H	L	19-37	Hogg (3P) Swales (T) Wyatt (T)

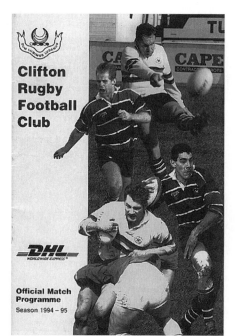

**Clifton
Rugby
Football
Club**

DHL
WORLDWIDE EXPRESS ®

**Official Match
Programme**
Season 1994 – 95

PROGRAMME DETAILS

Pages: 40

Advertising Rates: £200 full page

CLUB & GROUND DETAILS

Station Road, Cribbs Causeway, Henbury, Bristol BS10 7TP
Telephone: 0117 950 0445
Fax: 0117 950 2855

Total Capacity: 2,500
Seated: 250
Standing: 2,250
Simple Directions to Ground: As last years book
Nearest Railway Station: Bristol Parkway
Car Parking: 200 plus
Season Tickets: £35.00
Match Prices: Adults £4.00 Children Free OAPs £2.00
Membership: £35.00
Training Nights: Seniors Monday and Wednesday

CLIFTON R.F.C.

MATCH BY MATCH PLAYERS BY POSITION

Beresford	Phillips	Brain	Locke	Davis	Hogg	Jeffrey	Fisher	Ashford	Cox	Blake	Lewis	Swales	Hone	Wyatt	Reuben	Docas	Naivalurua	Heywood	Waddon	Dewdney	Futter	Burns	Crane
15	14	13	12	11	10	9	1	2	3	4	5	6	7	8									
15	14	13	12	11	10	9	1	2	3	4	5	6	7	8									R
15		13	12	11	10	9	1	2		4		6	7	8	3	5							
15	14	R	12		10	9	1	2		4		6	7	8	3	5	13						
15		11	12	14	10	9	1	2		4		6	7	8	3	5	13						4
	11	14	12	R	10	9	1	2					7	8	3	5	13	6					
	11	15	12	14	10	9	1	2					7	8	3	5	13	6					
15	11	12	14		10	9	1	2		4			7	8	3	5	13	6					
15		13	12	14	10	9	1	2					7		3	5		8	4				
15		13	12	14	10	9	1	2				6	7		3	5		8	4				
15	11	12	14		10	9	1	2	3	4		6	7			5	13			R			8
15	11	12	14				1	2	3	4		6	7	8			13			9			5
15	11	12	14			9	1	2	3	4		6	7	8			13						
15		12		14	10			2	3	4			7	8		5	13	6		9	11	1	
15		12		14	10		R	2	3				7	8		5	13	6	4	9	11	1	
15		12			10		R	2	3			6	7	8		5	13		4	9	11	1	
15		12			10			1	2	3		6	7	8		5	13		5	9	11		
15		12			10		R		3			6	7	8		5	13		4	9	11	1	

Also Played: M Lenthall R match 2; D Cottrell No 14 match 3, No 11 match 4; G Shipton R match 3; I Whitehall No 4 matches 6, 7; A Freeman No 15 match 6; P Hamid R match 7; S Hodges No 11 matches 9, 10; S Powell No 8 match 9, R match 10; P Cug No 10 matches 12, 13; R Horne No 5 match 13; P Crockers No 14 matches 16, 17, 19; L Bogira No 2 match 19; P Polledri R matches 5, 14

Courage League Records 1994-95

League Debuts: G Lewis, A Reuben, M Dodds, G Crane, I Whitehall, L Waddon, E Hodges, S Powell, P Futter, A Burns, D Dewdney, R Horne, K Bogira

Players used: 33

Ever Presents None – 3 17 Brain, Ashford, Hone

● No 8 Mark Wyatt continued to extend his numerous club records. Since making his debut in the opening game of the 1988-89 season Wyatt has played 82 out of 91 League games. He has played 24 more than his nearest rival, fellow back row forward Wayne Hone. He is also the club's leading try scorer with 37, 18 ahead of the next man on the list, winger Jon Phillips.

● Stand-off Simon Hogg tops the points scoring chart for the 4th consecutive season and takes his club points scoring record past 400 and 500.

● Try-scoring all-time list

	Tries	Apps	Strike Rate
M Wyatt	37	82	2.22
J Phillips	19	23	1.21

CLIFTON R.F.C.

COURAGE LEAGUE STATISTICS
compiled by Steve McCormack

Season	Div	P	W	D	L	F	T	C	P	D	A	T	C	P	D	Most Points	Most Tries
1987-88	SW1	10	6	0	4	210	33	18	13	1	112	17	7	9	1	60 Roger Gilbert	7 Mike Speakman
1988-89	SW1	10	9	0	1	237	28	16	25	6	76	6	2	15	1	64 Simon Harvey	4 Mark Trott
1989-90	AL5	10	8	1	1	240	31	16	21	7	122	18	7	10	2	83 Simon Harvey	6 Mark Trott Mark Wyatt
1990-91	3	12	6	1	5	172	25	12	13	3	186	23	4	18	3	32 Phil Cue	8 Dan Cottrell
1991-92	3	12	9	0	3	298	44	22	25	1	132	14	5	19	3	100 Simon Hogg	8 Matt Brain
1992-93	3	11	4	2	5	206	28	9	15	1	175	18	11	20	1	71 Simon Hogg	5 Mark Wyatt Doug Woodman
1993-94	4	18	16	2	0	477	54	24	40	13	205	17	6	35	1	222 Simon Hogg	16 John Phillips
1994-95	3	18	5	1	12	242	25	12	26	5	344	33	19	40	7	116 Simon Hogg	4 Matt Brain Mark Wyatt
Total		101	63	7	31	2082	268	129	178	37	1352	146	71	167	19		

BIGGEST WIN — **Home:** 64-7 v Bournemouth 19.9.87 SW1 **Away:** 42-12 v Oxford 26.11.88 SW1

BIGGEST DEFEAT — **Home:** 19-37 v Rugby 29.4.95 CL3 **Away:** 32-43 v Leeds 24.4.93 CL3

MOST TRIES in a match — **For:** 10 v Bournemouth 19.9.87 SW1 **Against:** 6 v West Hartlepool 20.10.90 CL3 v Leeds 24.4.94 CL3

MOST CONSECUTIVE — **Wins:** 10 **Defeats:** 7

MOST APPEARANCES — **Forward:** 82 Mark Wyatt **Back:** 56 Simon Hogg

MOST CONSECUTIVE APPEARANCES 54 Wayne Hone

CONSECUTIVE SCORING MATCHES — **Tries:** 3 John Phillips **Points:** 26 Simon Hogg

	IN A SEASON	IN A CAREER	IN A MATCH
MOST POINTS	222 Simon Hogg 1993-94 CL4	509 Simon Hogg 1991-95	25 Simon Harvey v Taunton 8.4.89 Home SW1
MOST TRIES	16 John Phillips 1993-94 CL4	37 Mark Wyatt 1988-95	4 Dan Cottrell v Askeans 4.1.92
MOST CONVERSIONS	24 Simon Hogg 1993-94	58 Simon Hogg 1991-95	9 Roger Gilbert v Bournemouth 19.9.87 Home SW1
MOST PENALTIES	30 Simon Hogg 1993-94	97 Simon Hogg 1991-95	6 Simon Harvey v Weston Super Mare 10.9.88 Home SW1 v Taunton 8.4.89 Home SW1
MOST DROP GOALS	14 Simon Hogg 1993-94	23 Simon Hogg 1991-95	2 Simon Harvey v Sudbury 14.10.89 Home D4S Phil Cue v Lydney 23.3.90 Away CL3 Simon Hogg v Leeds 30.10.93 Home CL4 v Sheffield 4.12.93 Away CL4

EXETER F.C.

NICKNAME: EXE   **FOUNDED:** 1872

CLUB OFFICIALS

President
R J Roach
Chairman
W J Baxter
Club Secretary
B P (Tug) Wilson
11 Washbrook View, Ottery St Mary,
Devon EX11 1EP
Tel: (H) 01404 813316 (W) 01884
243200
Fixtures Secretary
S Grainger
8 Linda Close, Exeter EX1 3EU
Tel: (H) 01392 53162
Press Officer
See Club Secretary for details

Review of the Season

From an early stage of the season it seemed that Exeter would finally find it too difficult to retain League Four status and so it proved. At the final count they were six points adrift of Richmond, who were the lowest placed survivors in the table.

However, the Pilkington Cup scotched the idea that they were a bunch of no-hopers as they won through four rounds before finally succumbing in the last eight to Wasps - a massive 31-0 at home but a sign that they have the determination and ability with luck to bounce back. Their victims in the cup had been North Walsham (32-7 away), Launceston (30-7 away), Rugby 9-7 (at home) and visiting Aspatria (18-6).

Now they must regroup and take note of the fact that their most consistent players last season were fullback Stewart, wing Dovell, experienced scrum-half Andy Maunder, tighthead Harris and lock Langley. They are a good nucleus on whom to build recovery plans.

Photo: CW Sport Photography

Colours: Black shirts, black shorts   **Change Colours**: Black/white strip shirt

EXETER F.C.

COURAGE LEAGUE
MATCH DETAILS 1994-95

No	Date	Opponents	Ven	Result		Scorers
1	Sep 10	Morley	A	W	13-6	Czerpak (P) Stewart (T) Brotchie (T)
2	Sep 17	Rosslyn Park	H	L	9-11	Czerpak (2P) Tutchings (1DG)
3	Sep 24	Blackheath	A	L	7-21	Lambert (T) Stewart (1C)
4	Oct 1	Rugby	H	L	11-15	Stewart (2P) Chatterton (T)
5	Oct 15	Harrogate	H	L	13-14	Stewart (1C 1P 1D) Beauchamp (T)
6	Oct 22	Otley	A	L	3-16	Stewart (1D)
7	Oct 29	Bedford	H	L	3-19	Beauchamp (1P)
8	Nov 12	Clifton	A	L	15-29	Oxland (4P) Stewart (1P)
9	Jan 7	Richmond	H	L	3-14	Patidor (1P)
10	Jan 14	Rosslyn Park	A	W	11-10	Dovell (T) Green (2P)
11	Feb 11	Morley	H	D	12-2	Green (4P)
12	Mar 3	Harrogate	A	L	3-17	Green (1D)
13	Mar	Rugby	A	L	11-17	Green (2P) Chatterton (T)
14	Mar 25	Otley	H	W	18-11	Stewart (1C 2P) Doyle (T) Maunder (T)
15	Apr 1	Bedford	A	L	10-23	Chatterton (T)
16	Apr 8	Richmond	A	L	5-41	Dovell (T)
17	Apr 15	Clifton	H	L	6-15	Patidar (2P)
18	Apr 29	Blackheath	H	L	0-28	

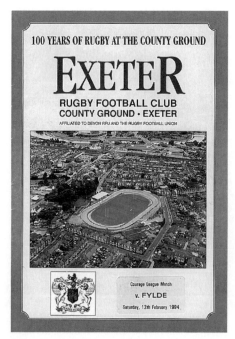

100 YEARS OF RUGBY AT THE COUNTY GROUND

EXETER

RUGBY FOOTBALL CLUB
COUNTY GROUND · EXETER
AFFILIATED TO DEVON RFU AND THE RUGBY FOOTBALL UNION

Courage League Match
v. FYLDE
Saturday, 12th February 1994

PROGRAMME DETAILS

Pages: 36 (A4)

Editor: Tony Lee
Advertising Rates: Full page £450

CLUB & GROUND DETAILS

County Ground, Church Road, St Thomas, Exeter EX2 9BQ
Telephone: 01392 78750

Total Capacity: 6,000
Seated: 1,750
Standing: 4,250
Simple Directions to Ground: Jcn 30 M5 head on A377 to town centre, Sainsbury Store turn left (Cowick Street) under railway bridge traffic lights turn left then right turn (100 yds)
Nearest Railway Station: Exeter St Davids
Car Parking: 200
Season Tickets: Adults £35.00 Children/OAPs £17.50
Match Prices: Adults £5.00 Children/OAPs £2.50
Membership: Seniors £20.00 Juniors £3.00
Training Nights: Tuesdays and Thursdays

EXETER F.C.

MATCH BY MATCH PLAYERS BY POSITION

Stewart	Doyle	Tutchings	Turner	Dovell	Czerpak	Maunder	Harris	Sitch	Sluman	Batchelor	Langley	Southern	Hutchinson	Brotchie	Gibbons	Bess	Beauchamp	Thomas	Chatterton	Baxter	Green	Brooking	Westgate
15	14	13	12	11	10	9	3	2	1	4	5	6	7	8				R					
15	14	13	12	11	10	9		2	3	6	5		7	8	1	4							
10	14	13	12	11				2	3	5	4		7	8	1	R	15						
10		13	12	11		9	3	2			4		7		1	5	15		14	6			
10		13	12	11		9		2	3			6	7	8	1	5	15		14	4			
		13	12	11		9	3				4	7	R	8	1	5	15		14	6			
15	14	13	12	11		9	3			5	4		7		1	R				6			
	14		12	11		9	3			5			7		1		8						
		15	13	14	11	9	3			8	4	6			1			R	12	5	10	2	
		15	13	14	11	9	3			8	4		6		1				12	5	10	2	
		15	13	14	11	9	3			8	4	6			1					5	10	2	
15					11		3			8	4	6			1			12	14	5	10	2	
15	12				11	9	3			8	4	6			1			13	14	5	10		
15		13			11	9	3			8	4		6		1			12	14	5	10	R	
15	13	12			11	9	3			8	4	6			1	5			14		10	2	
15		13			11	9	3				4	6	7			5		12	14	8			
15		13			11	9		3		8	4		7		1	6				12	14		
15		13			11	9	3			8	4		7		1	6			11	14			

Also Played: R Walker No 6 match 3; R Lambert No 9 match 3, No 11 match 6, R match 18; D Oxland No 10 matches 7, 8, No 9 match 13; M Cathery No 9 matches 4, 8, No 6 match 9; M Wooltarton No 2 matches 7, 8, 9; M Patidor No 10 matches 9, 17, 18; S Westcott No 2 matches 14, 15, 17, 18; M Rose No 13 match 13; M Webb No 12 match 19; J Bartlett No 5 match 18; J Sussex No 1 match 17; L Ingledon No 12 match 18

Courage League Records 1994-95

League Debuts: 11 – J Czerpak, A Brotchie, M Beauchamp, J Thomas, M Woolturton, M Patidar, K Brooking, S Westcott, M Rose, M Webb, J Bartlett
Players used: 35
Ever Presents 0 – Most 17 Harry Langley
Most appearances: 102 Andy Maunder

● Exeter's scrum half Andy Maunder became the first player in the National Divisions to make 100 League appearances, doing so on 8th April v Richmond. He beat Wakefield's Dave Scully to this feat by a week. He finished the season on 102, the same as Scully

● Meanwhile second row forward Harry Langley holds the Courage record for most appearances by a forward, 95, one ahead of Harlequins' prop Andy Mullins. Maunder is also joint holder of the record for consecutive League appearances, 88, a record he shares with Rotherham flanker Richard Selkirk. Both had their sequences broken last season.

● With leading points scorer Andy Green out injured for the majority of the season, Ian Stewart shared some of the kicking duties and moved into second place on Exeter's all-time list, also becoming the second player to top 100 points.

● Mark Chatterton's 3 tries saw him top the try scorer's list for a second time and took his total to 14 and into 2nd place on the all time list.

	Tries	Apps	Strike Rate
A Maunder	23	102	4.43
M Chatterton	14	73	5.21
A Green	13	77	5.92

EXETER F.C.

COURAGE LEAGUE STATISTICS
compiled by Steve McCormack

Season	Div	P	W	D	L	F	T	C	P	D	A	T	C	P	D	Most Points	Most Tries
1987-88	3	11	3	2	6	128	15	4	16	4	197	27	16	19	0	42 Andy Green	3 Andy Green. Mike Gathery
1988-89	3	11	4	0	7	142	17	7	14	6	180	22	10	20	4	65 Malcolm Collins	5 Andy Maunder
1989-90	3	11	5	1	5	149	15	7	25	0	153	17	5	19	6	99 Andy Green	2 Andy Green Andy Maunder John Davis Simon Dovell
1990-91	3	12	7	2	3	160	20	7	22	0	139	16	6	21	0	92 Andy Green	4 Jeff Tutchings
1991-92	3	12	8	2	2	203	29	12	19	2	138	14	5	22	2	77 Andy Green	4 Mark Chatterton. John Davis
1992-93	3	11	8	1	2	247	25	10	31	3	169	16	7	24	1	122 Andy Green	5 Andy Maunder
1993-94	3	18	9	1	8	308	32	20	34	2	271	23	15	38	4	125 Andy Green	5 Andy Maunder
1994-95	3	18	3	1	14	153	11	4	26	4	319	30	17	43	2	35 Ian Stewart	3 Mark Chatterton
TOTALS		104	47	10	47	1490	164	71	187	21	1566	165	81	206	19		

BIGGEST WIN   **Home:** 48-13 v Askeans 10.10.92 CL3   **Away:** 41-0 v Havant 26.2.94 CL3

BIGGEST DEFEAT   **Home:** 28-33 v Leeds 13.3.93 CL3   **Away:** 13-48 v Fylde 3.10.87 CL3

MOST TRIES in a match   **For:** 7   **Against:** 3 v Fylde 3.10.87 CL3

MOST CONSECUTIVE   **Wins:** 6   **Defeats:** 8

MOST APPEARANCES   **Forward:** 95 Harry Langley   **Back:** 102 Andy Maunder

MOST CONSECUTIVE APPEARANCES   88 Andy Maunder 12.9.87 to 17.9.94

CONSECUTIVE SCORING MATCHES   **Tries:** 3 Andy Maunder, John Davis

Points: 32 Andy Green

	IN A SEASON	IN A CAREER	IN A MATCH
MOST POINTS	125 Andy Green 1993-94 CL3	595 Andy Green 1987-95	20 Andy Green v Met Police 10.11.90 Home CL3
MOST TRIES	5 Andy Maunder 1988-89 CL3 1992-93 CL3 1993-94 CL3	23 Andy Maunders 1987-95	3 Mike Cathery v Birmingham 26.3.88 Home CL3 Andy Green v Met Police 10.11.90 Home CL3 Mike Chatterton v Headingley 23.11.91 Home CL3 Harry Langley v Broughton park 24.4.93 CL3
MOST CONVERSIONS	16 Andy Green 1993-94 CL3	53 Andy Green 1987-95	3 Andy Green on 6 occasions
MOST PENALTIES	31 Andy Green 1992-93 CL3	131 Andy Green 1987-95	5 Andy Green v West Hartlepool 28.10.Home CL3 v Sheffield 28.3.92 Home CL3 v Plymouth 14.11.92 Home CL3
MOST DROP GOALS	4 Andy Green 1987-88 CL3	13 Andy Green 1987-95	2 Andy Green v Sheffield 23.4.88 Home CL3

HAVANT R.F.C.

NICKNAME: HAV   **FOUNDED:** 1951

CLUB OFFICIALS

President
Phil West
Chairman
Harry Wilkinson
Club Secretary
Colin Sewell
6 Font Close, Fareham, Hants PO14 4PH
Tel: (H) 01489 583417 (W) 01489 583417
Fixtures Secretary
Mick Chalk
16 Highclere Avenue, Leigh Park,
Havant, Hants PO9 4RB
Tel: (H)01705 472239 (W) 01705 723749
Press Officer
Ray Quinn
Tel: (W) 01705 241122

Review of the Season

For Havant and coach Owen Jarrett, the 1994-95 season was genuinely a case of so near, yet so far.

Up until Christmas, the Hampshire side were right on the inside track in a four horse race for promotion.

A stunning 32-29 win over pace-setters Rotherham in October, thanks to Adam Jewitt's late smash-and-grab try and Pete Russell's conversion, had sounded an ominous warning to their rivals.

It was to be the Yorkshire team's only reverse of the season.

But Havant failed to capitalise on a useful pre-Christmas start of six wins from eight, and were to falter in the New Year with the awayday blues.

Successive draws at Redruth and Plymouth put the skids under the Hooks Lane outfit's promotion bandwagon.

But it was bogey-side Aspatria, who had put paid to Havant's promotion bid two seasons earlier, who inflicted a numbing 18-19 defeat at Bower Park with a match-winning penalty four minutes from time.

An 18-22 loss at home to promotion rivals Reading – the only blot on an otherwise impeccable Hooks Lane copybook, extinguished Havant's flickering hopes of division three rugby.

Their away form and the lack of consistency with kicking ultimately cost Havant the chance of a step up.

However for Owen Jarrett and his troops, consolation could be drawn from a remarkable turnaround in spirit and application among the players after a torrid season the previous year.

Winger Jimmy Bates and flanker Nick Roach remained ever-presents in the league team with 18 starts each. Roach also claimed the laurels in the try-scoring stakes with 10, one ahead of winger Jewitt.

A year tinged with disappointment but still a promising springboard with which to approach the coming season.

Colours: Navy blue and white 4" hoops, navy shorts   **Change Colours**: Red

HAVANT R.F.C.

COURAGE LEAGUE
MATCH DETAILS 1994-95

No	Date	Opponents	Ven	Result	Scorers
1	Sep 10	Redruth	H	W 23-16	Ashworth (5P) Roach (T) Firkin (1D)
2	Sep 17	Leeds	A	W 18-6	Ashworth (1C 1P) Roach (T) Russell (T D)
3	Sep 24	Aspatria	H	W 24-8	Ashworth (1C 2P) Bates (2T) Russell (2P)
4	Oct 1	Broughton P	A	W 15-12	Russell (1C 1P) Firkin (T) Jewitt (T)
5	Oct 15	Reading	A	L 15-18	Russell (1C 1P) Bates (T) Pen Try
6	Oct 22	Rotherham	H	W 32-29	Russell (1C 5P) Middleton (2T) Jewitt (T)
7	Oct 29	Liverpool St H	A	L 12-22	Russell (1C) Middleton (T) Jones (T)
8	Nov 12	Askeans	H	W 50-13	Russell (1T 5C) Ashworth (T) Redden (T) Jewitt (2T) Bates (T) Roach (T)
9	Jan 7	Plymouth	A	D 17-17	Chapman (3P) Firkin (1D) Jewitt (T)
10	Jan 14	Redruth	A	D 22-22	Ashworth (2C 1P) Roach (2T) Firkin (T)
11	Feb 11	Leeds	H	W 10-3	Bates (T) Ward (T)
12	Feb 25	Aspatria	A	L 18-19	Powley (P) Roach (2T) Jewitt (T)
13	Mar 4	Broughton P	H	W 37-22	Russell (2C 1P) Ford (T) Bates (T) Jewitt (2T) Roach (T) Jones (T)
14	Mar 25	Reading	H	L 18-22	Russell (1T 1P) Powley (T) Knight (T)
15	Apr 1	Rotherham	A	L 10-35	Russell (1C 1D) Rouse (T)
16	Apr 8	Liverpool St H	H	W 17-7	Russell (2C 1P) Jewitt (T) Pen Try
17	Apr 15	Askeans	A	L 23-35	Russell (1C 1P) Whirehead (T) Bates (T) Roach (T) Rouse (T)
18	Apr 29	Plymouth	H	W 27-25	Russell (1C 1D) Rushin (1C) Wright (2T) Loveday (T) Roach (T)

HAVANT RUGBY FOOTBALL CLUB
GROUND: HOOKS LANE, FRASER ROAD,
BEDHAMPTON, HAVANT, HANTS. PO9 3EJ
Telephone: 01705-477843

SEASON 1994 - 1995

OFFICIAL
PROGRAMME

PROGRAMME DETAILS

Pages: 48

Editor:
Advertising Rates: £250.00 full page £150.00 half page
£85.00 quarter page

CLUB & GROUND DETAILS

Havant R.F.C., Hooks Lane, Fraser Road, Bedhampton,
Havant, Hants PO9 3EJ
Telephone: 01705 477843
Fax: 01705 492311

Total Capacity: 2,700
Seated: 200
Standing: 2,500
Simple Directions to Ground: As per last season
Nearest Railway Station: Havant or Bedhampton
(infrequent)
Car Parking: 200 adjacent to clubhouse
Season Tickets: £3.00 League Cup £2.00 other
Match Prices: £2.00
Membership: £25.00
Training Nights: Tuesdays and Thursdays

HAVANT R.F.C.

MATCH BY MATCH PLAYERS BY POSITION

Ashworth	Bates	Boydell	Powley	Coulson	Firkin	Jones	Rees	Whitehead	Cameron	Rouse	Ward	Redden	Roach	Knight	Morgan	Middleton	Russell	Jewit	Pearce	Davey	Chapman	Ford	Perry
15	14	13	12	11	10	9	1	2	3	4	5	6	7	8									
15	14	13	12			9		2	3		5		7	8	4	6	10	11					
15	14	13	12			9	1	2	3		5		7	8	4	6	10	11					
	14	13	12	15		9	1	2	3		5		7		4	6	10	11					
15	14	13	12	R		9	1	2	3		5		7		4	6	10	11	8				
15	14	13	12			9	1	2	3		5		7	8		6	10	11	4				
15	14		12			9	1	2	3		5		7	8		6	10	11	4				
15	14	13	12			9	1			5	4	6	7	8			10	11					
	14	13	12	15			1			5	4		7	8		6		11			9		
15	14		13	10			1			5	4		7	8		6		11			9	3	
	14	13	12	15			1			5	4		7	8		6		11			9	3	
	14		12	15			1			5	4		7	8		6		11			9	3	
	14		13	9			1	2		5	4		7	8		6	10	11				3	
	14		12	15			1	2		5	4		7			6	10	11	8	13	9	3	
	14			15			1	2		5			7	8	4	6	10	12		13	9	3	
	14			15			1	2		5			7	8	4	6	10	12		13	9	3	
	14			15			1	2		5			7	8	4	6	10	11		13	9	3	
	14			9			1	2		4	5		7	8			10	11		13		3	

Also Played: R Myal No 1 match 2; J Hammond R Match 3; J Davenport No 8 match 4; J Tolcher No 13 match 7; A Ugston No 11 matches 15, 16; M Jarrett No 12 matches 17, 18; H Rushin No 15 matches 13, 18; N Croker No 3 match 8; M Brady No 3 matches 8, 9, 10, 11, 12; M Loveday No 6 match 18, G Edwards No 3 match 9; N Servini No 13 match 12 No 12 match 13

Courage League Records 1994-95

League Debuts: S Coulson, J Firken, J Cameron, P Redden, K Middleton, J Davenport, J Tolcher, M Brady, N Croker, A Weston, T Chapman, J Ford, M Jarrett, H Rushin, M Loveday, G Edwards, N Servini
Players used: 35
Ever Presents 2 J Bates, N Roach

● Pete Russell and Rob Ashworth continued their ding dong battle to remain top of Havant's all time points scoring list. Ashworth started the season in front but by the end of it Russell was 5 points up

	Pts	T	C	P	D	App	Ave
P Russell	284	7	48	47	5		
R Ashworth	279	4	20	71	2		

● Russell equalled Ashworth's record of finishing leading scorer 3 times. Russell's 2 drop goals saw him equal Perry's career total of 5. Ashworth and Russell both set a new record of 5 penalties in a match whilst Russell equalled his own record of 5 conversions in a match

● If that contest was close it has nothing on the battle to be leading try scorer. We now have 3 men tied on 20 tries each. Pride of place goes to flanker Nick Roach who scored a club record 10 tries beating Will Knight's previous best of 9. knight started the season as the club's joint top try scorer with 17, a record he shared with Andy Wilson. The record is now 20 and shared between Knight, Roach and Jimmy Bates.

HAVANT R.F.C.

COURAGE LEAGUE STATISTICS
compiled by Steve McCormack

Season	Div	P	W	D	L	F	T	C	P	D	A	T	C	P	D	Most Points	Most Tries
1987-88	ALS	10	5	0	5	116	17	6	8	102						39 Chris Manktellow	3 Chris Manktellow
1988-89	ALS	10	8	1	1	177	22	13	19	2	92					61 Peter Coomb	6 Peter Coomb
1989-90	ALS	10	5	1	4	132	17	8	3	126						43 Rob Ashworth	5 Andy Wilson
1990-91	D4S	12	5	0	7	157	15	8	27		173					97 Rob Ashworth	2 by 4 players
1991-92	D4S	12	11	0	1	301	45	23	24	1	91					129 Pete Russell	9 Will Knight
1992-93	3	11	8	1	2	185	23	5	20		93					54 Rob Ashworth	3 Mark Sheldon Paul Jenkins Andy Wilson
1993-94	3	18	3	0	5	203	22	15	20	1	432	51	26	3	1	32 Pete Russell	4 Nick Roach
199-95	4	18	10	2	6	390	51	21	27	4	330	32	17	45	2	85 Pete Russell	10 Nick Roach
TOTALS		101	55	5	31	1661	212	99	158	15	1439						

BIGGEST WIN **Home:** 50-13 v Askeans 12.11.94 CL4 **Away:** 56-3 v Southend 14.3.92 D4S

BIGGEST DEFEAT **Home:** 0-41 v Exeter 26.2.94 CL3 **Away:** 6-46 v Rosslyn Park 12.3.94 CL3

MOST TRIES in a match **For**: 10 v Southend 14.3.92 D4S **Against:** 7 v Exeter 26.2.94 v Rosslyn Park 12.3.94

MOST CONSECUTIVE **Wins:** 13 **Defeats:** 8

MOST APPEARANCES **Forward:** **Back:**

MOST CONSECUTIVE APPEARANCES

CONSECUTIVE SCORING MATCHES **Tries:** 4 Jim Bates

Points: 14 Rob Ashworth

	IN A SEASON	IN A CAREER	IN A MATCH
MOST POINTS	129 Peter Russell 1991-92	284 Peter Russell 1988-95	20 Peter Russell v Southend Home 14.3.92 D4S
MOST TRIES	10 Nick Roach 1994-95	20 Will Knight 1988-95 Nick Roach 1991-95 Jimmy Bates 1991-95	3 Andy Wilson v Sudbury 23.9.89 Home D4S v Ealing 11.1.92 Home D4S Jim Bates v Southend 14.3.92 Home D4S Nick Roach v Southend 14.3.92 Home D4S
MOST CONVERSIONS	23 Peter Russell 1991-92	48 Peter Russell 1989-95	5 Peter Russell v Southend 14.3.92 v Askeans 12.1.95 Home v Askeans 12.11.94 CL4
MOST PENALTIES	27 Rob Ashworth 1990-91	71 Rob Ashworth 1988-95	5 Rob Ashworth v Redruth 10-9-84 Home CL4 Peter Russell v Rotherham 22.10.94 Home CL4
MOST DROP GOALS	3 Andy Perry 1987-88	5 AndyPerry 1987-91 Peter Russell 1989-95	2 Andy Perry v Lydney 7.11.87 Home D4S

LEEDS R.U.F.C.

NICKNAME: **FOUNDED:** June 1991

CLUB OFFICIALS

President
F S C Browning
Chairman
Mike Palmer-Jones
Club Secretary
Mike Bidgood
4 West Hill Avenue, Leeds LS7 3QH
Tel: (H)0113 2682784 (W) 0113 2625382
Fixtures Secretary
Les Jackson
4 Gledhow Wood Avenue, Leeds LS8 1NY
Tel: (H) 0113 2665544 (W) 0113 2665544
Press Officer
Mike Bidgood
Tel: (H) 0113 2682784 (W) 0113 2625382

Review of the Season

A club which bears the name of LEEDS will be disappointed that the best they can achieve in a competitive season is fifth place in League Four, but this was the fate of the club at the conclusion of last season and fans will need to see a big improvement if they will continue to give their support. They were never in contention for promotion.

The Pilkington Cup brought with it an immediate and decisive exit at Aspatria (23-0), so now they must seriously consider future strategy.

Their most consistent players were centre Ralph Bennett, the top points scorer, fly-half Kevin Bowling, fullback Stuart Langley, left wing Thornton, loosehead Head, the front jumper Burkenshaw and the openside flanker Lancaster. On them will the future probably depend, but one cannot emphasise too strongly that a team bearing the name of Leeds should be nearer the top flight.

Colours: Royal blue, old gold, white   **Change Colours**: Red hoops

LEEDS R.U.F.C.

COURAGE LEAGUE
MATCH DETAILS 1994-95

No	Date	Opponents	Ven	Result		Scorers
1	Sep 10	Aspatria	A	W	22-11	Eddie (1C) Bennett (T) Moule (T) Singleton (T) Salkeld (T)
2	Sep 11	Havant	H	L	6-18	Eddie (2P)
3	Sep 24	Reading	A	L	19-24	Eddie (1C 3P 1D) Eagle (T)
4	Oct 1	Rotherham	H	L	8-17	Eddie (1P) Eagle (T)
5	Oct 15	Liverpool St H	A	L	10-35	Bowling (1C 1P) Eagle (T)
6	Oct 22	Askeans	H	W	35-10	Bennett (1T 2C 2P) Bartliffe (T) Griffin (T) Douglas (T) Thornton (T)
7	Oct 29	Plymouth	A	W	17-13	Bennett (1C) Bowling (1C 1D) Griffin (T) Bartliffe (T)
8	Nov 12	Redruth	H	W	19-0	Bennett (1C 4P) Thornton (T)
9	Jan 7	Broughton P	A	W	11-0	Spowart (1P 1D) Lancaster (T)
10	Jan 14	Aspatria	H	W	12-3	Eddie (4P)
11	Feb 11	Havant	A	L	3-10	Bennett (1P)
12	Feb 25	Reading	H	L	18-23	Langley (1T 1C 1P) Griffin (T) Bennett (1P)
13	Mar 4	Rotherham	A	L	18-34	Bennett (1C 2P) Bartliffe (2T)
14	Mar 25	Liverpool St H	H	L	20-26	Bennett (5P) Bartliffe (T)
15	Apr 1	Askeans	A	L	14-15	Langley (2P) Eagle (1D) Thornton (T)
16	Apr 8	Plymouth	H	W	30-25	Langley (3C 3P) Griffin (2T) Thornton (T)
17	Apr 15	Redruth	A	L	13-20	Langley (1C 2P) Bennett (T)
18	Apr 29	Broughton P	H	W	60-8	Langley (1T 1C) Cutter (T) Lancaster (3T) Bennett (1T 4C) Whitford (T) Griffin (T) Thornton (2T)

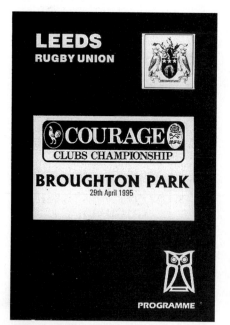

PROGRAMME DETAILS

Pages: 36
Advertising Rates: A5 Monochrome £195.00

CLUB & GROUND DETAILS

Leeds R.U.F.C., Clarence Field, Bridge Road, Kirkstall, Leeds
LS5 3BN
Telephone: 01132 755029
Fax:

Total Capacity: 7,850
Seated: 850
Standing: 7,000
Simple Directions to Ground: From A1 (North). Leave A1 at
Wetherby and take A58 to Leeds and follow road for 7 miles to Leeds
Outer Ring Road (A61200. Turn right at the roundabout and pass
straight across next 3 roundabouts. The third is the A660 Otley Road
which is about 6 miles from the Wetherby Road. After approximately
300 yards turn left at the lights into Spen Lane and follow the road for
about 1 1/2 miles to the next set of lights. Turn right onto Kirkstall
Lane which leads down to the lights at the junction with A65 and
Bridge Road. Go through the lights and the entrance to the Leeds
RUFC is 100 yards on the left opposite Clover Warehouse, turning into
the "Funtazia" car park. *Continued p 280.*
Nearest Railway Station: Leeds City / Headingley
Car Parking: 200 in ground
Season Tickets: £30.00 Adults £3.00 Children £11.00 OAPs
Match Prices:
Membership: £3.00
Training Nights: Tuesdays and Thursdays

LEEDS R.U.F.C.

MATCH BY MATCH PLAYERS BY POSITION

Eagle	Douglas	Hartley	Bennett	Thornton	Bowling	Head	Salkeld	Machell	Burkinshaw	Wilde	James	Lancaster	Moule	Woolaston	Swarbrigg	Griffen	Curtis	Bartliffe	Freeman	Roberts	Morgan	Whitford	Langley
15	14	13	12	11	10	1	2	3	4		6	7	8										
		13	12	11	10	1	R		4		6	7	8	2									
15		13	12	11	10	1	2		4		6	7	8		9								
15	13		12	11	10	1			4	R		7	8	2	9	6							
15		13	12	11	10	1	R	3	4	5	6				9	7	8	14					
	13		12	11	10	1		3	4		6	7		2	9	8	5	14					
			12	11	10	1		3	4	5	6			2	9	7	8	14	13	R			
		,,12		11	10	1		3	4	5	8	7		2	9	6	14	13					
	14		12	11	10	1		3	4			7	6	2			8		13		9		
15			12	11	10	1		3	4			7	6	2			8		13		9		
			12		10	1	2		4	5					9		8		13	2	15	11	
		13		11	10	1	2	3	4	5		7	8		9	7			14	12			
			12	11	10	1	2	3	4	5		7		R		6	8	15	13		9	14	
	14		12	11	10	1	2		4	5		7	8		9	6		15		3			
	14		12	11		1	2		4	5		7	8			6				3	9	13	
	14		12	11	10	1	2		4	5		7			9	6	8			3		13	
	14		12	11	10	1	2		4	5		7				6	8			3	9	13	
	14	13		11	10	1	2		4	R		7		R		6	8	15		3	9	12	

Also Played: Singleton No 9 matches 1, 2; Jenkins No 5 matches 1, 2, 3; D Eddie R match 1 No 14 matches 2, 3, 4, 10; R Broderick No 3 match 2; M Cutter No 3 matches 3, 4; A Fraser No 5 match 4; A Ogle No 2 match 5; C Spowart No 15 match 9 No 10 match 15; H Barratt No 5 matches 9, 10, No 6 match 11; C Raducanu No 5 match 18

Courage League Records 1994-95

League Debuts: 13 R Bennett, A Jenkins, A Ogle, P Curtis, S Bartliffe, C Freeman, N Roberts, S Langley, C Spowart, R Morgan, H Barratt, C Raducanu
Players used: 35
Ever Presents 3 R Bennet, C Head, P Burkinshaw
Most appearances: 41 Chris Thornton

● Recorded their biggest ever win in the final game of the season when they beat Broughton Park 60-8. In the process they ran in 10 tries which was also a record. Three came from Stuart Lancaster who equalled Chris Thornton's record of a League hat trick

● Ralph Bennett in his first season for the club top scored with 83 points from 18 games and would have challenged David Breakwell's seasonal record of 97 but for the fact that the kicking was shared between 5 players

● Bennett managed to become the first player to kick 5 penalties in a match, doing so v Liverpool St Helens at home in March. He also equalled Ben Lloyd's record of 4 conversions in a match.

● Winger Chris Thornton extends his club try scoring record to 15. Flanker Phil Griffin who holds the record for a forward with 7 is second overall to Thornton.

LEEDS R.U.F.C.

COURAGE LEAGUE STATISTICS

compiled by Steve McCormack

Season	Div	P	W	D	L	F	T	C	P	D	A	T	C	P	D	Most Points	Most Tries
1992-93	3	11	7	0	4	228	28	17	16	2	220	24	11	24	2	45 Ben Lloyd	7 Chris Thornton
1993-94	4	18	7	0	11	243	23	16	26	6	318	32	13	36	8	97 David Breakwell	3 Penalty Try
1994-95	4	18	8	0	10	335	36	19	35	4	291	30	15	34	3	83 Ralph Bennett	6 Phil Griffin. Chris Thornton
TOTALS		47	22	0	35	806	87	52	77	12	829	86	39	94	13		

BIGGEST WIN **Home:** 60-8 v Broughton Park, 29.4.95 CL4 **Away:** 33-28 v Exeter 13.3.93 CL3

BIGGEST DEFEAT **Home:** 20-26 v Liverpool St H 25.3.94 CL4 **Away:** 11-35 v Havant 26.9.92 CL3 / 10-35 v Liverpool St H 15.10.93 CL4

MOST TRIES in a match **For**: 10 v Broughton Park 29.4. 95 CL4 **Against:** 5 v Plymouth 9.4.94 CL4

MOST CONSECUTIVE **Wins:** 6 **Defeats:** 5

MOST APPEARANCES **Forward:** 37 Paul Burkinshaw **Back:** 41 Chris Thornton

MOST CONSECUTIVE APPEARANCES 24 David Breakwell 26.9.92 to 5.3.94

CONSECUTIVE SCORING MATCHES **Tries:** 4 Chris Thornton

Points: 9 David Breakwell

	IN A SEASON	IN A CAREER	IN A MATCH
MOST POINTS	97 David Breakwell 1993-94 CL4	134 David Breakwell 1992-94	20 David Breakwell v Aspatria 27.10.93 Home CL3
MOST TRIES	7 Chris Thornton 1992-93 CL3	15 Chris Thornton 1992-95	3 Chris Thornton v Exeter 13.3.93 Away CL3 Stuart Lancaster v Broughton Park 29.4.95 Home CL4
MOST CONVERSIONS	12 David Breakwell 1993-94 CL4	19 David Breakwell 1992-94	4 Ben Lloyd v Askeans 13.2.93 Home CL3 Ralph Bennett v Broughton Park 29.4.95 Home CL4
MOST PENALTIES	20 David Breakwell 1993-94 CL4	26 David Breakwell 1992-94	5 Ralph Bennett v Liverpool St H 23.3.95 Home CL4
MOST DROP GOALS	4 Dan Eddie 1993-94 CL4	8Dan Eddie 1992-95	2 Dan eddie v Broughton Park 19.2.94 CL4

Directions to ground continued

From M1. Leave M1 at Junction 47 and follow signs for City Centre. The road winds a lot but pass Hilton Hotel on the left and then under bridge to lights at City Square. Stay in left lane at lights and pass Queens Hotel on left and road becomes Wellington Street (A65 to Ilkley). Pass Holiday Inn on left and then Yorkshire Post again on the left. Pass under the fly-over and follow A65 for two miles. At second set of lights turn left into Bridge Road and the entrance to the Leeds RUFC is 100 yards on the left opposite Clover Warehouse, turning into the "Funtazia" car park.

From M62/M621. Leave M62 at Junction 27 and follow M621 to City Centre. Leave at Junction 2 immediately past Elland Road (Leeds United Ground). Take the first exit at the sliproad roundabout signed A58,A61,A65. Follow the road to lights at entry to large gyratory. Leave at the third exit (under a bridge) still towards A58,A61 etc. Keep in left lanes and exit down to the A65 (Ilkley). You will see the Yorkshire Post tower on the right of the road at this junction. Follow A65 for two miles. At second set of lights turn left into Bridge Road and the entrance to the Leeds RUFC is 100 yards on the left opposite Clover Warehouse, turning into the "Funtazia" car park.

LIVERPOOL ST HELENS F.C.

NICKNAME: LSH   **FOUNDED:** Liverpool 1857 (merged 1986)

CLUB OFFICIALS
President
Ian Clark
Chairman
W S McGowan
Club Secretary
E C Hyland
22 Salisbury Road, Cressington Park,
Liverpool L19 0PJ
Tel: 0151 4278831
Fixtures Secretary
J D Robertson
36 Beryl Road, Wirral L47 9RT
Tel: (H) 0151 6775611 (W) 0151 4277535
Press Officer
C J Brown
47 Cowley Hill Lane, St Helens
WA10 2AR
(W + H) 01744 759075

Review of the Season

Although LIVERPOOL ST HELENS finished third in League Four they ended the season six points behind second placed Reading. who joined Rotherham in being promoted, but the two top clubs were outstanding candidates for honours and in the new campaign prospects should be better with competition -in theory at least - less difficult.

Even so the club must plan to ascend on the basis that every match will be like a cup-tie and in this respect they did not shine in the recent season, losing their place in the Pilkington Cup in their first outing - 15-10 at Camp Hill.

Consistency in 1994-95 came mainly from fullback and leading scorer Andy Higgin, who has been around for some time, and he was well aided by other experienced players in wing Sephton and centre Wellens. Other reliable players were another centre in Davies, lock Hughes, No8 Lupton and prop Gill.

Together they can add up in a new season to a realistic promotion challenge. League Four is not good enough for the City of Liverpool.

Colours: Red, blue, white and black hoops   **Change Colours:** White – red trim

LIVERPOOL ST HELENS F.C.

COURAGE LEAGUE
MATCH DETAILS 1994-95

No	Date	Opponents	Ven	Result	Scorers
1	Sep 10	Broughton P	H	W 30-3	Higgins (1T 3C 3P) Jones (T) Jackson (T)
2	Sep 17	Askeans	A	W 9-6	Higgins (2P 1D)
3	Sep 24	Plymouth	H	W 24-5	Higgins (3P) Jones (2T) Davies (T)
4	Oct 1	Redruth	A	D 11-11	Higgins (2P) Walker (T)
5	Oct 15	Leeds	H	W 35-10	Higgins (1T 3C 3P) Gaskell (2T) Davies (T)
6	Oct 22	Aspatria	A	L 6-16	Higgins (2P)
7	Oct 29	Havant	H	W 22-12	Higgins (2C 1P) Williams (2T) Gaskell (T)
8	Nov 12	Reading	A	L 6-28	Higgins (1P 1D)
9	Jan 7	Rotherham	H	L 14-18	Higgins (2C) K Simms (T) Eldoy (T)
10	Jan 14	Broughton P	A	W 25-12	Higgins (1T 2C 2P) Davies (T) Sephton (T)
11	Feb 11	Askeans	H	W 14-3	Higgins (2C) K Simms (T) Wood (T)
12	Feb 25	Plymouth	A	D 17-17	Wellens (1T 3P 1D)
13	Mar 4	Redruth	H	W 49-21	Wellens (2C) Jones (T) Davies (T) Williams (T) Walker (2T) Sephton (2T) Humphries (2T)
14	Mar 25	Leeds	A	W 26-20	Higgins (1C 3P) K Simms (T) Sephton (2T)
15	Apr 1	Aspatria	H	W 42-5	Higgins (1T 4C 3P) Liddle (T) Davies (T) Williams (T) Sephton (T)
16	Apr 8	Havant	A	L 7-17	Higgins (1C) Sephton (T)
17	Apr 15	Reading	H	D 14-14	Higgins (2C) Wellens (T) Humphreys (T)
18	Apr 29	Rotherham	A	L 23-25	Higgins (2C 2P) Wellens (1D) Walker (T) Wood (T)

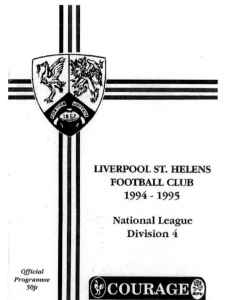

LIVERPOOL ST. HELENS
FOOTBALL CLUB
1994 - 1995

National League
Division 4

Official
Programme
50p

PROGRAMME DETAILS
Price: 50p
Pages: 20

Advertising Rates: Full page £300 + VAT

CLUB & GROUND DETAILS
Liverpool St Helens F.C., Moss Lane, Windle, St Helens
WA11 7PL
Telephone: 01744 25708
Fax:

Total Capacity: 2,300
Seated: 300
Standing: 2,000
Simple Directions to Ground: M6 Junction 23. A580
(Liverpool) 5 miles A570 (Southport) 100 yards, small lane
on left to ground
Nearest Railway Station:
Car Parking: 200
Season Tickets: £40.00
Match Prices: Adults £3.50 Children/OAPs £1.00
Membership: £40.00
Training Nights: Tuesdays and Thursdays

LIVERPOOL ST HELENS F.C.

MATCH BY MATCH PLAYERS BY POSITION

Higgins	Walker	Simms K	Simms N	Jones	Wellens	Elroy	Gill	Whittle	Hudsons	Hughes S	Jackson	Hughes N	Gaskell	Hendry	Davies	Lupton	Grigg	Williams I	Sephton	Bettinson	Wood	O'Keefe
15	14	13	12	11	10	9	1	2	3	4	5	6	7	8								
15	14		12	11	10	9	1	2	3	4		6	7	8	13	5						
10	14	13		11		9	1		3	4		6		8	12	5	2			15	7	
15	14			11	10	9	1		3	4		6		8	13	5	2			12	7	
10		13	14			9	3			4		6		8	12	5	2	7	15			
10		12	11			9	3			4	R	6		8	13	5	2	7	15			
15	14	13			10	9	3	2		4		6		8	12			7				
10	14	13					3	2	1	4		6			12	8		7	11	15		
10	14	13		11		9	1			4		6			12	8	2	7	15		3	5
15	R	13	14		10	9	1			4		6			12	8	2	7	11	R	3	5
15		13	14		10		1			4		7			12	8	2		11		6	3
15	14	12			13					4		6				8	2	7	11		3	
R			14	12			1			4					13	8	2	7	11		6	3
15	14	13			10		1			4					12	8	2	7	11		6	3
15	14	13					1			4					12	8	2	7	11		6	3
15	11	13			10			1		4					12	8	2	7	14		6	3
15	11	13			10		3	1		4	R	6			12	8	2	7	14			
15	11	13			10		1			4		7			12	8	2		14		6	3

Also Played: M Lawson No 11 match 5; S Metcalfe No 1 matches 5, ; C Harrison R, match 6, No 1 match 7; N Preston R match 6; C Walker No 11 match 7; D Dahinton No 5 matches 7, 8, 11, 15, 16; S Humphreys R matches 12, 15, 17, 18, No 15 match 13; C Hayes No 9 match 8; N Gregory No 10 matches 12, 13, 15; D Shove No 1 match 12;

Courage League Records 1994-95

League Debuts: N Jones, D Jackson, M Lawson, S Metcalfe, C Walker, C Hayes, S O'Keefe, M Liddle, S Humphreys, N Gregory, D Shove
Players used: 34
Ever Presents S Hughes

● Andy Higgin resumed his kicking duties with the departure of Simon Mason to Newcastle Gosforth. Higgin broke Mason's record for points in a season scoring 155 to Mason's 140

	Pts	T	C	P	D	App	Ave
A Higgin	155	4	24	27	2	17	9.12
S Mason	140	3	16	30	1	15	9.33

● Higgin also broke Mason's record of 16 conversions in a season. Higgin, who was finishing top of the points scoring list for the third time now holds the club's career records for points, conversions, penalties and drop goals

● Winger Mark Sephton tops the try scoring list for a third consecutive season and 5th in total. His 7 tries sees his career total go up to 35, 25 more than the next on the list Kevin Simms and Graham Eldoy who both have 10

● Higgin twice equalled Sephton and Dean Crompton's record of 20 points in a match before finally setting a new mark in the game at home to Aspatria. In that game Higgin managed 22 points from a try, 4 conversions and 3 penalties.

LIVERPOOL ST HELENS F.C.

COURAGE LEAGUE STATISTICS
compiled by Steve McCormack

Season	Div	P	W	D	L	F	T	C	P	D	A	T	C	P	D	Most Points	Most Tries
1987-88	2	11	8	1	2	154	18	8	19	3	97	10	6	13	2	34 Tosh Askew	3 Ian Gibbons. John Shinwell
1988-89	1	11	1	0	10	116	9	4	22	2	254	37	20	22	0	55 Tosh Askew	3 Brendan Hanavan
1989-90	2	11	8	2	1	154	20	7	18	2	106	12	5	14	2	66 Tosh Askew	6 Mark Sephton
1990-91	1	12	0	0	12	88	9	5	13	1	349	57	35	16	1	31 Andy Higgins	2 Mark Sephton. Peter Buckton
1991-92	2	12	0	0	12	87	14	5	7	0	418	65	37	27	1	26 Paul Ramsden	4 Mark Elliott
1992-93	3	11	5	0	6	203	22	12	19	4	130	13	4	18	1	98 Andy Higgins	8 Mark Sephton
1993-94	4	18	11	1	6	396	44	22	43	1	275	25	12	37	5	140 Simon Mason	9 Mark Sephton
1994-95	4	18	10	3	5	374	44	26	30	4	243	27	15	26		155 Andy Higgins	7 Mark Sephton
TOTALS		104	43	7	54	1372	180	89	171	17	1872	246	134	173	12		

BIGGEST WIN	**Home:** 77-5 v Aspatria 13.3.93 CL3	**Away:** 31-5 v Broughton Park 23.10.93 CL4
BIGGEST DEFEAT	**Home:** 6-49 v Morely 14.3.92 CL2	**Away:** 4-76 Newcastle Gosforth 29.2.92 CL2
MOST TRIES in a match	**For:** 12 v Aspatria 13.3.93	**Against:** 13 v Newcastle Gosforth 29.2.92
MOST CONSECUTIVE	**Wins:** 6	**Defeats:** 24
MOST APPEARANCES	**Forward:**	**Back:**
MOST CONSECUTIVE APPEARANCES		
CONSECUTIVE SCORING MATCHES	**Tries:** 3 Nick Walker	
	Points: 14 Andy Higgin	

	IN A SEASON	IN A CAREER	IN A MATCH
MOST POINTS	155 Andy Higgin 1994-95 CL4	340 Andy Higgin 1990-95	22 Andy Higgin v Aspatria 1.4.95 Home CL4
MOST TRIES	9 Mark Sephton 1993-94 CL4	34 Mark Sephton 1989-95	4 Mark Sephton v Aspatria 13.3.93 Home CL3
MOST CONVERSIONS	24 Andy Higgin 1994-95 CL4	44 Andy Higgin 1990-95	7 Andy Higgin v Aspatria 13.3.93 Home CL3
MOST PENALTIES	30 Simon Mason 1993-94 CL4	68 Andy Higgin 1990-95	5 Tosh Askew v Bedford 30.4.88 Away CL2 v Moseley 26.11.88 Away CL1 Simon Mason v Sudbury 18.12.93 Home CL4
MOST DROP GOALS	4 Andy Higgin 1992-93 CL4	6 Andy Higgin 1990-95	2 Nick Simms v Blackheath 9.1.88 Home CL2 Tosh Askew v Headingley 14.10.89 Home CL2

LONDON WELSH R.F.C.

NICKNAME: **FOUNDED:** 1885

CLUB OFFICIALS

President
Kelvin Bryon
Chairman
Ernie Williams
Club Secretary
Pete Taylor
Ensign House, Brighton Road,
Addlestone, Surrey KT15 1PG
Tel: (H) 01344 842070 (W) 01932 857433
Fixtures Secretary
Colin Bosley
21 Ellesmere Avenue, London NW7 3EX
Tel: (H) 0181 9060799
Press Officer
Allan Price
Tel: (H) 01483 472944 (W) 0171 8157924

Review of the Season

Welsh dreams of promotion were finally realised in the most dramatic fashion. It really did seem that the Welsh would go through the season undefeated, yet not to be promoted. But on the final day of the season, Lydney suffered an agonising defeat at Henley, and with the Welsh winning at Met. Police, the fifth division title and promotion were theirs. In truth, the Welsh were comprehensively the best side in the division, scoring 146 points more than their nearest challengers and conceding fewer points than any other side. In fact, the Welsh total of 409 points, at more than 34 a game, was the best in the National Leagues. They were also the only undefeated league side in England. Flair with discipline was a hallmark of London Welsh play in 1994-95. It not only helped them win promotion, but also overcame Hawick (44-15), who finished fourth in the Scottish first division and were fielding their full league side, and second division champions Saracens (31-27), who were also at stength. There were some monumental victories. The league defeat of Sudbury (88-7) provided the greatest margin of victory in the history of National League rugby, while Maidstone were beaten by 92-6, to set up a new scoring record in a domestic game.

Colin Charvis had a magnificent season at Number Eight. He was selected to the Welsh 2000 Elite squad, which identifies young players with great international potential, and also scored 19 tries, which broke John Taylor's long-standing try-scoring record for a forward. Four players scored more than ten tries, with young David Lubliner (15) showing fine form on the right wing. Rhodri Phillips and Michael Dawes each scored 11 tries. The goal-kicking of new fly-half Craig Raymond was a real bonus for a club not noted for their place-kicking prowess. He played in 18 games, scored in every one of them, and compiled 240 points. During the second half of the season, his kicking was world class, with 50 goals from 68 attempts, at 74%.

Back: Mike Gosling (Playing Controller), Peter Shaw, Guy Leleu, Colin Charvis, Dai Harries, Neil Thomas, Graeme Peacock, Lee Thomas, Mark Herbert, Nigel Rees (Coach), Front: Rhodri Phillips, Michael Dawes, Richard Thomas, Andy Tucker, Alistair Sandilands, Robbie Jones, Huw Roberts, Peter Walters, Gerallt Phillips
Colours: Scarlet, white shorts   **Change Colours**: Green

LONDON WELSH R.F.C.

COURAGE LEAGUE
MATCH DETAILS 1994-95

No	Date	Opponents	Ven	Result	Scorers
1	Sep 13	Tabard	H	W 37-7	R Phillips (1T 3C 2P) Nicholas (T) Dawes (2T) Charvis (T)
2	Sep 24	Henley	A	W 34-6	R Phillips (2C 1P) Dawes (1T 1C) Sandilands (T) Charvis (2T) Nicholas (T)
3	Oct 1	Walsham	H	W 31-6	Dawes (5C) Newcombe (T) Tucker (T) Charvis (T) L Thomas (T) Leleu (T)
4	Oct 15	Weston S Mare	A	W 22-6	R Phillips (1C) Newcombe (T) Dawes (T) Nicholas (T) Walters (T)
5	Oct 22	Basingstoke	H	W 23-8	Dawes (1C 2P) Sandilands (T) Charvis (T) C Davies (T)
6	Oct 29	Camborne	A	D 21-21	Dawes (1C 3P) Nicholas (T) Charvis (T)
7	Jan 7	High Wycombe	H	W 69-6	Raymond (2T 4C 2P) Newcombe (2T) Lubliner (2T) Harries (2T) R Thomas (T) L Thomas (T) Charvis (T)
8	Jan 14	Lydney	A	D 17-17	Raymond (4P) Enoch (T)
9	Feb 11	Berryhill	H	W 29-15	Raymond (2C 5P) Newcombe (T) Lubliner (T)
10	Mar 4	Barking	A	W 19-15	Raymond (1C 4P) Tucker (T)
11	Mar 25	Sudbury	H	W 88-7	Raymond (7C 4P) Dawes (1C) S Thomas (T) Tucker (T) Lubliner (4T) Pike (3T) R Phillips (2T) Herbert (T)
12	Apr 8	Met Police	A	W 19-13	Raymond (C 4P) S Thomas (T)

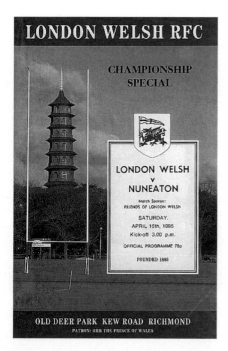

PROGRAMME DETAILS
Price: 75p
Pages: 36

Advertising Rates: £400.00 page

CLUB & GROUND DETAILS
London Welsh R.F.C., Old Deer Park, Kew Road, Richmond, Surrey TW9 2AZ
Telephone: 0181 9401604
Fax: 0181 9402368

Total Capacity: 7,200
Seated: 1,200
Standing: 6,000
Simple Directions to Ground: Half mile north of Richmond BR Station, adjacent to south side of Kew Gardens
Nearest Railway Station: Richmond (BR and Underground)
Car Parking: 200
Season Tickets: £50.00 Adults £20.00 OAPs/Children
Match Prices: £4.00 Adults £1.50 OAPs/Children
Membership: £50.00 Seniors £20.00 Juniors/OAPs
Training Nights: Tuesdays and Thursdays

LONDON WELSH R.F.C.

MATCH BY MATCH PLAYERS BY POSITION

Shaw	Pike	Dawes	Leleu	Sandilands	Phillips K	Nicholas	Herbert	Tucker	Thomas R	Peacock	Thomas N	Thomas L	Newcombe	Charvis	Harries	Walters	Phillips G	Jones	Lubliner	Richards	Raymond	Pritchard	Thomas
15	14	13	12	11	10	9	1	2	3	4	5	6	7	8	R								
15		13	12	11	10	9	1	2	3	4	5	6	7	8		14							
15		13	12	11	10		1	2	3	4	5	6	7	8	R	14	9						
		12		11	10	9	1	2	3	4	5	6	7	8		14		15	13				
		10	12	11		9	1	2	3	4	5	6	7	8		14	R	15	13				
		10	12		15	9	1	2	3	4	5	6	7	8	R	14			13				
15	11	13						2	3		5	6	7	8	4		9		14	12	10	1	
15	1	13						2	3	4	5		7	8			9		14	12	10	1	
	11				15		1	2	3	4	5		8	7			9		14	12	10		1
	11	13			15		1	2	3	4	5	6	7	8			9		14	12	10		
	11	13			15		1	2	3	4			7	8	6		9		14		10		1
	11	13			15		1	2	3	8					4		9		14		10		1

Also Played: C Davies R match 5; P Enoch R match 7, No 6 matches 8, 9; R Westlake No 6 match 12; M Russell No 7 match 12; D Davies No 5 matches 11, 12.

Courage League Records 1994-95

Players used: 28
Ever Presents 2 A Tucker. R Thomas
Most appearances: 60 Graeme Peacock

● Record breaking season for Welsh as they finally won their way back into the top 4 divisions on the last day of the league season

● They scored more points, tries and penalties than ever before whilst conceding a record low number of points and tries

● New stand off Craig Raymond scored an incredible 109 points in just 6 games – easily the quickest 100 points in Courage history and gave him an average of over 18 points per match against a record for a player scoring 100 points in a season. He missed the first half of the season awaiting registration

● Those 109 points moved him into 3rd place on the club's all time list

	Pts	T	C	P	D	App	Ave
B Phillips	140	12	14	16	3	41	3.41
M Hamlin	111	2	28	15	-	12	9.25
C Raymond	109	2	15	23	-	6	18.17

● No 8 Colin Charvis becomes the club's top forward try scorer passing Andy Tucker's record of 12. Charvis finishes the season on 16 – 14 ahead and third place on the all time list

	Tries	Apps	Strike Rate
M Bell	26	33	1.65
M Douglas	18	41	2.27
C Charvis	16	31	1.93

● Forward Graeme Peacock passes Julian Davies' club record of 53 appearances, ending the season on 60. Peacock is one of those rare breed of forwards who also kicks goals – his 81 career points include 10 conversions and 6 penalties

LONDON WELSH R.F.C.

COURAGE LEAGUE STATISTICS
compiled by Steve McCormack

Season	Div	P	W	D	L	F	T	C	P	D	A	T	C	P	D	Most Points	Most Tries
1987-88	2	11	3	2	6	153	24	6	14	1	185	23	6	25	2	25 Nathan Humphreys	5 Richard Wintle
1988-89	2	11	1	1	9	125	18	7	13	0	235	32	16	23	2	23 Nathan Humphreys	4 Guy Leleu
1989-90	3	11	3	0	8	141	19	7	15	2	179	20	12	21	4	25 Lee Evans	3 Gareth Hughes Mark Thomas Jim Williams
1990-91	D4S	12	7	0	5	235	34	15	22	1	165	16	10	26	1	30 Gareth Hughes	6 Mickey Bell
1991-92	D4S	12	9	0	3	292	49	21	16	2	160	15	8	25	3	43 Graeme Peacock	7 Mark Douglas. Steve Thomas
1992-93	D4S	12	10	0	2	353	50	29	15	0	170	19	9	18	1	111 Mike Hamlin	6 Andy Tucker Mickey Bell
1993-94	D4S	12	5	3	4	216	25	11	22	1	140	9	4	28	1	41 David Shufflebotham	6 Peter Walters
1994-95	D4S	12	10	2	0	409	52	28	31	0	126	8	4	25	1	107 Craig Raymond	7 Colin Charvis David Lubliner
TOTALS		93	48	8	37	1924	271	124	148	7	1360	142	69	191	15		

BIGGEST WIN   **Home:** 88-7 v Sudbury 25.3.95 D5S   **Away:** 49-6 v Sidcup 16-11-91 D4S

BIGGEST DEFEAT   **Home:** 3-28 v Lydney 18.11.90 CL3   **Away:** 4-37 v Saracens 22.10.88 CL2

MOST TRIES in a match   **For:** 12 v Sudbury 25.3.95 D5S   **Against:** 6 v Saracens 22.10.88 CL2

MOST CONSECUTIVE   **Wins:** 9   **Defeats:** 6

MOST APPEARANCES   **Forward:** 60 Graeme Peacock   **Back:** 52 Guy Leleu

MOST CONSECUTIVE APPEARANCES   33 Graeme Peacock

CONSECUTIVE SCORING MATCHES   **Tries:** 5 Mickey Bell (Twice)

Points: 7 Graeme Peacock. Mike Hamlin

	IN A SEASON	IN A CAREER	IN A MATCH
MOST POINTS	111 Mike Hamlin 1992-93 D4S	140 Rhodri Phillips 1990-95	26 Craig Raymond v Sudbury 25.3.95 D5S
MOST TRIES	7 Mark Douglas and Steve Thomas 1991-92 D4S Colin Charvis and David Lubliner 1994-95 D5S	20 Mickey Bell 1989-94	4 Mickey Bellv North Walsham 13.10.90 Home D4S David Lubliner v Sudbury 25.3.95 D5S
MOST CONVERSIONS	28 Mike Hamlin 1992-93 D4S	28 Mike Hamlin 1992-93	7 Craig Raymond v Sudbury 25.3.95 Home D5S
MOST PENALTIES	23 Craig Raymond 1994-95 D5S	23 Craig Raymond 1994-95	5 Lee Evans v Met. Police 25.4.92 Home D4S David Shufflebotham v Weston Super Mare 26.11.93 Home D4S Rhodri Phillips v Berry hill 29.1.94 Away D5S Craig Raymond v Berry hill 11.2.95 Home D5S
MOST DROP GOALS	2 Lee Evans 1989-90 D3 Rhodri Phillips 1991-92 D4S	3 Rhodri Phillips 1990-95	1 on 7 occasions by 4 players

PLYMOUTH ALBION R.F.C.

NICKNAME: Albion   **FOUNDED:** 1876

CLUB OFFICIALS

President
Robert Hicks M.P.
Chairman
Clive Cross
Club Secretary
Roger Bowden
7 Winnow Close, Staddiscombe,
Plymouth, Devon PL9 9RZ
Tel: (H) 01752 491642
Fixtures Secretary
Andy Watts
52 Brook Road, Ivybridge, Devon
Tel: (H) 01752 896293
Press Officer
Paddy Marsh
Tel: 01752 794981

Review of the Season

Nothing would be more worrying for fans in general if PLYMOUTH ALBION were to drop out of the main swing of the National Leagues, but in the past campaign only one point separated them from Askeans and a descent into one of the regional fifth leagues and a last ditch gallant loss at Havant was not a final disaster because both the Kent club and Broughton Park lost on the same day and went down.

The Pilkington Cup brought no relief from gloom as an initial visit to Basingstoke was enough to see their departure (a close 13-10 scoreline).

Where can encouragement be found to prevent the South West from becoming a rugby backwater? Playing consistency came from top scorer and fly-half Martin Thompson, Richard Thompson at fullback and the wing Les Oman, with brave forward efforts from hooker Steve Pooley, the back-row men Roger Bailey and looseahead Stewart Coleman. Can they with others turn the tide?

Colours: Cherry, green and white   **Change Colours**: Green

PLYMOUTH ALBION R.F.C.

COURAGE LEAGUE
MATCH DETAILS 1994-95

No	Date	Opponents	Ven	Result	Scorers
1	Sep 10	Reading	A	L 17-27	Slade (2C) M Thompson (1P) Vallence (T) Osborne (T)
2	Sep 17	Rotherham	H	L 15-27	M Thompson (4P 1D)
3	Sep 24	Liverpool St H	A	L 5-24	Harrison (T)
4	Oct 1	Askeans	H	W 29-6	M Thompson (1T 3C 1P) Vallence (T) Walklin (T) Osborne (T)
5	Oct 15	Broughton P	H	L 21-24	M Thompson (1C 3P) M Goldsmith (T) Walklin (T)
6	Oct 22	Redruth	A	L 14-25	M Thompson (3P) Burnham (T)
7	Oct 29	Leeds	H	L 13-17	M Thompson (1C 1P 1D) Pennell (T)
8	Nov 12	Aspatria	A	L 8-26	M Thompson (1P)Trott (T)
9	Jan 7	Havant	H	D 17-17	R Thompson (D) Walklin (T) Oman (3P)
10	Jan 14	Reading	H	W 31-30	R Thompson (T) Harrison (T) Trott (1C 1P) Walklin (T) Cameron (T) Oman (2P)
11	Feb 25	Liverpool St H	H	D 17-17	M Thompson (2C 1P) Oman (T) Saunders (T)
12	Mar 4	Askeans	A	L 8-15	M Thompson (1P) Oman (T)
13	Mar 11	Rotherham	A	L 23-35	M Thompson (2C 3P) Oman (T) Harrison (T)
14	Mar 25	Broughton P	A	L 9-19	M Thompson (3P)
15	Apr 1	Redruth	H	W 24-8	M Thompson (2P) R thompson (1D) Oman (2T) Harrison (T)
16	Apr 8	Leeds	A	L 25-30	M Thompson (2C 2P) Burnham (T) M Goldsmith (T) Bailey (T)
17	Apr 15	Aspatria	H	W 23-11	M Thompson (1T 1C 2P) Walklin (T) M Scott (T)
18	Apr 29	Havant	A	L 25-27	M Thompson (1C 1P) Oman (T) Pooley (2T) Walklin (T)

THE
ALBION
—Review—
SPONSORED BY

Match Day Programme
AND
Official Journal of Plymouth Albion R.F.C.

COURAGE
NATIONAL
LEAGUE
DIVISION 4

LUCKY PROGRAMME
NO. 225

PROGRAMME DETAILS

Pages: 48

Advertising Rates: Full page £200.00 half page £100.00
quarter page £50.00

CLUB & GROUND DETAILS

Plymouth Albion RFC, Beacon Park, Peverell, Plymouth
PL2 2JP
Telephone: 01752 772924

Total Capacity: 2,500
Seated: 500
Standing: 2,000
Simple Directions to Ground: On approaching Plymouth
follow the Plymouth Argyle F.C. signs 200 yds past Safeway
Superstore at 2nd set of traffic lights turn right.
Nearest Railway Station: North Road Plymouth
Car Parking: 70 both ends of ground
Season Tickets:
Match Prices: Adults £3.50 Children/OAPs £1.25
Membership: £10.00
Training Nights: Mondays and Wednesdays

PLYMOUTH ALBION R.F.C.

MATCH BY MATCH PLAYERS BY POSITION

Slade	Trinder	Vallence	Lejeume	Oman	Thompson	Thomas	Bullock	Pooley	Smith	Harrison	Osborne	Goldsmith M	Goldsmith I	Daniel R	Bailey	Saunders	Cameron	Walkin	Burnham	Trott	Coleman	Thompson	Stansfield
15	14	13	11	10	9	1	2	3	4	5	6	7	8										
15	14	13	12	11	10	9	2	3	4	5				7	8	6							
15	14	13	12	11	10	9	2	3	4	5				7	8	1	6						
11	13			10	9	1	2	3	4	5				7	8		6	14	12				
15	13		11	10			2	R	4		8				6	3		14	12	9	1		
11	12			10		3	2	R	4		8				6			14	13	9	1		
12				10			2	3	4		8				6		7	14	13	9	1		
			12	11	10		2		4	5	8			7	6	3		14	13	9	1	15	
			11		9		2	6	4	5	8			7		3		14	12		1	10	13
			11		9		2		4	5	8				6	3	7	14	12	10	1	15	13
			11	10	9		2		4		6			8		3	7	14	12		1	15	13
			11	10	9		2		4					7	8	3	6	14	12		1	15	13
	13		11	10	9	3	2		4		6			8			7	14			1	15	12
	13			10	9	3	2		4	5	8				6	R		14	11		1	15	12
	13		11	10			2		4	5	8			R	6	3		14		9	1	15	12
	13		14	10			2			8	5				6	3	7	11		9	1	15	12
	13		11	10			2		4	8	5				6	3		14		9	1	15	12
			11	10			2		4	8	5					3	R	14	13	9	1	15	12

Also Played: I Davies No 1 match 2; J Underwood R match 3; A Turner No 15 matches 4, 6, 7, 9; C Passmore No 5 matches 5, 11, 12, 13; M Manton R match 14 No 4 match 16; M Banner R matches 7, 16, 17; M Pennell No 11 match 7; T Chapman No 5 matches 6, 7; M Scott No 7 matches 5, 6, 14, 15, 17, 18, R match 8

Courage League Records 1994-95

League Debuts: D Le Jeume, R Daniel, H Turner, A Burnham, P Stansfield, M Manton
Players used: 31
Ever Presents: 1 No 5 Pooley
Most appearances: 54 Nick Saunders

● Prop Nick Saunders passes Ian Russell's club record of 53 appearances on the last day of the season to end up on 54 whilst Steve Walkin passes Nick Leonard's record appearances for a back, again on the last day of the season 46 to 45.

● Stand off Martin Thompson breaks Mark Slade's career record of 169 points and becomes the first Plymouth player to pass 200 points. He also broke Martin Livesey's 7 year record of 108 points in a season.

	Pts	T	C	P	D	App	Ave
1987-88 Thompson	129	2	13	29	2	16	8.06
1994-95 Livesey	108	2	23	17	1	9	12.00

● Steve Walkin tops the try scoring list for the third time, 1st in 4 years though. He extends his club career record to 25 and with 108 points moves into third place on the all time points list equal with Martin Livesey

PLYMOUTH ALBION R.F.C.

COURAGE LEAGUE STATISTICS
compiled by Steve McCormack

Season	Div	P	W	D	L	F	T	C	P	D	A	T	C	P	D	Most Points	Most Tries
1987-88	3	11	8	0	3	276	41	23	21	1	125	11	3	22	3	108 Martin Livesey	8 Kevin Nurns
1988-89	3	11	11	0	0	311	47	27	19	4	89	5	3	18	3	101 Dominic Cundy	8 Steve Walklin
1989-90	2	11	5	0	6	206	32	15	16	0	164	17	12	21	3	36 Charlie Gabbitas	4 Ian Russell. Steve Walklin
1990-91	2	12	4	0	8	129	9	6	23	4	210	30	15	18	2	44 Kevin Thomas	2 Charlie Gabbitas
1991-92	2	12	3	0	9	153	16	7	25	0	209	23	12	27	4	62 Mark Slade	2 by 5 players
1992-93	3	11	0	0	11	130	16	4	13	1	305	38	20	22	3	26 Martin Thompson	3 Mark Haimes
1993-94	4	18	9	0	9	286	31	13	31	4	416	47	26	41	2	90 Martin Thompson	5 Roger Bailey
1994-95	4	18	4	2	12	324	35	16	35	4	381	42	21	38	5	129 Martin Thompson	6 Steve Walklin
TOTALS		104	44	2	58	1815	227	111	183	18	1899	213	112	207	25		

BIGGEST WIN — **Home:** 57-3 v Met. Police 26.11.88. Cl3 — **Away:** 46-3 v Birmingham 17.10.87 CL3

BIGGEST DEFEAT — **Home:** 3-35 v Havant 13-3-93 CL3 — **Away:** 21-54 v Newcastle Gosforth 28.3.92 CL2

MOST TRIES in a match — **For**: 9 v Birmingham 17.10.87 CL3 — **Against:**

MOST CONSECUTIVE — **Wins:** 11 — **Defeats:** 16

MOST APPEARANCES — **Forward:** 51 Nick Saunders — **Back:** 46 Steve Walklin

MOST CONSECUTIVE APPEARANCES — 43 Kevin Turton 12.9.87 to 23.3.91

CONSECUTIVE SCORING MATCHES — **Tries:** 3 by 7 players

Points: 11 Martin Thompson

	IN A SEASON	IN A CAREER	IN A MATCH
MOSTPOINTS	129 Martin Thompson 1994-95 CL4	260 Martin Thompson 1989-95	25 Dominic Cundy v Metropolitan Police 26.11.88 CL3
MOST TRIES	8 Kevin Norris 1987-88 CL3	25 Steve Walklin 1987-95	4 Steve Walklin v Birmingham 17.10.87 Away CL3 Ian Russell v Fylde 31.10.87 Away CL3
MOST CONVERSIONS	23 Martin Livesey 1987-88 CL3	26 Martin Thompson 1989-95	8 Dominic Cundy v Metropolitan Police 26.11.88 Home CL3
MOST PENALTIES	29 Martin Thompson 1994-95 Cl4	54 Martin Thompson 1989-95	6 Mark Slade v Bedford 14.12.91 CL2
MOST DROP GOALS	3 Dominic Cundy 1988-89 CL3 Martin Thompson 1989-95	7 Martin Thompson 1989-95	Dominic Cundy v Wakefield 10.9.88 Home CL2

REDRUTH R.F.C.

NICKNAME: The Reds   **FOUNDED:** 1875

CLUB OFFICIALS

President
W J Bishop O.B.E.
Chairman
Gerard Curtis
Club Secretary
Ivor Horscroft
Silver Fields, Chapel Street, Redruth
TR15 2DI
Tel: (H & W) 01209 215941
Fixtures Secretary
Jerry Penna
Chy-Auhlon, North Country, Redruth
TR16 4BZ
Tel: (H) 01209 211520 (W) 01872
322000 ext 3221

Colours: Red shirt, white shorts

Review of the Season

The future of rugby's credibility in the South West depends on clubs like REDRUTH and a few others, so a final League Four position of seventh out of ten does not encourage optimism, even though at the last count they were five points clear of a relegation place, even though the ultimate game saw them lose 32-19 at Aspatria. Survival from their opening Pilkington Cup match at Askenas (19-12) followed by a 31-0 rout at Blackheath will reinforce the view that improvements in playing form are needed.

The best of their players last season were fullback and wing Simon Blake, who was top points scorer, the wing Andy Knowles was a strong runner and the pack played gallantly, but does this add up to a revival in Cornwall?

Fans will wait, see and hope.

Change Colours: Black shirt

REDRUTH R.F.C.

COURAGE LEAGUE
MATCH DETAILS 1994-95

No	Date	Opponents	Ven	Result		Scorers
1	Sep 10	Havant	A	L	16-23	Blake (2P) Gomer (T) Cowie (T)
2	Sep 17	Reading	H	L	23-28	Blake (2C 3P) Cowie (T) G Williams (T)
3	Sep 24	Rotherham	A	L	17-31	Blake (2C 1P) Wilkins (T) D Williams (T)
4	Oct 1	Liverpool St H	H	D	11-11	Blake (2P) C Whitworth (T)
5	Oct 15	Askeans	A	W	19-12	Blake (1C 3P 1D) S Whitworth (T)
6	Oct 22	Plymouth	H	W	25-14	Blake (1C 6P) Wills (T)
7	Oct 29	Broughton P	A	W	14-8	Blake (2P 1D) Knowles (T)
8	Nov 12	Leeds	A	L	0-17	
9	Jan 7	Aspatria	H	W	18-23	Blake (1T 1C 2P) Wyatt (T)
10	Jan 14	Havant	H	D	22-22	Blake (1C 5P) Sullivan (T)
11	Feb 11	Reading	A	L	11-29	Blake (2P) Yelland (T)
12	Feb 25	Rotherham	H	L	13-19	Blake (1T 1P) Hambly (T)
13	Mar 4	Liverpool St H	A	L	21-49	Blake (3C) S Whitworth (T) Sullivan (T) G Williams (T)
14	Mar 25	Askeans	H	W	28-16	Blake (2C 3P) Douch (T) Knowles (T) Wilkins (T)
15	Apr 1	Plymouth	A	L	8-24	Blake (1T 1P)
16	Apr 8	Broughton P	H	W	24-14	Blake (3C 1P) Congo (T) Yelland (T) Hambly (T)
17	Apr 15	Leeds	H	W	20-13	Blake (1T 1C 1P) Knowle (T) Cook (T)
18	Apr 29	Aspatria	A	L	19-32	Blake (1C 4P) Hussey (T)

PROGRAMME DETAILS

Advertising Rates: £350.00 full page

CLUB & GROUND DETAILS

Redruth A.F.C., Recreation Ground, Redruth TR15 1SY
Telephone: 01209 215520
Fax: 01209 314438

Total Capacity: 15,670
Seated: 670
Standing: 15,000
Simple Directions to Ground: A30 west through Cornwall,
leave at Redruth exit over twin roundabout, past Avers
garage, ground signposted on left
Nearest Railway Station: Redruth
Car Parking: 100 at ground
Season Tickets: £22.00 Adults £15.00 Children/OAPs
Match Prices: £1.00
Membership: £5.00
Training Nights: Mondays and Wednesdays

REDRUTH R.F.C.

MATCH BY MATCH PLAYERS BY POSITION

Thomas	Gomez	Wilkins	Whitworth	Williams D	Blake	Whitworth	Cowie	Rutter	Tonkin	O'Sullivan	Cook	Williams G	O'Dwyer	Hawkin	Hussey	Douch	Yelland	Hambly	Knowles	Clifton Griffiths	Wills	Sullivan	Congo
15	14	13	12	11	10	9	1	2	3	4	5	6	7	8	R	R							
15	14	13	12	11	10	9	1	2	3	6	5	8	7		R		4						
15	14	13	12	11	10		1	2	3	6	5	8	7		9		4						
15		13		11	10	9	1	2	3	5	6	7	8		14		4	12					
15		13	12		10	9	1		3	5	6		8	11			4		14	2	7	R	
15		13	12		10	9	1		3	5	6		8		14		4		11	2	7		
15			12		10				3	5	6		8		9		4	13	11	2	7		
15			12		10	9			3	5	6	7	8		14			13	11	2			
		13			10	9			3	5	6		8	11		1	4	12	14	2	7		
15		13		11	10	9			3	5	6		8			1	4	12	14	2	7		
15			12		10	14	9		3	5	6		8			1	4	13	11	2	7		
			12		10	15	R		3	5			8		9	1	4	13	14		7		6
15			12		10	14			3	5	6		8		9	1	4	13	11		7		
15			12		10	14	9		3	5			8			1	4	13	11				6
15			12		10	14	9		3	5			8			1	4	13	11				6
15		13			10	14	9	R	3	5	6		8			1	4	12	11		7		
		13			10	14	15	9	1	3	7	5	6	8			4	12	11				
			12		10	9		2	3	4			7	8	14	1	5		11				6

Also Played: J Wyatt No 14 match 7, No 15 matches 9,18; M Bryant No 1 Match 7; P Vickery No 1 match 8; M Phillips R match 9; D Penberthy No 7 match 8; M Stearn No 11 match 12, B Tregoning No 2 matches 12,1= 13, 14, 15; T Cowling R matches 13, 15; B Andrew No 7 matches 14, 15, No 2 matches 16, 17; E Slick R match 15; T Mead R match 16, No 13 match 18; C Sibwell R match 17

Courage League Records 1994-95

League Debuts: S O'Dwyer, N Yelland, N Hambly, P Vickery, A Sullivan, P Congo
Players used: 32
Ever Presents 1 S Blake
Most appearances: 71 Tony Cook

● Stand off/winger/full back Simon Blake re-wrote Redruth's scoring records. He smashed his own record of points in a season

	Pts	T	C	P	D	App	Ave
1994-95	179	4	18	39	2	18	9.94
1990-91	95	3	16	17	-	11	8.64

● Blake topped the points scoring list for a fourth time. He equalled his own record of 20 points in a match in the game v Plymouth at home in October. He previously did this in Redruth's first ever league game back in September 1987. In the match above v Plymouth he set a record of 6 penalties in a match

● Winger Andy Knowles, who scored 2 tries in that first ever league match, extended his club tries scoring record to 24 from 57 matches

● Second row forward Tony Cook extended his club record for consecutive appearances to 61 before missing the match v Broughton Park last October with a knee injury. Cook ends the season with 70 appearances just one ahead of Stuart Whitworth

REDRUTH R.F.C.

COURAGE LEAGUE STATISTICS

compiled by Steve McCormack

Season	Div	P	W	D	L	F	T	C	P	D	A	T	C	P	D	Most Points	Most Tries
1987-88	SW1	10	9	0	1	214	37	12	10	4	107	10	5	18	1		
1988-89	ALS	10	6	1	3	136	19	9	18		81	6	3	17	-		
1989-90	ALS	10	7	0	3	151	20	7	18	1	84	6	3	18	-		
1990-91	D4S	12	12	0	0	225	34	16	19	0	79	7	13	13	1		
1991-92	3	12	6	1	5	155	14	3	28	3	123	10	1	23	4		
1992-93	3	11	7	2	2	175	17	9	23	1	125	13	3	18	0		
1993-94	3	18	2	0	16	178	9	2	41	2	488	63	34	33	2		
1994-95	4	18	6	2	10	309	30	18	39	2	387	44	16	39	6		
TOTALS		101	55	6	40	1543	180	76	190	13	1474	159	68	179	14		

BIGGEST WIN	**Home:** 42-6 v St Ives 19.9.87 SW1	**Away:** 39-6 v Salisbury 23.9.89 ALS
BIGGEST DEFEAT	**Home:** 9-39 v Rosslyn Park 26.3.94 CL3	**Away:** 13-60 v Coventry 30.4.94 CL3
MOST TRIES in a match	**For:** 7 v Salisbury 23.9.89 ALS	**Against:** 10 v Fylde 9.4.94
MOST CONSECUTIVE	**Wins:** 16	**Defeats:** 9
MOST APPEARANCES	**Forward:** 71 Tony Cook	**Back:** 70 Stu Whitworth
MOST CONSECUTIVE APPEARANCES	61 Tony Cook 30.3.90 to 22.10.94	
CONSECUTIVE SCORING MATCHES	**Tries:** 3 John Willis Andy Knowles, Marcel Gomez (twice	
	Points: 11 Kevin Thomas	

	IN A SEASON	IN A CAREER	IN A MATCH
MOST POINTS	179 Simon Blake 1994-95 CL4	409 Simon Blake 1987-95	
MOST TRIES	7 Jonathan Willis 1988-89 ALS	24 Andy Knowles 1987-95	
MOST CONVERSIONS	18 Simon Blake 1994-95 CL4	44 Simon Blake 1987-95	
MOST PENALTIES	39 Simon Blake 1994-95 CL4	88 Simon Blake 1987-95	
MOST DROP GOALS	4 Peter Bradley 1987-88 SW1	4 Peter Bradley 1987-88	

WALSALL R.F.C.

NICKNAME: **FOUNDED:** 1922

CLUB OFFICIALS

President
D H Peacock
Chairman
R M Harding
Club Secretary
S Caleb E Tillott
6 Lichfield Road, Sandhills, Walsall
Wood, Walsall WS9 9PE
Tel: (H) 01543 372667
Fixtures Secretary
M I Friar
8A Bacon Street, Walsall WS1 2DL
Tel: (H) 01922 36243 (W) 01788 541222
Press Officer
K H W Clews
Tel: 01902 631947

Review of the Season

Walsall's progressive achievements of recent years bore wonderful fruit with the clear-cut championship of Courage League 5 North, four other major titles and a host of new records, both club and individual.

The bare statistics are a telling story in themselves: in all games (just 32) came 1022 points, including 132 tries, 55 of them by wingers, of whom Jon Rowe, with 30 scores, and Malcolm Walker, 20 scores, finished 1st and 2nd in the Unisys National Tryscoring Chart.

Fly-half Richard Mills set a new club record of 312 points in 27 appearances and his full total of 369 points for the season, including 57 for Staffordshire, put him at the head of both Overall Scorers and Kickers in the Unisys Charts.

The Staffordshire Cup was retained and a unique Staffordshire Grand-Slam was completed by victories in the County Sevens, County Colts Cup and County Colts Sevens.

But beyond mere figures is the fact that it was all done in explosive, attractive, expansive style, not least in the twelve League matches, which produced 47 tries and 389 points for Walsall, despite mid-season setbacks with defeat at Stourbridge and a home draw with Kendal.

The loss at Stourbridge came the week after similarly disappointing departure from the Pilkington Cup for a second season running at the hands of Wharfedale at the 2nd Round stage, a defeat amply avenged later in the League with a tremendous 50-8 away victory soon after a record-breaking 61-0 away League demolition of Sheffield in which nine tries were scored before another eight at Wharfedale.

Of the seven defeats suffered by Walsall in all games, five coincided with County Championship matches when Walsall contributed ten players to Staffordshire and had nine others out nursing injuries.

Walsall's squad is very much home-grown, the League side still containing eight men who featured in Walsall's promotion from Midland Division One in 1989-9, but strengthened last season by the return to his home club of Barbarian and ex-England B captain Richard Moon and the arrival of RAF Combined Services back Steve Lazenby.

Colours: Scarlet jerseys, black shorts, scarlet stockings
Change Colours: Black shirts, (red collar and cuffs), black shorts, black stockings

WALSALL R.F.C.

COURAGE LEAGUE
MATCH DETAILS 1994-95

No	Date	Opponents	Ven	Result		Scorers
1	Sep 24	Barker's Butts	A	W	29-8	Mills (1C 4P) Walker (T) Rowe (T) Flynn (T)
2	Oct 1	Winnington Park	H	W	49-3	Mills (4C 2P) Pen Try Haley (T) Rowe (2T) Till G (2T) Moon (T)
3	Oct 15	Stourbridge	A	L	8-13	Walker (T) Mills (1P)
4	Oct 22	Hereford	H	W	40-6	Mills (4C 4P) Rowe (2T) Moon (T) Friar (T)
5	Oct 29	Stoke	A	W	30-11	Walker (T) Moon (T) Mills (C 5P D)
6	Jan 7	Kendal	H	D	8-8	Coleman (T) Mills (1P)
7	Jan 14	Nuneaton	A	W	27-11	Mills (1C 5P) Walker (T) Mills (T)
8	Feb 25	Sheffield	A	W	61-0	Mills (1T 5C 2P) Till G (3T) Till P (T) Walker (T) Lazenby (2T) Burns (T)
9	Mar 11	Birmingham S	H	W	33-3	Mills (4C) Pen Try Till G (T) Rowe (T) Walker (T) Tayler (T)
10	Mar 25	Wharfedale	A	W	50-8	Mills (5C) Till P (T) Rowe (3T) Till G (2T) Rose (2T)
11	Apr 1	Lichfield	H	W	25-19	Mills (1C 6P) Moon (T)
12	Apr 8	Preston	H	W	29-20	Mills (3C 1P) Rowe (2T) Till G (T) Rose (T)

PROGRAMME DETAILS

Pages: 44

Advertising Rates: £275 Full Page

CLUB & GROUND DETAILS

Walsall R.F.C., Broadway, (Delves Road), Walsall WS1 3JY
Telephone: 01922 26818

Total Capacity: 2,250
Seated: 250
Standing: 2,000
Simple Directions to Ground: From NE (A38/A461) almost into Walsall, take Ring Road left, after three roundabouts Ground first on right. Form NW (M6) From J9 follow sign left for Walsall and quickly fork right onto Ring Road, after three sets of more traffic lights, Ground fourth left. From S/SW (M5, M40/42, M1/6) head for M6/Jct 7, take sign for Walsall, after 2 miles take roundabout left onto Ring Road, Ground first on right
Nearest Railway Station: Walsall or Bescott
Car Parking: 100 adjacent to club
Season Tickets:
Match Prices: £3.00 (League and Cup)
Membership: £15.00
Training Nights: Tuesdays and Thursdays

WALSALL R.F.C.

MATCH BY MATCH PLAYERS BY POSITION

Friar	Rowe	Watson	Flynn	Walker	Mills	Moon	Tayler	Hayley	Jones	Harding	Ellis	Burns	Till G	Coleman	Rose	Tillott	Morgan	Lazenby	Till P	Stewart	Godfrey	King
15	14	13	12	11	10	9	1	2	3	4	5	6	7	8								
15	14		12	11	10	9	1	2	3	4	5		7	8	13	6						
15	14	13		11	10	9	1	2	3	4	5	6	7	8	12	R						
15	14	13		11	10	9	1	2	3	4	5	6	7	8	12							
15	14	13		11	10	9	1	2	3	4		6	7	8	12			5				
15	14	,11	10	9	1	2	3	4			6	7	8	12			13	5	R			
	14		12	11	10	9	1	2	3	4	6	7			13		15	8		5		
15	14			11	10	9	1	2	3	4	6	7	8	12			13	5				
15	14			11	10	9	1	2	3	4	6	7	8	12			13	5	9			
15	14			11	10	9	1	2	3	4	6	7	8	12			13	5				
15	14			11	10	9	1	2	3	4	6	7	8	12			13	5				
15	14			11	10	9	1	2	3	4	6	7	8	12			13	5				R

Courage League Records 1994-95

- A record breaking season for stand-off Richard Mills who smashed his previous seasonal best by 65 points. It also saw him break the club record for conversions and penalties with 29 and 31 respectively. The 164 was also a divisional record. This was Mills' 5th consecutive season as the club's top scorer.

- Gary Till and Jon Rowe equalled Roger Broadbent's record of 3 tries in a Courage League match. Till and Rowe share the record of career tries – 15

	Tries	Apps	Strike Rate
Gary Till	15	35	2.33
Jon Rowe	15	39	2.60

- Second row Rob Harding extends his club record of appearances to 79. Since making his debut back in November 1987 Harding has missed just 6 matches after being involved in a car accident in 1992-93.

WALSALL R.F.C.

COURAGE LEAGUE STATISTICS

compiled by Steve McCormack

Season	Div	P	W	D	L	F	T	C	P	D	A	T	C	P	D	Most Points	Most Tries
1987-88	MID1	10	5	1	4	183	28	16	9	4	100	15	5	10		53 John Dowdswell	5 Charlie Herriotts
1988-89	MID1	10	10	0	0	210	27	18	19	3	71	10	2	9		95 John Dowdswell	4 Malcolm Walker
1989-90	ALN	10	2	0	8	143	17	9	15	4	183	22	10	23	2	31 John Dowdswell	4 Simon Leaver. Matt McCluney
1990-91	ALN	12	5	0	7	149	16	8	19	4	176	23	9	19	3	75 Richard Mills	3 Nick Millward. Dave Wild
1991-92	D4N	12	3	1	8	139	11	4	24	5	187	24	14	20	1	99 Richard Mills	4 Duncan Marshall
1992-93	D4N	12	6	0	6	165	15	9	24	0	179	19	15	16	2	90 Richard Mills	3 Mike Friar. Gary Till. Jon Rowe
1993-94	D5N	12	7	0	5	166	13	7	29	0	148	11	9	22	3	81 Richard Mills	3 Gary Till
1994-95	D5N	12	10	1	1	389	47	29	31	1	110	10	3	17	1	164 Richard Mills	11 Jon Rowe
TOTALS		90	48	3	39	1544	174	100	170	1154	134	67	136	12			

BIGGEST WIN   **Home:** 60-13 v Stafford 7.11.87 MIDI   **Away:** 61-0 v Sheffield 25.2.95 D5N

BIGGEST DEFEAT   **Home:** 23-27 v Rotherham 26.3.94 D5N   **Away:** 0-36 v Otley 10.11.90 D4N

MOST TRIES in a match   **For:** 10 v Stafford 7.11.87 MIDI   **Against:** 5 (Three times)

MOST CONSECUTIVE   **Wins:** 10   **Defeats:** 7

MOST APPEARANCES   **Forward:** R. Harding 79   **Back:** R Mills 75

MOST CONSECUTIVE APPEARANCES   R Harding 49

CONSECUTIVE SCORING MATCHES   **Tries:** 3 Malcolm Walker

Points: 14 John Dowdswell. Richard Mills

	IN A SEASON	IN A CAREER	IN A MATCH
MOST POINTS	164 Richard Mills 1994-95 D5N	525 Richard Mills 1988-95	22 Richard Mills v Nuneaton 14.1.95 Away D5N
MOST TRIES	11 Jon Rowe 1994-95	15 Jon Rowe 1990-95 Gary Till 1992-95	3 Roger Broadbent v Stafford 7.11.87 Home MIDI Gary Till v Sheffield 25.2.95 Away D5N Jon Rowe v Wharfedale 25.3.95 Away D5N
MOST CONVERSIONS	29 Richard Mills 1994-95 D5N	53 Richard Mills 1988-95	7 John Dowdswell v Stockwood Park 22.10.88 Home MIDI
MOST PENALTIES	31 Richard Mills 1994-95 D5N	117 Richard Mills 1988-95	6 John Dowdswell v Stockwood Park 22.10.88 Home MIDI Richard Mills v Lichfield 1.4.95 Home D5N
MOST DROP GOALS	5 Richard Mills 1994-95 D5N	14 Richard Mills 1988-95	2 Richard Mills v Hereford 12.1.88 Away Midi v Birmingham Solihull 12.1.90 Away D4N

LEAGUE 5 NORTH

LEAGUE 5 SOUTH

MEMBER CLUBS
1995-96

**League 5 North & 5 South Registrar
and Official:**
M J Wilson
Michael Humphreys & Partners Ltd
68 South Lambeth Road
Vauxhall
London SW8 1RL
Tel: (B) 0171-820 9911
Fax: 0171 820 9259

NATIONAL LEAGUE FIVE NORTH STATISTICS 1993/94

RESULTS

		1	2	3	4	5	6	7	8	9	10	11	12	13
1	B'ham & S'hull			16-11	14-3	20-15	6-7			8-15			10-17	12-9
2	Bradford & B	26-5			16-0	22-34			11-14					27-26
3	Durham		19-11			21-13			3-13		27-15	14-16		
4	Hereford		17-12					10-25		3-3	16-9		20-10	15-15
5	Kendal			3-3	11-6			16-6		8-16			6-14	6-3
6	Lichfield	12-5			12-22	16-8				10-13			7-18	5-0
7	Nuneaton	9-8	6-20				9-3		11-23		8-8	19-18		
8	P Grasshoppers	17-16				11-3	20-15	21-12					25-7	18-10
9	Rotherham		54-19	76-3				26-6	11-10		37-8	54-18		
10	Stoke on Trent	9-11	18-13			11-5	17-5		19-3			10-12		
11	Stourbridge	19-3	11-3		15-11	34-15	0-16		10-6					
12	Walsall		16-15	22-16				17-0		23-27	6-13	12-0		
13	Winnington Park			66-3				24-12		26-3	24-16	15-9	9-6	

WEEK BY WEEK POSITIONS

	13/11	11/12	29/1	26/2	12/3	26/3	30/4
Birmingham & S	4	5	8	11	9	11	9
Bradford & B	12	8	7	6	7	9	13
Durham	6	11	11	9	6	8	12
Hereford	2	3	4	5	5	6	8
Kendal	7	12	12	12	11	13	10
Lichfield	10	6	9	10	12	10	7
Nuneaton	11	10	13	13	13	12	11
P Grasshoppers	1	1	1	1	1	2	2
Rotherham	5	2	2	3	2	1	1
Stoke on Trent	8	7	5	7	8	5	6
Stourbridge	13	13	10	8	10	7	5
Walsall	9	9	3	2	3	3	3
Winnington Park	3	4	6	4	4	4	4

PLAYING RECORD

	PLD	W	D	L	F	A	PD	Pts
Rotherham	12	10	1	1	335	142	193	21
Preston Grasshoppers	12	10	0	2	191	128	63	20
Walsall	12	7	0	5	166	148	18	14
Winnington Park	12	6	1	5	227	132	95	13
Stourbridge	12	6	0	6	162	188	-26	12
Stoke on Trent	12	5	1	6	153	167	-14	11
Lichfield	12	5	0	7	118	138	-20	10
Hereford	12	4	2	6	126	153	-27	10
Birmingham & Solihull	12	5	0	7	128	162	-34	10
Kendal	12	4	1	7	142	171	-29	9
Nuneaton	12	4	1	7	122	200	-78	9
Durham City	12	4	1	7	159	279	-120	9
Bradford & Bingley	12	4	0	8	189	210	-21	8

NATIONAL LEAGUE FIVE SOUTH STATISTICS 1993/94

RESULTS

	1	2	3	4	5	6	7	8	9	10	11	12	13
1 Basingstoke			20-9		12-9	10-16			10-26		13-17	12-9	
2 Berry Hill	14-7			13-6	24-34				3-3		16-12	15-6	
3 Camvorne		17-16		38-13			23-3	2-25			3-3		32-17
4 High Wycombe	13-11				16-13	6-6			0-23		23-14	7-14	
5 London Welsh			17-17				3-3	56-3	12-8		0-12		39-7
6 Lydney		8-13	23-3				33-7	16-7			6-13		15-3
7 Maidstone	19-58	6-14		6-20					14-26		3-50	9-23	
8 Met. Police	28-13	19-9		15-6			3-10		16-3			13-31	
9 North Walsham			8-13		13-6	11-13					15-9	6-6	11-14
10 Reading	32-3	21-6		17-0			41-0	26-0	32-3				
11 Southend		17-3	10-18		13-15	18-26		29-28		11-14			14-18
12 Tabard			25-9		12-12	17-16				13-22	19-6		8-9
13 W Super Mare	18-22	15-3		5-10		29-6		12-5			16-15		

WEEK BY WEEK POSITIONS

	13/11	4/12	11/12	8/1	29/1	26/2	12/3	26/3	9/4	23/4	30/4
Basingstoke	7	6	4	8	6	9	11	11	11	11	11
Berry Hill	12	10	8	6	9	7	5	7	6	7	7
Camborne	6	7	7	3	5	6	7	4	4	4	4
H Wycombe	4	5	9	7	3	4	6	8	9	9	9
L. Welsh	11	9	10	10	8	11	9	6	5	6	6
Lydney	2	2	2	2	2	2	2	2	2	2	2
Maidstone	10	12	13	13	13	13	13	13	13	13	13
Met. Police	13	13	12	12	11	8	10	9	10	10	10
North Walsham	5	4	6	9	10	10	8	10	7	8	8
Reading	1	1	1	1	1	1	1	1	1	1	1
Southend	9	11	11	11	12	12	12	12	12	12	12
Tabard	3	3	3	4	7	5	3	3	3	3	3
Weston-Super-Mare	8	8	5	5	4	3	4	5	8	5	5

PLAYING RECORD

	PLD	W	D	L	F	A	PD	Pts
Reading	12	10	1	1	248	61	187	21
Lydney	12	7	2	3	181	111	70	16
Tabard	12	6	2	4	183	136	47	14
Camborne	12	6	2	4	197	180	17	14
Weston-Super-Mare	12	7	0	5	163	180	-17	14
London Welsh	12	5	3	4	216	140	76	13
Berry Hill	12	6	1	5	146	154	-8	13
North Walsham	12	5	2	5	148	136	12	12
High Wycombe	12	5	1	6	120	173	-53	11
Metropolitan Police	12	5	0	7	167	174	-7	10
Basingstoke	12	5	0	7	191	210	-19	10
Southend	12	3	0	9	203	208	-5	6
Maidstone	12	1	0	11	86	386	-300	2

NATIONAL LEAGUE FIVE NORTH STATISTICS 1994-95

PLAYING RECORD AND POINTS BREAKDOWN

	P	W	D	L	F	A	Pts	HOME							AWAY						
								W	D	L	F	A	Pts		W	D	L	F	A	Pts	
Walsal	12	10	1	1	389	110	21	5	1	0	184	59	11		5	0	1	205	51	10	
Kendal	12	9	1	2	226	162	19	6	0	0	156	65	12		3	1	2	70	97	7	
Preston G	12	8	1	3	187	137	17	6	0	0	109	59	12		2	1	3	78	78	5	
Wharfdale	12	6	1	5	209	198	13	3	1	2	123	116	7		3	0	3	86	82	6	
Lichfield	12	6	0	6	217	208	12	4	0	2	105	78	8		2	0	4	112	130	6	
Stourbridge	12	6	0	6	166	174	12	3	0	3	71	70	6		3	0	3	95	104	6	
Stoke on Trent	12	5	1	6	154	154	11	3	1	2	86	84	7		2	0	4	68	70	4	
Winnington Park	12	5	1	6	173	214	11	3	0	3	107	95	6		2	1	3	66	119	5	
Sheffield	12	5	0	7	156	197	10	4	0	2	101	114	8		1	0	5	55	83	2	
B'ham & S'hull	12	5	0	7	167	226	10	3	0	3	93	87	6		2	0	4	74	139	4	
Nuneaton	12	4	0	8	129	161	8	2	0	4	68	87	4		2	0	4	61	74	4	
Barkers Butts	12	4	0	8	98	233	8	2	0	4	31	81	4		2	0	4	67	152	4	
Hereford	12	1	2	9	153	250	4	1	1	4	93	102	3		0	1	5	60	148	1	

RESULTS

		1	2	3	4	5	6	7	8	9	10	11	12	13
1	Barkers Butts						6-5		5-3	0-20	3-12	8-29	9-12	
2	B'ham & S'hull	8-9				16-23	24-12	3-20		23-17	19-6			
3	Hereford	15-20	9-10		16-23	26-20		13-13				14-16		
4	Kendal	51-6	28-26			16-6		24-11		9-3	28-13			
5	Lichfield	38-11					13-15	6-3	15-8	20-12	13-29			
6	Nuneaton			11-6	9-12				15-9			11-27	16-17	6-16
7	Preston G	24-8					9-3		19-10	18-13	27-19		12-6	
8	Sheffield		28-5	40-9	14-9							0-61	3-25	16-5
9	Stoke on Trent			16-9			6-11		19-12			11-30	25-13	9-9
10	Stourbridge						16-15		10-13	0-3		13-8	17-13	15-18
11	Walsall		33-3		25-19		29-20							49-3
12	Wharfdale		22-8	13-13	41-8	15-22						8-50		24-15
13	Winnington Pk	16-13	19-22	28-17	9-10	32-22	3-11							

WEEK BY WEEK POSITIONS

	17/9	24/9	1/10	15/10	22/10	29/10	7/1	14/1	11/2	25/2	4/3	25/3	8/4
Barkers Butts	11	13	12	13	13	13	13	13	13	10	9	11	12
Birmingham & Solihull	5	7	4	6	8	8	11	11	11	12	11	10	10
Hereford	13	9	8	8	10	12	12	12	12	13	13	13	13
Kendal	6	3	6	3	5	4	4	4	4	3	3	3	2
Lichfield	12	12	10	11	11	10	8	9	9	8	7	4	5
Nuneaton	8	10	11	10	9	7	10	10	10	11	12	12	11
Preston Grasshoppers	3	1	1	1	1	1	1	1	1	1	1	2	3
Sheffield	1	4	3	5	4	6	6	8	8	9	10	9	9
Stoke on Trent	9	8	9	7	7	9	7	6	6	5	6	7	7
Stourbridge	2	2	5	2	2	3	5	5	5	6	4	5	6
Walsall	7	5	2	4	3	2	2	2	2	2	1	1	1
Wharfdale	4	6	7	9	6	5	3	3	3	4	5	6	4
Winnington Park	10	11	13	12	12	11	9	7	7	7	8	8	8

NATIONAL LEAGUE FIVE SOUTH STATISTICS 1994-95

PLAYING RECORD AND POINTS BREAKDOWN

	P	W	D	L	F	A	Pts	HOME						AWAY					
								W	D	L	F	A	Pts	W	D	L	F	A	Pts
London Welsh	12	10	2	0	409	126	22	6	0	0	277	49	12	4	2	0	132	77	10
Lydney	12	10	1	1	263	131	21	5	1	0	142	47	11	5	0	1	121	84	10
Weston Super Mare	12	8	0	4	194	160	16	3	0	3	95	108	6	5	0	1	99	52	10
N Walsham	12	7	1	4	233	190	15	5	0	1	138	76	10	2	1	3	95	114	5
Barking	12	7	0	5	223	173	14	2	0	4	84	86	4	5	0	1	139	87	10
Tabard	12	7	0	5	207	208	14	4	0	2	102	81	8	3	0	3	105	127	6
Met Police	12	5	0	7	183	175	10	3	0	3	94	75	6	2	0	4	89	100	4
Camborne	12	4	2	6	174	188	10	2	2	2	90	86	6	2	0	4	84	102	4
Henley	12	5	0	7	190	299	10	2	0	4	118	163	4	3	0	3	72	136	6
High Wycombe	12	4	0	8	192	261	8	3	0	3	104	78	6	1	0	5	88	183	2
Berry Hill	12	3	0	9	133	229	6	3	0	3	77	105	6	0	0	6	56	124	0
Sudbury	12	3	0	9	150	352	6	2	0	4	84	153	4	1	0	5	66	199	2
Basingstoke	12	2	0	10	122	181	4	2	0	4	81	80	4	0	0	6	41	101	0

RESULTS

		1	2	3	4	5	6	7	8	9	10	11	12	13
1	Barking				11-6		37-5	14-19	6-18	16-26				0-12
2	Basingstoke	20-24		24-3		14-5	6-16			9-10				8-22
3	Berry Hill	16-15			14-13		19-23		0-16	21-18				7-20
4	Camborne		15-6					21-21	12-17		15-15	18-13	9-14	
5	High Wycombe	11-20		15-13	13-23		49-6			11-3				5-13
6	Henley				27-24			6-34	33-30			21-26	18-31	13-18
7	London Welsh		23-8	29-15		69-6					31-6	88-7	37-7	
8	Lydney		18-5			21-7		17-17			18-12	42-3	26-3	
9	Met Police				23-0		11-16	13-19	15-17			13-9		19-14
10	N Walsham	10-17	15-8	30-9		47-21	14-6			22-15				
11	Sudbury	9-40	14-11	17-13		9-31					16-24		19-34	
12	Tabard	21-23	16-3	9-3		23-18				21-17	12-17			
13	Weston S Mare				14-18			6-22	18-23		22-21	17-8	18-16	

WEEK BY WEEK POSITIONS

	17/9	24/9	1/10	15/10	22/10	29/10	7/1	14/1	11/2	25/2	4/3	25/3	8/4
Barking	12	8	3	3	3	3	3	3	3	3	4	5	5
Basingstoke	11	7	8	6	7	9	9	9	9	11	12	13	13
Berry Hill	8	12	13	13	12	13	12	12	13	12	13	11	11
Camborne	3	5	4	4	5	7	8	7	8	8	9	8	8
Henley	6	9	10	11	10	10	11	11	11	9	8	10	9
High Wycombe	10	11	12	12	13	12	13	13	12	10	10	9	10
London Welsh	1	1	1	1	1	1	1	1	1	2	2	2	1
Lydney	5	3	2	2	2	2	2	2	2	1	1	1	2
Met Police	2	2	6	5	6	8	6	6	4	5	6	7	7
N Walsham	9	4	7	10	8	6	5	5	6	7	5	4	4
Sudbury	7	10	11	9	11	11	10	10	10	13	11	12	12
Tabard	13	13	9	8	9	5	7	8	7	6	7	6	6
Weston Super Mare	4	6	5	7	4	4	4	4	5	4	3	3	3

COURAGE CHAMPIONSHIP STATISTICS 1987–1995

DIVISION FIVE NORTH
(FORMERLY DIVISION FOUR NORTH, AREA LEAGUE NORTH)

	CHAMPIONS	RUNNERS-UP	RELEGATED
1987-88	Rugby	Durham	Derby Solihull Birkenhead Park
1988-89	Roundhay	Broughton Park	Birmingham
1989-90	Broughton Park	Morley	None
1990-91	Otley	Lichfield	Stoke on Trent Birmongham Solihull
1991-92	Aspatria	Hereford	Vale of Lune Northern
1992-93	Harrogate	Rotherham	Towcastrians
1993-94	Rotherham	Preston Grasshoppers	Bradford & Bingley Durham City
1994-95	Walsall	Kendal	Hereford Barkers Butts

TEAM RECORDS

Most points for in a season: 424 Otley 1990-91
Most points against in a season: 286 Towcestrians 1992-93
Least points for in a season: 29 Birmingham 1988-89
Least points against in a season: 67 Roundhay 1987-88
Most wins in a season: 11 Otley 1990-91, Aspatria 1991-92
Least wins in a season: 0 Solihull 1987-88, Birmingham 1988-89, Stoke 1989-90
Most defeats in a season: 10 Solihull 1987-88, Birmingham 1988-89, Stoke 1989-90,
Birmingham & Solihull 1990-91, Northern 1991-92, Towcestrians 1992-93
Least defeats in a season: 1 9 times
Most draws in a season: 3 Northern 1990-91
Biggest home win: 79-0 Roundhay v Birmingham 1988-89
Biggest away win: 61-0 Walsall v Sheffield 1994-95
Highest scoring draw: 21-21 Winnington Park v Walsall 1991-92
Lowest scoring draw: 0-0 Roundhay v Northern 1987-88
Lowest winning score: 3-0 Stoke v Stourbridge 1994-95
Highest score by losing side: 26 Bradford & Bingley 27, Winnington Park 26 1993-94,
Kendal 28 Birmingham Solihull 1994-95

COURAGE CHAMPIONSHIP STATISTICS 1987–1995

DIVISION FIVE SOUTH
(FORMERLY DIVISION FOUR SOUTH, AREA LEAGUE SOUTH)

	CHAMPIONS	RUNNERS-UP	RELEGATED
1987-88	Askeans	Sidcup	Streatham/Croydon
1988-89	Lydney	Havant	Sidcup Stroud Ealing
1989-90	Met Police	Clifton	Salisbury
1990-91	Redruth	Basingstoke	Maidenhead Cheltenham
1991-92	Havant	Basingstoke	Sidcup, Ealing
1992-93	Sudbury	London Welsh	Thurrock
1993-94	Reading	Lydney	Southend Maidstone
1994-95	London Welsh	Lydney	Sudbury Basingstoke

TEAM RECORDS

Most points for in a season: 409 London Welsh 1994-95
Most points against in a season: 386 Maidstone 1993-94
Least points for in a season: 64 Maidstone 1989-90
Least points against in a season: 61 Reading 1993-94
Most wins in a season: 12 Redruth 1990-91
Least wins in a season: 0 Streatham/Croydon 1987-88, Sidcup 1988-89, Ealing 1991-92
Most defeats in a season: 11 Ealing 1991-92, Maidstone 1993-94
Least defeats in a season: 0 Redruth 1990-91, Sudbury 1992-93, London Welsh 1994-95
Most draws in a season: 3 Berry Hill 1992-93, London Welsh 1993-94
Biggest home win: 88-7 London Welsh v Sudbury 1994-95
Biggest away win: 58-19 Basingstoke v Maidstone 1993-94
Highest scoring draw: 18-18 Berry Hill v Weston Super Mare
Lowest scoring draw: 3-3 3 times
Lowest winning score: 3-0 Redruth v Southend 1989-90
Highest score by losing side: 30-33 Lydney v Henley 1994-95

BIRMINGHAM & SOLIHULL RFC

NICKNAME: Bees   **FOUNDED:** 1989 (Merger Birmingham R.F.C. and Solihull R.U.F.C.)

CLUB & GROUND DETAILS
Sharmans Cross Road, Solihull
Telephone: 0121 705 7995

Total Capacity: 1,500
Standing: 1,500
Nearest Railway Station: Solihull
Car Parking: 50
Season Tickets: N/A
Match Prices: N/A
Membership: Seniors £35.00 (£40.00 October) Juniors £5.00
Training Nights: Tuesday and Thursday
Club Shop Manager: David Radburn 0121 709 1088
Colours: Red black gold white quarters

CLUB OFFICIALS
President
Christopher Gifford
Chairman
Michael Norman
Director of Coaching
Nigel Horton
Club Secretary
Kirk Simpson
103 St Bernard's Road, Solihull B92 7DQ
Tel: (H) 0121 682 2708 (W) 0121 233 2298
Fixtures Secretary
Alan Morden
Station Farm, 40 Old Station Road, Hampton in Arden, Solihull B92 0HF
Tel: (H) 01675 442462 (W) 0121 643 2736
Press Officer
Gareth Hitchins
Tel: (H) 1021 308 4687 (W) 0121 373 1080
Commercial Managers
Greville Edwards
David Radburn
1st XV Captain: Simon Taylor
1st XV Coaches: Nigel Horton & John White

Preston Grasshoppers centres Jim Moore and Andy Taylorson attempt to breach the Birmingham & Solihull defence

Broughton Park forward Alex Kloss in determined mood against Askeans, John Clifford and captain Graham Higginbotham in support

Photo: John Fryer

BROUGHTON PARK F.C.

NICKNAME: Park   **FOUNDED:** 1882

Back to the Future

The past 1994-95 season was the Park's poorest ever, the single league win after Christmas added to three previous wins not being enough to avoid relagation.

But the Club does not intend to dwell in the past. Moves are afoot to sell the ground and release resources for developing the undoubted potential in the club.

Off the field, newly installed Director of Rugby, John Livsey, heads a team of ex-players committed to developing the 'Park of the future'. Chief coack Frank O'Rourke will organise the coaching input. Present players will have strong competition from recent Colts and the increasing signings made to strengthen the 1st XV squad.

Powerful wing, Martin Kelly, is the new Club Captain and has the task of leading the players in a revival of Park's playing fortunes. The signs are good with Park's young forwards maturing quickly and now able to provide a platform for fifteen man rugby.

CLUB PLAYING RECORD 1994-95

National League: Four
Final League Position at end of 1994-95 Season: 10th
League Playing Record: P 18, W 4, D 0, L 14, Pts F 218, Pts A 429
Season Playing Record: P 34, W 8, D 0, L 25, Pts F 440, Pts A 826

Achievements/Competitions Won During 1994-95 Season:

U14s won Lancashire Cup. Coached by Kevin O'Brien.
Colts runners up in Lancashire Cup.

MOST CAPPED PLAYERS

A. Neary   England 43, Lions 1
K. O'Brien   Ireland 3
B. Jackson   England 2
M. Leadbetter   England 2

LEADING APPEARANCES FOR THE CLUB

K. O'Brien   596   22 Seasons
M. Kelly   32   1994-95

LEADING SCORERS

A. Rimmer, Stand Off, 28 games, 44 Penalties, 12 Conversions, 1 Drop Goal, Total 159 pts.
M. Kelly, Wing, 16 Tries, Fifth Season as leading try scorer.
Leading Scorer in Club's History: K. O'Brien
Record points scorer in a season: K. O'Brien
Player of the Year 1994-95: G. Higgingbotham

BROUGHTON PARK F.C.

CLUB & GROUND DETAILS

Chelsfield Grove, Chorlton, Manchester M21 5SU
Telephone: 0161 881 2481
Fax:

Total Capacity: 3,300
Seated: 300
Standing: 3,000
Simple Directions to Ground: Leave M56 at J3. Follow signs for Manchester Centre on Princess Parkway. At fifth set of lights turn left into Mauldeth Road West. The ground is 3/4 mile on right.
Nearest Railway Station: Ouccadukkt
Car Parking: 150-200
Season Tickets: -
Match Prices: Adults £2.00 Children/OAPs £1
Membership: Seniors £35.00 Juniors £10.00
Training Nights: Tuesday and Thursday

Colours: Black and white hoops
Change Colours: Red jersey

CLUB OFFICIALS

President
L Morgan
Chairman
G Peart
Club Secretary
R W Greenall
260 Barlow Moor Road, Chorlton, Manchester M21 8HA
Tel: (H) 0161 861 0457
Fixtures Secretary
D W Ramsbottom
9 Yew Tree Grove, Heald Green, Cheshisre SK8 3TJ
Tel: (H) 0161 437 3017
Press Officer
D Evans
Tel: (H) 0161 881 6705

KENDAL R.U.F.C.

NICKNAME:

FOUNDED: 1905

CLUB OFFICIALS

President
R A Short
Chairman
I W Hutton
Club Secretary
Paul A Ruiz
29 Mint Street, Kendal LA9 6DS
Tel: (H) 01539 720686 (W) 01539 734039
Fixtures Secretary
A R Quarry
14 Collinfield, Kendal LA9 5JD
Tel: (H) 01539 731640 (W) 01900 602623
Match Secretary
R Wilson 01539 740449
Press Officer
John Hutton
Tel: (H) 01539 733152

CLUB PLAYING RECORD 1994-95

National League: 5 North
Final League Position: 2nd
League Playing record: P 12, W 9, D 1, L 2, Pts F 226, Pts A 162
Season Playing record: P 34, W 25, D 2, L 7, Pts F 666, Pts A 431

Team: Kendal 1st XV 1994-95 after their Jennings Bitter Cumbria Cup Victory.   *Photo: Times & Star, Workington*

KENDAL R.U.F.C.

Action: 941-174-27. No8 Peter Kremer passing to prop-forward Billy Coxan in the league game against Birmingham at Mintbridge on the 24th September. Photo: Westmorland Gazette

CLUB & GROUND DETAILS

Mint Bridge, Shap Road, Kendal LA9 6DL
Telephone: 01539 734039
Fax:
Total Capacity: 1,300
Seated: 300
Standing: 1,000
Simple Directions to Ground: M6 J36 A591 A6 Follow signs for penrith, keep left of Duke of Cumberland 400 m on left.
Nearest Railway Station: Kendal via Oxenholme
Car Parking: 100
Season Tickets:
Match Prices: Adults £2.50 OAPs 50p
Membership: Seniors £25.00 Juniors Free or £1.00
Training Nights: Tuesday and Thursday

Colours: Black and amber
Change Colours: Green

LICHFIELD R.U.F.C.

NICKNAME: **FOUNDED:** 1874

CLUB OFFICIALS

President
Wilf Linney
Chairman
James Greenhorn
Club Secretary
Shaun D Godfrey
1 Old College House, Dam Street, Lichfield, Staffs WS13 6AA
Tel: (H) 01543 268539 (W) 0171 548 2840
Fixtures Secretary
Steve Barr
2 Barley Croft, Whittington, Lichfield, Staffs WS13
Tel: (H) 01543 432605 (W) 01922 414480
Press Officer
Mrs Emma Ridgway
Tel: (H) 01543 432972 (W) 0121 230 5035
Director of Playing
Dave Lewis
1st XV Manager
Mark Davis

CLUB PLAYING RECORD 1994-95

National League: 5 North
Final League Position:
League Playing record: P 12, W 6, D 0, L 6, Pts F 217, Pts A 208
Season Playing record: P 29, W 20, D 0, L9, Pts F 783, Pts A 394

Back (l to r): Peter Whitting (Physio), Mark Moysey, Charlie Prince, Paul Fairs, Jason Powell, Ian Grant, Mark Bishop, Scott Howes, Neil Law, James Mitchell, Chris Ward
Front (l to r): Trevor Cartwright, Mike Prince, Gary Smith, Dan Bourne (Capt), Mark Davis, Tony Bartlett, Dave Richards, Barry Broad (Coach)

LICHFIELD R.U.F.C

Centre of picture: Lichfield Captain Danny Bourne (green shirt) tries to prize the ball from the opposition.

CLUB & GROUND DETAILS

Cooke Fields, Tamworth Road, Lichfield, Staffordshire WS14
Telephone: 01543 263020
Fax:

Total Capacity: 4,250
Seated: 250
Standing: 4,000
Simple Directions to Ground: A51 from Lichfield toward Tamworth, Ground situated next to A38 on left behind Horse & Jockey pub.
Nearest Railway Station: Lichfield City or Trent Valley
Car Parking: 300
Season Tickets: Adults £17.50 Children/OAPs £10.00
Match Prices: Adults £2.50 Children/OAPs £2.00
Membership: Seniors £27.50 Juniors £15.00
Training Nights: Tuesday and Thursday

Colours: Myrtle green shirts, navy blue shorts, red socks
Change Colours: Yellow shirts

NUNEATON R.F.C.

NICKNAME: Nuns   **FOUNDED:** 1879

CLUB OFFICIALS

President
Keith Howells
Chairman
Derek Cake
Club Secretary
Marian Gunn
151 Windermere Avenue, Nuneaton, Warwickshire CV11 6HN
Tel: (H) 01203 387515
Fixtures Secretary
John Davies
3 Saints Way, Nuneaton, Warwickshire CV10 0UU
Tel: (H) 01203 370011 (W) 01203 344800
Press Officer
John Lumsden
Tel: (H) 01203 385559/325355
Playing Administrator
Steve Redfern

CLUB PLAYING RECORD 1994-95

National League: 5 North
Final League Position:
League Playing record: P 12, W 4, D 0, L 8, Pts F 131, Pts A 159
Season Playing record: P 31, W 13, D 0, L, 18, Pts F 468, Pts A 605

Back row: Dave Warden (Match Secretary), Steve Redfern (Coach), Clive Medford, Paul Vowles, Karl Ashfield, Mark Mitchell (Club Captain), Darren Barry, George Mumford, Bill Boffey, Alan Jones, Tony Simms (1st XV Captain), Paul Flowers, Dave Lyons (Coach), Paul Barton (Medical Assistant).
Front row: Andy Nicholls, Tim Bates, Simon Reid, Martin Owen, Mark Elvidge, Andy Moore, Paul Jones.

NUNEATON R.F.C.

CLUB & GROUND DETAILS

Harry Cleaver Ground, Attleborough Road, Nuneaton, Warwickshire CV11 4JP
Telephone: 01203 283925
Fax: 01203 383925

Total Capacity: 3,000
Seated: 500
Standing: 2,500
Simple Directions to Ground: M1-M6 Jcn 3, A444 Nuneaton, follow signs for Rugby/Lutterworth. Pass school and Leisure Centre on left, bear left into Attleborough Road. Turn left into lane just past Rugger Tavern on left.
Nearest Railway Station: Nuneaton Trent Valley
Car Parking: 175
Season Tickets: Adults £30.00 Children/OAPs £10.00
Match Prices: Adults £3.00 Children/OAPs £1.50
Membership: Seniors £20.00, Juniors £2.50
Training Nights: Tuesday and Thursday

Colours: Black/red/white hoops
Change Colours: Red or white

PRESTON GRASSHOPPERS R.F.C.

NICKNAME: **FOUNDED:** 1869

CLUB OFFICIALS

President
Les Anson
Chairman
David Taylorson
Club Secretary
John Hetherington
51 Kilworth Height, Fulwood, Preston PR2 3NU
Tel: (H) 01772 712162 (W) 01772 764715
Fixtures Secretary
John M Powell
121 Bare Lane, Bare, Morecambe LA4 4RD
Tel: 01524 424514
Press Officer
John Hetherington
Tel: (H) 01772 712162 (W) 01772 764715

CLUB PLAYING RECORD 1994-95

National League: 5 North
Final League Position:
League Playing record: P 12, W 8, D 1, L 3, Pts F 187, Pts A 137
Season Playing record: P 39, W 24, D 2, L 13, Pts F 910, Pts A 563

PRESTON GRASHOPPERS R.F.C.

Dave Whittingham – 1994-95 Player of the Year

Les Anson, who after serving the club for 42 years in a variety of roles, becomes 'Hoppers' new President.
Photo: Lancashire Evening Post

CLUB & GROUND DETAILS

Lightfood Green, Fulwood, Preston PR4 0AP
Telephone: 01772 863456
Fax:

Total Capacity: 3,000
Seated: 250
Standing: 2,750
Simple Directions to Ground: M6 Junction 32. Follow Garstand sign, turn left towards Preston, in 50 yards left again. Follow Ingol signs. Ground is approx 1 mile from motorway on right.
Nearest Railway Station: Preston
Car Parking: 300+
Season Tickets: N/A
Match Prices: Adults £4.00 Members £2.00 Children/OAPs £2.00
Membership: Seniors £32.00 Juniors £9.00
Training Nights: Monday, Wednesday & Thursday

Colours: Navy blue and white
Change Colours: Green

Chairman of Rugby
Bob Bailey
Chairman of Selectors
Keith Moore
Administration Officer
Ken Moore
Bar Chairman
Robbie Jarvis
Finance Chairman
John Muirhead
Hon. Treasurer
Jim Powdrell
1st XV Captain
Mike Bailey
1st XV Coach
John Morgan

SANDAL R.U.F.C.

NICKNAME: **FOUNDED:** 1927

Champions 1994-95 – Courage League Division One

After four seasons in North Division One, having been runners-up last year and never having finished outside the top four, Sandal this year are worthy Champions, even though they headed the table by only one point, the narrowest of margins.

Sandal have been chased hard all season by Stockton, who finished in 2nd place, Manchester in 3rd, and Bradford & Bingley who faded only in the final furlong to finish in 4th place. At the end, only a single point separated each of the top four teams.

Under the captaincy of scrum-half ANDREW TURTON, Sandal lost only one League match all season, that somewhat surprisingly, against West Park Bramhope (6- 15) although they were well beaten on the day. Three games were drawn – an indication of just how tight North One was – against Wigton (A) (13-13), Manchester (H) (9-9) and Stockton (A) (6-6). Those last two results are particularly significant, penalty goals from fly-half MARK HARDCASTLE saving the day for Sandal on each occasion.

Eight games were won, and of those the most satisfying were away victories at Tynedale (21-8), Bradford & Bingley (17-16), and Huddersfield (16-9). Home victories were achieved against Durham City (12-9), Widnes (24-17), York (19- 10), Hull Ionians (27-9), and finally, and most satisfying of them all, an emphatic 57-5 home victory over Middlesbrough to ensure promotion.

Qualifying for the Pilkington Cup via the County Cup route, Sandal progressed to Round 4 of the National Knock-out competition, disposing of Wigton, Winnington park and Camp Hill before falling to Lydney in Round 4.

Whilst Sandal's successes are based very much on their traditional expansive 15-man game in which every player contributes to the full, there have been some fine individual performances. None more so than leading points scorer, fly half MARK HARDCASTLE, whose prolific goal-kicking has taken him beyond the 250 points mark for the sixth season in succession.

Leading try scorers (with 10 apiece) are brothers MARK and DAVID WOLFF whilst JIM DAVIS has made good progress in the centre alongside the experienced former England man, BRYAN BARLEY. Amongst the forwards, JASON MORTIMER has had an outstanding season in the second-row, whilst NICK SYKES and JON HANSON, both Yorkshire Under 21 caps, are two young props who will more than cope with the challenges of National Division Five Rugby.

Standing (l to r): Sue Crabbe (Club Doctor), Vicki Banton (Physio), Ken Fleming, Steve Barnes, Glynn Thompson, Jon Adams, Allan Gibb, Keith Walker, Glenn Barker, Duncan Allott.
Seated (l to r): Nick Powell, Bryan Barley, Mark Hardcastle, Alan Davies (President), Andrew Turton (captain), Jon Hanson, Gary Lig, Jim Davis.
Absent are Mark Wolff, Andrew Wolff, David Wolff, Jason Mortimer, Nick Sykes.

SANDAL R.U.F.C.

Sandal leading try scorer, wingman David Wolff, is held in the tackle, but support is at hand from (left) lock Keith Walker and (right) No 8 Allan Gibb.

Photo: Wakefield Express Newspaper

CLUB & GROUND DETAILS

Milnthorpe Green, Standbridge Lane, Sandal, Wakefield, W. Yorks
Telephone: 01924 250661
Fax:

Total Capacity: 1,500
Seated: -
Standing: 1,500
Simple Directions to Ground: Jct 39 M1 onto A636 direction Wakefield; after 3/4 mile turn right at roundabout onto Asdale Road; after 1 mile, Club on left.
Nearest Railway Station: Wakefield (Westgate or Kirkgate)
Car Parking: 200
Season Tickets:
Match Prices: Adults £2.50 League & Cup, £2.00 Other Children/OAPs £1.00
Membership: Seniors £26.50 Juniors £11.00
Training Nights: Tuesday & Thursday

Colours: Maroon, gold and white
Change Colours: Gold, maroon and white

CLUB OFFICIALS

President
Mr H A Davies
Chairman
Mr H H Newton
Club Secretary
Mr L R Bedford
14 Lindale Mount, Alverthorpe, Wakefield, West Yorks WF2 0BH
Tel: (H) 10924 379263
Fixtures Secretary
Mr C Critchett
48 Sinclair Garth, Sandal, Wakefield, W. Yorks WF2 6RE
Tel: 01924 254329
Press Officer
Mr P Harrison
Tel: 01924 863457
1st XV Captain
Bryan Barley
1st XV Coach
Martin Shuttleworth

SHEFFIELD R.U.F.C.

NICKNAME: FOUNDED: 1902

CLUB OFFICIALS

President
Q R (Robert) Dean
Chairman
D M (Mike) Howarth
Club Secretary
Jim Goulding
34 Whinfell Court, Whirlow, Sheffield S11 9QA
Tel: (H) 01142 620543 (W) 01709 555416
Fixtures Secretary
Q R (Robert) Dean
94 Riverdale Road, Sheffield S10 3FD
Tel: (H) 01142 301021 (W) 01142 377036
Press Officer
Ian Harris
Tel: (H) 01142 351491
Chairman of Playing
Graham Sulley
Chairman of International Administration
Mike Brackley
Chairman of Finance
John Phillips
1st XV Captain
Nick Crapper
1st XV Coach
Allan Broomhead

CLUB & GROUND DETAILS

Abbeydale Sports Club, Abbeydale Road South, S17 3LG
Telephone: 01142 367011
Fax: 01142 621054

Total Capacity: 1,250
Seated: 250
Standing: 1,000
Simple Directions to Ground: As in last years directory
Nearest Railway Station: Dore/Totley
Car Parking: 200
Season Tickets: N/A
Match Prices:
Membership: Seniors £35.00 Juniors £10.00
Training Nights: Tuesday and Thursday

Colours: Blue/white hoops, navy blue shorts, red socks
Change Colours: Red shirts

Leading Appearances for Club:

Name	Appearances	Season
1 W M (Bill) Reichwald	515	1974-1995
2 H (Harry) Johnson	340	1956-1974
3 D (Dave) Watson	330	1979-1995

Leading Scorers in all games (1994/95):

Name	Position	No of games	Tries	Penalties	Conversions	Drop Goals	Total
1 A Stoddard	Wing	14	4	22	11	—	108
2 J Morley	Centre	27	5	17	10	—	96
3 M Allatt	Fullback	24	6	—	—	—	30

Leading scorer in Club's history: Alan Old   1,665   1976-1986

Record points scorer in a season: Mark Rodgers   297   1992-1993

322

LEAGUE 5 NORTH PROGRAMMES

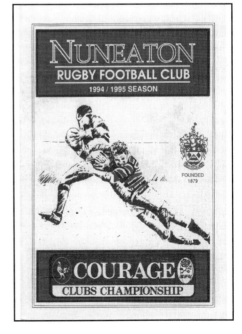

STOKE-ON-TRENT R.U.F.C.

NICKNAME: **FOUNDED:** 1884

CLUB OFFICIALS

President
Fhil Tarakaniec
Chairman
Tony Brindley
Club Secretary
Stephen Beck
10 Hillside Close, Fulford, Stoke-on-Trent ST11 9RU
Tel: 01782 398090 (W) 0121 631 3555
Fixtures Secretary
Eric Hardisty
8 Maple Gardens, Stone, Staffs ST15 0EJ
Tel: (H) 01785 813641 (W) 0121 554 6423
Press Officer
Tom Maskrey
Tel (H) 01782 313346
Chairman of Junior Rugby
Brian Ellis
Chairman of Selection
Paul Lukasawicz
1st XV Captain
Nigel Binns
1st XV Coach
Simon Robson

CLUB PLAYING RECORD 1994-95

National League: 5 North
Final League Position:
League Playing record: P 12, W 5, D 1, L 6, Pts F 154, Pts A 154
Season Playing record: P 31, W 15, D 1, L 15, Pts F 475, Pts A 497

STOKE-ON-TRENT R.U.F.C.

Action from Stoke-on-Trent v Birkenhead Park. Prop Richard Bradly driving forward ball in hand.

CLUB & GROUND DETAILS

Hartwell Lane, Nr Barlaston, Stoke-on-trent ST3 7NG
Telephone: 01782 372807
Fax:

Total Capacity: 2,120
Seated: 120
Standing: 2,000
Simple Directions to Ground: From the north use either the M6 or M1. From M1, follow the A38 then A50. Turn left at first seet of traffic lights on the outskirts of the city (A520). After approx. 3 miles, take road signposted Barlaston. Club 1 mile on left. From M6 leave at J.15, follow A34 south, then take road to Barlaston. The Club is through the village 1 mile on the right. From the south leave at J.14, follow A34 north, directions then as above.
Nearest Railway Station: Stoke-on-Trent
Car Parking: 200
Season Tickets:
Match Prices: Adults £2.00 OAPs Free
Membership: Seniors £26.00 Juniors £2.00
Training Nights: Monday and Thursday

Colours: Dark blue and light blue stripes
Change Colours: Red

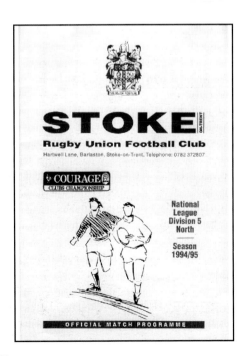

STOKE
Rugby Union Football Club
Hartwell Lane, Barlaston, Stoke-on-Trent, Telephone: 0782 372807

COURAGE
CLUBS CHAMPIONSHIP

National
League
Division 5
North

Season
1994/95

OFFICIAL MATCH PROGRAMME

STOURBRIDGE R.F.C.

NICKNAME: **FOUNDED:** 1876

CLUB OFFICIALS

President
Norman Robertson
Chairman
T.B.A.
Club Secretary
R (Bob) Browne
41 Western Road, West Hagley, Stourbridge DY9 0JY
Tel: (H) 01562 882020 (W) 0121 423 2345
Fixtures Secretary
C H J Smith
San Malo, New Wood, Stourton, Stourbridge
Tel: (H) 01384 390125
Press Officer
C W Davies
Tel: (H) 01384 376201
Commercial Manager
Mark Denison

CLUB & GROUND DETAILS

Bridgnorth Road, Stourton, Stourbridge DY7 6QZ
Telephone: 01384 393889
Fax:

Total Capacity: 3,300
Seated: 300
Standing: 3,000
Simple Directions to Ground:
Nearest Railway Station: Stourbridge Junction
Car Parking: 300+
Season Tickets: -
Match Prices: Adults £2.50 Children/OAPs Free
Membership:
Training Nights: Tuesday and Thursday 7 pm

Colours: Navy blue (broad) and white (narrow) stripes
Change Colours: Broad red and white hoops, trimmed with narrow navy blue

Back Row: Dave Fourness (Coach), Scott Badcock, Jim Reed-Daunter, Phil Ralph, Jon Taylor, Neil Mitchell, Howard Baldwin, Simon Bayley, Dave Smallman, Harry Jeavons-Fellows, Alun Tapper, Nick Perry (Manager), Maggie Morley (Physio)
Front Row: Chris Mann, Anthony Dawson, Rob Merritt, Lyn Jenkins (President), Tom Jeavons-Fellows (Captain), Steve Morley (Chairman of Selectors), Mark Wilson, Simon Pennington, Richard Trigg

STOURBRIDGE R.F.C.

1994-95 Players

Player	Appearances
Jeavons-Fellows, Tom	28
Mann, Chris	28
Jeavons-Fellows, Harry	25
Dawson, Tigger	24
Merritt, Rob	24
James, Adrian	23
Tapper, Alun	23
Trigg, Richard	23
Smallman, Dale	21
Taylor, John	21
Wilson, Mark	20
Penning, Simon	19
Mitchell, Neil	18
Baylie, Simon	17
Badcock, Scott	16
Ralph, Phil	14
Baldwin, Howard	13
Reed-Daunter, Jim	13
Crees, Mark	11
Edwards, Brian	9
Perry, Nick	8
Phillips, Steve	8
Tibbetts, Nick	8
Hill, Simon	7
Crowfoot, Martin	6
Edwards, Robin	6
Horton, Nick	6
Parsons, Chris	6
Baxter, Ross	5
Farrar, Phil	5
Lewis, Simon	5
Astley, Kevin	4
Bishop, Clive	4
Waddington, Nick	4
Evans, Chris	3
Mees, Simon	3
Moseley, Andy	3
Aimes, Mike	2
Dyson, Jeremy	2
Jones, Peter	2
Kennedy, Mark	2
Priestnall, Ed	2
Priestnall, Steve	2
Smith, Jon	2
Thompson, Jim	2
Davies, Ceri	1
Harris, Mike	1
Mason, Pete	1
Rorison, Peter	1
Whitehead, Richard	1

Did it go over?

WHARFEDALE R.U.F.C.

NICKNAME: Greens, 'Dale, Dalesmen   FOUNDED: 1923

Review of the Season

The 94/95 season proved to be one of consolidation for the Dalesmen . . . both on and off the field. The 1st XV finished a creditable 4th in their first season of National league rugby in spite of being deprived of the services of key players through injury for parts of the campaign. The most convincing league victory was a 41-8 triumph over Kendal who eventually finished runners up to Walsall. The Pilkington Cup brought home wins over Stoke and Walsall but The Greens were edged out at Rotherham, losing 33-30 in the final minute.

      Off-the-field developments included a further clubhouse extension . . . the latest stage in a £1/4 million up-grading of facilities which began with the introduction of the Courage Leagues in 87-88. Captain, No. 8 Stuart Hird proved as inspirational as ever in his 16th season with the club, prop John Metcalfe played in all of Yorkshire's County Championship games and influential full back Neil Heseltine recovered from injury in time to join the County squad. Winger Alex Howarth followed his 409 points last season with 317, to finish 6th in the National 'charts'.

      Wharfedale look forward to making a strong challenge in all competitions in the 95-96 season.

WHARFEDALE R.U.F.C.

The newly extended Clubhouse (official opening Saturday 2nd September 1995 with the home game v Otley)

CLUB & GROUND DETAILS

Wharfedale Avenue, Threshfield, Skipton, North Yorks BD23 5ND
Telephone: 01756 752547
Fax:

Total Capacity: 2,120
Seated: 120
Standing: 2,000
Simple Directions to Ground: Take B6256 from Skipton Bypass. After 8 miles turn right in Threshfield, then left after 400 yds.
Nearest Railway Station: Skipton
Car Parking: 120
Season Tickets: N/A
Match Prices: £2.00
Membership: Seniors £2.00 Juniors N/A
Training Nights: Monday, Wednesday, starts 1st week in July

Colours: Emerald green shirts, white shorts
Change Colours: Navy blue shirts, white shorts

CLUB OFFICIALS

President:
J S Spencer
Chairman
F W House
Club Secretary
G H Brown
Wharfemead, Wood Lane, Crassington, Skipton, North Yorkshire BD23 5ND
Tel: (H) 01756 752410
Fixtures Secretary
J M Harrison
Old Hall Farm, Threshfield, Skipton, North Yorks
Tel: (H) 01756 752777
Press Officer
Keith Lewis
Tel: (H) 01535 634318

WINNINGTON PARK R.F.C.

NICKNAME: PARK   **FOUNDED:** 1907

Review of the Season

A season which promised well ended in disappointment. Winnington Park lost the Cheshire Cup in a hard encounter with Macclesfield, were knocked out of the Pilkington Cup by Sandal and finished in the wrong half of the league. Again an early season bad spell of injuries deprived Park of key players and in total 54 were used during the season. The squad was obviously not settled. Another feature was lack of consistency in goal kicking and when ace 2nd team kicker Scott Ashall who notched 40 points in one match was given his chance he failed to deliver at the higher level. A bonus for Winnington was the return from Australia of Nick Yardley who excelled later in the season at either No 7 or No 8 and the continued progression of 2nd row Paul Rees who played for the Anti-Assassins and continues to demonstrate increasing skill levels. Paul was a unanimous choice for the Player of the Year. Leading points scorer was Rob Oliver with 98 points and leading try scorers were Aidrian Bird, Paul Rees and Ian Taylor.

The season ended on a high note with a tour of Portugal and a captain's dinner at which no buns were thrown! At the dinner we bade farewell to Dave Nicholls who had led Winnington Park for the past two years and vice Captain Chris Sutton who has for years been a tower of strength in the centre. Steve Foster one of our past prolific points scorers has moved to the Midlands and will be playing next year for Rugby. We wish all our ex-players well and look forward to welcoming the young talent which we continue to develop. A rugby club is more than just its first XV and the youth, junior and mini teams continue to flourish and supply a stream of talented players. Ian Davies, now firmly established at tight lead prop and invited to train with the England U21 squad, Paul Rees and Nick Yardley are all products of this system.

Vince Murphy has stepped down from chief coach to concentrate on playing vets rugby again though we will still have his talents and services available. Doug Hill will lead an extended coaching team with some illustrious helpers and Ian Taylor who performed magnificently at hooker has been elected 1st team captain.

Roy Palin has accepted the invitation to continue as President for a further year, John Downham takes over as Hon Secretary and Chris Gleave and Peter Worral continue to share the fixture arrangements. As ever Winnington Park are truly amateur and ever optimistic.

CLUB OFFICIALS

President
T R Palin
Chairman
W G Cragg
Club Secretary
J C W Downham
216 London Road, Leftwich, Northwich, Cheshire CW9 8AQ
Tel: (H) 01606 48962 (W) 01565 633294
Fixtures Secretary
C F G Leave
Westerley, West Road, Weaverham, Northwich, Cheshire CW8 3HH
Tel: (H) 01606 853999 (W) 01925 752016
Press Officer
R Dean (Bob)
Tel: (H&W) 01606 43084

CLUB & GROUND DETAILS

Burrows Hill, Hartford, Northwich, Cheshire CW8 3AA
Telephone: 01606 74242
Fax:

Total Capacity: 5,000
Seated: -
Standing: 5,000
Simple Directions to Ground: One mile from Hartford turn off A556, turn left by traffic lights at Hartford Church into

Bradburns Lane, then right into Beach Road B5152. Burrows Hill is first left and ground is second entrance on right.
Nearest Railway Station: Hartford
Car Parking: 500
Season Tickets:
Match Prices: £2.00 or £4.00 OAPs half price Children free
Membership: Seniors £30.00 Juniors £16.00
Training Nights: Tuesdays and Thursdays

Colours: White with sky and royal blue circlet
Change Colours: Red and white hoops

LEAGUE 5 NORTH PROGRAMMES

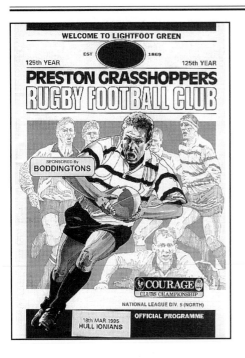

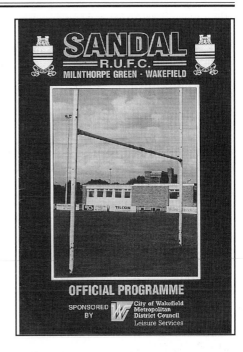

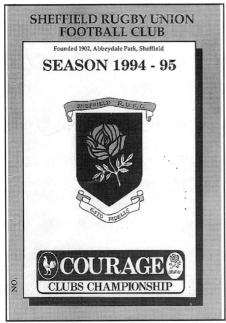

WORCESTER R.F.C.

NICKNAME: **FOUNDED:**

FOUNDED 1871

CLUB OFFICIALS

President
D Hodgson
Chairman
M Robins
Club Secretary
A C Harling
6 The Grove, Claines, Worcester WR3 7NZ
Tel: (H) 01905 454900 (W) 01562 822295
Fixtures Secretary
R Paul
139 Liverpool Road, Ronkswood, Worcester
Tel: (H) 01905 355565
Press Officer
A C Harling (as above)
Coaching Director
Phil Maynard
Commercial Manager
Richard Cummings

Back row (l to r): C Douglas (Asst. Director of Coaching), P Maynard (Director of Coaching), A Harling, C Mills, N Tisdale, R Dyde, P Shillingford, J Moffatt, S Cookson, G Blakeway, P Drew
Middle (l to r): M James, C Allen, N Stoodley (Capt), J Wootton, I Watts
Front (l to r): A Taft, A McLaughlin, A Crawford, N Lyman, S Bradley

WORCESTER R.F.C.

Worcester's Cpatain P Shillingford in a Courage League Match v Stafford

CLUB & GROUND DETAILS
Sixways, Pershore Lane, Hindlip, Worcester
Telephone: 01905 471173/454183
Fax:

Total Capacity: Unlimited
Seated: -
Standing: Unlimited
Simple Directions to Ground: Junction 6, M5, (Worcester North) take B4168 to Droitwich, 300 yards on left.
Nearest Railway Station: Worcester Foregate Street
Car Parking: 250
Season Tickets: Adults £20.00 Children/OAPs N/A
Match Prices: Adults £2.00 Children/OAPs £1.00
Membership: Seniors £40.00 Juniors £10.00
Training Nights: Monday & Thursday

Colours: Navy, gold band
Change Colours: White with navy and gold band

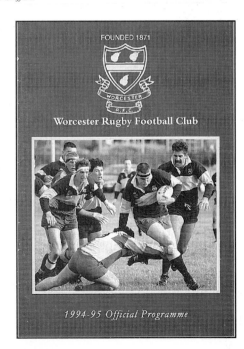

FOUNDED 1871

Worcester Rugby Football Club

1994-95 Official Programme

Rugby Programmes are now well worth collecting

The all round improvement in the standard of the Courage Championship programmes last season was impressive and without a doubt it was encouraged by the excellent 'Rugby Programe Club' which has created a real interest in these publications. Many clubs have found ideal volunteers to take on the job of programme editor but I wonder whether senior club officials have really looked around to see how many young members would be suitable to help with the work.

Most clubs have real enthusiasts who would love to be officially involved. They probably don't fit the description of the typical rugby official in fact they may be young, bright teenagers who are dedicated to the club and have energy, ideas and just need encouragement.

A good programe is a wonderful advertisement for the club and it not only gives the spectators the teams but can publicise the club functions, future fixtures, fund raising schemes and create interest amongst prospective new members.

The programme with the right blend of advertising and features can also make a club a good profit. It will be interesting to see next season's publications as I am sure more and more clubs will be taking a real pride in their marketing – TONY WILLIAMS.

Rugby Programme Club
1994/95 programme survey analysis

	Category	Points max
1	Cover pice	10
2	Cover design	20
3	Fixture and date on cover	10
4	A5 size	10
5	Programme indexing	5
6	Total pages	10
7	% editorial	10
8	Paper quality	20
9	Team line-ups	10
10	Match preview notes	20
11	Opponents analysis	10
12	Past match statistics (of this fixture)	5
13	Club news	10
14	Supporters club notes	5
15	Division news	10
16	Current season fixtures (league & other)	5
17	Are results up to date	5
18	Player appearances	5
19	All games match by match players details	15
20	Previous match reviews	5
21	Action photos	
22	News from other divisions	5
23	Junior XV fixtures and news	5
24	Local/district rugby news 5	
25	Player profile	5
26	Current team photo of home side	5
27	Quiz	5
28	Guest Writer	5
29	Lucky programme prize	3
30	General style, design, presentation "feel"	20
31	Anything else worthwhile – 5 max/item	

The Rugby Programme Club, an organisation for collectors of rugby programmes and memorabilia, have undertaken their third annual survey of match programmes in Britain and Ireland. We have made awards for the leading programmes. For the 1994/95 season the main awards won by the Courage League Clubs were:

Club Programme of the Year	Bristol
Runner Up	Otley
Most improved programme	London Irish

All clubs in Division 1 to 5 were invited to submit examples of their programmes for consideration. Sadly not all replied. The Courage League Directory mentioned the survey last season and we were pleased to receive further entries from smaller clubs. Analysis is undertaken by a small committee awarding points against 30 aspects of programme make-up. In addition an allowance is made to clubs without the resources of clubs in Division 1. Of the English clubs who entered, the top ten are summarised here.

On the whole we are pleased to report that the standard of programmes for league matches has improved on previous seasons. The aspects which showed the greatest improvements were match and player statistics – with match-by-match details starting to appear regularly – and general club news. The latter of these is important as it can be said that the programme is the "organ" of the rugby club, a simple and appropriate means of discriminating information. On the down side we considered it surprising how many clubs produced programmes which only made a cursory reference to the afternoon's game, other than team line-ups.

There were some remarkable examples of the vision, energy and commitment of programme editors from clubs of a status lower than many who produced programmes of a dreary and uninformative nature. We believe it is important to raise the standard of programme to provide information of home and away supporters as well as potentially generate income and ensure club sponsors get value for money.

The Rugby Programme Club will repeat this exercise next season. All clubs are encouraged to submit entries. At the end of the season they will receive detailed analysis of their programme which may assist its future development.

Those requiring information about the Rugby Programme Club should write to:-
David Fox, 9 Pine Close, Thornbury, Bristol BS21 1AS enclosing an A5 size SAE. Clubs wishing to enter the 1995/96 survey should send 2 different league programmes to the above address.

Bristol – A programme in which match preview, club and general information is of the highest order. Look out for local rugby news and reports on junior XV games.

Otley – Terrific programme from Division 3. Excellent match preview notes, club news and commentary on today's opponents.

Leicester – Exceptional statistical section and highly relevant and informative club news.

London Irish – Transformed last season's standard programme into one which gives current information, statistics and previews to a high standard.

Orrell – Fabulous cover. Look out for excellent Division 1 news and statistics in particular.

Saracens – Good club news. Nice mix of humour in the programme. Nice idea to put team line-ups on back cover.

Wasps – Particularly good match preview notes and divisional news.

Reading – Nicely designed programme with good preview notes and opponent analysis.

Old Whitgiftians – Outstanding programme with virtually no adverts! Nice feature is the enclosed reproduction of old programmes featuring Olf Whitgiftians from long ago.

Bath – Not as good as previous season but good nonetheless. Good domestic information.

ASKEANS R.F.C.

NICKNAME: FOUNDED: 1929

CLUB OFFICIALS

President
H P Robinson
Chairman
W J Ruston
Club Secretary
Graham Terry
End Waye, Brookhurst Gardens, Southborough, Tunbridge Wells, Kent TN4 0UA
Tel: (H) 01892 528996
Fixtures Secretary
Mick Sidgwick
53 Borkwood Way, Orpington, Kent BR6 9PB
Tel: 01689 867436
Press Officer
Patrick Barrow
0181 319 2984

CLUB & GROUND DETAILS

60A Broad Walk, Kidbrooke SE3 8NB
Telephone: 0181 852 8596
Fax:

Total Capacity: 1,000
Seated: 200
Standing: 800
Simple Directions to Ground: A2 from Central London or Kent. BroadWalk is just off A2 between Blackheath and Eltham.
Nearest Railway Station: Kidbrooke
Car Parking: 120
Season Tickets: £50.00
Match Prices: Adults £4.00 Children/OAPs £2.00
Membership: Seniors £60.00 Juniors £10.00
Training Nights: Tuesday and Thursday

Colours: Blue, black, white
Change Colours: White

Askeans 1994-95

ASKEANS R.F.C.

Askeans' skipper Richard Hennah against Havant

Leading Appearances for Club

Name	Appearances	Season
1 G V Wickens	546	1953-79
2 P Dessent	465	1968-86
3 S Homewood	427	1972-88

Leading Scorers in all games (1994/95):

Name	Pos.	P	T	P	C	DG	Ttl
Richard Larkin	Fly Half	23	1	56	15	7	224
Howard Evans	Scrum Half	22	7				35
Robbie Graham	Wing	9	7				35

Leading scorer in Club's history: John Field

Record points scorer in a season: John Field   257 in 1986-7

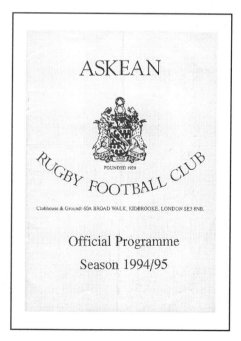

ASKEAN

FOUNDED 1929

Clubhouse & Ground: 60A BROAD WALK, KIDBROOKE, LONDON SE3 8NB.

Official Programme

Season 1994/95

BARKING R.U.F.C.

NICKNAME: **FOUNDED:** 1930

CLUB OFFICIALS

President
W Marshall
Chairman
L Consiglio
Club Secretary
George Darley
12 Glenton Way, Rise Park, Romford, Essex RM1 4AF
Tel: 01708 764828
Fixtures Secretary
Graham Comley
26 Beltinge Road, Harold Wood, Essex RM3 0UJ
Tel: (H) 0181 599 5791 (W) 0171 696 3186
Press Officer
Jeff Caney
0181 505 1191

CLUB PLAYING RECORD 1994-95

National Division: Five South
Final League Position at end of 1994/95 Season:
League Playing record: P 12, W 7, D 0, L 5, Pts F 223, Pts A 173
Season Playing record: P 32, W 23, D 0, L 9, Pts F 829, Pts A 398
1995-96 1st XV Captain: Dean Cutting
1995-96 1st XV Coach: Mike Lovett

BARKING R.U.F.C.

Barking on the 'Attack'

CLUB & GROUND DETAILS

Goresbrook, Gale Street, Dagenham, Essex RM9 4TY
Telephone: 0181 595 7324
Fax:

Total Capacity: 100
Seated: -
Standing: 100
Simple Directions to Ground: A13 from London over Reipple Road flyover, 1st turning on left at 400 yds, Gale Street.
Nearest Railway Station: Beacontree Station (Districtline) 1/2 mile
Car Parking: 150
Season Tickets: N/A
Match Prices: Adults £2.50 Children/OAPs £1.00
Membership: Seniors £33.00 Juniors Free
Training Nights: Tuesdays and Thursdays

Colours: Cardinal & gray hoops - navy blue shorts - red socks
Change Colours: Orange

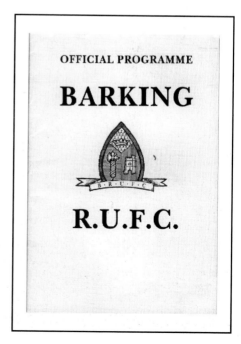

OFFICIAL PROGRAMME

BARKING

R · U · F · C

R.U.F.C.

BERRY HILL R.F.C.

NICKNAME: FOUNDED: 1893

CLUB OFFICIALS

President
R W Jenkins JP
Chairman
John Evans
Club Secretary
T J Baldwin
Hill Brink, Joyford Hill,
Coleford, Glos GL16 7AH
Tel: 01594 832539
Director of Rugby
Ian Seymour
Fixtures Secretary
G R Goddard
71A Cheltenham Road,
Gloucester GL2 0JG
01452 306749
Press Officer
John Belcher
01594 832249

CLUB & GROUND DETAILS

Lakers Road, Berry Hill, Coleford, Glos GL16 7LY
Telephone: 01594 833295
Fax:

Total Capacity: 600
Seated: Nil
Standing: 600
Simple Directions to Ground: A4136 Gloucester
to Monmouth road, turn into Park Road at Five
Acres, then into Lakers Road.
Nearest Railway Station: Gloucester
Car Parking: 100
Season Tickets: -
Match Prices: £2.00 Children/OAPs 50p
Membership: Seniors £5.00 Juniors £3.00
Training Nights: Monday and Wednesday

Colours: Black and amber
Change Colours: Red

CLUB PLAYING RECORD 1994-95

National Division: Five South
Final League Position at end of 1994/95 Season:
League Playing record: P 12, W 3, D 0, L 9, Pts F 133, Pts A 229
Season Playing record: P 36, W 12, D 3, L 21, Pts F 494, Pts A 656

1995-96 1st XV Captain: Nicky Harris
1995-96 1st XV Coach: Neil Jones
1995-96 1st XV Manager: John Cole

Back (l to r): T Ruck, K Mapps, D Edwards, G Jones, T Price, I Bell, G Alexander, J Powell, D Kear, J Evans, P Greenaway (Coach)
Front (lto r): D Powell (First Aid), J Bennett, A Jones, M Harris (Capt), P Tingle, P Baldwin, M Smith

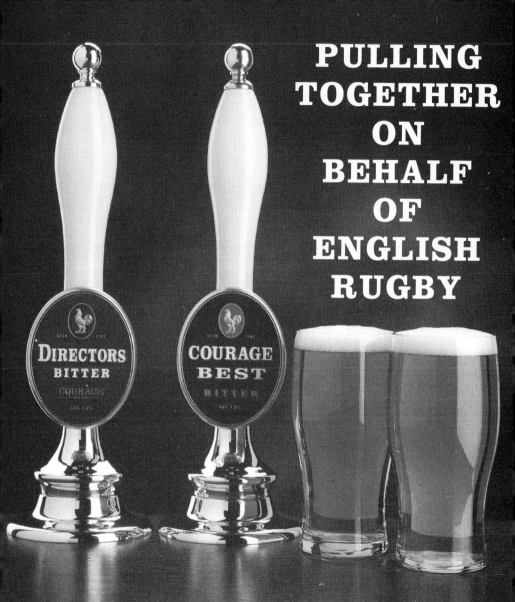

PULLING TOGETHER ON BEHALF OF ENGLISH RUGBY

Proud Sponsors of The Courage Clubs Championship and the England Squad

COURAGE
CLUBS CHAMPIONSHIP

CAMBERLEY R.F.C.

NICKNAME: **FOUNDED:** 1931

CLUB OFFICIALS

President
Harry Gibson
Chairman
Bob Hughes
Club Secretary
P J Bland
20 Moulsham Lane, Yateley, Camberley, Surrey GU17 7QY
Tel: (H) 01252 878934 (W) 01252 890097
Fixtures Secretary
W Fletcher
63 Rockwood Avenue, Owlsmoor, Camberley, Surrey GU13 9PD
Tel: (H) 01344 777701
Treasurer
M Courtness
Press Officer
D Hughes
Tel: (H) 01252 613869

CLUB & GROUND DETAILS

Camberley R.F.C., Watchetts Recreation Ground, Park Road, Camberley, Surrey GU15 2SR
Telephone: 01276 25395
Fax:

Total Capacity:
Seated:
Standing:
Simple Directions to Ground: M3 Junction 4, follow signs to Camberley. At Whites Garage in Frimley Road turn right into Park Road
Nearest Railway Station: Camberley
Car Parking: 100 next to clubhouse
Season Tickets:
Match Prices:
Membership:
Training Nights: Tuesdays and Thursdays

Colours: Black with amber collar
Change Colours: Black and yellow hoops

LEAGUE 5 SOUTH PROGRAMMES

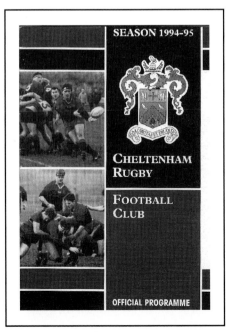

CAMBORNE R.F.C.

NICKNAME: Cherry and Whites   **FOUNDED:** 1878

CLUB OFFICIALS

President
D L C Roberts
Chairman
R Harris
Club Secretary
John Dunstan
The Retreat, 11 Station Hill, Praze an Beeble, Camborne TR14 0JT
Tel: (H) 01209 831373 (W) 01736 795456
Fixtures Secretary
David Smith
65 Hughville Street, Camborne, Cornwall
Tel: 01209 716992
Press Officer
John Dunstan
Tel: (H) 01209 831373 (W) 01736 795456

Leading Appearances for Club:

Name	Appearances	Season
1 Nigel Pellowe	1,003	1969-93
2 Bobby Tonkin	771	1967-85
3 Frank Butler	530	1968-88

Leading Scorers in all games (1994/95):

Name	Position	P	T	P	C	DG	Ttl
D Chapman	Fly Half/Full Back	17	2	25	16	2	123
S Moyle	Fly Half	25	5	9	16	2	90
T Adams	Lock	28	15	–	–	–	75

CLUB & GROUND DETAILS

Camborne R.F.C., The Recreation Ground, Camborne,
Cornwall
Telephone: 01209 713227
Fax:

Total Capacity: 9,977
Seated: 777
Standing: 9,200
Simple Directions to Ground: Leave A30 Camborne/Redruth
bypass at Junction "Camborne West" following signs for
Recreation Ground
Nearest Railway Station: Camborne
Car Parking: 40 Crane Park Camborne
Season Tickets: £25.00
Match Prices: Adults £2.50 Children/OAPs £1.50
Membership: Seniors £25.00 Juniors £25.00
Training Nights: Mondays and Wednesdays

Colours: Cherry and white
Change Colours: Blue

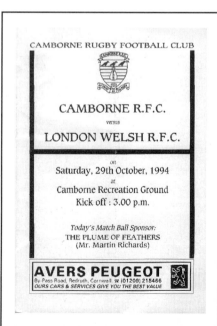

LEAGUE 5 SOUTH PROGRAMMES

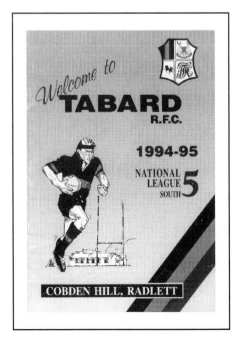

CHELTENHAM R.F.C.

NICKNAME: **FOUNDED:** 1889

Review of the Season

After being runners-up in the South West One league the previous season, Cheltenham gained promotion to National League 5(S), without losing a single league game, but drawing against Brixham.

Promotion depended on the result of the last league game in April against Newbury, on the Newbury ground, with Cheltenham emerging winners by 26 pts, to 17 pts., in a nail-biting encounter.

Their biggest win in the league was against Stroud (37-0), and they ended with a total of 275 pts., with 111 pts. against.

Overall, Cheltenham won 28 games, with notable successes against Moseley, Coventry and London Irish.

But they suffered a grevious loss when their coach, Dave Protherough, was tragically killed in a road accident early on in the season. He had inspired the club to aim for the highest possible national league status.

Over 60 players turned out for the first XV., and there was considerable back- up strength available in the United side, which went out to win the West of England 2nd. XVs. merit table for the first time, scoring over 1,000 points against leading second XVs.

Cheltenham now confidently face, national league rugby for the first time in 105 years, and with a successful first season for their U21 team, can claim to provide games from U8 through to senior level, as well as having two ladies sides.

CLUB OFFICIALS

President
Peter Stephens
Chairman
Chris Mourton
Club Secretary
Thomas Parker
39 Long Mynd Avenue, Cheltenham, Glos GL551 5QT
Tel: (H) 01242 521076

Fixtures Secretary
M D Edwards
2 Greenbank Cotts, Guiting Power, Cheltenham GL54 5UT
Tel: (H) 01452 850232 (W) 01452 419666
Player Manager
John Wood
Press Officer
T Parker
Tel: (H) 01242 521076

Leading Appearances for Club:

Name	Appearances	Season
Mal Preedy	29	1994-95
Matthew Watts	29	1994-95
Peter Lodge	28	1994-95

Leading Scorers in all games (1994/95):

Name	Position	P	T	P	C	DG	Ttl
M Watts	Fly Half	29	4	44	51	6	272
Paul Edwards	Wing	27	21	–	–	–	105
Phil Watters	Full Back	21	8	7	1	1	66

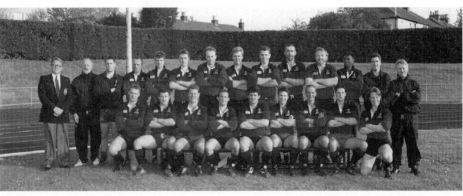

Photo: Simon Vickers

CHELTENHAM R.F.C.

Flanker John Wood leading a drive on the Newbury line, during Cheltenham's game at Newbury, in the last league game of the season, which Cheltenham won, to secure promotion to National League 5(S).   Photo: Gloucestershire Echo

CLUB & GROUND DETAILS

Cheltenham R.F.C., Prince of Wales Stadium, Tommy Taylor's Lane, Cheltenham GL50 4NJ
Telephone: 01242 525393
Fax:

Total Capacity: 3,500
Seated: 500
Standing: 3,000
Simple Directions to Ground: From M5 (South): Leave at Junction 11, proceed towards Cheltenham, 1/2 mile to roundabout near Golden Valley Hotel. Straight on to second roundabout (GCHQ building on left). Bear left along Princess Elizabeth Way to roundabout near Kingsditch Industrial Estate. Straight over into Kingsditch Lane, first turning right (Swindon Road), over railway bridge. Bear left where road forks (St Pauls Road), pass under railway bridge and first turning left up Folly Lane to stadium on left.
From North, M5 motorway: Leave at Junction 10, then approx. 1 1/2 miles along A4019 until roundabout near Kingsditch Industrial Estate. Turn left into Kingsditch Lane and continue as directions from M5 South.
From London (A40) & Cirencester: Proceed towards Cheltenham until junction of London Road and Cirencester Road (traffic Lights), Holy Apostles Church. Continue past Hales Road lights, to next lights, turn right into Hewlett Road – following signs for A435 (Evesham) – All Saints Road, Pittville Circus, Wellington Road. Then right at lights towards Evesham to roundabout outside racecourse. Turn left into Swindon Lane. Take third turning left (signed Recreation Centre), straight to stadium on right.
Nearest Railway Station: Cheltenham
Car Parking: 300 adjacent to ground
Season Tickets: Adults £25.00 Children/OAPs £12.00
Match Prices: £2.50
Membership: Seniors £20.00 Juniors £10.00
Training Nights: Mondays and Thursdays (seniors) Tuesdays and Thursdays (juniors)

Colours: Red and black
Change Colours: White

CLUB PLAYING RECORD 1994-95

National Division: Five South
Final League Position at end of 1994/95 Season:
League Playing record: P 12, W 11, D 1, L 0, Pts F 275, Pts A 111
Season Playing record: P 33, W 28, D 1, L 5, Pts F 849, Pts A 411

HENLEY R.F.C.

NICKNAME: **FOUNDED:** 1930

CLUB OFFICIALS

President
A Hobbs
Chairman
G Horner
Club Secretary
P J Allen
8 St Katherines Road, Henley, Oxon RG9 1PJ
Tel: (H) 01491 575154 (W) 0181 7887272
Fixtures Secretary
P Emerson
16 St Marys Close, Henley, Oxon RG9 1RD
Tel: (H) 01491 578606 (W) 01734 02455
Press Officer
N Armstead
Tel:
Commercial Manager
P Woodall

CLUB & GROUND DETAILS

Henley R.F.C., 'Dry Leas', Marlow Road, Henley, Oxon
Telephone: 01491 574499
Fax:

Total Capacity: 1,200
Seated: None
Standing: 1,200
Simple Directions to Ground: Centre of Henley follow signs to Marlow
Ground on left approx 100 yds from roundabout
Nearest Railway Station: Henley
Car Parking: 150 adjacent to ground
Season Tickets: £20.00
Match Prices: -
Membership: Seniors £35.00 Juniors £10.00
Training Nights: Mondays and Thursdays

Colours: Gold with blue (navy) and green hoops
Change Colours: Dark green

HENLEY R.F.C.

Photo: Adrian Lewington

HIGH WYCOMBE R.U.F.C.

NICKNAME: WYCS   **FOUNDED:** 1929 (present form) originally 1891

CLUB OFFICIALS

President
John Brine
Chairman
Dr Eric Wilgher
Club Secretary
Don Dickerson
3 Talbot Avenue, High Wycombe, Bucks HP13 5HE
Tel: (H) 01494 532024 (W) 01494 441211
Fixtures Secretary
George Brown
Deerleap, Primrose Hill, Widmerend, High Wycombe, Bucks HP15 6NU
Tel: (H) 01494 716700
Press Officer
David Harrod
Tel: (H) 01494 711562 (W) 01344 779333

CLUB PLAYING RECORD 1994-95

National Division: Five South
Final League Position at end of 1994/95 Season:
League Playing record: P 12, W 4, D 0, L 8, Pts F 192, Pts A 261
Season Playing record: P 33, W 15, D 0, L 18, Pts F 697, Pts A 693

1995-96 1st XV Captain: Elliott Forester
1995-96 Team Secretary: Mike Baud

High Wycombe First XV in new club shirts early Autumn 1994

HIGH WYCOMBE R.U.F.C.

CLUB & GROUND DETAILS

High Wycombe R.U.F.C., Kingsmead Road, High Wycombe, Bucks HP11 1JB
Telephone: 01494 524407
Fax:

Total Capacity: Unlimited
Seated:
Standing: Unlimited
Simple Directions to Ground: From East – off Junction 3 M40 (Wycombe East) to roundabout. First left to mini roundabout under motorway viaduct. Turn right. 800 yards road takes sharp right hand bend. Do not go round bend but take road which runs off at apex of the bend (Kingsmead Road). Club 1 mile on right.
From West – Off Junction 4 M40 (Wycombe Central) follow A404 (Amersham) signs into town centre. Take A40 (Beaconsfield) to the East. Follow A40 until Red Lion Pub on left (1 1/2 miles approx.). Take next turn right into Abbey Barn Road. Follow 800 yards around sharp left hand bend into Kingsmead Road. Club 1 mile on left.
Nearest Railway Station: High Wycombe (Marylebone Line)
Car Parking: unlimited
Season Tickets:
Match Prices: £2.00
Membership: £100.00 life £15.00 annual
Training Nights: Tuesdays

Colours: Broad green hoop and narrow black, white and green hoops
Change Colours: Broad black hoop and narrow black,whiteand green hoops

LYDNEY R.F.C.

NICKNAME: Severnsiders   **FOUNDED:** 1887

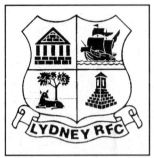

CLUB OFFICIALS

President
T C Bailey
Chairman
Dr Peter Catlin
Club Secretary
A John Jones
5 Kimberley Close, Lydney, Glos GL15 5 AE
Tel: (H) 01594 842709 (W) 01594 841470 (Fax) 01594 844604
Fixtures Secretary
R Powell
Skaint Maestro, Lydney, Glos
Tel; (H) 01594 562820 (W) Mobile 0860 497301
Press Officer
Ken Hyde
Tel: 01594 841351
Social Manageress
Diane Emery
Shop Manageress
Ann Sargent
Tel: 01594 502822

CLUB & GROUND DETAILS

Lydney R.F.C., Regentsholm, Regents Street, Lydney, Glos GL1 5SR
Telephone: 01594 842479
Fax:

Total Capacity: 3,320
Seated: 320
Standing: 3,000
Simple Directions to Ground: From Gloucester (A48) Turn left at Swan Hotel. 1st left into Fairfield Road, 2nd right into ground
Nearest Railway Station: Lydney 1 1/2 miles
Car Parking: 80 on ground
Season Tickets: Adults £30.00 Children/OAPs £15.00
Match Prices: Adults £3.00 Children/OAPs £1.50
Membership: Seniors £15.00 Juniors £5.00
Training Nights: Tuesdays and Thursdays

Colours: Black and white hoops
Change Colours: Red

1st XV Coaching Panel: Rod Sealy, Brian Vine, Andy Wyman, Paul Nowell
1st XV Manager: Gordon Sargent
1st XV Captain: Nick Nelmes

Leading Scorers in all games (1994/95):

Name	Position	Games	T	P	C	DG	Ttl
R Mills	Centre	5	25	11	1		125
A Halford	Wing	4	22	7			100
M Stubbs	Wing	12					60

Leading socrer in Club's history: John Morris   487
Record points scorer in a season: John Morris   487

METROPOLITAN POLICE GROUND
at Imber Court, East Molesey

METROPOLITAN POLICE R.F.C.

NICKNAME: **FOUNDED:** 1923

CLUB OFFICIALS

President
Sir Paul Condon
Chairman
David Veness
Club Secretary
David Barham
MPAA Office, Room G11, Wellington House, Buckingham Gate, London SW1E 6BE
Tel: (H) 0181 4224966 (W) 0171 2307109
Fixtures Secretary
Robert Williams
Enquiries, Hendon Police Station, 133 Brent Street, London NW4 4DA
Tel: (H) 0181 3492319 (W) 0181 2004771
Press Officer
Andy Fairweather
Tel: (H) 081 3184098 (W) Mobile 0956 200574

CLUB PLAYING RECORD 1994-95

National Division: Five South
Final League Position at end of 1994/95 Season:
League Playing record: P 12, W 5, D 0, L 17, Pts F 183, Pts A 175
Season Playing record: P 35, W 16, D 0, L 19, Pts F 706, Pts A 587

1st XV Manager 95-96: Frank Armstrong
1st XV Captain 95-96: Kevin Walsh

Back row (l to r): Frank Armstrong (Team Manager), Mark Swevin, Steve Williams, Richard Bannister, Richard Galvin, Andy Kearns, Phil Thompson, Ian Warlow, Mike Booth, Harry Monk, Andy Carter, Rowly Williams (Coach)
Front row (l to r): Paul Totham, Derek Baraam, Simon Welch, Leighton Davies, Richard Jenkins, Kevon Walsh (Capt), Paul Wakefield, Paul Galvin, Ross Ferry

METROPOLITAN POLICE R.F.C.

Clear off side by Paul Galvin but good shot of pack enjoying the sunshine!!

CLUB & GROUND DETAILS

Metropolitan Police R.F.C., (Imber Court) Sports Club, Ember Lane, East Molesey KT8 0BT
Telephone: 0101 3901267
Fax: 0181 3989755

Total Capacity: 3,250
Seated: 750
Standing: 2,500
Simple Directions to Ground: M25 junction 12, M3 to London junction 1, A308 to Hampton Court, turn right A309 next roundabout(??) into Ember Court Road. Club at end of road.
Nearest Railway Station: Thames Ditton and Esher
Car Parking: 200
Season Tickets: -
Match Prices: Adults £3.00 Children/OAPs £1.50
Membership: Seniors £20.00
Training Nights: Thursday

Colours: Blue and white hoops
Change Colours: Gold shirts with blue collar and sleeves

Leading Scorers in all games (1994/95):

Name	Position	P	T	P	C	DG	Ttl
M Slevin	O-Half/Wing	22	7	36	24	2	197
A Carter	Wing	27	15	4	2		91
J Lunn	Full Back	25	1	10	4		43

Player of the Year – Richard Galvin
Had an excellent season with total commitment both in defence and attack.

NORTH WALSHAM R.F.C.

NICKNAME: **FOUNDED:** 1962

CLUB OFFICIALS

President
Cyril Durrant
Chairman
Mike Biggs
Club Secretary
John Wheeley
Dobeck, Thurne, Gt. Yarmouth NR29 3BY
Tel: (H) 01692 670294
Fixtures Secretary
Keith Jarvis
The Chilterns, 2D Millfield Road, North Walsham NR28 0EB
Tel: (H) 01692 406429 (W) 01263 732341
Press Officer
Toni Marcantonio
Tel: (H) 01493 751837 (W) 01362 654285
Commercial Manager: Pat Dye
Director of Coaching: Dick Flatters
1st XV Captain 95-96: Nick Greenhall
1st XV Coach 95-96: Nick Youngs

CLUB & GROUND DETAILS

Norwich Road, Scottow, Norwich NR10 5BU
Telephone: 01692 538461
Fax:

Total Capacity: 1,000
Seated: Nil
Standing: 1,000
Simple Directions to Ground: Leave Norwich on B1150 to North Walsham. Continue through Cottishall towards N. Walsham. Ground is on left after passing Three Horse Shoes pub.
Nearest Railway Station: North Walsham
Car Parking: Ample
Season Tickets: -
Match Prices: £3.00
Membership: Seniors £40.00
Training Nights: Tuesday & Thursday

Colours: Green with black band and white stripe
Change Colours: White/black shorts

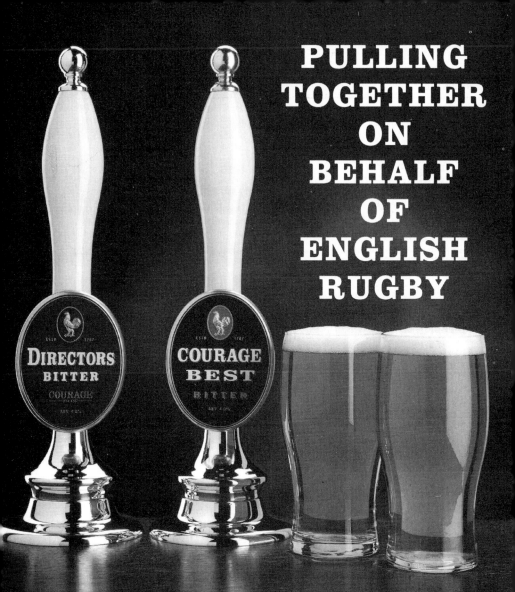

PULLING TOGETHER ON BEHALF OF ENGLISH RUGBY

**Proud Sponsors of
The Courage Clubs Championship
and the England Squad**

TABARD R.F.C.

NICKNAME: Tabs   **FOUNDED:** 1951

Tabard Rugby Football Club

Tabard, under skipper Richard Malone, had another successful season with a league position of sixth, reaching round three of the Pilkington Cup and again winning the Honda Herts Presidents Cup. The league got off to a hesitant start before straight wins against Sudbury, Metropolitan Police and Henley gave them the foundation they needed. A good run in the Pilkington Cup with wins over Sherborne, Weston-Super-Mare and High Wycombe put them into the third round against Richmond, a game closer than the 24-16 scoreline indicated and one which gave the media opportunity to debate a penalty try conceded early on.

Away from the leagues Tabard had good games against Saracens and Northampton second teams as well as the Leicester development squad and in the Honda Herts Presidents Cup, beat Letchworth to win the cup for a record seventh time.

Stand off Nick Churchman kept the points mounting up but had to settle with a club record of 299 and flanker Steve Armstrong led the try scorers with 9 and also played the most games, only missing one throughout the season.

The club is looking for another solid performance next year with hooker Mark Trippick as Captain and Tim Smithers joining the coaching squad led by Ivor Jones.

CLUB OFFICIALS

President
D T Burrows
Chairman
T F Clark
Club Secretary
Piers S R Wood
67a Falcon Road, Battersea, London SW11 2PG
Tel: (H) 0171 924 1520 (W) 0171 246 3753

Fixtures Secretary
C Carmichael
10 Chandos Road, Boreham Wood, Herts WD6 1UU
Tel: (H) 0181 953 9006 (W) 0181 953 9246
Press Officer
P C Cook
Tel: (H) 0181 207 5564 (W) 0171 492 4997

CLUB PLAYING RECORD 1994-95

National Division: Five South
Final League Position at end of 1994/95 Season:
League Playing record: P 12, W 7, D 0, L 5, Pts F 207, Pts A 208
Season Playing record: P 31, W 20, D 2, L 9, Pts F 579, Pts A 462

1st XV Captain 95-96: Mark Trippick
1st XV Coach 95-96: Ivor Jones

Team before Herts Cup Final   *Photo: Cindy Hardy*

TABARD R.F.C.

Nick Churchman on the way to scoring against London Welsh Photo: Cindy Hardy

CLUB & GROUND DETAILS

Cobden Hill, Readlett WD7 7LN
Telephone: 01923 855561
Fax:

Total Capacity: 2,000
Seated: -
Standing: 2,000
Simple Directions to Ground: On A5183 Watling
Street, from Elstree turn right after entry into Radlett,
blind entrance by high brick wall. (Cat & Fiddle pub
is 100 m past entry on left)
Nearest Railway Station: Radlett
Car Parking: 200
Season Tickets: -
Match Prices: Adults £2.00 Children/OAPs £1.00
Membership: Seniors £30.00 Juniors £10.00
Training Nights: Tuesday and Thursday

Colours: Navy, broad gold band edged with red
Change Colours: Red/gold/navy quarters

Leading Scorers in all games (1994-95):

Name	Position	P	T	P	C	DG	Ttl
N Churchman	Stand off	28	4	68	33	3	299
S Armstrong	Flanker	30	9				45
D Robjohns	Centre	25	6				30

Leading scorer in Club's history: N Churchman
Record points scorer in a season: N Churchman

Dick Malone (Tabard Captain) at front of line out. Other faces Jed Siollemia and Martin Richards

WESTON-SUPER-MARE R.F.C.

NICKNAME: Seasiders **FOUNDED:** 1875

CLUB OFFICIALS
President
Dr G Papworth
Chairman
J Brentnall
Club Secretary
H C Hope
24 Feniton Clovelly Road, Worle, Weston-Super-mare, Avon BS22 0LN
Tel: (H) 01934 511834 (W) 01934 625643
Chairman of Marketing
Andrew Cashmore
Chairman of Rugby Comm.
Bill Poole
Fixtures Secretary
R Main
142 Quantock Road, Weston-Super-Mare, Avon BS23 4DP
Tel: (H) 01934 417864
Press Officer
Bernard Pauncefort OBE
Tel: 01934 626174

CLUB PLAYING RECORD 1994-95
National Division: Five South
Final League Position at end of 1994/95 Season:
League Playing record: P 12, W 8, D 0, L 4, Pts F 194, Pts A 160
Season Playing record: P 35, W 25, D 0, L 9, Pts F 891, Pts A 449

Tour Party to Germany

WESTON SUPER MARE R.F.C.

Weston-Super-Mare v Gordano

CLUB & GROUND DETAILS

Recreation Ground, Drove Road, Weston-Super-Mare, Avon BS23 3PA
Telephone: 01934 623118 (Office 625643)
Fax:
Chairman of Ground/Buildings: John Fry
Chairman of Bar: Andrew Simmonds
Total Capacity: 6,499
Seated: 499
Standing: 6,000
Simple Directions to Ground: M5 Junction 21, follow A370 into New Bristol Road then Locking Road. Into Weston 2.5 miles. 3rd set of traffic lights - left over railway bridge. 4th exit off roundabout.
Nearest Railway Station: Weston-Super-Mare
Car Parking: 200
Season Tickets: Adults From £20.00 to £30.00 Children £7.50 OAPs £12.00
Match Prices: Adults from £2.00 to £4.00 Children/OAPs £1.00
Membership: Seniors £30.00 Juniors £7.50
Training Nights: Monday and Wednesday

Colours: Royal blue, red and white hoops
Change Colours: Blue or red

Team Captain (1995-96) and Player of the Year (1994-95) Paul Thatcher

Wharfdale flanker Russ Buckroyd is bundled into touch by the defence in his side's 25-3 win over Sheffield in Courage League Five at Abbeydale

Photo: Gordon Bunney

THE REGIONAL DIVISIONS

NORTHERN

MIDLAND

LONDON & SOUTH EAST

SOUTH WEST

NORTHERN DIVISION

CHAIRMAN, League Sub-Committee
Bob Archer, Brookfield House, Scotland Head, Winlaton, Tyne & Wear NE21 6PL (H) 0191 414 3532

N.E. CO-ORDINATOR AND YORKSHIRE REPRESENTATIVE
Les Bentley, 32 Moorhead Terrace, Shipley, W. Yorkshire BD18 4LB (H) 01274 585460

N.W. CO-ORDINATOR AND LANCASHIRE REPRESENTATIVE
Bill Chappell, Seawood House, Carter Road, Kents Bank, Grange-over-Sands, Cumbria LA11 7AS (H) 01539 533456

DURHAM REPRESENTATIVE
Dr Lee Hetherington., 97 Kells Lane, Gateshead, Tyne & Wear NE9 5XX (H) 0191 487 9128

NORTHUMBERLAND REPRESENTATIVE
Dudley Gibbs, Sandy Ford, Healey, Nr Riding Mill, Northumberland NE44 6BA (H) 01434 682 496 (B) 01207 500 957

CHESHIRE REPRESENTATIVE
Mike Lord, 68 Hoole Road, Chester, Cheshire CH2 3NL (H) 01244 312702 (B) 0151 356 6241

CUMBRIA REPRESENTATIVE
Jack Hamer, 55 Rush Green Road, Lymm, Cheshire WA13 9PS (H) 01925 755584 (W) 0151 548 6756

LEAGUE SECRETARIES
North One D Ellis, 19 Beadon Avenue, Waterloo, Huddersfield, West Yorkshire HD5 8QZ (H) 01484 421046
North Two Mike Smith, The Lowe, Wainstalls, Halifax, W. Yorkshire HX2 7TR (H & Fax) 01422 882879
North East One I. Clark, 109 Dryden Road, Low Fell, Gateshead, Tyne and Wear NE9 5TS (H) 0191 421 8271
North East Two J. Scott, 8 Main Street, Cherry Burton, Beverley, East Yorks HU17 7RF (H) 01964 551340 (B) 01612 237981
Durham/North One S. Harrison, 9 Gillside Grove, Roker, Sunderland, Tyne & Wear SR6 9PQ (H) 0191 548 4272
Durham/North Two Mrs Joyce Baty, 5 Brooklands, Ponteland, Northumberland NE20 9LZ (H) 01661 823527
Durham/North Three Anthony Brown, 22 Mill Crescent, Hebburn, Tyne & Wear NE31 1UQ (H)

0191 469 3716
Yorkshire One P J Lee, 64 Station Road, Burley-in-Wharfedale, Ilkley, W Yorks LS29 7NG (H) 01943 862599
Yorkshire Two Ron Lewis, 33 Swift Way, Sandal, Wakefield, W. Yorkshire WF2 6SQ (H) 01924 253049
Yorkshire Three H Ormerod, 11 Kirklands Avenue, Baildon, W. Yorkshire BD17 6EQ (H) 01274 591005
Yorkshire Four P Hazledine, 90 Fairburn Drive, Garforth, Leeds LS25 2JD (H) 0113 866035
Yorkshire Five A.S. McNally, 28 Cherry Tree Road, Armthorpe, Doncaster, S Yorks (H) 01302 834252
North West One Alan Johnson, 6 Rugby Drive, Tytherington, Macclesfield, Cheshire (H) 01625 614697
North West Two Ivon Hodgeson, Kimberley End, 22 Capesthorn Close, Holmes Chapel, Cheshire CW4 7EW(H) 01477 533406
Cumbria/North Lancs Roger Bott, 123 Albert Road West, Heaton, Bolton, Lancs BL1 5ED (H) 01204 841376
Cumbria Bill Hopkinson, Far Hey Farm, Littleborough, Rochdale, Lancs OL15 9NS (H) 01706 379879 (B) 01706 47474 x 4531
North Lancs One Colin Barton, 4 Oulderhill Drive, Rochdale, Lancs OL11 5LB (H) 01706 350312
North Lancs Two Ian Scott Brown, Brumsholme, Pendleview, Grindleton, Nr. Clitheroe, Lancs BB7 4QU (H) 01200 440102 (B) 01254 582749 / 57846
Cheshire/South Lancs Mike Massey, Fieldside, Grange Road, Bowden, Cheshire WA14 3EE (H) 0161 928 2997
Cheshire Ken Punshon, 24 Newcombe Road, Holcombe Brook, Nr. Bury, Lancs BL0 9UT (H) 01204 884886
South Lancs Vic Thomas, 5 Portree Close, Winton, Eccles, Manchester M30 8LX (H) 0161 788 7274

NORTHERN DIVISION

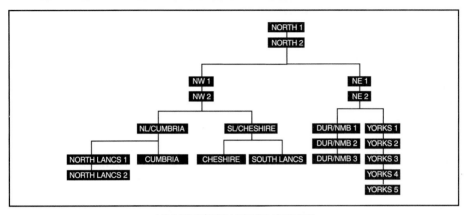

ADMINISTRATIVE RULES

On League Saturdays, both Clubs will telephone the match result through to their League Secretary. Both clubs will also confirm within 48 hours the result and score in writing together with the list of players and replacements featuring in the match to the League Secretary on a card signed by the referee.

a.   In the case of Northern Division Leagues 1 and 2, North West Leagues 1 and 2 and North East Leagues 1 and 2, such telephone calls shall be made not later than 5.30pm on the evening of the game and the League Secretary shall report the results to Snowdon Sports Editorial, PO Box 154, Sheffield S10 4BW. Tel: Sheffield 0114 230 3093 (24 hour answering copy line).

b.   The remaining League Secretaries will telephone the results as soon as possible, but in any case not later than 3.00pm on the Sunday following the games to Snowdon Sports Editorial at the above numbers.

c.   In Northern Division Leagues 1 and 2 the League Secretaries will remit to the Chairman the scores and results in writing within 48 hours. The remaining League Secretaries will remit the results and the scores in writing to their North East or North West co-ordinator within 48 hours.

d.   In the case of an abandoned match the Secretary of the League must be supplied by the home Club with a certificate signed by the Referee indicating the point at which the match was abandoned, and the score.

e.   These arrangements do not prohibit local publicity and Clubs are advised to maintain and improve local publicity by informing their local press as usual.

f.   Any Club failing to notify the result in accordance with this Rule shall on the first occasion during a

season be fined £15, on the second and third occasion £25. If the fines are not paid there will be a recommendation to the RFU that the Club be suspended or expelled from the League. Should payment of fines not be honoured within 28 days of the date of the invoice, the offending club will lose 2 league points.

RESCHEDULED MATCHES

A match postponed or abandoned under Regulation 11 (a) or (b) or a match not played on the appointed day for reasons acceptable to the Organising Committee SHALL be played on the NEXT AVAILABLE Saturday.

A Saturday is deemed to be "available" UNLESS one of the following conditions applies:

a)   Either Club has, on that day, a scheduled Courage League match.

b)   Either Club has, on that day, a Pilkington Cup or Shield match.

c)   Either Club has, on that weekend, a match in a Competition under the authority of their Constituent Body BUT **NOT** a Merit Table match.

d)   Either Club has a demand on one or more of their effectively registered players to play in a representative match under the authority of the RFU, their Division or their Constituent Body on that day.

e)   In addition, the Northern Division Organising Committee may – at its absolute discretion and usually at the start of a season – declare a specific Saturday "unavailable" where it falls on or close to a public holiday or where it is considered inappropriate to play for other particular reasons.

NORTHERN CHAMPIONS ROLL OF HONOUR 1994/95

North 1
Sandal
North 2
Macclesfield
North West 1
Sedgley Park
North West 2
Leigh
North East 1
Blaydon
North East 2
Ashington
Cumbria/Lancashire North
Windermere
Cumbria
Carnforth
Lancashire North 1
Metrovick
Lancashire North 2
Eccles
Cheshire & Lancashire South
Aspull

Cheshire
Congleton
Lancashire South
Newton-le-Willows
Durham & Northumberland 1
Percy Park
Durham & Northumberland 2
Winlaton Vulcans
Durham & Northumberland 3
Barnard Castle
Yorkshire 1
Wheatley Hills
Yorkshire 2
Wibsey
Yorkshire 3
Wetherby
Yorkshire 4
Mosborough
Yorkshire 5
Rawmarsh

Macclesfield RUFC – Cheshire Cup Winners 1994/95

NORTH DIVISION
FEATURED CLUBS

MACCLESFIELD

MACCLESFIELD have for some time been one of the most consistent clubs in the North Division and their achievement not only their league – North Two – but also the Cheshire County Cup by beating League Five North team Winnington Park in the final suggests that it may not be long before they shake off their junior club label.

This all means that from the humble origins of North West Two they are only one step away from that big time dream after two further promotions and a recent season where no league game was lost. In fact, only four defeats were suffered in all matches during the season and their victories included games against higher placed clubs and their county cup success, which means Pilkington Cup entry next season (they meet North One champions Sandal in Round One), was gained despite the fact that they had to enter in the first round and then meet good sides like Caldy (beaten by 70 points) and then a strong Sale side in the semi-final.

Their rise in the North's pecking order proves that any ambitious club has a chance of rubbing shoulders with the best if they try hard enough and Macclesfield are one of many determined outfits in possibly the toughest of the divisional competitions. Who will bet against further promotion and senior status in the very near future?

They have the support and the facilities plus the talent to do so.

WHEATLEY HILLS

WHEATLEY HILLS, who were undefeated champions of Yorkshire One, are another ambitious club like neighbours Doncaster, who were a featured team last season and have justified our confidence in them. This was ample consolation for a near miss in 1993-94, when promotion was taken from them in the last minute of their final match.

Their success is fine testimony to a youth policy, which has not only created a superb first team squad, but has also produced such excellent players as David Scully, the Wakefield scrum-half who must one day add full England honours to the sevens triumphs he has enjoyed. Wheatley Hills are basically a young outfit led by lock Martin Gillvray on the field and coached by No 8 Andy Gough, who is in his third season in charge. Apart from their unbeaten league record they had an excellent overall season with 23 matches won out of 30 and only seven lost for a 720-369 points difference.

The club's strength in depth was demonstrated by a second string which had a 25 to nine win-loss record, a 574-286 points situation and victory in the South Yorkshite Trophy to show for their efforts, while the thirds won 26 games out of 31 with five lost and 1,030 points scored against only 231 from opponents. They also run a fourth XV (13 wins from 27 matches) and a colts side.

For Wheately Hills next season in North East Two is seen as a stage on the way to big things. Last campaign may have been their best so far, but better must be on the way.

Wheatley Hills

NORTHERN DIVISION

NORTH ONE
1995-96
FIXTURES

September 16 1995 (Week 3)
West Park Bramhope	v	Manchester
Bridlington	v	Tynedale
Bradford & Bingley	v	Middlesbrough
Widnes	v	Wigton
Huddersfield	v	Hull Ionians
York	v	Stockton

September 23 1995 (Week 4)
Stockton	v	West Park Bramhope
Hull Ionians	v	York
Wigton	v	Huddersfield
Middlesbrough	v	Widnes
Tynedale	v	Bradford & Bingley
Macclesfield	v	Bridlington

September 30 1995 (Week X1)
West Park Bramhope	v	Hull Ionians
Manchester	v	Stockton
Bradford & Bingley	v	Macclesfield
Widnes	v	Tynedale
Huddersfield	v	Middlesbrough
York	v	Wigton

October 14 1995 (Week 6)
Hull Ionians	v	Manchester
Wigton	v	West Park Bramhope
Middlesbrough	v	York
Tynedale	v	Huddersfield
Macclesfield	v	Widnes
Bridlington	v	Bradford & Bingley

October 21 1995 (Week 7)
West Park Bramhope	v	Middlesbrough
Manchester	v	Wigton
Stockton	v	Hull Ionians
Widnes	v	Bridlington
Huddersfield	v	Macclesfield
York	v	Tynedale

October 28 1995 (Week 8)
Wigton	v	Stockton
Middlesbrough	v	Manchester
Tynedale	v	West Park Bramhope
Macclesfield	v	York
Bridlington	v	Huddersfield
Bradford & Bingley	v	Widnes

November 11 1995 (Week 10)
West Park Bramhope	v	Macclesfield
Manchester	v	Tynedale
Stockton	v	Middlesbrough
Hull Ionians	v	Wigton
Huddersfield	v	Bradford & Bingley
York	v	Bridlington

January 6 1996 (Week 17)
Middlesbrough	v	Hull Ionians
Tynedale	v	Stockton
Macclesfield	v	Manchester
Bridlington	v	West Park Bramhope
Bradford & Bingley	v	York
Widnes	v	Huddersfield

January 13 1996 (Week 18)
West Park Bramhope	v	Bradford & Bingley
Manchester	v	Bridlington
Stockton	v	Macclesfield
Hull Ionians	v	Tynedale
Wigton	v	Middlesbrough
York	v	Widnes

February 10 1996 (Week 22)
Tynedale	v	Wigton
Macclesfield	v	Hull Ionians
Bridlington	v	Stockton
Bradford & Bingley	v	Manchester
Widnes	v	West Park Bramhope
Huddersfield	v	York

February 17 1996 (Week 23)
West Park Bramhope	v	Huddersfield
Mancehster	v	Widnes
Stockton	v	Bradford & Bingley
Hull Ionians	v	Bridlington
Wigton	v	Macclesfield
Middlesbrough	v	Tynedale

February 24 1996 (Week 24)
Macclesfield	v	Middlesbrough
Bridlington	v	Wigton
Bradford & Bingley	v	Hull Ionians
Widnes	v	Stockton
Huddersfield	v	Manchester
York	v	West Park Bramhope

March 30 1996 (Week X7)
Manchester	v	York
Stockton	v	Huddersfield
Hull Ionians	v	Widnes
Wigton	v	Bradford & Bingley
Middlesbrough	v	Bridlington
Tynedale	v	Macclesfield

NORTH ONE

BRADFORD & BINGLEY RFC
Ground Address: Wagon Lane, Aireview, Bingley, West Yorkshire. Tel: 01274 775441 Fax: 01274 775442
Club Secretary: Mr JS Oddy, The Coach House, Warren Farm, Slate Quarry Lane, Eldwick, Bingley, Yorkshire BD16 3NP. Tel: (H) 01274 563254 Tel: (W) 01274 729792
Fixtures Secretary: Mr WK Wilkinson, Green Acres, Station Lane, Birkenshaw, Bradford, West Yorkshire. Tel: (H) 01274 681231 Fax: 01274 681231
Club Colours: Red, amber & black hoops, black shorts.

BRIDLINGTON RUFC
Ground Address: Dukes Park, Queensgate, Bridlington, East Yorkshire YO15 5SL. Tel: 01262 676405
Club Secretary: JP Preston, c/o The Clubhouse, Dukes Park, Queensgate, Bridlington, East Yorkshire YO15 5LN. Tel: (H) 01262 850071 Tel: (W) 01262 603979
Fixtures Secretary: John Chambers, c/o The Clubhouse, Dukes Park, Queensgate, Bridlington, East Yorkshire YO15 5LN. Tel: (H) 01377 217532 Tel (W) 01262 672088
Club Colours: Navy with irregular amber hoops.

HUDDERSFIELD RUFC
Ground Address: Tandem Ground, Waterloo, Huddersfield HD5 0AN. Tel: 01484 423864
Club Secretary: AR Field, 54 Quarry Lane, Lascelles Hall, Huddersfield HD5 0AR. Tel: (H) 01484 534318 Tel: (W) 01484 424055
Fixtures Secretary: B Starbuck, 2 The Cottages, Upperthong, Holmfirth, Huddersfield HD7 2UX. Tel: (H) 01484 686059 Tel (W) 0113 2591999
Club Colours: White shirt, claret & gold hoops, white shorts.

HULL IONIANS RUFC
Ground Address: Brantingham Park, Brantingham Road, Elloughton, Brough, North Humberside HU15 1HX. Tel: 01482 667342
Club Secretary: Peter Sharp, 38 Corby Park, North Ferriby, North Humberside HU14 3AY. Tel: (H) 01482 631819 Tel: (W) 01482 803933
Fixtures Secretary: John Clayton, 45 Chestnut Avenue, Willerby, Hull HU10 6PD. Tel: (H) 01482 651667
Club Colours: Red, white, blue, green quarters, royal blue shorts.

MACCLESFIELD RUFC
Ground Address: Priory Park, Priory Lane, Macclesfield SK10 4AE. Tel: 01625 827899
Club Secretary: T McCreery, 20 Carnoustie Drive, Macclesfield SK10 2TB. Tel: (H) 01625 615488 Tel: (W) 0161 832 5085
Fixtures Secretary: A Johnson, 6 Rugby Drive, Macclesfield SK10 2JD. Tel: (H) 01625 614697
Club Colours: Blue with white hoops.

MANCHESTER FC
Ground Address: Grove Park, Grove Lane, Cheadle Hulme, Cheadle, Cheshire, SK8 7NB. Tel: 0161 485 1115
Club Secretary: Norman R Thomas, 94 Kitts Moss Lane, Bramhall, Cheshire, SK7 2BQ. Tel: (H) 0161 439 3385 Tel: (W) 0161 367 9000
Fixtures Secretary: Derek W Partington, 28 Crossfield Drive, Worsley, Greater Manchester, M28 4GP. Tel: (H) 0161 790 6742
Club Colours: Red and white hooped jerseys, white shorts, red socks.

MIDDLESBROUGH RUFC
Ground Address: Acklam Park, Green Lane, Acklam, Cleveland, Middlesbrough TS5 7SL. Tel: 01642 818567
Club Secretary: Don Brydon, 20 Westwood Avenue, Linthorpe, Middlesbrough, Cleveland TS5 5PY. Tel: (H) 01642 819954 Tel: (W) 01642 264047
Fixtures Secretary: John Cunningham, 2 Bush Street, Linthorpe, Middlesbrough TS5 6BN. Tel: (H) 01642 818192 Tel (W) 01429 275453
Club Colours: Maroon jerseys, white shorts.

FINAL TABLE

	P	W	D	L	F	A	Pts
Sandal	12	8	3	1	227	126	19
Stockton	12	8	2	2	196	111	18
Manchester	12	7	3	2	217	166	17
Bradford & Bingley	12	8	0	4	230	166	16
Hull Ionians	12	5	1	6	198	196	11
Huddersfield	12	5	1	6	163	167	11
Widnes	12	5	1	6	163	188	11
York	12	5	1	6	157	198	11
Middlesbrough	12	5	1	6	162	206	11
West Park Bramhope	12	5	1	6	197	162	9
Tynedale	12	4	1	7	184	154	9
Wigton	12	3	1	8	132	238	7
Durham City	12	2	0	10	124	272	4

STOCKTON RUFC
Ground Address: c/o Norton Cricket Field, Station Road, Norton, Stockton, Cleveland TS20 1PE. Tel: 01642 554031
Club Secretary: John Robinson, 17 Rook Lane, Norton, Stockton, Cleveland TS20 1SB. Tel: (H) 01642 557288
Fixtures Secretary: Brendon Thornton, 23 Loweswater Crescent, Stockton, Cleveland TS18 4PY. Tel: (H) 01642 613745
Club Colours: Red shirts, white shorts.

TYNEDALE RFC
Ground Address: Tynedale Park, Corbridge, Northumberland NE45 5AY. Tel: 01434 632996/7
Club Secretary: A Smith, West Fell, Corbridge, Northumberland NE45 5RZ. Tel: (H) 01434 632044 Tel: (W) 0191 477 1412
Fixtures Secretary: JA Suddes, Glendalough, West Hextol, Hexham, Northumberland. Tel: (H) 01434 603989
Club Colours: Royal blue & white horizontal stripes.

WEST PARK BRAMHOPE RUFC
Ground Address: The Sycamores, Bramhope, Leeds LS16 9JR. Tel: 0113 2671437
Club Secretary: Mr Andy Oddy, Bonito, 89 The Birches, Bramhope, Leeds LS16 9DP. Tel: (H) 0113 2673316
Fixtures Secretary: Mr Mick Openshaw, 5 Victoria Grove, Horsforth, Leeds LS18 4ST. Tel: (H) 0113 2587338
Club Colours: Yellow & black abstract.

WIDNES RUFC
Ground Address: Heath Road, Widnes, Cheshire WA8 7NU. Tel: 0151 424 2575
Club Secretary: John Hollins, 5 Iris Close, Widnes, Cheshire. Tel: (H) 0151 423 1906 Tel: (W) 0151 422 4223
Fixtures Secretary: Ray Heapey, 108 Coroners Lane, Widnes, Cheshire. Tel: (H) 0151 424 6565
Club Colours: Red & black bands, black shorts.

WIGTON RUFC
Ground Address: Lowmoor Road, Wigton, Cumbria CA7 9QT. Tel: 106973 42206
Club Secretary: Malcolm Sunter, Alpha, Lowmoor Road, Wigton, Cumbria CA7 9QR. Tel: (H) 016973 42917 Tel: (W) 01228 519258
Fixtures Secretary: Allan Robson, 2 Station Hill, Wigton, Cumbria. Tel: (H) 016973 42310 Tel (W) 01228 45810
Club Colours: Green shirt, white shorts, green socks, white tops.

YORK RUFC
Ground Address: Clifton Park, Shipton Road, York YO3 6RE. Tel: 01904 623602
Club Secretary: Brian McClure, 15 Stubden Grove, York YO3 4UY. Tel: (H) 01904 691026
Fixtures Secretary: Peter Ayers, Orchard House, The Village, Skelton, York YO3 6YQ. Tel: (H) 01904 470351
Club Colours: Green, black & white hoops with black shorts.

NORTHERN DIVISION

NORTH TWO 1995-96 FIXTURES

September 16 1995 (Week 3)
Northern	v	Vale of Lune
West Park	v	Old Crossleyans
Birkenhead Park	v	Hartlepool Rovers
New Brighton	v	Blaydon
Sedgley Park	v	Alnwick
Doncaster	v	Durham City

September 23 1995 (Week 4)
Durham City	v	Northern
Alnwick	v	Doncaster
Blaydon	v	Sedgley Park
Hartlepool Rovers	v	New Brighton
Old Crossleyans	v	Birkenhead Park
Halifax	v	West Park

September 30 1995 (Week X1)
Northern	v	Alnwick
Vale of Lune	v	Durham City
Birkenhead Park	v	Halifax
New Brighton	v	Old Crossleyans
Sedgley Park	v	Hartlepool Rovers
Doncaster	v	Blaydon

October 14 1995 (Week 6)
Alnwick	v	Vale of Lune
Blaydon	v	Northern
Hartlepool Rovers	v	Doncaster
Old Crossleyans	v	Sedgley Park
Halifax	v	New Brighton
West Park	v	Birkenhead Park

October 21 1995 (Week 7)
Northern	v	Hartlepool Rovers
Vale of Lune	v	Blaydon
Durham City	v	Alnwick
New Brighton	v	West Park
Sedgley Park	v	Halifax
Doncaster	v	Old Crossleyans

October 28 1995 (Week 8)
Blaydon	v	Durham City
Hartlepool Rovers	v	Vale of Lune
Old Crossleyans	v	Northern
Halifax	v	Doncaster
West Park	v	Sedgley Park
Birkenhead Park	v	New Brighton

November 11 1995 (Week 10)
Northern	v	Halifax
Vale of Lune	v	Old Crossleyans
Durham City	v	Hartlepool Rovers
Alnwick	v	Blaydon
Sedgley Park	v	Birkenhead Park
Doncaster	v	West Park

January 6 1996 (Week 17)
Hartlepool Rovers	v	Alnwick
Old Crossleyans	v	Durham City
Halifax	v	Vale of Lune
West Park	v	Northern
Birkenhead Park	v	Doncaster
New Brighton	v	Sedgley Park

January 13 1996 (Week 18)
Northern	v	Birkenhead Park
Vale of Lune	v	West Park
Durham City	v	Halifax
Alnwick	v	Old Crossleyans
Blaydon	v	Hartlepool Rovers
Doncaster	v	New Brighton

February 10 1996 (Week 22)
Old Crossleyans	v	Blaydon
Halifax	v	Alnwick
West Park	v	Durham City
Birkenhead Park	v	Vale of Lune
New Brighton	v	Northern
Sedgley Park	v	Doncaster

February 17 1996 (Week 23)
Northern	v	Sedgley Park
Vale of Lune	v	New Brighton
Durham City	v	Birkenhead Park
Alnwick	v	West Park
Blaydon	v	Halifax
Hartlepool Rovers	v	Old Crossleyans

February 24 1996 (Week 24)
Halifax	v	Hartlepool Rovers
West Park	v	Blaydon
Birkenhead Park	v	Alnwick
New Brighton	v	Durham City
Sedgley Park	v	Vale of Lune
Doncaster	v	Northern

March 30 1996 (Week X7)
Vale of Lune	v	Doncaster
Durham City	v	Sedgley Park
Alnwick	v	New Brighton
Blaydon	v	Birkenhead Park
Hartlepool Rovers	v	West Park
Old Crossleyans	v	Halifax

NORTH TWO

ALNWICK RUFC
Ground Address: Greensfield, St James, Alnwick, Northumberland. Tel: 01665 602342
Club Secretary: Tim Flood, Witton Shield House, Netherwitton, Morpeth, Northumberland NE61 4NL. Tel: (H) 01670 772327 Tel: (W) 0191 252 6857
Fixtures Secretary: John Ainsworth, 10 Cornhill Estate, Alnwick, Northumberland NE66 1RX. Tel: (H) 01665 605196 Tel (W) 01665 510505
Club Colours: Royal blue jersey with gold lion rampant badge, white shorts, royal blue socks with gold tops.

BIRKENHEAD PARK FC
Ground Address: Park Road North, Birkenhead, Merseyside L41 8AA. Tel: 0151 652 4646
Club Secretary: MG Thomas, 22 Oldfield Way, Heswall, Wirral. Tel: (H) 0151 342 5098
Fixtures Secretary: RC Hardman, 32 Shamrock Road, Claughton, Birkenhead L41 0EQ. Tel: (H) 0151 652 5204 Tel (W) Ring club
Club Colours: Red, white & navy blue hoops.

BLAYDON RUFC
Ground Address: Crow Trees Ground, Hexham Road, Swalwell, Newcastle-upon-Tyne NE16 3BN. Tel: 0191 420 0505/6
Club Secretary: GH March, 'Twickers', 48A Spen Burn, Ashtree Court, High Spen, Rowlands Gill, Tyne & Wear NE39 2DN. Tel: (H) 01207 545397
Fixtures Secretary: JM Huxley, 'The Mount', 59 Sunniside Road, Sunniside, Newcastle-upon-tyne NE16 5NF. Tel: (H) 0191 488 7280
Club Colours: Scarlet jerseys, white collar, white shorts, red stockings, 2 blue bands.

DONCASTER RUFC
Ground Address: Armthorpe Road, Doncaster DN2 5QB. Tel: 01302 770275
Club Secretary: John Lowe, 57 Wroot Road, Finningley Village, Doncaster, South Yorkshire DN9 3DR. Tel: (H) 01302 770275 Tel: (W) Mobile: 01585 397 353
Fixtures Secretary: Roger Linsley, 53 St Mary's Road, Tickhill, Doncaster DN11 9JJ. Tel: (H) 01302 742646 Tel (W) 01302 866906
Club Colours: Blue, red & white hoops.

DURHAM CITY RFC
Ground Address: Hollow Drift, Green Lane, Durham City DH1 3JU. Tel: 0191 386 1172
Club Secretary: Mr R Elston, 18 Mayorswell Field, Claypath, Durham City DH1 1JW. Tel: (H) 0191 386 3245 Tel: (W) 01207 507001
Fixtures Secretary: Mr J Thompson, 'Cherry Tree House', West End, Bradshaw, Co Durham. Tel: (H) 01388 528071 Tel (W) 01388 762522
Club Colours: Blue & gold hoops, white shorts.

HALIFAX RUFC
Ground Address: Standeven Memorial Ground, Ovenden Park, Keighley Road, Halifax, West Yorkshire HX2 8AR. Tel: (& Fax) 01422 365926
Club Secretary: AV Edwards, 6 Heath Street, Savile Park, Halifax, West Yorkshire HX3 0DJ. Tel: (H) 01422 356314 Tel: (W) 01422 360272
Fixtures Secretary: RA Childs, Fir Tree Cottage, Wentworth Grove, Bradshaw, Halifax, West Yorkshire HX2 9QN. Tel: (H) 01422 244608 Tel (W) 01836 376497
Club Colours: Dark blue, light blue & white hoops.

HARTLEPOOL ROVERS FC
Ground Address: The New Friarage, West View Road, Hartlepool, Cleveland TS24 0BP. Tel: 01424 267741
Club Secretary: Bill Dale, 21 Knapton Avenue, Wolviston Court, Billingham, Cleveland TS22 5DJ. Tel: (H) 01642 556314
Fixtures Secretary: T Lowe, Alma House, Junction Road, Norton, Cleveland. Tel: (H) 01624 530093
Club Colours: White shirts, black shorts, red socks.

NEW BRIGHTON RUFC
Ground Address: Reeds Lane, Moreton, Wirral L46 3RH. Tel: 0151 677 1873
Club Secretary: Mrs Beryl M Bowes, 4 Murrayfield Drive, Moreton, Wirral L46 3RS. Tel: (H) 0151 678 2654 Tel: (W)

FINAL TABLE

	P	W	D	L	F	A	Pts
Macclesfield	12	12	0	0	314	106	24
Bridlington	12	11	0	1	232	101	22
New Brighton	12	9	0	3	376	140	18
West Park St Helens	12	8	1	3	316	205	17
Northern	12	8	0	4	206	115	16
Doncaster	12	7	0	5	136	155	14
Birkenhead Park	12	4	1	7	177	188	9
Old Crossleyans	12	4	2	6	141	240	8*
Hartlepool Rovers	12	4	0	8	110	212	8
Alnwick	12	3	0	9	155	276	6
Halifax	12	4	0	8	146	229	4*
Vale of Lune	12	2	0	10	146	296	4
Northwich	12	0	0	12	65	260	0

0151 224 3409
Fixtures Secretary: Mr Bernard Murphy, 43 Brookfield Gardens, West Kirby, Wirral L48 4EL. Tel: (H) 0151 625 8835 Tel (W) 0151 647 7969
Club Colours: Light blue/darkblue/white.

NORTHERN FC
Ground Address: McCracken Park, Great North Road, Gosforth, Newcastle upon Tyne NE18 8AP. Tel: 0191 236 3369
Club Secretary: Ian F Cook, 100 High Street, Gosforth, Newcastle upon Tyne NE3 1HB. Tel: (H) 0191 268 9642 Tel: (W) 0191 218 0881
Fixtures Secretary: Julian B Hayes, 21 Meadow Road, West Monkseaton, Whitley Bay, Tyne & Wear. Tel: (H) 0191 253 4520
Club Colours: White shirts, blue shorts, red socks.

OLD CROSSLEYANS RUFC
Ground Address: Standeven House, Broomfield Avenue, Halifax, West Yorkshire HX3 0JF. Tel: 01422 363000
Club Secretary: Richard A Davies, 4 Warley Dene, Holme Road, Warley, Halifax, West Yorkshire HA2 7RS. Tel: (H) 01422 832218
Fixtures Secretary: Derek Ainley, 1 Savile Heath, Manor Heath Road, Halifax, West Yorkshire. Tel: (H) 01422 368233 Tel (W) 01422 822217
Club Colours: Blue & amber.

SEDGLEY PARK RUFC
Ground Address: The Clubhouse, Park Lane, Whitefield, Manchester M45 7DZ. Tel: 0161 766 5050
Club Secretary: Mark G Mold, 32 Vicarage Avenue, Cheadle Hulme, Cheadle, Cheshire SK8 7JW. Tel: (H) 0161 486 0496 Tel: (W) 0161 794 4755
Fixtures Secretary: Rob Williamson, 17 Boundary Drive, Bradley Fold, Bolton BL2 6SE. Tel: (H) 01204 705868 Tel (W) 0161 202 1714
Club Colours: Claret & old gold thin hooped shirts.

VALE OF LUNE RUFC
Ground Address: Powderhouse Lane, Lancaster LA1 2TT. Tel: 01524 64029
Club Secretary: Peter Fell, 55 Stanhope Avenue, Morecambe, Lancashire LA3 3AL. Tel: (H) 01524 416519
Fixtures Secretary: Mr FW Swarbrick, 116 Prospect Street, Lancaster. Tel: (H) 01524 37601 Tel (W) 01524 64055
Club Colours: Cherry & white hooped shirts & socks, navy blue shorts.

WEST PARK (ST HELENS) RFC
Ground Address: Eccleston Hill, Prescot Road, St Helens, Merseyside. Tel: 01744 26138
Club Secretary: William Bold, 76 Greenfield Road, St Helens, Merseyside WA10 6FL. Tel: (H) 01744 26138 Tel: (W) 01744 26138
Fixtures Secretary: JE Briers, 51 Daresbury Road, Eccleston, St Helens, Merseyside. Tel: (H) 01744 734665
Club Colours: Green & gold.

NORTHERN DIVISION

NORTH WEST ONE
1995-96
FIXTURES

September 16 1995 (Week 3)
Blackburn	v	Netherhall
Wilmslow	v	Penrith
Carlisle	v	Sandbach
Northwich	v	Chester
Cockermouth	v	Oldershaw
Lymm	v	Leigh

September 23 1995 (Week 4)
Leigh	v	Blackburn
Oldershaw	v	Lymm
Chester	v	Cockermouth
Sandbach	v	Northwich
Penrith	v	Carlisle
Ashton on Mersey	v	Wilmslow

September 30 1995 (Week X1)
Blackburn	v	Oldershaw
Netherhall	v	Leigh
Carlisle	v	Ashton on Mersey
Northwich	v	Penrith
Cockermouth	v	Sandbach
Lymm	v	Chester

October 14 1995 (Week 6)
Oldershaw	v	Netherhall
Chester	v	Blackburn
Sandbach	v	Lymm
Penrith	v	Cockermouth
Ashton on Mersey	v	Northwich
Wilmslow	v	Carlisle

October 21 1995 (Week 7)
Blackburn	v	Sandbach
Netherhall	v	Chester
Leigh	v	Oldershaw
Northwich	v	Wilmslow
Cockermouth	v	Ashton on Mersey
Lymm	v	Penrith

October 28 1995 (Week 8)
Chester	v	Leigh
Sandbach	v	Netherhall
Penrith	v	Blackburn
Ashton on Mersey	v	Lymm
Wilmslow	v	Cockermouth
Carlisle	v	Northwich

November 11 1995 (Week 10)
Blackburn	v	Ashton on Mersey
Netherhall	v	Penrith
Leigh	v	Sandbach
Oldershaw	v	Chester
Cockermouth	v	Carlisle
Lymm	v	Wilmslow

January 6 1996 (Week 17)
Sandbach	v	Oldershaw
Penrith	v	Leigh
Ashton on Mersey	v	Netherhall
Wilmslow	v	Blackburn
Carlisle	v	Lymm
Northwich	v	Cockermouth

January 13 1996 (Week 18)
Blackburn	v	Carlisle
Netherhall	v	Wilmslow
Leigh	v	Ashton on Mersey
Oldershaw	v	Penrith
Chester	v	Sandbach
Lymm	v	Northwich

February 10 1996 (Week 22)
Penrith	v	Chester
Ashton on Mersey	v	Oldershaw
Wilmslow	v	Leigh
Carlisle	v	Netherhall
Northwich	v	Blackburn
Cockermouth	v	Lymm

February 17 1996 (Week 23)
Blackburn	v	Cockermouth
Netherhall	v	Northwich
Leigh	v	Carlisle
Oldershaw	v	Wilmslow
Chester	v	Ashton on Mersey
Sandbach	v	Penrith

February 24 1996 (Week 24)
Ashton on Mersey	v	Sandbach
Wilmslow	v	Chester
Carlisle	v	Oldershaw
Northwich	v	Leigh
Cockermouth	v	Netherhall
Lymm	v	Blackburn

March 30 1996 (Week X7)
Netherhall	v	Lymm
Leigh	v	Cockermouth
Oldershaw	v	Northwich
Chester	v	Carlisle
Sandbach	v	Wilmslow
Penrith	v	Ashton on Mersey

NORTH WEST ONE

ASHTON-ON-MERSEY RUFC
Ground Address: Banky Lane, off Carrington Lane, Ashton-on-Mersey, Sale, Cheshire M33 5NP. Tel: 0161 973 6637
Club Secretary: Mr MJ Nobbs, 116 Mercer Street, Newton-le-Willows, Merseyside WA12 9TL. Tel: (H) 01925 220350 Tel: (W) 0151 548 3499
Fixtures Secretary: Mr P Stokes, 109 Buxton Crescent, Sale Cheshire M33 3LG. Tel: (H) 0161 282 3242
Club Colours: Maroon shirts, navy shorts, maroon/white socks.

BLACKBURN RUFC
Ground Address: Ramsgreave Drive, Blackburn BB1 8NB. Tel: 01254 247669
Club Secretary: Mr LC Blow, 41 East Park Avenue, Blackburn BB1 8DT. Tel: (H) 01254 247669 Tel: (W) Mobile: 0370 474885
Fixtures Secretary: G Bancroft, 3 Higher House Close, Livesey, Blackburn BB2 4RN. Tel: (H) 01254 201366 Tel (W) 0850 920373
Club Colours: Royal blue shirts, white shorts, red & white socks.

CARLISLE RFC
Ground Address: Warwick Road, Carlisle, Cumbria CA1. Tel: 01228 21300
Club Secretary: NJ Laycock, 90 Greystone Road, Carlisle, Cumbria CA1 2DD. Tel: (H) 01228 22895 (not after 10pm) Tel: (W) 01228 20277
Fixtures Secretary: DD Morton, 14 Naworth Drive, Lowry Hill, Carlisle, Cumbria. Tel: (H) 01228 515486
Club Colours: Navy blue, white & red.

CHESTER RUFC
Ground Address: Hare Lane, Vicars Cross, Chester CH3 7BD. Tel: 01244 336017
Club Secretary: P Rhodes, The Hollies, off Carriage Drive, Frodsham, via Warrington, Cheshire WA6 6EF. Tel: (H) 01928 731485 Tel: (W) 0151 229 2404
Fixtures Secretary: C Cawthorn, 21 Oaklands Avenue, Tattenhall, Nr Chester. Tel: (H) 01829 70498 Tel (W) 01244 603420
Club Colours: Red shirts, white shorts.

COCKERMOUTH RFC
Ground Address: Laithwaite, Low Road, Cockermouth, Cumbria. Tel: 01900 824884
Club Secretary: Mr Chris Garrard, Bent Dyke, Dean Lonning, Eaglesfield, Cockermouth, Cumbria. Tel: (H) 01900 822835 Tel: (W) 01900 823592
Fixtures Secretary: Andrew Quarry, 14 Cullinsfield, Kendal. Tel: (H) 01539 731640 Tel (W) 01900 602623
Club Colours: Black & amber.

LEIGH RUFC
Ground Address: Round Ash Park, Hand Lane, Leigh, Lancashire WN7 3NA. Tel: 01942 673526
Club Secretary: Mark Downs, 3 Melling Close, Leigh, Lancashire WN7 3NQ. Tel: (H) 01942 676704
Fixtures Secretary: Tom Hughes, 2 Launceston Road, Hindley Green, Wigan, Lancashire WN2 4TQ. Tel: (H) 01942 257427 Tel (W) 01695 733061
Club Colours: Black with amber band.

LYMM RFC
Ground Address: Beechwood, Crouchley Lane, Lymm, Warrington, Cheshire WA13 0AT. Tel: 01925 753212
Club Secretary: Varun Maharaj, 5 Farrell Road, Stockton Heath, Warrington WA4 6LR. Tel: (H) 01925 264566 Tel: (W) 01204 532611
Fixtures Secretary: C Monks, 8 Newlands Road, Stockton Heath, Warrington, Cheshire WA4 2DS. Tel: (H) 01925 262904
Club Colours: Green, black & white hoops, black shorts.

NETHERHALL RUFC
Ground Address: Netherhall Park, Netherhall Road,

FINAL TABLE

	P	W	D	L	F	A	Pts
Sedgley Park	12	12	0	0	421	60	24
Chester	12	7	2	3	159	144	16
Lymm	12	7	1	4	215	192	15
Netherhall	12	7	1	4	220	208	15
Wilmslow	12	6	1	5	214	140	13
Oldershaw	12	7	0	5	259	172	12*
Ashton on Mersey	12	6	1	5	133	171	11*
Sandbach	12	5	0	7	191	240	10
Carlisle	12	5	0	7	132	190	10
Cockermouth	12	5	1	6	134	156	9*
Blackburn	12	3	1	8	138	208	7
Stockport	12	2	0	10	135	243	4
Wigan	12	2	0	10	84	311	4

Maryport, W Cumbria. Tel: 01900 815833
Club Secretary: P Bartlett, 66 Garborough Close, Crosby, Nr Maryport, W Cumbria, CA15 6RZ. Tel: (H) 01900 818420 Tel: (W) 01946 692261
Fixtures Secretary: L Rumney, 4 Orchard Cose, Seaton, Workington, W Cumbria. Tel: (H) 01900 871440
Club Colours: Claret and gold.

NORTHWICH RUFC
Ground Address: Moss Farm Leisure Centre, Moss Road, Winnington, Northwich, Cheshire. Tel: 01606 79987
Club Secretary: Alan Langston, 23 Carlton Road, Witton Park, Northwich, Cheshire CW9 5PW. Tel: (H) 01606 41039
Fixtures Secretary: Keith Naylor, Flat 3, Hillside House, Old Vicarage Lane, Hartford, Northwich, Cheshire CW8 1QD. Tel: (H) 01606 782573 Tel (W) 01270 255155
Club Colours: Black shirts, black shorts.

OLDERSHAW RUFC
Ground Address: Belvidere Playing Fields, Belvidere Road, Wallasey, Merseyside. Tel: 0151 638 4379
Club Secretary: Martin Lloyd, 10 The Oval, Wallasey, Merseyside L45 6UY. Tel: (H) 0151 639 8389 Tel: (W) 0151 242 1064
Fixtures Secretary: Peter Purland, 63 Croxteth Road, Liverpool, Merseyside L8 3SF. Tel: (H) 0151 733 4854
Club Colours: Navy blue with gold hoops.

PENRITH RUFC
Ground Address: Winters Park, Penrith, Cumbria CA11 8RG. Tel: 01768 863151
Club Secretary: Keith Davis, Ivybank, 59 Lowther Street, Penrith, Cumbria CA11 7UQ. Tel: (H) 01768 866089 Tel: (W) 01768 217339
Fixtures Secretary: William F Mounsey, The Luham, Edenhall, Penrith CA11 8TA. Tel: (H) 01768 881202
Club Colours: Myrtle green & white hoops, white shorts.

SANDBACH RUFC
Ground Address: Bradwall Road, Sandbach, CW11 9AP. Tel: 01270 762457
Club Secretary: John Gater, 7 Colley Lane, Sandbach, Cheshire CW11 0HE. Tel: (H) 01270 764035 Tel: (W) 01260 283815
Fixtures Secretary: Graham Armstrong, 14 Langley Close, Sandbach CW11 0YS. Tel: (H) 01270 760446
Club Colours: Green with red, yellow & white stripe.

WILMSLOW RUFC
Ground Address: Memorial Ground, Pownall Park, Kings Road, Wilmslow SK9 5PZ. Tel: 01625 522274
Club Secretary: David Pike, 12 Fairbourne Drive, Wilmslow SK9 6JF. Tel: (H) 01625 525616
Fixtures Secretary: JI Blackburn, 14 Telfer Court, Middlewich CW10 0TD. Tel: (H) 01606 837200
Club Colours: Sky blue, maroon & white jerseys, white shorts, maroon stockings.

NORTHERN DIVISION

NORTH WEST TWO 1995-96 FIXTURES

November 11 1995 (Week 10)

Vagabonds 1995 (IOM)	v	Stockport
Rossendale	v	Windermere
Wigan	v	Fleetwood
Merseyside Police	v	Aspull
Old Aldwinians	v	Egremont
Caldy	v	Kirkby Lonsdale

September 16 1995 (Week 3)

Vagabonds 1995 (IOM)	v	Rossendale
Kirkby Lonsdale	v	Windermere
Egremont	v	Fleetwood
Old Salians	v	Aspull
Old Aldwinians	v	Merseyside Police
Caldy	v	Wigan

September 23 1995 (Week 4)

Wigan	v	Vagabonds 1995 (IOM)
Merseyside Police	v	Caldy
Aspull	v	Old Aldwinians
Fleetwood	v	Old Salians
Windermere	v	Egremont
Stockport	v	Kirkby Lonsdale

September 30 1995 (Week X1)

Vagabonds 1995 (IOM)	v	Merseyside Police
Rossendale	v	Wigan
Egremont	v	Stockport
Old Salians	v	Windermere
Old Aldwinians	v	Fleetwood
Caldy	v	Aspull

October 14 1995 (Week 6)

Merseyside Police	v	Rossendale
Aspull	v	Vagabonds 1995 (IOM)
Fleetwood	v	Caldy
Windermere	v	Old Aldwinians
Stockport	v	Old Salians
Kirkby Lonsdale	v	Egremont

October 21 1995 (Week 7)

Vagabonds 1995 (IOM)	v	Fleetwood
Rossendale	v	Aspull
Wigan	v	Merseyside Police
Old Salians	v	Kirkby Lonsdale
Old Aldwinians	v	Stockport
Caldy	v	Windermere

October 28 1995 (Week 8)

Aspull	v	Wigan
Fleetwood	v	Rossendale
Windermere	v	Vagabonds 1995 (IOM)
Stockport	v	Caldy
Kirkby Lonsdale	v	Old Aldwinians
Egremont	v	Old Salians

January 6 1996 (Week 17)

Fleetwood	v	Merseyside Police
Windermere	v	Wigan
Stockport	v	Rossendale
Kirkby Lonsdale	v	Vagabonds 1995 (IOM)
Egremont	v	Caldy
Old Salians	v	Old Aldwinians

January 13 1996 (Week 18)

Vagabonds 1995 (IOM)	v	Egremont
Rossendale	v	Kirkby Lonsdale
Wigan	v	Stockport
Merseyside Police	v	Windermere
Aspull	v	Fleetwood
Caldy	v	Old Salians

February 10 1996 (Week 22)

Windermere	v	Aspull
Stockport	v	Merseyside Police
Kirkby Lonsdale	v	Wigan
Egremont	v	Rossendale
Old Salians	v	Vagabonds 1995 (IOM)
Old Aldwinians	v	Caldy

February 17 1996 (Week 23)

Vagabonds 1995 (IOM)	v	Old Aldwinians
Rossendale	v	Old Salians
Wigan	v	Egremont
Merseyside Police	v	Kirkby Lonsdale
Aspull	v	Stockport
Fleetwood	v	Windermere

February 24 1996 (Week 24)

Stockport	v	Fleetwood
Kirkby Lonsdale	v	Aspull
Egremont	v	Merseyside Police
Old Salians	v	Wigan
Old Aldwinians	v	Rossendale
Caldy	v	Vagabonds 1995 (IOM)

March 30 1996 (Week X7)

Rossendale	v	Caldy
Wigan	v	Old Aldwinians
Merseyside Police	v	Old Salians
Aspull	v	Egremont
Fleetwood	v	Kirkby Lonsdale
Windermere	v	Stockport

NORTH WEST TWO

ASPULL RFC
Ground Address: Woodshaw Park, Woods Road, Aspull,
Wigan, Lancs. Tel: 01942 831611
Club Secretary: David Simpson, 5 Whitecroft, Wigan
WN3 5PS. Tel: (H) 01257 421421 Tel: (W) 01942 492221
Fixtures Secretary: GW Gregson, 26 Lyndon Avenue,
Shevington, Wigan, Lancashire WN6 8BT. Tel: (H) 01257
421421 Tel (W) 01942 492221
Club Colours: Sky & navy hoops.

CALDY RFC
Ground Address: Paton Field, Lower Caldy Cross Roads,
Telegraph Road, Caldy, Wirral. Tel: 0151 625 8043
Club Secretary: RB Flashman, 26 Milton Cresent, Heswall,
Wirral. Tel: (H) 0151 342 5300 Tel: (W) 0151 653 0566
Fixtures Secretary: K Doolan, 37 Peartree Close, Great
Sutton Street, Wirral. Tel: (H) 0151 348 0119
Club Colours: Sable, claret, silver & gold hoops.

EGREMONT RUFC
Ground Address: Bleach Green, Egremont, Cumbria. Tel:
01946 820645
Club Secretary: WHF Moran, 58 Dent View, Egremont,
Cumbria CA22 2ET. Tel: (H) 01946 822119 Tel: (W)
019467 72443 Fax: 019467 72446
Fixtures Secretary: JWA Crichton, 25 Springfield
Gardens, Bigrigg, Egremont, Cumbria. Tel: (H) 01946
811933 Tel (W) 01946 72443
Club Colours: Black & gold stripes.

FLEETWOOD RUFC
Ground Address: Melbourne Avenue, Fleetwood,
Lancashire. Tel: 01253 874774
Club Secretary: Trevor Michael Jones, 'The Cottage',
Derby Road, Poulton le Fylde, Lancashire, FY6 7AF. Tel:
(H) 01253 899352 Tel: (W) 01253 873030
Fixtures Secretary: Brian Olsen, 32 Huntingdon Road,
Anchorsholme, Thornton Cleveleys, Lancashire, FY5 1SR.
Tel: (H) 01253 854758 Tel (W) 01253 866336
Club Colours: Green jerseys, navy blue shorts, green &
gold stockings.

KIRKBY LONSDALE RUFC
Ground Address: The Club House, Underley Park, Kirkby
Lonsdale, via Carnforth, Lancs. Tel: 015242 71780
Club Secretary: Richard Harkness, Meadowgarth,
Fairbank, Kirkby Lonsdale. Tel: (H) 015242 71137 Tel:
(W) 01524 72111
Fixtures Secretary: Paul Newell, Primrose Cottage,
Thorns Lane, Sedbergh, Cumbria. Tel: (H) 015396 20091
Club Colours: Red, black, amber hoops & socks, black shorts.

MERSEYSIDE POLICE RUFC
Ground Address: Police Sports Ground, Riversdale Road,
Aigburty, Liverpool 19, Mersyside. Tel: 0151 427 2208
Club Secretary: D/Sgt Andy Ward, 229 Pensby Road,
Heswall, Wirral, Merseyside L61 5UA. Tel: (H) 0151 342
8825 Tel: (W) 01244 533500
Fixtures Secretary: Constable Fred Evans, 42 Greenheys
Road, Wallasey, Merseyside L44 5UO. Tel: (H) 0151 638
1448 Tel (W) 0151 709 6010 x5206
Club Colours: Blue/black/white quarters, black shorts.

OLD ALDWINIANS RUFC
Ground Address: Audenshaw Park, Droylsden Road,
Audenshaw, Manchester M34 5SN. Tel: 0161 301 1001
Club Secretary: C Daly, 60 Green Lane, Hollingworth,
Hyde, Cheshire SK14 8JQ. Tel: (H) 01457 762402
Fixtures Secretary: Alan Whalley, 190 Greenside Lane,
Droylsden, Manchester M43 7UR. Tel: (H) 0161 370 0921
Tel (W) 0161 223 1353 x246
Club Colours: Red & white hoops, blue shorts.

OLD SALIANS RUFC
Ground Address: Rookwood, Clarendon Crescent, off
Dane Road, Sale, Cheshire. Tel: 0161 973 7250
Club Secretary: R Alderson, 179 Flixton Road, Urmston
M41 5ED. Tel: (H) 0161 746 9821 Tel: (W) 0161 224 7201

FINAL TABLE

	P	W	D	L	F	A	Pts
Leigh	12	11	0	1	231	130	22
Penrith	12	9	1	2	285	131	19
Kirkby Lonsdale	12	8	0	4	228	171	16
Old Salians	12	7	2	3	142	120	16
Fleetwood	12	7	1	4	211	144	15
Merseyside Police	12	7	0	5	152	1161	14
Old Aldwinians	12	5	0	7	190	177	10
Vagabonds (IOM)	12	5	0	7	124	175	10
Rossendale	12	5	0	7	132	193	10
Caldy	12	3	1	8	186	191	7
Egremont	12	2	1	9	118	205	5
St Edward's OB	12	3	1	8	138	265	5*
Ruskin Park	12	2	1	9	134	208	3*

Fixtures Secretary: Andrew Parkinson, 22 Alexandra
Road, Sale, Cheshire. Tel: (H) 0161 976 3904
Club Colours: Navy blue shirts with white chest band,
navy shorts & socks.

ROSSENDALE RUFC
Ground Address: Marl Pits Sports Centre, Newchurch
Road, Rawtenstall, Rossendale, Lancs BB4 7SW. Tel:
01706 229152
Club Secretary: Mr P Brotherton, 47 Poulton Avenue,
Accrington, Lancs BB5 5EP. Tel: (H) 01254 234310 Tel:
(W) 01282 772511
Fixtures Secretary: Mr T Kelly, 111 Pinkington Terrace,
Broadway, Haslingden, Rossendale, Lancs BB4 4EH. Tel:
(H) 01706 217361
Club Colours: Maroon & white.

STOCKPORT RUFC
Ground Address: Bridge Lane Memorial Ground,
Headland Road, Bridge Lane, Bramhall, Stockport,
Cheshire. Tel: 0161 439 2150
Club Secretary: Mike Drew, 191 Moor Lane, Woodford,
Stockport SK7 1PF. Tel: (H) 0161 439 5439
Fixtures Secretary: Martin Wroe, Moor Lane, Woodford,
Stockport. Tel: (H) 0161 440 8536
Club Colours: Red, white, green.

VAGABONDS (IOM) RUFC
Ground Address: Glencrutchery Road, Douglas, Isle of
Man. Tel: 01624 661996
Club Secretary: Ian Forrest, Croft House, Church Road,
Santon, Isle of Man. Tel: (H) 01624 822297 Tel: (W)
01624 638300
Fixtures Secretary: Steve Wilson, 49 St Catherines Close,
Douglas, Isle of Man. Tel: (H) 01624 673029 Tel (W)
01624 671118
Club Colours: White shirts with black & yellow band,
black shorts, black & yellow hooped socks.

WIGAN RUFC
Ground Address: Douglas Valley, Wingates Road, off
Leyland Mill Lane, Wigan, Lancashire. Tel: 01924 242556
Club Secretary: Graham Heeley, 30 Darley Road,
Hawkley Hall, Wigan WN3 5PG. Tel: (H) 01924 201360
Tel: (W) 0161 486 6211
Fixtures Secretary: Dave Clarke, 224 Billinge Road, Pemberton,
Wigan, Lancashire WN5 9HX. Tel: (W) 01942 207771
Club Colours: Black & white irregular hoops.

WINDERMERE RUFC
Ground Address: Dawes Meadow, Longlands, Bowness
on Windermere, Cumbria LA23 3AS. Tel: 015394 43066
Club Secretary: Jonathan C Stephenson, 22 Meadow
Road, Wallasey, Merseyside LA44 5WD. Tel: (H) 015394
45448 Tel: (W) 015394 88622 (Tel & Fax)
Fixtures Secretary: Guy W Aspinwall, 6 Brow Crescent,
Windermere, Cumbria LA23 2EZ. Tel: (H) 015394 88019
Club Colours: Amber.

NORTHERN DIVISION

CUMBRIA & LANCASHIRE NORTH 1995-96 FIXTURES

November 11 1995 (Week 10)
Trafford MV v Tyldsley
St Benedicts v Carnforth
Ormskirk v Keswick
Vickers v Workington
Upper Eden v Furness
Caldervale v Rochdale

September 16 1995 (Week 3)
Trafford MV v St Benedicts
Rochdale v Carnforth
Furness v Keswick
Moresby v Workington
Upper Eden v Vickers
Caldervale v Ormskirk

January 6 1996 (Week 17)
Keswick v Vickers
Carnforth v Ormskirk
Tyldsley v St Benedicts
Rochdale v Trafford MV
Furness v Caldervale
Moresby v Upper Eden

September 23 1995 (Week 4)
Ormskirk v Trafford MV
Vickers v Caldervale
Workington v Upper Eden
Keswick v Moresby
Carnforth v Furness
Tyldsley v Rochdale

January 13 1996 (Week 18)
Trafford MV v Furness
St Benedicts v Rochdale
Ormskirk v Tyldsley
Vickers v Carnforth
Workington v Keswick
Caldervale v Moresby

September 30 1995 (Week X1)
Trafford MV v Vickers
St Benedicts v Ormskirk
Furness v Tyldsley
Moresby v Carnforth
Upper eden v Keswick
Caldervale v Workington

February 10 1996 (Week 22)
Carnforth v Workington
Tyldsley v Vickers
Rochdale v Ormskirk
Furness v St Benedicts
Moresby v Trafford MV
Upper Eden v Caldervale

October 14 1995 (Week 6)
Vickers v St Benedicts
Workington v Trafford MV
Keswick v Caldervale
Carnforth v Upper Eden
Tyldsley v Moresby
Rochdale v Furness

February 17 1996 (Week 23)
Trafford MV v Upper Eden
St Benedicts v Moresby
Ormskirk v Furness
Vickers v Rochdale
Workington v Tyldsley
Keswick v Carnforth

October 21 1995 (Week 7)
Trafford MV v Keswick
StBenedicts v Workington
Ormskirk v Vickers
Moresby v Rochdale
Upper eden v Tyldsley
Caldervale v Carnforth

February 24 1996 (Week 24)
Tyldsley v Keswick
Rochdale v Workington
Furness v Vickers
Moresby v Ormskirk
Upper Eden v St Benedicts
Caldervale v Trafford MV

October 28 1995 (Week 8)
Workington v Ormskirk
Keswick v St Benedicts
Carnforth v Trafford MV
Tyldsley v Caldervale
Rochdale v Upper Eden
Furness v Moresby

March 30 1996 (Week X7)
St Benedicts v Caldervale
Ormskirk v Upper Eden
Vickers v Moresby
Workington v Furness
Keswick v Rochdale
Carnforth v Tyldsley

CUMBRIA & LANCASHIRE NORTH

CALDER VALE RUFC
Ground Address: Holden Road, Reedley, Burnely, Lancashire BB10 2LE. Tel: 01282 424337
Club Secretary: Mr WK Seed, 30 Moorland Drive, Brierfield, Nelson, Lancashire BB9 5ER. Tel: (H) 01222 614172 Tel: (W) 01282 474291
Fixtures Secretary: Mr M Wilton, 93 Talbot Drive, Brickcliffe, Burnley BB10 2RT. Tel: (H) 01282 457963 Tel (W) 01282 696321
Club Colours: Royal blue & gold hoops.

CARNFORTH RFC
Ground Address: Carnforth High School, Kellet Road, Carnforth, Lancashire.
Club Secretary: John S Marsden, Whinfell, Eden Mount Way, Carnforth, Lancashire LA5 9XN. Tel: (H) 01524 734832 Fax: 01524 736639 Tel: (W) 0860 848151
Fixtures Secretary: Steve Vose, 15 Clifton Drive, Bare, Morecambe, Lancashire LA4 6SR. Tel: (H) 01524 832041
Club Colours: Green & black hoops.

FURNESS RUFC
Ground Address: Strawberry Grounds, Abbey Road, Barrow-in-furness, Cumbria. Tel: 01229 825226
Club Secretary: John Mallinson, 64 Hawcoat Lane, Barrow-in-Furness, Cumbria LA14 4HQ. Tel: (H) 01229 823151 Tel: (W) 01229 837727
Fixtures Secretary: Graham Brannon, 64 Norfolk Street, Barrow-in-Furness, Cumbria. Tel: (H) 01229 811098
Club Colours: Blue & white.

KESWICK RUFC
Ground Address: Davidson Park, Keswick, Cumbria. Tel: 017687 72823
Club Secretary: ME Bowman, 3 Briar Rigg, Keswick, Cumbria CA12 4NW. Tel: (H) 017687 74878
Fixtures Secretary: AJ Branthwaite, 15 St Herberts Street, Keswick, Cumbria. Tel: (H) 017687 74234
Club Colours: Navy, green, gold hoops, white shorts.

MORESBY RUFC
Ground Address: Walk Mill Park, Moresby Parks, Whitehaven, Cumbria. Tel: 01946 695984
Fixtures Secretary: Syd Bray, 19 Sneckyeat Road, Hensingham, Whitehaven, Cumbria CA28 8PE. Tel: (H) 601946 694199
Club Colours: Red & white.

ORMSKIRK RUFC
Ground Address: Green Lane, Ormskirk, Lancs. Tel: 01695 572523
Club Secretary: LA Bumford, 28 Gores Lane, Formby, Mersyide L37 3NY. Tel: (H) 01704 878702 Tel: (W) 0151 934 4428
Fixtures Secretary: Alan Worthington, 21 Sefton Gardens, Aughton, Ormskirk, Lancs L39 6RY. Tel: (H) 01695 423762 Tel (W) 01695 572405
Club Colours: Dark green, light green & blue hoops.

ROCHDALE RUFC
Ground Address: Moorgate Avenue, Bamford, Rochdale, Greater Manchester OL11 5LU. Tel: 01706 46863
Club Secretary: JBL McManus, 27 Hunstanton Drive, Brandlesholme, Bury, Lancs, BL8 1EG. Tel: (H) 0161 761 4371 Tel: (W) 0161 740 4993
Fixtures Secretary: MP Deasey, 17 Honeysuckle Way, Rochdale, Greater Manchester OL12 6XL. Tel: (H) 01706 356094 Tel (W) 01706 353208
Club Colours: Maroon & white hoops.

ST BENEDICTS RUFC
Ground Address: Newlands Avenue, Mirehouse, Whitehaven, Cumbria.
Club Secretary: MJ Morgan, 264 Meadow Road, Mirehouse, Whitehaven, Cumbria. Tel: (H) 01946 64076
Fixtures Secretary: A Relph, 145 Balmoral Road, Whitehaven, Cumbria. Tel: (H) 01946 62490
Club Colours: Amber & black.

FINAL TABLE

	P	W	D	L	F	A	Pts
Windermere	12	12	0	0	316	97	24
Workington	12	10	0	2	223	125	20
Calder Vale	12	8	0	4	230	67	16
Upper Eden	12	7	1	4	163	161	15
Rochdale	12	7	0	5	127	138	14
Vickers	12	5	1	6	139	124	11
St Benedict's	12	5	0	7	148	155	10
Moresby	12	5	0	7	144	182	10
Tyldesley	12	4	0	8	145	200	8
Furness	12	4	0	8	111	174	8
Keswick	12	4	0	8	144	211	8
Ormskirk	12	4	0	8	137	234	8
De la Salle (Saf'd)	12	2	0	10	87	266	4

TRAFFORD METROVICK RFCC
Ground Address: MacPherson Park, Finneybank Road, Sale, Cheshire M33 1LR. Tel: 0161 976 7061
Club Secretary: Mr D French, 8 Shandon Avenue, Northenden, Manchester M22 4DP. Tel: (H) 0161 902 9963 Tel: (W) 061 248 7009
Fixtures Secretary: Mr Bryn Maddick, 1 Pollen Close, Sale, Cheshire M33 3LS. Tel: (H) 0161 962 9948 Tel (W) 0161 877 7760
Club Colours: Black & white hooped jersey, white shorts, black socks with white tops.

TYLDESLEY RUFC
Ground Address: Well Street, Tyldesley. Tel: 01942 882967
Club Secretary: Fred Eckersley, 48 Hough Lane, Tyldesley M29 8NW. Tel: (H) 01942 876074 Tel: (W) 0161 794 6215
Fixtures Secretary: Alf Yates, 6 Parkfield Close, Astley, Tyldesley, Manchester M29 7GM. Tel: (H) 01942 874651
Club Colours: Blue jerseys, white shorts.

UPPER EDEN RUFC
Ground Address: Pennine Park, Westgarth Road, Kirkby Stephen, Cumbria CA17 4AB. Tel: 017683 71585
Club Secretary: MS Reed, 87 High Street, Kirkby Stephen, Cumbria CA17 4SH. Tel: (H) 017683 72197
Fixtures Secretary: G Todd, Melbecks House, Melbecks, Kirkby Stephen, Cumbria CA17 4AB. Tel: (H) 017683 71562
Club Colours: Black & white hoops.

VICKERS RUFC
Ground Address: Hawcoat Park, Hawcoat Lane, Barrow in Furness, Cumbria. Tel: 01229 825296
Club Secretary: Mr T Mason, 48 Croslands Park, Barrow in Furness, Cumbria LA13 9NH. Tel: (H) 01229 821624 Tel: (W) 01229 820628
Fixtures Secretary: Mr C High, 19 Cowlarns Road, Barrow in Furness, Cumbria LA14 4HJ. Tel: (H) 01229 826886
Club Colours: Maroon & white.

WORKINGTON RUFC
Ground Address: Ellis Sports Ground, Mossbay Road, Workington CA14 3XZ. Tel: 01900 62625
Club Secretary: M Heaslip, 32 Elizabeth Street, Workington CA14 3XZ. Tel: (H) 01900 66339 Tel: (W) 01900 65656
Fixtures Secretary: JA Heaslip, 3 St Michael's Road, Workington CA14 3EZ. Tel: (H) 01900 602449
Club Colours: Black & white hoops.

NORTHERN DIVISION

CUMBRIA 1995-96 FIXTURES

September 16 1995 (Week 3)
Whitehaven v Smith Bros
Millom v Creighton
British Steel v Ambleside

September 23 1995 (Week 4)
Creighton v British Steel
Smith Bros v Millom
Greengarth v Silloth

September 30 1995 (Week X1)
Cumbria Constabulary v Ambleside
Whitehaven v Greengarth
British Steel v Smith Bros

October 14 1995 (Week 6)
Creighton v Cumbria Constabulary
Greengarth v Millom
Silloth v Whitehaven

October 21 1995 (Week 7)
Cumbria Constabulary v Smith Bros
Ambleside v Creighton
Millom v Silloth
British Steel v Greengarth

October 28 1995 (Week 8)
Smith Bros v Ambleside
Silloth v British Steel
Whitehaven v Millom

November 11 1995 (Week 10)
Cumbria Constabulary v Greengarth
Creighton v Smith Bros
British Steel v Whitehaven

January 6 1996 (Week 17)
Greengarth v Ambleside
Silloth v Cumbria Constabulary
Millom v British Steel

January 13 1996 (Week 18)
Cumbria Constabulary v Whitehaven
Ambleside v Silloth
Creighton v Greengarth

February 10 1996 (Week 22)
Greengarth v Smith Bros
Silloth v Creighton
Whitehaven v Ambleside
Millom v Cumbria Constabulary

February 17 1996 (Week 23)
Cumbria Constabulary v British Steel
Ambleside v Millom
Creighton v Whitehaven
Smith Bros v Silloth

378

CUMBRIA

AMBLESIDE RUFC
Ground Address: Galava Park, Borrans Road, Ambleside, Cumbria LA22 0UL. Tel: 015394 32536
Club Secretary: Mrs J Irwin, No. 1 Hodge Howe Cottages, Windermere, Cumbria LA23 2EZ. Tel: (H) 015394 42025
Fixtures Secretary: Mr N Fecitt, Hart Head Farm, Rydal, Ambleside, Cumbria. Tel: (H) 015394 33772 Tel (W) 015394 32296
Club Colours: Black.

BRITISH STEEL RUFC
Ground Address: Moss Bay Works, Moss Bay, Workington, Cumbria. Tel: 01900 603570
Club Secretary: B Moore, 6 Ellerbeck Lane, Workington, Cumbria. Tel: (H) 01900 67228
Club Colours: Red, white & blue hoops, black shorts.

CREIGHTON RUFC
Ground Address: Carrs Field, Caxton Road, off Newton Road, Carlisle. Tel: 01228 21169
Club Secretary: David J Thomlinson, 146 Moorhouse Road, Carlisle CA2 7QR. Tel: (H) 01228 35111 Tel: (W) 01228 24379
Fixtures Secretary: John Graham, 117 Pinecroft, Newfield, Kingstown Road, Carlisle CA3 0DB. Tel: (H) 01228 26705
Club Colours: Navy blue, red collars/cuffs, white shorts, red socks.

CUMBRIA CONSTABULARY RUFC
Ground Address: Winters Park, Penrith (by kind permission of Penrith RUFC). Tel: 01768 863151
Club Secretary: Philip Hutton, 24 Landsdown Close, Kendal, Cumbria LA9 7SB. Tel: (H) 01539 722092
Fixtures Secretary: Tom Hurst, Rosehill Cottage, Edenhall, Penrith CA11 8SX. Tel: (H) 01768 881020 Tel (W) 01768 64355 x7522
Club Colours: Black & myrtle green quarters.

GREENGARTH RUFC
Ground Address: Greengarth Hostel, Holmbrook, Cumbria. Tel: 01946 725800
Club Secretary: Ian Sharp, 1 Pelham Drive, Calderbridge, Seascale, Cumbria CA20 1BB. Tel: (H) 01946 841744 Tel: (W) 01946 820206
Fixtures Secretary: SJ Hall, 57 Coniston Avenue, Seascale, Cumbria. Tel: (H) 019467 28663
Club Colours: Maroon & gold.

MILLOM RUFC
Ground Address: Wilson Park, Haverigg, Millom, Cumbria. Tel: 01229 770901
Club Secretary: Pauline Hartley, The Cottage, Standsbridge, The Green, Millom, Cumbria. Tel: (H) 01229 770910 Tel: (W) 01229 772300
Fixtures Secretary: Ian Stavelton, 10 Buttermere Drive, Millom. Tel: (H) 01229 773743
Club Colours: White/blue.

SILLOTH RUFC
Ground Address: Old Marshalling Yard, Eden Street, Silloth, Carlisle, Cumbria CA5 4AD. Tel: 016973 32229
Club Secretary: David Henderson, 8 Beaconsfield Terrace, Silloth, Cumbria CA5 4HE. Tel: (H) 016973 31076
Fixtures Secretary: Richard Smith, 54b Skinburness Road, Silloth, Cumbria. Tel: (H) 016973 31687
Club Colours: Green & black hoops.

SMITH BROS RUFC
Ground Address: Seven Fields, Bransty Road, Whitehaven, Cumbria CA28 9RW. Tel: 01946 65905
Club Secretary: M Worsley, 1 Coach House, Cleator Moor Road, Whitehaven, Cumbria CA28 8TX. Tel: (H) 01946 66946
Fixtures Secretary: I Barber, 53 Griffel Road, Parton, Whitehaven, Cumbria. Tel: (H) 01946 62576
Club Colours: Blue & white hoops.

FINAL TABLE

	P	W	D	L	F	A	Pts
Carnforth	8	7	0	1	226	37	14
Creighton	8	6	1	1	118	51	13
Millom	8	6	0	2	191	66	12
Whitehaven	8	5	0	3	144	53	10
Smith Brothers	8	4	1	3	103	142	9
Ambleside	8	3	0	5	140	83	6
Green Garth	8	3	0	5	71	95	6
British Steel	8	1	0	7	35	277	2
Silloth	8	0	0	8	48	272	0

WHITEHAVEN RUFC
Ground Address: The Playground, Richmond Terrace, Whitehaven, Cumbria. Tel: 01946 695253
Club Secretary: Ernest McConnell, 38 Loop Road South, Whitehaven, Cumbria CA28 7SE. Tel: (H) 01946 692225
Fixtures Secretary: Mr WG Anderson, 18 Hensingham Road, Whitehaven, Cumbria. Tel: (H) 01946 692844
Club Colours: Maroon & white hoops.

NORTHERN DIVISION

November 11 1995 (Week 10)

De La Salle (Salford)	v	Dunkenfield
Eccles	v	Heaton Moor
Blackpool	v	Littleborough
Colne & Nelson	v	Ashton under Lyne
Thornton Cleveleys	v	Bury
North Manchester	v	Oldham

September 16 1995 (Week 3)

De La Salle (Salford)	v	Eccles
Oldham	v	Heaton Moor
Bury	v	Littleborough
Bolton	v	Ashton under Lyne
Thornton Cleveleys	v	Colne & Nelson
North Manchester	v	Blackpool

January 6 1996 (Week 17)

Littleborough	v	Colne & Nelson
Heaton Moor	v	Blackpool
Dukenfield	v	Eccles
Oldham	v	De La Salle (Salford)
Bury	v	North Manchester
Bolton	v	Thornton Cleveleys

September 23 1995 (Week 4)

Blackpool	v	De La Salle (Salford)
Colne & Nelson	v	North Manchester
Ashton under Lyne	v	Thornton Cleveleys
Littleborough	v	Bolton
Heaton Moor	v	Bury
Dukenfield	v	Oldham

January 13 1996 (Week 18)

De La Salle (Salford)	v	Bury
Eccles	v	Oldham
Blackpool	v	Dukenfield
Colne & Nelson	v	Heaton Moor
Ashton under Lyne	v	Littleborough
North Manchester	v	Bolton

September 30 1995 (Week X1)

De La Salle (Salford)	v	Colne & Nelson
Eccles	v	Blackpool
Bury	v	Dukenfield
Bolton	v	Heaton Moor
Thornton Cleveleys	v	Littleborough
North Manchester	v	Ashton under Lyne

February 10 1996 (Week 22)

Heaton Moor	v	Ashton under Lyne
Dukenfield	v	Colne & Nelson
Oldham	v	Blackpool
Bury	v	Eccles
Bolton	v	De La Salle (Salford)
Thornton Cleveleys	v	North Manchester

October 14 1995 (Week 6)

Colne & Nelson	v	Eccles
Ashton udner Lyne	v	De La Salle (Salford)
Littleborough	v	North Manchester
Heaton Moor	v	Thornton Cleveleys
Dukenfield	v	Bolton
Oldham	v	Bury

February 17 1996 (Week 23)

De La Salle (Salford)	v	Thornton Cleveleys
Eccles	v	Bolton
Blackpool	v	Bury
Colne & Nelson	v	Oldham
Ashton under Lyne	v	Dukenfield
Littleborough	v	Heaton Moor

October 21 1995 (Week 7)

De La Salle (Salford)	v	Littleborough
Eccles	v	Ashton under Lyne
Blackpool	v	Colne & Nelson
Bolton	v	Oldham
Thornton Cleveleys	v	Dukenfield
North Manchester	v	Heaton Moor

February 24 1996 (Week 24)

Dukenfield	v	Littleborough
Oldham	v	Ashton under Lyne
Bury	v	Colne & Nelson
Bolton	v	Blackpool
Thornton Cleveleys	v	Eccles
North Manchester	v	De La Salle (Salford)

October 28 1995 (Week 8)

Ashton under Lyne	v	Blackpool
Littleborough	v	Eccles
Heaton Moor	v	De La Salle (Salford)
Dukenfield	v	North Manchester
Oldham	v	Thornton Cleveleys
Bury	v	Bolton

March 30 1996 (Week X7)

Eccles	v	North Manchester
Blackpool	v	Thornton Cleveleys
Colne & Nelson	v	Bolton
Ashton under Lyne	v	Bury
Littleborough	v	Oldham
Heaton Moor	v	Dukenfield

NORTH LANCS ONE

ASHTON-UNDER-LYNE RC
Ground Address: Gambrel Bank, St Albans Avenue,
Ashton-under-Lyne OL6 8TU. Tel: 0161 330 1361
Club Secretary: Dennis Gee, 26 Burnedge Lane,
Grasscroft, Oldham, Lancs OL4 4EA. Tel: (H) 01457
872823 Tel: (W) 0161 303 9482
Fixtures Secretary: Neil Mather, 2 Castle Walk,
Ashton-under-Lyne, Lancs. Tel: (H) 0161 339 6697 Tel
(W) 0161 626 6521
Club Colours: Red, amber & black hoops.

BLACKPOOL RUFC
Ground Address: Fleetwood Road, Bispham, Blackpool,
Lancashire FY5 1RN. Tel: 01253 853308
Club Secretary: Cliff Wainscott, 15 Stafford Avenue,
Poulton-le-Fylde, Lancs FY6 8BJ. Tel: (H) 01253 885151
Fixtures Secretary: Ian Taylor, Vine Cottage, 3 Gosforth
Road, Blackpool, Lancs FY2 9UB. Tel: (H) 01253 358183
Tel (W) 01253 75104
Club Colours: Red & blue hoops.

BOLTON RUFC
Ground Address: Mortfield Pavilion, Avenue St, off
Chorley Old Road, Bolton BL1 3AW. Tel: 01204 363710
Club Secretary: RD Pemberton, Grasmere House, 4
Wilkinson St, Leigh, Lancs WN7 4DG. Tel: (H) 01942
678257
Fixtures Secretary: DA Patchett, Badger Cottage, 2
Richmill Terrace, Ramsbottom BL0 9EW. Tel: (H) 01706
826298
Club Colours: Red & white hoops.

BURY RUFC
Ground Address: Radcliffe Road, Bury, Lancs. Tel: 0161
764 1528
Club Secretary: GJ Hilton, 66 Twiss Green Lane,
Culcheth, Warrington WA3 4DQ. Tel: (H) 01925 762119
Tel: (W) 01925 762975
Fixtures Secretary: M Freschini, 15 Watling Street, Elton,
Bury. Tel: (H) 0161 764 9051
Club Colours: Red, gold & blue hooped jerseys, navy blue
shorts, red stockings.

COLNE & NELSON RUFC
Ground Address: Holt House, Harrison Drive, Colne,
Lancs. Tel: 01282 863339
Club Secretary: Keith Thornton, 12 Camden Street,
Nelson, Lancashire BB9 0BL. Tel: (H) 01282 613612 Tel:
(W) 01282 415500 & 415511
Fixtures Secretary: Duncan Bolton, 7 White Lee Avenue,
Trawden, Colne, Lancashire BB8 9SD. Tel: (H) 01282
869321 Tel (W) 01282 818883
Club Colours: All black.

DE LA SALLE (SALFORD) RUFC
Ground Address: Lancaster Road, Salford, Manchester
M6. Tel: 0161 789 2261
Club Secretary: John Malone, 57 Hayfield Road, Salford,
Manchester M6 8QA. Tel: (H) 0161 281 6011
Fixtures Secretary: JIm Collins, 8 Oakwood Drive,
Salford, Manchester M6 7NQ. Tel: (H) 0161 281 3761 Tel
(W) 0161 775 7928
Club Colours: Scarlet & gold hoops.

DUKINFIELD RUFC
Ground Address: Blocksages Playing Fields, Birch Lane,
Dukinfield, Cheshire. Tel: 0161 343 2769
Club Secretary: Ernie Taylor, 52 Gower Road, Hyde,
Cheshire SK14 5AD. Tel: (H) 0161 366 9541 Tel: (W)
01706 47422
Fixtures Secretary: Alan Hilton, Old St Georges Vicarage,
Pennine View, Heyrod, Stalybridge, Cheshire. Tel: (H)
0161 338 3410
Club Colours: Blue & gold hoops.

ECCLES RFC
Ground Address: Gorton Street, Peel Green, Eccles,
Manchester M30 8LX. Tel: 0161 789 2613

FINAL TABLE

	P	W	D	L	F	A	Pts
Metrovick	12	11	1	0	235	77	23
Blackpool	12	9	0	3	220	133	18
Bolton	12	9	0	3	187	120	18
Oldham	12	8	2	2	154	128	18
Thornton Cleveleys	12	8	1	3	196	100	17
Ashton-under-Lyne	12	6	1	5	173	180	13
Bury	12	5	2	5	117	165	12
Heaton Moor	12	5	0	7	130	155	10
Dukinfield	12	3	1	8	151	151	7
Colne & Nelson	12	3	0	9	115	143	6
North Manchester	12	3	0	9	115	211	6
Chorley	12	2	0	10	109	206	4
Burnage	12	2	0	10	80	213	4

Club Secretary: AC Brunt, 3 Beanfields, Worsley,
Manchester M28 2PJ. Tel: (H) 0161 794 4114 Tel: (W)
0831 486574
Fixtures Secretary: AE Chettoe, 11 Glynrene Drive,
Wardley, Worsley, Manchester M27 3GL. Tel: (H) 0161
794 5642 Tel (W) 0161 790 7711/2
Club Colours: Blue & white hoops, white shorts, blue &
white stockings.

HEATON MOOR RUFC
Ground Address: Green Lane, Heaton Moor, Stockport
SK4 2NF. Tel: 0161 432 3407
Club Secretary: Peter Jackson, 35 Stanley Road, Heaton
Moor, Stockport SK4 4HW. Tel: (H) 0161 442 9061 Tel:
(W) 01928 717070
Fixtures Secretary: Peter Shaw, 20 Lowerfield Drive,
Offerton, Stockport. Tel: (H) 0161 456 9758 Tel (W) 0161
499 9900 x3313
Club Colours: Black, red & gold.

LITTLEBOROUGH RUFC
Ground Address: Rakewood, Hollingworth Lake,
Littleborough, Lancs OL15 0AP. Tel: 01706 370220
Club Secretary: John Dawson, 11 Coleridge Drive,
Smithy Bridge, Littleborough, Lancs OL15 0RA. Tel: (H)
01706 373707 Tel: (W) 0161 872 2141
Fixtures Secretary: Mr Harry Hanson, 639 Oldham Road,
Royton, Lancs. Tel: (H) 0161 624 7880
Club Colours: Green, black & amber.

NORTH MANCHESTER RUFC
Ground Address: Tudor Lodge, Victoria Avenue, Moston,
Manchester M10 9SH (No mail to ground address). Tel:
0161 682 9234
Club Secretary: BH Stott, 8 Barlea Avenue, New Moston,
Manchester M40 3WL. Tel: (H) 0161 682 0541
Fixtures Secretary: P McCabe, 6 Millpool Walk,
Harpurney, Manchester M9 4DX. Tel: (H) 0161 202 3038
Club Colours: Green, black & white hoops.

OLDHAM RUFC
Ground Address: Manor Park, Bryth Road, Bardsley,
Oldham, Lancs. Tel: 0161 624 6383
Club Secretary: TJ Brown, 12 Tilton St, Oldham, Lancs
OL1 4JA. Tel: (H) 0161 620 1878 Tel: (W) 01254 57139
Fixtures Secretary: T Park Esq, Flat 71, Imogen Court,
Regent Park, Ordsall, Salford. Tel: (H) 0161 832 4551
Club Colours: Red & white hoops, blue shorts.

THORNTON CLEVELEYS RUFC
Ground Address: Fleetwood Road, Thornton Cleveleys,
Lancashire. Tel: 01253 854104
Club Secretary: Michael Johnson, 15 Beryl Avenue,
Thornton Cleveleys, Lancs FY5 3PA. Tel: (H) 01253
822857 Tel: (W) 01253 822857
Club Colours: Red, black & amber hoops.

NORTHERN DIVISION

NORTH LANCS TWO
1995-96
FIXTURES

September 16 1995 (Week 3)
Broughton v Clitheroe
Marple v Chorley
Burnage v British Aerospace
Shell Carrington v Lostock

September 23 1995 (Week 4)
British Aerospace v Shell Carrington
Chorley v Burnage
Clitheroe v Marple

September 30 1995 (Week X1)
Old Bedians v Lostock
Burnage v Clitheroe
Shell Carrington v Chorley

October 14 1995 (Week 6)
British Aerospace v Old Bedians
Clitheroe v Shell Carrington
Broughton v Marple

October 21 1995 (Week 7)
Old Bedians v Chorley
Lostock v British Aerospace
Burnage v Broughton

October 28 1995 (Week 8)
Chorley v Lostock
Clitheroe v Old Bedians
Broughton v Shell Carrington
Marple v Burnage

November 11 1995 (Week 10)
Lostock v Clitheroe
British Aerospace v Chorley
Shell Carrington v Marple

January 6 1996 (Week 17)
Clitheroe v British Aerospace
Broughton v Old Bedians
Burnage v Shell Carrington

January 13 1996 (Week 18)
Old Bedians v Marple
Lostock v Broughton
Chorley v Clitheroe

February 10 1996 (Week 22)
Broughton v British Aerospace
Marple v Lostock
Burnage v Old Bedians

February 17 1996 (Week 23)
Old Bedians v Shell Carrington
Lostock v Burnage
British Aerospace v Marple
Chorley v Broughton

NORTH LANCS TWO

BAE WARTON RFC
Ground Address: Bank Lane Playing Fields, Bank Lane, Warton, Lancashire PR4 1AX. Tel: 01772 854002/01772 852788
Club Secretary: Peter S Mill, 7 Ashton Gate, Ashton on Ribble, Preston, Lancashire PR2 1NF. Tel: (H) 01772 769512 Tel: (W) 01772 853244
Fixtures Secretary: Matthew Jagger, 6 Hazel Coppice, Lea, Preston, Lancashire. Tel: (H) 01772 769152 Tel (W) 01772 855583
Club Colours: Blue & white quarters.

BROUGHTON RUFC
Ground Address: Yew St, Broughton, Salford M7 9HL. Tel: 0161 792 2920
Club Secretary: Paul Walsh, 6 Grassfield Avenue, Lower Broughton, Salford M7 9HW. Tel: (H) 0161 792 1571
Fixtures Secretary: John Barrow, 31 Brown Street, Salford. Tel: (H) 0161 743 0902
Club Colours: Blue with yellow/red/yellow stripe midway.

BURNAGE FC
Ground Address: Varley Park, Battersea Road, Heaton Mersey, Stockport SK4 3EA. Tel: 0161 432 2150
Club Secretary: MG Crawley, 9 Leeside, Heaton Mersey, Stockport, Cheshire SK4 2DN. Tel: (H) 0161 442 4581 Tel: (W) 01625 512811
Fixtures Secretary: R Cook, c/o Burnage FC, Varley Park, Battersea Road, Heaton Mersey, Stockport SK4 3EA.
Club Colours: Black shirt, shorts, socks.

CHORLEY RUFC
Ground Address: Brookfields, Chancery Road, Astley Village, Chorley, Lancashire PR7 1XP. Tel: 01257 268806
Club Secretary: Ken Potter, Lindisfarne, 97 The Farthings, Astley Park, Chorley PR7 1SH. Tel: (H) 01257 267411 Tel: (W) 01695 53485 Fax: 01695 51205
Fixtures Secretary: Tim Holland, 45 Stump Lane, Chorley PR6 0AL. Tel: (H) 01257 416980 Tel (W) 01257 242344
Club Colours: Black & white quarters.

CLITHEROE RUFC
Ground Address: Littlemoor Park, Littlemoor Road, Clitheroe, Lancs. Tel: 01200 22261
Club Secretary: John Hyde, Moorhey Cottage, Knowle Green, Longridge, Preston PR3 2XE. Tel: (H) 01254 878402 Tel: (W) 01282 415543
Fixtures Secretary: Phil Isherwood, 160 Chatburn Road, Clitheroe BB7 2AZ. Tel: (H) 01200 23781 Tel (W) 01254 824033
Club Colours: Maroon & gold.

LOSTOCK RFC
Ground Address: Lostock RFC, Lostock Lane, Lostock, Bolton.
Club Secretary: R Fletcher, 19 Shaftesbvury Avenue, Lostock, Bolton, Lancs BL6 4AP. Tel: (H) 01204 698362
Fixtures Secretary: D Ball, 18 Lenora Street, Bolton, Lancs. Tel: (H) 01204 63629
Club Colours: All black.

MARPLE RUFC
Ground Address: Wood Lane, Marple, Stockport, Cheshire.
Club Secretary: Mr MJ Cleverly, 16 Lyme Grove, Marple, Stockport, Cheshire SK6 7NW. Tel: (H) 0161 449 8393
Fixtures Secretary: Mr N Hawkley, Bottomlock Cottage, Marple Bridge, Stockport, Cheshire SK6 5LB. Tel: (H) 0161 449 9985 Tel (W) 0161 273 3300
Club Colours: Red & black shirts, black shorts.

MONTELL RFC
Ground Address: Montell Polyolefinf, Carrington Works, Urmston, Manchester. Tel: 0161 776 3000
Club Secretary: Dave Yates, 37 Overdale Crescent, Flixton, Manchester, M41 5GR. Tel: (H) 0161 747 2242
Fixtures Secretary: Tony Kelly, 332 Liverpool Rd, Irlam, Manchester, M30 6AN. Tel: (H) 0161 775 7743 Tel (W)

FINAL TABLE

	P	W	D	L	F	A	Pts
Eccles	8	7	0	1	113	70	14
Littleborough	8	6	1	1	166	68	13
Marple	8	6	0	2	213	44	12
Old Bedians	8	6	0	2	171	25	12
British Aerospace	8	4	0	4	34	162	8
Broughton	8	2	1	5	138	96	5
Shell Carrington	8	3	0	5	85	163	2*
Clitheroe	8	1	0	7	53	124	0*
Lostock	8	0	0	8	24	275	-2*

0161 745 7425
Club Colours: Red & yellow.

OLD BEDIANS RFC
Ground Address: Underbank Farm, Millgate Lane, East Didsbury, Manchester M20 5QX. Tel: 0161 445 8862
Club Secretary: AP Horner, 73 Lee Crescent, Gorse Hill, Stretford, Manchester M32 0TN. Tel: (H) 0161 865 5524 Tel: (W) 0161 228 3681
Fixtures Secretary: G Tucker, 3 Palatine Avenue, Withington, Manchester M20. Tel: (H) 0161 445 2358
Club Colours: Royal blue shirts, white shorts.

NORTHERN DIVISION

CHESHIRE & LANCASHIRE SOUTH 1995-96 FIXTURES

September 16 1995 (Week 3)
Crewe & Nantwich v Kersal
Sefton v Congleton
South Liverpool v Newton le Willows
Port Sunlight v Parkonians
Ruskin Park v St Edwards OB
Eagle v Warrington

September 23 1995 (Week 4)
Warrington v Crewe & Nantwich
St Edwards OB v Eagle
Parkonians v Ruskin Park
Newton le Willows v Port Sunlight
Congleton v South Liverpool
Wirral v Sefton

September 30 1995 (Week X1)
Crewe & Nantwich v St Edwards OB
Kersal v Warrington
South Liverpool v Wirral
Port Sunlight v Congleton
Ruskin Park v Newton le Willows
Eagle v Parkonians

October 14 1995 (Week 6)
St Edwards OB c Kersal
Parkonians v Crewe & Nantwich
Newton le Willows v Eagle
Congleton v Ruskin Park
Wirral v Port Sunlight
Sefton v South Liverpool

October 21 1995 (Week 7)
Crewe & Nantwich v Newton le Willows
Kersal v Parkonians
Warrington v St Edwards OB
Port Sunlight v Sefton
Ruskin Park v Wirral
Eagle v Congleton

October 28 1995 (Week 8)
Parkonians v Warrington
Newton le Willows v Kersal
Congleton v Crewe & Nantwich
Wirral v Eagle
Sefton v Ruskin Park
South Liverpool v Port Sunlight

November 11 1995 (Week 10)
Crewe & Nantwich v Wirral
Kersal v Congleton
Warrington v Newton le Willows
St Edwards OB v Parkonians
Ruskin Park v South Liverpool
Eagle v Sefton

January 6 1996 (Week 17)
Newton le Willows v St Edwards OB
Congleton v Warrington
Wirral v Kersal
Sefton v Crewe & Nantwich
South Liverpool v Eagle
Port Sunlight v Ruskin Park

January 13 1996 (Week 18)
Crewe & Nantwich v South Liverpool
Kersal v Sefton
Warrington v Wirral
St Edwards OB v Congleton
Parkonians v Newton le Willows
Eagle v Port Sunlight

February 10 1996 (Week 22)
Congleton v Parkonians
Wirral v St Edwards OB
Sefton v Warrington
South Liverpool v Kersal
Port Sunlight v Crewe & Nantwich
Ruskin Park v Eagle

February 17 1996 (Week 23)
Crewe & Nantwich v Ruskin Park
Kersal v Port Sunlight
Warrington v South Liverpool
St Edwards OB v Sefton
Parkonians v Wirral
Newton le Willows v Congleton

February 24 1996 (Week 24)
Wirral v Newton le Willows
Sefton v Parkonians
South Liverpool v St Edwards OB
Port Sunlight v Warrington
Ruskin Park v Kersal
Eagle v Crewe & Nantwich

March 30 1996 (Week X7)
Kersal v Eagle
Warrington v Ruskin Park
St Edwards OB v Port Sunlight
Parkonians v South Liverpool
Newton le Willows v Sefton
Congleton v Wirral

CHESHIRE & LANCASHIRE SOUTH

ALTRINCHAM (KERSAL) RFC
Ground Address: Stelfox Avenue, Timperley, Altrincham, Cheshire. Tel: 0161 973 9157
Club Secretary: Dominic Leach, 10 Addison Road, Hale, Altrincham, Cheshire WA15 9BU. Tel: (H) 0161 941 3085 Tel: (W) 0161 929 1851
Fixtures Secretary: PRL Blakeman, 32 Glebelands Road, Knutsford, Cheshire. Tel: (H) 01565 634276
Club Colours: Red, black & white hoops, blue shorts.

CONGLETON RUFC
Ground Address: Clubhouse: 78 Park Street, Congleton, Cheshire CW12. Tel: 01260 273338
Club Secretary: Dennis Thorley, 46 Bladon Crescent, Alsager, via Stoke-on-Trent, Cheshire ST7 2BG. Tel: (H) 01270 878293 Tel: (W) 0161 223 1301 x3132
Fixtures Secretary: Ken Williams, 2 Sprink Lane, Buglawton, Congleton, Cheshire CW12. Tel: (H) 01260 279202
Club Colours: Red/white/red/black hoops, black shorts.

CREWE AND NANTWICH RUFC
Ground Address: The Vagrants, Newcastle Road (A500). Willaston, Nantwich, cheshire CW5 7EP. Tel: 01270 69506
Club Secretary: AG Jones, 9 Gingerbread Lane, Nantwich, Cheshire CW5 6NH. Tel: (H) 01270 625737 Tel: (W) 01270 625737
Fixtures Secretary: RL Christie, 127A Welsh Row, Nantwich, Cheshire CW5 5ET. Tel: (H) 01270 629637 (after 8pm) Tel (W) 01270 624160
Club Colours: White with single black circlet.

EAGLE RUFC
Ground Address: Thornton Road, Great Sankey, Warrington, Cheshire. Tel: 01925 632926
Club Secretary: Vince Sandwell, 23 Waterworks Lane, Winwick, Warrington, Cheshire WA2 8LH. Tel: (H) 01925 650367 Tel: (W) 01925 830007
Fixtures Secretary: Alan Knight, 7 Trefoil Close, Birchwood, Warrington, Cheshire. Tel: (H) 01925 831490
Club Colours: Black & white hoops.

NEWTON-LE-WILLOWS RUFC
Ground Address: Newton-le-Willows Sports Club, Crow Lane East, Newton-le-Willows, Merseyside. Tel: 01925 224591
Club Secretary: DN Hughes, 127 Birley Street, Newton-le-Willows, Merseyside WA12 9UN. Tel: (H) 01925 221304 Tel: (W) 0161 797 1225
Fixtures Secretary: O O'Neill, 236 Crow Lane West, Newton-le-Willows, Merseyside. Tel: (H) 01925 221366
Club Colours: Amber & blue.

PARKONIAN RUFC
Ground Address: H Martin Curphey Memorial Ground, Holm Lane, Oxton, Birkenhead, Merseyside L43 2HU. Tel: 0151 652 3105
Club Secretary: Mr PL Mullen, 8 Deerwood Crescent, Little Sutton, South Wirral L66 1SE. Tel: (H) 0151 339 1270 Tel: (W) 0151 448 6280
Fixtures Secretary: Mr E Potter, 24 Thornton Road, Higher Begington, Merseyside. Tel: (H) 0151 608 1582
Club Colours: Maroon, blue & white hooped jerseys & stockings, white shorts.

PORT SUNLIGHT RFC
Ground Address: Leverhulme Playing Field, Green Lane, Bromborough, Wirral, Merseyside. Tel: 0151 334 3677
Club Secretary: Alan Haigh, 13 Charlotte's Meadow, Bebington, Wirral, Merseyside L63 3JH. Tel: (H) 051 334 1304 Tel: (W) 0151 231 3132
Fixtures Secretary: Chris Dodd, 16 Thornton Road, Bebington, Wirral, Merseyside L63 5PS. Tel: (H) 0151 608 7022
Club Colours: Black & white hoops.

RUSKIN PARK RFC
Ground Address: Ruskin Drive, St Helens, Merseyside WA10 6RP. Tel: 01774 22893

FINAL TABLE

	P	W	D	L	F	A	Pts
Aspull	12	12	0	0	280	45	24
Eagle	12	8	0	4	183	161	16
South Liverpool	12	7	0	5	209	144	14
Crewe & Nantwich	12	7	0	5	193	177	14
Wirral	12	8	0	4	133	127	14*
Altrincham Kersal	12	6	1	5	142	138	13
Warrington	12	5	0	7	152	146	10
Sefton	12	5	0	7	156	186	10
Port Sunlight	12	5	0	7	86	147	10
Old Parkonians	12	5	0	7	157	146	8*
Southport	12	4	0	8	137	176	8
Old Anselmians	12	3	1	8	112	213	7
Vulcan	12	2	0	10	88	222	4

Club Secretary: Steve Mitchell, 13 Whitebeam Gardens, Chestnut Grove, Rainhill, Merseyside. Tel: (H) 0151 431 1171 Tel: (W) 01744 20021
Fixtures Secretary: G White, 25 Dodd Avenus, Eccleston, St Helens. Tel: (H) 01744 756478
Club Colours: Royal blue, white & black hoops.

SEFTON RUFC
Ground Address: Thornhead Lane, Leyfield Road, West Derby, Liverpool L12 9EY. Tel: 0151 228 9092
Club Secretary: Graham Price, 5 Avalon Road, West Derby, Liverpool L12 9ER. Tel: (H) 0151 220 1043 Tel: (W) 0151 487 0606
Fixtures Secretary: Bernard Houghton, 14 Gateacre Vale Road, Liverpool L25 5NP. Tel: (H) 0151 428 3740
Club Colours: Red/white hoops, blue shorts.

SOUTH LIVERPOOL RUFC
Ground Address: Bridgefield Forum Leisure Centre, Halewood, Knowsley, Liverpool L26. Tel: 0151 443 2123
Club Secretary: Mr Lawrence Sherrington, 14 Brook Way, Great Sankey, Warrington, Cheshire. Tel: (H) 01925 726768
Fixtures Secretary: Mr Dave Edge, 93 Millwood Road, Speke, Liverpool L24 2HR. Tel: (H) 0151 425 4018 Tel (W) 0151 486 2930
Club Colours: Amber & black quarters.

ST EDWARD'S OLD BOYS RUFC
Ground Address: Bishops Court, North Drive, Sandfield Park, West Derby, Liverpool 12. Tel: 0151 228 1414
Club Secretary: S Smith, 107 Church Road, Woolton, Liverpool L25 6DB. Tel: (H) 0151 428 2799
Fixtures Secretary: R Reilly, 130 Quarry Street, Woolton, Liverpool 25. Tel: (H) 0151 428 3296
Club Colours: Royal blue, gold chest band.

WARRINGTON RUFC
Ground Address: Bridge Lane, Appleton, Warrington, Cheshire. Tel: 01925 264591
Club Secretary: GP Robinson, 8 Bellhouse Lane, Graddenhall, Warrington WA4 2SD. Tel: (H) 01925 261644
Fixtures Secretary: P Andrews, 6 Alexandra Street, Warrington WA1 3SE. Tel: (H) 01925 413638
Club Colours: Red, green & white.

WIRRAL RFC
Ground Address: Old Wirralians Memorial Ground, Thornton Common Road, Clatterbridge, Wirral, Mersyside. Tel: 0151 334 1309
Club Secretary: Mr P Darch, 19 Tanar Close, Spital, Bebington, Wirral, Merseyside L63 9AN. Tel: (H) 0151 346 1299 Tel: (W) 0151 639 8181
Fixtures Secretary: Mr ICT Ritchie, 49 Meadow Lane, Willaston, Wirral, Merseyside. Tel: (H) 0151 327 5695 Tel (W) 0151 236 4702
Club Colours: Maroon & white hoops.

NORTHERN DIVISION

CHESHIRE
1995-96
FIXTURES

September 16 1995 (Week 3)
Helsby	v	Shell Stanlow
Wallasey	v	Bowden
Old Anselmians	v	Moore
Whitehouse Park	v	Prenton

September 23 1995 (Week 4)
Hoylake	v	Helsby
Moore	v	Whitehouse Park
Bowden	v	Old Anselmians
Holmes Chapel	v	Wallasey

September 30 1995 (Week X1)
Helsby	v	Prenton
Shell Stanlow	v	Hoylake
Old Anselmians	v	Holmes Chapel
Whitehouse Park	v	Bowden

October 14 1995 (Week 6)
Prenton	v	Shell Stanlow
Moore	v	Helsby
Holmes Chapel	v	Whitehouse Park
Wallasey	v	Old Anselmians

October 21 1995 (Week 7)
Helsby	v	Bowden
Shell Stanlow	v	Moore
Hoylake	v	Prenton
Whitehouse Park	v	Wallasey

October 28 1995 (Week 8)
Moore	v	Hoylake
Bowden	v	Shell Stanlow
Holmes Chapel	v	Helsby
Old Anselmians	v	Whitehouse Park

November 11 1995 (Week 10)
Helsby	v	Wallasey
Shell Stanlow	v	Holmes Chapel
Hoylake	v	Bowden
Prenton	v	Moore

January 6 1996 (Week 17)
Bowden	v	Prenton
Holmes chapel	v	Hoylake
Wallasey	v	Shell Stanlow
Old Anselmians	v	Helsby

January 13 1996 (Week 18)
Helsby	v	Whitehouse Park
Shell Stanlow	v	Old Anselmians
Hoylake	v	Wallasey
Prenton	v	Holmes Chapel
Moore	v	Bowden

February 10 1996 (Week 22)
Holmes Chapel	v	Moore
Wallasey	v	Prenton
Old Anselmians	v	Hoylake
Whitehouse Park	v	Shell Stanlow

February 17 1996 (Week 23)
Hoylake	v	Whitehouse Park
Prenton	v	Old Anselmians
Moore	v	Wallasey
Bowden	v	Holmes Chapel

CHESHIRE

BOWDON RUFC
Ground Address: Clay Lane, Timperley, Cheshire. Tel: 0161 980 8321
Club Secretary: Tom St John Sloan, 7 Leigh Road, Hale, Altrincham WA15 9BG. Tel: (H) 0161 941 5865 Tel: (W) 0161 929 0105
Fixtures Secretary: Frank Norton, 36 Greenwalk, Timperley, Altrincham. Tel: (H) 0161 980 8195 Tel (W) 01925 834639
Club Colours: Burgundy, black, white hoops.

HELSBY RUFC
Ground Address: Helsby Sports & Social Club, Chester Road, Helsby, Warrington. Tel: 01928 722267
Club Secretary: Eric Lamb, 5 Firbank Road, Elton, Nr Chester, Cheshire CH2 4LY. Tel: (H) 01928 724039 Tel: (W) 0151 350 4392
Fixtures Secretary: Tony Ryder, 64 Chester Road, Helsby WA6 0DW. Tel: (H) 01928 723733
Club Colours: Black & amber.

HOLMES CHAPEL RUFC
Ground Address: Goostrey Lane, Goostrey, Cheshire (do not use for post).
Club Secretary: Mr S Ranger, 16 BalmoralDrive, Holmes Chapel, Cheshire CW4 7HY. Tel: (H) 01477 533765 Tel: (W) 0850 003869
Fixtures Secretary: Mr J Leary, 7 Swanlow Drive, Winsford, Cheshire. Tel: (H) 01606 554614 Tel (W) 01606 593411
Club Colours: Blue & gold hoops.

HOYLAKE RFC
Ground Address: Melrose Avenue, Hoylake, Wirral, Merseyside L47 3AU. Tel: 0151 632 2538
Club Secretary: Mrs Susan Kurton, 7 Meadowcroft Road, Meols, Wirral, Merseyside L47 6BG. Tel: (H) 0151 632 5540 Tel: (W) 0151 678 7456
Fixtures Secretary: Ali Green, 48 Bovetside, West Kirby, Wirral, Merseyside. Tel: (H) 0151 625 7813
Club Colours: Red, green & white.

MOORE RUFC
Ground Address: Moss Lane, Moore, Nr Warrington, Cheshire WA4 6UP. Tel: 01925 740473
Club Secretary: John Stockton, 3 Hays Lane, Appleton, Cheshire WA4 6EJ. Tel: (H) 01925 266025
Fixtures Secretary: Peter Woollacott, 6 Woodlands Drive, Thelwall, Warrington, Cheshire WA4 2EU. Tel: (H) 01925 266576
Club Colours: Black with gold band.

OLD ANSELMIANS RUFC
Ground Address: Malone Field, Eastham Village Road, Eastham, Wirral. Tel: 0151 327 1613
Club Secretary: Tony Neville, 33 Stapleton Avenue, Greasby, Wirral L49 2QT. Tel: (H) 0151 678 4154 Tel: (W) 0151 350 1696
Fixtures Secretary: Tony McArdle, 18 Greenbank Drive, Heswall, Wirral L61 5UF. Tel: (H) 0151 342 1470
Club Colours: Blue, gold & white.

PRENTON RUFC
Ground Address: The Club House, Prenton Dell, Prenton Dell Road, Prenton, Wirral, Merseyside L43 3BS. Tel: 0151 608 1501
Club Secretary: Paul Foster, 8 Rake Close, Upton, Wirral, Merseyside L49 0XD. Tel: (H) 0151 678 6634 Tel: (W) 01244 694694
Fixtures Secretary: John tyler, 265 Greasby Road, Wirral, Merseyside L49 2PW. Tel: (H) 0151 608 8808
Club Colours: Maroon, gold & black.

SHELL (STANLOW) RFU
Ground Address: The Shell Club, Chester Road, Whitby, Ellesmere Port, South Wirral, Cheshire. Tel: 0151 355 2364/2704
Club Secretary: Mr ARJ Dale, 12 Archers Way, Great

FINAL TABLE

	P	W	D	L	F	A	Pts
Congleton	9	9	0	0	265	66	18
Wallasey	9	8	0	1	244	80	16
Shell Stanlow	9	6	0	3	156	99	12
Bowdon	9	5	1	3	198	117	11
Prenton	9	4	0	5	127	115	8
Helsby	9	2	2	5	73	72	6
Holmes Chapel	9	2	0	7	67	250	4
Whitehouse Park	9	2	0	7	71	216	2*
Hoylake	9	3	1	5	117	185	1*
Moore	9	2	0	7	84	202	-4*

Sutton, South Wirral, Cheshire L66 2RY. Tel: (H) 0151 339 7823 Tel: (W) 0151 355 2157 x206
Fixtures Secretary: Mr G Fennion, 19 Belgrave Drive, Ellesmere Port L65 7EJ. Tel: (H) 0151 356 1952 Tel (W) 01244 281281
Club Colours: Amber shirts, white shorts, red socks.

WALLASEY RUFC
Ground Address: Cross Lane, Leasowe Road, Wallasey, Wirral, Merseyside. Tel: 0151 638 1486
Club Secretary: Mr JA Burton, 14 Seaview Lane, Irby, Wirral, Merseyside L61 3UL. Tel: (H) 0151 648 4341 Tel: (W) 0161 236 3707
Fixtures Secretary: Mr A Rae, 8 Inchcape Road, Wallasey, Wirral, Merseyside L45 8JR. Tel: (H) 0151 638 6903 Tel (W) 0151 933 6446
Club Colours: Red, black, white hoops.

WHITEHOUSE PARK RFC
Ground Address: c/o Halton Sports, Murdishaw Avenue, Runcorn, Cheshire. Tel: 01928 714815
Club Secretary: Mr JM Gore, 1 Halsall Close, New Sutton Park, Runcorn, Cheshire WA7 6LT. Tel: (H) 01928 712284
Fixtures Secretary: Mr F Williams, 20 Rawdon Close, Palacefields, Runcorn, Cheshire WA7 2QQ. Tel: (H) 01928 718 738
Club Colours: Blue & white hoops.

NORTHERN DIVISION

LANCASHIRE SOUTH
1995-96
FIXTURES

September 16 1995 (Week 3)
Southport v Didsbury Toc H
Liverpool Colliate v Lucas
Birchfield v Mossley Hill
Douglas v Hightown
Halton v Vulcan

September 23 1995 (Week 4)
Vulcan v Southport
Hightown v Halton
Mossley Hill v Douglas (IOM)
Lucas v Birchfield
St Mary's OB v Liverpool Colliate

September 30 1995 (Week X1)
Southport v Hightown
Didsbury Toc H v Vulcan
Birchfield v St Mary's OB
Douglas (IOM)
Halton v Mossley Hill

October 14 1995 (Week 6)
Hightown v Didsbury Toc H
Mossley Hill v Southport
Lucas v Halton
St Mary's OB v Douglas (IOM)
Liverpool Colliate v Birchfield

October 21 1995 (Week 7)
Southport v Lucas
Didsbury Toc H v Mossley Hill
Vulcan v Hightown
Douglas (IOM)
Halton v St Mary's OB

October 28 1995 (Week 8)
Mossley Hill v Vulcan
Lucas v Didsbury Toc H
St Mary's OB v Southport
Liverpool Colliate v Halton
Birchfield v Douglas (IOM)

November 11 1995 (Week 10)
Southport v Liverpool Colliate
Didsbury Toc H v St Mary's OB
Vulcan v Lucas
Hightown v Mossley Hill
Halton v Birchfield

January 6 1996 (Week 17)
Lucas v Hightown
St Mary's OB v Vulcan
Liverpool Colliate v Didsbury Toc H
Birchfield v Southport
Douglas (IOM)

January 13 1996 (Week 18)
Southport v Douglas(IOM)
Didsbury Toc H v Birchfield
Vulcan v Liverpool Colliate
Hightown v St Mary's OB
Mossley Hill v Lucas

February 10 1996 (Week 22)
St Mary's OB v Mossley Hill
Liverpool Colliate v Hightown
Birchfield v Vulcan
Douglas (IOM)
Halton v Southport

February 17 1996 (Week 23)
Didsbury Toc H v Halton
Vulcan v Douglas (IOM)
Hightown v Birchfield
Mossley Hill v Liverpool Colliate
Lucas v St Mary's OB

LANCASHIRE SOUTH

BIRCHFIELD (LANCS) RUFC
Ground Address: Albright & Wilson Recreational Club, Birchfield Road, Widnes, Cheshire WA8 0TB. Tel: 0151 424 3222
Club Secretary: Stuart Ashton, 11 Eltham Close, Widnes, Cheshire WA8 0RG. Tel: (H) 0151 424 6344
Fixtures Secretary: Mr MH Cuthbert, 145 Shackleton Close, Old Hall, Warrington, Cheshire WA5 5QF. Tel: (H) 01925 638567
Club Colours: Maroon.

DIDSBURY TOC H RFC
Ground Address: Ford Lane, Didsbury, Manchester. Tel: 0161 446 2146
Club Secretary: Peter JM Bradley, 8 Barnard Avenue, Heaton Moor, Stockport SK4 4EP. Tel: (H) 0161 432 0496 Tel: (W) 0161 788 9611
Fixtures Secretary: Richard Mortimer, 34 Meadows Road, Sale. Tel: (H) 0161 976 5461
Club Colours: Black jersey with broad amber band.

DOUGLAS (IOM) RUFC
Ground Address: The Clubhouse, Port-E-Chee, Douglas, Isle of Man. Tel: 01624 676493
Club Secretary: P E Garrett, 3 Ridgeway Street, Douglas, Isle of Man. Tel: (H) 01624 629037 Tel: (W) 01624 624535
Fixtures Secretary: G Taylor, 7 Larch Hill, Hightonwood Hill, Tromode, Douglas, Isle of Man. Tel: (H) 01624 672396 Tel (W) 01624 626586
Club Colours: Maroon with gold band.

HALTON RUFC
Ground Address: ICI Recreation Ground, Liverpool Road, Widnes, Cheshire. Tel: 0151 424 2355
Club Secretary: SG Dennett, 267 Lunts Heath Road, Widnes, Cheshire WA8 9BB. Tel: (H) 0151 424 3978
Fixtures Secretary: (Acting) J Brady, 22 Highfield Crescent, Widnes, Cheshire. Tel: (H) 0151 423 1566
Club Colours: Blue & white hoops.

HIGHTOWN RUFC
Ground Address: Thirlmere Road, Hightown, Merseyside, L38. Tel: 0151 929 2330
Club Secretary: PO Sharman, 32 Cavendish Road, Crosby, Liverpool, L28 6XB. Tel: (H) 0151 474 6275 Tel: (W) 0151 474 6275
Fixtures Secretary: R Baker, 17 Mornington Avenue, Crosby, Liverpool. Tel: (H) 0151 920 7381 Tel (W) 0151 236 0559
Club Colours: Blue/white/brown quartered shirts, blue shorts & socks.

LIVERPOOL COLLEGIATE OLD BOYS RUFC
Ground Address: Peter Lloyd Leisure Centre, Millbank, Mill Lane, West Derby, Liverpool L13. Tel: 0151 228 7132
Club Secretary: RJ Smith, 4 Staveley Road, Grassendale, Liverpool L19 9AS. Tel: (H) 0151 427 6534 Tel: (W) 0151 229 4556
Fixtures Secretary: IM Smith, 107 Doulton Street, West Park, St Helens, Merseyside WA10 4NZ. Tel: (H) 01744 614987
Club Colours: Light blue/dark blue hoops.

LUCAS MERSEYSIDE RUFC
Ground Address: Walton Sports Centre, Walton Hall Avenue, Liverpool L4 9XP. Tel: 0151 523 3472
Club Secretary: I Whitehead, 14 Aylton Road, Liverpool L36 2LU. Tel: (H) 0151 449 2137 Tel: (W) 0151 524 6555
Fixtures Secretary: R Chesworth, 27 Moss Side, Dovecot, Liverpool L14 0SS. Tel: (H) 0151 489 1352
Club Colours: Royal blue.

MOSSLEY HILL RUFC
Ground Address: Mossley Hill Road, Liverpool L18.
Club Secretary: A Pealing, 5 Fieldfare Close, Liverpool L25 4UB. Tel: (H) 0151 280 1174 Tel: (W) 0151 228 3565
Fixtures Secretary: JC Parr, 42 The Copse, Woolton Road L18 3NH. Tel: (H) 0151 738 1247

FINAL TABLE

	P	W	D	L	F	A	Pts
Newton-le-Willows	9	9	0	0	423	74	18
Liverpool Coll'iate	9	7	0	2	146	60	14
St Mary's OB	9	6	0	3	189	84	12
Didsbury Toc H	9	4	1	4	163	150	9
Birchfield	9	5	0	4	189	160	8*
Douglas	9	4	0	5	135	128	8
Mossley Hill	9	3	1	5	94	178	7
Lucas	9	1	0	8	60	359	2
Halton	9	4	0	5	146	199	0*
Hightown	9	1	0	8	100	253	-2*

Club Colours: Maroon & gold hoops or quarters.

SOUTHPORT RUFC
Ground Address: Waterloo Road, Hillside, Southport, Merseyside PR8 4QW. Tel: 01704 569906
Club Secretary: Mr AR Coakley, 'The Old Vicarage', 2A St Peter's Road, Birkdale, Southport, Merseyside PR8 4BY. Tel: (H) 01704 550629 Tel: (W) 0589 323938
Fixtures Secretary: Mrs M Jackson, 43 Kenilworth Road, Ainsdale, Southport, Merseyside. Tel: (H) 01704 578362
Club Colours: Red, black & amber hoops.

ST MARY'S OLD BOYS RUFC
Ground Address: 17 Moor Lane, Crosby, Liverpool 23. Tel: 0151 924 1774
Club Secretary: Paul McCann, 3 Dumfries Way, Melling Mount, Kirkby. Tel: (H) 0151 548 0659
Fixtures Secretary: Peter Moore, 77 Freshfield Road, Formby, Merseyside. Tel: (H) 017048 78537
Club Colours: Maroon, yellow, blue hoops.

VULCAN RUFC
Ground Address: The Sportsfield, Wargrave Road, Newton-le-Willows, Merseyside. Tel: 01925 224180
Club Secretary: Paul Tither, 19 Grosvenor Gardens, Newton-le-Willows, Merseyside WA12 8LY. Tel: (H) 01925 222006 Tel: (W) 01925 417080
Fixtures Secretary: J Bajer, 5 Heylock Close, Newton-le-Willows, Merseyside WA12 2SD. Tel: (H) 01925 226653
Club Colours: Black & amber.

NORTHERN DIVISION

NORTH EAST ONE 1995-96 FIXTURES

November 11 1995 (Week 10)
Ashington v Morpeth
Redcar v Roundhegians
Selby v Driffield
North Ribblesdale v Gateshead Fell
Cleckheaton v Pontefract
Keighley v Old Brodleians

September 16 1995 (Week 3)
Ashington v Redcar
Old Brodleians v Roundhegians
Pontefract v Driffield
Horden v Gateshead Fell
Cleckheaton v North Ribblesdale
Keighley v Selby

September 23 1995 (Week 4)
Selby v Ashington
North Ribblesdale v Keighley
Gateshead Fell v Cleckheaton
Driffield v Horden
Roundhegians v Pontefract
Morpeth v Old Brodleians

September 30 1995 (Week X1)
Ashington v North Ribblesdale
Redcar v Selby
Pontefract v Morpeth
Horden v Roundhegians
Cleckheaton v Driffield
Keighley v Gateshead Fell

October 14 1995 (Week 6)
North Ribblesdale v Redcar
Gateshead Fell v Ashington
Driffield v Keighley
Roundhegians v Cleckheaton
Morpeth v Horden
Old Brodleians v Pontefract

October 21 1995 (Week 7)
Ashington v Driffield
Redcar v Gateshead Fell
Selby v North Ribblesdale
Horden v Old Brodleians
Cleckheaton v Morpeth
Keighley v Roundhegians

October 28 1995 (Week 8)
Gateshead Fell v Selby
Driffield v Redcar
Roundhegians v Ashington
Morpeth v Keighley
Old Brodleians v Cleckheaton
Pontefract v Horden

January 6 1996 (Week 17)
Driffield v North Ribblesdale
Roundhegians v Selby
Morpeth v Redcar
Old Brodleians v Ashington
Pontefract v Keighley
Horden v Cleckheaton

January 13 1996 (Week 18)
Ashington v Pontefract
Redcar v Old Brodleians
Selby v Morpeth
North Ribblesdale v Roundhegians
Gateshead Fell v Driffield
Keighley v Horden

February 10 1996 (Week 22)
Roundhegians v Gateshead Fell
Morpeth v North Ribblesdale
Old Brodleians v Selby
Pontefract v Redcar
Horden v Ashington
Cleckheaton v Keighley

February 17 1996 (Week 23)
Ashington v Cleckheaton
Redcar v Horden
Selby v Pontefract
North Ribblesdale v Old Brodleians
Gateshead Fell v Morpeth
Driffield v Roundhegians

February 24 1996 (Week 24)
Morpeth v Driffield
Old Brodleians v Gateshead Fell
Pontefract v North Ribblesdale
Horden v Selby
Cleckheaton v Redcar
Keighley v Ashington

March 30 1996 (Week X7)
Redcar v Keighley
Selby v Cleckheaton
North Ribblesdale v Horden
Gateshead Fell v Pontefract
Driffield v Old Brodleians
Roundhegians v Morpeth

390

NORTH EAST ONE

ASHINGTON JW RFC
Ground Address: Recreation Ground, High Market,
Ashington, Northumberland. Tel: 01670 814123
Club Secretary: S Leithead, 5 Woodlands, Ulgham, Morpeth,
Northumberland. Tel: (H) 01670 790386
Fixtures Secretary: A Armstrong, 25 Dunsdale Drive,
Eastfield Vale, Bramlington, Northumberland NE23 9GA. Tel:
(H) 01670 736891 Tel (W) 01670 533303
Club Colours: Royal blue & amber hoops, white shorts.
CLECKHEATON RUFC
Ground Address: Moorend, Cleckheaton, West Yorkshire
BD19 3UD. Tel: 01274 873410
Club Secretary: Mr Ian G Worley, 342 Whitehall Road,
Westfield, Wyke, Bradford, West Yorkshire BD12 9DP. Tel:
(H) 01274 677526
Fixtures Secretary: Mr Jack Wood, Traquair, 705 Halifax
Road, Cleckheaton, West Yorkshire BD19 6LJ. Tel: (H) 01274
873532 Tel (W) 01274 872423
Club Colours: Red & white hoops, black shorts, red socks with
two white hoops.
DRIFFIELD RUFC
Ground Address: Kellythorpe, Driffield, East Yorkshire YO25
9DN. Tel: 01377 256598
Club Secretary: Steve Edwards, Cedar Cottage, St John's
Road, Driffield, East Yorkshire YO25 7RS. Tel: (H) 01377
253757
Fixtures Secretary: John Harrison, 9 Parsonage Close,
Nafferton, Driffield YO25 0LH. Tel: (H) 01377 253032 Tel
(W) 01377 253032
Club Colours: Blue, black, white hoops.
GATESHEAD FELL RFC
Ground Address: Hedley Lawson Park, Eastwood Gardens,
Gateshead NE9 5BE. Tel: 0191 420 0207
Club Secretary: Matthew Alan Nunn, 30 Limetrees Gardens,
Low Fell, Gateshead NE9 5BE. Tel: (H) 0191 420 3089 Fax:
0191 420 3089
Fixtures Secretary: Newton Wood, 18 Lyndhurst Grove, Low
Fell, Gateshead NE9 5AU. Tel: (H) 0191 420 7409
Club Colours: Dark blue & light blue (narrow rings), white
shorts, red socks.
HORDEN WELFARE RFC
Ground Address: Northumberland Street, Horden, Peterlee,
Co. Durham SR8 4PL. Tel: 0191 586 3501
Club Secretary: William Featonby, 20 Morpeth Street,
Horden, Co. Durham SR8 4BB. Tel: (H) 0191 586 6973
Fixtures Secretary: John Fenwick, 1 Leyburn Place, Peterlee,
Co. Durham. Tel: (H) 0191 586 6540
Club Colours: Claret & blue.
KEIGHLEY RUFC
Ground Address: Skipton Road, Utley, Keighley, West
Yorkshire BD20 6DT. Tel: 01535 602174
Club Secretary: Michael T Greaves, Holmlea, Summerhill
Lane, Steeton, Keighley, West Yorkshire BD20 6RX. Tel: (H)
01535 653192 Tel: (W) 01535 605646
Fixtures Secretary: Joe Midgley, 21 Woodville Road,
Keighley, West Yorkshire BD20 6JA. Tel: (H) 01535 214545
Tel (W) 01535 605311
Club Colours: White, emerald & scarlet hoops.
MORPETH RFC
Ground Address: Grange House Field, Mitford Road,
Morpeth, Northumberland NE61 1RJ. Tel: 01670 512508
Club Secretary: Ken Fraser, Solway House, De Merley Road,
Morpeth, Northumberland NE61 1HZ. Tel: (H) 01670 511208
Tel: (W) 01642 244144 x209 Fax: 01642 245207
Fixtures Secretary: Bill Hewitt, The Birches, Lane End Farm,
Felton, Northumberland. Tel: (H) 01670 787757
Club Colours: Scarlet & white hooped shirts, white shorts,
scarlet socks with white tops.
NORTH RIBBLESDALE RUFC
Ground Address: Grove Park, Greenfoot, Settle, North
Yorkshire. Tel: 01729 822755
Club Secretary: RT Graveson, Attermire House, Castle Hill,
Settle, North Yorkshire BD24 9EU. Tel: (H) 01729 823559 Tel:
(W) 01729 825252
Fixtures Secretary: AM Davidson, Gasker, Lawkland,
Austwick, Lancaster LA2. Tel: (H) 01729 825595

FINAL TABLE

	P	W	D	L	F	A	Pts
Blaydon	12	11	0	1	212	116	22
Horden	12	9	0	3	248	135	18
Keighley	12	9	0	3	233	162	18
Driffield	12	8	0	4	213	114	16
Gateshead Fell	12	8	0	4	235	159	16
Old Brodleians	12	7	0	5	218	216	14
Morpeth	12	6	0	6	156	174	12
Cleckheaton	12	5	0	7	169	166	10
Pontefract	12	5	0	7	159	182	10
Roundhegians	12	3	1	8	126	227	7
Selby	12	3	1	8	177	232	5*
Redcar	12	2	0	10	96	281	4
Thornensians	12	1	0	11	114	191	2

Club Colours: Blue with white hoops.
OLD BRODLEIANS RUFC
Ground Address: Woodhead, Denholme Gate Road,
Hipperholme, Nr Halifax, West Yorkshire HX3 8JU. Tel:
01422 202708
Club Secretary: Mr Simon Heaton, Sutcliffe Wood Farm,
Hove Edge, Brighouse, West Yorkshire HD6 2QW. Tel: (H)
01484 721628 Tel: (W) 01274 687719
Fixtures Secretary: Mr M Hey, 2 Sunnybank Crescent,
Sowerby Bridge, Halifax, West Yorkshire HX6 2PL. Tel: (H)
01422 839614 Tel (W) 01924 490803
Club Colours: Black, red & white shirt, black shorts.
PONTEFRACT RFC
Ground Address: Moor Lane, Carleton, Pontefract, West
Yorkshire WF8 3RX. Tel: 01977 702650
Club Secretary: R Peacock, 12 Fair View, Carleton,
Pontefract, West Yorkshire WF8 3NT. Tel: (H) 01977 702284
Tel: (W) 01977 677421
Fixtures Secretary: M Higgitt, The Chimes, Common Lane,
Upton, Pontefract, West Yorkshire WF9 1DF. Tel: (H) 01977
643605
Club Colours: Royal blue shirts with white V, white shorts.
REDCAR RUFC
Ground Address: Mackinlay Park, Green Lane, Redcar,
Cleveland TS10 3RW. Tel: 01642 482733
Club Secretary: Dr David R Palmer, c/o Redcar Rugby Union
Football Club, Mackinlay Park, Green Lane, Redcar, Cleveland
TS10 3RW. Tel: (H) 01831 780655 Tel: (W) 01642 482733
Fixtures Secretary: Terry J Baxter, 12 The Crescent, Redcar,
Cleveland TS10 3AU. Tel: (H) 01642 483900
Club Colours: Black shirts, black shorts.
ROUNDHEGIANS RUFC
Ground Address: The Memorial Ground, Chelwood Drive,
Leeds 8. Tel: 0113 2667377
Club Secretary: Mr PA Hobson, 3 Ashgrove Mount, Kippax,
Leeds LS25 7RD. Tel: (H) 0113286 7106 Tel: (W) 01422
362461
Fixtures Secretary: Mr G English, 109 Swithenbank Avenue,
Gawthorpe, Ossett, West Yorkshire WF5 9RS. Tel: (H) 01924
265858
Club Colours: Green, black & white shirts, black shorts.
SELBY RUFC
Ground Address: Sandhill Lane, Leeds Road, Selby, West
Yorkshire YO8 0JP. Tel: 01757 703608
Club Secretary: MWM Blackwell, 10 Fenwicks Lane, Fulford,
York YO1 4PL. Tel: (H) 01904 633517 Tel: (W) 01757 289111
Fixtures Secretary: MJP Sharp, 7 The Causeway, Thorpe
Willoughby, Selby, North Yorkshire. Tel: (H) 01757 702737
Tel (W) 01904 646651
Club Colours: Red, green & gold hoops.

NORTHERN DIVISION

NORTH EAST TWO
1995-96
FIXTURES

September 16 1995 (Week 3)
Goole v Percy Park
Hull v Rockcliffe
Whitby v Darling Mowden Park
Bramley v Beverley
Thornensians v Wheatley Hills
Blyth v Westoe

September 23 1995 (Week 4)
Westoe v Goole
Wheatley Hills v Blyth
Beverley v Thornensians
Darl Mowden Park v Bramley
Rockcliffe v Whitby
Ripon v Hull

September 30 1995 (Week X1)
Goole v Wheatley Hills
Percy Park v Westoe
Whitby v Ripon
Bramley v Rockcliffe
Thornensians v Darl Mowden Park
Blyth v Beverley

October 14 1995 (Week 6)
Wheatley Hills v Percy Park
Beverley v Goole
Darl Mowden Park v Blyth
Rockcliffe v Thornensians
Ripon v Bramley
Hull v Whitby

October 21 1995 (Week 7)
Goole v Darl Mowden Park
Percy Park v Beverley
Westoe v Wheatley Hills
Bramley v Hull
Thornensians v Ripon
Blyth v Rockcliffe

October 28 1995 (Week 8)
Beverley v Westoe
Darl Mowden Park v Percy Park
Rockcliffe v Goole
Ripon v Blyth
Hull v Thornensians
Whitby v Bramley

November 11 1995 (Week 10)
Goole v Ripon
Percy Park v Rockcliffe
Westoe v Darl Mowden Park
Wheatley Hills v Beverley
Thornensians v Whitby
Blyth v Hull

January 6 1996 (Week 17)
Darl Mowden Park v Wheatley Hills
Rockcliffe v Westoe
Ripon v Percy Park
Hull v Goole
Whitby v Blyth
Bramley v Thornensians

January 13 1996 (Week 18)
Goole v Whitby
Percy Park v Hull
Westoe v Ripon
Wheatley Hills v Rockcliffe
Beverley v Darl Mowden Park
Blyth v Bramley

February 10 1996 (Week 22)
Rockcliffe v Beverley
Ripon v Wheatley Hills
Hull v Westoe
Whitby v Percy Park
Bramley v Goole
Thornensians v Blyth

February 17 1996 (Week 23)
Goole v Thornensians
Percy Park v Bramley
Westoe v Whitby
Wheatley Hills v Hull
Beverley v Ripon
Darl Mowden Park v Rockcliffe

February 24 1996 (Week 24)
Ripon v Darl Mowden Park
Hull v Beverley
Whitby v Wheatley Hills
Bramley v Westoe
Thornensians v Percy Park
Blyth v Goole

March 30 1996 (Week X7)
Percy Park v Blyth
Westoe v Thornensians
Wheatley Hills v Bramley
Beverley v Whitby
Darl Mowden Park v Hull
Rockcliffe v Ripon

NORTH EAST TWO

BEVERLEY RUFC
Ground Address: Beaver Park, Norwood, Beverley, North Humberside. Tel: 01480 870306
Club Secretary: Andrew Winter, 4 The Vineyards, Leven, Beverley, North Humberside HU17 5LD. Tel: (H) 01964 543981 Tel: (W) 01482 885027
Fixtures Secretary: Rob Jenner, 3 Spark Mill Terrace, Beverley, North Humberside. Tel: (H) 01482 868944
Club Colours: Green, brown & white.

BLYTH RFC
Ground Address: Plessey Road, Blyth, Northumberland. Tel: 01670 352063
Club Secretary: Dennis Reynolds, 21 Druridge Crescent, Blyth, Northumberland NE24 4SB. Tel: (H) 01670 360841
Fixtures Secretary: J Norris, 10 Dene View Drive, Blyth, Northumberland NE24 5PU. Tel: (H) 01670 369177 Tel (W) 0191 200 4000
Club Colours: Emerald green & black.

BRAMLEY RUFC
Ground Address: The Warrels, Grosmount Terrace, Warrels Road, Bramley, Leeds LS13 3NY. Tel: 0113 257 7787
Club Secretary: Andrew Hurdley, Hall Farm, Hall Road, Little Preston, Leeds LS26 8UT. Tel: (H) 0113 286 0131 Tel: (W) 01274 741433
Fixtures Secretary: Brian Parkin, 4 Westroyd Crescent, Pudsey, Leeds LS28 8JD. Tel: (H) 0113 256 3127
Club Colours: Green with black & gold band.

DARLINGTON MOWDEN PARK RFC
Ground Address: 22 Yiewsley Drive, Darlington, Co Durham DL3 9XS. Tel: 01325 465932
Club Secretary: GF Nevill, 44 Leith Road, Darlington, Co Durham DL3 8BG. Tel: (H) 01325 469001
Fixtures Secretary: GF Nevill, 44 Leith Road, Darlington, Co Durham DL3 8BG. Tel: (H) 01325 469001
Club Colours: Blue & white stripes.

GOOLE RUFC
Ground Address: The Clubhouse, Murham Avenue, Goole, North Humberside DN14 6PA. Tel: 01405 762018
Club Secretary: IR Higgins, 14 The Meadow, Howden, Goole, North Humberside DN14 7DX. Tel: (H) 01430 430037 Tel: (W) 01405 768621
Fixtures Secretary: P Shand, Hallgarth, 22 Ledgate Lane, Burton Salmon, Leeds LS25 5JY. Tel: (H) 01977 677660 Tel (W) 01977 703357
Club Colours: Navy blue & gold quarters.

HULL RUFC
Ground Address: Haworth Park, Emmott Road, Beverley Road, Hull HU6 7AB. Tel: 01482 802119
Club Secretary: Dominic Ward, 78 St Margaret's Avenue, Cottingham, Hull HU16 5NB. Tel: (H) 01482 842292 Tel: (W) 01482 35242
Fixtures Secretary: Robin Mason, 223 Beverley Road, Kirkella, Hull HU10 7AG. Tel: (H) 01482 657495 Tel (W) 01482 652528
Club Colours: Black with gold & red hoop.

PERCY PARK RFC
Ground Address: The Clubhouse, Preston Avenue, North Shields, Tyne & Wear NE29. Tel: 0191 257 5710
Club Secretary: AC Baker, 30 The Garth, Winlaton, Tyne & Wear NE21 6DD. Tel: (W) 0191 414 4869 Fax: 0191 414 8672
Fixtures Secretary: J Elliott, 13 Brundon Avenue, Whitley Bay, Tyne & Wear NE26 1SL. Tel: (H) 0191 252 6109
Club Colours: Black & white hoops, black shorts.

RIPON RUFC
Ground Address: Mallorie Park, Ripon, North Yorkshire HG4 2QD. Tel: 01765 604675
Club Secretary: Mike Viner, 20 Church Close, Tollerton, York YO6 2ES. Tel: (H) 01347 838180 Tel: (W) 01609 780780 x2915

FINAL TABLE

	P	W	D	L	F	A	Pts
Ashington	12	8	1	3	209	112	17
North Ribblesdale	12	8	1	3	161	129	17
Westoe	12	7	2	3	145	135	16
Darlington Mowden P	12	7	1	4	168	106	15
Hull	12	7	1	4	171	116	15
Blyth	12	6	0	6	160	176	12
Bramley	12	6	0	6	150	238	12
Ripon	12	4	2	6	136	131	10
Whitby	12	5	0	7	142	144	10
Goole	12	4	2	6	129	150	10
Beverley	12	5	0	7	145	168	10
Whitley Bay Rocklf	12	4	0	8	73	200	8
Novocastrians	12	2	0	10	112	196	4

Fixtures Secretary: Andy Proud, 1 Ure Bank Terrace, Ripon, North Yorkshire HG4 1JG. Tel: (H) 01765 605474 Tel (W) 01423 500066
Club Colours: Blue, black & white hoops.

THORNENSIANS RUFC
Ground Address: The Clubhouse, Coulman Street, Thorne, Nr Doncaster, South Yorkshire DN8 5BU. Tel: 01405 812746
Club Secretary: Ian Robson, Windyridge Cottage, Fieldside, Thorne, Doncaster, South Yorkshire DN8 4BD. Tel: (H) 01405 812360 Tel: (W) 01405 812200
Fixtures Secretary: Colin Thompson, 2 Orchard Croft, Bawtry, Doncaster, South Yorkshire. Tel: (H) 01302 719956
Club Colours: Blue, white & black hoops.

WESTOE RFC
Ground Address: Dean Road, South Shields, Tyne & Wear. Tel: 0191 456 1506
Club Secretary: John R Wells, 240 Mowbray Road, South Shields, Tyne & Wear NE33 3NW. Tel: (H) 0191 455 2260 Tel: (W) 0191 427 3500
Fixtures Secretary: D Aller, 7 Wood Tee, South Shields. Tel: (H) 0191 456 9531 Tel (W) 0191 456 1115
Club Colours: Red, sky and dark blue hoops.

WHEATLEY HILLS RUFC
Ground Address: Wheatley Hills Sports Ground, Brunel Road, York Road Industrial Estate, Doncaster, Yorkshire DN5 8PT. Tel: 01302 781472
Club Secretary: AR Dunkerley, 1 Mayfields, Scawthorne, Doncaster, Yorkshire DN5 7VA. Tel: (H) 01302 782214
Fixtures Secretary: I Blessed, 75 Chestnut Avenue, Wheatley, Doncaster DN2 5SR. Tel: (H) 01302 341614
Club Colours: Maroon & gold quartered shirts, maroon shorts.

WHITBY RUFC
Ground Address: Whiteleys Road, Whitby, North Yorkshire. Tel: 01947 602008
Club Secretary: F Howarth, 18 Lime Grove, Whitby, North Yorkshire YO21 1LP. Tel: (H) 01947 600692
Fixtures Secretary: A Wardell, 88 Thames Avenue, Guisborough TS14 8AR. Tel: (H) 01287 635931
Club Colours: Maroon.

WHITLEY BAY ROCKCLIFF RFC
Ground Address: Hillheads, Lovaine Avenue, Whitley Bay, Tyne & Wear. Tel: 0191 251 3704
Club Secretary: Ian Richardson, 3 Westfield Avenue, West Monkseaton, Whitley Bay, Tyne & Wear NE25 8NW. Tel: (H) 0191 251 2372 Fax: 0191 251 2372 Tel: (W) 0191 250 1864
Fixtures Secretary: Mr M Hopper, 19 Briarsyde, Benton, Newcastle-upon-Tyne NE12 9SL. Tel: (H) 0191 270 2098
Club Colours: Cardinal red & gold shirts, white shorts.

NORTHERN DIVISION

DURHAM & NORTHUMBERLAND ONE 1995-96 FIXTURES

November 11 1995 (Week 10)

Winlaton Vulcans	v	Novocastrians
Hartlepool TDSOB	v	Darlington
Ponteland	v	Darlington RA
Medicals	v	Ryton
North Shields	v	Acklam
North Durham	v	Sunderland

September 16 1995 (Week 3)

Winlaton Vulcans	v	Hartlepool TDSOB
Sunderland	v	Darlington
Acklam	v	Darlington RA
Bishop Auckland	v	Ryton
North Shields	v	Medicals
North Durham	v	Ponteland

September 23 1995 (Week 4)

Ponteland	v	Winlaton Vulcans
Medicals	v	North Durham
Ryton	v	North Shields
Darlington RA	v	Bishop Auckland
Darlington	v	Acklam
Novocastrians	v	Sunderland

September 30 1995 (Week X1)

Winlaton Vulcans	v	Medicals
Hartlepool TDSOB	v	Ponteland
Acklam	v	Novocastrians
Bishop Auckland	v	Darlington
North Shields	v	Darlington RA
North Durham	v	Ryton

October 14 1995 (Week 6)

Medicals	v	Hartlepool TDSOB
Ryton	v	Winlaton Vulcans
Darlington RA	v	North Durham
Darlington	v	North Shields
Novocastrians	v	Bishop Auckland
Sunderland	v	Acklam

October 21 1995 (Week 7)

Winlaton Vulcans	v	Darlington RA
Hartlepool TDSOB	v	Ryton
Ponteland	v	Medicals
Bishop Auckland	v	Sunderland
North Shields	v	Novocastrians
North Durham	v	Darlington

October 28 1995 (Week 8)

Ryton	v	Ponteland
Darlington RA	v	Hartlepool TDSOB
Darlington	v	Winlaton Vulcans
Novocastrians	v	North Durham
Sunderland	v	North Shields
Acklam	v	Bishop Auckland

January 6 1996 (Week 17)

Darlington RA	v	Medicals
Darlington	v	Ponteland
Novocastrians	v	Hartlepool TDSOB
Sunderland	v	Winlaton Vulcans
Acklam	v	North Durham
Bishop Auckland	v	North Shields

January 13 1996 (Week 18)

Winlaton Vulcans	v	Acklam
Hartlepool TDSOB	v	Sunderland
Ponteland	v	Novocastrians
Medicals	v	Darlington
Ryton	v	Darlington RA
North Durham	v	Bishop Auckland

February 10 1996 (Week 22)

Darlington	v	Ryton
Novocastrians	v	Medicals
Sunderland	v	Ponteland
Acklam	v	Hartlepool TDSOB
Bishop Auckland	v	Winlaton Vulcans
North Shields	v	North Durham

February 17 1996 (Week 23)

Winlaton Vulcans	v	North Shields
Hartlepool TDSOB	v	Bishop Auckland
Ponteland	v	Acklam
Medicals	v	Sunderland
Ryton	v	Novocastrians
Darlington RA	v	Darlington

February 24 1996 (Week 24)

Novocastrians	v	Darlington RA
Sunderland	v	Ryton
Acklam	v	Medicals
Bishop Auckland	v	Ponteland
North Shields	v	Hartlepool TDSOB
North Durham	v	Winlaton Vulcans

March 30 1996 (Week X7)

Hartlepool TDSOB	v	North Durham
Ponteland	v	North Shields
Medicals	v	Bishop Auckland
Ryton	v	Acklam
Darlington RA	v	Sunderland
Darlington	v	Novocastrians

DURHAM & NORTHUMBERLAND ONE

ACKLAM RUFC
Ground Address: Talbot Park, Saltersgill Avenue, Middlesborough, Cleveland TS4 3PR. Tel: 01642 321397
Club Secretary: Paul Pearson, 32 Foxgloves, Coulby Newham, Middlesborough, Cleveland TS8 0XA. Tel: (H) 01642 597195 Tel: (W) 01325 461231
Fixtures Secretary: David Lynch, 58 Sandmoor Road, New Marske, Cleveland TS11 8DJ.
Club Colours: Black, green & white.

BISHOP AUCKLAND RUFC
Ground Address: West Mills Playing Fields, Bridge Road, Bishop Auckland, Co Durham DL14 7PA. Tel: 01388 602922
Club Secretary: Mr KA Wilkinson, 7 Victoria Avenue, Bishop Auckland, Co Durham DL14 7JH. Tel: (H) 01388 605768 Tel: (W) 01388 603388
Fixtures Secretary: Mr E Farrer, 35 Windermere Drive, West Auckland, Co Durham DL14 9LF. Tel: (H) 01388 832810
Club Colours: Navy & sky blue.

DARLINGTON RFC
Ground Address: Blackwell Meadows, Grange Road, Darlington, Co Durham, DL1 5NR. Tel: 01325 363777
Club Secretary: Mr APF Foster, 45 Hartford Road, Darlington, Co Durham, DL3 8HF. Tel: (H) 01325 466501 Tel: (W) 01325 381818
Fixtures Secretary: Mr DE Gardner, Balder View, Cothorstone, Barnard Castle. Tel: (H) 01833 650543 Tel (W) 01833 690305
Club Colours: Black and white hoops.

DARLINGTON RAILWAY ATHLETIC RUFC
Ground Address: Brinkburn Road, Darlington, Co Durham. Tel: 01325 468125
Club Secretary: Owen Jackson, 36 Westgate Road, Darlington, Co Durham DL3 0SZ. Tel: (H) 01325 487606 Tel: (W) 0191 3834039
Fixtures Secretary: Pat Blewitt, 35 Cumberland Street, Darlington, Co Durham. Tel: (H) 01325 350076
Club Colours: Black & amber hoops.

MEDICALS RFC
Ground Address: Medical Athletic Ground, Cartington Terrace, Heaton, Newcastle-upon-Tyne. Tel: 0191 276 1473
Club Secretary: Dr AR Greenwood, 45 Church Road, Gosforth, Newcastle-upon-Tyne NE3 1UE. Tel: (H) 0191 285 0686 Tel: (W) 0191 491 5600
Fixtures Secretary: Mr P Fisher, 13 Swanton Close, Meadow Rise, Kenton, Newcastle-upon-Tyne NE5 4SL. Tel: (H) 0191 2713559
Club Colours: Maroon shirt, white collar, white shorts.

NORTH DURHAM RFC
Ground Address: Prince Consort Road, Gateshead, Tyne & Wear NE8 1WS. Tel: 0191 478 3071
Club Secretary: Brian Dodds, 15 Ladyhaugh Drive, Whickham, Newcastle upon Tyne NE16 5TE. Tel: (H) 0191 488 6714 Tel: (W) 0191 491 3030
Fixtures Secretary: Mr T Tate, 14 Alverstone Avenue, Low Fell, Gateshead, Tyne & Wear NE9 6UJ. Tel: (H) 0191 491 3083
Club Colours: Red & white hoops, navy shorts, bottle green socks.

NORTH SHIELDS RFC
Ground Address: Preston Playing Fields, Preston Village, North Shields, Tyne & Wear. Tel: 0191 257 7352
Club Secretary: David Daniels, 1 Highcross Road, North Shields, Tyne & Wear NE30 3JG. Tel: (H) 0191 252 6395 Tel: (W) 0191 253 1329
Fixtures Secretary: Mr AG Shield, 9 Cresswell Avenue, North Shields, Tyne & Wear. Tel: (H) 0191 259 0402
Club Colours: Royal blue & white hoops, white shorts.

NOVOCASTRIANS RFC
Ground Address: Sunderland Park, The Drive, High Heaton, Newcastle upon Tyne, NE7 7SY. Tel: 0191 266 1247
Club Secretary: RB Pollock, 101 Marine Avenue, Whitley Bay, Tyne & Wear, NE26 3LN. Tel: (H) 0191 251 1562 Tel: (W) 0191 296 0303
Fixtures Secretary: RJ Jay, 10 Lyndhurst Crescent, Low Fell, Gateshead, Tyne & Wear NE9 6BA. Tel: (H) 0191 487 3393 Tel (W) 0191 386 2714

FINAL TABLE

	P	W	D	L	F	A	Pts
Percy Park	12	11	0	1	396	63	22
Sunderland	12	10	1	1	301	89	21
Acklam	12	10	1	1	203	100	21
Darlington	12	9	0	3	333	76	18
Ryton	12	8	0	4	244	208	16
W Hartlepool TDSOB	12	7	0	5	207	177	12*
North Durham	12	5	1	6	164	219	11
North Shields	12	3	2	7	165	125	8
Darlington RA	12	3	1	8	105	275	7
Bishop Auckland	12	3	0	9	142	284	6
Ponteland	12	3	0	9	88	255	6
Guisborough	12	2	0	10	87	326	4
Wallsend	12	1	0	11	77	315	2

Club Colours: Red, black & white hooped shirts & socks, white shorts.

PONTELAND RFC
Ground Address: Ponteland Leisure Centre, Callerton Lane, Ponteland, Northumberland NE20 9EG. Tel: 01661 825441
Club Secretary: Simon Philp, 61 Jackson Avenue, Ponteland NE20 9UY. Tel: (H) 01661 872773
Fixtures Secretary: Joyce Baty, 5 Brooklands, Ponteland, Northumberland NE20 9LZ. Tel: (H) 01661 823527
Club Colours: Maroon shirts, black & white hoops, white shorts.

RYTON RUFC
Ground Address: Main Road, Ryton, Tyne & Wear NE40 3AG. Tel: 0191 413 3820
Club Secretary: JA Trodden, 63 Horsley Avenue, Ryton, Tyne & Wear NE40 4XQ. Tel: (H) 0191 413 2700 Tel: (W) 01670 713451
Fixtures Secretary: G Wright, 30 South Grove, Ryton, Tyne & Wear. Tel: (H) 0191 413 1986
Club Colours: Royal blue & white.

SUNDERLAND RFC
Ground Address: Ashbrooke, West Lawn, Sunderland, Tyne & Wear SR2 7HH. Tel: 011 528 4536
Club Secretary: Mr J Martin, 11 Roker Park Terrace, Sunderland SR6 9LY. Tel: (H) 0191 567 7045 Tel: (W) 0191 427 3562
Fixtures Secretary: Mr A Scott-Gray, 37 Glenesk Road, Sunderland SR2 9BN. Tel: (H) 0191 522 6188 Tel (W) 0191 430 1446
Club Colours: Red, black, gold hoops, white shorts.

WEST HARTLEPOOL TECHNICAL DAY SCHOOL OLD BOYS RUFC
Ground Address: Wiltshire Way, Throston Grange, Hartlepool, Cleveland. Tel: 01429 233548
Club Secretary: Mr D Bramley, 63 Hutton Avenue, Hartlepool, Cleveland TS26 9PP. Tel: (H) 01429 263157 Tel: (W) 01642 433363
Fixtures Secretary: Mr A Cheshire, 22 Loyalty Road, Hartlepool, Cleveland. Tel: (H) 01429 234659 Tel (W) 01642 604661
Club Colours: Royal blue & white hoops/quarters.

WINLATON VULCANS RFC
Ground Address: Axwell View Playing Fields, Winlaton, Blaydon-on-Tyne, NE21 6NF. Tel: 0191 414 2502
Club Secretary: Timothy Williams, 29 Huntley Cres, Winlaton, Blaydon-on-Tyne, NE21 6EU. Tel: (H) 0191 414 4636 Tel: (W) 0191 414 2502
Fixtures Secretary: Ian Bilclough, 8 Holly Ave, Winlaton Mill, Blaydon-on-Tyne, NE21 6SL. Tel: (H) 0191 414 8560
Club Colours: Black shirts, white collar, black shorts & socks.

NORTHERN DIVISION

DURHAM & NORTHUMBERLAND TWO 1995-96 FIXTURES

November 11 1995 (Week 10)
Richmondshire	v	Wallsend
Wensleydale	v	Hartlepool BBOB
Billingham	v	Seaham
Consett	v	Hartlepool
Barnard Castle	v	Chester le Street
Houghton	v	Guisborough

September 16 1995 (Week 3)
Richmondshire	v	Wensleydale
Guisborough	v	Hartlepool BBOB
Chester le Street	v	Seaham
Sedgefield	v	Hartlepool
Barnard Castle	v	Consett
Houghton	v	Billingham

January 6 1996 (Week 17)
Seaham	v	Consett
HartlepoolBBOB	v	Billingham
Wallsend	v	Wensleydale
Guisborough	v	Richmondshire
Chester le Street	v	Houghton
Sedgefield	v	Barnard Castle

September 23 1995 (Week 4)
Billingham	v	Richmondshire
Consett	v	Houghton
Hartlepool	v	Barnard Castle
Seaham	v	Sedgefield
Hartlepool BBOB	v	Chester le Street
Wallsend	v	Guisborough

January 13 1996 (Week 18)
Richmondshire	v	Chester le Street
Wensleydale	v	Guisborough
Billingham	v	Wallsend
Consett	v	Hartlepool BBOB
Hartlepool	v	Seaham
Houghton	v	Sedgefield

September 30 1995 (Week X1)
Richmondshire	v	Consett
Wensleydale	v	Billingham
Chester le Street	v	Wallsend
Sedgefield	v	Hartlepool BBOB
Barnard Castle	v	Seaham
Houghton	v	Hartlepool

February 10 1996 (Week 22)
Hartlepool BBOB	v	Hartlepool
Wallsend	v	Consett
Guisborough	v	Billingham
Chester le Street	v	Wensleydale
Sedgefield	v	Richmondshire
Barnard Castle	v	Houghton

October 14 1995 (Week 6)
Consett	v	Wensleydale
Hartlepool	v	Richmondshire
Seaham	v	Houghton
Hartlepool BBOB	v	Barnard Castle
Wallsend	v	Sedgefield
Guisborough	v	Chester le Street

February 17 1996 (Week 23)
Richmondshire	v	Barnard Castle
Wensleydale	v	Sedgefield
Billingham	v	Chester le Street
Consett	v	Guisborough
Hartlepool	v	Wallsend
Seaham	v	Hartlepool BBOB

October 21 1995 (Week 7)
Richmondshire	v	Seaham
Wensleydale	v	Hartlepool
Billingham	v	Consett
Sedgefield	v	Guisborough
Barnard Castle	v	Wallsend
Houghton	v	Hartlepool BBOB

February 24 1996 (Week 24)
Wallsend	v	Seaham
Guisborough	v	Hartlepool
Chester le Street	v	Consett
Sedgefield	v	Billingham
Barnard Castle	v	Wensleydale
Houghton	v	Richmondshire

October 28 1995 (Week 8)
Hartlepool	v	Billingham
Seaham	v	Wensleydale
Hartlepool BBOB	v	Richmondshire
Wallsend	v	Houghton
Guisborough	v	Barnard Castle
Chester le Street	v	Sedgefield

March 30 1996 (Week X7)
Wensleydale	v	Houghton
Billingham	v	Barnard Castle
Consett	v	Sedgefield
Hartlepool	v	Chester le Street
Seaham	v	Guisboroough
Hartlepool BBOB	v	Wallsend

DURHAM & NORTHUMBERLAND TWO

BARNARD CASTLE RUFC
Ground Address: The Clubhouse, Birch Road, Barnard Castle, Co Durham DL12 8JP. Tel: 01833 631766
Club Secretary: Tim Worley, 17 Newgate, Barnard Castle, Co Durham DL12 8NQ. Tel: (H) 01833 637608 Tel: (W) 01833 690305
Fixtures Secretary: John Stead, Tutta Beck Farmhouse, Rokeby, Nr Barnard Castle, Co Durham DL12 9RY. Tel: (H) 01833 690214
Club Colours: All black.

BILLINGHAM RUFC
Ground Address: c/o Billingham Synthonia Golf Club, Central Avenue, Billingham, Cleveland TS23 1LR. Tel: 01642 365556
Club Secretary: John Ker, 4 Anlaby Close, Billingham, Cleveland TS23 3RA. Tel: (H) 01642 560536 Tel: (W) (& Fax) 01642 560692
Fixtures Secretary: Colin Wakenshaw, 30 Grampian Road, Billingham, Cleveland TS23 2PH. Tel: (H) 01642 535374

CHESTER-LE-STREET RFC
Ground Address: Donald Owen Clarke Centre, Riverside Park, Chester-le-Street, Co Durham. Tel: 0191 388 4121
Club Secretary: Paul Langley, 58 Rydal Road, Chester-le-Street, Co Durham DH2 3DT. Tel: (H) 0191 388 5989 Tel: (W) 0191 383 3443
Fixtures Secretary: Graham Rodger, 3 Fife Avenue, Chester-le-Street, Co Durham. Tel: (H) 0191 389 1713
Club Colours: Navy blue shirts & shorts, red socks.

CONSETT & DISTRICT RFC
Ground Address: Belle Vue Park, Medomsley Road, Consett, Co Durham. Tel: 01207 590662
Club Secretary: Mr John O'Connor, 26 Woodlands Road, Shotley Bridge, Consett, Co Durham DH8 0DE. Tel: (H) 01207 501794 Tel: (W) 0191 489 9588 Fax: 0191 428 0075
Fixtures Secretary: Mr David Herdman, 33 The Briary, Shotley Bridge, Consett, Co Durham. Tel: (H) 01207 581385
Club Colours: Black/amber quarters.

GUISBOROUGH RUFC
Ground Address: Belmangate, Guisborough, Cleveland TS14 7BB. Tel: 01287 632966
Club Secretary: DF Childs, 32 Boston Drive, Marton, Cleveland TS7 8LZ. Tel: (H) 01642 314081
Fixtures Secretary: GR Crooks, 51 Farndale Drive, Pinehills, Guisborough, Cleveland TS14 8JJ. Tel: (H) 01287 633244
Club Colours: Black & amber.

HARTLEPOOL BOYS BRIGADE OLD BOYS RFC
Ground Address: Old Friarage, Headland, Hartlepool (Ground only).
Club Secretary: GK Faint, 11 Nesbyt Road, Hartlepool, Cleveland TS24 9NB. Tel: (H) 01429 265674
Fixtures Secretary: I Mulrooney, 65 Percy Street, Hartlepool, Cleveland TS26 0HT. Tel: (H) 01429 278082 Tel (W) 01429 260471
Club Colours: White with broad black band, black shorts, black & white hooped socks.

HARTLEPOOL RFC
Ground Address: Mayfield Park, Easington Road, Hartlepool, Cleveland TS24 9BA. Tel: 01429 266445
Club Secretary: Keith Dobson, 15 John Howe Gardens, Hartlepool, Cleveland TS24 9NQ. Tel: (H) 01429 261236 Tel: (W) 01429 266522 x2263
Fixtures Secretary: Gary Mayes, 62 Whitrout Road, Hartlepool, Cleveland TS24 9PW. Tel: (H) 01429 262984
Club Colours: All black.

HOUGHTON RUFC
Ground Address: Dairy Lane, Houghton le Spring, Tyne & Wear DH4 5BW. Tel: 0191 584 1460
Club Secretary: David Winthrop, Hillcroft, 14 North Road, Houghton le Spring, Tyne & Wear DH5 9JU. Tel: (H) 0191 517 0716 Tel: (W) 0191 567 0094

FINAL TABLE

	P	W	D	L	F	A	Pts
Winlaton Vulcans	12	11	0	1	341	55	22
Medicals	12	10	0	2	278	71	20
Wensleydale	12	8	1	3	186	140	17
Hartlepool	12	8	0	4	231	117	16
Chester-le-Street	12	7	1	4	164	94	15
Seaham	12	7	0	5	152	153	12*
Billingham	12	5	1	6	106	150	11
Hartlepool BBOB	12	5	0	7	125	231	10
Richmondshire	12	4	0	8	80	212	8
Houghton	12	3	1	8	103	220	7
Consett	12	4	0	8	117	194	6*
Seghill	12	2	2	8	108	189	6
Seaton Carew	12	1	0	11	93	258	2

Fixtures Secretary: John Felton, 37 Larchwood, Harraton Wood, Washington, Tyne & Wear NE38 9BT. Tel: (H) 0191 416 1467 Tel (W) 0191 487 7171
Club Colours: Black shirts with white hoop, black shorts, black stockings with white tops.

RICHMONDSHIRE RUFC
Ground Address: The Playing Fields, Theakston Lane, Richmond, North Yorkshire DL10 4LL. Tel: 01748 850515
Club Secretary: Mr S Speakman, 36 Victoria Road, Richmond, North Yorkshire DL10 4AU. Tel: (H) 01748 825579 Tel: (W) 01748 850111
Fixtures Secretary: Mr R Dixon, 3 St Nicholas Drive, Richmond, North Yorkshire DL10 7DY. Tel: (H) 01748 825360
Club Colours: Red, gold & white hoops.

SEAHAM RUFC
Ground Address: New Drive Playing Fields. Club: 27 Cornelia Terrace, Seaham, Co Durham. Tel: 0191 581 2331
Club Secretary: Alan Mason, 1 Membury Close, Sunderland, Tyne & Wear. Tel: (H) 0191 520 0282 Tel: (W) 0191 279 4342
Fixtures Secretary: Alan Mason, 1 Membury Close, Sunderland, Tyne & Wear. Tel: (H) 0191 520 0282 Tel (W) 0191 279 4342
Club Colours: Red shirts.

SEDGEFIELD RUFC
Ground Address: Sedgefield Community College, Sedgefield, Stockton-on-Tees, Cleveland. Tel: 01740 621097
Club Secretary: Neil Hetherington, 1 The Meadows, Sedgefield, Stockton-on-Tees, Cleveland TS21 2DL. Tel: (H) 01740 621179 Tel: (W) 0836 292665
Fixtures Secretary: Mr M Price, 50 West End, Sedgefield, Stockton-on-Tees, Cleveland. Tel: (H) 01740 622792
Club Colours: Red & black quarters.

WALLSEND RFC
Ground Address: Sam Smith's Pavilion, Benfield School Campus, Benfield School, Benfield Road, Walkergate, Newcastle-Upon-Tyne NE6. Tel: 0191 265 9357
Club Secretary: Brian J Thirlaway, 25 Blanchland Close, Battle Hill Estate, Wallsend, Tyne & Wear, NE28 9DU. Tel: (H) 0191 234 4877
Fixtures Secretary: Robert Lowery, 27 Boyd Crescent, Wallsend, Tyne & Wear NE28 7SG. Tel: (H) 0191 234 2400
Club Colours: Myrtle green jerseys with gold trim, white shorts, green socks.

WENSLEYDALE RUFC
Ground Address: Cawkhill Park, Wensley Road, Leyburn, North Yorkshire. Tel: 01969 623067
Club Secretary: David Ward, 3 Kelberdale Terrace, Leyburn, North Yorkshire DL8 5AP. Tel: (H) 01969 624462 Tel: (W) 01969 622046
Fixtures Secretary: Ian Burdon, Lane House Farm, Jervaulx, Ripon, North Yorkshire. Tel: (H) 01677 460226
Club Colours: Black & amber hoops.

NORTHERN DIVISION

DURHAM & NORTHUMBERLAND THREE 1995-96 FIXTURES

November 11 1995 (Week 10)
Benton v Wearside
Newton Aycliffe v Seaton Carew
Prudhoe Hospital v Washington
Hartlepool Athletic v Jarrovians
Durham Constabulary v Seghill
Alston Moor v Belmont

September 16 1995 (Week 3)
Benton v Newton Aycliffe
Belmont v Seaton Carew
Seghill v Washington
South Tyneside Collge v Jarrovians
Durham Constabulary v Hartlepool Athletic
Alston Moor v Prudhoe Hospital

September 23 1995 (Week 4)
Prudhoe Hospital v Benton
Hartlepool Athletic v Alston Moor
Jarrovians v Durham Constabulary
Washington v South Tyneside College
Seaton Carew v Seghill
Wearside v Belmont

September 30 1995 (Week X1)
Benton v Hartlepool Athletic
Bewton Aycliffe v Prudhoe Hospital
Seghill v Wearside
South Tyneside College v Seaton Carew
Durham Constabulary v Washington
Alston Moor v Jarrovians

October 14 1995 (Week 6)
Hartlepool Athletic v Newton Aycliffe
Jarrovians v Benton
Washington v Alston Moor
Seaton Carew v Durham Constabulary
Wearside v South Tyneside College
Belmont v Seghill

October 21 1995 (Week 7)
Belmont v Washington
Newton Aycliffe v Jarrovians
Prudhoe v Hartlepool Athletic
South Tyneside College v Belmont
Durham Constabulary v Wearside
Alston Moor v Seaton Carew

October 28 1995 (Week 8)
Jarrovians v Prudhoe Hospital
Washington v Newton Aycliffe
Seaton Carew v Benton
Wearside v Alston Moor
Belmont v Durham Constabulary
Seghill v South Tyneside College

January 6 1996 (Week 17)
Washington v Hartlepool Athletic
Seaton Carew v Prudhoe Hospital
Wearside v Newton Aycliffe
Belmont v Benton
Seghill v Alston Moor
South Tyneside College v Durham Constabulary

January 13 1996 (Week 18)
Benton v Seghill
Newton Aycliffe v Belmont
Prudhoe Hospital v Wearside
Hartlepool Athletic v Seaton Carew
Jarrovians v Washington
Alston Moor v South Tyneside College

February 10 1996 (Week 22)
Seaton Carew v Jarrovians
Wearside v Hartlepool Athletic
Belmont v Prudhoe Hospital
Seghill v Newton Aycliffe
South Tyneside College v Benton
Durham Constabulary v Alston Moor

February 17 1996 (Week 23)
Benton v Durham Constabulary
Newton Aycliffe v South Tyneside College
Prudhoe Hospital v Seghill
Hartlepool Athletic v Belmont
Jarrovians v Wearside
Washington v Seaton Carew

February 24 1996 (Week 24)
Wearside v Washington
Belmont v Jarrovians
Seghill v Hartlepool Athletic
South Tyneside College v Prudhoe Hospital
Durham Constabulary v Newton Aycliffe
Alston Moor v Benton

March 30 1996 (Week X7)
Newton Aycliffe v Alston Moor
Prudhoe Hospital v Durham Constabulary
Hartlepool Athletic v South Tyneside College
Jarrovians v Seghill
Washington v Belmont
Seaton Carew v Wearside

398

DURHAM & NORTHUMBERLAND THREE

ALSTON MOOR RUFC
Ground Address: Bluebell Inn, Townfoot, Alston, Cumbria CA9 3HZ. Tel: 01434 381566
Club Secretary: Barbara Hindley, The Mill Cottage, Station Road, Alston, Cumbria CA9 3HZ. Tel: (H) 01434 382650 Tel: (W) 016977 2212
Fixtures Secretary: S Lax, Monument View, Townfoot, Alston, Cumbria. Tel: (H) 01434 381801
Club Colours: Royal blue & black hoops.

BELMONT RUFC
Ground Address: Gilesgate Moor Sports & Social Club, Belmont, Durham. Tel: 0191 386 4615
Club Secretary: James MG Nangle, 5 Winchester Road, Newton Hall, Durham DH1 5QU. Tel: (H) 0191 386 0827
Fixtures Secretary: Mike Weetman, 20 Willow Tree Avenue, Gilesgate, Durham. Tel: (H) 0191 384 7513
Club Colours: Light blue/dark blue quarters.

BENTON RUFC
Ground Address: Darsley Park, Civil Service Sports Ground, Old Whitley Road, Newcastle-upon-Tyne. Tel: 0191 266 2726
Club Secretary: Colin Reid, 114 Northumberland Street, Wallsend, Tyne & Wear NE28 7PX. Tel: (H) 0191 262 4913 Tel: (W) 0191 218 7558
Fixtures Secretary: Geoff Parker, 9 Wilson Terrace, Forest Hall, Newcastle-upon-Tyne 12, Tyne & Wear. Tel: (H) 0191 268 5808 Tel (W) 0191 225 4171
Club Colours: White shirts with broad blue hoop, blue shorts, red socks.

DURHAM CONSTABULARY RUFC
Ground Address: Sports Complex, Police Headquarters, Aykley Heads, Durham. Tel: 0191 386 4929 x2128
Club Secretary: Paul Baty, Spennymoor Police Office, Dundass Street, Spennymoor DL16 6AR. Tel: (W) 01388 814411 x 2712
Fixtures Secretary: Peter Davis, Complaints & Discipline, Police Headquarters, Aykley Head's, Durham. Tel (W) 0191 3864929 x2295 Fax:0191 3752290
Club Colours: Blue/yellow.

HARTLEPOOL ATHLETIC RFC
Ground Address: Oakesway Estate, Hartlepool, Co Durham TS24 0RN. Tel: 01429 274715
Club Secretary: Jim Ainslie, Archway Cottage, 10 Regent Street, Hartlepool, Co Durham TS24 0QN. Tel: (H) 01429 260003 Tel: (W) 0836 258317
Fixtures Secretary: John Bentham, 22 Tempest Road, Hartlepool, Co Durham TS24 9QH. Tel: (H) 01429 222239
Club Colours: Sky blue.

JARROVIANS RUFC
Ground Address: Lukes Lane Estate Recreation Ground, Hebburn, Tyne & Wear. Tel: 0191 489 3291
Club Secretary: Steve Softley, 20 Gladstone Street, Hebburn, Tyne & Wear NE31 2XJ. Tel: (H) 0191 489 0789 Tel: (W) 0191 477 2271 x3250
Fixtures Secretary: Dave King, 46 Lichfield Way, Fellsgate, Jarrow, Tyne & Wear NE32 4VW. Tel: (H) 0191 489 1611 Tel (W) 0191 427 1717 x5071
Club Colours: Black & amber hoops.

NEWTON AYCLIFFE RUFC
Ground Address: Moore Lane, Newton Aycliffe, Co Durham, DL5 5AG. Tel: 01325 312768
Club Secretary: Mr Shaun Pettit, 2 Zetland Hunt, TheChase, Newton Aycliffe, Co Durham DL5 7LQ. Tel: (H) 01325 311569 Tel: (W) 01388 777310
Fixtures Secretary: Mr Brian Parsonage, 353 Rowan Place, Newton Aycliffe, co Durham DL5 7BB. Tel: (H) 01325 310515 Tel (W) 0860 705640
Club Colours: Green, amber & maroon.

PRUDHOE HOSPITAL RFC
Ground Address: Prudhoe Hospital Sports & Social Club, Prudhoe, Northumberland. Tel: 01661 33068
Club Secretary: Mr G Bridgewater, 15 Paddock Wood, Prudhoe, Northumberland, NE42 5BJ. Tel: (H) 01661 832772
Fixtures Secretary: L Franchetti, 6 Park Lane, Prudhoe, Northumberland NE42 5LN. Tel: (H) 01661 832784
Club Colours: Red, blue quarters, white shorts, red stockings.

FINAL TABLE

	P	W	D	L	F	A	Pts
Barnard Castle	9	9	0	0	286	48	18
Sedgefield	9	8	0	1	211	75	16
Jarrovians	9	6	1	2	195	83	13
Newton Aycliffe	9	6	0	3	153	96	12
Wearside	9	5	0	4	143	125	10
Hartlepool Athletic	9	3	0	6	93	177	6
Belmont	9	3	0	6	92	241	6
Benton	9	2	0	7	32	157	4
Prudhoe	9	1	1	7	52	169	3
Washington	9	1	0	8	46	132	0*

SEATON CAREW RUFC
Ground Address: Hornby Park, Elizabeth Way, Seaton Carew, Hartlepool, Cleveland TS25 2AB. Tel: 01429 260945
Club Secretary: Paul McManus, 9 Ruswarp Grove, Seaton Carew, Hartlepool, Cleveland TS25 2BA. Tel: (H) 01429 233189 Tel: (W) 01429 268821 Fax: 01429 860704
Fixtures Secretary: Colin P Chappell, 19 Endeavour Close, Seaton Carew, Hartlepool, Cleveland TS25 1EY. Tel: (H) 01429 868058 Tel (W) 01429 269739 Fax: 01429 269739
Club Colours: Maroon & gold hoops.

SEGHILL RUFC
Ground Address: Welfare Park, Seghill, Cramlington, Northumberland NE23 7ER. Tel: 0191 237 0414
Club Secretary: Stewart Grainger, 16 Carrick Drive, Parklands, Blyth NE24 3SX. Tel: (H) 01670 355 909
Fixtures Secretary: G Fenwick, 20 Wheatfield Grove, Benton, Newcastle-upon-Tyne, NE12 8DN. Tel: (H) 0191 266 5146 Tel (W) 0191 266 5146
Club Colours: Red & black.

SOUTH TYNESIDE COLLEGE RUFC
Ground Address: South Tyneside College, Grosvenor Road, South Shields, Tyne & Wear NE34 6ET. Tel: 0191 427 3500
Club Secretary: R Smith, 87 Coleman Avenue, South Shields, Tyne & Wear NE34 9AG. Tel: (H) 0191 454 2359 Tel: (W) 0191 427 3571
Fixtures Secretary: C Moule, 2 Portland Close, Chester le Street, Co Durham. Tel: (H) 0191 388 7548 Tel (W) 0191 427 3577
Club Colours: Black with two black hoops & one gold hoop.

WASHINGTON RUFC
Ground Address: Northern Arga Playing Fields, c/o Stephenson Industrial Estate, Washington, Tyne & Wear. Tel: 0191 419 0258
Club Secretary: Mr Leslie Peter Cash, 206 Stevenage Road, Washington, Tyne & Wear NE37 3DD. Tel: (H) 0191 417 6298
Fixtures Secretary: C Parks, 1 The Poplars, Biddick, Washington, Tyne & Wear NE38 7DR. Tel: (H) 0191 416 8420
Club Colours: Royal blue/amber hooped jersey, blue shorts, amber socks.

WEARSIDE RUFC
Ground Address: Fulwell Quarry Reclamation Site, Newcastle Road, Sunderland, Tyne & Wear.
Club Secretary: Jonathan Ridley, 143 Atkinson Road, Fulwell, Sunderland, Tyne & Wear SR6 9AY. Tel: (H) 0191 549 6523 Tel: (W) 0191 565 6256 x45441
Fixtures Secretary: Jeff Fowler, 8 Kirkwood Avenue, Hastings Hill, Sunderland, Tyne & Wear. Tel: (H) 0191 534 5191 Tel (W) 0191 276 1161 Mobile: 0589 127352
Club Colours: Royal blue & scarlet hoops.

NORTHERN DIVISION

YORKSHIRE ONE
1995-96
FIXTURES

September 16 1995 (Week 3)

Yarnbury	v	Sheffield Oaks
Ilkley	v	Halifax Vandals
Wibsey	v	Wath
Old Otliensians	v	Pocklington
Castleford	v	Leodiensians
Barnsley	v	Malton & Norton

September 23 1995 (Week 4)

Malton & Norton	v	Sheffield Oaks
Leodiensians	v	Barnsley
Pocklington	v	Castleford
Wath	v	Old Otliensians
Halifax Vandals	v	Wibsey
Bradford Salem	v	Ilkley

September 30 1995 (Week X1)

Yarnbury	v	Leodiensians
Sheffield Oaks	v	Malton & Norton
Wibsey	v	Bradford Salem
Old Otliensians	v	Halifax Vandals
Castleford	v	Wath
Barnsley	v	Pocklington

October 14 1995 (Week 6)

Leodiensians	v	Sheffield Oaks
Pocklington	v	Yarnbury
Wath	v	Barnsley
Halifax Vandals	v	Castleford
Bradford Salem	v	Old Otliensians
Ilkley	v	Wibsey

October 21 1995 (Week 7)

Yarnbury	v	WathSheffield Oaks
Malton & Norton	v	Leodiensians
Old Otliensians	v	Ilkley
Castleford	v	Bradford Salem
Barnsley	v	Halifax Vandals

October 28 1995 (Week 8)

Pocklington	v	Malton & Norton
Wath	v	Sheffield Oaks
Halifax Vandals	v	Yarnbury
Bradford Salem	v	Barnsley
Ilkley	v	Castleford
Wibsey	v	Old Otliensians

November 11 1995 (Week 10)

Yarnbury	v	Bradford Salem
Sheffield Oaks	v	Halifax Vandals
Malton & Norton	v	Wath
Leodiensians	v	Pocklington
Castleford	v	Wibsey
Barnsley	v	Ilkley

January 6 1996 (Week 17)

Wath	v	Leodiensians
Halifax Vandals	v	Malton & Norton
Bradford Salem	v	Sheffield Oaks
Ilkley	v	Yarnbury
Wibsey	v	Barnsley
Old Otliensians	v	Castleford

January 13 1996 (Week 18)

Yarnbury	v	Wibsey
Sheffield Oaks	v	Ilkley
Malton & Norton	v	Bradford Salem
Leodiensians	v	Halifax Vandals
Pocklington	v	Wath
Barnsley	v	Old Otliensians

February 10 1996 (Week 22)

Halifax Vandals	v	Pocklington
Bradford Salem	v	Leodiensians
Ilkley	v	Malton & Norton
Wibsey	v	Sheffield Oaks
Old Otliensians	v	Yarnbury
Castleford	v	Barnsley

February 17 1996 (Week 23)

Yarnbury	v	Castleford
Sheffield Oaks	v	Old Otliensians
Malton & Norton	v	Wibsey
Leodiensians	v	Ilkley
Pocklington	v	Bradford Salem
Wath	v	Halifax Vandals

February 24 1996 (Week 24)

Bradford Salem	v	Wath
Ilkley	v	Pocklington
Wibsey	v	Leodiensians
Old Otliensians	v	Malton & Norton
Castleford	v	Sheffield Oaks
Barnsley	v	Yarnbury

March 30 1996 (Week X7)

Sheffield Oaks	v	Barnsley
Malton & Norton	v	Castleford
Leodiensians	v	Old Otliensians
Pocklington	v	Wibsey
Wath	v	Ilkley
Halifax Vandals	v	Bradford Salem

YORKSHIRE ONE

BARNSLEY RUFC
Ground Address: Barnsley Cricket & Athletic Club, Shaw Lane, Barnsley, South Yorshire. Postal address: PO Box 123, Barnsley S75 1YU. Tel: 01226 203509
Club Secretary: M Marshall, 4 Westbourne Grove, Barnsley, South Yorkshire S75 1AE. Tel: (H) 01226 771473
Fixtures Secretary: S Roper, 20 Loxley Road, Burton Grange, Barnsley, South Yorkshire S71 5NR. Tel: (H) 01226 285687 Tel (W) 01484 429696 x273
Club Colours: Red, white, blue hoops.

BRADFORD SALEM RFC
Ground Address: Shay Lane, Heaton, Bradford BD9 6SL. Tel: 01274 496430
Club Secretary: Martin G Walker, 24 Roydscliffe Road, Heaton, Bradford, West Yorksire BD9 5PU. Tel: (H) 01274 492470 Tel: (W) 01274 882214
Fixtures Secretary: John Dobson, 2 Highfield Drive, Heaton, Bradford, West Yorkshire BD9 6HN. Tel: (H) 01274 487517 Tel (W) 01422 330022
Club Colours: Royal blue, gold, black hoops, black shorts, blue socks.

CASTLEFORD RUFC
Ground Address: Willowbridge Lane, Whitwood, Castleford, West Yorkshire WF10. Tel: 01977 554762
Club Secretary: Todd Staweckl, 18 Woodbine Street, Ossett, West Yorkshire WF5 9LN. Tel: (H) 01924 263454 Tel: (W) 01924 276104/279885
Fixtures Secretary: E Mills, 1a Pinfold Lane, Methley, Leeds LS26 9AU. Tel: (H) 01977 515784 Tel (W) 01924 413056
Club Colours: Red & blue hoops.

HALIFAX VANDALS RFC Tel: 01422 831703
Club Secretary: Andrew Ward, 124 Ravenstone Drive, Greetland, Halifax HX4 8DY. Tel: (H) 01422 371999 Tel: (W) 01422 824186
Fixtures Secretary: Cyril Clegg, 28 Vicar Park Drive, Norton Tower, Halifax. Tel: (H) 01422 359813
Club Colours: Royal blue & white narrow stripes, blue shorts.

ILKLEY RUFC
Ground Address: Stacks Field, Denton Road, Ilkley, West Yorkshire LS29 0BZ. Tel: 01943 607037
Club Secretary: Mr G Whiteley, Springs End House, 44 Springs Lane, Ilkley, West Yorkshire LS29 8TH. Tel: (H) 01943 609792 Tel: (W) 0113 2440785
Fixtures Secretary: Mr K Bernard, 36 Dale View, Ilkley, West Yorkshire LS29 9BP. Tel: (H) 01943 602945 Tel (W) 0113 2451000
Club Colours: Red, white & black.

LEODIENSIAN RUFC
Ground Address: Cragg Lane, off King Lane, Alwoodley, Leeds LS17 5PR. Tel: 0113 267 3409
Club Secretary: Mr MW Brighten, 16 Alwoodley Gardens, Alwoodley, Leeds, LS17 7BQ. Tel: (H) 0113 2672410 Tel: (W) 0113 230 0632
Fixtures Secretary: M Crook, 40 Cookridge Drive, Leeds 16. Tel: (H) 0113 267 3651 Tel (W) 01535 636116
Club Colours: Navy blue and gold.

MALTON & NORTON RUFC
Ground Address: Pasture Lane, Peasey Hill, Malton, North Yorkshire. Tel: 01653 694657
Club Secretary: CO Whincup, Arboretum, Keld Head Hall, Middleton Road, Pickering, North Yorkshire YO18 8NR. Tel: (H) 01751 477170 Tel: (W) 01723 584141 x2341
Fixtures Secretary: Mr JQ Knock, 3 Lime Avenue, Stockton Lane, York. Tel: (H) 01751 472228 Tel (W) 01653 692424
Club Colours: Red, white & black hooped shirts.

OLD OTLIENSIANS RUFC
Ground Address: Chaffers Field, Pool Road, Otley, West Yorkshire. Tel: 01943 461476
Club Secretary: D Taylor, 39 The Whartons, Otley, West Yorkshire LS21 2AG. Tel: (H) 01943 850913 Tel: (W)

FINAL TABLE

	P	W	D	L	F	A	Pts
Wheatley Hills	12	12	0	0	343	90	24
Wath	12	10	0	2	255	119	20
Ilkley	12	7	1	4	171	122	15
Yarnbury	12	7	1	4	149	121	15
Barnsley	12	7	1	4	139	129	15
Malton & Norton	12	6	1	5	178	198	13
Leodiensians	12	6	0	6	179	197	12
Sheffield Oaks	12	5	0	7	128	201	10
Bradford Salem	12	4	0	8	171	179	8
Pocklington	12	4	0	8	155	204	8
Castleford	12	3	2	7	125	210	8
Old Otliensians	12	2	0	10	115	200	4
Hemsworth	12	2	0	10	138	276	2*

01274 334051
Fixtures Secretary: AS Normanton, 26 Roseberry Crescent, Great Ayton, Middlesbrough, Cleveland. Tel: (H) 01642 723199 Tel (W) 01642 467144
Club Colours: Navy blue, royal blue & white.

POCKLINGTON RUFC
Ground Address: Percy Road, Pocklington, East Yorkshire YO4 2QB. Tel: 01759 303358
Club Secretary: MB Herring, 34 Hill Rise Drive, Market Weighton, York YO4 3JZ. Tel: (H) 01430 872156 Tel: (W) 01482 666198
Fixtures Secretary: JB Rudsdale, 3 Beckside, Wilberfoss, York YO4 5NS. Tel: (H) 01759 380312
Club Colours: Navy & white hoops.

SHEFFIELD OAKS RUFC
Ground Address: Limestone Cottage, Claywheels Lane, Sheffield 6. Tel: 0114 285 3268
Club Secretary: Mr A Thomas, 144 Lyminster Road, Wadsley Bridge, Sheffield, South Yorkshire S6 1HZ. Tel: (H) 0114 232 6774
Fixtures Secretary: Mr G Davies, Griffs Lodge, Stopes Road, Stannington, Sheffield S6 6BW. Tel: (H) 0114 233 5829
Club Colours: Royal blue & gold hoops.

WATH UPON DEARNE RUFC
Ground Address: Moor Road, Wath upon Deane, Rotherham, South Yorkshire. Tel: 01709 872399
Club Secretary: S Poxton, 19 Packham road, Wath upon Dearne, Rotherham, South Yorkshire. Tel: (H) 01709 874154
Fixtures Secretary: S Corns, 83 Chapel Street, Wath upon Dearne, Rotherham, South Yorkshire. Tel: (H) 01709 874911
Club Colours: Blue with maroon & gold bands.

WIBSEY RUFC
Ground Address: Northfield Road, Wibsey, Bradford, West Yorkshire BD6. Tel: 01274 671643
Club Secretary: Martin Spencer, 188 St Enoch's Road, Wibsey, Bradford, West Yorkshire BD6 3BT. Tel: (H) 01274 605566 Tel: (W) 01274 390400
Fixtures Secretary: Mr Arthur Deacon, 18 Overton Drive, Horton Bank Top, Bradford BD6. Tel: (H) 01274 574905
Club Colours: Red & green.

YARNBURY (HORSFORTH) RUFC
Ground Address: Brownberrie Lane, Horsforth, Leeds LS18 5HB. Tel: 0113 2581346
Club Secretary: Paul Trigg, 16 Moorland Grove, Moortown, Leeds LS17 6HS. Tel: (H) 0113 2664680 Tel: (W) 01274 531602
Fixtures Secretary: John Riley, 65 Broadgate Lane, Horsforth, Leeds 18 5AB. Tel: (H) 0113 2589131 Tel (W) 01924 441818
Club Colours: Blue, black & white uneven hoops, navy shorts.

NORTHERN DIVISION

YORKSHIRE TWO
1995-96
FIXTURES

November 11 1995 (Week 10)

Aireborough	v	Moortown
Sheffield Tigers	v	West Leeds
Dinnington	v	Skipton
Old Modernians	v	Hessle
Wetherby	v	Northallerton
Hemsworth	v	Huddersfield YMCA

September 16 1995 (Week 3)

Aireborough	v	Sheffield Tigers
Huddersfield YMCA	v	West Leeds
Northallerton	v	Skipton
Scarborough	v	Hessle
Wetherby	v	Old Modernians
Hemsworth	v	Dinnington

January 6 1996 (Week 17)

Skipton	v	Old Modernians
West Leeds	v	Dinnington
Moortown	v	Sheffield Tigers
Huddersfield YMCA	v	Aireborough
Northallerton	v	Hemsworth
Scarborough	v	Wetherby

September 23 1995 (Week 4)

Dinnington	v	Aireborough
Old Modernians	v	Hemsworth
Hessle	v	Wetherby
Skipton	v	Scarborough
West Leeds	v	Northallerton
Moortown	v	Huddersfield YMCA

January 13 1996 (Week 18)

Aireborough	v	Northallerton
Sheffield Tigers	v	Huddersifeld YMCA
Dinnington	v	Moortown
Old Modernians	v	West Leeds
Hessle	v	Skipton
Hemsowrth	v	Scarborough

September 30 1995 (Week X1)

Aireborough	v	Old Modernians
Sheffield Tigers	v	Dinnington
Northallerton	v	Moortown
Scarborogh	v	West Leeds
Wetherby	v	Skipton
Hemsworth	v	Hessle

February 10 1996 (Week 22)

West Leeds	v	Hessle
Moortown	v	Old Modernians
Huddersfield YMCA	v	Dinnington
Northallerton	v	Sheffield Tigers
Scarborough	v	Aireborough
Wetherby	v	Hemsworth

October 14 1995 (Week 6)

Old Modernians	v	Sheffield Tigers
Hessle	v	Aireborough
Skipton	v	Hemsworth
West Leeds	v	Wetherby
Moortown	v	Scarborough
Huddersfield YMCA	v	Northallerton

February 17 1996 (Week 23)

Aireborough	v	Wetherby
Sheffield Tigers	v	Scarborough
Dinnington	v	Northallerton
Old Modernians	v	Huddersfield YMCA
Hessle	v	Moortown
Skipton	v	West Leeds

October 21 1995 (Week 7)

Aireborough	v	Skipton
Sheffield Tigers	v	Hessle
Dinnington	v	Old Modernians
Scarborough	v	Huddersfield YMCA
Wetherby	v	Moortown
Hemsworth	v	West Leeds

February 24 1996 (Week 24)

Moortown	v	Skipton
Huddersfield YMCA	v	Hessle
Northallerton	v	Old Modernians
Scarborough	v	Dinnington
Wetherby	v	Sheffield Tigers
Hemsworth	v	Aireborough

October 28 1995 (Week 8)

Hessle	v	Dinnington
Skipton	v	Sheffield Tigers
West Leeds	v	Aireborough
Moortown	v	Hemsworth
Huddersfield YMCA	v	Wetherby
Northallerton	v	Scarborough

March 30 1996 (Week X7)

Sheffield Tigers	v	Hemsworth
Dinnington	v	Wetherby
Old Modernians	v	Scarborough
Hessle	v	Northallerton
Skipton	v	Huddersfield YMCA
West Leeds	v	Moortown

YORKSHIRE TWO

AIREBOROUGH RUFC
Ground Address: Green Lane Cricket Club, Nunroyd Park, Yeadon, Nr Leeds, West Yorkshire L19. Tel: 01943 878299
Club Secretary: AM Tullie, 55 Warren Lane, Eldwick, Bingley, West Yorkshire BD16 3BS. Tel: (H) 01274 569631 Tel: (W) 0113 243 6671
Fixtures Secretary: C Clarke, 55 Coppice View, Idle, Nr Bradford, West Yorkshire BD10 8UF. Tel: (H) 01274 610896 Tel (W) 01274 544466
Club Colours: Maroon & white.

DINNINGTON RUFC
Ground Address: Lodge Lane, Dinnington, Sheffield, South Yorkshire, S31 7PB. Tel: 01909 562044
Club Secretary: Mike Burke, 4 Greenway Court, Main Street, North Anston, Sheffield, South Yorkshire, S31 7BD. Tel: (H) 01909 565206
Fixtures Secretary: W Gilboby, 16 Devonshire Drive, North Anstone, Sheffield S31 7AQ. Tel: (H) 01909 562997
Club Colours: Blue, white & gold hoops.

HEMSWORTH RUFC
Ground Address: Moxon Fields, Lowfield Road, Hemsworth, Pontefract, West Yorkshire WF9 4JT. Tel: 01977 610078
Club Secretary: Mark Roberts, 'The Elms', Stockingate, South Kirby, Pontefract WF9 3QX. Tel: (H) 01977 644379 Tel: (W) 01977 644379
Fixtures Secretary: Neil Jennings, 8 Churchfield Terrace, Cudworth, Barnsley, South Yorkshire. Tel: (H) 01226 710181
Club Colours: Navy blue.

HESSLE RUFC
Ground Address: Livingstone Road, Hessle, North Humberside HU13 0HS. Tel: 01482 643430
Club Secretary: TJ Sleight, 69 Tranby Avenue, Hessle, North Humberside HU13 0PX. Tel: (H) 01482 643262 Tel: (W) 01482 448111
Fixtures Secretary: P Denton, 7 Maplewood Avenue, Hull HU5 5YE. Tel: (H) 01482 561338
Club Colours: Green, black & white irregular hooped shirts, white shorts.

HUDDERSFIELD YMCA RFC
Ground Address: Laund Hill Sports Ground, Salendine Nook, Huddersfield, West Yorkshire. Tel: 01484 654052
Club Secretary: Ian Leask, 3 Cheviot Way, Mirfield, West Yorkshire WF14 8HW. Tel: (H) 01924 496448 Tel: (W) 01484 654052
Fixtures Secretary: Gary Schofield, 7 Stonefield Avenue, Crosland Moor, Huddersfield HD4 5QF. Tel: (H) 01484 651738
Club Colours: Black/red hoops, black shorts, red socks.

MOORTOWN RUFC
Ground Address: Moss Valley, (off The Avenue), Alwoodley Park, Leeds, West Yorkshire. Tel: 0113 267 8243
Club Secretary: Mr GP Spark, 7 Hall Cliffe Grove, Horbury, Wakefield, West Yorkshire WF4 6DE. Tel: (H) 01924 271808 Tel: (W) 01924 273442
Fixtures Secretary: Mr C Forbes, 19 The Mount, Alwoodley, Leeds, West Yorkshire LS17 7RH. Tel: (H) 0113 267 5974
Club Colours: Maroon, green & white.

NORTHALLERTON RUFC
Ground Address: Brompton Lodge, Northallerton Road, Brompton, Northallerton, North Yorkshire DL6 2PZ. Tel: 01609 773496
Club Secretary: GW Cartwright, 76 Thirsk Road, Northallerton, North Yorkshire. Tel: (H) 01609 772881
Fixtures Secretary: Mr A Bradley, 15 Borrowby Avenue, Northallerton, North Yorkshire. Tel: (H) 01609 772743
Club Colours: Green, yellow & amber.

OLD MODERNIANS RUFC
Ground Address: The Clubhouse, Cookridge Lane, Cookridge, Leeds, West Yorkshire LS16 7ND. Tel: 0113 267 1075
Club Secretary: KR Shotton, c/o 25 Crowlees Road, Mirfield, West Yorkshire WF14 9PJ. Tel: (W) 01484 533231
Fixtures Secretary: D Carter, 81 Green Lane, Cookridge, Leeds, West Yorkshire. Tel: (H) 0113 267 9718
Club Colours: Red & black hoops, black shorts.

FINAL TABLE

	P	W	D	L	F	A	Pts
Wibsey	12	12	0	0	272	95	24
Halifax Vandals	12	9	0	3	222	143	18
Northallerton	12	8	0	4	147	120	16
Old Modernians	12	8	1	3	172	104	15*
Moortown	12	5	2	5	143	140	12
West Leeds	12	6	0	6	158	161	12
Aireborough	12	6	0	6	201	215	12
Huddersfield YMCA	12	5	1	6	109	181	11
Sheffield Tigers	12	5	0	7	164	222	10
Dinnington	12	4	1	7	180	187	9
Hessle	12	3	1	8	111	132	7
Scarborough	12	1	3	8	114	187	5
York Railway Inst	12	1	1	10	129	235	3

SCARBOROUGH RUFC
Ground Address: The Club House, Scalby Road, Scarborough, North Yorkshire YO12 6EE. Tel: 01723 363039
Club Secretary: Mrs S E Hanson, c/o Scarborough RUFC, The Club House, Scalby Road, Scarburgh, North Yorkshire YO12 6EE. Tel: (W) 01723 363039
Fixtures Secretary: AT Downes, c/o SRUFC, The Club House, Scalby Road, Scarborough YO12 6EE. Tel: (H) 01723 584315
Club Colours: Navy, maroon & white.

SHEFFIELD TIGERS RUFC
Ground Address: Hathersage Road, Dore Moor, Sheffield S17 3AB. Tel: 0114 2360075
Club Secretary: Martin Caine, 20 Sandy Acres Drive, Waterthorpe, Sheffield S19 6LS. Tel: (H) 0114 248 9052 Tel: (W) 0115 962 0532
Fixtures Secretary: Ron Lewis, 33 Swift Way, Sandal, Wakefield WF2 6SQ. Tel: (H) 01924 253049 Tel (W) 0113 243 5301
Club Colours: Maroon & white hoops, black shorts.

SKIPTON RUFC
Ground Address: Coulthorpe Memorial Grounds, Sandylands, Carleton New Road, Skipton, Yorkshire BD23 2AZ. Tel: 01756 793148
Club Secretary: Andrew Clark, 200 Moorview Way, Skipton, North Yorkshire BD23 2TN. Tel: (H) 01756 798137 Fax: 01756 701155 Tel: (W) 01836 560140
Fixtures Secretary: Andy Abell, 22 Regent Road, Skipton, North Yorkshire BD23 1AN. Tel: (H) 01756 798798 Tel (W) 01756 793377
Club Colours: Cardinal red shirts, white shorts, red socks.

WEST LEEDS RUFC
Ground Address: Blue Hill Lane, Wortley, Leeds LS12 4NZ. Tel: 0113 263 9869
Club Secretary: Ms Jill Dowson, 66 Cow Close Road, Leeds LS12 5PD. Tel: (H) 0113 279 8322 Tel: (W) 0113 245 7111
Fixtures Secretary: John MacAndrew, 27 Rooms Fold, Morley, Leeds LS27 9PS. Tel: (H) 0113 252 0369
Club Colours: Navy, old gold & white.

WETHERBY RUFC
Ground Address: The Club House, Grange Park, Wetherby, West Yorkshire. Tel: 01937 582461
Club Secretary: Mr Chris Nussey, 62 Wighill Lane, Tadcaster, North Yorkshire LS24 8EX. Tel: (H) 01937 833494 Tel: (W) 0113 276 0730
Fixtures Secretary: Keith Astbury, 2 Fir Tree Avenue, Garforth, Leeds LS25 2JN. Tel: (H) 0113 286 2347
Club Colours: Red & white hooped jerseys, white shorts, red socks.

NORTHERN DIVISION

YORKSHIRE THREE
1995-96
FIXTURES

September 16 1995 (Week 3)

Mosborough	v	Heath
Old Rishworthians	v	Knottingley
Marist	v	Leeds Corinthians
Baildon	v	Phoenix Park
Rodillians	v	Hullensians
Ossett	v	York RI

September 23 1995 (Week 4)

York RI	v	Mosborough
Hullensians	v	Ossett
Phoenix Park	v	Rodillians
Leeds Corinthians	v	Baildon
Knottingley	v	Marist
Lawnswood	v	Old Rishworthians

September 30 1995 (Week X1)

Mosborough	v	Hullensians
Heath	v	York RI
Marist	v	Lawnswood
Baildon	v	Knottingley
Rodillians	v	Leeds Corinthians
Ossett	v	Phoenix Park

October 14 1995 (Week 6)

Hullensians	v	Heath
Phoenix Park	v	Mosborough
Leeds Corinthians	v	Ossett
Knottingley	v	Rodillians
Lawnswood	v	Baildon
Old Rishworthians	v	Marist

October 21 1995 (Week 7)

Mosborough	v	Leeds Corinthians
Heath	v	Phoenix Park
York RI	v	Hullensians
Baildon	v	Old Rishworthians
Rodillians	v	Lawnswood
Ossett	v	Knottingley

October 28 1995 (Week 8)

Phoenix Park	v	York RI
Leeds Corinthians	v	Heath
Knottingley	v	Mosborough
Lawnswood	v	Ossett
Old Rishworthians	v	Rodillians
Marist	v	Baildon

November 11 1995 (Week 10)

Mosborough	v	Lawnswood
Heath	v	Knottingley
York RI	v	Leeds Corinthians
Hullensians	v	Phoenix Park
Rodillians	v	Marist
Ossett	v	Old Rishworthians

January 6 1996 (Week 17)

Leeds Corinthians	v	Hullensians
Knottingley	v	York RI
Lawnswood	v	Heath
Old Rishworthians	v	Mosborough
Marist	v	Ossett
Baildon	v	Rodillians

January 13 1996 (Week 18)

Mosborough	v	Marist
Heath	v	Old Rishworthians
York RI	v	Lawnswood
Hullensians	v	Knottingley
Phoenix Park	v	Leeds Corinthians
Ossett	v	Baildon

February 10 1996 (Week 22)

Knottingley	v	Phoenix Park
Lawnswood	v	Hullensians
Old rishworthians	v	York RI
Marist	v	Heath
Baildon	v	Mosborough
Rodillians	v	Ossett

February 17 1996 (Week 23)

Mosborough	v	Rodillians
Heath	v	Baildon
York RI	v	Marist
Hullensians	v	Old Rishworthians
Phoenix Park	v	Lawnswood
Leeds Corinthians	v	Knottingley

February 24 1996 (Week 24)

Lawnswood	v	Leeds Corinthians
Old Rishworthians	v	Phoenix Park
Marist	v	Hullensians
Baildon	v	York RI
Rodillians	v	Heath
Ossett	v	Mosborough

March 30 1996 (Week X7)

Heath	v	Ossett
York RI	v	Rodillians
Hullensians	v	Baildon
Phoenix Park	v	Marist
Leeds Corinthians	v	Old Rishworthians
Knottingley	v	Lawnswood

YORKSHIRE THREE

BAILDON RUFC
Ground Address: Jenny Lane, Baildon, Shipley, West Yorkshire BD17 6RS. Tel: 01274 582644
Club Secretary: RB Hawkins, 30 Moorfield Drive, Baildon, Shipley, West Yorkshire BD17 6LQ. Tel: (H) 01274 580292
Fixtures Secretary: Mr JR Jennings, 15 Moorfield Drive, Baildon, Shipley, West Yorkshire BD17 6LQ. Tel: (H) 01274 593632 Tel (W) 01943 608765
Club Colours: Red, black & white hooped jerseys.

HEATH RUFC
Ground Address: North Dean, Stainland Road, West Vale, Halifax, West Yorkshire HX4 8LS. Tel: 01422 372920
Club Secretary: Craig Bedford, 58 Hollins Lane, Sowerby Bridge, Halifax HX6 2RP. Tel: (H) 01422 834473 Tel: (W) 01422 373462
Fixtures Secretary: Gary Mason, 16 Scar Bottom Road, Halifax, West Yorkshire. Tel: (H) 01422 349271 Tel (W) 01422 371909
Club Colours: Emerald, gold, claret.

HULLENSIANS RUFC
Ground Address: Springhead Lane, Anlaby Common, Hull. Tel: 01482 651086
Club Secretary: Mark Bayston, 31 Glenfield Drive, Kirkell, Hull HU10 7UL. Tel: (H) 01482 659793 Tel: (W) 01482 830367
Fixtures Secretary: Tim Robinson, 79 Huntley Drive, Chanterlands Avenue, Hull HU5 4DP. Tel: (H) 01482 348181 Tel (W) 01482 323631
Club Colours: Red & black.

KNOTTINGLEY RUFC
Ground Address: The Club House, Marsh Lane, Knottingley, West Yorkshire WF11 9DE. Tel: 01977 672438
Club Secretary: Mr DD Heald, 51 Pontefract Road, Knottingley, West Yorkshire WF11 8RD. Tel: (H) 01977 672496 Tel: (W) 01977 672496
Fixtures Secretary: Colin Davison, 66 Simpsons Lane, Knottingley, West Yorkshire. Tel: (H) 01977 674373 Tel (W) 01977 703377
Club Colours: Blue & white regular hoops, blue shorts.

LAWNSWOOD RUFC
Ground Address: Lawnswood Sports Ground, Otley Road, Leeds LS16 6HQ. Tel: 0113 2678168
Club Secretary: David G Smith, 46 Highfield Avenue, Wortley, Leeds LS12 4BY. Tel: (H) 0113 2790365 Tel: (W) 0113 2380002
Fixtures Secretary: Dr RW Marshall, 38 Barthorpe Crescent, Leeds LS17 5PE. Tel: (H) 0113 2685755 Tel (W) 0113 2332599
Club Colours: Green/black hoops.

LEEDS CORINTHIANS RUFC
Ground Address: Middleton District Centre, Leeds 10. Tel: 0113 2711574
Club Secretary: Mr Malcolm Naylor, 9 Staithe Gardens, Middleton, Leeds LS10 3NA. Tel: (H) 0113 2705919
Fixtures Secretary: Mr Graham Mapplebeck, 33 Oakley Street, Thorpe, Wakefield WF3 3DX. Tel: (H) 01924 828809 Tel (W) 0113 2457205
Club Colours: All black with gold trim.

MARIST RUFC
Ground Address: Cranbrook Avenue, Hull. Tel: 0182 859216
Club Secretary: Kevin Johnson, 11 Roborough Close, Hull HU7 4RN. Tel: (H) 0182 828973 Tel: (W) 0182 781202
Fixtures Secretary: Ralph Ayre, 92 Auckland Avenue, Cottingham Road, Hull HU6 7SH. Tel: (H) 0182 804166
Club Colours: Royal blue & white.

MOSBOROUGH RUFC
Ground Address: Mosborough Miners WMC, Station Road, Mosborough, Sheffield 19. Tel: 01142 485546
Club Secretary: Lawrence S Hannon, 12 Stonegravels Croft, Halfway, Sheffield S19 5HP. Tel: (H) 01142 488425 Tel: (W) 01246 854650
Fixtures Secretary: S Collins, Manor View, Brampton-en-le-Mothen, Rotherham S66 9BD. Tel: 01709 531732
Club Colours: Black & white hoops.

FINAL TABLE

	P	W	D	L	F	A	Pts
Wetherby	12	10	0	2	243	88	20
Skipton	12	9	2	1	237	114	20
Old Rishworthians	12	8	2	2	195	103	18
Stanley Rodillians	12	7	1	4	150	140	15
Heath	12	7	0	5	155	156	14
Phoenix Park	12	6	1	5	148	135	13
Marist	12	6	1	5	156	163	13
Ossett	12	5	1	6	132	231	11
Knottingley	12	3	3	6	118	130	9
Hullensians	12	4	0	8	115	124	8
Lawnswood	12	3	1	8	123	187	7
Leeds Corinthians	12	3	1	8	59	125	7
Burley	12	0	1	11	85	220	1

OLD RISHWORTHIAN RUFC
Ground Address: The Clubhouse, Copley, Halifax, West Yorkshire. Tel: 01422 353919
Club Secretary: DW Butler, Keepers, Shaw Lane, Holywell Green, Halifax, West Yorkshire HX4 9DW. Tel: (H) 01422 371672 Tel: (W) 01484 721223
Fixtures Secretary: R Wadsworth, 7 Newstead Terrace, Newstead, Halifax, West Yorkshire HX1 4TA. Tel: (H) 01422 323172 Tel (W) 01482 845740
Club Colours: Maroon, white & black hoops.

OSSETT RUFC
Ground Address: Spring Mill, off Queens Drive, Ossett, West Yorkshire. Tel: 01924 273618
Club Secretary: DJ Dearnley, 4 Crown Point Close, Ossett, West Yorkshire WF5 8RH. Tel: (H) 01924 278991 Tel: (W) 01274 727886
Fixtures Secretary: IR Whitehead, 20 Westfield Street, Ossett WF5 8JE. Tel: (H) 01924 264629
Club Colours: Black/red quarters, black shorts.

PHOENIX PARK RUFC
Ground Address: Oval Ball, Stoney Royd, Farsley, Leeds. Tel: 01132 553439
Club Secretary: Michael Ryan, 280 Whitehall Road, Wyke, Bradford BD12 9DX. Tel: (H) 01274 727886
Fixtures Secretary: John Duckworth, 38 Soho Mills, Thornton Road, Bradford BD1 2DW. Tel (W) 01274 394801
Club Colours: Royal blue & gold.

STANLEY RODILLIANS RUFC
Ground Address: Manley Park, Lee Moor Road, Stanley, Wakefield, West Yorkshire. Tel: 01924 823619
Club Secretary: RJ Matthews, 27 Newlands Walk, Stanley, Wakefield, West Yorkshire WF3 4DT. Tel: (H) 01924 828727 Tel: (W) 01924 823135
Fixtures Secretary: I Young, 21 Eastfield Drive, Woodlesford, Leeds LS26 8SO. Tel: (H) 0113 2826743 Tel (W) 01742 671131
Club Colours: Green, black, white hoops, black shorts.

YORK RI RUFC
Ground Address: Railway Institute Sports Ground, New Lane, Acomb, York YO2 4NU. Tel: 01904 798930
Club Secretary: GH Wogan, 47 Melton Avenue, Rawcliffe Lane, York YO3 6QQ. Tel: (H) 01904 641489 Tel: (W) 01904 654247
Fixtures Secretary: WF Cooper, Moorcroft, Lucy Hall Drive, Baildon, Shipley, West Yorkshire BD17 5BG. Tel: (H) 01274 584355
Club Colours: Royal blue & white hooped shirts, black shorts, royal blue socks.

NORTHERN DIVISION

YORKSHIRE FOUR
1995-96
FIXTURES

November 11 1995 (Week 10)

Rawmarsh	v	Adwick le Street
Garforth	v	Edlington & Wickersley
BP Chemicals	v	Stocksbridge
Danum Phoenix	v	Withernsea
New Earswick	v	Burley
Hornsea	v	Rowntrees

September 16 1995 (Week 3)

Rawmarsh	v	Garforth
Rowntrees	v	Edlington & Wickersley
Burley	v	Stocksbridge
De La Salle (Sheffield)	v	Withernsea
New Earswick	v	Danum Phoenix
Hornsea	v	BP Chemicals

January 6 1996 (Week 17)

Stocksbridge	v	Danum Phoenix
Edlington & Wickersley	v	BP Chemicals
Adwick le Street	v	Garforth
Rowntrees	v	Rawmarsh
Burley	v	Hornsea
De La Salle (Sheffield)	v	New Earswick

September 23 1995 (Week 4)

BP Chemicals	v	Rawmarsh
Danum Phoenix	v	Hornsea
Withernsea	v	New Earswick
Stocksbridge	v	De La Salle (Sheffield)
Edlington & Wickersley	v	Burley
Adwick le Street	v	Rowntrees

January 13 1996 (Week 18)

Rawmarsh	v	Burley
Garforth	v	Rowntrees
BP Chemicals	v	Adwick le Street
Danum Phoenix	v	Edlington & Wickersley
Withernsea	v	Stocksbridge
Hornsea	v	De La Salle (Sheffield)

September 30 1995 (Week X1)

Rawmarsh	v	Danum Phoenix
Garforth	v	BP Chemicals
Burley	v	Adwick le Street
De La Salle (Sheffield)	v	Edlington & Wickersley
New Earswick	v	Stocksbridge
Hornsea	v	Withernsea

February 10 1996 (Week 22)

Edlington & Wickersley	v	Withernsea
Adwick le Street	v	Danum Phoenix
Rowntrees	v	BP Chemicals
Burley	v	Garforth
De La Salle (Sheffield)	v	Rawmarsh
New Earswick	v	Hornsea

October 14 1995 (Week 6)

Danum Phoenix	v	Garforth
Withernsea	v	Rawmarsh
Stocksbridge	v	Hornsea
Edlington & Wickersley	v	New Earswick
Adwick le Street	v	De La Salle (Sheffield)
Rowntrees	v	Burley

February 17 1996 (Week 23)

Rawmarsh	v	New Earswick
Garforth	v	De La Salle (Sheffield)
BP Chemicals	v	Burley
Danum Phoenix	v	Rowntrees
Withernsea	v	Adwick le Street
Stocksbridge	v	Edlington & Wickersley

October 21 1995 (Week 7)

Rawmarsh	v	Stocksbridge
Garforth	v	Withernsea
BP Chemicals	v	Danum Phoenix
De La Salle (Sheffield)	v	Rowntrees
New Earswick	v	Adwick le Street
Hornsea	v	Edlington & Wickersley

February 24 1996 (Week 24)

Adwick le Street	v	Stocksbridge
Rowntrees	v	Withernsea
Burley	v	Danum Phoenix
De La Salle (Sheffield)	v	BP Chemicals
New Earswick	v	Garforth
Hornsea	v	Rawmarsh

October 28 1995 (Week 8)

Withernsea	v	BP Chemicals
Stocksbridge	v	Garforth
Edlington & Wickersley	v	Rawmarsh
Adwick le Street	v	Hornsea
Rowntrees	v	New Earswick
Burley	v	De La Salle (Sheffield)

March 30 1996 (Week X7)

Garforth	v	Hornsea
BP Chemicals	v	New Earswick
Danum Phoenix	v	De La Salle (Sheffield)
Withernsea	v	Burley
Stocksbridge	v	Rowntrees
Edlington & Wickersley	v	Adwick le Street

YORKSHIRE FOUR

ADWICK-LE-STREET RUFC
Ground Address: Church Lane Playing Fields, Adwick-le-Street, Doncaster, South Yorkshire.
Club Secretary: RJTerry, 7 Cranfield Drive, Skellow, Doncaster, South Yorkshire DN6 8RS. Tel: (H) 01302 727580 Tel: (W) 01977 605100
Fixtures Secretary: Michael Flanagan, 31 Alexandra Road, Bentley, Doncaster, South Yorkshire. Tel: (H) 01302 872429
Club Colours: Light blue & dark blue hoops, navy shorts, red hose.

BP CHEMICALS RUFC
Ground Address: BP Sports & Social Club, Salt End, Hedon Road, Hull HU12 8DS. Tel: (H) 01482 377574
Club Secretary: Ian Batty, 349 Ings Road, Sutton-on-Hull, Hull HU7 4UY. Tel: (H) 01482 377574
Fixtures Secretary: Steve West, 2 Manor Road, Preston, Nr Hull HU12 8SQ. Tel: (H) 01482 891371 Tel (W) 01482 896251 x2844
Club Colours: Maroon & gold.

BURLEY RUFC
Ground Address: The Club House, Abbey Road, Leeds LS5 3NG. Tel: 0113 275 7400
Club Secretary: Terry McCreedy, 42 Fearnville Place, Leeds LS8 3DY. Tel: (H) 0113 265 5065 Tel: (W) 01274 727524
Fixtures Secretary: John Sanderson, 5 Southolme Close, Leeds LS5 3LP. Tel: (H) 0113 278 7772
Club Colours: Maroon & white.

DANUM PHOENIX RUFC
Ground Address: Du Pont Sports & Social Club, Wheatley Hall Road, Doncaster, South Yorkshire DN2 4LT. Tel: 01302 364307
Club Secretary: Martin O'Hara, The Townhouse, 27 Bennetthorpe, Donaster DN2 6AA. Tel: (H) 01302 349753
Fixtures Secretary: Michael Tollerfield, 75 Appleton Way, Scawthorpe, Doncaster DN5 9NE. Tel: (H) 01302 875700
Club Colours: All black with red & yellow band on shirts.

DE LA SALLE (SHEFFIELD) RUFC
Ground Address: De La Salle Association Club, behind Beauchief Hall, off Abbey Lane, Sheffield. Tel: 0114 236 7756
Club Secretary: Maureen Buckley, 93 Ingram Road, Sheffield S2 2SB. Tel: (H) 0114 272 0246
Fixtures Secretary: Tony Buckley, 93 Ingram Road, Sheffield S2 2SB. Tel: (H) 0114 272 0246
Club Colours: Green & gold hoops.

EDLINGTON AND WICKERSLEY RUFC
Ground Address: Granby Road WMC, Broomhouse Lane, Edlington, Doncaster DN12. Tel: 01302 862404
Club Secretary: Mick Gulliver, 24 Elsham Close, Bramley, Rotherham S66 0XZ. Tel: (H) 01709 546823
Fixtures Secretary: Steve Houghton, 150 Pear Tree Avenue, Bramley, Rotherham S66 0NF. Tel: (H) 01709 531758
Club Colours: Green shirts, black shorts & socks.

GARFORTH RUFC
Ground Address: Garforth Community College, Lidget Lane, Garforth Leeds LS25 1LJ.
Club Secretary: George Shaw, 32 Rose Court, Garforth, Leeds LS25 1NS. Tel: (H) 0113 286 7193
Fixtures Secretary: Mr F Child, Eden Villa, 8 Lowther Avenue, Garforth, Leeds LS25 1EP. Tel: (H) 0113 286 8625 Tel (W) 0113 275 2115
Club Colours: Black to chest then royal blue, gold & scarlet.

HORNSEA RUFC
Ground Address: Clubhouse, Westwood Avenue, Hornsea HU18 1BB. Tel: 01964 534181
Club Secretary: Nic Marshall, 4 Paddock View, Beverley Road, Withernwick HU11 4UA. Tel: (H) 01964 527966 Tel: (W) 01964 536939

FINAL TABLE

	P	W	D	L	F	A	Pts
Mosborough	12	11	1	0	250	43	23
Baildon	12	10	0	2	271	74	20
Stocksbridge	12	9	1	2	190	83	19
Hornsea	12	9	0	3	195	79	16*
Rowntrees	12	7	1	4	161	141	15
BP Chemicals	12	5	0	7	108	141	10
Withernsea	12	5	0	7	131	200	10
Yorkshire Main	12	4	3	5	87	162	9*
De la Salle (Sheff)	12	4	0	8	90	170	9
Adwick le Street	12	3	0	9	82	154	6
Danum Phoenix	12	3	1	8	97	185	5*
Garforth	12	2	1	9	99	204	5
Knaresborough	12	2	0	10	71	196	2*

Fixtures Secretary: Mrs Lesley Wood, 15 Cheyne Garth, Hornsea HU18 1BE. Tel: (H) 01964 5361856
Club Colours: Black with green & white hoops across chest.

NEW EARSWICK RFC
Ground Address: White Rose Avenue, New Earswick, York. Tel: 01904 750103
Club Secretary: Howard Elders, 26 Priory Wood Way, Huntington, York YO3 9JG. Tel: (H) 01904 652471
Fixtures Secretary: Bryan Bates, 16 Beech Place, Strenshall, York YO3 5AS. Tel: (H) 01904 491296 Tel (W) 01904 642961
Club Colours: Claret & white hoops.

RAWMARSH RUFC
Ground Address: Rawmarsh Leisure Centre, Barbers Avenue, Rawmarsh, Rotherham, South Yorkshire. Tel: 01709 522191
Club Secretary: Alan Parker, 3 McManus Avenue, Rawmarsh, Rotherham, S Yorkshire, S62 7RD. Tel: (H) 01709 522795
Fixtures Secretary: Eric Perkins, 21 Harding Avenue, Rawmarsh, Rotherham, S Yorkshire, S62 7ED. Tel: (H) 01709 526786
Club Colours: Black, amber trim.

ROWNTREE RUFC
Ground Address: Mille Crux, Huxby Road, York. Tel: 01904 623933
Club Secretary: Ashleigh Miles Walters, 32 Chelkar Way, Clifton, York YO3 6ZH. Tel: (H) 01904 690066 Tel: (W) 01904 603325
Fixtures Secretary: Graeme Lavender, 52 Wilton Rise, Holgate Road, York YO2 4BT. Tel: (H) 01904 626897 Tel (W) 01904 411176
Club Colours: Red, black & white.

STOCKSBRIDGE RUFC
Ground Address: Stone Moor Road, Bolstone, Sheffield.
Club Secretary: Julian McGowan, 12 Weats Grove, Penistone, Sheffield S30 6GU. Tel: (H) 01226 765814 Tel: (W) 0113 238 0093
Fixtures Secretary: Chris Lambert, 616 Manchester Road, Stocksbridge, Sheffield S30 5DY. Tel: (H) 0114 288 5223 Tel (W) 0831 141432
Club Colours: Royal blue & white hoops, blue shorts.

WITHERNSEA RUFC
Ground Address: Plough Inn, Holymn, North Humberside HU19 2RS. Tel: 01964 614209
Club Secretary: Mr AC Ellis, 11-17 Seaside Road, Withernsea HU19 2DL. Tel: (H) 01964 613278 Tel: (W) 01964 613278
Fixtures Secretary: Mr P Vickerman, 216 Queen Street, Withernsea. Tel: (H) 01964 614654
Club Colours: White & blue hoops.

NORTHERN DIVISION

YORKSHIRE FIVE 1995-96 FIXTURES

February 24 1996 (Week 24)
Pudsey v Knaresborough
Menwith Hill v Harlow Nomads
Yorkshire Copperworks v Armthorpe Markham

September 30 1995 (Week X1)
Knaresborough v Menwith Hill
Pudsey v Yorkshire Copperworks
Armthorpe Markham v Harlow Nomads

October 14 1995 (Week 6)
Knaresborough v Armthorpe Markham
Menwith Hill v Pudsey
Yorkshire Copperworks v Harlow Nomads

October 21 1995 (Week 7)
Harlow Nomads v Knaresborough
Menwith Hill v Yorkshire Copperworks
Pudsey v Armthorpe Markham

October 28 1995 (Week 8)
Yorkshire Copperworks v Knaresborough
Armthorpe Markham v Menwith Hill
Pudsey v Harlow Nomads

November 11 1995 (Week 10)
Knaresborough v Pudsey
Harlow Nomads v Menwith Hill
Armthorpe Markham v Yorkshire Copperworks

January 6 1996 (Week 17)
Menwith Hill v Knaresborough
Yorkshire Copperworks v Pudsey
Harlow Nomads v Armthorpe Markham

January 13 1996 (Week 18)
Armthorpe Markham v Knaresborough
Pudsey v Menwith Hill
Harlow Nomads v Yorkshire Copperworks

February 10 1996 (Week 22)
Knaresborough v Harlow Nomads
Yorkshire Copperworks v Menwith Hill
Armthorpe Markham v Pudsey

February 17 1996 (Week 23)
Knaresborough v Yorkshire Copperworks
Menwith Hill v Armthorpe Markham
Harlow Nomads v Pudsey

YORKSHIRE FIVE

ARMTHORPE MARKHAM RUFC
Ground Address: Cricket Field, Church Street,
Armthorpe, Doncaster. Club House: c/o Armthorpe
Markham Sports & Social Club, Church Street, Armthorpe.
Tel: 01302 831247
Club Secretary: KM & Mrs AS McNally, 28 Cherry Tree
Road, Armthorpe, Doncaster, DN3 2HP. Tel: (H) 01302
834252 Tel: (W) 0585 262961
Fixtures Secretary: KM & Mrs AS McNally, 28 Cherry
Tree Rd, Armthorpe, Doncaster, DN3 2HP. Tel: (H) 01302
834252 Tel (W) 0585 262961
Club Colours: Red, blue, black, white, quarters, red socks.

HARLOW NOMADS RUFC
Ground Address: c/o Harrogate Grammar School, Arthurs
Avenue, Harrogate, North Yorkshire HG2 0DZ.
Club Secretary: Mel Hill, Flat 1, 13 Dragon Avenue,
Harrogate, North Yorkshire HG1 5DS. Tel: (H) 01423
508041 Tel: (W) 0113 246 4662
Fixtures Secretary: Tony Rogerson, 13 Grosvenor Road,
Harrogate, North Yorkshire HG1 4EG. Tel: (H) 01423
564481
Club Colours: Royal blue & yellow hoops.

KNARESBOROUGH RUFC
Ground Address: Hay-a-Park, Park Lane, off Chain Lane,
Knaresborough, North Yorkshire. Tel: 01423 862525
Club Secretary: Mr C Mabbott, c/o 6 Pine Close,
Wetherby, West Yorkshire LS22 7XU. Tel: (H) 0113 266
0286 Tel: (W) 01937 581977
Fixtures Secretary: Mr P Lynsky, 22 Park Crest,
Knaresborough, North Yorkshire HG5 0BT. Tel: (H) 01423
869082
Club Colours: Navy/gold hooped shirts, navy shorts &
socks.

MENWITH HILL RUFC
Ground Address: Menwith Hill Station, Harrogate, North
Yorkshire HG3 2RF. Tel: 01423 777781
Club Secretary: R Bent, Sports Centre, Menwith Hill
Station, Harrogate, North Yorkshire. Tel: (W) 01423
777781
Fixtures Secretary: M Kirkbride, Sports Centre, Menwith
Hill Station, Harrogate. Tel (W) 01423 777781
Club Colours: Yellow shirts with green trim.

PUDSEY RUFC
Ground Address: Bankhouse Inn, Bankhouse Lane,
Pudsey LS28 8EB. Tel: 0113 256 4662
Club Secretary: MG Woodhead, 28 The Heights,
Bankhouse Lane, Pudsey LS28 8LZ. Tel: (H) 0113 256
9900 Tel: (W) 0113 257 2275 Fax: 0113 255 3224
Fixtures Secretary: JE Day, Bankhouse Inn, Bankhouse
Lane, Pudsey LS28 8EB. Tel: (H) 0113 256 4662
Club Colours: Black/red/green/white.**YORKSHIRE
COPPERWORKS RUFC**
Ground Address: Haigh Park Road, Stourton, Leeds 10.
Club Secretary: M Coleman, 10 Oakfield Avenue,
Rothwell, Leeds LS26 0NJ. Tel: (H) 0113 282 3774 Tel
(W) 0113 270 1107
Fixtures Secretary: Richard Garnham, 10 Swithens Grove,
Rothwell, Leeds LS26 0TL. Tel: (H) 0113 282 3774 Tel
(W) 0113 270 1107
Club Colours: Blue & old gold.

FINAL TABLE

	P	W	D	L	F	A	Pts
Rawmarsh	5	4	0	1	108	49	8
New Earswick	5	3	0	2	80	67	6
Yorkshire CW	5	3	0	2	61	44	4*
Harlow Nomads	5	3	0	2	63	59	4*
Menwith Hill	5	2	0	3	80	88	4
Quakers Armthorpe Markham	5	0	0	5	50	135	0

IF EVERY CLUB BOUGHT TEN DIRECTORIES EVERY CLUB COULD HAVE ITS PHOTO IN NEXT YEARS BOOK!

We have received these photos from 14 Regional Divisions and we would like to have room for more.

Blaydon is a club which, has despite its traditions, lain dormant for many years, but the appointment of Newcastle Gosforth coach Steve Gustard as Director of Rugby and the arrival of Banty Johnson and Steve Bainbridge from the same club, saw a league season with only one defeat and victory in the final game clinched the North East Division 1 Championship and promotion to North 11.

The club previously well known for its connection with Blaydon Races, the Geordie National Anthem, and its now famous Sunday Morning Car Boot Sale, attracting larger numbers than Wimbledon in the Premier Soccer League, are at last on the move, guided by an enthusiastic Executive Committee chaired by Barrie Urwin and financially directed by peter Stokoe. They are on a sound footing running 7 sides every Saturday and junior sides at most levels on Sundays. Rugby is booming at Blaydon, sponsorship is being attracted and new President, Jim Huxley feels that this success, linked with proposed £¾ million clubhouse improvements, enables the future to be faced with great optimism and Blaydon's goal to become number 3 in the North East is well within their sights.

Cleckheaton winning team v Doncaster (Heineken Yorkshire Shield Final)
Back: N Smith, R Widdop, G Piper, J Hammond, A Binns, D Turton, M Womersley, M Collins, P
Hemingway, D Bonner (Coach)
Front: S Burnhill, R Oldroyd, I Gatenby, T Evans, A Foster, G Stead, P Burnhill

Whitchurch captain Phil Mullock scores against Derby – Midlands One

Back Row (l to r): N Bell, T White, T Horsfall, P Maguire, S Foley, P Burr, S McLeod, R Speeks, J Convery,
G Allison, A Meeke, M Elliot, M Snowball, N Stephenson, C Bennet, D McCarrick
Front Row (l to r): K Allison, K Thobular, M Roddam, D Guy (Coach), J Wilson (Treasurer), K Scott
(Cpatain), A Archer (Chairman), T Williams (Secretary), A Rutherfield, J McGray

MIDLAND DIVISION

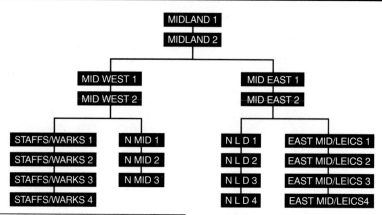

OFFICIALS 1995-96

CHAIRMAN
David Robins, The Clubhouse, Upper Chase Road, Malvern WR14 2BU (H) 01684 564826 (B) 01684 560247 (Fax) 01684 893125

HON. SECRETARY
Michael Wilson, 6 New Road, Easton-on-the-Hill, Stamford, Lincs. PE9 3NN (H) 01780 64019

LEAGUE SECRETARIES
Midland One David Coe, 18 Watermeadow Close, Great Oakley, Corby NN18 8JD (H) 01536 460052 (B) 01536 402551 x 3107 (Fax) 01536 402680
Midland Two Geoff Goodall, 38 Presthills Road, Hinckley, Leics LE10 1AJ (H) 01455 238742 (B) 01203 562650
Midland East One Mike Bracey, 154 Manor Road, Barton-le-Clay, Bedford MK45 4NU (H) 01582 881237
Midland West One Pat Dalley, 153 Masshouse Lane, Kings Norton, Birmingham B38 9AD (H) 0121 680 7237
Midland East Two Brian Johnston, 9 Nursery Close, Atworth, Melksham, Wilts SN12 8HX (H) 01225 790658 (B) 01249 442771 (Fax) 01249 442865
Midland West Two Simon Peace, 12 Alfreda Avenue, Holywood, Worcs B47 5BP (H) 0121 474 4142 (B) 0121 744 4505
Staffs/Warks One Keith Dale, 14 St Anthony's Drive, Newcastle, Staffs ST5 2JE (H) 01782 615770
Staffs/Warks Two Bruce Braithwaite, 4 Badgers Croft, Eccleshall, Staffs ST21 6DS (H) 01785 851114 (B) 01785 277330

Staffs/Warks Three & Four Ray Roberts, 261 Alwyn Road, Bilton, Rugby, Warks CV22 7RP (H) 01788 810276
North Midland One Chris Parsons, 15 Silverbirch Drive, Wythall, Worcs B47 5RB (H) 0121 474 4785
North Midland Two John McNally, 490 Brook Lane, Moseley, Birmingham B13 0BZ (H) 0121 604 6180 (B) 0121 783 7232 (Fax) 0121 789 8306
North Midland Three Nigel Banwell, 16 Riverside Close, Upton upon Severn, Worcs WR8 0JN (H) 01684 592 046
Notts/Lincs & Derby One Kevin Price, 10 Seagrave Road, Thrussington, Leicestershire. LE7 4UG (H) 01664 424388
Notts/Lincs & Derby Two Paul Raymont, 18 Longhill Rise, Kirkby-in-Ashfield, Nottinghamshire NG19 9FL (H) 01623 750990
Notts/Lincs & Derby Three David H Murphy, The Old Carpenters Arms, 32 High Street, Little Bytham, Grantham, Lincolnshire NG33 4QX (H) 01780 410692
Notts/Lincs & Derby Four Andrew Woodall, 3 Brough Cottages, Brough, Bradwell, Derbyshire S30 2HG (H) 01433 620698
East Midland/Leicestershire One Philip Osborne, Ashthorne, Teeton Road, Ravensthorpe, Northampton NN6 8EJ (H) 01684 770772 (B) 01327 705785
East Midland/Leicestershire Two Michael King, 53 Kettering Road, Market Harborough, Leics. LE16 8AN (H) 01858 467267
East Midland/Leicestershire Three Bob Ingledew, 15 Martin Close, Bedford MK41 7JY. (H) 01234 268482
East Midland/Leicestershire Four Paul Adams, 323a Bedford Road, Kempston, Beds. MK42 8QB. (H) 01234 853390 (Fax) 01234 857552

MIDLAND DIVISION

ADMINISTRATIVE RULES

NOTIFICATION OF RESULTS

Club Secretaries are responsible for their club's compliance with the rules of notification of results.

The home club shall notify the appropriate party the result of a league match by telephone by the time stated in the Administrative Instructions.

Both clubs in confirmation of the match played shall return by FIRST CLASS MAIL, the official Match Result Card, completed in all respects to the appropriate officer of the league in accordance with the Administrative Instructions.

Failure to telephone and card in the match results within the time limits laid down shall incur an immediate fine of £15. A second offence a fine of £25 and a third and subsequent offence £25 and a deduction of two league points.

Offending clubs will be notified of fines imposed. Failure to pay within 28 days will result in the offending club being deducted two league points.

There is no right of appeal.

If, 28 days after the last league game, any fine is not paid, the Division will write to the RFU requesting the offending clubs explusion.

ADMINISTRATIVE INSTRUCTIONS

a.   League results to be telephoned to Russells by 5.00pm on the Saturday of the game.
Telephone: 0116 2872 991, Fax: 0116 2872 991.

b.   Match result card to be posted by first class mail on the Monday following the Saturday game.

c.   Notification and collection of fines will be administered by the appropriate League Secretary.

COMPUTER PRINTOUTS FOR PLAYERS' REGISTRATIONS

If Clubs require updated printouts for new players a **stamped addressed envelope must be enclosed** with the relevant registration forms and forwarded to the Registrar, PO Box 183, Leicester LE3 8BZ. Otherwise it will be assumed that an updated printout is not required. It is essential that all Clubs appoint an officer to be responsible for all registration matters.

POSTPONED GAMES

The home club shall notify the appropriate party and the League Secretary of a postponed fixture.

RESCHEDULED MATCHES

A match postponed or abandoned under Regulation 11(a) or (b) or a match not played on the appointed day for reasons acceptable to the Organising Committee SHALL be played on the NEXT AVAILABLE Saturday.

A Saturday is deemed to be 'available' UNLESS one of the following conditions applies:

a. Either Club has, on that day, a scheduled Courage League match.

b. Either Club has, on that day, a Pilkington Cup or Shield match.

c. Either Club has, on that weekend, a match in a Competition under the authority of their Constituent Body, but **NOT** a Merit Table match.

d. Either Club has a demand on one or more of their effectively registered players to play in a representative match under the authority of the RFU, their Division or their Constituent Body on that day.

e. In addition, the Midland Division Committee may – at its absolute discretion and usually at the start of a season declare a specific Saturday "unavailable" where it falls on or close to a public holiday or where it is considered by the committee inappropriate to play for other particular reasons.

MIDLANDS CHAMPIONS ROLL OF HONOUR 1994/95

Midlands 1
Worcester
Midlands 2
Leighton Buzzard
Midlands West 1
Newport (Shropshire)
Midlands West 2
Luctonians
Midlands East 1
Scunthorpe
Midlands East 2
Ilkeston
Staffs/Warwicks 1
Stoke Old Boys
Staffs/Warwicks 2
Silhillians
Staffs/Warwicks 3
Old Warwickians
Staffs/Warwicks 4
Rugby Welsh
North Midlands 1
Malvern

North Midlands 2
Erdington
North Midlands 3
Wulfrun
Notts, Lincs & Derby 1
Ashbourne
Notts, Lincs & Derby 2
Buxton
Notts, Lincs & Derby 3
Castle Donington
Notts, Lincs & Derby 4
Cleethorpes
East Midlands/Leics 1
Old Northamptonians
East Midlands/Leics 2
Rushden & Higham
East Midlands/Leics 3
Kempston
East Midlands/Leics 4
Burbage

Newport (Salop)

414

MIDLAND DIVISION FEATURED CLUBS

NEWPORT (SALOP)

NEWPORT (SALOP) were promotded for a third successive season after winning Midlands West One with an unbeaten record, which included only one drawn match, and a 248-103 points difference. Overall the first team lost only three of their fixtures with that one draw and their victims included National League Five North sides Walsall (the champions) and Hereford. In the North Midlands Cup they suffered a narrow semi-final defeat at the hands of National League Stourbridge and the Shropshire Cup was won for a third season in succession. An annus mirabilis indeed!

Each Saturday, the club fields four senior teams and a colts side, while on Sunday mornings the youth section has coaching for players from under seven to under 17 and this brought success for the Under 16s and Under 15s as they won their appropriate North Midlands knock-out competitions.

Club captain is Mick Trumper, himself and RFU club coach who has with the help of other experienced coaches formed a dedicated squad of players, whose skills and fitness have been improving by leaps and bounds over recent seasons. This has led to enterprising and open rugby, which is enjoyed by everyone.

Facilities at the club in its fine setting are superb and at least as good as any in the Midlands and their successful youth policy is already paying dividends to the extent that they are the envy of all rivals.

RUSHDEN & HIGHAM

RUSHDEN & HIGHAM, founded in humble circumstances in 1950, have rewarded the confidence and efforts of their loyal members and enthusiastic backroom staff by enjoying a marvellous season, which saw them win East Midlands & Leicestershire Two with the only 100 per cent record in the East Midlands and an appearance in the Pilkington Shield quarter-finals in which they lost bravely to eventual winners Bedford Queens, whose efforts durint the season we also salute.

The club runs four senior sides and a colts XV, while there are also strong mini and junior sections. The top side is led by Northampton Police Sergeant Mick Pegley and they enjoyed a superb overall record apart from perfection in their league, which saw the first dozen matches won. Mick has brought the average age of the side, which was at one time a bit long in the tooth, to 26, although stand-off Charlie McGowan can boast of celebrating 43 birthdays.

Honours during their short history have been limited – they won the East Midlands Knock-Out Cup in 1972 and 1984 and appeared in the 1984-85 John Player Cup as a rseult of the latter success – and their CV claims that they are champions consumers of beer wherever they go, but this should be taken with a large dose of saline. They are a club which can be underestimated at great peril by any detractors and are definately on the way up.

Rushden & Higham

MIDLAND DIVISION

MIDLAND ONE
1995-96
FIXTURES

September 16 1995 (Week 3)

Camp Hill	v	Whitchurch
Hereford	v	Leamington
Leighton Buzzard	v	Barker's Butts
Mansfield	v	Westleigh
Syston	v	Burton
Wolverhampton	v	Stafford

September 23 1995 (Week 4)

Barker's Butts	v	Wolverhampton
Burton	v	Leighton Buzzard
Broadstreet	v	Mansfield
Leamington	v	Syston
Stafford	v	Camp Hill
Westleigh	v	Hereford

September 30 1995 (Week X1)

Camp Hill	v	Barker's Butts
Hereford	v	Broadstreet
Leighton Buzzard	v	Leamington
Syston	v	Westleigh
Whitchurch	v	Stafford
Wolverhampton	v	Burton

October 14 1995 (Week 6)

Barker's Butts	v	Whitchurch
Burton	v	Camp Hill
Broadstreet	v	Syston
Leamington	v	Wolverhampton
Mansfield	v	Hereford
Westleigh	v	Leighton Buzzard

October 21 1995 (Week 7)

Camp Hill	v	Leamington
Leighton Buzzard	v	Broadstreet
Stafford	v	Barker's Butts
Syston	v	Mansfield
Whitchurch	v	Burton
Wolverhampton	v	Westleigh

October 28 1995 (Week 8)

Burton	v	Stafford
Broadstreet	v	Wolverhampton
Hereford	v	Syston
Leamington	v	Whitchurch
Mansfield	v	Leighton Buzzard
Westleigh	v	Camp Hill

November 11 1995 (Week 10)

Barker's Butts	v	Burton
Camp Hill	v	Broadstreet
Leighton Buzzard	v	Hereford
Stafford	v	Leamington
Whitchurch	v	Westleigh
Wolverhampton	v	Mansfield

January 6 1996 (Week 17)

Broadstreet	v	Whitchurch
Hereford	v	Wolverhampton
Leamington	v	Barker's Butts
Mansfield	v	Camp Hill
Syston	v	Leighton Buzzard
Westleigh	v	Stafford

January 13 1996 (Week 18)

Barker's Butts	v	Westleigh
Burton	v	Leamington
Camp Hill	v	Hereford
Stafford	v	Broadstreet
Whitchurch	v	Mansfield
Wolverhampton	v	Syston

February 10 1996 (Week 22)

Broadstreet	v	Barker's Butts
Hereford	v	Whitchurch
Leighton Buzzard	v	Wolverhampton
Mansfield	v	Stafford
Syston	v	Camp Hill
Westleigh	v	Burton

February 17 1996 (Week 23)

Barker's Butts	v	Mansfield
Burton	v	Broadstreet
Camp Hill	v	Leighton Buzzard
Leamington	v	Westleigh
Stafford	v	Hereford
Whitchurch	v	Syston

February 24 1996 (Week 24)

Broadstreet	v	Leamington
Hereford	v	Barker's Butts
Leighton Buzzard	v	Whitchurch
Mansfield	v	Burton
Syston	v	Stafford
Wolverhampton	v	Camp Hill

March 30 1996 (Week X7)

Barker's Butts	v	Syston
Burton	v	Hereford
Leamington	v	Mansfield
Stafford	v	Leighton Buzzard
Westleigh	v	Broadstreet
Whitchurch	v	Wolverhampton

MIDLANDS ONE

BARKER'S BUTTS RFC
Ground Address: Pickford Grange Lane, Allesley,
Coventry CV5 9AR. Tel: 01676 522192
Club Secretary: John I Evans, 70 Norman Place Road,
Coundon, Coventry CV6 2BT. Tel: (H) 01203 335780
Fixtures Secretary: H E Paine, 43 Sutton Avenue, Eastern
Green, Coventry CV5 7EG. Tel: (H) 01203 474261
Club Colours: Blue & gold.
BROADSTREET RFC
Ground Address: Ivor Preece Field, Brandon Road,
Coventry. Tel: 01203 453982 (club house); 01203 451706
(caretaker)
Club Secretary: Mr CJ McGinty, 60 Caludon Road, Stoke,
Coventry CV2 4LP. Tel: (H) 01203 441210 or 01203
679261
Fixtures Secretary: Mr D Wilkinson, 4 Court Leet, Binley
Woods, Coventry CV3 2JR. Tel: (H) 01203 543548
Club Colours: Red with white & green bands, navy shorts.
BURTON ON TRENT FC
Ground Address: Peel Croft, Lichfield Street,
Burton-on-Trent, Staffs DE14 3RH. Tel: 01283 564510
Club Secretary: Mr J Lowe, 20 The Chevin, Stretton,
Burton-on-Trent, Staffs DE13 0XU. Tel: (H) 01283 534422
Fixtures Secretary: Mr P Richard, 20 Olton Road,
Mickleover, Derby DE5 5PL. Tel: (H) 01332 516901
Club Colours: White with black sash, white shorts.
CAMP HILL RFC
Ground Address: Haslucks Green Road, Shirley, Solihull,
West Midlands. Tel: 0121 744 4175
Club Secretary: Russell Homer, c/o Kidsons Impey, Bank
House, 8 Charry Street, Birmingham B2 5AD. Tel: (H)
0121 631 2631 Tel: (W) 0121 631 2631
Fixtures Secretary: Graham Scutt, 130 Longmore Road,
Solihull, West Midlands B90 3EE. Tel: (H) 0121 744 4495
Tel (W) 0121 744 4495
Club Colours: Maroon & light blue.
HEREFORD RFC
Ground Address: Belvedere Lane, Wyeside, Hereford
NR4 9UT. Tel: 01432 273410
Club Secretary: Mr Michael Littlefield, The Rides, 13
Burwood Close, Hereford HR1 1DQ. Tel: (H) 01432
275468 Tel: (W) 01432 356310
Fixtures Secretary: Mr Neil Coulson, Stockmans Cottage,
Netherton Farm, Harewood End, Hereford HR2 8LA. Tel:
(H) 01989 730418 Tel (W) 01989 562377
Club Colours: White/black.
LEAMINGTON RUFC
Ground Address: Moorefields, Kenilworth Road,
Blackdown, Leamington Spa, Warks CV32 6RG. Tel:
01926 425584
Club Secretary: Mr LF Smith, 103 Telford Avenue,
Leamington Spa CV32 7HG. Tel: (H) 01926 423391
Fixtures Secretary: Peter Waring, 4 Borrowell Terrace,
Kenilworth, Warwickshire CV8 1ER. Tel: (H) 01926
56865
Club Colours: Royal blue with single scarlet & gold hoops.
LEIGHTON BUZZARD
Ground Address: Wrights Meadow, Leighton Road,
Stanbridge, Leighton Buzzard, Beds LU7 9HR. Tel: 01525
371322
Club Secretary: J McCormack, 15 Neptune Gardens,
Leighton Buzzard, Beds LU7 8NW. Tel: (H) 01525 378194
Tel: (W) 0181 343 2133
Fixtures Secretary: A Hodey, 36 Woodman Close,
Leighton Buzzard, Beds LU7 8NU. Tel: (H) 01525 379976
Tel (W) 01462 851515
Club Colours: Navy blue & white regular hoops.
MANSFIELD RUFC
Ground Address: Eakring Road, Mansfield, Notts NG18
3EW. Tel: 01623 649834
Club Secretary: Keith Bingley, Keepers Cottage, Lamins

FINAL TABLE	P	W	D	L	F	A	Pts
Worcester	12	11	1	0	278	82	23
Burton	12	10	0	2	209	156	20
Whitchurch	12	7	1	4	240	157	15
Westleigh	12	6	2	4	135	114	14
Mansfield	12	5	1	6	167	197	11
Stafford	12	5	1	6	155	209	11
Wolverhampton	12	5	0	7	215	173	10
Camp Hill	12	4	2	6	157	175	10
Syston	12	5	0	7	169	227	10
Leamington	12	4	2	6	157	200	10
Camp Hill	12	4	2	6	157	175	10
Bedworth	12	3	2	7	135	200	8
Towcestrians	12	3	1	8	177	229	7
Derby	12	3	1	8	116	191	7

Lane, Bestwood Park, Nottingham NG6 8UJ. Tel: (H)
01602 208943 Tel: (W) 01623 25821
Fixtures Secretary: Kevin Swithenbank, 40 Summercourt
Drive, Ravenshead, Notts NG15 9FT. Tel: (H) 01623
793726 Tel (W) 01623 649834
Club Colours: Blue & white hoops, navy shorts.
STAFFORD RUFC
Ground Address: County Ground, Castlefields, Newport
Road, Stafford ST16 1BG. Tel: 01785 211241
Club Secretary: PL Hill, 39 Rising Brook, Stafford ST17
9DE. Tel: (H) 01785 59583
Fixtures Secretary: BJ Bowen, 18 Greenfield Road,
Stafford ST17 0PU. Tel: (H) 01785 663378
Club Colours: Black & amber irregular hoops.
SYSTON RFC
Ground Address: Barkby Road, Queniborough,
Leicestershire LE7 3FE. Tel: (W) 01623 1223
Club Secretary: Mr JD Newton, 62 Fosse Way, Syston,
Leicester LE7 1NE. Tel: (H) 0116 269 4647
Fixtures Secretary: Mr B Sturgess, 28 Harwin Drive,
Evington, Leicester. Tel: (H) 0116 273 5674 Tel (W)
01580 890275
Club Colours: Navy & saxe hoops, navy shorts.
WESTLEIGH RFC
Ground Address: Lutterworth Road, Blaby, Leicester. Tel:
0116 2771010
Club Secretary: D Herd, 2 Ridgeway, Littlethorpe,
Leicester. Tel: (H) 0116 2849318
Fixtures Secretary: Chris Barker, 66 Carisbrooke Road,
Leicester. Tel: (H) 0116 2708676
Club Colours: Black & white hoops.
WHITCHURCH RFC
Ground Address: Edgeley Park, Whitchurch, Shropshire.
Tel: 01948 663316
Club Secretary: Neil Prunier, 9 St Mary's Street,
Whitchurch, Shropshire SY13 1QU. Tel: (H) 01948
663012 Tel: (W) 01948 663012
Fixtures Secretary: N Speakes, 9 Talbot Street,
Whitchurch, Shropshire. Tel: (H) 01948 665573
Club Colours: Red shirts, white shorts.
WOLVERHAMPTON RUFC
Ground Address: Rear Castlecroft Road, Castlecroft,
Wolverhampton WV3 8NA. Tel: 01902 763900
Club Secretary: Dr DJ Rutherford, Rose Cottage, 3
Woodlands Cottages, Penn, Wolverhampton WV4 4DG.
Tel: (H) 01902 335926 Tel: (W) 01902 24847
Fixtures Secretary: Mr J Hurst-Knight, 5 Westgate Villas,
High Town, Bridgnorth, Shropshire. Tel: (H) 01746
765563
Club Colours: Black shirt, black shorts, black socks.

MIDLAND DIVISION

MIDLAND TWO 1995-96 FIXTURES

November 11 1995 (Week 10)
Bedford Athletic v Hinckley
Bedworth v Matlock
Belgrave v Paviors
Derby v Keresley
Sutton Coldfield v Scunthorpe
Towcestrians v Newport

September 16 1995 (Week 3)
Bedford Athletic v Belgrave
Newport v Paviors
Scunthorpe v Matlock
Stockwood Park v Keresley
Sutton Coldfield v Derby
Towcestrians v Bedworth

January 6 1996 (Week 17)
Hinckley v Belgrave
Matlock v Derby
Newport v Bedford Athletic
Paviors v Bedworth
Scunthorpe v Towcestrians
Stockwood Park v Sutton Coldfield

September 23 1995 (Week 4)
Bedworth v Bedford Athletic
Derby v Towcestrians
Hinckley v Newport
Keresley v Sutton Coldfield
Matlock v Stockwood Park
Paviors v Scunthorpe

January 13 1996 (Week 18)
Bedford Athletic v Scunthorpe
Bedworth v Hinckley
Belgrave v Newport
Derby v Paviors
Keresley v Matlock
Towcestrians v Stockwood Park

September 30 1995 (Week X1)
Bedford Athletic v Derby
Belgrave v Bedworth
Scunthorpe v Hinckley
Stockwood Park v Paviors
Sutton Coldfield v Matlock
Towcestrians v Keresley

February 10 1996 (Week 22)
Hinckley v Derby
Newport v Bedworth
Paviors v Keresley
Scunthorpe v Belgrave
Stockwood Park v Bedford Athletic
Sutton Coldfield v Towcestrians

October 14 1995 (Week 6)
Derby v Belgrave
Hinckley v Stockwood Park
Keresley v Bedford Athletic
Matlock v Towcestrians
Newport v Scunthorpe
Paviors v Sutton Coldfield

February 17 1996 (Week 23)
Bedford Athletic v Sutton Coldfield
Bedworth v Scunthorpe
Belgrave v Stockwood Park
Derby v Newport
Keresley v Hinckley
Matlock v Paviors

October 21 1995 (Week 7)
Bedford Athletic v Matlock
Bedworth v Derby
Belgrave v Keresley
Stockwood Park v Newport
Sutton Coldfield v Hinckley
Towcestrians v Paviors

February 24 1996 (Week 24)
Hinckley v Matlock
Newport v Keresley
Scunthorpe v Derby
Stockwood Park v Bedworth
Sutton Coldfield v Belgrave
Towcestrians v Bedford Athletic

October 28 1995 (Week 8)
Hinckley v Towcestrians
Keresley v Bedworth
Matlock v Belgrave
Newport v Sutton Coldfield
Paviors v Bedford Athletic
Scunthorpe v Stockwood Park

March 30 1996 (Week X7)
Bedworth v Sutton Coldfield
Belgrave v Towcestrians
Derby v Stockwood Park
Keresley v Scunthorpe
Matlock v Newport
Paviors v Hinckley

418

MIDLANDS TWO

BEDFORD ATHLETIC RUFC
Ground Address: The Clubhouse, Putnoe Wood,
Wentworth Drive, Putnoe, Bedford. Tel: 01234 350874
Club Secretary: BM Eynon, 133 Dudley Street, Bedford
MK40 3SY. Tel: (H) 01234 214929 Tel: (W) 0973 382766
Fixtures Secretary: J Ross, 63 Avon Drive, Bedford
MK41 7UR. Tel: (H) 01234 343151 Tel (W) 01234 225116
Club Colours: Black & white hooped shirts, dark blue
shorts, black socks.
BEDWORTH RUFC
Ground Address: Rectory Fields, Smarts Road, Bedworth,
Warks CV12 8DS. Tel: 01203 312025
Club Secretary: David Hatfield, 17 New Road, Ash
Green, Nr Coventry CV7 9AS. Tel: (H) 01203 365160 Tel:
(W) 01203 362399
Fixtures Secretary: Alan Sheppard, 15 Warwick Gardens,
Nuneaton CV10 8DB. Tel: (H) 01203 33434
Club Colours: Green shirts, white shorts.
BELGRAVE RFC
Ground Address: Belgrave Pastures, Thurcaston Road,
Abbey Lane, Belgrave, Leicester LE4. Tel: 0116 2663033
Club Secretary: Michael John Goddard,
271a Birstall Road, Birstall, Leicester, LE4 4DJ. Tel: (H)
0116 2677383 Tel: (W) 0802 263676
Fixtures Secretary: Kevin Hick, 3 Coplow Crescent, Syston,
Leicester. Tel: (H) 0116 260 8617 Tel (W) 0116 273 9501
Club Colours: Red & black hoops, black shorts.
DERBY RFC
Ground Address: Kedleston Road, Derby DE22 2TF. Tel:
01332 344341
Club Secretary: Paul Teager, 26 Windmill Rise, Belper,
Derbyshire DE56 1GQ. Tel: (H) 01773 822350 Tel: (W)
01332 627279
Fixtures Secretary: Jerry Gregson, 45 West Avenue
South, Chellaston, Derby DE73 1SH. Tel: (H) 01332
701312 Tel (W) 01332 661461
Club Colours: Black & amber hoops, black shorts.
HINCKLEY RFC
Ground Address: Leicester Road, Hinckley. Tel: 01455
615010
Club Secretary: FJ Swift, 8 The Rills, Hinckley LE10
1NA. Tel: (H) 01455 250270
Fixtures Secretary: P Green, 10 Falmouth Close,
Nuneaton. Tel: (H) 01203 345267
Club Colours: Amber & black.
KERESLEY RFC
Ground Address: Burrow Hill Lane, Corley, Nr Coventry
CV7 8BE. Tel: 01676 540082
Club Secretary: Paul Vuckovic, 31 Bassett Road,
Coundon, Coventry, West Midlands CV6 1LF. Tel: (H)
01203 592469 Tel: (W) 01926 430350
Fixtures Secretary: Mr Lawrence Caswell, 28 Thompsons
Road, Keresley, Coventry CV7 8JW. Tel: (H) 01203 337219
Club Colours: Royal blue, scarlet & white jerseys and
stockings, navy blue shorts.
MATLOCK RUFC
Ground Address: Cromford Meadows, Cromford, Nr
Matlock, Derbyshire. Tel: 01629 822821
Club Secretary: CG Baker, Badger House, Lumb Lane,
Darley Dale, Matlock, Derbyshire DE4 2HP. Tel: (H)
01629 735294 Tel: (W) 01629 735294
Fixtures Secretary: D Pearson, Greyfriars, Bakewell
Road, Matlock, Derbyshire DE4 3BN. Tel: (H) 01629
55440 Tel (W) 01773 841152
Club Colours: Blue, gold & grey quartered shirts, royal
blue socks, navy blue shorts.
NEWPORT (SALOP) RUFC
Ground Address: The Old Showground, Forton Road,
Newport, Shropshire. Tel: 01952 810021
Club Secretary: Christopher Cann, 3 Chetwynd End,
Newport, Salop TF10 7JJ. Tel: (H) 01952 810194 Tel: (W)

FINAL TABLE

	P	W	D	L	F	A	Pts
Leighton Buzzard	12	11	0	1	210	131	22
Broad Street	12	10	0	2	291	129	20
Stockwood Park	12	9	0	3	208	153	18
Hinckley	12	8	1	3	286	134	17
Belgrave	12	7	0	5	225	163	14
Paviors	12	6	0	6	153	134	12
Matlock	12	5	1	6	170	176	11
Bedford Athletic	12	5	0	7	177	204	10
Keresley	12	4	1	7	125	198	9
Sutton Coldfield	12	5	0	7	162	177	8*
Peterborough	12	3	0	9	149	242	6
Newark	12	1	1	10	109	249	3
Willenhall	12	2	0	10	98	273	2*

01952 820028
Fixtures Secretary: David Vasilionka, 53 Fisher's Lock,
Newport, Salop. Tel: (H) 01952 810755
Club Colours: Maroon & white hoops.
PAVIORS RFC
Ground Address: Burntstump Hill, Arnold, Nottingham
NG5 8PQ. Tel: 0115 963 0384
Club Secretary: DI Hudson, The School House, Eakring Road,
Kneesall, Newark, Notts NG22 0AG. Tel: (H) 01623 861072
Fixtures Secretary: Len Hines, 20 Stiles Road, Arnold,
Nottingham NG5 6RE. Tel: (H) 0115 9269061
Club Colours: Red with green band.
SCUNTHORPE RUFC
Ground Address: Heslam Park, The Queensway (Entrance
from Ashby Road), Scunthorpe, South Humberside. Tel:
01724 843013
Club Secretary: Mr AS Bagshaw, 51 Old Brumby Street,
Scunthorpe, South Humberside DN16 2AJ. Tel: (H) 01724
849838 Tel: (W) 01724 280666
Fixtures Secretary: Mr N Cleal, 18 Cheltenham Close,
Bottesford, Scunthorpe, South Humberside. Tel: (H) 01724
856801 Tel (W) 01724 843411
Club Colours: Lincoln green.
STOCKWOOD PARK RFC
Ground Address: London Road, Luton, Beds LU1 2BY.
Tel: 01582 28044
Club Secretary: KJ Janes, 166 Brompton Close, Luton, Beds
LU3 3QU. Tel: (H) 01582 576855 Tel: (W) 01582 576855
Fixtures Secretary: RA Poulter, St Helier, Kings Walden
Road, Offley, Hitchin, Herts SG5 3DU. Tel: (H) 01482
768656 Tel (W) 01438 742366
Club Colours: Red with broad yellow band, blue shorts.
SUTTON COLDFIELD RFC
Ground Address: Walmley Road, Walmley, Sutton
Coldfield, West Midlands. Tel: 0121 351 5323
Club Secretary: Tim Gallagher, 61 Gorge Road, Sedgley,
Dudley, West Midlands DY3 1LE. Tel: (H) 01902 887605
Tel: (W) 01902 305961
Fixtures Secretary: Roger Smoldon, 69 Station Road,
Sutton Coldfield, West Midlands B22 5JY. Tel: (H) 0121
354 7771 Tel (W) 0121 422 0131
Club Colours: Emerald green shirts, white shorts.
TOWCESTRIANS RFC
Ground Address: Greens Norton Road, Towcester,
Northamptonshire NN12 8AW. Tel: 01327 350141
Club Secretary: Mr Richard Bodily, 36 Goodwood, Great
Holm, Milton Keynes, Buckinghamshire MK8 9DZ. Tel:
(H) 01908 562153
Fixtures Secretary: Geoff Hanson, 21 High Street,
Creaton, Northampton, Northants. Tel: (H) 01604 505491
Tel (W) 01604 505670
Club Colours: Maroon with white edged amber band,
black shorts.

MIDLAND DIVISION

MIDLAND WEST ONE 1995-96 FIXTURES

September 16 1995 (Week 3)
Willenhall	v	Kings Norton
Bromsgrove	v	Dudley
Old Leamingtonians	v	Luctonians
Longton	v	Newbold
Aston	v	Kenilworth
Old Laurentians	v	Leek

September 23 1995 (Week 4)
Kings Norton	v	Bromsgrove
Leek	v	Willenhall
Kenilworth	v	Old Laurentians
Newbold	v	Aston
Luctonians	v	Longton
Old Halesonians	v	Old Leamingtonians

September 30 1995 (Week X1)
Dudley	v	Kings Norton
Bromsgrove	v	Leek
Longton	v	Old Halesonians
Aston	v	Luctonians
Old Laurentians	v	Newbold
Willenhall	v	Kenilworth

October 14 1995 (Week 6)
Leek	v	Dudley
Kenilworth	v	Bromsgrove
Newbold	v	Willenhall
Luctonians	v	Old Laurentians
Old Halesonians	v	Aston
Old Leamingtonians	v	Longton

October 21 1995 (Week 7)
Kings Norton	v	Leek
Bromsgrove	v	Newbold
Dudley	v	Kenilworth
Aston	v	Old Leamingtonians
Old Laurentians	v	Old Halesonians
Willenhall	v	Luctonians

October 28 1995 (Week 8)
Kenilworth	v	Kings Norton
Newbold	v	Dudley
Luctonians	v	Bromsgrove
Old Halesonians	v	Willenhall
Old Leamingtonians	v	Old Laurentians
Longton	v	Aston

November 11 1995 (Week 10)
Kings Norton	v	Newbold
Bromsgrove	v	Old Halesonians
Dudley	v	Luctonians
Leek	v	Kenilworth
Old Laurentians	v	Longton
Willenhall	v	Old Leamingtonians

January 6 1996 (Week 17)
Luctonians	v	Kings Norton
Newbold	v	Leek
Old Halesonians	v	Dudley
Old Leamingtonians	v	Bromsgrove
Longton	v	Willenhall
Aston	v	Old Laurentians

January 13 1996 (Week 18)
Kings Norton	v	Old Halesonians
Bromsgrove	v	Longton
Dudley	v	Old Leamingtonians
Leek	v	Luctonians
Kenilworth	v	Newbold
Willenhall	v	Aston

February 10 1996 (Week 22)
Old Leamingtonians	v	Kings Norton
Aston	v	Bromsgrove
Longton	v	Dudley
Luctonians	v	Kenilworth
Old Halesonians	v	Leek
Old Laurentians	v	Willenhall

February 17 1996 (Week 23)
Kings Norton	v	Longton
Bromsgrove	v	Old Laurentians
Dudley	v	Aston
Leek	v	Old Leamingtonians
Kenilworth	v	Old Halesonians
Newbold	v	Luctonians

February 24 1996 (Week 24)
Aston	v	Kings Norton
Willenhall	v	Bromsgrove
Old Laurentians	v	Dudley
Old Halesonians	v	Newbold
Old Leamingtonians	v	Kenilworth
Longton	v	Leek

March 30 1996 (Week X7)
Kings Norton	v	Old Laurentians
Dudley	v	Willenhall
Leek	v	Aston
Kenilworth	v	Longton
Newbold	v	Old Leamingtonians
Luctonians	v	Old Halesonians

MIDLANDS WEST ONE

ASTON OLD EDWARDIANS FC
Ground Address: Sunnybank Avenue, Perry Common, Birmingham, West Midlands B44 0HP. Tel: 0121 373 5746
Club Secretary: Malcolm A Perrott, 21 Ivy Road, Sutton Coldfield, West Midlands B73 5EB. Tel: (H) 0121 355 2639
Fixtures Secretary: A Stafford, 54 Station Road, Marston Green, Solihull, West Midlands B37 7BA. Tel: (H) 0121 779 6288 Tel (W) 0121 356 1395
Club Colours: Red, white & myrtle green hooped shirts, white shorts, green socks.

BROMSGROVE RFC
Ground Address: Finstall Park, Finstall Road, Bromsgrove, Worcestershire B60 3DH. Tel: 01527 874690
Club Secretary: JA Watson, 7 Bowmore Road, Harwood Park, Bromsgrove Worcs B60 2HH. Tel: (H) 01527 875467 Tel: (W) 0121 458 2000 x3656
Fixtures Secretary: PR Amphlett, Birds Farm, Uphampton, Ombersley, Droitwich, Worcs WR9 0JS. Tel: (H) 01905 620514 Tel (W) 01905 620514
Club Colours: White shirts with red, black & red hoops, white shorts.

DUDLEY KINGSWINFORD RFC
Ground Address: Heathbrook, Swindon Road, Wall Heath, Kingswinford, West Midlands DY6 0AW. Tel: 01384 287006
Club Secretary: David Evans, 156 Common Road, Wombourne, West Midlands WV5 0LT. Tel: (H) 01902 894463 Tel: (W) 01902 316327
Fixtures Secretary: WR Jones, 54 Dingle View, Sedgley, West Midlands DY3 3LE. Tel: (H) 01902 6746852056 Tel (W) 0121 557 3949
Club Colours: Cambridge blue & navy hoops, black shorts.

KENILWORTH RFC
Ground Address: Jack Davies Memorial Ground, Glasshouse Lane, Kenilworth CV8 2AJ. Tel: 01926 53945
Club Secretary: WJ Whitesmith, 4 Glasshouse Lane, Kenilworth CV8 2AJ. Tel: (H) 01926 59465 Tel: (W) 01926 851113 Fax: 01926 851394
Fixtures Secretary: Dai Davies, 33 Fishponds Road, Kenilworth CV8 1EY. Tel: (H) 01926 54824
Club Colours: Blue & yellow.

KINGS NORTON RFC
Ground Address: Kings Norton RFC, Ash Lane, Hopwood, Birmingham, B48 7BB. Tel: 0121 445 3340
Club Secretary: GSC MacIver, 11 Chapel Walk, Kings Norton, Birmingham B30 3LW. Tel: (H) 0121 459 2279
Fixtures Secretary: K Evans, 21 Belbroughton Road, Halesowen, West Midlands B63 4ND. Tel: (H) 0121 501 1750 Tel (W) 0121 444 2864
Club Colours: Red and gold hoops, white shorts, red socks.

LEEK RUFC
Ground Address: Birchall Playing Fields, Cheddleton Road, Leek, Stoke-on-Trent, Staffordshire. Tel: 01538 383 697
Club Secretary: Andrew Chandler, Woodside, Clay Lake, Endon, Stoke-on-Trent ST9 9DD. Tel: (H) 01782 503964
Fixtures Secretary: E Birch, 12 Sandybrook Lane, Birchall, Leek. Tel: (H) 01538 385 963
Club Colours: Blue & white narrow hoops, white shorts, blue socks.

LONGTON RFC
Ground Address: Roughcote Lane, Caverswall, Nr Stoke on Trent, Staffs ST11 9EG. Tel: 01782 394449
Club Secretary: Mr Alan Miller, 5 The Dreys, Trentham, Stoke on Trent ST4 8DU. Tel: (H) 01782 641845 Tel: (W) 01782 315188
Fixtures Secretary: Mr Dave Watt, 4 Whitesands Grove, Meir Park, Stoke on Trent. Tel: (H) 01782 397292 Tel (W) 01782 599052
Club Colours: Black & amber.

LUCTONIANS RFC
Ground Address: Mortimer Park, Hereford Road,

FINAL TABLE

	P	W	D	L	F	A	Pts
Newport	12	11	1	0	248	103	23
Longton	12	9	0	3	227	92	18
Old Laurentians	12	8	0	4	191	96	16
Bromsgrove	12	8	0	4	153	109	16
Dudley	12	8	0	4	157	107	14*
Aston Old Edwardian	12	6	1	5	208	207	13
Newbold	12	6	1	5	220	123	11*
Kings Norton	12	4	0	8	99	196	8
Leek	12	4	0	8	113	218	8
Old Halesonians	12	3	1	8	128	186	7
Old Leamingtonians	12	3	0	9	150	211	6
Newcastle (Staffs)	12	3	0	9	73	228	6
Ludlow	12	2	2	8	67	158	4*

Kingsland, Leominster, Herefordshire. Tel: 01568 708345
Club Secretary: Huw Davies, The Bell House, Kingsland, Leominster, Herefordshire HR6 9RU. Tel: (H) 01568 708450 Tel: (W) 01432 362130
Fixtures Secretary: Peter Furlong. Tel: (H) 01568 708469
Club Colours: Black & white.

NEWBOLD-ON-AVON RFC
Ground Address: The Clubhouse, Parkfield Road, Newbold-on-Avon, Rugby, Warks CV21 1EZ. Tel: 01788 565811
Club Secretary: Adrian Johnston, 46 Warren Road, Rugby, Warks CV22 5LG. Tel: (H) 01788 560804
Fixtures Secretary: Ken Perks, 152 Dunchurch Road, Rugby, Warks CV22 6DR. Tel: (H) 01788 577741 Tel (W) 01788 572572
Club Colours: Red & black quarters.

OLD HALESONIANS RFC
Ground Address: Wassell Grove, Hagley, Nr Stourbridge, West Midlands DY9 9JY. Tel: 01562 883036
Club Secretary: Simon J Hussey, 67 Carol Crescent, Halesowen, West MIdlands. Tel: (H) 0121 550 5725 Tel: (W) 0121 522 6084
Fixtures Secretary: Mr Peter Sidaway, 40 Sandringham Road, Halesowen, West Midlands B62 8TJ. Tel: (H) 0121 561 4013
Club Colours: Royal blue/amber shirts.

OLD LAURENTIAN RFC
Ground Address: Fenley Field, Limetree Avenue, Rugby CV22 7QT. Tel: 01788 810855
Club Secretary: AE Willis, 45 Frobisher Road, Rugby CV22 7HS. Tel: (H) 01788 813481 Tel: (W) 01203 203564
Fixtures Secretary: Ray Roberts, 261 Alwyn Road, Rugby CV2 7RP. Tel: (H) 01788 810276
Club Colours: Maroon, green & yellow, green shorts.

OLD LEAMINGTONIANS RFC
Ground Address: The Crofts, Bericote Road, Leamington Spa, Warks CV32 6JX. Tel: 01926 424991
Club Secretary: Mr Denis Fisher, 14 New Street, Cubbington, Leamington Spa, Warwickshire CV32 6QP. Tel: (H) 01926 422131
Fixtures Secretary: Mike F Russell, The Gables Bungalow, 64 Kenilworth Road, Leamington Spa, Warwickshire CV32 6JX. Tel: (H) 01926 427540
Club Colours: Blue & gold hoops.

WILLENHALL RUFC
Ground Address: Bognop Road, Essington, Nr Wolverhampton, South Staffordshore. Tel: 01922 405694
Club Secretary: Elfyn Pugh, 9 Five Fields Road, Willenhall, West Midlands WV12 4NZ. Tel: (H) 01902 607747 Tel: (W) 0197 885 2141
Fixtures Secretary: Brian Wood, 189 Station Street, Cheslyn Hay, Walsall WS6 7EH. Tel: (H) 01922 416259
Club Colours: Maroon.

MIDLAND DIVISION

MIDLAND WEST TWO
1995-96
FIXTURES

September 16 1995 (Week 3)
Malvern	v	Ludlow
Shrewsbury	v	Stoke Old Boys
Stratford	v	Old Yardleians
Tamworth	v	Newcastle (Staffs)
Nuneaton Old Eds	v	Old Coventrians
Woodrush	v	Dixonians

September 23 1995 (Week 4)
Dixonians	v	Malvern
Old Coventrians	v	Woodrush
Newcastle (Staffs)	v	Nuneaton Old Eds
Old Yardleians	v	Tamworth
Stoke Old Boys	v	Stratford
Selly Oak	v	Shrewsbury

September 30 1995 (Week X1)
Malvern	v	Old Coventrians
Ludlow	v	Dixonians
Stratford	v	Selly Oak
Tamworth	v	Stoke Old Boys
Nuneaton Old Eds	v	Old Edwardians
Woodrush	v	Newcastle (Staffs)

October 14 1995 (Week 6)
Old Coventrians	v	Ludlow
Newcastle (Staffs)	v	Malvern
Old Yardleians	v	Woodrush
Stoke Old Boys	v	Nuneaton Old Eds
Selly Oak	v	Tamworth
Shrewsbury	v	Stratford

October 21 1995 (Week 7)
Malvern	v	Old Yardleians
Ludlow	v	Newcastle (Staffs)
Dixonians	v	Old Coventrians
Tamworth	v	Shrewsubry
Nuneaton Old Eds	v	Selly Oak
Woodrush	v	Stoke Old Boys

October 28 1995 (Week 8)
Newcastle (Staffs)	v	Dixonians
Old Yardleians	v	Ludlow
Stoke Old Boys	v	Malvern
Selly Oak	v	Woodrush
Shrewsbury	v	Nuneaton Old Eds
Stratford	v	Tamworth

November 11 1995 (Week 10)
Malvern	v	Selly Oak
Ludlow	v	Stoke Old Boys
Dixonians	v	Old Yardleians
Old Coventrians	v	Newcaslte (Staffs)
Nuneaton Old Eds	v	Stratford
Woodrush	v	Shrewsbury

January 6 1996 (Week 17)
Old Yardleians	v	Old Coventrians
Stoke Old Boys	v	Dixonians
Selly Oak	v	Ludlow
Shrewsbury	v	Malvern
Stratford	v	Woodrush
Tamworth	v	Nuneaton Old Eds

January 13 1996 (Week 18)
Malvern	v	Stratford
Ludlow	v	Shrewsubry
Dixonians	v	Selly Oak
Old Coventrians	v	Stoke Old Boys
Newcastle (Staffs)	v	Old Yardleians
Woodrush	v	Tamworth

February 10 1996 (Week 22)
Stoke Old Boys	v	Newcastle (Staffs)
Selly Oak	v	Old Coventrians
Shrewsubry	v	Dixonians
Stratford	v	Ludlow
Tamworth	v	Malvern
Nuneaton Old Eds	v	Woodrush

February 17 1996 (Week 23)
Malvern	v	Nuneaton Old Eds
Ludlow	v	Tamworth
Dixonians	v	Stratford
Old Coventrians	v	Shrewsbury
Newcastle (Staffs)	v	Selly Oak
Old Yardleians	v	Stoke Old Boys

February 24 1996 (Week 24)
Seely Oak	v	Old Yardleians
Shrewsbury	v	Newcastle (Staffs)
Stratford	v	Old Coventrians
Tamworth	v	Dixonians
Nuneaton Old Eds	v	Ludlow
Woodrush	v	Malvern

March 30 1996 (Week X7)
Ludlow	v	Woodrush
Dixonians	v	Nuneaton Old Eds
Old Coventrians	v	Tamworth
Newcastle (Staffs)	v	Stratford
Old Yardleians	v	Shrewsbury
Stoke Old Boys	v	Selly Oak

MIDLANDS WEST TWO

DIXONIANS RFC
Ground Address: 31a Fountain Road, Edgbaston, Birmingham B17 8NJ. Tel: 0121 434 3313
Club Secretary: Vivian Shingler, Timberhonger House, Timberhonger, Bromsgrove, Worcs B61 9ET. Tel: (H) 01527 861686 Tel: (W) 0121 544 4788
Fixtures Secretary: Daved Hall, 32 Jerrards Drive, Sutton Coldfield, West Midlands B75 7TJ. Tel: (H) 0121 378 2839
Club Colours: Maroon, green & black jerseys, black shorts & stockings.

LUDLOW RFC
Ground Address: The Linney, Ludlow, Shropshire SY8 1EE. Tel: 01584 875762
Club Secretary: Colin Spanner, 58 Henley Orchards, Ludlow SY8 1TN. Tel: (H) 01584 873107 Tel: (W) 01584 872333 Fax: 0584 876459
Fixtures Secretary: Rob Flemons, Ford House, Orleton, Nr Ludlow SY8 4HW. Tel: (H) 01568 780334 Tel (W) 01562 820505 x2545
Club Colours: Red shirts, black shorts.

MALVERN RFC
Ground Address: Spring Lane, Malvern, Worcs. WR14 1AJ. Tel: 01684 573728
Club Secretary: MG Davies, 102 Fruitlands, Malvern, Worcs WR14 4XB. Tel: (H) 01684 567835 Tel: (W) 01222683152
Fixtures Secretary: W Pomeroy, 50 Barnards Green Road, Malvern Worcs WR14 3LW Tel: (H) 01684 562279 Tel: (W) 01684 894786
Club Colours: Maroon, light blue and gold.

NEWCASTLE (STAFFS) RUFC
Ground Address: Lilleshall Road, Claxton, Newcastle-under-Lyme, Staffordshire. Tel: 01782 617042
Club Secretary: RJO Websdale, 61 Westlands, Seabridge, Newcastle-under-Lyme, Staffordshire ST5 3LJ. Tel: (H) 01782 633784 Tel: (W) 01782 839380
Fixtures Secretary: D Westrup, 153 Congleton Road, Sandbach, Cheshire CW11 0SR. Tel: (H) 01270 766538 Tel (W) (& Fax) 01352 712536
Club Colours: Maroon & white hoops, black shorts & socks.

NUNEATON OLD EDWARDIANS RFC
Ground Address: Weddington Road, Nuneaton, Warks. Tel: 01203 386778
Club Secretary: John Jones, 168 Hinckley Road, Nuneaton, Warks CV11 6LP. Tel: (H) 01203 387719 Tel: (W) 01455 553081
Fixtures Secretary: John Sparkes, 140 Lutterworth Road, Nuneaton, Warks CV11 6PE. Tel: (H) 01203 326029 Tel (W) 01203 402121 x2750
Club Colours: Red & white hoops.

OLD COVENTRIANS RFC
Ground Address: Tile Hill Lane, Coventry CV4 9DE. Tel: 01203 715273
Club Secretary: Mr RC Richards, 28 Woodland Avenue, Coventry CV2 6DB. Tel: (H) 01203 670080
Fixtures Secretary: Mr I Knowles, 23 Meadow Road, Wolston, Nr Coventry CV8 8HL. Tel: (H) 01203 545692
Club Colours: Old gold, red & black quarters, black shorts.

OLD YARDLEIANS RFC
Ground Address: Tile House Lane, Shirley, Solihull, West Midlands B90 1PW. Tel: 0211 744 3380
Club Secretary: Mick Ison, 28 Quinton Close, Solihull, West Midlands B92 9BL. Tel: (H) 0121 743 5311
Fixtures Secretary: Tommy Power, 16 Charfield Road, Birmingham B30 1QS. Tel: (H) 0121 459 1622
Club Colours: Green/old gold/maroon.

SELLY OAK RFC
Ground Address: Holders Lane, Moseley, Birmingham.
Club Secretary: Alan Badsey, 49 Green Meadow Road,

FINAL TABLE

	P	W	D	L	F	A	Pts
Luctonians	12	12	0	0	591	61	24
Kenilworth	12	10	0	2	422	132	20
Old Coventrians	12	8	1	3	238	225	17
Tamworth	12	7	1	4	181	113	15
Dixonians	12	6	1	5	179	158	13
Nuneaton Od Edward	12	6	0	6	195	211	12
Selly Oak	12	6	1	5	250	200	11*
Stratford-on-Avon	12	5	0	7	184	184	10
Old Yardleians	12	4	1	7	142	244	9
Woodrush	12	4	0	8	159	238	8
Shrewsbury	12	3	1	8	154	329	7
Dunlop	12	3	0	9	99	259	6
Coventry Welsh	12	1	0	11	42	482	2

Selly Oak, Birmingham B29 4DD. Tel: (H) 0121 475 5717 Tel: (W) 0121 420 2623
Fixtures Secretary: Barry Pearce, 9 Langford Avenue, Great Barr, Birmingham B43 5NH. Tel: (H) 0121 358 4442 Tel (W) 0121 360 8500
Club Colours: Black & white hooped shirts with red spangles, blue shorts.

SHREWSBURY RUFC
Ground Address: Sundorne Castle, Uffington, Shrewsbury SY4 4RR. Tel: 01743 353380
Club Secretary: Graham S Jackson, 99 Highfields, Shrewsbury, Shropshire SY2 5PJ. Tel: (H) 01743 361802
Fixtures Secretary: Nigel Hughes, 34 Leamore Crescent, Belle Vue, Shrewsbury. Tel: (H) 01743 360383
Club Colours: Narrow sky blue & navy hoops.

STOKE OLD BOYS RFC
Ground Address: Brookvale Avenue, Binley, Coventry. Tel: 01203 453631
Club Secretary: Mr Brian Jose, 33 Hothorpe Close, Binley, Coventry CV3 2HX. Tel: (H) 01203 457127 Tel: (W) 01203 335121 x245
Fixtures Secretary: Mr James Monaghan, 65 Conifer Paddock, Binley, Coventry CV3 2RE. Tel: (H) 01203 451198
Club Colours: Maroon & white hoops, blue shorts.

STRATFORD-UPON-AVON RFC
Ground Address: Pearcroft, Loxley Road, Stratford-upon-Avon. Tel: 01789 297796
Club Secretary: Ron Grant, 4 St Gregory's Road, Stratford-upon-Avon, Warks CV37 6UH. Tel: (H) 01789 266722 Tel: (W) 0121 502 7116
Fixtures Secretary: Mrs A Prentice, 2 Byron Road, Stratford-upon-Avon CV37 7JP. Tel: (H) 01789 269892 Tel (W) 01789 414979
Club Colours: Black & white shirts, white shorts.

TAMWORTH RUFC
Ground Address: Wiggaton Park, Tamworth, Staffs B79 8ED. Tel: 01827 68794
Club Secretary: Craig Parker, 36 Ethelfleda Road, Hockley, Tamworth, Staffs B78 5HS. Tel: (H) 01827 285147 Tel: (W) 01827 310300
Fixtures Secretary: Gordon Pensley, 44 Avon, Hockley, Tamworth, Staffs. Tel: (H) 01827 285211
Club Colours: Maroon, black & white.

WOODRUSH RFC
Ground Address: Icknield Street, Forhill, Birmingham B38 0EL. Tel: 01564 822878
Club Secretary: SH Edwards, 6 Tanwood Close, Callow Hill, Redditch B97 5YU. Tel: (H) 01527 544281
Fixtures Secretary: Mr R Gardiner, 'Brambles', Packhorse Lane, Wythall, Nr Birmingham B38 0DN. Tel: (H) 0121 436 5649 Tel (W) 01527 552815 x2376
Club Colours: Emerald green & white hoops, black shorts.

MIDLAND DIVISION

STAFFORDSHIRE & WARWICKSHIRE ONE 1995-96 FIXTURES

November 11 1995 (Week 10)

Coventry Saracens	v	Southam
Atherstone	v	Manor Park
Eccleshall	v	Rugby St Andrews
GPT (Coventry)	v	GEC St Leonards
Silhillians	v	Dunlop
Coventry Welsh	v	Coventrians

September 16 1995 (Week 3)

Coventry Saracens	v	Atherstone
Coventrians	v	Manor Park
Dunlop	v	Rugby St Andrews
Trinity Guild	v	GEC St Leonards
Silhillians	v	GPT (Coventry)
Coventry Welsh	v	Eccleshall

September 23 1995 (Week 4)

GPT (Coventry)	v	Coventry Welsh
GEC St Leonards	v	Silhillians
Rugby St Andrews	v	Trinity Guild
Manor Park	v	Dunlop
Southam	v	Coventrians
Eccleshall	v	Coventry Saracens

September 30 1995 (Week X1)

Coventry Saracens	v	GPT (Coventry)
Atherstone	v	Eccleshall
Dunlop	v	Southam
Trinity Guild	v	Manor Park
Silhillians	v	Rugby St Andrews
Coventry Welsh	v	GEC St Leonards

October 14 1995 (Week 6)

GPT (Coventry)	v	Atherstone
GEC ST Leonards	v	Coventry Saracens
Rugby St Andrews	v	Coventry Welsh
Manor Park	v	Silhillians
Southam	v	Trinity Guild
Coventrians	v	Dunlop

October 21 1995 (Week 7)

Coventry Saracens	v	Rugby St Andrews
Atherstone	v	GEC St Leonards
Eccleshall	v	GPT (Coventry)
Trinity Guild	v	Coventrains
Silhillians	v	Southam
Coventry Welsh	v	Manor Park

October 28 1995 (Week 8)

GEC St Leonards	v	Eccleshall
Rugby St Andrews	v	Atherstone
Manor Park	v	Coventry Saracens
Southam	v	Coventry Welsh
Coventrians	v	Silhillians
Dunlop	v	Trinity Guild

January 6 1996 (Week 17)

Rugby St Andrews	v	GPT (Coventry
Manor Park	v	Eccleshall
Southam	v	Atherstone
Coventrians	v	Coventry Saracens
Dunlop	v	Coventry Welsh
Trinity Guild	v	Silhillians

January 13 1996 (Week 18)

Coventry Saracens	v	Dunlop
Atherstone	v	Coventrians
Eccleshall	v	Southam
GPT (Coventry)	v	Manor Park
GEC St Leonards	v	Rugby St Andrews
Coventry Welsh	v	Trinity Guild

February 10 1996 (Week 22)

Manor Park	v	GEC ST Leonards
Southam	v	GPT (Coventry)
Coventrians	v	Eccleshall
Dunlop	v	Atherstone
Trinity Guild	v	Coventry Saracens
Silhillians	v	Coventry Welsh

February 17 1996 (Week 23)

Coventry Saracens	v	Silhillians
Atherstone	v	Trinity Guild
Eccleshall	v	Dunlop
Rugby St Andrews	v	Manor Park
GPT (Coventry)	v	Coventrians
GEC St Leonards	v	Southam

February 24 1996 (Week 24)

Coventrians	v	GEC St Leonards
Southam	v	Rugby St Andrews
Dunlop	v	GPT (Coventry)
Trinity Guild	v	Eccleshall
Silhillians	v	Atherstone
Coventry Welsh	v	Coventry Saracens

March 30 1996 (Week X7)

Atherstone	v	Coventry Welsh
Eccleshall	v	Silhillians
GPT (Coventry)	v	Trinity Guild
GEC St Leonards	v	Dunlop
Rugby St Andrews	v	Coventrians
Manor Park	v	Southam

STAFFS & WARWICKS ONE

ATHERSTONE RFC
Ground Address: Ratcliffe Road, Atherstone, Warks. Tel: 01827 714934
Club Secretary: David Boal, Thurmaston House, 74 South Street, Atherstone, Warks CV9 1DZ. Tel: (H) 01827 713145
Fixtures Secretary: Keith Berry, 10 Goodere Drive, Polesworth, Tamworth, Staffs. Tel: (H) 01827 893138
Club Colours: All black.
COVENTRIANS RFC
Ground Address: Black Pad, off Yelverton Road, Radford, Coventry. Tel: 01203 682885
Club Secretary: JH Parke, 47 High Street, Ryton-on-Dunsmore, Nr Coventry CV8 3FJ. Tel: (H) 01203 304394
Fixtures Secretary: JS Daniel, 116 Mill Farm Park, Marston Jabbett, Nuneaton CV12 9SF. Tel: (H) 01203 373470
Club Colours: Blue/white quarters.
COVENTRY SARACENS
Ground Address: Bredon Avenue, Binley, Coventry. Tel: 01203 453557
Club Secretary: Brian Craner, 71 Westhill Road, Coundon, Coventry, West Midlands CV6 2AD. Tel: (H) 01203 590280 Tel: (W) 01203 832996
Fixtures Secretary: Roger Hancox, 23 Rugby Lane, Stretton on Dunsmore, Rugby LE10 3LL. Tel: (H) 01203 542252 Tel: (W) 01203 687167
Club Colours: Black shirts with red & green V, black shorts.
COVENTRY WELSH RFC
Ground Address: Burbages Lane, Longford, Coventry CV6 6AY. Tel: 01203 360303
Club Secretary: c/o Mr J Horan, 91 Hollfast Road, Coundon, Coventry, West Midlands. Tel: (H) 01203 335047
Fixtures Secretary: Mr T Davis, 123 (D) Park Gate Road, Holbrooks, Coventry, West Midlands. Tel: (H) 01203 581977 Tel (W) 01203 667738 x3399
Club Colours: Red shirts, black shorts.
DUNLOP RFC
Ground Address: Burnaby Road, Holbrooks, Coventry. Tel: 01203 662394
Club Secretary: James Harnett, 19 Stepping Stones Road, Coundon, Coventry CV5 8JJ. Tel: (H) 01203 601995 Tel: (W) 01203 416255
Fixtures Secretary: John Ormsby, 5 Postbridge Road, Stivychall, Coventry CV3 5AG. Tel: (H) 01203 410313 Tel (W) 01203 511155
Club Colours: Black & amber hoops, black shorts.
ECCLESHALL RUFC
Ground Address: Badenhall Farm, Stone Road, Eccleshall, Staffs ST21 6AP. Tel: 01785 851902
Club Secretary: KE Levitt, 46 Old Road, Stone, Staffs ST15 8HR. Tel: (H) 01785 818234
Fixtures Secretary: A Christmas, Tudor Cottage, Newcastle Road, Baldwins Gate, Newcastle, Staffs. Tel: (H) 01782 680118 Tel (W) 0121 359 1113
Club Colours: Black with gold & emerald hoop.
GEC ST LEONARDS RUFC
Ground Address: GEC Protection Control, St Leonards Avenue, Stafford, Staffs. Tel: 01785 58070
Club Secretary: J A Whibley, 26 Hall Close, Stafford, Staffs, ST17 4JJ. Tel: (H) 01785 53201 Tel: (W) 01785 53201
Fixtures Secretary: Mr I McLeod, 17 St Augustine's Road, Rugeley, Staffs WS15 1NF. Tel: (H) 01889 579365 Tel (W) 01860 694548
Club Colours: Black with gold band.
GPT (COVENTRY) RFC
Ground Address: GPT Sports Pavilion, Allard Way, Coventry. Tel: 01203 451157

FINAL TABLE

	P	W	D	L	F	A	Pts
Stoke Old Boys	12	11	0	1	362	88	22
Southam	12	9	0	3	225	89	18
Coventry Saracens	12	8	0	4	229	118	16
Rugby St Andrews	12	8	0	4	273	166	16
Trinity Guild	12	8	0	4	261	168	16
GEC Coventry	12	8	0	4	188	121	16
Manor Park	12	6	0	6	141	163	12
Atherstone	12	5	1	6	205	149	11
GEC St Leonards	12	5	1	6	140	201	9*
Eccleshall	12	3	2	7	141	316	6*
Uttoxeter	12	2	2	8	107	358	6
Trentham	12	1	1	10	75	248	3
Old Wheatleyans	12	0	1	11	83	245	1

Club Secretary: RG Everitt, PP16.5 Berkley House, 245 Broad Street, Birmingham B1 2HQ. Tel: (H) 01203 456670
Tel: (W) 0121 230 4638
Fixtures Secretary: GN Goodall, 38 Priesthills Road, Hinckley, Leics LE10 1AJ. Tel: (H) 01455 238742 Tel (W) 01203 562656
Club Colours: Red, blue & green hoops.
MANOR PARK RFC
Ground Address: Griff Coton Sports Club, Heath End Road, Nuneaton, Warks. Tel: 01203 386798
Club Secretary: WJ Newcombe, 489 Heath End Road, Nuneaton, Warks CV10 7HD. Tel: (H) 01203 374476
Fixtures Secretary: S Atkinson, 10 East Avenue, Bedworth, Warks CV12 9EH. Tel: (H) 01203 312274
Club Colours: Red & black hooped jerseys, black shorts & hose.
RUGBY ST ANDREWS RFC
Ground Address: Hillmorton Grounds, Ashlawn Road, Rugby. Tel: 01788 542786
Club Secretary: Jim Corry, 3 Holme Way, Barby, Rugby CV23 8UQ. Tel: (H) 01788 891039 Tel: (W) 01455 232763
Fixtures Secretary: John Hunt, 14 Northcott Road, Rugby. Tel: (H) 01788 574496
Club Colours: Blue & navy hoops, navy shorts.
SILHILLIANS RUFC
Ground Address: Copt Heath, Warwick Road, Solihull, West Midlands B93 9LW. Tel: 01564 777680
Club Secretary: GR Loader, 4 Shackleton Drive, Perton, Wolverhampton, West Midlands WV6 7SA. Tel: (H) 01902 742695 Tel: (W) 01902 353522
Fixtures Secretary: Mr I Hateley, 5 Brookvale Grove, Olton, Solihull, West Midlands. Tel: (H) 0121 707 1738 Tel (W) 0121 708 1830
Club Colours: Maroon, blue & white shirts, blue shorts.
SOUTHAM RUFC
Ground Address: Kineton Road, Southam, Nr Rugby, Warks. Tel: 01926 813674
Club Secretary: I Harvey, Rookery Nook, Priors Marston. Tel: (H) 01327 60709
Fixtures Secretary: P Neal, 48 George Street, Stockton, Warks. Tel: (H) 01926 817402
Club Colours: Blue/white.
TRINITY GUILD RFC
Ground Address: Rowley Road, Baginton, Coventry CV8 3AL. Tel: 01203 305928
Club Secretary: DH Williams, 122 Grange Road, Longford, Coventry, Warks CV6 6DA. Tel: (H) 01203 360833 Tel: (W) 01203 666655 x2420
Fixtures Secretary: K Lightowler, 37 Oakfield Road, Coundon, Coventry CV6 1ED. Tel: (H) 01203 598932
Club Colours: Maroon, old gold, dark blue hoops.

MIDLAND DIVISION

STAFFORDSHIRE & WARWICKSHIRE TWO 1995-96 FIXTURES

November 11 1995 (Week 10)
Alcester	v	Pinley
Berkswell & Balsall	v	Old Wheatleyans
Cannock	v	Handsworth
Earlsdon	v	Shipston on Stour
Spartans	v	Old Warwickians
Wednesbury	v	Uttoxeter

September 16 1995 (Week 3)
Berkswell & Balsall	v	Cannock
Old Warwickians	v	Pinley
Spartans	v	Earlsdon
Trentham	v	Shipston on Stour
Uttoxeter	v	Handsworth
Wednesbury	v	Alcester

January 6 1996 (Week 17)
Handsworth	v	Alcester
Old Warwickians	v	Wednesbury
Old Wheatleyans	v	Cannock
Pinley	v	Earlsdon
Trentham	v	Spartans
Uttoxeter	v	Berkswell & Balsall

September 23 (Week 4)
Alcester	v	Berkswell & Balsall
Earlsdon	v	Wednesbury
Handsworth	v	Old Warwickians
Old Wheatleyans	v	Uttoxeter
Pinley	v	Trentham
Shipston on Stour	v	Spartans

January 13 1996 (Week 18)
Alcester	v	Old Wheatleyans
Berkswell & Balsall	v	Old Warwickians
Cannock	v	Uttoxeter
Earlsdon	v	Handsworth
Shipston on Stour	v	Pinley
Wednesbury	v	Trentham

September 30 1995 (Week X1)
Berkswell & Balsall	v	Earlsdon
Cannock	v	Alcester
Old Warwickians	v	Old Wheatleyans
Spartans	v	Pinley
Trentham	v	Handsworth
Wednesbury	v	Shipston on Stour

February 10 1996 (Week 22)
Handsworth	v	Shipston on Stour
Old Warwickians	v	Cannock
Old Wheatleyans	v	Earlsdon
Spartans	v	Wednesbury
Trentham	v	Berkswell & Balsall
Uttoxeter	v	Alcester

October 14 1995 (Week 6)
Earlsdon	v	Cannock
Handsworth	v	Spartans
Old Wheatleyans	v	Trentham
Pinley	v	Wednesbury
Shipston on Stour	v	Berkswell & Balsall
Uttoxeter	v	Old Warwickians

February 17 1996 (Week 23)
Alcester	v	Old Warwickians
Berkswell & Balsall	v	Spartans
Cannock	v	Trentham
Earlsdon	v	Uttoxeter
Pinley	v	Handsworth
Shipston on Stour	v	Old Wheatleyans

October 21 1995 (Week 7)
Alcester	v	Earlsdon
Berkswell & Balsall	v	Pinley
Cannock	v	Shipston on Stour
Spartans	v	Old Wheatleyans
Trentham	v	Uttoxeter
Wednesbury	v	Handsworth

February 24 1996 (Week 24)
Old Warwickians	v	Earlsdon
Old Wheatleyans	v	Pinley
Spartans	v	Cannock
Trentham	v	Alcester
Uttoxeter	v	Shipston on Stour
Wednesbury	v	Berkswell & Balsall

October 28 1995 (Week 8)
Handsworth	v	Berkswell & Balsall
Old Warwickians	v	Trentham
Old Wheatleyans	v	Wednesbury
Pinley	v	Cannock
Shipston on Stour	v	Alcester
Uttoxeter	v	Spartans

March 30 1996 (Week X7)
Alcester	v	Spartans
Cannock	v	Wednesbury
Earlsdon	v	Trentham
Handsworth	v	Old Wheatleyans
Pinley	v	Uttoxeter
Shipston on Stour	v	Old Warwickians

STAFFS & WARWICKS TWO

ALCESTER RFC
Ground Address: Birmingham Road, King's Coughton, Alcester, Warwickshire B49 5QF. Tel: 01789 764061
Club Secretary: MJ Edwards, 8 Icknield Row, Alcester, Warwicks B49 5EW. Tel: (H) 01789 764096 Tel: (W) 01789 762285
Fixtures Secretary: Mr GK Rees, 2 Wain Close, alcester, Warwickshire B49 6LA. Tel: (H) 01789 764188
Club Colours: Red & black.

BERKSWELL & BALSALL RFC
Ground Address: Meeting House Lane, Balsall Common, Nr Coventry CV7 7QE. Tel: 01676 533825
Club Secretary: PC Wigley, 36 Kemps Green Road, Balsall Common, Nr Coventry CV7 7QE. Tel: (H) 01676 533036
Fixtures Secretary: Steve Wake, 33 Wildcroft Road, Whoberley, Coventry CV5 8AU. Tel: (H) 01203 711510 Tel (W) 0121 500 6188
Club Colours: Red shirts, black shorts, red socks.

CANNOCK RUFC
Ground Address: The Morgan Ground, Stafford Road, Huntington, Staffordshire WS12 4NU. Tel: 01543 467906
Club Secretary: Trevor Bailey, 22 Banbury Road, Cannock, Staffordshire, WS11 1NR. Tel: (H) 01543 504256 Tel: (W) 01543 490634
Fixtures Secretary: Neville Lawrence, 112 Cannock Road, Chadsmoor, Cannock, Staffordshire. Tel: (H) 01922 415810 Tel (W) 01543 503398
Club Colours: Blue & gold hoops.

EARLSDON RFC
Ground Address: Mitchell Avenue, Canley, Coventry CV4 8DY. Tel: 01203 464467
Club Secretary: JG Ward, 18 Wainbody Avenue, Green Lane, Coventry CV3 6BD. Tel: (H) 01203 419729
Fixtures Secretary: R Price, 25 Montrose Drive, Nuneaton CV10 7LX. Tel: (H) 01203 346190
Club Colours: Red & white.

HANDSWORTH RUFC
Ground Address: 450 Birmingham Road, Walsall, WS5 3JP (adjacent to the Bell Inn A34). Tel: 0121 357 6427
Club Secretary: Julian P Gudz, 3 St George's Court, Persehouse Street, Walsall, WS1 2AT. Tel: (H) 01922 645856 Tel: (W) 0121 556 5599
Fixtures Secretary: David Mew, 143 Birmingham Road, Wylde Green, Sutton Coldfield, B72 1LX. Tel: (H) 0121 354 4518 Tel (W) 01922 614056
Club Colours: Red & white hooped shirts.

OLD WARWICKIAN RFC
Ground Address: Old Warwickian Sports Ground, Hampton Road, Warwick, Warwickshire. Tel: 01926 496295
Club Secretary: Patrick Wing, 57 Broadfern Road, Knowle, Solihull B93 9OE. Tel: (H) 01564 779947
Fixtures Secretary: Andrew Marshall, Far Westfields Farm House, Moreton Morrell, Leamington Spa, Warks. Tel: (H) 01926 651750 Tel (W) 01926 651750
Club Colours: Maroon & white hooped jerseys.

OLD WHEATLEYANS RFC
Ground Address: Norman Place Road, Coundon, Coventry. Tel: 01203 334888
Club Secretary: Richard Leigh, 8 Orchard Crescent, Coventry CV3 6HS. Tel: (H) 01203 501998 Tel: (W) 01203 688918
Fixtures Secretary: Dai Margetts, 2 Rochester Road, Earlsdon, Coventry CV5 6AD. Tel: (H) 01203 672952
Club Colours: Blue, maroon & gold.

PINLEY RFC
Ground Address: The Croft, Wyken Croft, Coventry, West Midlands CV2 3HS. Tel: 01203 602059
Club Secretary: MD Brown, 75 Dennis Road, Wyken, Coventry, West Midlands CV2 3HS. Tel: (H) 01203 455449 Tel: (W) 01203 363353
Fixtures Secretary: B Lester, 7 Tiverton Road, Wyken, Coventry, West Midlands CV2 3DN. Tel: (H) 01203 443605

FINAL TABLE	P	W	D	L	F	A	Pts
Silhillians	12	9	0	3	207	128	18
Coventrians	12	9	0	3	161	89	18
Berkswell & Balsall	12	8	1	3	213	80	17
Pinley	12	7	2	3	218	131	16
Cannock	12	8	0	4	168	154	16
Handsworth	12	7	0	5	172	102	14
Spartans	12	6	1	5	238	112	13
Wednesbury	12	6	1	5	126	179	13
Shipston-on-Stour	12	6	0	6	173	119	12
Earlsdon	12	5	1	6	167	96	11
Linley	12	2	0	10	129	211	4
Warwickshire Police	12	2	0	10	85	198	4
Harbury	12	0	0	12	35	493	0

Club Colours: Red/black quarters.

SHIPSTON ON STOUR RUFC
Ground Address: Mayo Road, Shipston on Stour, Warks. Tel: 01608 662107
Club Secretary: Richard Slatter, Woodhills Farm, Todenham, Moreton in Marsh, Glos GL56 9PH. Tel: (H) 01608 650453 Tel: (W) 01608 650453
Fixtures Secretary: Robert Hawkins, Washbrook, Ilmington, Shipston on Stour, Warks CV36 4LZ. Tel: (H) 01608 688216
Club Colours: Black shirts, shorts & stockings.

SPARTANS RUFC
Ground Address: Coppice Lane, Middleton, Nr Tamworth, Staffordshire. Tel: 0121 308 5857
Club Secretary: Sarah McGrovy, 33 Alexandra Mews, Victoria Road, Tamworth, Staffs B79 7HT. Tel: (H) 01827 63132
Fixtures Secretary: Phil Morris, 24 Moat Drive, Drayton Bassett, Tamworth, Staffs B78 3UG. Tel: (H) 01827 260383 Tel (W) 0121 767 7856
Club Colours: Black shirts, black shorts.

TRENTHAM RUFC
Ground Address: Oak Tree Road, Trentham, Stoke-on-Trent, Staffordshire. Tel: 01782 642320
Club Secretary: M Riley, 7 Waterbeck Grove, Trentham, Stoke-on-Trent, Staffordshire ST4 8BG. Tel: (H) 01782 644874 Tel: (W) 01925 824511
Fixtures Secretary: M Procter, Holly House, Barn Court, Clayton, Newcastle, Staffordshire. Tel: (H) 01782 623292 Tel (W) 014775 71321
Club Colours: Green & white hoops.

UTTOXETER RFC
Ground Address: Oldfields Sports Centre, Springfield Road, Uttoxeter, Staffs. Tel: 01889 564347
Club Secretary: Simon Bailey, Stoneleigh Cottage, Cubley, Nr Ashbourne, Derbyshire DE6 2EY. Tel: (H) 01335 330306 Tel: (W) 01889 593031
Fixtures Secretary: Barry Watson, 78 Hall Road, Rolleston-on-Dove, Burton-on-Trent, Staffordshire DE13 9BY. Tel: (H) 01283 813538
Club Colours: Navy with red & gold hoops, blue shorts, red socks.

WEDNESBURY RUFC
Ground Address: Hydes Road Playing Field, Hydes Road, Wednesbury. Clubhouse: 14 Bridge Street, Wednesbury. Tel: 0121 502 2477
Club Secretary: Mr Peter Hughes, 28 Alder Road, Wednesbury, West Midlands WS10 9PX. Tel: (H) 0121 556 5005 Tel: (W) 01922 721898
Fixtures Secretary: Mr Robert F Smith, 31 Doe Bank Road, Ocker Hill, Tipton, West Midlands. Tel: (H) 0121 556 6748 Tel (W) 01902 752926
Club Colours: Black & white hoops, black shorts.

MIDLAND DIVISION

STAFFORDSHIRE & WARWICKSHIRE THREE 1995-96 FIXTURES

November 11 1995 (Week 10)
Burntwood	v	Linley
Claverdon	v	Bloxwich
Harbury	v	Coventry Tech
Rubery Owen	v	Rugeley
Warks Police	v	Rugby Welsh
Wheaton Aston	v	Standard

September 16 1995 (Week 3)
Harbury	v	Burntwood
Rugby Welsh	v	Linley
Shottery	v	Rugeley
Standard	v	Bloxwich
Warks Police	v	Claverdon
Wheaton Aston	v	Rubery Owen

September 23 1995 (Week 4)
Bloxwich	v	Shottery
Claverdon	v	Harbury
Coventry Tech	v	Rugby Welsh
Linley	v	Standard
Rubery Owen	v	Warks Police
Rugeley	v	Wheaton Aston

September 30 1995 (Week X1)
Burntwood	v	Claverdon
Harbury	v	Rubery Owen
Shottery	v	Linley
Standard	v	Coventry Tech
Warks Police	v	Rugeley
Wheaton Aston	v	Bloxwich

October 14 1995 (Week 6)
Bloxwich	v	Warks Police
Coventry Tech	v	Shottery
Linley	v	Wheaton Aston
Rugby Welsh	v	Standard
Rubery Owen	v	Burntwood
Rugeley	v	Harbury

October 21 1995 (Week 7)
Burntwood	v	Rugeley
Claverdon	v	Rubery Owen
Harbury	v	Bloxwich
Shottery	v	Rugby Welsh
Warks Police	v	Linley
Wheaton Aston	v	Coventry Tech

October 28 1995 (Week 8)
Bloxwich	v	Burntwood
Coventry Tech	v	Warks Police
Linley	v	Harbury
Rugby Welsh	v	Wheaton Aston
Rugeley	v	Claverdon
Standard	v	Shottery

January 6 1996 (Week 17)
Bloxwich	v	Rubery Owen
Coventry	v	Burntwood
Linley	v	Claverdon
Rugby Welsh	v	Harbury
Shottery	v	Wheaton Aston
Standard	v	Warks Police

January 13 1996 (Week 18)
Burntwood	v	Rugby Welsh
Claverdon	v	Coventry Tech
Harbury	v	Standard
Rubery Owen	v	Linley
Rugeley	v	Bloxwich
Warks Police	v	Shottery

February 10 1996 (Week 22)
Coventry Tech	v	Rubery Owen
Linley	v	Rugeley
Rugby Welsh	v	Claverdon
Shottery	v	Harbury
Standard	v	Burntwood
Wheaton Aston	v	Warks Police

February 17 1996 (Week 23)
Bloxwich	v	Linley
Burntwood	v	Shottery
Claverdon	v	Standard
Harbury	v	Wheaton Aston
Rubery Owen	v	Rugby Welsh
Rugeley	v	Coventry Tech

February 24 1996 (Week 24)
Coventry Tech	v	Bloxwich
Rugby Welsh	v	Rugeley
Shottery	v	Claverdon
Standard	v	Rubery Owen
Warks Police	v	Harbury
Wheaton Aston	v	Burntwood

March 30 1996 (Week X7)
Bloxwich	v	Rugby Welsh
Burntwood	v	Warks Police
Claverdon	v	Wheaton Aston
Linley	v	Coventry Tech
Rubery Owen	v	Shottery
Rugeley	v	Standard

STAFFS & WARWICKS THREE

BLOXWICH RFC
Ground Address: TP Riley School, Lichfield Road, Bloxwich, Walsall. Tel: 01922 710463
Club Secretary: James WE Rudge, 5 Primrose Close, Pelsall, Walsall, West Midlands WS3 5BT. Tel: (H) 01922 693690 Tel: (W) 01509 219990
Fixtures Secretary: Anthony Allen, 16 Sorrel Close, Featherstone, Staffs WV10 7TX. Tel: (H) 01902 739835 Tel (W) 01902 864726
Club Colours: Green & black (black & white chest hoops), black shorts.

BURNTWOOD RUFC
Ground Address: Burntwood Recreation Centre, High Street, Burntwood, Nr Walsall, Staffs WS7 8XH. Tel: 01543 682911
Club Secretary: Kevin Broadhead, 12 School Walk, Chaseterrace, Walsall, Staffs WS7 8NQ. Tel: (H) 01543 279038
Fixtures Secretary: Alan Wood, 72 Hunter Avenue, Burntwood, Mr Walsall, Staffordshire WS7 9AQ. Tel: (H) 01543 677513
Club Colours: Red/green/white hoops.

CLAVERDON RFC
Ground Address: Ossetts Hole Lane, Yarningale Common, Claverdon, Warks. Tel: 01926 843133
Club Secretary: Basil Sayer, The White House, 45 Station Road, Balsall Common, Coventry CV7 7FN. Tel: (H) 01676 532164 Tel: (W) 01933 224444
Fixtures Secretary: Chris Goldwater, Home Farm, Blackwell, Shipston on Stour, Warks. Tel: (H) 01608 682773 Tel (W) 0121 454 6188 x4393
Club Colours: Red & white.

COVENTRY TECHNICAL RFC
Ground Address: Mitchell Avenue, off Charter Avenue, Canley, Coventry, West Midlands. Tel: 01203 471733
Club Secretary: N Franklin, 42 Haynestone Road, Coundon, Coventry CV6 1GJ. Tel: (H) 01203 335560
Fixtures Secretary: Tony Jones, Flat 2, 128 Murrary Road, Rugby, Warwickshire CV21 7Jr. Tel: (H) 01788 547911
Club Colours: Green/gold/brown.

HARBURY RFC
Ground Address: Waterloo Fields, Middle Road, Harbury, Warwickshire. Tel: 01926 613462
Club Secretary: Graham Lewis, Rose Cottage, Bridge Lane, Ladbroke, Warwickshire CV33 0DE. Tel: (H) 01926 815196
Fixtures Secretary: Jerry Birkbeck, 22 Campion Terrace, Leamington Spa, Warwickshire CV32 4SX. Tel: (H) 01926 424053
Club Colours: Cherry & white hoops.

LINLEY & KIDSGROVE RUFC
Ground Address: Bathpool Park Ski Centre, Kidsgrove, Staffordshire.
Club Secretary: Jason Swingewood, 6 Clandon Avenue, Tunstall, Stoke-on-Trent, Staffordshire ST6 5UT. Tel: (H) 01782 837647 Tel: (W) 0151 934 6233
Fixtures Secretary: Alan Hodgekinson, 50 Greenbank Road, Tunstall, Stoke-on-Trent, Staffordshire ST6 7EY. Tel: (H) 01782 838201 Tel (W) 01782 312614
Club Colours: Green & gold quarters.

RUBERY OWEN RFC
Ground Address: High Hill Centre, High Hill, Essington, West Midlands WV11 2DW. Tel: 01922 492795
Club Secretary: Michael Richard Chandler, 32 Coppice Road, Walsall Wood, Walsall, West Midlands WS9 9BL. Tel: (H) 01543 370678 Tel: (W) 01384 400999
Fixtures Secretary: Graham Smith, 7 Oakwood Close, Essington, West Midlands. Tel: (H) 01922 400222
Club Colours: Black.

RUGBY WELSH RFC
Ground Address: Clubhouse: Bakehouse Lane, Rugby CV21 2DB. Ground: (Council pitch remote from

FINAL TABLE

	P	W	D	L	F	A	Pts
Old Warwickians	11	10	0	1	334	73	20
Alcester	11	9	1	1	250	44	19
Bloxwich	11	9	0	2	167	90	18
Rubery Owen	11	7	1	3	194	81	15
Claverdon	11	6	0	5	132	119	12
Burntwood	11	5	0	6	160	123	10
Rugeley	11	4	1	6	125	173	9
Wheaton Aston	11	5	0	6	143	138	8*
Coventry Technical	11	5	0	6	151	202	8*
Standard	11	3	1	7	171	169	7
Old Oaks	11	0	0	11	67	356	0
Warwick	11	1	0	10	55	381	-2*

clubhouse) Alwyn Road Recreation Ground, Bilton. Tel: Clubhouse: 01788 565605. No phone at ground.
Club Secretary: Roy Thompson, 1 Heather Close, Rugby CV22 6SB. Tel: (H) 01788 577796 Tel: (W) 01788 545062
Fixtures Secretary: John Rowland, 76 Pytchley Road, Rugby CV22 5NF. Tel: (H) 01788 574421 Tel (W) 01788 563467
Club Colours: Red shirts, white shorts, red & white socks.

RUGELEY RUFC
Ground Address: Hagley Park, Rugeley, Staffs. Tel: 01889 582266 Mobile: 0421 449869
Club Secretary: David Ensor, 36 Anson Street, Rugeley, Staffs WS15 2BA. Tel: (H) 01889 578920
Fixtures Secretary: K Archer, 61 Redbrock Lane, Rugeley, Staffs. Tel: (H) 01889 570154
Club Colours: Amber shirts, black shorts.

SHOTTERY RFC
Ground Address: Shottery Fields, Shottery Road, Stratford-upon-Avon, Warwickshire. Tel: 01789 400252
Club Secretary: Neil Povey, 11 Beach Croft, High Street, Henley in Arden, Warwickshire B95 5AC. Tel: (H) 01564 793587
Fixtures Secretary: Phil Whiting, 5 St Raith's Court, Gunnings Road, Alcester B49 6AH. Tel: (H) 01789 400252
Club Colours: Blue shirts, blue shorts.

STANDARD RFC
Ground Address: Tanners Lane, Tile Hill, Coventry. Tel: 01203 675186
Club Secretary: Chris Hughes, 108 Earlsdon Avenue, South Coventry CV5 6DN. Tel: (H) 01203 679552
Fixtures Secretary: Henry Kantor, 4 Bowfell Close, Mount Nod, Coventry CV5 7JF. Tel: (H) 01203 463855 Tel (W) 01926 643067
Club Colours: Dark blue, light blue & white hoops.

WARWICKSHIRE CONSTABULARY RFC
Ground Address: Police HQ, Leek Wootton, Warwick, Warwickshire. Tel: 01926 415000
Club Secretary: AG Mumford, 11 Barton Road, Bedworth, Warwickshire CV12 8HG. Tel: (H) 01203 640109 Tel: (W) 01203 643111
Fixtures Secretary: AG Mumford, 11 Barton Road, Bedworth, Warwickshire CV12 8HG. Tel: (H) 01203 640109 Tel (W) 01203 643111
Club Colours: Maroon/navy.

WHEATON ASTON RUFC
Ground Address: The Monkton Recreation Centre, Pinfold Lane, Penuridge, Staffs. Tel: 01785 712264
Club Secretary: Mr Barry Dalby, 3 Kiddemore Green, Brewood, Staffs ST19 9BQ. Tel: (H) 01902 850926 Tel: (W) 01952 463335
Fixtures Secretary: Mr R Jones, Preston Hill Farm, Penuridge, Staffs. Tel: (H) 01785 712214
Club Colours: Black/gold.

MIDLAND DIVISION

STAFFORDSHIRE & WARWICKSHIRE FOUR 1995-96 FIXTURES

September 16 1995 (Week 3)
Jaguar   v   Stone
Michelin   v   Fife St
Warwick   v   Old Oaks

September 23 1995 (Week 4)
Ford   v   Jaguar
Old Oaks   v   Michelin
Stone   v   Warwick

September 30 1995 (Week X1)
Fife St   v   Old Oaks
Michelin   v   Stone
Warwick   v   Ford

October 14 1995 (Week 6)
Ford   v   Michelin
Jaguar   v   Warwick
Stone   v   Fife St

October 21 1995 (Week 7)
Fife St   v   Ford
Michelin   v   Jaguar
Old Oaks   v   Stone

October 28 1995 (Week 8)
Ford   v   Old Oaks
Jaguar   v   Fife St
Warwick   v   Michelin

November 11 1995 (Week 10)
Fife St   v   Warwick
Old Oaks   v   Jaguar
Stone   v   Ford

January 6 1996 (Week 17)
Fife St   v   Michelin
Old Oaks   v   Warwick
Stone   v   Jaguar

January 13 1996 (Week 18)
Jaguar   v   Ford
Michelin   v   Old Oaks
Warwick   v   Stone

February 10 1996 (Week 22)
Ford   v   Warwick
Old Oaks   v   Fife St
Stone   v   Michelin

February 17 1996 (Week 23)
Fife St   v   Stone
Michelin   v   Ford
Warwick   v   Jaguar

February 24 1996 (Week 24)
Ford   v   Fife St
Jaguar   v   Michelin
Stone   v   Old Oaks

March 30 1996 (Week X7)
Fife St   v   Jaguar
Michelin   v   Warwick
Old Oaks   v   Ford

April 13 1996 (Week 30)
Ford   v   Stone
Jaguar   v   Old Oaks
Warwick   v   Fife St

STAFFS & WARWICKS FOUR

FIFE STREET RUFC
Ground Address: Ambleside Sports Club, Ambleside
Way, Nuneaton. Tel: 01203 371033
Club Secretary: Lynn Gillespie, 60 Bristol Road,
Earlsdon, Coventry CV5 6LH. Tel: (H) 01203 675401 Tel:
(W) 01203 831919
Fixtures Secretary: Mr A Ratcliffe, 526 Kingswood Road,
Nuneaton CV10 8QQ. Tel: (H) 01203 349456
Club Colours: Green, red & white hoops.

FORD LEAMINGTON RFC
Ground Address: Newbold Comyn, Newbold Terrace,
Leamington Spa, Warwickshire.
Club Secretary: Mr D Guest, 22 Dudley Green, Lillington,
Leamington Spa, Warwickshire. Tel: (H) 01926 886159
Fixtures Secretary: Martin McAndrew, 14 Redland Road,
Leamington Spa, Warwickshire CV31 2PB. Tel: (H) 01926
886678
Club Colours: Blue, black & white hoops, black shorts.

JAGUAR RFC
Ground Address: Jaguar Sports and Social Club,
Middlemarch Road, Radford, Coventry, Warks.
Club Secretary: Martin Mills, 51 Dawes Close, Stoke
Mews, Coventry, CV2 4LL. Tel: (H) 01203 459314 Tel:
(W) 01203 235527
Fixtures Secretary: Martin Mills, 51 Dawes Close, Stoke
Mews, Coventry, CV2 4LL. Tel: (H) 01203 459314 Tel
(W) 01203 235527
Club Colours: Black with yellow trim.

MICHELIN RUFC
Ground Address: Michelin Sports Centre, Rosetree
Avenue, Trent Vale, Stoke-on-Trent. Tel: 01782 402899
Club Secretary: Paul Gill, 20 Foxwood Close, Walton,
Stone, Staffs ST15 0LN. Tel: (H) 01785 815711 Tel: (W)
01782 372372
Fixtures Secretary: Stuart Mold, 33 Meadowbrook Court,
Little Stoke, Stone, Staffs ST15 8LX. Tel: (H) 01782
819212 Tel (W) 01782 718731
Club Colours: Blue & gold hoops.

OLD OAKS RFC
Ground Address: Shelfield Comm School.
Club Secretary: Martin Berry, 70 Charles Crescent,
Pelsall, Nr Walsall, West Midlands WS3 5BH. Tel: (H)
01922 694839
Fixtures Secretary: J soden, 19 Colins Road, Shire Oak,
Brownhills, West Midlands. Tel: (H) 01543 374790
Club Colours: Royal blue & scarlet quarters, navy shorts,
1 red sock, 1 blue sock.

STONE RUFC
Ground Address: Alleynes School, Oulton Road, Stone,
Staffs.
Club Secretary: Mrs F Foster, 17 Granville Terrace, Stone,
Staffs ST15 8DF. Tel: (H) 01785 817230 Tel: (W) 01925
418181
Fixtures Secretary: M Upton, 11 St Michael's Mount,
Stone, Staffs ST15 8PZ. Tel: (H) 01785 815950 Tel (W)
0836 516728
Club Colours: Green/maroon.

WARWICK RFC
Ground Address: Hampton Fields, Hampton Road,
Warwick. Tel: 01926 410972
Club Secretary: Peter O'Rourke, 96 Clinton Lane,
Kenilworth, Warwickshire CV8 1AX. Tel: (H) 01926
58239 Tel: (W) 0831 510696
Fixtures Secretary: Nicholas Adams, 17 Church Street,
Warwick CV34 4AB. Tel: (H) 01926 403015 Tel (W)
01973 427021
Club Colours: Purple and black hoops.

FINAL TABLE	P	W	D	L	F	A	Pts
Rugby Welsh	7	7	0	0	235	50	14
Shottery	7	6	0	1	229	36	12
Ford	7	4	0	3	127	54	8
Stone	7	4	0	3	91	127	8
Michelin	7	4	0	3	146	93	4*
Jaguar (Coventry)	7	2	0	5	78	104	4
Onley Park	7	0	0	7	31	243	-2*
Fife Street	7	1	0	6	43	273	-2*

MIDLAND DIVISION

September 16 1995 (Week 3)

Bridgnorth	v	Evesham
Erdington	v	Old Griffinians
Kidderminster	v	Old Centrals
Telford	v	Bromyard
Veseyans	v	Edwardians
Warley	v	Five Ways

September 23 1995 (Week 4)

Five Ways	v	Bridgnorth
Edwardians	v	Warley
Bromyard	v	Veseyans
Old Centrals	v	Telford
Old Griffinians	v	Kidderminster
Pershore	v	Erdington

September 30 1995 (Week X1)

Bridgnorth	v	Edwardians
Evesham	v	Five Ways
Kidderminster	v	Pershore
Telford	v	Old Griffinians
Veseyans	v	Old Centrals
Warley	v	Bromyard

October 14 1995 (Week 6)

Edwardians	v	Evesham
Bromyard	v	Bridgnorth
Old Centrals	v	Warley
Old Griffinians	v	Veseyans
Pershore	v	Telford
Erdington	v	Kidderminster

October 21 1995 (Week 7)

Bridgnorth	v	Old Centrals
Evesham	v	Bromyard
Five Ways	v	Edwardians
Telford	v	Erdington
Veseyans	v	Pershore
Warley	v	Old Griffinians

October 28 1995 (Week 8)

Bromyard	v	Five Ways
Old Centrals	v	Evesham
Old Griffinians	v	Bridgnorth
Pershore	v	Warley
Erdington	v	Veseyans
Kidderminster	v	Telford

November 11 1995 (Week 10)

Bridgnorth	v	Pershore
Evesham	v	Old Griffinians
Five Ways	v	Old Centrals
Edwardians	v	Bromyard
Veseyans	v	Kidderminster
Warley	v	Erdington

January 6 1996 (Week 17)

Old Centrals	v	Edwardians
Old Griffinians	v	Five Ways
Pershore	v	Evesham
Erdington	v	Bridgnorth
Kidderminster	v	Warley
Telford	v	Veseyans

January 13 1996 (Week 18)

Bridgnorth	v	Kidderminster
Evesham	v	Erdington
Five Ways	v	Pershore
Edwardians	v	Old Griffinians
Bromyard	v	Old Centrals
Warley	v	Telford

February 10 1996 (Week 22)

Old Griffinians	v	Bromyard
Pershore	v	Edwardians
Erdington	v	Five Ways
Kidderminster	v	Evesham
Telford	v	Bridgnorth
Veseyans	v	Warley

February 17 1996 (Week 23)

Bridgnorth	v	Veseyans
Evesham	v	Telford
Five Ways	v	Kidderminster
Edwardians	v	Erdington
Bromyard	v	Pershore
Old Centrals	v	Old Griffinians

February 24 1996 (Week 24)

Pershore	v	Old Centrals
Erdington	v	Bromyard
Kidderminster	v	Edwardians
Telford	v	Five Ways
Veseyans	v	Evesham
Warley	v	Bridgnorth

March 30 1996 (Week X7)

Evesham	v	Warley
Five Ways	v	Veseyans
Edwardians	v	Telford
Bromyard	v	Kidderminster
Old Centrals	v	Erdington
Old Griffinians	v	Pershore

NORTH MIDLANDS ONE

BRIDGNORTH RFC
Ground Address: The Bull, Bridge Street, Bridgnorth, Shropshire WV15 5AA. Tel: 01746 762796
Club Secretary: Pete Shimmin, 7 Buck Cottage, Sheinton, Cressage, Shropshire SY5 6DJ. Tel: (H) 01952 510604 Tel: (W) 01746 766488
Fixtures Secretary: Alun Stoll, Ty'r Ysgol, Vicarage Road, Penn, Wolverhampton WV4 5HP. Tel: (H) 01902 332025 Tel (W) 01902 332025
Club Colours: Black shirts/shorts.

BROMYARD RFC
Ground Address: Mintridge, Stoke Lacy, Bromyard, Herefordshire. Tel: 01885 488152 (to mid Sept); 01885 483933 (from mid Sept)
Club Secretary: Mick Warren, The Chestnuts, Munderfield, Bromyard, Herefordshire HR7 4JT. Tel: (H) 01885 490684 Tel: (W) 01885 490480
Fixtures Secretary: Gerry Houghton, 3 Valley View, Bredenbury, Bromyard, Herefordshire HR7 4UJ. Tel: (H) 01885 488387 Tel (W) 01885 488387
Club Colours: Green & gold shirts, black shorts.

EDWARDIAN FC
Ground Address: The Memorial Ground, Streetsbrook Road, Solihull, West Midlands B90 3PE. Tel: 0121 744 6831
Club Secretary: Chris Nevin, 21 Wroxhall Road, Solihull, West Midlands B91 1DR. Tel: (H) 0121 704 1870 Tel: (W) 0121 625 6621
Fixtures Secretary: Steve Abercrombie, 35 Green Lane, Shirley, Solihull, West Midlands B90 1AP. Tel: (H) 0121 608 6195 Tel (W) 0121 430 7508
Club Colours: Old gold, claret & navy irregular hoops.

ERDINGTON RFC
Ground Address: Birches Green Playing Fields, Kingsbury Road, Erdington, Birmingham. Tel: 0121 373 7597
Club Secretary: Derek Owen, 129 Bradbury Road, Solihull, West Midlands B92 8AL. Tel: (H) 0121 706 4699 Tel: (W) 01527 64252 x3307
Fixtures Secretary: Keith Robinson, 5 Ullenhall Road, Walmley, Sutton Coldfield, West Midlands B76 8QG. Tel: (H) 0121 351 2740
Club Colours: White shirts with single blue hoop, blue shorts.

EVESHAM RFC
Ground Address: Evesham Sports Club, Albert Road, Evesham, Worcs. Tel: 01386 446469
Club Secretary: J Patrick Hartley, Nightingale House, Bishampton, Pershore, Worcs, WR10 2NH. Tel: (H) 01386 462325 Tel: (W) 01527 876776
Fixtures Secretary: Ian Moreton, 'Frensham' Lenchwick, Evesham, Worcs. Tel: (H) 01386 870566 Tel (W) 01386 443311
Club Colours: Navy/maroon hoops.

FIVE WAYS OLD EDWARDIANS FC
Ground Address: Masshouse, Ash Lane, Hopwood, Birmingham. Tel: 0121 445 4909
Club Secretary: Richard Lisseter, 138 Chatsworth Road, Halesowen, West Midlands B62 8TH. Tel: (H) 0121 559 6549 Tel: (W) 0121 550 1724
Fixtures Secretary: Paul Hipkiss, 37 The Crescent, Cradley Heath, West Midlands. Tel: (H) 0121 550 4280
Club Colours: Navy blue & amber.

KIDDERMINSTER CAROLIANS RFC
Ground Address: Marlpool Lane, Kidderminster, Worcs DY11 5HP. Tel: 01562 740043
Club Secretary: Mr Wallace Boyd, 7 Belvedere Crescent, Meadow Rise, Bewdley, Worcs DY12 1JX. Tel: (H) 01299 404171 Tel: (W) 0121 643 6611
Fixtures Secretary: Mr T Carder, 218 Puxton Drive, Kidderminster DY11 5HJ. Tel: (H) 01562 747910 Tel (W) 01902 774044
Club Colours: Black shirts with gold hoops, black shorts.

OLD CENTRALS RFC
Ground Address: Bournevale, off Little Hardwick Road, Aldridge, West Midlands. Tel: 0121 353 2856
Club Secretary: DE Smith, 14 St Andrews, Amington, Tamworth B77 4RA. Tel: (H) 01827 50018 Tel: (W) 0121 384 7000
Fixtures Secretary: R Stain, 147 Green Road, Moseley,

FINAL TABLE

	P	W	D	L	F	A	Pts
Malvern	12	11	1	0	329	85	23
Telford	12	11	0	1	269	101	22
Edwardians	12	8	1	3	215	141	17
Evesham	12	8	1	3	187	134	17
Five Ways Old Eds	12	6	0	6	220	211	12
Old Griffinians	12	6	0	6	208	213	12
Old Centrals	12	6	0	6	205	217	12
Vereyans	12	6	0	6	168	220	12
Pershore	12	4	0	8	192	197	8
Bridgnorth	12	3	2	7	141	265	8
Warley	12	3	1	8	132	206	7
Kidderminster	12	3	0	9	182	213	6
Droitwich	12	0	0	12	115	360	0

Birmingham. Tel: (H) 0121 778 6804 Tel (W) 0121 554 0184
Club Colours: Maroon, green, gold hoops, navy shorts.

OLD GRIFFINIANS RFC
Ground Address: Billsley Common, Kings Heath, Birmingham.
Club Secretary: Rick Adie, 33 Middlemore Road, Northfield, Birmingham B31 3UD. Tel: (H) 0121 624 7504 Tel: (W) 0121 453 1778
Fixtures Secretary: Bernard Malin, 59 Spiceland Road, Northfield, Birmingham B31 1NL. Tel: (H) 0121 475 3788
Club Colours: Black.

PERSHORE RFC
Ground Address: Mill Lane, Wyre Piddle, Pershore, Worcestershire. Tel: 01386 554105
Club Secretary: Sam Cook, 7 Allsebrook Gardens, Badsey, Evesham, Worcestershire WR11 4HJ. Tel: (H) 01386 831494
Fixtures Secretary: Phil Green, 25 Drovers Way, Astwood Farm, Worcester WR3 8QD. Tel: (H) 01905 756442 Tel (W) 01684 293482
Club Colours: Black with two scarlet hoops, black shorts.

TELFORD HORNETS RFC
Ground Address: Town Park, Hinkshay Road, Dawley, Telford, Shropshire TF4 3NZ. Tel: 01952 505440
Club Secretary: Martin Dolphin, 10 Canonbie Lea, Madeley, Telford, Shropshire TF7 5RL. Tel: (H) 01952 684904 Tel: (W) 01952 294424
Fixtures Secretary: Andy Vickers, 35 Grovefields, Leegomery, Telford, Shropshire TF2 4YL. Tel: (H) 01952 243551
Club Colours: Black with gold chest band.

VESEYANS RFC
Ground Address: Little Hardwick Road, Streetly, Sutton Coldfield, West Midlands. Tel: 0121 353 5388
Club Secretary: Stuart Crowther, 31 Jerrard Drive, Sutton Coldfield, West Midlands B75 7TD. Tel: (H) 0121 378 4090 Tel: (W) 0121 607 1377
Fixtures Secretary: Stewart Davies, 153 Thornbridge Avenue, Great Barr, Birmingham B42 4AF. Tel: (H) 0121 357 6506 Tel (W) 0121 351 3833
Club Colours: Black & white hooped shirts, black shorts.

WARLEY RFC
Ground Address: Broomfield, The Uplands, Smethwick, Warley, West Midlands B67 6BJ. Tel: 0121 558 0084
Club Secretary: Keiron Ward, 72 Oak Road, Oldbury, Warley, West Midlands B68 0BD. Tel: (H) 0121 422 4639
Fixtures Secretary: Peter Davies, 60 Park Road, Smethwick, Warley, West Midlands B67 5HS. Tel: (H) 0121 420 3141
Club Colours: Red & white hoops, black shorts, red & white socks.

MIDLAND DIVISION

NORTH MIDLANDS TWO 1995-96 FIXTURES

November 11 1995 (Week 10)

Birmingham Welsh	v	Ross on Wye
Birmingham City Off	v	Stourport
Bournville	v	Birmingham Civil Ser
Droitwich	v	Old Salts
Upton on Severn	v	Redditch
Tenbury	v	Kynoch

September 16 1995 (Week 3)

Birmingham Welsh	v	Birmingham City Off
Kynoch	v	Stourport
Redditch	v	Birmingham Civil Ser
Wulfrun	v	Old Salts
Upton on Severn	v	Droitwich
Tenbury	v	Bournville

January 6 1996 (Week 17)

Kynoch	v	Birmingham Welsh
Redditch	v	Tenbury
Birmingham Civil Ser	v	Droitwich
Stourport	v	Bournville
Ross on Wye	v	Birmingham City Off
Wulfrun	v	Upton on Severn

September 23 1995 (Week 4)

Bournville	v	Birmingham Welsh
Droitwich	v	Tenbury
Old Salts	v	Upton on Severn
Birmingham Civil Ser	v	Wulfrun
Stourport	v	Redditch
Ross on Wye	v	Kynoch

January 13 1996 (Week 18)

Birmingham Welsh	v	Redditch
Bournville	v	Ross on Wye
Droitwich	v	Stourport
Old Salts	v	Birmingham Civil Ser
Birmingham City Off	v	Kynoch
Tenbury	v	Wulfrun

September 30 1995 (Week X1)

Birmingham Welsh	v	Droitwich
Birmingham City Off	v	Bournville
Redditch	v	Ross on Wye
Wulfrun	v	Stourport
Upton on Severn	v	Birmingham Civil Ser
Tenbury	v	Old Salts

February 10 1996 (Week 22)

Wulfrun	v	Birmingham Welsh
Stourport	v	Old Salts
Ross on Wye	v	Droitwich
Kynoch	v	Bournville
Redditch	v	Birmingham City Off
Upton on Severn	v	Tenbury

October 14 1995 (Week 6)

Old Salts	v	Birmingham Welsh
Droitwich	v	Birmingham City Off
Birmingham Civil Ser	v	Tenbury
Stourport	v	Upton on Severn
Ross on Wye	v	Wulfrun
Kynoch	v	Redditch

February 17 1996 (Week 23)

Birmingham Welsh	v	Upton on Severn
Birmingham City Off	v	Wulfrun
Bournville	v	Redditch
Droitwich	v	Kynoch
Old Salts	v	Ross on Wye
Birmingham Civil Ser	v	Stourport

October 21 1995 (Week 7)

Birmingham Welsh	v	Birmingham Civil Ser
Birmingham City Off	v	Old Salts
Bournville	v	Droitwich
Wulfrun	v	Kynoch
Upton on Severn	v	Ross on Wye
Tenbury	v	Stourport

February 24 1996 (Week 24)

Tenbury	v	Birmingham Welsh
Ross on Wye	v	Birmingham Civil Ser
Kynoch	v	Old Salts
Redditch	v	Droitwich
Wulfrun	v	Bournville
Upton on Severn	v	Birmingham City Off

October 28 1995 (Week 8)

Stourport	v	Birmingham Welsh
Old Salts	v	Bournville
Birmingham Civil Ser	v	Birmingham City Off
Ross on Wye	v	Tenbury
Kynoch	v	Upton on Severn
Redditch	v	Wulfrun

March 30 1996 (Week X7)

Birmingham Civil Ser	v	Kynoch
Droitwich	v	Wulfrun
Old Salts	v	Redditch
Stourport	v	Ross on Wye
Birmingham City Off	v	Tenbury
Bournville	v	Upton on Severn

NORTH MIDLANDS TWO

BIRMINGHAM CITY OFFICIALS RFC
Ground Address: Land Rover Social Club, Bilsmore
Green, Off Rowood Drive, Solihull, West Midlands, B92
9LN. Tel: 0121 742 7155
Club Secretary: Mr DG Armstrong, 6 Yenton Court,
Chester Road, Erdington, Birmingham, B24 0EB. Tel: (H)
0121 382 8513
Fixtures Secretary: Mr M Cooper, 182 Elmay Road,
Sheldon, Birmingham, B26 2QY. Tel: (H) 0121 604 7147
Club Colours: Navy with red and amber band.

BIRMINGHAM CIVIL SERVICE RFC
Ground Address: Old Damson Lane, Elmdon, Solihull,
West Midlands. Tel: 0121 782 0423 or 0121 782 2151
Club Secretary: Dick Webb, 51 Ladbrook Road, Solihull,
West Midlands B91 3RW. Tel: (H) 0121 705 2812
Fixtures Secretary: Bill Pratt, 230 Alcester Road,
Hollywood, Worcs B47 5HQ. Tel: (H) 01564 822401
Club Colours: Red shirts with 5' white hoop, blue shorts,
red socks.

BIRMINGHAM WELSH RFC
Ground Address: Catherine de Barnes Lane, Bickenhill,
Solihull, West Midlands. Tel: 01675 442995
Club Secretary: Martin Whateley, 19 Wimbourne Road,
Sutton Coldfield, Birmingham B76 2SU. Tel: (H) 0121 378
3446 Tel: (W) 0121 357 7488
Fixtures Secretary: Julian CP Griffiths, 39 School Road,
Moseley, Birmingham B13 9TF. Tel: (H) 0121 449 2471
Tel (W) 0121 233 2838
Club Colours: Scarlet & green quarters, black shorts.

BOURNVILLE RFC
Ground Address: Rowheath, Heath Road, Bournville,
Birmingham B30. Tel: 0121 458 1711
Club Secretary: Mr Michael Palmer, 15 Cutlers Rough
Close, Northfield, Birmingham B31 1LK. Tel: (H) 0121
475 0480 Tel: (W) 0121 454 2304
Fixtures Secretary: Mr John Rice, Warden's Flat, MOGH,
3 College Walk, Selly Oak, Birmingham B29 6ZE. Tel: (H)
0121 415 4255 Tel (W) 0121 472 0163
Club Colours: Maroon with blue & yellow hoops on
sleeves.

DROITWICH RFC
Ground Address: The Clubhouse, Hanbury Road,
Droitwich Spa, Worcs. Tel: 01905 770384
Club Secretary: RJ Shelley, 12 King George Avenue,
Droitwich WR9 7BP. Tel: (H) 01905 770438 Tel: (W)
01384 413841
Fixtures Secretary: Richard Latham, 16 Maytree Hill,
Meadow View, Droitwich. Tel: (H) 01905 773589 Tel (W)
0121 585 5716
Club Colours: Black & gold.

KYNOCH RFC
Ground Address: Holford Drive, Perry Barr, Birmingham
B42 2TU. Tel: 0121 356 4369
Club Secretary: John K Ross, 127 Leopold Avenue,
Handsworth Wood, Birmingham B20 1EX. Tel: (H) 0121
358 3277
Fixtures Secretary: Ray Jones, 17 Kenneth Grove,
Erdington, Birmingham B23 7TT. Tel: (H) 0121 356 9277
Club Colours: Black & white hoops.

OLD SALTLEIANS RFC
Ground Address: Watton Lane, Water Orton,
Birmingham. Tel: 0121 748 3380
Club Secretary: Richard English, 3 The Maltings,
Aldridge W59 0NL. Tel: (H) 01922 56088 Tel: (W) 01543
251478
Fixtures Secretary: Kelvin Roberts, 2 Newmarsh Road,
Minworth B76 8XW. Tel: (H) 0121 351 1473
Club Colours: Red & gold hoops, blue shorts.

REDDITCH RFC
Ground Address: Bromsgrove Road, Redditch.
Club Secretary: Bryn Richards, 29 Ladbrook Close,

FINAL TABLE

	P	W	D	L	F	A	Pts
Erdington	12	12	0	0	327	60	24
Bromyard	12	9	1	2	368	105	19
Birmingham City Off	12	9	0	3	282	96	18
Birmingham Civ Ser	12	9	0	3	158	117	18
Redditch	12	7	0	5	159	133	14
Old Saltleians	12	7	0	5	127	158	14
Tenbury	12	6	0	6	164	153	12
Kynoch	12	5	1	6	180	218	11
Ross-on-Wye	12	5	0	7	157	282	10
Upton-on-Severn	12	4	0	8	159	162	8
Birmingham Welsh	12	3	0	9	149	208	6
Bournville	12	1	0	11	78	278	2
Market Drayton	12	0	0	12	63	401	-2*

Oakenshaw, Redditch, Worcs B98 7XR. Tel: (H) 01527
542870
Fixtures Secretary: Dave Hitchin, 2 Haresfield Close,
Southcrest, Redditch. Tel: (H) 01527 65345 Tel (W) 01527
572592
Club Colours: Light & dark blue quarters.

ROSS-ON-WYE RUFC
Ground Address: Ross Sports Centre, Wilton Road,
Ross-on-Wye, Herefordshire. Tel: 01989 63256
Club Secretary: Mr C Warwick, New Street,
Ross-on-Wye, HR9 7DA. Tel: (H) 01989 563612
Fixtures Secretary: Mr D Cooke, 22 Brampton Avenue,
Ross-on-Wye. Tel: (H) 01989 564626
Club Colours: Blue/white hoops.

STOURPORT RFC
Ground Address: Stourport Cricket & Rugby Club,
Walshes Meadow, Dunley Road, Stourport-on-Severn,
Worcestershire. Tel: 01299 822210
Club Secretary: Andy Foster, Lime-Kilns, Pensax,
Abberley, Worcs WR6 6XH. Tel: (H) 01299 896631
Fixtures Secretary: Mark Jenner, 10 Kingsway,
Stourport-on-Severn, Worcs DY13 8NL. Tel: (H) 01299
824872 Tel (W) 0121 322 3370
Club Colours: Navy jersey with gold V, navy shorts.

TENBURY RFC
Ground Address: Palmers Meadow, Tenbury Wells,
Worcs. Tel: Clubhouse 01584 810456
Club Secretary: Roger Bowkett, The White House,
Kyrewood, Tenbury Wells, Worcs WR15 8SQ. Tel: (H)
01584 810694 Tel: (W) 01584 810351
Fixtures Secretary: Mick Spicer, 19 Castle Close,
Burford, Tenbury Wells, Worcs WR15 8AY. Tel: (H)
01584 819541 Tel (W) 01584 810567
Club Colours: Emerald & black hooped jerseys, black
shorts.

UPTON UPON SEVERN
Ground Address: Sports Club, Upton-on-Severn. Tel:
01684 594445
Club Secretary: Geoff Marchant, 2 Avon Bank, Defford,
Worcester WR8 9BD. Tel: (H) 01386 750486
Fixtures Secretary: NP Banwell, 16 Riverside Close,
Upton upon Severn, Worcester WR8 0JN. Tel: (H) 01684
592046
Club Colours: Black & white quarters.

WULFRUN RUFC
Ground Address: Wednesfield High School, Lakefield
Road, Wednesfield, Wolverhampton, West Midlands.
Club Secretary: Chris Withers, 1 D'Eyncourt Road,
Wednesfield, Wolverhampton. Tel: (H) 01902 732809
Fixtures Secretary: Chris Turner, 148 Warstones Drive,
Warstones, Wolverhampton, West Midlands WV4 6NJ.
Tel: (H) 01902 653018
Club Colours: Green with black V.

MIDLAND DIVISION

NORTH MIDLANDS THREE
1995-96
FIXTURES

September 16 1995 (Week 3)
Market Drayton v Bredon
Old Moseleians v Ledbury
Witton v Bishop's Castle
Yardley & District v Birchfield

September 23 1995 (Week 4)
Birchfield v Market Drayton
Bishop's Castle v Yardley & District
Cleobury v Witton
Oswestry v Harborne

September 30 1995 (Week X1)
Bredon v Birchfield
Market Drayton v Bishop's Castle
Old Moseleians v Oswestry
Witton v Ledbury
Yardley & District v Cleobury

October 14 1995 (Week 6)
Bishop's Castle v Bredon
Cleobury v Market Drayton
Harborne v Old Moseleians
Ledbury v Yardley & District

October 21 1995 (Week 7)
Birchfield v Bishop's Castle
Bredon v Cleobury
Market Drayton v Ledbury
Witton v Oswestry

October 28 1995 (Week 8)
Cleobury v Birchfield
Harborne v Witton
Ledbury v Bredon
Oswestry v Yardley & District

November 11 1995 (Week 10)
Birchfield v Ledbury
Bishop's Castle v Cleobury
Market Drayton v Oswestry
Witton v Old Moseleians
Yardley & District v Harborne

January 6 1996 (Week 17)
Harborne v Market Drayton
Ledbury v Bishop's Castle
Old Moseleians v Yardley & District
Oswestry v Bredon

January 13 1996 (Week 18)
Birchfield v Oswestry
Bredon v Harborne
Cleobury v Ledbury
Market Drayton v Old Moseleians

February 10 1996 (Week 22)
Harborne v Birchfield
Old Moseleians v Bredon
Oswestry v Bishop's Castle
Witton v Yardley & District

February 17 1996 (Week 23)
Birchfield v Old Moseleians
Bishop's Castle v Harborne
Cleobury v Oswestry
Market Drayton v Witton

February 24 1996 (Week 24)
Harborne v Cleobury
Old Moseleians v Bishop's Castle
Oswestry v Ledbury
Witton v Bredon
Yardley & District v Market Drayton

March 30 1996 (Week X7)
Birchfield v Witton
Bredon v Yardley & District
Cleobury v Old Moseleians
Ledbury v Harborne

NORTH MIDLANDS THREE

BIRCHFIELD RUFC
Ground Address: Moor Lane Sports & Social Club, Moor Lane, Witton, Birmingham B6 7AA. Tel: 0121 356 2142
Club Secretary: Dave Simcox, 32 Holland Road, Sutton Coldfield, West Midlands B72 1RQ. Tel: (H) 0121 354 3727 Tel: (W) 0635 523456
Fixtures Secretary: Roger Booth, 151 Chester Road, Streetly, Sutton Coldfield B74 3NE. Tel: (H) 0121 353 9332 Tel (W) 0121 777 3222 x3825
Club Colours: Green & black hoops.

BISHOP'S CASTLE & ONNY VALLEY RUFC
Ground Address: Love Lane, Bishop's Castle, Shropshire.
Club Secretary: John Smith, Hillington, Union Street, Bishop's Castle Shropshire. Tel: (H) 01588 638225
Fixtures Secretary: Darren Price, 14A The Flat, High Street, Bishop's Castle, Shropshire. Tel: (H) 01588 638971 Tel (W) 01588 637746
Club Colours: Green & red hoops.

BREDON STAR RFC
Ground Address: Bredon Playing Fields, Kemerton Rd, Bredon, Nr Tewkesbury, Glos. Tel: 01684 772831
Club Secretary: Carol Julie Malpass, 33 Plantation Crescent, Bredon, Nr Tewkesbury, Glos. Tel: (H) 01684 72831
Fixtures Secretary: Neil Evans, Apple Orchard, Chapel Lane, Kinshan, Nr Tewkesbury, Glos GL20 8US. Tel: (H) 01684 772645 Tel (W) Mobile: 0973 171451
Club Colours: Red & black hoops.

CLEOBURY MORTIMER RFC
Ground Address: Lacon Chiloe School, Cleobury Mortimer, Nr Kidderminster, Worcs DY14 8PE. Tel: 01299 271317
Club Secretary: Richard Redfern, 43 Furlongs Road, Cleobury Mortimer, Nr Kidderminster, Worcs DY14 8AR. Tel: (H) 01299 270472 Tel: (W) 01299 270395 Fax: 01299 27101
Fixtures Secretary: Stephen Hems, High Street, Cleobury Mortimer, Nr Kidderminster, worcs. Tel: (H) 01299 270392
Club Colours: Red & green quarters.

HARBORNE RFC
Ground Address: Playing Fields, Metchley, Park Road, Harborne, Birmingham. Tel: 0121 427 2690
Club Secretary: David Davis, 78 Wilmington Road, Quinton, Birmingham. Tel: (H) 0121 422 4693 Tel: (W) 0121 626 6170
Fixtures Secretary: Simon Parker, 14 Mill Gardens, Smethwick, Oldbury, West Midlands. Tel: (H) 0121 420 3523
Club Colours: Green, red & black band.

LEDBURY RFC
Ground Address: Ross Road Playing Field, Ross Road, Ledbury. Tel: 01531 633926
Club Secretary: Mrs Sally Rowberry, 53 Oatleys Crescent, Ledbury, Herefordshire HR8 2BY. Tel: (H) 01531 633926
Fixtures Secretary: Mike Nolan, Norwich House, Oatleys Road, Ledbury, Herefordshire. Tel: (H) 01531 635243
Club Colours: Black & white.

MARKET DRAYTON RFC
Ground Address: Greenfields, Greenfields Lane, Market Drayton, Shropshire. Tel: 01630
Club Secretary: Rob Davies, 73 Longslow Road, Market Drayton, Shropshire TF9 3BP. Tel: (H) 01630 655069
Fixtures Secretary: Adrian Barker, 1 Pine Close, Farcroft Estates, Market Drayton, Shropshire. Tel: (H) 01630 653202 Tel (W) 01630 653177
Club Colours: Black with green stripe.

OLD MOSELEIANS RFC
Ground Address: Lugtrout Lane, Solihull, West Midlands. Tel: 0121 705 7847
Club Secretary: John Stefani, 6 Stand Street, Warwick

FINAL TABLE

	P	W	D	L	F	A	Pts
Wulfrun	10	9	0	1	225	71	18
Stourport	10	8	0	2	141	96	16
Bishops Castle	10	8	0	2	244	105	14*
Yardley & District	10	8	0	2	185	72	14*
Ledbury	10	6	1	3	276	92	11*
Birchfield	10	4	1	5	184	144	9*
Oswestry	10	4	0	6	79	190	8
Witton	10	2	0	8	127	200	4
Old Moseleians	10	3	0	7	109	176	2*
Cleobury Mortimer	10	2	0	8	120	196	2*
Bredon Star	10	0	0	10	31	379	0

CV34 6HR. Tel: (H) 01926 497275 Tel: (W) 01926 464511
Fixtures Secretary: Mick Fielding, 96 Vera Road, Yardley, Birmingham B26 1TT. Tel: (H) 0121 783 6333 Tel (W) 0121 707 7111
Club Colours: Black shirts with red & white chest band, black shorts.

OSWESTRY RFC
Ground Address: Park Hall, Oswestry, Shropshire. Tel: 01691 652949
Club Secretary: Nick Ashley, 46 Maserfield, Oswestry SY11 1SB. Tel: (H) 01691 655164 Tel: (W) 01691 666505
Fixtures Secretary: Peter Hunt, Birch Farm, Trefonen, Oswestry. Tel: (H) 01691 652620 Tel (W) 01691 652143
Club Colours: Black & red hooped shirts, black shorts.

WITTON RFC
Ground Address: Ansells Sports & Social Club, Aldridge, Road, Perry Barr, Birmingham B42 2TP. Tel: 0121 356 4296
Club Secretary: Alex Reed, 4A Rectory Road, Sutton Coldfield, West Midlands B75 7AL. Tel: (H) 0121 321 2036 Tel: (W) 0121 351 5451
Fixtures Secretary: Carl Sadler, 634 Queslett Road, Great Barr, Birmingham B43 7DU. Tel: (H) 0121 681 4293
Club Colours: Gold shirts with black V, black shorts.

YARDLEY & DISTRICT RFC
Ground Address: Colehall Lane, Stechford, Birmingham. Tel: 0121 789 8450
Club Secretary: David Adderley, 16 Bantams Close, Kitts green, Birmingham B33 0LY. Tel: (H) 0121 789 6735 Tel: (W) 0121 693 6401 Mobile: 0831 847111
Fixtures Secretary: John Shaw, 3 Barbourne Close, Solihull, West Midlands B91 3TL. Tel: (H) 0121 705 3292 Tel (W) 0121 700 3182
Club Colours: Blue & gold hoops.

MIDLAND DIVISION

MIDLANDS EAST ONE 1995-96 FIXTURES

November 11 1995 (Week 10)

Amber Valley	v	Ilkeston
Ampthill	v	Vipers
Biggleswade	v	Long Buckby
Huntingdon	v	Kettering
Peterborough	v	Newark
Stoneygate	v	Spalding

September 16 1995 (Week 3)

Amber Valley	v	Ampthill
Newark	v	Vipers
Spalding	v	Long Buckby
Stewarts & Lloyds	v	Kettering
Stoneygate	v	Huntingdon
Peterborough	v	Biggleswade

September 23 1995 (Week 4)

Biggleswade	v	Amber Valley
Huntingdon	v	Peterborough
Kettering	v	Stoneygate
Long Buckby	v	Stewarts & Lloyds
Vipers	v	Spalding
Ilkeston	v	Newark

September 30 1995 (Week X1)

Amber Valley	v	Huntingdon
Ampthill	v	Biggleswade
Peterborough	v	Kettering
Spalding	v	Ilkeston
Stewarts & Lloyds	v	Vipers
Stoneygate	v	Long Buckby

October 14 1995 (Week 6)

Huntingdon	v	Ampthill
Kettering	v	Amber Valley
Long Buckby	v	Peterborough
Ilkeston	v	Stewarts & Lloyds
Newark	v	Spalding
Vipers	v	Stoneygate

October 21 1995 (Week 7)

Amber Valley	v	Long Buckby
Ampthill	v	Kettering
Biggleswade	v	Huntingdon
Peterborough	v	Vipers
Stewarts & Lloyds	v	Newark
Stoneygate	v	Ilkeston

October 28 1995 (Week 8)

Kettering	v	Biggleswade
Long Buckby	v	Ampthill
Vipers	v	Amber Valley
Ilkeston	v	Peterborough
Newark	v	Stoneygate
Spalding	v	Stewarts & Lloyds

January 6 1996 (Week 17)

Long Buckby	v	Huntingdon
Ilkeston	v	Ampthill
Newark	v	Amber Valley
Spalding	v	Peterborough
Stewarts & Lloyds	v	Stoneygate
Vipers	v	Biggleswade

January 13 1996 (Week 18)

Amber Valley	v	Spalding
Ampthill	v	Newark
Biggleswade	v	Ilkeston
Huntingdon	v	Vipers
Kettering	v	Long Buckby
Peterborough	v	Stewarts & Lloyds

February 10 1996 (Week 22)

Ilkeston	v	Huntingdon
Newark	v	Biggleswade
Spalding	v	Ampthill
Stewarts & Lloyds	v	Amber Valley
Stoneygate	v	Peterborough
Vipers	v	Kettering

February 17 1996 (Week 23)

Amber Valley	v	Stoneygate
Ampthill	v	Stewarts & Lloyds
Biggleswade	v	Spalding
Huntingdon	v	Newark
Kettering	v	Ilkeston
Long Buckby	v	Vipers

February 24 1996 (Week 24)

Ilkeston	v	Long Buckby
Newark	v	Kettering
Spalding	v	Huntingdon
Stewarts & Lloyds	v	Biggleswade
Stoneygate	v	Ampthill
Peterborough	v	Amber Valley

March 30 1996 (Week X7)

Ampthill	v	Peterborough
Biggleswade	v	Stoneygate
Huntingdon	v	Stewarts & Lloyds
Kettering	v	Spalding
Long Buckby	v	Newark
Vipers	v	Ilkeston

MIDLANDS EAST ONE

AMBER VALLEY RUFC
Ground Address: Pye Bridge, Lower Somercotes, Alfreton, Derbyshire DE55 1NF. Tel: 01773 541 308
Club Secretary: Sue Ferguson, 60 Warwick Road, Somercotes, Alfreton, Derbyshire DE55 1SO. Tel: (H) 01773 606956 Tel: (W) 01773 602106
Fixtures Secretary: Tom Uniache, 34 Beaulieu Way, The Spinney, Swanwick, Alfreton, Derbyshire. Tel: (H) 01773 541953
Club Colours: Black/maroon/amber.

AMPTHILL & DISTRICT RUFC
Ground Address: Dillingham Park, Woburn Road, Ampthill, Bedford MK45 2HX. Tel: 01525 403303
Club Secretary: Richard Churchill, The Bungalow, Park Gardens, Bletchley, Milton Keynes MK3 6HT. Tel: (H) 01908 379089
Fixtures Secretary: Graham Whitehall, 72 Bluebell Close, Flitwick, Bedfod MK45 1NR. Tel: (H) 01525 715411
Club Colours: Maroon & amber.

BIGGLESWADE RUFC
Ground Address: Langford Road, Biggleswade, Beds SG18 9RA. Tel: 01767 312463
Club Secretary: Mike Williams, 8 Laurel Way, Ickleford, Hitchin, Herts SG5 3UP. Tel: (H) 01462 454782 Tel: (W) 01462 424224
Fixtures Secretary: Mike Pearson, 1 Marlowe Court, Eaton Ford, St Neots, Cambs PE19 3LG. Tel: (H) 01480 385077 Tel (W) 01480 385077
Club Colours: Navy with red hoop.

HUNTINGDON RUFC
Ground Address: The Racecourse, Brampton, Huntingdon.
Club Secretary: Jonathan Buckingham, The Gables, Chestnut Grove, Great Stukely, Huntingdon. Tel: (H) 01480 455888 Tel: (W) 01480 414411
Fixtures Secretary: Tim Tack, 37 Egremont Road, Hardwick, Cambridge CB3 7XR. Tel: (H) 01954 211140 Tel (W) 0223 833121
Club Colours: Green shirts, blue shorts, green socks.

ILKESTON RUFC
Ground Address: Gallows Inn Fields, Nottingham Road, Ilkeston, Derbyshire. Tel: 0115 932 3048
Club Secretary: Ean Wykes, 8 Carman Close, Watnall, Notts NG16 1JX. Tel: (H) 0115 9384307 Tel: (W) 0115 9384093
Fixtures Secretary: Colin Fox, 36 Nuthall Circle, Kirk Hallam, Ilkeston, Derbyshire DE7 4GU. Tel: (H) 0115 9308421 Tel (W) 0115 9443569
Club Colours: White, green & blue hoops.

KETTERING RFC
Ground Address: Waverley Road, Kettering, NN15 6NT. Tel: 01536 85588
Club Secretary: Peter May, 8 St Clement's Court, Highfield Road, Kettering, Northants. Tel: (H) 01536 415804
Fixtures Secretary: Rob Bowley, Messyage Farmhouse, 10 Lower Benefield, Peterborough. Tel: (H) 01832 205382
Club Colours: Royal blue & white hoops.

LONG BUCKBY RFC
Ground Address: Station Road, Long Buckby, Northamptonshire NN6 7QA. Tel: 01327 842222
Club Secretary: P J Osborne, Ashthorne, Teeton Road, Ravensthorpe, Northamptonshire NN6 8EJ. Tel: (H) 01604 770772 Tel: (W) 01327 705785
Fixtures Secretary: S Ruddlesdin, 37 Rockhill Road, Long Buckby, Northamptonshire NN6 7QS. Tel: (H) 01327 842933
Club Colours: Emerald green.

NEWARK RUFC
Ground Address: Kelham Road, Newark, Nottinghamshire. Tel: 01636 702355
Club Secretary: Edward Hine, Flat 3, 10 Peveril Drive,

FINAL TABLE

	P	W	D	L	F	A	Pts
Scunthorpe	12	11	0	1	366	86	22
Long Buckby	12	11	0	1	285	83	22
Spalding	12	7	1	4	137	185	15
Kettering	12	7	0	5	172	99	14
Ampthill	12	7	0	5	189	141	14
Stoneygate	12	5	1	6	163	140	11
Stewart's & Lloyds	12	5	1	6	124	146	11
Biggleswade	12	5	1	6	131	165	11
Amber Valley	12	5	1	6	87	121	11
Vipers	12	5	0	7	135	152	10
Wellingborough	12	4	0	8	133	141	8
Northampton BB	12	2	0	10	85	207	4
Chesterfield	12	1	1	10	66	407	3

The Park, Nottingham NG7 1DE. Tel: (H) 0115 947 5086 Tel: (W) 0115 929 3434
Fixtures Secretary: Hugh Daybell, The Homestead, Coddington, Newark, Nottinghamshire. Tel: (H) 01636 702197
Club Colours: Navy blue with white band.

PETERBOROUGH RUFC
Ground Address: Second Drove, Fengate, Peterborough. Tel: 01733 69413
Club Secretary: B A Hedges, 85 Apsley Way, Longthorpe, Peterborough, PE3 9NZ. Tel: (H) 01733 332287
Fixtures Secretary: MJ Proud, 64 Ramsey Road, Warboys, PE17 3RW. Tel: (H) 01487 822951
Club Colours: Red, gold, silver.

SPALDING RFC
Ground Address: Memorial Field, St Thomas Road, Spalding, Lincs PE11 2TT. Tel: 01775 725191
Club Secretary: J Constable, 14 Amsterdam Gardens, Spalding, Lincs PE11 3HY. Tel: (H) 01775 723790 Tel: (W) 01775 711911
Fixtures Secretary: P Sly, Redhouse Cottage, Scoldhall Lane, Surfleet, Spalding, Lincs PE11 4BJ. Tel: (H) 01775 680844
Club Colours: Maroon & navy blue hoops.

STEWARTS & LLOYDS RFC
Ground Address: Occupation Road, Corby, Northants NN17 1EH. Tel: 01536 400317
Club Secretary: JM Thompson, 5 Howe Crescent, Corby, Northants NN17 2RY. Tel: (H) 01536 400317
Fixtures Secretary: Vernon Cook, 52 Coldermeadow Avenue, Corby, Northants. Tel: (H) 01536 741971 Tel (W) Mobile: 0421 518320
Club Colours: Black shirts & shorts, black & white socks.**STONEYGATE FC**
Ground Address: Covert Lane, Scraptoft, Leics LE7 9SP. Tel: 0116 241 9188
Club Secretary: SM Morris, 203 Evington Lane, Evington, Leicester LE5 6DJ. Tel: (H) 0116 273 5927 Tel: (W) 0116 262 8596
Fixtures Secretary: M Herbert, 6 Spencer Street, Oadby, Leicester. Tel: (H) 0116 2714229 Tel (W) 0116 255 2694
Club Colours: Cardinal red & white hoops, navy blue shorts.

VIPERS RFC
Ground Address: Blaby Bypass, Whetstone, Leicester. Tel: 0116 286 4777
Club Secretary: Mr Paul Hutchinson, 260 Queens Road, Nuneaton, Warwickshire CV11 5LY. Tel: (H) 01203 373950 Tel (W) 0585 708767
Fixtures Secretary: Ian Reid, 52 Stanhope Road, Wigston, Leicester LE3 2BF. Tel: (H) 0116 281 0472
Club Colours: Green with black & gold hoops.

MIDLAND DIVISION

MIDLANDS EAST TWO 1995-96 FIXTURES

November 11 1995 (Week 10)
Coalville v Kibworth
Ashbourne v Lutterworth
Chesterfield v Old Northamptonians
Northampton BB v Lincoln
Moderns v Mellish
Wellingborough v South Leicester

September 16 1995 (Week 3)
Coalville v Ashbourne
South Leicester v Lutterworth
Mellish v Old Northamptonians
West Bridgford v Lincoln
Moderns v Northampton BB
Wellingborough v Chesterfield

January 6 1996 (Week 17)
Old Northamptonians v Northampton BB
Lutterworth v Chesterfield
Kibworth v Ashbourne
South Leicester v Coalville
Mellish v Wellingborough
West Bridgford v Moderns

September 23 1995 (Week 4)
Chesterfield v Coalville
Northampton BB v Wellingborough
Lincoln v Moderns
Old Northamptonians v West Bridgford
Lutterworth v Mellish
Kibworth v South Leicester

January 13 1996 (Week 18)
Coalville v Mellish
Ashbourne v South Leicester
Chesterfield v Kibworth
Northampton BB v Lutterworth
Lincoln v Old Northamptonians
Wellingborough v West Bridgford

September 30 1995 (Week X1)
Coalville v Northampton BB
Ashbourne v Chesterfield
Mellish v Kibworth
West Bridgford v Lutterworth
Moderns v Old Northamptonians
Wellingborough v Lincoln

February 10 1996 (Week 22)
Lutterworth v Lincoln
Kibworth v Northampton BB
South Leicester v Chesterfield
Mellish v Ashbourne
West Bridgford v Coalville
Moderns v Wellingborough

October 14 1995 (Week 6)
Northampton BB v Ashbourne
Lincoln v Coalville
Old Northamptonians v Wellingborough
Lutterworth v Moderns
Kibworth v West Bridgford
South Leicester v Mellish

February 17 1996 (Week 23)
Coalville v ModernsAshbourne
Chesterfield v Mellish
Northampton BB v South Leicester
Lincoln v Kibworth
Old Northamptonians v Lutterworth

February 24 1996 (Week 24)
Kibworth v Old Northamptonians
South Leicester v Lincoln
Mellish v Northampton BB
West Bridgford v Chesterfield
Moderns v Ashbourne
Wellingborough v Coalville

October 21 1995 (Week 7)
Coalville v Old Northamptonians
Ashbourne v Lincoln
Chesterfield v Northampton BB
West Bridgford v South Leicester
Moderns v Kibworth
Wellingborough v Lutterworth

October 28 1995 (Week 8)
Lincoln v Chesterfield
Old Northamptonians v Ashbourne
Lutterworth v Coalville
Kibworth v Wellingborough
South Leicester v Moderns
Mellish v West Bridgford

March 30 1996 (Week X7)
Ashbourne v Wellingborough
Chesterfield v Moderns
Northampton BB v West Bridgford
Lincoln v Mellish
Old Northamptonians v South Leicester
Lutterworth v Kibworth

MIDLANDS EAST TWO

ASHBOURNE RUFC
Ground Address: The Recreation Ground, Cokayne Avenue, Ashbourne, Derbyshire.
Club Secretary: Steve Jones, 20 North Leys, Ashbourne, Derbyshire DE6 1DQ. Tel: (H) 01335 344753 Tel: (W) 01335 343821
Fixtures Secretary: Ian Jones, 18 Oak Crescent, Ashbourne, Derbyshire. Tel: (H) 01335 344894 Tel (W) 01335 343243
Club Colours: Navy & old gold hoops.

CHESTERFIELD RUFC
Ground Address: Sheffield Road, Stonegravels, Chesterfield. Tel: 01246 232321
Club Secretary: PI Jackson, 396 Old Road, Chesterfield S40 3QF. Tel: (H) 01246 568287 Tel: (W) 01246 270112
Fixtures Secretary: M Lord, 34 Pennine Way, Loundsley Green, Chesterfield. Tel: (H) 01246 274105
Club Colours: Red & white hoops, white shorts.

COALVILLE RFC
Ground Address: Memorial Ground, Broomleys Road, Coalville, Leicester. Tel: 01530 812090
Club Secretary: Peter Smith, 50 Parkdale, Ibstock, Leics LE67 1JW. Tel: (H) 01530 262113 Tel: (W) 01530 832085
Fixtures Secretary: John Bird, 51 Battram Road, Ellistown, Leicester. Tel: (H) 01530 230186
Club Colours: Navy shirts with amber chest band & white shorts.

KIBWORTH RUFC
Ground Address: Northampton Road, Market Harborough, Leicestershire. Tel: 01858 464210
Club Secretary: David R Coe, 18 Watermeadow Close, Great Oakley, Corby, Northamptonshire NN18 8JD. Tel: (H) 01536 460052 Tel: (W) 01858 402551 x3107
Fixtures Secretary: E Gregory, 5 Manor Road, Great Bowden, Market Harborough, Leicestershire LE16 7HE. Tel: (H) 01858 465550
Club Colours: Black shirts, black shorts.

LINCOLN RFC
Ground Address: The Lindum, St Giles Avenue, Wragby Road, Lincoln LN2 4PE. Tel: 01522 528592
Club Secretary: Mr John Graves, 7 Holdensby Road, Cherryfield, Lincoln. Tel: (H) 01522 511500
Club Colours: Red, white & green hoops, green shorts, red socks.

LUTTERWORTH RFC
Ground Address: Ashby Lane, Bitteswell, Nr Lutterworth, Leics LE17 4SQ. Tel: 01455 557329
Club Secretary: Colin Hudson, Mason & Bowns Cottage, Ashby Parva, Nr Lutterworth, Leics LE17 5HY. Tel: (H) 01455 209053 Tel: (W) 01788 577191
Fixtures Secretary: Chris Payne, Cawder Ghyll, Shawell, Nr Lutterworth, Leics LE17 6AG. Tel: (H) 01788 860442
Club Colours: Red, green & white hoops.

MELLISH RFC
Ground Address: The Memorial Ground, Plains Road, Mapperley, Nottingham NG5 3RT. Tel: 0115 926 6653
Club Secretary: Mark Wrench, 1 Arndale Road, Sherwood, Nottingham NG5 3GT. Tel: (H) 0115 926 4991
Fixtures Secretary: Sid Harris, 2 Tilstock Court, Watnall, Nottingham NG16 1JZ. Tel: (H) 0115 938 5456
Club Colours: Yellow, green & black hoops.

MODERNS RFC
Ground Address: Ferryfield, Main Road, Wilford, Nottingham. Tel: 0115 9811374
Club Secretary: Brian Walls, The Fold, Hacking Lane, Kinoulton, Notts. Tel: (H) 01949 841297
Fixtures Secretary: Alistair Clark, 17 Mountsorrel Drive, Abbey Park, West Bridgford, Nottingham NG2 6LJ. Tel: (H) 0115 981 9207 Tel (W) 0115 978 1203
Club Colours: Red & white hoops, white shorts.

FINAL TABLE

	P	W	D	L	F	A	Pts
Ilkeston	12	10	0	2	230	113	20
Huntingdon	12	9	0	3	275	151	18
West Bridgford	12	8	0	4	223	177	18
Lutterworth	12	7	1	4	189	136	15
Moderns	12	7	0	5	265	188	14
Kibworth	12	7	0	5	223	153	14
Coalville	12	7	0	5	126	125	14
South Leicester	12	6	1	5	205	144	13
Lincoln	12	5	0	7	174	199	10
Mellish	12	4	1	7	118	209	9
Luton	12	3	0	9	98	153	8
Grimsby	12	2	1	9	107	223	5
Worksop	12	1	0	11	86	348	-2*

NORTHAMPTON BOYS BRIGADE OLD BOYS RFC
Ground Address: St Andrews Mill, St Andrews Road, Northampton NN1 2PG. Tel: 01604 32460
Club Secretary: Mrs S Jeffery, 218 Eastern Avenue, North Kingsthorpe, Northampton NN2 7AT. Tel: (H) 01604 717947
Fixtures Secretary: Mr P Johnson, 164 Gladstone Road, Northampton NN5 7EL. Tel: (H) 01604 586421
Club Colours: Light blue, dark blue & maroon hoops.

OLD NORTHAMPTONIANS RFC
Ground Address: Sports Field, Billing Road, Northampton. Tel: 01604 34045
Club Secretary: Keith Napier, 627 Wellingborough Road, Northampton NN3 3HR. Tel: (H) 01604 415269 Tel: (W) 01604 33329
Fixtures Secretary: David Summers, 32A Ashburnham Road, Abington, Northampton NN1 4AN. Tel: (H) 01604 715261 Tel (W) 01604 28430
Club Colours: Cardinal, navy & gold hoops.

SOUTH LEICESTER RFC
Ground Address: Welford Road, Wigston Magna, Leicester LE18 1TE. Tel: 0116 2882066
Club Secretary: Richard Dowdall, 4 Bodmin Avenue, Wigston Magna, Leicester LE18 4HB. Tel: (H) 0116 2856407
Fixtures Secretary: David Cottom, 11 Heather Way, Countesthorpe, Leicester LE8 3WU. Tel: (H) 0116 2773615
Club Colours: Green & white hoops.

WELLINGBOROUGH RFC
Ground Address: Cut Throat Lane, Great Doddington, Wellingborough, Northants NN29 7TZ. Tel: 01933 222260
Club Secretary: Bob Stevenson, 12 South Street, Wollaston, Northants NN29 7RX. Tel: (H) 01933 664538 Tel: (W) 01933 226077
Fixtures Secretary: Ian Brown, 71 Fulwell Road, Bozeat, Northants NN29 7LX. Tel: (H) 01933 663622
Club Colours: White shirts with red band, navy shorts.

WEST BRIDGFORD RFC
Ground Address: The Memorial Ground, Stamford Road, West Bridgford, Nottingham. Tel: 0115 9232506
Club Secretary: K Howells, 117 Mount Pleasant, Keyworth, Nottingham NE12 5ES. Tel: (H) 0115 937 4468
Fixtures Secretary: B Najdan, 41 Blake Road, West Bridgford, Nottingham. Tel: (H) 0115 9816853
Club Colours: Black with red & gold hoops, black shorts & stockings.

MIDLAND DIVISION

NOTTS, LINCS & DERBYS ONE 1995-96 FIXTURES

November 11 1995 (Week 10)
Buxton	v	Glossop
East Retford	v	Stamford
Long Eaton	v	Melbourne
Nottingham Casuals	v	Kesteven
Sleaford	v	Grimsby
Southwell	v	East Leake

September 16 1995 (Week 3)
East Retford	v	Buxton
Grimsby	v	Glossop
Kesteven	v	East Leake
Nottingham Casuals	v	Long Eaton
Sleaford	v	Southwell
Worksop	v	Melbourne

January 6 1996 (Week 17)
East Leake	v	Long Eaton
Glossop	v	Southwell
Grimsby	v	East Retford
Kesteven	v	Sleaford
Stamford	v	Buxton
Worksop	v	Nottingham Casuals

September 23 1995 (Week 4)
East Leake	v	Worksop
Glossop	v	Kesteven
Long Eaton	v	Sleaford
Melbourne	v	Nottingham Casuals
Southwell	v	East Retford
Stamford	v	Grimsby

January 13 1996 (Week 18)
Buxton	v	Grimsby
East Retford	v	Kesteven
Long Eaton	v	Glossop
Melbourne	v	East Leake
Sleaford	v	Worksop
Southwell	v	Stamford

September 30 1995 (Week X1)
Buxton	v	Southwell
East Retford	v	Long Eaton
Kesteven	v	Stamford
Nottingham Casuals	v	East Leake
Sleaford	v	Melbourne
Worksop	v	Glossop

February 10 1996 (Week 22)
Glossop	v	Melbourne
Grimsby	v	Southwell
Kesteven	v	Buxton
Nottingham Casuals	v	Sleaford
Stamford	v	Long Eaton
Worksop	v	East Retford

October 14 1995 (Week 6)
East Leake	v	Sleaford
Glossop	v	Nottingham Casuals
Grimsby	v	Kesteven
Long Eaton	v	Buxton
Melbourne	v	East Retford
Stamford	v	Worksop

February 17 1996 (Week 23)
Buxton	v	Worksop
East Leake	v	Glossop
East Retford	v	Nottingham Casuals
Long Eaton	v	Grimsby
Melbourne	v	Stamford
Southwell	v	Kesteven

October 21 1995 (Week 7)
Buxton	v	Melbourne
East Retford	v	East Leake
Nottingham Casuals	v	Stamford
Sleaford	v	Glossop
Southwell	v	Long Eaton
Worksop	v	Grimsby

February 24 1996 (Week 24)
Grimsby	v	Melbourne
Kesteven	v	Long Eaton
Nottingham Casuals	v	Buxton
Sleaford	v	East Retford
Stamford	v	East Leake
Worksop	v	Southwell

October 28 1995 (Week 8)
East Leake	v	Buxton
Glossop	v	East Retford
Grimsby	v	Nottingham Casuals
Kesteven	v	Worksop
Melbourne	v	Southwell
Stamford	v	Sleaford

March 30 1996 (Week X7)
Buxton	v	Sleaford
East Leake	v	Grimsby
Glossop	v	Stamford
Long Eaton	v	Worksop
Melbourne	v	Kesteven
Southwell	v	Nottingham Casuals

NOTTS, LINCS & DERBY ONE

BUXTON RUFC
Ground Address: Fairfield Centre, Victoria Park Road, Buxton, Derbyshire. Tel: 01298 24081
Club Secretary: David Robson, 20 Errwood Avenue, Buxton SK17 9BD. Tel: (H) 01298 22432 Tel: (W) 01298 26121
Fixtures Secretary: Ian Gould, 24 Queens Road, Buxton, Derbyshire SK17 7ET. Tel: (H) 01298 27683 Tel (W) 01298 768356
Club Colours: Blue, gold, red irregular hoops.

EAST LEAKE RFC
Ground Address: Costock Road Pavilion, Costock Road Playing Fields, Costock Road, East Leake, Nr Loughborough, Leics.
Club Secretary: Paul R Cobbin, Myrtle Cottages, 60 Loughborough Road, Hathern, Leicestershire LE12 5JA. Tel: (H) 01509 646354 Tel: (W) 01374 773514
Fixtures Secretary: Mike Kirton, 138 Loughborough Road, Hathern, Leics LE12 5JB. Tel: (H) 01509 646472 or 842212 Tel (W) 01850 101635
Club Colours: Maroon shirts, black shorts.

EAST RETFORD RUFC
Ground Address: Ordsall Road, East Retford, Nottinghamshire. Tel: 01777 703243
Club Secretary: EM Henderson, 51 Trent Street, Retford, Nottinghamshire DN22 6NG. Tel: (H) 01777 706987 Tel: (W) 01909 476724
Fixtures Secretary: B Dudley, 21 Southfall Close, Rawskill, Nottinghamshire. Tel: (H) 01777 818616 Tel (W) 0191 483 2451
Club Colours: Emerald & amber hoops, royal blue shorts.

GLOSSOP RUFC
Ground Address: Hargate Hill Lane, Charlesworth, Broadbottom, Hyde, Cheshire, SK13 9JL. Tel: 01457 864553
Club Secretary: Alastair May, 6 Kinder Grove, Romiley, Stockport, SK6 4EU. Tel: (H) 0161 427 5774 Tel: (W) 01457 864553
Fixtures Secretary: Dave Gerrard, 11 Burnside, Hadfield, Hyde, Cheshire, SK14 8DX. Tel: (H) 01457 865014 Tel (W) 01142 735030
Club Colours: Blue and white quartered shirts.

GRIMSBY RUFC
Ground Address: Springfield Road, Scartho, Grimsby, Sth Humberside, DN33 3JF. Tel: 01472 878594
Club Secretary: Geoff Norton, 157 Chichester Road, Cleethorpes, South Humberside, DN35 0JN. Tel: (H) 01472 696629 Tel: (W) 01472 254450
Fixtures Secretary: Roy Campodonic, 35 Bulwick Avenue, Grimsby, South Humberside DN33 3BH. Tel: (H) 01472 825904
Club Colours: Royal blue shirts, white shorts.

KESTEVEN RUFC
Ground Address: Wood Nook, Nr Grantham, Lincolnshire. Tel: 01476 64887
Club Secretary: Mr NJ Pert, 8 High Street, Ropsley, Nr Grantham. Tel: (H) 01476 585352 Tel: (W) 01476 616314
Fixtures Secretary: Mr D Gilbert, 3 Bluetown, Skillington, Nr Grantham. Tel: (H) 01476 860676
Club Colours: Black shirts, white shorts.

LONG EATON RFC
Ground Address: West Park, Long Eaton, Notts. Tel: 0115 946 0907
Club Secretary: Tony Suiter, 102 Trowell Grove, Long Eaton, Notts NG10 4BB. Tel: (H) 0115 972 1267 Tel: (W) 0115 9344776
Fixtures Secretary: Martin Smith, 4 Hawthorn Avenue, Long Eaton, Notts NG10 3NF. Tel: (H) 0973 379510 Tel (W) 0973 379510
Club Colours: Blue & white quarters, black shorts.

FINAL TABLE

	P	W	D	L	F	A	Pts
Ashbourne	12	10	0	2	196	113	20
Stamford	12	8	0	4	247	134	16
Glossop	12	7	1	4	186	116	15
Kesteven	12	7	2	3	186	118	14*
Nottingham Casuals	12	6	1	5	241	170	13
Long Eaton	12	6	1	5	150	140	13
Southwell	12	6	1	5	141	141	13
East Leake	12	6	0	6	164	158	12
Sleaford	12	5	0	7	166	183	10
Melbourne	12	5	0	7	128	174	10
Leesbrook	12	4	1	7	158	205	9
Bakewell Mannerians	12	2	1	9	102	271	5
Dronfield	12	2	0	10	93	235	4

MELBOURNE RFC
Ground Address: Melbourne Recreation Ground, Cock Shut Lane, Melbourne, Derbyshire. Tel: 01332 865330
Club Secretary: Miss Debbie Clarke, 48 Station Road, Melbourne, Derby DE73 1EB. Tel: (H) 01332 864966
Fixtures Secretary: Mr D Carlier, 21 Selina Close, Melbourne, Derby. Tel: (H) 01332 864446 Tel (W) 01332 864446
Club Colours: Bottle green.

NOTTINGHAM CASUALS RFC
Ground Address: Canal Side, Meadow Road, Beeston Rylands, Nottingham NG9 1JG. Tel: 0115 925 0135
Club Secretary: A Rothera, 36 Harcourt Street, Beeston, Nottingham NG9 1EY. Tel: (H) 0115 925 7427 Tel: (W) 0115 951 4489
Fixtures Secretary: J Lillestone, 16 Chapel Fields, Swinford, Leics LE17 6BS. Tel: (H) 01788 860530
Club Colours: White with maroon hoops.

SLEAFORD RFC
Ground Address: Sleaford RFC, East Road, Sleaford. Tel: 01529 303335
Club Secretary: Mark Ainger, 28 Summerfield Drive, Sleaford, Lincs. Tel: (H) 01529 307054
Fixtures Secretary: George Marsh, 37 Meadowfield, Sleaford, Lincs. Tel: (H) 01529 303859
Club Colours: Red & black hoops, black shorts, red socks.

SOUTHWELL RUFC
Ground Address: Pentelowes, Park Lane, Southwell, Notts. Tel: 01636 812576
Club Secretary: Paul Nicholas Robinson, The Hall Farm, Main Street, Farnsfield, NG22 8EY. Tel: (H) 01623 882010 Tel: (W) 0116 289200
Fixtures Secretary: Phil Gordon, Beggars Behind, Main Street, Morton, Notts. Tel: (H) 01636 830485
Club Colours: Maroon shirts, navy blue shorts.

STAMFORD RUFC
Ground Address: Hambleton Road, Stamford, Lincs. Tel: 01780 52180
Club Secretary: NM Jolly, 21 Chatsworth Road, Stamford, Lincs. Tel: (H) 01780 52134 Tel: (W) 01780 720501
Fixtures Secretary: A Baker, 27 Queens Walk, Stamford, Lincs. Tel: (H) 01780 56367
Club Colours: Purple/black/white.

WORKSOP RUFC
Ground Address: Stubbing Lane, Worksop, Notts. Tel: 01909 484247
Club Secretary: Mr ME Murphy, 86 Bridge Street, Worksop, Notts S80 1JF. Tel: (H) 01777 870952 Tel: (W) 01909 500544
Fixtures Secretary: Nick Gibson, 12 Maple Drive, Worksop, Notts S81 0LR. Tel: (H) 01909 487506 Tel (W) 01629 580000 x7558
Club Colours: Black & white hoops, black shorts.

MIDLAND DIVISION

November 11 1995 (Week 10)

All Spartans	v	Rolls Royce
Boston	v	Boots Athletic
Castle Donington	v	Ashfield Swans
Keyworth	v	North Kesteven
Leesbrook Asterdale	v	Bakewell Mannerians
Market Rasen & Louth	v	Dronfield

September 16 1995 (Week 3)

Bakewell Mannerians	v	Ashfield Swans
Boston	v	Castle Donington
Dronfield	v	North Kesteven
Leesbrook Asterdale	v	Keyworth
Market Rasen & Louth	v	All Spartans
Nottingham Police	v	Rolls Royce

September 23 1995 (Week 4)

All Spartans	v	Leesbrook Asterdale
Ashfield Swans	v	Dronfield
Boots Athletic	v	Bakewell Mannerians
Keyworth	v	Boston
North Kesteven	v	Nottingham Police
Rolls Royce	v	Market Rasen & Louth

September 30 1995 (Week X1)

Boston	v	All Spartans
Castle Donington	v	Keyworth
Dronfield	v	Boots Athletic
Leesbrook Asterdale	v	Rolls Royce
Market Rasen & Louth	v	North Kesteven
Nottingham Police	v	Ashfield Swans

October 14 1995 (Week 6)

All Spartans	v	Castle Donington
Ashfield Swans	v	Market Rasen & Louth
Bakewell Mannerians	v	Dronfield
Boots Athletic	v	Nottingham Police
North Kesteven	v	Leesbrook Asterdale
Rolls Royce	v	Boston

October 21 1995 (Week 7)

Boston	v	North Kesteven
Castle Donington	v	Rolls Royce
Keyworth	v	All Spartans
Leesbrook Asterdale	v	Ashfield Swans
Market Rasen & Louth	v	Boots Athletic
Nottingham Police	v	Bakewell Mannerians

October 28 1995 (Week 8)

Ashfield Swans	v	Boston
Bakewell Mannerians	v	Market Rasen & Louth
Boots Athletic	v	Leesbrook Asterdale
Dronfield	v	Nottingham Police
North Kesteven	v	Castle Donington
Rolls Royce	v	Keyworth

January 6 1996 (Week 17)

Ashfield Swans	v	Keyworth
Bakewell Mannerians	v	Boston
Boots Athletic	v	Castle Donington
Dronfield	v	Leesbrook Asterdale
North Kesteven	v	All Spartans
Nottingham Police	v	Market Rasen & Louth

January 13 1996 (Week 18)

All Spartans	v	Ashfield Swans
Boston	v	Dronfield
Castle Donington	v	Bakewell Mannerians
Keyworth	v	Boots Athletic
Leesbrook Asterdale	v	Nottingham Police
Rolls Royce	v	North Kesteven

February 10 1996 (Week 22)

Ashfield Swans	v	Rolls Royce
Bakewell Mannerians	v	Keyworth
Boots Athletic	v	All Spartans
Dronfield	v	Castle Donington
Market Rasen & Louth	v	Leesbrook Asterdale
Nottingham Police	v	Boston

February 17 1996 (Week 23)

All Spartans	v	Bakewell Mannerians
Boston	v	Market Rasen & Louth
Castle Donington	v	Nottingham Police
Keyworth	v	Dronfield
North Kesteven	v	Ashfield Swans
Rolls Royce	v	Boots Athletic

February 24 1996 (Week 24)

Bakewell Mannerians	v	Rolls Royce
Boots Athletic	v	North Kesteven
Dronfield	v	All Spartans
Leesbrook Asterdale	v	Boston
Market Rasen & Louth	v	Castle Donington
Nottingham Police	v	Keyworth

March 30 1996 (Week X7)

All Spartans	v	Nottingham Police
Ashfield Swans	v	Boots Athletic
Castle Donington	v	Leesbrook Asterdale
Keyworth	v	Market Rasen & Louth
North Kesteven	v	Bakewell Mannerians
Rolls Royce	v	Dronfield

NOTTS, LINCS & DERBY TWO

ALL SPARTANS RUFC
Ground Address: Sutton Lawn, Station Road, Sutton in
Ashfield, Notts. Tel: 01623 554554
Club Secretary: Peter Graney, 14 St Edmund's Avenue, Mans,
Woodhouse, Notts NG19 9JX. Tel: (H) 01623 653048
Fixtures Secretary: John Chambers, Tideswell, 12 Berry Hill
Lane, Mansfield, Notts NG18 4BQ. Tel: (H) 01623 641391
Club Colours: Blue shirts with amber hoop, black shorts, blue
socks.

ASHFIELD SWANS RUFC
Ground Address: Ashfield School, Sutton Road, Kirkby in
Ashfield, Nottinghamshire. Tel: 01623 752403
Club Secretary: Stephen Trainer, 12 Belfry Close, Broadlands
Park, Kirkby-in-Ashfield, Notts NG17 8NS. Tel: (H) 01623
443744 Tel: (W) 0115 965 7276
Fixtures Secretary: Paul Raymont, 18 Longhill Rise, Kirkby
in Ashfield, Nottinghamshire NG19 9FL. Tel: (H) 01623
750990
Club Colours: Red & black hoops.

BAKEWELL MANNERIANS RUFC
Ground Address: The Showground, Coombs Road, Bakewell,
Derbyshire.
Club Secretary: Tom Furness, Fern Bank, Brookfield Lane,
Bakewell, Derbyshire DE45 1AN. Tel: (H) 01629 812863 Tel:
(W) 01629 580000 x7186
Fixtures Secretary: John Oldfield, Oldfield Design, Riverside
Works, Buxton Road, Bakewell, Derbyshire DE45 1GJ. Tel:
(H) 01629 814911 Tel (W) 01629 813301
Club Colours: Dark blue, light blue & white hooped shirts,
navy shorts.

BOOTS ATHLETIC RUFC
Ground Address: Boots Sports Ground, Holme Road, Lady
Bay, West Bridgford, Nottingham. Tel: 01159 492388/01159
813112
Club Secretary: Mike Freemantle, 18 Kirkby Close,
Southwell, Notts NG25 0DG. Tel: (H) 01636 816433 Tel: (W)
01636 830302
Fixtures Secretary: Greg Haywood, Slaughterhouse Cottage,
Main Street, Epperstone, Notts NG14 6AD. Tel: (H) 0115 966
4629 Tel (W) 0115 947 0712
Club Colours: Navy/sky blue quarters.

BOSTON RFC
Ground Address: Great Fen Road, Boardsides, Wyberton,
Boston, Lincs PE2 7PB. Tel: 01205 362683
Club Secretary: Mrs Lynn Creasey, 48 Glen Drive, Boston,
Lincs PE21 7QB. Tel: (H) 01205 356753 Tel: (W) 01205
313002
Fixtures Secretary: Mr Tim Bembridge, 5 Blackthorne Lane,
Boston, Lincs PE21 9PB. Tel: (H) 01205 351973
Club Colours: Blue & white hoops.

CASTLE DONINGTON RUFC
Ground Address: The Spittal Playing Fields, The Spittal,
Castle Donington, Derbyshire.
Club Secretary: Adrian Hackett, The Old Bakery, Thringstone,
Leicestershire LE67 5AP. Tel: (H) 01530 223599 Tel: (W)
0831 675987
Fixtures Secretary: Mr P Parry, 80 Suthers Road, Kegworth,
Derbyshire DE74 2DE. Tel: (H) 01509 672148 Tel (W) 01509
672148
Club Colours: Red & black quartered shirtss, black shorts, red
& black hooped socks.

DRONFIELD RUFC
Ground Address: Dronfield School, Stubley Lane, Dronfield
Woodhouse, Nr Sheffield. Tel: Clubhouse: 0114 289 0913
Club Secretary: Dr RCC Nixon, 129 Ridgeway Road,
Sheffield S12 2SQ. Tel: (H) 0114 239 8510 Tel: (W) 01709
828500
Fixtures Secretary: Mick Rodgers, 56 Ribblesdale Drive,
Sheffield S12 3XE. Tel: (H) 0114 247 2846
Club Colours: Red shirts, black shorts.

KEYWORTH RFC
Ground Address: The Pavilion, Willoughby Lane,
Widmerpool, Nottinghamshire NG2 6EZ. Tel: 01159 375579
Club Secretary: MP Tyrrell, 60 Peterborough Road, Farcet,
Peterborough, Cambs PE7 3BN. Tel: (H) 01733 310468
Fixtures Secretary: Brian Lund, 15 Debdale Lane, Keyworth,

FINAL TABLE

	P	W	D	L	F	A	Pts
Buxton	12	11	0	1	288	95	22
East Retford	12	10	1	1	409	148	21
Mkt Rasen & Louth	12	8	0	4	254	130	16
Keyworth	12	8	0	4	167	109	16
Ashfield Swans	12	8	0	4	173	116	16
All Spartans	12	7	0	5	173	140	14
Boston	12	6	0	6	133	173	12
Rolls Royce	12	6	0	6	117	190	10*
Nottinghamshire Con	12	5	1	6	105	115	9*
North Kesteven	12	5	0	7	173	138	8*
Bingham	12	1	1	10	75	333	3
Barton & District	12	0	2	10	86	295	2
Meden Vale	12	0	1	11	78	249	1

Notts. Tel: (H) 01159 374 079 Tel (W) Ans: 01159 374076
Club Colours: Black with gold stripes or gold with black
stripes.

LEESBROOK ASTERDALE RUFC
Ground Address: Asterdale Centre, Borrowash Road,
Spondon, Derby. Tel: 01332 668656
Club Secretary: c/o Draefern Ltd, Victoria
Chambers, 60 London Road, Derby DE1 2PA. Tel: (W) 01332
290188
Fixtures Secretary: Derek Chambers, 17 St John's Drive,
Chaddesden, Derby DE21 6SD. Tel: (H) 01332 668980
Club Colours: Black, white, green & blue quarters.

MARKET RASEN & LOUTH RUFC
Ground Address: Willingham Road, Market Rasen, Lincs LN8
3RE. Tel: 01673 843162
Club Secretary: B Harper, Newgoby, Church Lane, Manby,
Louth, Lincs, LN11 8HL. Tel: (H) 01507 327318 Tel: (W)
01507 327318
Fixtures Secretary: J Holt, Manesty, 1 Castle Hill, Caistor,
Lincoln, LN7 6UG. Tel: (H) 01472 851653 Tel (W) 01472
851653
Club Colours: Red & green hoops.

NORTH KESTEVEN RUFC
Ground Address: Memorial Fields, rear of Memorial Hall,
Newark Road, North Hykeham, Lincoln. Tel: 01522 680193
Club Secretary: Kevin Flynn, 20 Stenigot Close, Doddington
Park, Lincoln LN6 3PB. Tel: (H) 01522 692409 Tel: (W) 01780
720041 x7455
Fixtures Secretary: Nigel Thomas, 192 Hykeham Road,
Lincoln LN6 8AR. Tel: (H) 01522 696666
Club Colours: Black shirts with white, emerald & scarlet
bands, black shorts.

NOTTINGHAMSHIRE CONSTABULARY RFC
Ground Address: Mellish RFC, Plains Road, Mapperley,
Nottingham. Tel: 0115 926 6655
Club Secretary: Mr Ian Wintom, Olde Breck, 4 Hall Mews,
Main Street, Papplewick, Notts NG15 8FW. Tel: (H) 0115 964
0364 Tel: (W) 0115 948 2999 x5204
Fixtures Secretary: Martin Hewitt, 10 The Mount, Redhill,
Nottingham. Tel: (H) 0115 920 4996 Tel (W) 0115 942 0999
Club Colours: Black/bottle green quarters.

ROLLS-ROYCE RFC
Ground Address: Merrill Way, Allenton, Derby.
Club Secretary: Nigel Calladine, 131 Marjorie Road,
Chaddesden, Derby, DE21 4HP. Tel: (H) 01335 344554 Tel:
(W) 01335 344554
Fixtures Secretary: Cerith Davies, 66 Alwards Close,
Alvaston, Derby DE24 0FB. Tel: (H) 01332 572256
Club Colours: Maroon/sky blue quarters.

MIDLAND DIVISION

NOTTS, LINCS & DERBYS THREE 1995-96 FIXTURES

November 11 1995 (Week 10)

Barton & District	v	Cotgrave
Bingham	v	Nottinghamians
Cleethorpes	v	University of Derby
Meden Vale	v	Belper
Stamford College	v	Horncastle
Yarborough Bees	v	Tupton

September 16 1995 (Week 3)

Cleethorpes	v	Barton & District
Horncastle	v	Cotgrave
Ollerton	v	Belper
Stamford College	v	Bingham
Tupton	v	Nottinghamians
Yarborough Bees	v	Meden Vale

January 6 1996 (Week 17)

Cotgrave	v	Bingham
Horncastle	v	Cleethorpes
Nottinghamians	v	Meden Vale
Ollerton	v	Yarborough Bees
Tupton	v	Stamford College
University of Derby	v	Barton & District

September 23 1995 (Week 4)

Belper	v	Yarborough Bees
Bingham	v	Cleethorpes
Cotgrave	v	Tupton
Meden Vale	v	Stamford College
Nottinghamians	v	Ollerton
University of Derby	v	Horncastle

January 13 1996 (Week 18)

Barton & District	v	Horncastle
Belper	v	Nottinghamians
Bingham	v	University of Derby
Cleethorpes	v	Tupton
Meden Vale	v	Cotgrave
Stamford College	v	Ollerton

September 30 1995 (Week X1)

Barton & District	v	Bingham
Cleethorpes	v	Meden Vale
Ollerton	v	Cotgrave
Stamford College	v	Belper
Tupton	v	University of Derby
Yarborough Bees	v	Nottinghamians

February 10 1996 (Week 22)

Cotgrave	v	Belper
Horncastle	v	Bingham
Ollerton	v	Cleethorpes
Tupton	v	Barton & District
University of Derby	v	Meden Vale
Yarborough Bees	v	Stamford College

October 14 1995 (Week 6)

Belper	v	Cleethorpes
Cotgrave	v	Yarborough Bees
Horncastle	v	Tupton
Meden Vale	v	Barton & District
Nottinghamians	v	Stamford College
University of Derby	v	Ollerton

February 17 1996 (Week 23)

Barton & District	v	Ollerton
Belper	v	University of Derby
Bingham	v	Tupton
Cleethorpes	v	Yarborough Bees
Meden Vale	v	Horncastle
Nottinghamians	v	Cotgrave

October 21 1995 (Week 7)

Barton & District	v	Belper
Bingham	v	Meden Vale
Cleethorpes	v	Nottinghamians
Ollerton	v	Horncastle
Stamford College	v	Cotgrave
Yarborough Bees	v	University of Derby

February 24 1996 (Week 24)

Horncastle	v	Belper
Ollerton	v	Bingham
Stamford College	v	Cleethorpes
Tupton	v	Meden Vale
University of Derby	v	Nottinghamians
Yarborough Bees	v	Barton & District

October 28 1995 (Week 8)

Belper	v	Bingham
Cotgrave	v	Cleethorpes
Horncastle	v	Yarborough Bees
Nottinghamians	v	Barton & District
Tupton	v	Ollerton
University of Derby	v	Stamford College

March 30 1996 (Week X7)

Barton & District	v	Stamford College
Belper	v	Tupton
Bingham	v	Yarborough Bees
Cotgrave	v	University of Derby
Meden Vale	v	Ollerton
Nottinghamians	v	Horncastle

446

NOTTS, LINCS & DERBY THREE

BARTON & DISTRICT RUFC
Ground Address: Mill Lane, Barrow-on-Humber, South Humberside.
Club Secretary: Tom Phipps, 4 West Acridge, Barton-on-Humber, South Humberside. Tel: (H) 01652 632373 Tel: (W) 01724 847888
Fixtures Secretary: Andy Snowdon, Western Villa, High Burgage, Winteringham, South Humberside. Tel: (H) 01724 734629
Club Colours: Red & white hoops.

BELPER RUFC
Ground Address: Eyes Meadow, Duffield, Derbyshire.
Club Secretary: Chris Smith, Hillcrest, Hillcliffe Lane, Turnditch, Belper, Derbyshire DE5 2EA. Tel: (H) 01773 550702 Tel: (W) 01332 332248
Fixtures Secretary: Adrian Young, 1 Derwent Bridge Cottage, Makney Road, Duffield, Derbyshire. Tel: (H) 01332 842768 Tel (W) 01332 349457
Club Colours: Black & white hoops.

BINGHAM RUFC
Ground Address: The Town Pavilion, Brendan Grove, Wynhill, Bingham, Notts. Tel: 01949 832874
Club Secretary: John Perry, 29 Cogley Lane, Bingham, Notts. Tel: (H) 01949 837777
Fixtures Secretary: RJ Williams, Crown House, High Street, Collingham, Notts. Tel: (H) 01636 8233076
Club Colours: Green & red hoops.

CLEETHORPES RUFC
Ground Address: Wilton Road, Cleethorpes, South Humberside. Tel: 01472 812936
Club Secretary: Mr Alan Clark, 10 Cambridge Street, Cleethorpes, South Humberside DN35 8HB. Tel: (H) 01472 692716 Tel: (W) 01469 572464
Fixtures Secretary: Mr John Walsham, 38 Richmond Road, Cleethorpes. Tel: (H) 01472 699322
Club Colours: Gold with blue hoops.

COTGRAVE COLLIERY RUFC
Ground Address: Cotgrave Community Centre, Woodview, Cotgrave, Nottingham NE12 3PJ. Tel: 0115 989 2916
Club Secretary: Mr JP Robinson, 10 Fosse Walk, Cotgrave, Nottingham NG12 3NZ. Tel: (H) 0115 989 2501
Fixtures Secretary: Paul Cooke, 6 Ashlea Close, Cotgrave, Nottingham NG12 3PR. Tel: (H) 0115 989 9829 Tel (W) 0115 947 6111
Club Colours: Claret & blue quarters.

HORNCASTLE RFC
Ground Address: The Pavilion, Horncastle Playing Fields, Horncastle, Lincs. Tel: 01507 526 742
Club Secretary: Miss TJ Livingstone, 30 East Street, Horncastle, Lincs LN9 6AZ.
Fixtures Secretary: Jeff Bentley, 1 Albert Cottages, Chapel Lane, Legbourne, Louth, Lincs LN11 8LW. Tel: (H) 01507 600318
Club Colours: Green & gold quarters, black shorts.

MEDEN VALE RFC
Ground Address: Welbeck Colliery Miners Welfare Institute, Elkesley Road, Meden Vale, Mansfield, Notts. Tel: 01623 842267
Club Secretary: Garry Blake, 3 Coggins Lane, Old Church Warsop, Mansfield, Notts NG20 0RP. Tel: (H) 01623 846335
Fixtures Secretary: Garry Blake, 3 Coggins Lane, Old Church Warsop, Mansfield, Notts NG20 0RP. Tel: (H) 01623 846335
Club Colours: Black with white collar.

NOTTINGHAMIANS RFC
Ground Address: Adbolton Lane, West Bridgford, Nottingham. Tel: 0115 981 1372
Club Secretary: David Hampson, 43 Lenton Manor, Lenton, Nottingham NG7 2FW. Tel: (H) 0115 946 2121

FINAL TABLE						
	P	W	D	L	F	A	Pts
Castle Donington	12	9	2	1	313	107	20
Derby University	12	9	1	2	253	151	19
Boots Athletic	12	9	1	2	217	118	19
Stamford College	12	9	0	3	240	101	18
Nottinghamians	12	8	1	3	204	150	17
Cotgrave	12	7	2	3	290	139	16
Tupton	12	7	0	5	198	137	14
Belper	12	5	1	6	179	131	11
Horncastle	12	4	0	8	145	233	8
Ollerton & Beverct	12	3	0	9	158	336	6
Skegness	12	2	0	10	113	203	4
Bolsover	12	2	0	10	113	189	2*
Gainsborough	12	0	0	12	57	485	0

Tel: (W) 0115 946 2121
Fixtures Secretary: Phil Quinn, 80 Dunster Road, Newthorpe, Notts NG16 2DW. Tel: (H) 01773 710668 Tel (W) 0115 941 8418
Club Colours: Black, white & purple hoops.

OLLERTON RUFC
Ground Address: Boughton Village Hall Sports Field, Church Lane, Boughton, Newark, Notts.
Club Secretary: DG Price, Lathkill, Harrow Farm, Tuxford Road, Boughton, Newark, Notts NG22 9JZ. Tel: (H) 01623 860871
Fixtures Secretary: DG Price, Lathkill, Harrow Farm, Tuxford Road, Boughton, Newark, Notts NG22 9JZ. Tel: (H) 01623 860871
Club Colours: Yellow & blue hoops.

STAMFORD COLLEGE RFC
Ground Address: Stamford College of Further Education, Drift Road, Stamford, Lincs.
Club Secretary: Steve Pulley, 5 Fir Road, Stamford, Lincs. Tel: (H) 01780 66352
Fixtures Secretary: Steve Pulley 5 Fir Road, Stamford, Lincs. Tel: (H) 01780 66352
Club Colours: Red & green hoops.

TUPTON RUFC
Ground Address: Recreation Ground, North Side, Tupton, Chesterfield. Tel: 01246 862002
Club Secretary: Steve Robinson, 7 Gladstone Road, Chesterfield, Derbyshire S40 4TE. Tel: (H) 01246 202857 Tel: (W) 01246 217522
Fixtures Secretary: Bob Curry, 190 Queen Victoria Road, New Tupton, Derbyshire S42 6DW. Tel: (H) 01246 862059
Club Colours: Navy blue shirt with 3 yellow bands, navy blue shorts & socks.

UNIVERSITY OF DERBY RUFC
Ground Address: University of Derby, Kedleston Road, Derby, DE22 1GB. Tel: 01332 622222
Club Secretary: Laurence Byrn, c/o Students Union, University of Derby, Kedleston Road, Derby DE22 1GB. Tel: (W) Students Union: 01332 348846
Fixtures Secretary: Laurence Byrn, c/o Students' Union, University of Derby, Kedleston Rd, Derby DE22 1GB. Tel (W) Students Union: 01332 348846
Club Colours: Dark green & white quarters.

YARBOROUGH BEES RUFC
Ground Address: Yarborough Sports Centre, Riseholme Road, Lincoln. Tel: 01522 524228
Club Secretary: H Sampson, 7 Shannon Avenue, Lincoln LN6 7JG. Tel: (H) 01522 691631
Fixtures Secretary: Mr A Goude, 44 Rooklands, Scotter Lincs DN21 3TT. Tel: (H) 01724 867048
Club Colours: Maroon & amber.

MIDLAND DIVISION

NOTTS, LINCS & DERBYS FOUR 1995-96 FIXTURES

September 23 1995 (Week 4)
Bolsover v Whitwell
Gainsborough v Bilsthorpe
Metheringham v Bourne
RAF Waddington v Hope Valley
Skegness v Buxton Eagles

October 14 1995 (Week 6)
Bilsthorpe v Metheringham
Bourne v Skegness
Buxton Eagles v RAF Waddington
Hope Valley v Bolsover
Sutton Bonnington v Gainsborough

October 21 1995 (Week 7)
Bolsover v Buxton Eagles
Metheringham v Sutton Bonnington
RAF Waddington v Bourne
Skegness v Bilsthorpe
Whitwell v Hope Valley

October 28 1995 (Week 8)
Bilsthorpe v RAF Waddington
Bourne v Bolsover
Buxton Eagles v Whitwell
Gainsborough v Metheringham
Sutton Bonnington v Skegness

November 11 1995 (Week 10)
Bolsover v Bilsthorpe
Hope Valley v Buxton Eagles
RAF Waddington v Sutton Bonnington
Skegness v Gainsborough
Whitwell v Bourne

January 6 1996 (Week 17)
Bilsthorpe v Whitwell
Bourne v Hope Valley
Gainsborough v RAF Waddington
Metheringham v Skegness
Sutton Bonnington v Bolsover

January 13 1996 (Week 18)
Bolsover v Gainsborough
Buxton Eagles v Bourne
Hope Valley v Bilsthorpe
RAF Waddington v Metheringham
Whitwell v Sutton Bonnington

February 10 1996 (Week 22)
Bilsthorpe v Buxton Eagles
Gainsborough v Whitwell
Metheringham v Bolsover
Skegness v RAF Waddington
Sutton Bonnington v Hope Valley

February 17 1996 (Week 23)
Bolsover v Skegness
Bourne v Bilsthorpe
Buxton Eagles v Sutton Bonnington
Hope Valley v Gainsborough
Whitwell v Metheringham

February 24 1996 (Week 24)
Gainsborough v Buxton Eagles
Metheringham v Hope Valley
RAF Waddington v Bolsover
Skegness v Whitwell
Sutton Bonnington v Bourne

March 30 1996 (Week X7)
Bilsthorpe v Sutton Bonnington
Bourne v Gainsborough
Buxton Eagles v Metheringham
Hope Valley v Skegness
Whitwell v RAF Waddington

448

NOTTS, LINCS & DERBY FOUR

BILSTHORPE RUFC
Ground Address: Bilsthorpe Sports Ground, Eakring Road, Bilsthorpe, Newark, Notts.
Club Secretary: Peter G Steffen, 55 Crompton Road, Bilsthorpe, Newark, Notts NG22 8PS. Tel: (H) 01623 870906
Fixtures Secretary: Darren Wilford, 18 Sixth Avenue, Edwinstowe, Mansfield, Notts NG21 9PN. Tel: (H) 01623 824120
Club Colours: Green/gold/black hoops.

BOLSOVER RUFC
Ground Address: Oxcroft Miners' Welfare, Clowne Road, Stanfree, Chesterfield, Derbyshire.
Club Secretary: Lynda Knight, 224 Shuttleworth Road, Bolsover, Chesterfield, Derbyshire S44 6PA. Tel: (H) 01246 822418
Fixtures Secretary: Gerry Weedon, 55 Station Road, Bolsover, Chesterfield, Derbyshire. Tel: (H) 01246 824076
Club Colours: Blue, white & gold.

BOURNE RUFC
Ground Address: Milking Nook Drive, Spalding Road, Bourne, Lincs. Tel: 01778 393346
Club Secretary: Andrew J Rowe, 54 North Road, Bourne, Lincs PE10 9BT. Tel: (H) 01778 424353 Tel: (W) 01933 57511
Fixtures Secretary: Rob Haddon, Rough Hill Cottage, Dolans Lane, Edenham, Bourne, Lincs. Tel: (H) 01778 591336
Club Colours: Blue with gold band.

BUXTON EAGLES RUFC
Ground Address: Eagle Hotel, Eagle Parade, Buxton, Derbyshire. Tel: 01298 24521
Club Secretary: Mr Simon Shouls, 27 Burlow Road, Hardur Hill, Buxton, Derbyshire SK17 9HZ. Tel: (H) 01298 22294
Fixtures Secretary: Mr C France, 46 Fairfield Road, Buxton. Tel: (H) 01298 26158 Tel (W) 01298 24521
Club Colours: Black.

GAINSBOROUGH RUFC
Ground Address: Rose Leisure, North Warren Road, Gainsborough, Lincs. Tel: 01427 612915
Club Secretary: AC Lobley, Church View Cottage, Gringley Road, Walkeringham, Doncaster, South Yorkshire DN10 4HT. Tel: (H) 01427 890951 Tel: (W) 01427 612885
Fixtures Secretary: A Russel, Plot 29, The Meadows, Holme Lane, Messingham. Tel: (H) 01724 612915
Club Colours: Black.

HOPE VALLEY RUFC
Ground Address: Castleton Playing Fields, Hollowford Road, Castleton. Tel: c/o The Peak Hotel 01433 620247
Club Secretary: Ian Broad, 10 Farndale Road, Hillsborough, Sheffield S6 1SH. Tel: (H) 0114 233 8264
Fixtures Secretary: Andy Woodall, 3 Brough Cottages, Brough, Bradwell S30 2HG. Tel: (H) 01433 620698
Club Colours: Purple, green & white quarters, black shorts.

METHERINGHAM RUFC
Ground Address: Metheringham Village Playing Field, Princes Street, Metheringham, Lincoln.
Club Secretary: Mrs Jayne Brown, Old Coach House, High Street, Metheringham, Lincoln LN4 3EA. Tel: (H) 01526 322370 Tel: (W) 01526 Fax: 01526 320110
Fixtures Secretary: Mr M Bridge, 5 Wesley Close, Metheringham, Lincoln. Tel: (H) 01526 321997
Club Colours: Black & gold.

RAF WADDINGTON RUFC
Ground Address: RAF Waddington, Waddington, Lincs LN5 9NB. Tel: 01522 720271 (ask for gymnasium) or 01836 719771
Club Secretary: Ray Massey, 19 Kyme Road, Heckinton, Sleeford, Lincs NG34 9RS. Tel: (H) 01836 719771
Fixtures Secretary: Ray Massey, 19 Kyme Road,

FINAL TABLE	P	W	D	L	F	A	Pts
Cleethorpes	12	9	0	3	293	117	18
Yarborough Bees	12	7	2	3	239	81	16
Sutton Bonnington S	12	7	2	3	172	86	16
Bourne	12	8	1	3	194	88	15*
Whitwell	12	3	1	8	94	165	7
Hope Valley	12	3	0	9	54	378	6
Bilsthorpe	12	2	0	10	114	245	4

Heckinton, Sleeford, Lincs NG34 9RS. Tel: (H) 01836 719771
Club Colours: Black & gold quarters.

SKEGNESS RUFC
Ground Address: Wainfleet Road, Skegness. Tel: 01754 765699
Club Secretary: Alan Hawkes, Grunters Grange, East Keal, Spilsby, Lincs. Tel: (H) 01790 752788
Fixtures Secretary: Jeremy Kendall, Flat 1, 12 Prince Alfred Avenue, Skegness PE25 2UH. Tel: (H) 01754 761903
Club Colours: Royal blue & white hoops.

SUTTON BONNINGTON RFC
Ground Address: Sutton Bonnington School of Agriculture, Loughborough, Leicestershire. Tel: 01159 515151 x8462
Club Secretary: Michael Gardiner, Sutton Bonnington Guild Office, School of Agriculture, Loughborough, Leicestershire LE12 5RD. Tel: (H) 01159 515151 x8648
Fixtures Secretary: Matt Higgs. Sutton Bonnington Guild Office, School of Agriculture, Loughborough, Leicestershire LE12 5RD. Tel: (H) 01159 515151 x8648
Club Colours: Black, green & white stripes.

WHITWELL RUFC
Ground Address: Markland Campus, North Derbyshire Tertiary College, Sheffield Road, Creswell, Notts. Tel: 01909 724908
Club Secretary: Mrs Jill Marshall, 3 Duke Street, Whitwell, Worksop, Notts S80 4TH. Tel: (H) 01909 722060
Fixtures Secretary: Mark Passey, 40 Chesterfield Road, Barlborough S43 4TT. Tel: (H) 01246 570645
Club Colours: Black/green.

MIDLAND DIVISION

EAST MIDLANDS & LEICESTERSHIRE ONE 1995-96 FIXTURES

November 11 1995 (Week 10)

Aylestone St James	v	Northampton Old Scouts
Bedford Queens	v	Rushden & Higham
Dunstablians	v	Oakham
Luton	v	Northampton Men's Own
Melton Mowbray	v	Market Bosworth
St Neots	v	Oadby Wyggestonians

September 16 1995 (Week 3)

Aylestone St James	v	St Neots
Dunstablians	v	Bedford Queens
Luton	v	Rushden & Higham
Market Bosworth	v	Oadby Wyggestonians
Melton Mowbray	v	Luton
Oakham	v	Northampton Men's Own

January 6 1996 (Week 17)

Loughborough	v	Dunstablians
Market Bosworth	v	Aylestone St James
Northampton Men's Own	v	Bedford Queens
Northampton Old Scouts	v	St Neots
Oadby Wyggestonians	v	Luton
Oakham	v	Melton Mowbray

September 23 1995 (Week 4)

Bedford Queens	v	Melton Mowbray
Luton	v	Aylestone St James
Northampton Men's Own	v	Loughborough
Northampton Old Scouts	v	Market Bosworth
Oadby Wyggestonians	v	Oakham
Rushden & Higham	v	Dunstablians

January 13 1996 (Week 18)

Aylestone St James	v	Oakham
Bedford Queens	v	Oadby Wyggestonians
Luton	v	Northampton Old Scouts
Melton Mowbray	v	Loughborough
Rushden & Higham	v	Northampton Men's Own
St Neots	v	Market Bosworth

September 30 1995 (Week X1)

Aylestone St James	v	Bedford Queens
Dunstablians	v	Northampton Men's Own
Loughborough	v	Oadby Wyggestonians
Melton Mowbray	v	Rushden & Higham
Oakham	v	Northampton Old Scouts
St Neots	v	Luton

February 10 1996 (Week 22)

Dunstablians	v	Melton Mowbray
Loughborough	v	Aylestone St James
Market Bosworth	v	Luton
Northampton Old Scouts	v	Bedford Queens
Oadby Wyggestonians	v	Rushden & Higham
Oakham	v	St Neots

October 14 1995 (Week 6)

Bedford Queens	v	St Neots
Market Bosworth	v	Oakham
Northampton Men's Own	v	Melton Mowbray
Northampton Old Scouts	v	Loughborough
Oadby Wyggestonians	v	Dunstablians
Rushden & Higham	v	Aylestone St James

February 17 1996 (Week 23)

Aylestone St James	v	Dunstablians
Bedford Queens	v	Market Bosworth
Luton	v	Oakham
Northampton Men's Own	v	Oadby Wyggestonians
Rushden & Higham	v	Northampton Old Scouts
St Neots	v	Loughborough

October 21 1995 (Week 7)

Aylestone St James	v	Northampton Men's Own
Dunstablians	v	Northampton Old Scouts
Loughborough	v	Market Bosworth
Luton	v	Bedford Queens
Melton Mowbray	v	Oadby Wyggestonians
St Neots	v	Rushden & Higham

February 24 1996 (Week 24)

Dunstablians	v	St Neots
Loughborough	v	Luton
Market Bosworth	v	Rushden & Higham
Melton Mowbray	v	Aylestone St James
Northampton Old Scouts	v	Northampton Men's Own
Oakham	v	Bedford Queens

October 28 1995 (Week 8)

Market Bosworth	v	Dunstablians
Northampton Men's Own	v	St Neots
Northampton Old Scouts	v	Melton Mowbray
Oadby Wyggestonians	v	Aylestone St James
Oakham	v	Loughborough
Rushden & Higham	v	Luton

March 30 1996 (Week X7)

Bedford Queens	v	Loughborough
Luton	v	Dunstablians
Northampton Men's Own	v	Market Bosworth
Oadby Wyggestonians	v	Northampton Old Scouts
Rushden & Higham	v	Oakham
St Neots	v	Melton Mowbray

EAST MIDLANDS & LEICS ONE

AYLESTONE ST JAMES RFC
Ground Address: Covert Lane, Scraptoft, Leicester. Tel: 01162 419202
Club Secretary: KWI Ridge, 5 Canons Close, Narboro', Leicester. Tel: (H) 01162 866481 Tel: (W) 01162 608187
Fixtures Secretary: P Chapman, 8 Valentine Road, Leicester LE5 2GH. Tel: (H) 0116 2431826
Club Colours: Blue/white hoops.

BEDFORD QUEENS RUFC
Ground Address: Bedford Sporting Centre, Chester Road, Queens Park, Bedford. Tel: 01234 211151
Club Secretary: Mr James Cunningham, Flat 4, 16 Adelaide Square, Bedford, Beds MK40 2RW. Tel: (H) 01234 269085 Tel: (W) 01234 347111
Fixtures Secretary: Mr A Radnor, 133 Ireland, Shefford, Beds SG17 5GL. Tel: (H) 01462 816175 Tel (W) 01385 372897
Club Colours: Maroon & white hooped shirts, navy shorts.

DUNSTABLIANS RUFC
Ground Address: Bidwell Park, Bedford Road, Houghton Regis, Dunstable, Beds LU5 6JW. Tel: 01582 866555
Club Secretary: Mr Paul Freeman, 19 Preston Road, Toddington, Nr Dunstable, Beds LU5 6EG. Tel: (H) 01525 874550 Tel: (W) 01234 333492
Fixtures Secretary: Mr Dai Gabriel, 19 Hilly Fields, Dunstable, Beds LU6 3NS. Tel: (H) 01582 60262
Club Colours: Red, black & silver.

LOUGHBOROUGH RFC
Ground Address: The Clubhouse, Derby Road Playing Fields, Derby Road, Loughborough, Leics. Tel: 01509 261093
Club Secretary: Mrs Anne Murphy, 51 Park Road, Loughborough, Leics LE11 2ED. Tel: (H) 01509 231575
Fixtures Secretary: Mrs Anne Murphy, 51 Park Road, Loughborough, Leics LE11 2ED. Tel: (H) 01509 231575
Club Colours: Old gold & navy.

LUTON RFC
Ground Address: Newlands Road, Luton, Beds LU1 4BQ. Tel: 01582 20355
Club Secretary: PJ Wilson, 17 Burghley Close, Flitwick, Bedford MK45 1TF. Tel: (H) 01525 713409 Tel: (W) 01480 52451 x5232
Fixtures Secretary: Martin Alexander, 9 Glenfield Road, Luton, Beds LU3 2HZ. Tel: (H) 01582 598581
Club Colours: Green with red & white hoops.

MARKET BOSWORTH RFC
Ground Address: Cadeby Lane, Cadeby, Market Bosworth. Tel: 01455 291340
Club Secretary: Mr G Donnelly, 23 Norfolk Road, Desford, Leicester LE9 9HR. Tel: (H) 01455 823522 Tel: (W) 01455 232328
Fixtures Secretary: Mr P Spencer, 27 St George's Avenue, Hinckley, Leics LE10 0TE. Tel: (H) 01455 633364 Tel (W) 01455 230804
Club Colours: Blue, white & gold hoops.

MELTON MOWBRAY RFC
Ground Address: Saxby Road, Melton Mowbray, Leicestershire LE13 1BP. Tel: 01664 43342
Club Secretary: Mr Colin R Cross, 15 Fernie Avenue, Melton Mowbray, Leicestershire LE13 0HZ. Tel: (H) 01664 61702 Tel: (W) 01664 64111
Fixtures Secretary: Anthony Middleton, 13 Birch Close, Melton Mowbray, Leicestershire LE13 0QA. Tel: (H) 01664 67042
Club Colours: Maroon shirts, white shorts, maroon socks.

NORTHAMPTON MEN'S OWN RFC
Ground Address: Stoke Road, Ashton, Northampton NN7 2JN. Tel: 01604 862463
Club Secretary: John Goold, 38 Millway, Duston, Northampton NN5 6ES. Tel: (H) 01604 756297
Fixtures Secretary: Ernie Dalby, 39 Forest Road, Piddington, Northampton NN7 2DA. Tel: (H) 01604 870609 Tel (W) 01302 556398
Club Colours: White with blue hoop.

NORTHAMPTON OLD SCOUTS RFC
Ground Address: Rushmere Road, Northampton. Tel: 01604 33639
Club Secretary: Bob Letty, 49 Barley Hill Road, Southfields,

FINAL TABLE

	P	W	D	L	F	A	Pts
Old Northamptonians	12	10	1	1	128	127	21
Bedford Queens	12	10	1	1	254	114	21
Northampton Old Sco	12	9	0	3	295	166	18
Northampton MO	12	7	0	5	205	156	14
St Neots	12	7	0	5	179	149	14
Dunstablians	12	6	0	6	229	180	12
Oadby Wyggestonians	12	5	1	6	165	173	11
Melton Mowbray	12	5	1	6	149	161	11
Loughborough	12	4	2	6	134	219	10
Market Bosworth	12	4	0	8	167	168	8
Aylestone St James	12	4	0	8	87	218	8
Old Bosworthians	12	3	0	9	160	230	6
Daventry	12	1	0	11	86	329	2

Northampton NN3 5JA. Tel: (H) 01604 493727 Tel: (W) 01604 601326
Fixtures Secretary: Keith Shurville, 41 Churchill Avenue, Boothville, Northampton NN3 6NY. Tel: (H) 01604 494374 Tel (W) 01908 690333 x2406
Club Colours: Red, green, gold & navy hooped shirts, navy shorts.

OADBY WYGGESTONIAN RFC
Ground Address: Oval Park, Wigston Road, Oadby, Leicester. Tel: 0116 2714848
Club Secretary: Jim Kilgallen, 75 Leicester Road, Oadby, Leicester LE2 4DF. Tel: (H) 0116 2713987 Tel: (W) 0116 2858032
Fixtures Secretary: Jim Kilgallen, 75 Leicester Road, Oadby, Leicester LE2 4DF. Tel: (H) 0116 2713987 Tel (W) 0116 2858032
Club Colours: Black, white & gold hooped jerseys, black shorts.

OAKHAM RFC
Ground Address: The Showground, Barleythorpe Road, Oakham, Rutland, Leicestershire. Tel: 01572 724206
Club Secretary: Peter Bateman, 26 Well Street, Langham, Oakham, Rutland LE15 7JS. Tel: (H) 01572 756143 Tel: (W) 0116 2550020
Fixtures Secretary: Peter Bateman, 26 Well Street, Langham, Oakham, Rutland LE15 7JS. Tel: (H) 01572 756143 Tel (W) 0116 2550020
Club Colours: Black with broad amber band, black shorts.

RUSHDEN AND HIGHAM RFC
Ground Address: Manor Park, Bedford Road, Rushden, Northants NN10 0SA. Tel: 01933 312071
Club Secretary: Steve Miles, 9 Grange Road, Little Cransley, Kettering, Northants NN14 1PH. Tel: (H) 01536 790429 Tel: (W) 01604 235410
Fixtures Secretary: Terry Dancer, 4 Orwell Close, Raunds, Northants NN9 6SG. Tel: (H) 01933 624889
Club Colours: Black & white hoops.

ST NEOTS RUFC
Ground Address: The Common, St Neots PE19 1HA. Tel: 01480 474285
Club Secretary: Ray London, 14 St James Court, Eynesbury, St Neots PE19 2QQ. Tel: (H) 01480 390135 Tel: (W) 01480 812202 x249
Fixtures Secretary: Keith Sandford, 36 Avenue Road, St Neots, Cambs PE19 1LJ. Tel: (H) 01480 472812 Tel (W) 01234 274049
Club Colours: Light blue with navy hoop.

MIDLAND DIVISION

EAST MIDLANDS & LEICESTERSHIRE TWO 1995-96 FIXTURES

November 11 1995 (Week 10)

Kempston v Bugbrooke
Northampton Casuals v Brackley
Daventry v Wellingborough OG
Bedford Swifts v Old Ashbeians
St Ives v New Parks
Birstall v Old Bosworthians

September 16 1995 (Week 3)

Daventry v Bedford Swifts
St Ives v Northampton Casuals
Birstall v Kempston
Colworth House v Bugbrooke
Old Bosworthians v Brackley
New Parks v Wellingborough OG

January 6 1996 (Week 17)

New Parks v Bedford Swifts
Old Ashbeians v Daventry
Wellingborough OG v Northampton Casuals
Brackley v Kempston
Colworth House v Birstall
Old Bosworthians v St Ives

September 23 1995 (Week 4)

Northampton Casuals v Bedford Swifts
Old Ashbeians v New Parks
Wellingborough OG v Old Bosworthians
Brackley v Colworth House
Bugbrooke v Birstall
Kempston v St Ives

January 13 1996 (Week 18)

Bugbrooke v Brackley
Kempston v Wellingborough OG
Northampton Casuals v Old Ashbeians
Daventry v New Parks
Bedford Swifts v Old Bosworthians
St Ives v Colworth House

September 30 1995 (Week X1)

Daventry v Northampton Casuals
Bedford Swifts v Kempston
St Ives v Bugbrooke
Birstall v Brackley
Colworth House v Wellingborough OG
Old Bosworthians v Old Ashbeians

February 10 1996 (Week 22)

Colworth House v Bedford Swifts
Old Bosworthians v Daventry
New Parks v Northampton Casuals
Old Ashbeians v Kempston
Wellingborough OG v Bugbrooke
Birstall v St Ives

October 14 1995 (Week 6)

Bugbrooke v Bedford Swifts
Kempston v Daventry
New Parks v Old Bosworthians
Old Ashbeians v Colworth House
Wellingborough OG v Birstall
Brackley v St Ives

February 17 1996 (Week 23)

Brackley v Wellingborough OG
Bugbrooke v Old Ashbeians
Kempston v New Parks
Northampton Casuals v Old Bosworthians
Daventry v Colworth House
Bedford Swifts v Birstall

October 21 1995 (Week 7)

Northampton Casuals v Kempston
Daventry v Bugbrooke
Bedford Swifts v Brackley
St Ives v Wellingborough OG
Birstall v Old Ashbeians
Colworth House v New Parks

February 24 1996 (Week 24)

St Ives v Bedford Swifts
Birstall v Daventry
Colworth House v Northampton Casuals
Old Bosworthians v Kempston
New Parks v Bugbrooke
Old Ashbeians v Brackley

October 28 1995 (Week 8)

Wellingborough OG v Bedford Swifts
Brackley v Daventry
Bugbrooke v Northampton Casuals
Old Bosworthians v Colworth House
New Parks v Birstall
Old Ashbeians v St Ives

March 30 1996 (Week X7)

Wellingborough OG v Old Ashbeians
Brackley v New Parks
Bugbrooke v Old Bosworthians
Kempston v Colworth House
Northampton Casuals v Birstall
Daventry v St Ives

452

BEDFORD SWIFTS RUFC
Ground Address: Bedford Athletics Stadium, Barkers Lane, Bedford MK41 9SA. Tel: 01234 351115
Club Secretary: Trevor N Stewart, 64 Ravensden Road, Renhold, Bedford MK41 0JY. Tel: (H) 01234 771828 Tel: (W) 01767 681491
Fixtures Secretary: Mr Stan Davidson, 136 Chantry Avenue, Kempston, Beedford. Tel: (H) 01234 857529
Club Colours: Royal blue & amber hoops.

BIRSTALL RFC
Ground Address: Longslade Community College, Wanlip Lane, Birstall, Leicester LE4 4GH. Tel: 0116 2674211
Club Secretary: Mr C Blakesley, 39 Ashfield Drive, Anstey, Leicester LE7 7TA. Tel: (H) 0116 2351254 Tel: (W) 0121 722 4000
Fixtures Secretary: Mr J Cross, 10 Riverside Close, Birstall, Leicester LE4 4EH. Tel: (H) 0116 2673307
Club Colours: Black/green/white hoops.

BRACKLEY RUFC
Ground Address: Springfield Road, Pavillons Way, Brackley, Northants NN13 6LW. Tel: 01280 700685
Club Secretary: Mrs Sue Cooper, 30 Octavian Way, Brackley, Northants NN13 7BL. Tel: 01280 704711
Fixtures Secretary: C Page 6o Halse Road, Brackley, Northants NN13 6EG. Tel: (H) 01280 701732
Club Colours: Royal blue & white quarters.

BUGBROOKE RUFC
Ground Address: The Playing Fields, Pilgrims Lane, Bugbrooke, Northants. Tel: 01604 831137
Club Secretary: Mr John Gowen, 46 Granary Road, East Hunsbury, Northampton NN4 0XA. Tel: (H) 01604 705273 Tel: (W) 01604 671176
Fixtures Secretary: Mr Terry Newcombe, 31 Georges Avenue, Bugbrooke, Northants NN7 3PP. Tel: (H) 01604 831806
Club Colours: Bottle green shirts, gold collar & cuffs, green shorts, green socks with gold hoops.

COLWORTH HOUSE RUFC
Ground Address: Unilever Research, Colworth House, Sharnbrook, Bedford MK44 1LQ. Tel: 01234 222221
Club Secretary: Dr Paul Dunnett, Barden Cottage, 37 Sandy Road, Willington, Bedford MK44 3QS. Tel: (H) 01234 838671 Tel: (W) 01234 222857
Fixtures Secretary: Andy Souten, 19 Carisbrooke Way, Putnoe, Bedford MK41 8HR. Tel: (H) 01234 219363 Tel (W) 0585 934177
Club Colours: Emerald green with scarlet hoop, black shorts & socks.

DAVENTRY RFC
Ground Address: Stefen Hill, Western Avenue, Daventry, Northants NN11 4ST. Tel: 01327 703802
Club Secretary: Richard Roy, 5 Warwick Street, Daventry, Northants NN11 4AJ. Tel: (H) 01327 310477 Tel: (W) 01327 72921
Fixtures Secretary: Graham Woodliffe, Checkley Cottage, Chapel Street, Charwelton, Daventry, Northants NN11 3YU. Tel: (H) 01327 261461 Tel (W) 01327 709137
Club Colours: All black.

KEMPSTON RUFC
Ground Address: c/o Cutler Hammer Sports & Social Club, 134 High Street, Kempston, Beds. Tel: 01234 852499
Club Secretary: Mr J Duke, 21 Gulliver Close, Kempston, Beds MK42 8RB. Tel: (H) 01234 855426 Tel: (W) 0171 374 3641
Fixtures Secretary: Mr T Trinder, 41 Keeley Lane, Wootton, Beds. Tel: (H) 01234 853277
Club Colours: Red & black.

NEW PARKS RFC
Ground Address: New Parks Community College, Greencoat Road, Leicester LE3 6RN. Tel: 0116 2872115/6
Club Secretary: A Newcombe, 37 Copeland Avenue Forest Way, Leicester LE3 9BT. Tel: (H) 0116 2871618

FINAL TABLE

	P	W	D	L	F	A	Pts
Rushden & Higham	12	12	0	0	293	63	24
Oakham	12	11	0	1	307	58	22
Bedford Swifts	12	10	0	2	283	100	20
St Ives	12	7	0	5	283	100	14
Wellingborough OG	12	7	0	5	114	87	14
Brackley	12	6	1	5	103	104	13
Colworth House	12	5	0	7	163	183	10
Birstall	12	6	0	6	135	187	10*
Old Ashbeians	12	4	2	6	113	216	10
Bugbrooke	13	3	1	8	120	169	7
Northampton Casuals	12	2	2	8	116	200	6
Aylestonians	12	2	0	10	99	233	4
Wigston	12	0	0	12	53	405	-2*

Tel: (W) 0116 2759588
Fixtures Secretary: DP Bullock, 17 Digby Close, Leicester. Tel: (H) 0116 2890649
Club Colours: Light blue with black chevron.

NORTHAMPTON CASUALS RFC
Ground Address: Rushmills House, Bedford Road, Rushmills, Northampton. Tel: 01604 36716
Club Secretary: Mr S M Tee, 32 Duston Wildes, Duston, Northampton NN5 6ND. Tel: (H) 01604 587982 Tel: (W) 0121 440 5151
Fixtures Secretary: Mr MD Askew, 60 Hinton Road, Kingsthorpe, Northampton. Tel: (H) 01604 821148 Tel (W) 01604 454283
Club Colours: Black with amber band.

OLD ASHBEIANS RFC
Ground Address: Nottingham Road, Ashby, Leics. Tel: 01530 413992
Club Secretary: J Mitchell, 50 Pennine Way, Ashby, Leics LE65 1EW. Tel: (H) 01530 415284 Tel (W) 01623 413308
Fixtures Secretary: Andy Patrick, 20 Tithe Close, Thringstone, Mr Coalville, Leics LE67 8LZ. Tel: (H) 01530 222076
Club Colours: Maroon & sky blue hoops, navy shorts.

OLD BOSWORTHIANS RFC
Ground Address: Hinckley Road, Leicester Forest East, Leicestershire. Tel: 0116 238 7136
Club Secretary: Grahame D Spendlove-Mason, Croft House Farm, Post Office Lane, Newton Harcourt, Leics LE8 0FN. Tel: 0116 259 2965 Tel: (W) 01530 222489
Fixtures Secretary: Colin Hughes, 97 Rosslyn Road, Whitwick, Leics LE67 5PV. Tel: (H) 01530 834493 Tel (W) 01509 611011 x44102
Club Colours: Navy.

ST IVES RUFC
Ground Address: Somersham Road, St Ives, Huntingdon, Cambs PE19 4LY. Tel: 01480 464455
Club Secretary: Mike Prince, 59 Erica Road, St Ives, Huntingdon, Cambs PE17 6AG. Tel: (H) 01480 381091
Fixtures Secretary: Nick Nicholson, 6 Orchard Terrace, St Ives, Huntingdon, Cambs PE17 4QS. Tel: (H) 01480 381693
Club Colours: Royal blue shirts, black shorts.

WELLINGBOROUGH OLD GRAMMARIANS RFC
Ground Address: Memorial Sportsfield, Sanders Road, Finedon Road Industrial Estate, Wellingborough, Northants. Tel: 01933 279316 (ground) 01933 226188 (clubhouse)
Club Secretary: Paul Bush, 33 Newtown Road, Little Irchester, Wellingborough, Northants NN8 2DX. Tel: (H) 01933 441663 Tel: (W) 01604 31626
Fixtures Secretary: Paul Bush, 33 Newtown Road, Little Irchester, Wellingborough, Northants NN8 2DX. Tel: (H) 01933 441663 Tel (W) 01604 31626
Club Colours: Claret & white hoops, black shorts.

MIDLAND DIVISION

EAST MIDLANDS & LEICESTERSHIRE THREE 1995-96 FIXTURES

November 11 1995 (Week 10)

Anstey	v	Burbage
Aylestonians	v	Thorney
Corby	v	West Leicester
Old Newtonians	v	Deepings
Westwood	v	Northampton Heathens
Wigston	v	Vauxhall

September 16 1995 (Week 3)

Corby	v	Old Newtonians
Northampton Heathens	v	Deepings
Oundle	v	Burbage
Vauxhall	v	Thorney
Westwood	v	Aylestonians
Wigston	v	Anstey

January 6 1996 (Week 17)

Deepings	v	Aylestonians
Northampton Heathens	v	Corby
Oundle	v	Wigston
Thorney	v	Anstey
Vauxhall	v	Westwood
West Leicester	v	Old Newtonians

September 23 1995 (Week 4)

Anstey	v	Westwood
Aylestonians	v	Corby
Burbage	v	Wigston
Deepings	v	Vauxhall
Thorney	v	Oundle
West Leicester	v	Northampton Heathens

January 13 1996 (Week 18)

Anstey	v	Deepings
Aylestonians	v	West Leicester
Burbage	v	Thorney
Corby	v	Vauxhall
Old Newtonians	v	Northampton Heathens
Westwood	v	Oundle

September 30 1995 (Week X1)

Corby	v	Anstey
Old Newtonians	v	Aylestonians
Oundle	v	Deepings
Vauxhall	v	West Leicester
Westwood	v	Burbage
Wigston	v	Thorney

February 10 1996 (Week 22)

Deepings	v	Burbage
Northampton Heathens	v	Aylestonians
Oundle	v	Corby
Vauxhall	v	Old Newtonians
West Leicester	v	Anstey
Wigston	v	Westwood

October 14 1995 (Week 6)

Anstey	v	Old Newtonians
Burbage	v	Corby
Deepings	v	Wigston
Northampton Heathens	v	Vauxhall
Thorney	v	Westwood
West Leicester	v	Oundle

February 17 1996 (Week 23)

Anstey	v	Northampton Heathens
Aylestonians	v	Vauxhall
Burbage	v	West Leicester
Corby	v	Wigston
Old Newtonians	v	Oundle
Thorney	v	Deepings

October 21 1995 (Week 7)

Aylestonians	v	Anstey
Corby	v	Thorney
Old Newtonians	v	Burbage
Oundle	v	Northampton Heathens
Westwood	v	Deepings
Wigston	v	West Leicester

February 24 1996 (Week 24)

Northampton Heathens	v	Burbage
Oundle	v	Aylestonians
Vauxhall	v	Anstey
West Leicester	v	Thorney
Westwood	v	Corby
Wigston	v	Old Newtonians

October 28 1995 (Week 8)

Burbage	v	Aylestonians
Deepings	v	Corby
Northampton Heathens	v	Wigston
Thorney	v	Old Newtonians
Vauxhall	v	Oundle
West Leicester	v	Westwood

March 30 1996 (Week X7)

Anstey	v	Oundle
Aylestonians	v	Wigston
Burbage	v	Vauxhall
Deepings	v	West Leicester
Old Newtonians	v	Westwood
Thorney	v	Northampton Heathens

EAST MIDLANDS & LEICS THREE

ANSTEY RFC
Ground Address: Link Road Playing Fields, Link Road, Anstey, Leicester.
Club Secretary: Christopher Apperley, 4 Dalby Road, Anstey, Leicester. Tel: (H) 0116 2340 293
Fixtures Secretary: Julian Garner, 12 Woodgon Road, Anstey, Leicester. Tel: (H) 0116 236 2758 Tel (W) 0116 2340 403
Club Colours: Black shirts & shorts.

AYLESTONIANS RFC
Ground Address: Knighton Lane East, Leicester. Tel: 0116 283 4899
Club Secretary: Mr Clive Cooper, 31 Rockingham Close, Leicester. Tel: (H) 0116 274 0922
Fixtures Secretary: Mr Geoff Gaunt, 15 Brookes Avenue, Croft, Leicester. Tel: (H) 01455 282052
Club Colours: Red, white & navy hoops.

BURBAGE RFC
Ground Address: John Cleveland College, Butt Lane, Hinckley, Leics.
Club Secretary: CM Startin, 102 Strathmore Road, Hinckley, Leicsw LE10 0LR. Tel: (H) 01455 634073 Tel: (W) 01455 637841
Fixtures Secretary: R Sansome, 39 Duport Road, Burbage, Leics. Tel: (H) 01455 610266
Club Colours: Green & white hoops.

CORBY RFC
Ground Address: Northen Park, Rockingham Triangle, Corby, Northants NN17 2AE. Tel: 01536 204466
Club Secretary: George A Ewen, 24 Charnwood Road, Corby, Northants NN17 1XS. Tel: (H) 01536 201788 Tel: (W) 01536 265291
Fixtures Secretary: Alistair Micks, 3 Streatham Drive, Corby, Northants. Tel: (H) 01536 268496 Tel (W) 01536 265291
Club Colours: Red & white quarters, white shorts.

DEEPINGS RUFC
Ground Address: Linchfield Road, Deeping St James, Peterborough. Tel: 01778 345228
Club Secretary: Brian Kirby, 4 Woodcroft Close, Market Deeping, Peterborough PE6 8BT. Tel: (H) 01778 343048 Tel: (W) 01733 556173
Fixtures Secretary: Keith Smith, 17 Burchnall Close, Deeping St James, Peterborough PE6 8QJ. Tel: (H) 01778 346411 Tel (W) 0116 276 5755
Club Colours: Yellow, green & black hoops.

NORTHAMPTON HEATHENS RFC
Ground Address: The Racecourse, East Park Parade, Northampton. Tel: 01604 39250
Club Secretary: Martin Labrum, 101 Yeomans Meadow, Northampton NN4 9YX. Tel: (H) 01604 765287
Fixtures Secretary: Derek Hodgkinson, 5 Pine Trees, Weston Favell, Northampton NN3 3ET. Tel: (H) 01604 416442
Club Colours: 3' black with 1' amber hoops.

OLD NEWTONIANS RFC
Ground Address: Hinckley Road (A47), Leicester Forest East, Leicester LE3 3PJ. Tel: 0116 239 2389
Club Secretary: GA Clark, 250 Wigston Lane, Aylestone, Leicester LE2 8DH. Tel: (H) 0116 283 2309 Tel: (W) 0116 278 5288
Fixtures Secretary: Peter Muggleton (Muggo), 16 Bruxby Street, Syston, Leicester LE7 8NB. Tel: (H) 0116 269 4704 Tel (W) (Message only) 0116 253 0066 x4223
Club Colours: Navy with white, green, red, white central band.

OUNDLE RFC
Ground Address: Occupation Road, Oundle, Nr Peterborough. Tel: 01832 273101
Club Secretary: David Cooke, 10 Howards Meadow, Kings Cliffe, Nr Peterborough PE8 6YJ. Tel: (H) 01780 470440 Tel: (W) 01832 273433

FINAL TABLE

	P	W	D	L	F	A	Pts
Kempston	11	9	0	2	278	82	18
New Parks	11	8	0	3	314	104	16
Oundle	11	8	0	3	221	92	16
Corby	11	8	0	3	219	92	16
Old Newtonians	11	6	0	5	219	106	12
Northampton Heathen	11	6	0	5	204	169	12
Westwood	11	6	0	5	175	181	12
Vauxhall Motors	11	5	0	6	101	164	10
Deepings	11	5	0	6	133	199	10
Anstey	11	3	0	8	118	213	6
West Leicester	11	2	0	9	114	263	4
Old Wellingburians	11	0	0	11	47	478	0

Fixtures Secretary: Mr Fred King, 13 Chapel Street, Titchmarsh, Nr Kettering, Northants. Tel: (H) 01832 734659 Tel (W) 01767 677722
Club Colours: Red & white hoops on black shirt, black shorts.

THORNEY RUFC
Ground Address: Thorney Park, Wisbech Road, Thorney, Cambs.
Club Secretary: Mr Louis Deplancke, 7 Headlands Way, Whittlesey, Nr Peterborough, Cambs PE7 1RL. Tel: (H) 01733 204893 Tel: (W) 01480 456111 x2526
Fixtures Secretary: Mr Dick Turner, 1415 Lincoln Road, Peterborough. Tel: (H) 01733 571259 Tel (W) 01733 63232
Club Colours: Navy & gold quarters.

VAUXHALL MOTORS RUFC
Ground Address: Vauxhall Recreation Club, Gypsy Lane, Luton, Beds. Tel: 01582 418860
Club Secretary: W Underwood, 2 Hardwick Green, Luton, Beds LU3 3XA. Tel: (H) 01582 503153 Tel: (W) 01528 390002 Fax: 01582 390153
Fixtures Secretary: M Neate, 32 Gardeners Close, Flitwick, Beds MK45 5BU. Tel: (H) 01525 716393 Tel (W) 01582 420565 Fax:01582 415682
Club Colours: Blue & gold.

WEST LEICESTER RFC
Ground Address: Rowley Fields Community College, Lyncote Road, Leicester. Tel: Clubhouse: 0116 254 0634
Club Secretary: Geoff Topley, 8 Hillsborough Road, Glen Parva, Leicester LE2 9PL. Tel: (H) 0116 277 4119 Tel: (W) 0116 257 2241
Fixtures Secretary: Alan Lee, 15 Chestnut Close, Littlethorpe, Leicester LE9 5HN. Tel: (H) 0116 286 3557
Club Colours: Red shirts, white shorts, black socks.

WESTWOOD RUFC
Ground Address: Phorpres Club, London Road, Peterborough PE2 9LF. Tel: 01733 343561
Club Secretary: Kenneth Barnes, 17 St Peter's Walk, Yaxley, Peterborough PE7 3EY. Tel: (H) 01733 241382 Tel: (W) 01733 555777
Fixtures Secretary: Peter Tarttelin, Flat 20, Fenland Court, West End, Whittlesey, Peterborough PE7 1HR. Tel: (H) 01733 350632
Club Colours: Red & white hoops.

WIGSTON RFC
Ground Address: Leicester Road, Countesthorpe, Leicester. Tel: 0116 277 1153
Club Secretary: Steve Benton, 5 Ramsdean Avenue, Wigston, Leicester LE18 1DX. Tel: (H) 0116 288 9381 Tel: (W) 0116 255 6776 Fax: 0116 255 3088
Fixtures Secretary: Rich Alexander, 41 Estoril Avenue, Wigston, Leicester. Tel: (H) 0116 288 2788
Club Colours: Purple with black, gold & silver chest & arm bands.

MIDLAND DIVISION

EAST MIDLANDS & LEICESTERSHIRE FOUR 1995-96 FIXTURES

September 16 1995 (Week 3)
Braunstone v Clapham
Cosby v Biddenham
Loughborough Students v Shepshed

September 23 1995 (Week 4)
Biddenham v Loughborough Students
Clapham v Cosby
Shepshed v Old Wellingburians

September 30 1995 (Week X1)
Braunstone v Shepshed
Loughborough Students v Clapham
Old Wellingburians v Biddenham

October 14 1995 (Week 6)
Biddenham v Braunstone
Clapham v Old Wellingburians
Shepshed v Cosby

October 21 1995 (Week 7)
Cosby v Braunstone
Old Wellingburians v Loughborough Students
Shepshed v Biddenham

October 28 1995 (Week 8)
Biddenham v Clapham
Braunstone v Old Wellingburians
Loughborough Students v Cosby

November 11 1995 (Week 10)
Braunstone v Loughborough Students
Old Wellingburians v Cosby
Shepshed v Clapham

November 25 1995 (Week 12)
Biddenham v Cosby
Clapham v Braunstone
Shepshed v Loughborough Students

January 6 1996 (Week 17)
Cosby v Clapham
Loughborough Students v Biddenham
Old Wellingburians v Shepshed

January 13 1996 (Week 18)
Biddenham v Old Wellingburians
Clapham v Loughborough Students
Shepshed v Braunstone

February 10 1996 (Week 22)
Braunstone v Biddenham
Cosby v Shepshed
Old Wellingburians v Clapham

February 17 1996 (Week 23)
Biddenham v Shepshed
Braunstone v Cosby
Loughborough Students v Old Wellingburians

February 24 1996 (Week 24)
Clapham v Biddenham
Cosby v Loughborough Students
Old Wellingburians v Braunstone

March 30 1996 (Week X7)
Clapham v Shepshed
Cosby v Old Wellingburians
Loughborough Students v Braunstone

456

EAST MIDLANDS & LEICS FOUR

BIDDENHAM RFC
Ground Address: The Biddenham Pavilion, Deep
Spinney, Biddenham, Beds.
Club Secretary: Simon Quail, Bulsara, 6 Malcote Close,
Deep Spinney, Biddenham MK40 4QW. Tel: (H) 01234
348640 Tel: (W) 01438 758012
Fixtures Secretary: Mr Kevin Weedon, 11 Darlow Drive,
Biddenham, Beds MK40 4AX. Tel: (H) 01234 269194
Club Colours: Bottle green/old English cream quarters.
BRAUNSTONE TOWN RFC
Ground Address: Mossdale Meadows, Braunstone,
Leicester. Tel: 0116 263 0018
Club Secretary: Mrs A M Tyers, 46 Salcombe Drive,
Glenfield, Leicester LE3 8AF. Tel: (H) 0116 287 5276 Tel:
(W) 0016 255 9600 x4097
Fixtures Secretary: Mr P Tyers, 46 Salcombe Drive,
Glenfield, Leicester LE3 8AF. Tel: (H) 0116 875276
Club Colours: Burgundy.
CLAPHAM RUFC
Ground Address: Twinwoods Road, Clapham, Beds.
Club Secretary: DR Tough, Millbrook House, 109 High
Street, Riseley, Beds MK44 1DF. Tel: (H) 01234 708453
Tel: (W) 01428 3614563 314281
Fixtures Secretary: M Baker, 82 High Street, Oakley,
Beds MK43 7RH. Tel: (H) 01234 824092
Club Colours: Blue & gold quarters.
COSBY RFC
Ground Address: Victory Park, Park Road, Cosby,
Leicester. Tel: 0116 284 9244
Club Secretary: CW Elliott, 9 Wavertree Close, Cosby,
Leicester LE9 5TN. Tel: (H) 0116 284 1746 Tel: (W)
01530 510051
Fixtures Secretary: CW Elliott, 9 Wavertree Close,
Cosby, Leicester LE9 5TN. Tel: (H) 0116 284 1746 Tel
(W) 01530 510051
Club Colours: Black.
LOUGHBOROUGH STUDENTS RFC
Ground Address: Loughborough University of
Technology. Ashby Road, Loughborough, Leics. Tel:
01509 217766 (Students' Union) 01509 235593 (Athletic
Union)
Club Secretary: Charles Leslie, c/o Jim Saker,
Management Development Centre, Rutland Hall,
Loughborough University Business School, LE11 3TU.
Tel: (H) 01585 753946 Tel: (W) 01509 223140
Fixtures Secretary: Glyn James, 31 Melbourne Road,
Stamford, Lincs PE9 1UO. Tel: (H) 01780 51793
Club Colours: Black & white hoops.
OLD WELLINGBURIAN RFC
Ground Address: Embankment Club, Wellingborough.
Tel: 01933
Club Secretary: Nick Fry, 69 Sillswood, Olney, Bucks
MK46 5PN. Tel: (H) 01234 712959
Fixtures Secretary: Duncan Philips. Tel: (H) 01908
314677 Tel (W) 0171 256 6411
Club Colours: Green/gold/maroon.
SHEPSHED RFC
Ground Address: Hind Leys College Campus, Forest
Street, Shepshed, Leicestershire LE12 9DB.
Club Secretary: Mrs Sue Patterson, c/o Shepshed RFC,
Hind Leys College, Forest Street, Shepshed, Leicestershire
LE12 9DB. Tel: (H) 01509 265847
Fixtures Secretary: R Short, 40D Loughborough Road,
Shepshed, Leicestershire LE12 9DN. Tel: (H) 01509
503592 Tel (W) 01509 504511
Club Colours: Red & black quarters.

FINAL TABLE

	P	W	D	L	F	A	Pts
Burbage	12	11	0	1	286	78	22
Thorney	12	11	0	1	380	58	20*
Braunstone Town	12	7	0	5	132	169	14
Cosby	12	6	0	6	136	231	12
Biddenham	12	3	0	9	122	179	6
Shepshed	12	3	0	9	78	217	6
Clapham Twinwoods	12	1	0	11	78	280	2

LONDON & SOUTH EAST DIVISION

OFFICIALS 1995-96

COMPETITION SUB-COMMITEE

CHAIRMAN
R. Tennant, 57 Boveney Road, Forest Hill, London SE23 3NL (H) 0181 699 9025

SECRETARY
M.A. Ward, 3 Rookery Close, Oulton Broad, Lowestoft, Suffolk NR33 9NZ (H) 01502 501135 (Fax) 01502 712660

EASTERN COUNTIES
F.A.G. Ford, "Fairhaven", 36 Haynes Road, Hornchurch, Essex RM11 2HT (H) 01708 457807
HAMPSHIRE
Lt. Col. D. McF. Hathorn, 3 Broomacres, Fleet, Aldershot, Hampshire GU13 9UU (H) 01252 621565
HERTFORDSHIRE
D.J. Williams, 7 Sadlers Way, Hertford, Herts SG14 2DZ (H) 01992 586744
KENT
D. Attwood, 6 Somerset Gardens, Lewisham, London, SE13 7SY (H) 0181 691 2820
MIDDLESEX
D.C. Ransom, 2 Powis Court, The Rutts, Bushey Heath, Hertfordshire WD2 1LL (H) 0181 950 5871 (B) 0181 848 8744
SURREY
H. Brady, 16 Selwood Terrace, London SW7 3QG (H) 0171 370 1078
SUSSEX
P Sealey, 15 Hart Close, Uckfield, Sussex TN22 2DA (H) 01825 763293
CO-OPTED
F Pugh, 42 Duchess Drive, Newmarket, Suffolk CB8 8AG
L.E.A.F. FUND MANAGER
F Pugh, 42 Duchess Drive, Newmarket, Suffolk CB8 8AG
RFU REPRESENTATIVES (COMPETITION SUB-COMMITTEE)
B Williams, "Chez Nous", Main Road, Westerfield, Ipswich IP6 9AJ (H) 01473 213339 (B) 01305 866046
G.G. Smith, The Old Rectory, Provender Lane, Norton, Faversham, Kent ME13 0SU (H) 01795 521166

LEAGUE SECRETARIES
London One George Ford, "Fairhaven", 36 Haynes Road, Hornchurch, Essex RM11 2HT (H) 01708 457807

London Two North David Williams, 7 Sadlers Way, Hertford, Herts SG14 2DZ (H) 01992 586744
London Two South & London Three South-West Lt. Col. D. McF. Hathorn, 3 Broomacres, Fleet, Aldershot, Hampshire, GU13 9UU (H) 01252 621565
London Three North-West D Gershlick, 20A The Avenue, Potters Bar, Herts EN6 1EB (H) 01707 644433
London Three North-East M. J. Stott, Brick Kiln Farm, North Walsham, Norfolk NR28 9LH (H) 01692 403096.
London Three South-East Dennis Attwood, 6 Somerset Gardens, Lewisham, London SE13 7SY. (H) 0181 691 2820.
Hertfordshire/Middlesex D. Gershlick, 20A The Avenue, Potters Bar, Hertfordshire EN6 1EB (H) 01707 644433
Herts All Leagues John Gregory, 58 Luton Lane, Redbourne, Herts AL3 6PY (H) 01582 792798
Middlesex One R Willingale, Fairmile Farm Cottage, Cobham, Surrey KT11 1JY (H) 01932 866927
Middlesex Two P. Astbury, 32 Kneller Gardens, Isleworth, Middlesex TW7 7NW (H) 0181 898 5372.
Middlesex Three A. Rabjohn, 62 Central Avenue, Hounslow, Middlesex TW3 2QL (H) 0181 894 1850.
Middlesex Four Brian East, 17 Waterloo Road, London, N19 5NJ (H) 0171 272 5686 (W) 0171 208 2800
Hampshire One and Two J Sneezum, Bursledon Lodge, Salterns Lane, Old Bursledon, Southampton, Hampshire SO3 8DH (H) 01703 402286
Surrey General Greer Kirkwood, 63 Shaftesbury Way, Strawberry Hill, Twickenham TW2 5RW (H) 0181 898 1767
Surrey One John Laidman, 2 West Dene, Park Lane, Cheam, Sutton, Surrey SM3 8BW (H) 0181 643 2919
Surrey Two Paul Tanner, 1 Woodlands Way, Morden, Surrey SM4 4DS (0181 540 5784) (W) 01923 214123
Surrey Three John Mason, 30 Ryefield Road, London SE19 3QU (H) 0181 771 5815
Surrey Four R.V. Miller, Flat 3, 127 Barnet Wood Road, Ashtead, Surrey KT21 2LR (H) 01372 813419 (W) 01483 571212 - 6828
Eastern Counties One, Two Mike Tuck, 51 Highfield Road, Billericay, Essex CM11 2PE (H) 01277 655483.
Eastern Counties Three and Four Ron Hatch, 99 Ernest Road, Wivenhoe, Essex CO7 9LJ (H) 01206 823548
Eastern Counties Five Roger Wyatt, Stone Cottage, The Green, Beyton, Suffolk IP30 9AF (H) 01359 270410
Sussex all Leagues J.M. Carrington, 115 Cootes Avenue, Horsham, W. Sussex RH12 2AF (H) 01403 260556
Kent One and Two J. Carley, 11 Vlissingen Drive, Deal, Kent CT14 6TZ (H) 01304 381273
Kent Three and Four R. Fisher, 7 Manwood Close, Sittingbourne, Kent ME10 4QL (H) 01795 471433 (W) 01634 388765.

458

LONDON & SOUTH EAST DIVISION

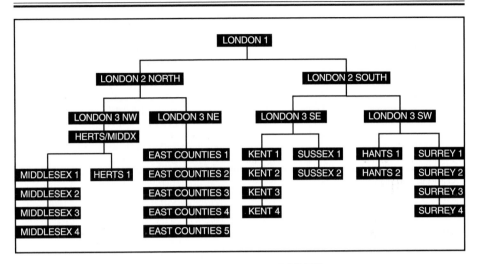

ADMINISTRATIVE RULES

1. REPORTING OF MATCH RESULTS

Match results shall be reported by the time specified on the particular instructions to each club. This report of a result is a FACT and is not open to excuse or reason for failure. Accordingly NO APPEAL will be accepted for failure to comply.

2. REPORTING OF POSTPONED MATCHES

Fixtures are scheduled for a particular day and the Results Service MUST receive a report of postponement in just the same way as if the game had been played. Please note that the Results Service OPENS 15 minutes BEFORE the notional time of no-side ie. the service recognises the NORMAL kick-off time according to the time of the season.

The Results Service and the League Administration are NOT one and the same thing and it is, therefore, insufficient simply to tell your League Secretary of a postponement. Failure to comply will incur the same penalty as failure to lodge a result.

3. PLAYING OF POSTPONED MATCHES

A match postponed or abandoned under Regulation 11 (a) or (b) or a match not played on the appointed day for reasons acceptable to the Organising Committee SHALL, henceforth, be played on the NEXT AVAILABLE SATURDAY.

A Saturday is deemed to be 'available' UNLESS one of the following conditions applies:

a. either Club has, on that day, a scheduled Courage League match.

b. Either Club has, on that day, a Pilkington Cup or Shield match.

c. either Club has, on that weekend, a match in a Competition within the authority of the Constituent Body, BUT NOT a Merit Table game.

d. either Club has, on that day, a demand on one or more of their 'effectively registered' players to play in a Representative game within the authority of the RFU, the Division or Constituent Body.

e. In addition, the Organising Committee (that is the London & SE Division Competition Sub-committee) may – at its absolute discretion and usually at the start of any season – decalre that a specific Saturday be deemed 'unavailable' where it falls on or close to a public holiday or where it is considered by the Committee inappropriate to play for another particular reason.

4. NEW APPLICATIONS TO JOIN LEAGUE

Application to join a league MUST be made IN WRITING and shall be in the hands of the Divisional Competition Secretary NOT LATER THAN 30th April. By this same date, the Club MUST have met ALL the entry criteria laid down in Courage League Regulation and those applied, from time to time, by the OrganisingCommittee.

LONDON & SOUTH EAST CHAMPIONS ROLL OF HONOUR 1994/95

London 1
Camberley
London 2 North
Staines
London 2 South
Charlton Park
London 3 North West
Hertford
London 3 North East
Colchester
London 3 South East
Brockleians
London 3 South West
Wimbledon
Herts/Middlesex
Mill Mill
Middlesex 1
Old Hamptonians
Middlesex 2
London Nigerians
Middlesex 3
London Exiles
Middlesex 4
Quintin
Hertfordshire
Tring
Eastern Counties 1
Lowestoft & Yarmouth
Eastern Counties 2
Ilford Wanderers
Eastern Counties 3
Fakenham

Eastern Counties 4
Billericay
Eastern Counties 5
Sawston
Kent 1
Sevenoaks
Kent 2
Ashford
Kent 3
Lordswood
Kent 4
Orpington
Sussex 1
Uckfield
Sussex 2
BA Wingspan
Sussex 3
Rye
Hampshire 1
Jersey
Hampshire 2
Andover
Hampshire 3
Fleet
Surrey 1
Old Whitgiftians
Surrey 2
Old Caterhamians
Surrey 3
Old Suttonians
Surrey 4
Kew Occasionals

Charlton Park

LONDON DIVISION FEATURED CLUBS

CHARLTON PARK

CHARLTON PARK, whose headquarters are at the Pippenhall Sports Ground in Eltham (South East London), enjoyed a resounding success in winning London South and will in the coming season be competing against the top clubs in the London and South East area with a realistic chance of becoming a senior side sooner rather than later.

In a dozen league matches they dropped only one points in drawing away at Old Wimbledonians last October at a time when they seemed to struggle to beat the opposition, but after that fourth match in the league their form improved and no opposiition again gave them any trouble with the luckless Protsmouth being beaten 55-8 at Eltham and Horsham suffering a 56-10 rout on their own ground in the final league game of the season.

Stars of an outfit which was a team in every sense have been skipper, fly-half and chief points gatherer John Field, fullback Kevin Ellis, scrum-half George Costi and a pack, which boasted such excellent performers as former Blackheath lock Goug Hursey and hooker Dave Hazelton, who scored nine tries in the competition including all three against Thanet Wanderers.

There is an excellent club house and friendly atmsophere and they especially mention the two Barrys – Sykes and Pritchard – for that. Charlton Park march on and we will follow their fortunes with great interest.

JERSEY

JERSEY, by finishing top of Hampshire One with all 12 matches won, find themselves back in London Three South West after three seasons and this time they mean to stay up. In a superb campaign overall they won 20 of their 24 fixtures for a 787-281 points position and the growing strength of the club is demonstrated by the fact that next season they will have three senior fifteens plus a colts side and veterans.

Their geographic situation means that they have a smaller fixture list than most, have large travelling expenses to meet league commitments and cannot expect to find star players in their midst, but at the same time the big clubs from England do not send out scouts to poach their better performers such as leading try scorer Justin Thomas, who crossed opponents' lines on 22 occasions.

The coaching is in the enthusiastic hands of Ol Burton and Ian Anderson and in 1994 they moved into a new club house, which cost a million pounds and so good are their facilities that Cardiff and Garrywoen paid them visits in 1994 for pre-season training and more can be expected to do so in the future.

Their league success hinged on a final game shoot-out against United Services (Portsmouth) with a fine 29-14 victory brining promotion. If in other competitions they were less successful the indications in one case were good for the game. In the Bass Hampshire Cup they lost narrowly to Gosport on a soggy day (10-9), while the Siam Cup (as old as the Calcutta Cup and fashioned in a similar manner) went back to Guernsey after an interval of eight years – sad for Jersey but a sign perhaps that Channel Islands rugby is in a nice competitive position with the others possible promotion candidates next season.

Channel Islanders have made their mark on the soccer scene and sooner rather than later rugby can be expected to find equivalents to Le Saux and Le Tissier from their clubs.

Jersey

LONDON & SOUTH EAST DIVISION

LONDON ONE
1995-96
FIXTURES

November 11 1995 (Week 10)
Guildford & Godalming v Staines
Old Colfeians v Sutton & Epsom
Old Mid-Whitgiftians v Charlton Park
Basingstoke v Harlow
Ruislip v Ealing
Esher v Sudbury

September 16 1995 (Week 3)
Guildford & Godalming v Old Colfeians
Sudbury v Sutton & Epsom
Ealing v Charlton Park
Southend v Harlow
Ruislip v Basingstoke
Esher v Old Mid-Whitgiftians

January 6 1996 (Week 17)
Charlton Park v Basingstoke
Sutton & Epsom v Old Mid-Whitgiftians
Staines v Old Colfeians
Sudbury v Guildford & Godalming
Ealing v Esher
Southend v Ruislip

September 23 1995 (Week 4)
Old Mid-Whitgiftians v Guildford & Godalming
Basingstoke v Esher
Harlow v Ruislip
Charlton Park v Southend
Sutton & Epsom v Ealing
Staines v Sudbury

January 13 1996 (Week 18)
Guildford & Godalming v Ealing
Old Colfeians v Sudbury
Old Mid-Whitgiftians v Staines
Basingstoke v Sutton & Epsom
Harlow v Charlton Park
Esher v Southend

September 30 1995 (Week X1)
Guildford & Godalming v Basingstoke
Old Colfeians v Old Mid-Whitgiftians
Ealing v Staines
Southend v Sutton & Epsom
Ruislip v Charlton Park
Esher v Harlow

February 10 1996 (Week 22)
Sutton & Epsom v Harlow
Staines v Basingstoke
Sudbury v Old Mid-Whitgiftians
Ealing v Old Colfeians
Southend v Guildford & Godalming
Ruislip v Esher

October 14 1995 (Week 6)
Basingstoke v Old Colfeians
Harlow v Guildford & Godalming
Charlton Park v Esher
Sutton & Epsom v Ruislip
Staines v Southend
Sudbury v Ealing

February 17 1996 (Week 23)
Guildford & Godalming v Ruislip
Old Colfeians v Southend
Old Mid-Whitgiftians v Ealing
Basingstoke v Sudbury
Harlow v Staines
Charlton Park v Sutton & Epsom

October 21 1995 (Week 7)
Guildford & Godalming v Charlton Park
Old Colfeians v Harlow
Old Mid-Whitgiftians v Basingstoke
Southend v Sudbury
Ruislip v Staines
Esher v Sutton & Epsom

February 24 1996 (Week 24)
Staines v Charlton Park
Sudbury v Harlow
Ealing v Basingstoke
Southend v Old Mid-Whitgiftians
Ruislip v Old Colfeians
Esher v Guildford & Godalming

October 28 1995 (Week 8)
Harlow v Old Mid-Whitgiftians
Charlton Park v Old Colfeians
Sutton & Epsom v Guildford & Godalming
Staines v Esher
Sudbury v Ruislip
Ealing v Southend

March 30 1996 (Week X7)
Old Colfeians v Esher
Old Mid-Whitgiftians v Ruislip
Basingstoke v Southend
Harlow v Ealing
Charlton Park v Sudbury
Sutton & Epsom v Staines

462

LONDON ONE

BASINGSTOKE RFC
Ground Address: Down Grange, Pack Lane, Basingstoke, Hampshire RG22 5HN. Tel: 01256 23308
Club Secretary: Brian Anderson, 9 Pelham Close, Old Basing, Basingstoke, Hants RG24 7HU. Tel: (H) 01256 59687
Fixtures Secretary: A Paynter, 152 Pack Lane, Kempshott, Basingstoke, Hants RG22 5HR. Tel: (H) 01256 27857 Tel (W) 01256 843191 x3760
Club Colours: Amber & blue.

CHARLTON PARK RFC
Ground Address: Pippenhall Sports Ground, Avery Hill Park, Footscray Road, Eltham, London SE9. Tel: 0181 850 0408
Club Secretary: Nick Hollier, 5 Brunswick Road, Bexleyheath, Kent DA6 8EL. Tel: (H) 0181 301 1210 Tel: (W) 0181 303 7777 x2419
Fixtures Secretary: Roger Foxon, 245 McLeod Road, Abbey Wood, London SE2 0YJ. Tel: (H) 0181 473 0004
Club Colours: Red & white hoops, blue shorts, red socks.

EALING FC
Ground Address: Berkeley Avenue, Greenford, Middlesex UB6 0NZ. Tel: 0181 422 0868
Club Secretary: Mr D Bugeja, 7 Bradley Gardens, Ealing, London W13 8HE. Tel: (H) 0181 997 9982 Tel: (W) 01344 872677
Fixtures Secretary: Mr P Monteith, 5 Bullfinch Close, Oakham, Rutland, Leicester LE15 6BS. Tel (W) 0171 204 2932
Club Colours: Dark green with white hoops.

ESHER RFC
Ground Address: 369 Molesley Road, Hersham, Surrey KT12 3PF. Tel: 01932 220295
Club Secretary: AR Till, 25 Motspur Park, New Malden, Surrey KT3 6PS. Tel: (H) 0181 942 1380
Fixtures Secretary: S Gardner, 72 Chesil Street, Winchester, Hants SO32 8HK. Tel: (H) 01962 869846
Club Colours: Black & amber.

GUILDFORD & GODALMING RFC
Ground Address: Broadwater, Guildford Road (A3100), Godalming, Surrey GU7 3BU. Tel: 01483 416199
Club Secretary: David Gambold, 10 Treebys Avenue, Jacobs Well, Guildford, Surrey GU4 7NT. Tel: (H) 01483 66304 Tel: (W) 01483 61365
Fixtures Secretary: Len Bodill, 4 Orchard Road, Burpham, Guildford, Surrey GU4 7JH. Tel: (H) 01483 570580
Club Colours: Green & white hoops, white shorts.

HARLOW RUFC
Ground Address: Ram Gorse, Elizabeth Way, Harlow, Essex CM20 2JQ. Tel: 01279 429750
Club Secretary: David Eynon, 12 Highfield, Harlow, Essex CM18 6HE. Tel: (H) 01279 426389 Tel: (W) 0181 554 1607 Fax: 0181 518 3251
Fixtures Secretary: John Pendleton, 59 Priory Court, Harlow, Essex CM18 7AZ. Tel: (H) 01729 439265
Club Colours: Red shirts with green trimmings & shorts.

OLD COLFEIANS RFC
Ground Address: Horn Park, Eltham Road, Lee, London SE12. Tel: 0181 852 1181
Club Secretary: Dai Andrew, 80 Dallinger Road, Lee, London SE12 0TH. Tel: (H) 0181 857 4036 Tel: (W) 0181 680 9011
Fixtures Secretary: John Nunn, The Mount, 27 Westmount Road, Eltham, London SE9 1JB. Tel: (H) 0181 265 7447
Club Colours: Blue, black, maroon & old gold bands, navy shorts & socks.

OLD MID-WHITGIFTIAN RFC
Ground Address: Lime Meadow Avenue, Sanderstead, Surrey CR2 9AS. Tel: 0181 657 2014
Club Secretary: Mike Morse, 'Winscombe Paddock', Beacon Road, Crowborough, East Sussex TN6 1UL. Tel: (H) 01829 655996
Fixtures Secretary: Andy Hillburn, 47A Foxearth Road,

FINAL TABLE

	P	W	D	L	F	A	Pts
Camberley	12	12	0	0	375	122	24
Esher	12	10	0	2	344	132	20
Ruislip	12	10	0	2	255	175	20
Harlow	12	7	0	5	337	210	14
Guildford & G'Ming	12	7	0	5	294	184	14
Ealing	12	7	0	5	175	153	14
Southend	12	6	0	6	243	249	12
Old Mid Whitgiftian	12	6	0	6	207	225	12
Sutton & Epsom	12	5	0	7	166	188	10
Old Colfeians	12	4	0	8	202	256	8
Streatham-Croydon	12	2	0	10	99	325	4
Eton Manor	12	2	0	10	129	259	2*
Maidstone	12	0	0	12	106	454	-2*

Selsdon, South Croydon, Surrey CR2 8EL. Tel: (H) 0181 657 1825 Tel (W) 0171 917 8888 x4435
Club Colours: Blue shirts, blue shorts.

RUISLIP RFC
Ground Address: West End Road, Ruislip, Middlesex HA4 6DR. Tel: 01895 633102
Club Secretary: Michael Searls, 16 Park Way, Rickmansworth, Herts WD3 2AT. Tel: (H) 01923 773903 Tel: (W) 0171 357 1000
Fixtures Secretary: Steve Hazell, Milestones, 23 Hopfield Avenue, Byfleet, Surrey. Tel: (H) 01932 354060 Tel (W) 0181 641 8510
Club Colours: Maroon & white hooped shirts, white shorts, maroon socks.

SOUTHEND RFC
Ground Address: Warners Bridge Park, Sumpters Way, Southend on Sea, Essex SS2 5RR. Tel: 01702 546682
Club Secretary: David Dilley, 106 Woodside, Leigh on Sea, Essex, SS9 4RB. Tel: (H) 01702 523553 Tel: (W) 01702 546682
Fixtures Secretary: Tom Webb, 28 St James Gardens, Westcliff on Sea, Essex. Tel: (H) 01702 342888
Club Colours: Chocolate and white.

STAINES RFC
Ground Address: The Reeves, Feltham Hill Road, Hanworth, Middlesex TW13 7NB. Tel: 0181 890 3051
Club Secretary: WR Johnston, 4 April Close, Feltham, Middlsex TW13 7JQ. Tel: (H) 0181 384 6330 Tel: (W) 0181 759 2141 x233
Fixtures Secretary: EJ de Voil, 94 Groveley Road, Sunbury-on-thames, Middlesex TW16 7LB. Tel: (H) 0181 890 6643 Tel (W) 0171 248 1117
Club Colours: Red & blue hoops, white shorts.

SUDBURY RUFC
Ground Address: 'Moorsfield', Great Cornard, Sudbury, Suffolk CO10 0JR. Tel: 01787 377547
Club Secretary: David Cardle, 'Bakersfield', School Road, Little Marplestead, Nr Halstead, Essex CO9 2RY. Tel: (H) 01787 475551 Tel: (W) 01933 442287
Fixtures Secretary: Gregory Underwood, 11 Bures Road, Great Cornard, Sudbury, Suffolk CO10 0EJ. Tel: (H) 01787 373045
Club Colours: Blue & maroon.

SUTTON & EPSOM RFC
Ground Address: Cuddington Court, Rugby Lane, West Drive, Cheam, Surrey SM2 7NF. Tel: 0181 642 0280
Club Secretary: DR Poole, Well Cottage, Loxwood Road, Wisborough Green, West sussex RH14 0DJ. Tel: (H) 01403 700594
Fixtures Secretary: I Frazer, 111 Benhill Road, Sutton, Surrey SM1 3RR. Tel: (H) 0181 643 4835 Tel (W) 0171 514 8549
Club Colours: Black & white jerseys (wide hoops).

LONDON & SOUTH EAST DIVISION

November 11 1995 (Week 10)

Thurrock	v	Finchley
Old Verulamians	v	Hertford
Brentwood	v	Woodford
Norwich	v	Colchester
Eton Manor	v	Cambridge
Bishop's Stortford	v	Romford & Gidea Park

September 16 1995 (Week 3)

Thurrock	v	Old Verulamians
Romford & Gidea Park	v	Hertford
Cambridge	v	Woodford
Cheshunt	v	Colchester
Eton Manor	v	Norwich
Bishop's Stortford	v	Brentwood

January 6 1996 (Week 17)

Woodford	v	Norwich
Hertford	v	Brentwood
Finchley	v	Old Verulamians
Romford & Gidea Park	v	Thurrock
Cambridge	v	Bishop's Stortford
Cheshunt	v	Eton Manor

September 23 1995 (Week 4)

Brentwood	v	Thurrock
Norwich	v	Bishop's Stortford
Colchester	v	Eton Manor
Woodford	v	Cheshunt
Hertford	v	Cambridge
Finchley	v	Romford & Gidea Park

January 13 1996 (Week 18)

Thurrock	v	Cambridge
Old Verulamians	v	Romford & Gidea Park
Brentwood	v	Finchley
Norwich	v	Hertford
Colchester	v	Woodford
Bishop's Stortford	v	Cheshunt

September 30 1995 (Week X1)

Thurrock	v	Norwich
Old Verulamians	v	Brentwood
Cambridge	v	Finchley
Cheshunt	v	Hertford
Eton Manor	v	Woodford
Bishop's Stortford	v	Colchester

February 10 1996 (Week 22)

Hertford	v	Colchester
Finchley	v	Norwich
Romford & Gidea Park	v	Brentwood
Cambridge	v	Old Verulamians
Cheshunt	v	Thurrock
Eton Manor	v	Bishop's Stortford

October 14 1995 (Week 6)

Norwich	v	Old Verulamians
Colchester	v	Thurrock
Woodford	v	Bishop's Stortford
Hertford	v	Eton Manor
Finchley	v	Cheshunt
Romford & Gidea Park	v	Cambridge

February 17 1996 (Week 23)

Thurrock	v	Eton Manor
Old Verulamians	v	Cheshunt
Brentwood	v	Cambridge
Norwich	v	Romford & Gidea Park
Colchester	v	Finchley
Woodford	v	Hertford

October 21 1995 (Week 7)

Thurrock	v	Woodford
Old Verulamians	v	Colchester
Brentwood	v	Norwich
Cheshunt	v	Romford & Gidea Park
Eton Manor	v	Finchley
Bishop's Stortford	v	Hertford

February 24 1996 (Week 24)

Finchley	v	Woodford
Romford & Gidea Park	v	Colchester
Cambridge	v	Norwich
Cheshunt	v	Brentwood
Eton Manor	v	Old Verulamians
Bishop's Stortford	v	Thurrock

October 28 1995 (Week 8)

Colchester	v	Brentwood
Woodford	v	Old Verulamians
Hertford	v	Thurrock
Finchley	v	Bishop's Stortford
Romford & Gidea Park	v	Eton Manor
Cambridge	v	Cheshunt

March 30 1996 (Week X7)

Old Verulamians	v	Bishop's Stortford
Brentwood	v	Eton Manor
Norwich	v	Cheshunt
Colchester	v	Cambridge
Woodford	v	Romford & Gidea Park
Hertford	v	Finchley

LONDON TWO NORTH

BISHOP'S STORTFORD RFC
Ground Address: Silver Leys, Hadham Road, Bishop's
Stortford, Hertfordshire CM23 2QE. Tel: 01279 652092
Club Secretary: RM Liddle, 95 Parsonage Lane, Bishop's
Stortford, Herts CM23 5BA. Tel: (H) 01279 651330 Tel:
(W) 01279 651330
Fixtures Secretary: Mrs Jenny Lancey, 41 Appleton
Fields, Bishop's Stortford, Herts CM23 4DR. Tel: (H)
01279 651061
Club Colours: Royal blue & white shirts & stockings,
white shorts.
BRENTWOOD RFC
Ground Address: King George's Playing Fields, Ingrave
Road, Brentwood, Essex. Tel: 01277 210267
Club Secretary: Mr RW Glasby, 59 Tyelands, Billericay,
Essex CM12 9PB. Tel: (H) 01277 631533 Tel: (W) 01702
74496
Fixtures Secretary: Mr A Joselyn, 15 Chandlers Walk,
Kelvedon Common, Brentwood, Essex CM15 0XL. Tel:
(H) 01277 373690 Tel (W) 0171 357 2770
Club Colours: Claret, grey & maroon hoops.
CAMBRIDGE RUFC
Ground Address: Grantchester Road, Cambridge CB3
9ED. Tel: 01223 312437
Club Secretary: Mr DJ Martin, 45 York Street, Cambridge
CB1 2PZ. Tel: (H) 01223 314705 Tel: (W) 01223 845985
Fixtures Secretary: Mr A Curtis, Kendal Lodge, Church
End, Coton, Cambridge CB3 7PN. Tel: (H) 01954 211724
Club Colours: Blood & sand.
CHESHUNT RFC
Ground Address: Rosedale Sports Club, Andrews Lane,
Rosedale, Cheshunt, Herts EN7 6TB. Tel: 01992 623983
Club Secretary: RP Jackson, 9 Hillside Crescent, Enfield,
Middlesex EN2 0HP. Tel: (H) 0181 342 0329 Tel: (W)
0171 283 6293
Fixtures Secretary: Peter Thompson, 7 Harrison's Walk,
Cheshunt, Herts EN8 8PT. Tel: (H) 01992 552225
Club Colours: Green & white hoops.
COLCHESTER RFC
Ground Address: Mill Road, Mile End, Colchester, C04
5JF. Tel: 02106 851610
Club Secretary: Ron Hatch, 99 Ernest Road, Wivenhoe,
C07 9LJ. Tel: (H) 01206 823548
Fixtures Secretary: Jon Roberts, 5 Spencer Close,
Maldon, CM9 6BX. Tel: (H) 01621 854043
Club Colours: Black.
ETON MANOR RFC
Ground Address: Eastway Sports Centre, Quartermile
Lane, Leyton, London E10. Tel: 0181 555 2670
Club Secretary: Mr John Ayling, 44 Lytton Road,
Leytonstone, London E11 1JH. Tel: (H) 0181 558 1800
Fixtures Secretary: Mr Martin Scott, 2 Preston Drive,
Wanstead, London E11 2JB. Tel: (H) 0181 530 4451
Club Colours: Dark blue with a light blue hoop, dark blue
shorts.
FINCHLEY RFC
Ground Address: Summers Lane, Finchley, London N12
0PD. Tel: 0181 445 3746
Club Secretary: Mr Carl Elliott, 3 Mount Pleasant Road,
Ealing, London W5 1SG. Tel: (H) 0181 998 9369 Tel: (W)
0171 600 0542
Fixtures Secretary: Mr Leo Gibbons, 132 Church Hill
Road, East Barnet, EN4 8XD. Tel: (H) 0171 368 7253 Tel
(W) 0171 377 3190
Club Colours: Scarlet & white hoops.
HERTFORD RFC
Ground Address: Highfields, Hoe Lane, Ware, Herts
SG12 9NZ. Tel: 01920 462975
Club Secretary: Mr Adrian Sparks, 29 Wilton Crescent,
Hertford, Herts SG13 8JS. Tel: (H) 01992 589364 Tel: (W)
01279 439161

FINAL TABLE

	P	W	D	L	F	A	Pts
Staines	12	11	0	1	318	107	22
Old Verulamians	12	9	0	3	239	178	18
Cheshunt	12	9	0	3	230	171	18
Bishop's Stortford	12	6	2	4	208	196	14
Norwich	12	6	1	5	188	132	13
Cambridge	12	5	2	5	157	160	12
Thurrock	12	5	0	7	201	204	10
Finchley	12	5	2	5	165	192	10*
Brentwood	12	4	2	6	140	171	10
Woodford	12	4	0	8	184	260	8
Romford & Gidea Pk	12	3	1	8	119	212	7
Chingford	12	3	0	9	141	240	6
Old Gaytonians	12	3	0	9	149	216	4*

Fixtures Secretary: Mr DJ Williams, 7 Sadlers Way,
Hertford, Herts SG14 2DZ. Tel: (H) 01992 586744
Club Colours: Black, royal blue & gold jerseys, black
shorts.
NORWICH RFC
Ground Address: Beeston Hyrne, North Walsham Road,
Norwich NR12 7BW. Tel: 01603 426259
Club Secretary: Ted Searle, Alan Boswell Insurance
Brokers Ltd, Cedar House, Carrow Road, Norwich NR1
1HP. Tel: (H) 01508 480364 Tel: (W) 01603 218000
Fixtures Secretary: Steve Henson, Kent House, The
Street, Old Costessey, Norwich NR8 5DB. Tel: (H) 01603
748351 Tel (W) 01603 685552
Club Colours: Maroon, green & gold.
OLD VERULAMIAN RFC
Ground Address: Cotlandswick, London Colney, Nr St
Albans, Hertfordshire AL2 1DW. Tel: 01727 822929
Club Secretary: AB Charlwood, 12 Waverley Road, St
Albans, Hertfordshire AL3 5BA. Tel: (H) 01727 846923
Fixtures Secretary: Mrs V Halford, 21 Marshalswick
Lane, St Albans, Hertfordshire AL1 4UR. Tel: (H) 01727
830732 Tel (W) 01920 830230
Club Colours: Royal blue with gold V, white shorts.
ROMFORD & GIDEA PARK RFC
Ground Address: Crow Lane, Romford, Essex RM7 0EP.
Tel: 01708 760068
Club Secretary: DGE Davies, 25 Stanley Avenue, Gidea
Park, Romford, Essex RM2 5DL. Tel: (H) 01708 724870
Tel: (W) 0181 592 4193
Fixtures Secretary: G Finch, 30 Warley Mount,
Brentwood, Essex CM14 5EN. Tel: (H) 01277 229817 Tel
(W) 0181 804 1980
Club Colours: Black jersey with purple & white bands
across chest and arms.
THURROCK RFC
Ground Address: Oakfield, Long Lane, Grays, Thurrock,
Essex. Tel: 01375 374877
Club Secretary: J Keefe, 20 Archates Avenue, Grays,
Essex RM16 6QS. Tel: (H) 01375 381763
Fixtures Secretary: Kevin Hymans, Clearwater, Argent
Street, Grays,Essex RM17 6PG. Tel: (H) 01375 383666
Club Colours: Black & white.
WOODFORD RFC
Ground Address: Highams, High Road, Woodford Green,
Essex IG8 9LB. Tel: 0181 504 6769
Club Secretary: Mr RF Perryman, 7 Brancepeth Gardens,
Buckhurst Hill, Essex IG9 5JL. Tel: (H) 0181 505 5973
Tel: (W) 0181 556 9721
Fixtures Secretary: Mr M Whiteley, 62 Beresford Road,
London E4. Tel: (H) 0181 524 2737 Tel (W) 0171 865 5870
Club Colours: Lavender, black & white.

LONDON & SOUTH EAST DIVISION

LONDON THREE NORTH WEST 1995-96 FIXTURES

November 11 1995 (Week 10)

Old Elizabethans	v	Old Merchant Taylors
Lensbury	v	Old Millhillians
Letchworth	v	Grasshoppers
Barnet	v	Old Gaytonians
Fullerians	v	Kingsburians
Mill Hill	v	Old Albanians

September 16 1995 (Week 3)

Old Elizabethans	v	Lensbury
Old Albanians	v	Old Millhillians
Kingsburians	v	Grasshoppers
Welwyn	v	Old Gaytonians
Fullerians	v	Barnet
Mill Hill	v	Letchworth

January 6 1996 (Week 17)

Grasshoppers	v	Barnet
Old Millhillians	v	Letchworth
Old Merchant Taylors	v	Lensbury
Old Albanians	v	Old Elizabethans
Kingsburians	v	Mill Hill
Welwyn	v	Fullerians

September 23 1995 (Week 4)

Letchworth	v	Old Elizabethans
Barnet	v	Mill Hill
Old Gaytonians	v	Fullerians
Grasshoppers	v	Welwyn
Old Millhillians	v	Kingsburians
Old Merchant Taylors	v	Old Albanians

January 13 1996 (Week 18)

Old Elizabethans	v	Kingsburians
Lensbury	v	Old Albanians
Letchworth	v	Old Merchant Taylors
Barnet	v	Old Millhillians
Old Gaytonians	v	Grasshoppers
Mill Hill	v	Welwyn

September 30 1995 (Week X1)

Old Elizabethans	v	Barnet
Lensbury	v	Letchworth
Kingsburians	v	Old Merchant Taylors
Welwyn	v	Old Millhillians
Fullerians	v	Grasshoppers
Mill Hill	v	Old Gaytonians

February 10 1996 (Week 22)

Old Millhillians	v	Old Gaytonians
Old Merchant Taylors	v	Barnet
Old Albanians	v	Letchworth
Kingsburians	v	Lensbury
Welwyn	v	Old Elizabethans
Fullerians	v	Mill Hill

October 14 1995 (Week 6)

Barnet	v	Lensbury
Old Gaytonians	v	Old Elizabethans
Grasshoppers	v	Mill Hill
Old Millhillians	v	Fullerians
Old Merchant Taylors	v	Welwyn
Old Albanians	v	Kingsburians

February 17 1996 (Week 23)

Old Elizabethans	v	Fullerians
Lensbury	v	Welwyn
Letchworth	v	Kingsburians
Barnet	v	Old Albanians
Old Gaytonians	v	Old Merchant Taylors
Grasshoppers	v	Old Millhillians

October 21 1995 (Week 7)

Old Elizabethans	v	Grasshoppers
Lensbury	v	Old Gaytonians
Letchworth	v	Barnet
Welwyn	v	Old Albanians
Fullerians	v	Old Merchant Taylors
Mill Hill	v	Old Millhillians

February 24 1996 (Week 24)

Old Merchant Taylors	v	Grasshoppers
Old Albanians	v	Old Gaytonians
Kingsburians	v	Barnet
Welwyn	v	Letchworth
Fullerians	v	Lensbury
Mill Hill	v	Old Elizabethans

October 28 1995 (Week 8)

Old Gaytonians	v	Letchworth
Grasshoppers	v	Lensbury
Old Millhillians	v	Old Elizabethans
Old Merchant Taylors	v	Mill Hill
Old Albanians	v	Fullerians
Kingsburians	v	Welwyn

March 30 1996 (Week X7)

Lensbury	v	Mill Hill
Letchworth	v	Fullerians
Barnet	v	Welwyn
Old Gaytonians	v	Kingsburians
Grasshoppers	v	Old Albanians
Old Millhillians	v	Old Merchant Taylors

LONDON THREE NORTH WEST

BARNET RFC
Ground Address: Byng Road, Barnet, herts. Tel: 0181 449 0040
Club Secretary: Nigel Oram, Bedwell End, Essendon, Hertsw AL9 6HL. Tel: (H) 01707 261238 Tel: (W) 0171 621 1224
Fixtures Secretary: Peter Glenister, 47 Bury Lane, Codicote, Hitchin, Herts SG4 8XX. Tel: (H) 01438 820692
Club Colours: Navy blue & claret.

FULLERIANS RFC
Ground Address: Coningesby Drive (end of Parkside Drive), Watford, Herts. Tel: 01923 224483
Club Secretary: Thomas, 3 Mitchell Close, Abbey Park, Abbot's Langley, Herts WD5 0TQ. Tel: (H) 01923 819308 Tel: (W) 01923 237674
Fixtures Secretary: J Ayres, 9 Church Grove, Little Chalfont, Bucks HP6 6SH. Tel: (H) 01494 763266
Club Colours: Black, red & greem hooped jerseys & socks, black shorts.

GRASSHOPPERS RFC
Ground Address: McFarlane Sports Field, McFarlane Lane, off Syon Lane, Osterley, Middlesex. Tel: 0181 568 0010
Club Secretary: Mr AJ Huckle, 13 Kings Road, Uxbridge, Middlesex UB8 2NW. Tel: (H) 01895 230582
Fixtures Secretary: Mr Andy Brown, 10 Boston Manor Road, Brentford, Middlesex. Tel: (H) 0181 560 4844 Tel (W) 0181 560 2583
Club Colours: Green, black & gold hoops.

KINGSBURIANS RFC
Ground Address: Northwick Park Pavilion, Northwick Park, The Fairway, North Wembley, Middlesex. Tel: 0181 904 4414
Club Secretary: Neil Keeler, 25 Lansdowne Road, Stanmore, Middlesex HA7 2RX. Tel: (H) 0181 954 7211 Tel: (W) 01442 844342
Fixtures Secretary: Bruce Bland, 10 Clitheroe Avenue, Rayners Lane, Harrow, Middlesex HA2 9UX. Tel: (H) 0181 868 5244 Tel (W) 0181 204 4442
Club Colours: Black & amber hoops, black shorts.

LENSBURY RFC
Ground Address: Lensbury Club, Broom Road, Teddington, Middx TW11 9NU. Tel: 0181 977 8821
Club Secretary: Mr M O'Gara, 13 Bryanston Avenue, Twickenham, Middx TW2 6HP. Tel: (H) 0181 898 7359 Tel: (W) 01252 816816
Fixtures Secretary: Mr S Riach, Deva, 12 Blackwood Close, West Byfleet, Surrey KT14 6PW. Tel: (H) 01932 340601 Tel (W) 01784 245058
Club Colours: Purple, orange & black.

LETCHWORTH GARDEN CITY RUFC
Ground Address: Baldock Road, Letchworth, Hertfordshire. Tel: 01462 682554
Club Secretary: John Donegan, 9 Byrd Walk, Baldock, Herts SG7 6LN. Tel: (H) 01462 491360 Tel: (W) 01462 442800
Fixtures Secretary: Graham Steele, 11 Rookes Close, Letchworth, Herts SG6 2SN. Tel: (H) 01462 676985 Tel (W) 0181 490 3631
Club Colours: Black & amber hoops, black shorts.

MILL HILL RFC
Ground Address: Page Street, Mill Hill, London NW7 2ER. Tel: 0181 203 0685
Club Secretary: Peter J Braddock, 43 Winstre Road, Boreham Wood, Hertfordshire WD6 5DR. Tel: (H) 0181 953 6500 Tel: (W) 0181 207 6373
Fixtures Secretary: Peter J Braddock, 43 Winstre Road, Boreham Wood, Hertfordshire WD6 5DR. Tel: (H) 0181 953 6500 Tel (W) 0181 207 6373
Club Colours: Chocolate & gold hoops.

OLD ALBANIAN RFC
Ground Address: Beech Bottom, Old Harpenden Road, St Albans, Herts. Tel: 01727 864476
Club Secretary: Peter Lipscomb, 35 Gurney Court Road, St Albans, Herts AL1 4QU. Tel: (H) 01727 760466 Tel: (W) 0181 784 5924
Fixtures Secretary: David Verdon, Pine Lodge, Hook Heath Road, Woking, Surrey. Tel: (H) 01483 764937 Tel (W) 0171 417 8096
Club Colours: Red, blue & gold hooped shirts.

FINAL TABLE

	P	W	D	L	F	A	Pts
Hertford	12	11	0	1	207	105	22
Grasshoppers	12	10	0	2	207	105	20
Lensbury	12	9	0	3	246	169	18
Old Albanians	12	8	0	4	210	138	15
Old Elizabethans	12	7	1	4	200	151	15
O Merchant Taylors	12	7	0	5	231	153	14
Letchworth	12	6	0	6	221	183	12
Old Millhillians	12	5	1	6	191	158	11
Welwyn	12	5	1	6	196	246	11
Barnet	12	4	0	8	174	224	8
Kingsburians	12	2	1	9	112	213	5
Upper Clapton	12	1	0	11	114	256	2
London New Zealand	12	1	0	11	69	293	2

OLD ELIZABETHANS (BARNET) RFC
Ground Address: Gypsy Corner, Mays Lane, Barnet, Hertfordshire EN5 2AG. Tel: 0181 449 9481
Club Secretary: Lincoln Way, Croxley Green, Nr Hertfordshire EN4 8DY. Tel: (H) 0181 368 4767 Tel: (W) 0181 290 4042
Fixtures Secretary: BJ Fuller, 109 Margaret Road, New Barnet, Herts EN4 9RA. Tel: (H) 0181 449 0590
Club Colours: Light blue & dark blue hoops, blue shorts.

OLD GAYTONIANS RFC
Ground Address: South Vale, Harrow, Middlesex HA1 3PN. Tel: 0181 423 4133
Club Secretary: Tony Usher, 9 Paynesfield Road, Bushey Heath, Herts WD2 1PQ. Tel: (H) 0181 950 2956 Tel: (W) 01784 241731
Fixtures Secretary: Brian Kennett, 102 Cleveland Road, London W13 0EL. Tel: (H) 0181 998 2879 Tel (W) 0181 231 2128
Club Colours: White with broad band of chocolate, green & blue.

OLD MERCHANT TAYLORS' FC
Ground Address: Durrants, Lincoln Way, Croxley Green, Nr Rickmansworth, Hertfordshire WD3 3ND. Tel: 01923 773014
Club Secretary: MG Foster, The White House, 16 New Road, Croxley Green, Hertfordshire WD3 3EL. Tel: (H) 01923 775793
Fixtures Secretary: GW Shilling, The Lodge, Wellingrove, Woodcock Hill, Rickmansworth, Herts WD3 1PT. Tel: (H) 01923 774506 Tel (W) 01923 774506
Club Colours: White jerseys, black shorts.

OLD MILLHILLIANS RFC
Ground Address: Pinner Park, Headstone Lane, North Harrow, Middlesex HA2 6BR. Tel: 0181 428 2281
Club Secretary: M Leon, Wildacre, Bushfield Road, Bovingdon, Herts HP3 0QR. Tel: (H) 01442 833665
Fixtures Secretary: P Foottit, 38 Birkbeck Road, London NW7 4AA. Tel: (H) 0181 906 3060 Tel (W) 0181 367 7711
Club Colours: Chocolate & white hoops.

WELWYN RFC
Ground Address: Handside Playing Fields, Hobbs Way, Colgrove, Welwyn Garden City, Herts. Tel: 01707 329116
Club Secretary: JM Sargeant, 67 Woodhall Lane, Welwyn Garden City, Herts AL7 3TG. Tel: (H) 01707 331186 Tel: (W) 01707 326318
Fixtures Secretary: N Aldridge, 9 Marsden Close, Welwyn Garden City, Herts AL7 6JF. Tel: (H) 01707 321012 Tel (W) 0181 758 6000
Club Colours: Maroon & white hooped shirts, blue shorts, maroon stockings.

467

LONDON & SOUTH EAST DIVISION

HERTFORDSHIRE/ MIDDLESEX 1995-96 FIXTURES

November 11 1995 (Week 10)

St Albans	v	St Mary's Hospital
Old Meadonians	v	Hendon
London New Zealand	v	Upper Clapton
Hemel Hempstead	v	Haringey
Old Hamptonian	v	Uxbridge
Hampstead	v	Centaurs

September 16 1995 (Week 3)

St Albans	v	Old Meadonians
Centaurs	v	Hendon
Uxbridge	v	Upper Clapton
Tring	v	Haringey
Old Hamptonian	v	Hemel Hempstead
Hampstead	v	London New Zealand

January 6 1996 (Week 17)

Upper Clapton	v	Hemel Hempstead
Hendon	v	London New Zealand
St Mary's Hospital	v	Old Meadonians
Centaurs	v	St Albans
Uxbridge	v	Hampstead
Tring	v	Old Hamptonian

September 23 1995 (Week 4)

London New Zealand	v	St Albans
Hemel Hempstead	v	Hampstead
Haringey	v	Old Hamptonian
Upper Clapton	v	Tring
Hendon	v	Uxbridge
St Mary's Hospital	v	Centaurs

January 13 1996 (Week 18)

St Albans	v	Uxbridge
Old Meadonians	v	Centaurs
London New Zealand	v	St Mary's Hospital
Hemel Hempstead	v	Hendon
Haringey	v	Upper Clapton
Hampstead	v	Tring

September 30 1995 (Week X1)

St Albans	v	Hemel Hempstead
Old Meadonians	v	London New Zealand
Uxbridge	v	St Mary's Hosptial
Tring	v	Hendon
Old Hamptonian	v	Upper Clapton
Hampstead	v	Haringey

February 10 1996 (Week 22)

Hendon	v	Haringey
St Mary's Hospital	v	Hemel Hempstead
Centaurs	v	London New Zealand
Uxbridge	v	Old Meadonians
Tring	v	St Albans
Old Hamptonian	v	Hampstead

October 14 1995 (Week 6)

Hemel Hempstead	v	Old Meadonians
Haringey	v	St Albans
Upper Clapton	v	Hampstead
Hendon	v	Old Hamptonian
St Mary's Hospital	v	Tring
Centaurs	v	Uxbridge

February 17 1996 (Week 23)

St Albans	v	Old Hamptonian
Old Meadonians	v	Tring
London New Zealand	v	Uxbridge
Hemel Hempstead	v	Centaurs
Haringey	v	St Mary's Hospital
Upper Clapton	v	Hendon

October 21 1995 (Week 7)

St Albans	v	Upper Clapton
Old Meadonians	v	Haringey
London New Zealand	v	Hemel Hempstead
Tring	v	Centaurs
Old Hamptonian	v	St Mary's Hospital
Hampstead	v	Hendon

February 24 1996 (Week 24)

St Mary's Hopital	v	Upper Clapton
Centaurs	v	Haringey
Uxbridge	v	Hemel Hempstead
Tring	v	London New Zealand
Old Hamptonian	v	Old Meadonians
Hampstead	v	St Albans

October 28 1995 (Week 8)

Haringey	v	London New Zealand
Upper Clapton	v	Old Meadonians
Hendon	v	St Albans
St Mary's Hospital	v	Hampstead
Centaurs	v	Old Hamptonian
Uxbridge	v	Tring

March 30 1996 (Week X7)

Old Meadonians	v	Hampstead
London New Zealand	v	Old Hamptonian
Hemel Hempstead	v	Tring
Haringey	v	Uxbridge
Upper Clapton	v	Centaurs
Hendon	v	St Mary's Hospital

HERTFORDSHIRE & MIDDLESEX

CENTAURS RFC
Ground Address: Gower Road, Syon Lane, Osterley, Middlesex TW7 5PY. Tel: 0181 560 4500
Club Secretary: Mr MD Royle, 218 Meadvale Road, Ealing, London, W5 1LT. Tel: (H) 0181 991 1439 Tel: (W) 01784 874177
Fixtures Secretary: Jerry Goldie, 23 Northumberland Avenue, Isleworth, Midd. TW7 5HZ. Tel: (H) 0181 568 7240 Tel (W) 0171 837 3627
Club Colours: Light blue & dark blue quarters.

HAMPSTEAD RFC
Ground Address: The Heath Extension, Hampstead Way, London NW11. Tel: 0171 794 4805
Club Secretary: Stephen John Loffler, 14 Grey Close, London NW11 6QG. Tel: (H) 0181 458 6512 Tel: (W) 0181 759 4822
Fixtures Secretary: Charles Scully, 4 Monmouth Close, Beaumont Park, Chiswick, London W4 5DQ. Tel: (H) 0181 987 9000 Tel (W) 01426 912234
Club Colours: Claret, gold & white.

HARINGEY RFC
Ground Address: New River Sports Centre, White Hart Lane, Wood Green, London N22 5QW. Tel: Clubhouse: 0181 888 9299. Reception: 0181 881 1926
Club Secretary: Glynne Jones, 44 Park Hall Road, East Finchley, London N2 9PX. Tel: (H) 0181 883 8091. Fax: 0181 883 8091
Fixtures Secretary: Colin Field, 4 Highview Close, Potters Bar, Herts. Tel: (H) 01707 645557 Tel (W) 0181 340 1771
Club Colours: Green, scarlet & white.

HEMEL HEMPSTEAD (CAMELOT) RUFC
Ground Address: The Club House, Chaulden Lane, Hemel Hempstead, Herts, HP1 2BS. Tel: 01442 230353 (Admin); 01442 213408 (Public)
Club Secretary: Mr JM Clapham, 49 Brook Court, Watling Street, Radlett, Herts, WD7 7JA. Tel: (H) 01923 852104 Tel: (W) 01923 852104
Fixtures Secretary: Mr AJ Wakefield, 23 Riverside Court, River Beach, Broomwater, Teddington, Middlesex. Tel: (H) 0181 977 0746 Tel (W) 0171 930 2399
Club Colours: Royal blue & white hoop.

HENDON RFC
Ground Address: Copthall Playing Fields, Great North Way, Hendon, London NW4. Tel: 0181 203 1737
Club Secretary: T Brownsell, 9 Winscombe Way, Stanmore, Middlesex HA7 3AX. Tel: (H) 0181 954 7060 Tel: (W) 0171 375 5526
Fixtures Secretary: C Silver, 7 Castellane Close, Stanmore, Middlesex HA7 3TN. Tel: (H) 0181 954 9641 Tel (W) 0171 734 4734
Club Colours: Green, black & white uneven stripes.

LONDON NEW ZEALAND RFC
Ground Address: c/o Osterley Sports & Social Club, Tentelow Lane, Osterley, Middx. Tel: 0181 574 3774
Club Secretary: Tudor Davies, 46 Lamorna Grove, Stanmore, Middx HA7 1PQ. Tel: (H) 0181 952 6822 Tel: (W) 0171 723 0022
Fixtures Secretary: Richard Peacock, Oakfell, Downley Common, High Wycombe, Bucks. Tel: (H) 01494 448157 Tel (W) 0181 907 7799
Club Colours: All black.

OLD HAMPTONIANS RFC
Ground Address: The Pavilion, Dean Road, Hampton, Middlesex. Tel: 0181 979 2784
Club Secretary: Ian Strutt, 132 Peregrine Road, Sunbury-on-Thames, Middlesex TW16 6JL. Tel: (H) 01932 782019 Tel: (W) 01941 106939
Fixtures Secretary: Nick Bugler, 31 Manoel Road, Twickenham, Middx TW2 5HJ. Tel: (H) 0181 755 0601 Tel (W) 0171 327 6391
Club Colours: Gold, silver & black hoops.

OLD MEADONIANS RFC
Ground Address: Riverside Lands, Chiswick, London W4. Tel: 0181 994 6956
Club Secretary: Maureen Willingale, Fairmile Farm Cottage, Denby Road, Cobham, Surrey KT11 1JY. Tel: (H) 01932 86627

FINAL TABLE

	P	W	D	L	F	A	Pts
Mill Hill	12	10	0	2	342	145	20
Fullerians	12	10	0	2	302	118	20
St Albans	12	9	1	2	282	168	19
Old Meadonians	11	8	1	2	208	102	17
Hampstead	12	6	1	5	246	154	13
Haringey	12	5	2	5	252	225	10*
Centaurs	12	6	0	6	202	219	10*
Hendon	12	5	0	7	128	229	10
Hemel Hempstead	11	4	0	7	137	217	8
St Mary's Hospital	11	3	1	7	162	231	7
Uxbridge	12	4	0	8	166	212	6*
Hitchin	11	2	0	9	126	387	4
Harpenden	12	1	0	11	131	277	2

Fixtures Secretary: Roger Willingale, Fairmile Farm Cottage, Denby Road, Cobham, Surrey KT11 1JY. Tel: (H) 01932 86692̄7
Club Colours: Maroon & blue hoops, white shorts.

ST ALBANS RFC
Ground Address: Boggeymead Spring, Oaklands Lane, Smallford, St Albans, Herts AL4 0HR. Tel: 01727 869945
Club Secretary: John Gregory, 58 Luton Lane, Redbourn, Herts AL3 7PY. Tel: (H) 01582 792798 Tel: (W) 0181 205 1213 x285
Fixtures Secretary: Gerry Thomas, 176 Park Street Lane, Park Street, St Albans AL2 2AT. Tel: (H) 01727 873004
Club Colours: Royal blue & gold hoops, navy shorts.

ST MARY'S HOSPITAL RFC
Ground Address: St Mary's Hospital Athletic Ground, Udney Park Road, Teddington, Middlesex. Tel: 0181 977 3100
Club Secretary: RAL Young, FRCS, West Middlesex University Hospital, Twickenham Road, Isleworth, Middx TW7 6AF. Tel: (H) 0181 891 0638 Tel: (W) 0181 565 5768
Fixtures Secretary: Professor P Sever FRCP, Dept of Clinical Pharmacology, St Mary's Hospital, 10th Floor, QEQM Wing, London W2. Tel (W) 0171 725 6455 or 1172
Club Colours: Navy blue shirt, shorts & socks.

TRING RFC
Ground Address: Pendley Sports Centre, Cow Lane, Tring, Herts. Tel: 01442 825710
Club Secretary: Malcolm Rose, 25 Grenadine Way, Tring, Herts HP23 5EA. Tel: (H) 01442 827165 Tel: (W) 01628 486969
Fixtures Secretary: Peter Wilson, 10A Woodley Grove, Enfield, Middx EN2 0EA. Tel: (H) 0181 842 4187
Club Colours: Black & gold.

UPPER CLAPTON RFC
Ground Address: The Clubhouse, Upland Road, Thornwood Common, Epping, Essex CM16 6NL. Tel: 01992 572588
Club Secretary: Kevin Hewitt, 10 Crescent Road, Station Road, Epping Essex. Tel: (H) 01992 561440 Tel: (W) 0171 490 2324
Fixtures Secretary: David Miller, 13 Rushfield, Sawbridgeworth, Herts CM21 9NF. Tel: (H) 01279 724849 Tel (W) 0181 309 6398
Club Colours: Red & white hoops 7' hoops.

UXBRIDGE RFC
Ground Address: Uxbridge Cricket Club, Park Road, Uxbridge, Middlesex UB8 1NR. Tel: 01895 823281
Club Secretary: Mr Kieran Dineen, 6 Asa Court, Old Station Road, Hayes, Middlesex UB3 4NA. Tel: (H) 0181 561 7763 Tel: (W) 0171 594 6069
Fixtures Secretary: Mr Ralph Allen, 54 Hyde Way, Hayes, Middx. Tel: (H) 0181 848 4142 Tel (W) 0181 759 9111
Club Colours: Black, white & red horizontally hooped shirts, black shorts, black, white & red socks.

LONDON & SOUTH EAST DIVISION

MIDDLESEX ONE
1995-96
FIXTURES

November 11 1995 (Week 10)
Old Pauline	v	Harrow
Hackney	v	Old Haberdashers
Roxeth Manor OB	v	Civil Service
Twickenham	v	Sudbury Court
London Nigerian	v	Belsize Park
Honourable Artillery Co	v	Wembley

September 16 1995 (Week 3)
Old Pauline	v	Hackney
Wembley	v	Old Haberdashers
Belsize Park	v	Civil Service
Old Actonians	v	Sudbury Court
London Nigerian	v	Twickenham
Honourable Artillery Co	v	Roxeth Manor OB

January 6 1996 (Week 17)
Civil Service	v	Twickenham
Old Haberdashers	v	Roxeth Manor OB
Harrow	v	Hackney
Wembley	v	Old Pauline
Belsize Park	v	Honourable Artillery Co
Old Actonians	v	London Nigerian

September 23 1995 (Week 4)
Roxeth Manor OB	v	Old Pauline
Twickenham	v	Honourable Artillery Co
Sudbury Court	v	London Nigerian
Civil Service	v	Old Actonians
Old Haberdashers	v	Belsize Park
Harrow	v	Wembley

January 13 1996 (Week 18)
Old Pauline	v	Belsize Park
Hackney	v	Wembley
Roxeth Manor OB	v	Harrow
Twickenham	v	Old Haberdashers
Sudbury Court	v	Civil Service
Honourable Artillery Co	v	Old Actonians

September 30 1995 (Week X1)
Old Pauline	v	Twickenham
Hackney	v	Roxeth Manor OB
Belsize Park	v	Harrow
Old Actonians	v	Old Haberdashers
London Nigerian	v	Civil Service
Honourable Artillery Co	v	Sudbury Court

February 10 1996 (Week 22)
Old Haberdashers	v	Sudbury Court
Harrow	v	Twickenham
Wembley	v	Roxeth Manor OB
Belsize Park	v	Hackney
Old Actonians	v	Old Pauline
London Nigerian	v	Honourable Artillery Co

October 14 1995 (Week 6)
Twickenham	v	Hackney
Sudbury Court	v	Old Pauline
Civil Service	v	Honourable Artillery Co
Old Haberdashers	v	London Nigerian
Harrow	v	Old Actonians
Wembley	v	Belsize Park

February 17 1996 (Week 23)
Old Pauline	v	London Nigerian
Hackney	v	Old Actonians
Roxeth Manor OB	v	Belsize Park
Twickenham	v	Wembley
Sudbury Court	v	Harrow
Civil Service	v	Old Haberdashers

October 21 1995 (Week 7)
Old Pauline	v	Civil Service
Hackney	v	Sudbury Court
Roxeth Manor OB	v	Twickenham
Old Actonians	v	Wembley
London Nigerian	v	Harrow
Honourable Artillery Co	v	Old Haberdashers

February 24 1996 (Week 24)
Harrow	v	Civil Service
Wembley	v	Sudbury Court
Belsize Park	v	Twickenham
Old Actonians	v	Roxeth Manor OB
London Nigerian	v	Hackney
Honourable Artillery Co	v	Old Pauline

October 28 1995 (Week 8)
Sudbury Court	v	Roxeth Manor OB
Civil Service	v	Hackney
Old Haberdashers	v	Old Pauline
Harrow	v	Honourable Artillery Co
Wembley	v	London Nigerian
Belsize Park	v	Old Actonians

March 30 1996 (Week X7)
Hackney	v	Honourable Artillery Co
Roxeth Manor OB	v	London Nigerian
Twickenham	v	Old Actonians
Sudbury Court	v	Belsize Park
Civil Service	v	Wembley
Old Haberdashers	v	Harrow

470

MIDDLESEX ONE

BELSIZE PARK RFC
Ground Address: c/o Hendon RFC, Copthall Sports Centre, Hendon Way, Hendon, London NW. Tel: 0171 794 4910
Club Secretary: Sebastian Colquhoun, 9 Regency Lawn, Croftdown Road, London NW5 1HF. Tel: (H) 0171 485 5767 Tel: (W) 0171 222 2020
Fixtures Secretary: Hugh Reeve-Tucker, 5 Algarve Road, London SW18 3EQ. Tel: (H) 0181 874 5907 Tel (W) 0171 234 4822
Club Colours: Lavender & black.

CIVIL SERVICE FC
Ground Address: Duke's Meadows, Riverside Drive, Chiswick, London W4. Tel: 0181 994 1202
Club Secretary: NG Alway, 20 Herndon Road, London, SW18 2DG. Tel: (H) 0181 870 6818 Tel: (W) 0171 583 5333
Fixtures Secretary: R Hulme, 64 Walmington Fold, London N12. Tel: (H) 0181 346 1557
Club Colours: Blue & white hoops.

HACKNEY RFC
Ground Address: Spring Hill Ground, Spring Hill, Hackney, London E5. Tel: 0181 806 5289
Club Secretary: Dave Clarke, 95 Queenswood Gardens, Wanstead, London E11 3SF. Tel: (H) 0181 530 3853 Tel: (W) 0181 514 5514
Fixtures Secretary: Bob Brown, 73 Purdy Street, Bow, London E3. Tel: (H) 0171 537 7306 Tel (W) 0171 729 5477
Club Colours: Gold, blue & green quarters.

HARROW RFC
Ground Address: Grove Field, Wood Lane, Stanmore, Middx HA7 4LF. Tel: 0181 954 2615
Club Secretary: Mrs Leslie Wyatt, 17 Rocklands Drive, Stanmore, Middx HA7 2JD. Tel: (H) 0181 907 1191
Fixtures Secretary: Mr Peter Pope, 16 Kenilworth Drive, Croxley Green, Hertfordshire. Tel: (H) 01923 241504 Tel (W) 01923 778111
Club Colours: Blue & white hoops.

HONOURABLE ARTILLERY COMPANY RFC
Ground Address: Honourable Artillery Company, Artillery Ground, Armoury House, City Road, London EC1V 2BQ. Tel: 0171 606 4655
Club Secretary: Colin Pritchard, c/o Armoury House, City Road, London EC1Y 2BQ.
Fixtures Secretary: Colin Pritchard, 31 Bedford Avenue, Little Chalfont, Bucks HP6 6PS. Tel: (H) 01494 762982
Club Colours: Broad dark blue & red hoops.

LONDON NIGERIAN RFC
Ground Address: Barnet Copthall Playing Fields, Great North Way, Hendon, London NW4. Tel: 0181 203 1737
Club Secretary: John Orchard, 30 Churston Gardens, London N11 2HL. Tel: (H) 0181 361 7903 Tel: (W) 0171 636 8623
Fixtures Secretary: Fola Odetoyinbo, 7 Hayne House, Penzance Place, Holland Park, London W11 4PF. Tel: (H) 0171 603 6233 Tel (W) 0171 837 4285
Club Colours: Green & white.

OLD ACTONIANS RFC
Ground Address: Gunnersbury Drive, off Popes Lane, Ealing, London W5. Tel: 0181 567 4556
Club Secretary: Mr Peter Mullen, 77 Warwick Road, London W5 5QE. Tel: (H) 0181 840 9235 Tel: (W) 0171 962 3426
Fixtures Secretary: Mr Donald Sommerville, 4 The Common, Ealing, London W5 3TR. Tel: (H) 0181 567 3002 Tel (W) 0181 567 3002
Club Colours: Blue & white hoops, red collar, white shorts.

OLD HABERDASHERS RFC
Ground Address: Croxdale Road, Theobald Street, Borehamwood, Hertfordshire WD6 4PY. Tel: 0181 953 1987

FINAL TABLE

	P	W	D	L	F	A	Pts
Old Hamptonians	12	11	0	1	336	125	22
Wembley	11	9	1	1	223	109	19
Old Paulines	12	7	1	4	192	129	15
Hackney	12	7	1	4	180	124	15
Harrow	11	7	0	4	195	105	14
Twickenham	12	7	0	5	244	189	14
Civil Service	12	6	2	4	176	184	14
Old Actonians	12	6	0	6	172	137	12
Old Haberdashers	12	4	1	7	136	248	9
Roxeth Manor OB	12	4	1	7	130	213	7*
Belsize Park	12	2	0	10	167	306	4
Sudbury Court	12	2	0	10	117	266	4
Antlers	12	1	1	10	118	251	3

Club Secretary: J Prest, 28 Aplins Close, Harpenden, Hertfordshire AL5 2QB. Tel: (H) 01582 761177
Fixtures Secretary: JJ Hanson, The Castle, School Lane, Old Brichetwood, Nr St Albans, Herts AL2 3XS. Tel: (H) 01923 673263 Tel (W) 0181 953 2178
Club Colours: Blue, white & magenta.

OLD PAULINE FC
Ground Address: St Nicholas Road, off Speer Road, Thames Ditton, Surrey KT7 0PW. Tel: 0181 398 1858
Club Secretary: Tim JD Cunis, 62 Derby Road, East Sheen, London SW14 7DP. Tel: (H) 0181 878 3099 Tel: (W) 0181 878 3099
Fixtures Secretary: John A Howard, 93A Richmond Park Road, Kingston-upon-Thames, Surrey KT2 6AF. Tel: (H) 0181 541 3817 Tel (W) 01372 464470
Club Colours: Red, white & black hoops, white shorts.

ROXETH MANOR OLD BOYS RFC
Ground Address: Queensmead School, Queens Walk, off Victoria Road, Ruislip, Middlesex. Tel: 0181 845 6010
Club Secretary: Mr DR Pearham, 26 Yeading Avenue, Harrow, Middlesex, HA2 9RN. Tel: (H) 0181 868 1799
Fixtures Secretary: Mr P Noot, Copthorne, Croft Road, Chalfont St Peter, Bucks. Tel: (H) 01753 888775
Club Colours: All black.

SUDBURY COURT RFC
Ground Address: The Pavilion, East Lane, North Wembley, Middx. Tel: 0181 904 8485
Club Secretary: Derek P Gray, 33 Northwick Park Road, Harrow, Middx. Tel: (H) 0181 427 4155
Fixtures Secretary: David Roxborough, 72A Locket Road, Harrow, Middx. Tel: (H) 0181 861 4362 Tel (W) 0181 951 1313
Club Colours: Dark blue, red & white.

TWICKENHAM RFC
Ground Address: Park Fields, South Road, Hampton, Middlesex. Tel: 0181 979 2427
Club Secretary: AR Kay, 29 Grange Avenue, Twickenham, Middlesex TW2 5TW. Tel: (H) 0181 898 7210 Tel: (W) 0181 898 7210
Fixtures Secretary: Martin R Mitchell, 41 Northolme Road, Highbury, London N5 2UX. Tel: (H) 0171 359 1224
Club Colours: Red & black irregular hoops.

WEMBLEY RFC
Ground Address: Roger Bannister's Sports Centre, Uxbridge Road, Watch End, Middx. Tel: 0181 420 1789
Club Secretary: Noreen Conlon, 62 Canterbury Way, Croxley Green, Rickmansworth, Herts WD3 3SS. Tel: (H) 01923 230640 Tel: (W) 0181 420 1789
Fixtures Secretary: Chris Green, 26 Anmersh Grove, Stanmore, Middx. Tel: (H) 0181 952 4850
Club Colours: Maroon & amber quarters.

LONDON & SOUTH EAST DIVISION

MIDDLESEX TWO 1995-96 FIXTURES

September 16 1995 (Week 3)

Bank of England	v	Hayes
Old Isleworthians	v	Enfield Ignatians
London Exiles	v	Feltham
London French	v	Hammersmith & Fulham
Thamesians	v	Old Abbotstonians
Pinner & Grammarians	v	Antlers

September 23 1995 (Week 4)

Antlers	v	Bank of England
Old Abbotstonians	v	Pinner & Grammarians
Hammersmith & Fulham	v	Thamesians
Feltham	v	London French
Enfield Ignatians	v	London Exiles
Barclays Bank	v	Old Isleworthians

September 30 1995 (Week X1)

Bank of England	v	Old Abbotstonians
Hayes	v	Antlers
London Exiles	v	Barclays Bank
London French	v	Enfield Ignatians
Thamesians	v	Feltham
Pinner & Grammarians	v	Hammersmith & Fulham

October 14 1995 (Week 6)

Old Abbotstonians	v	Hayes
Hammersmith & Fulham	v	Bank of England
Feltham	v	Pinner & Grammarians
Enfield Ignatians	v	Thamesians
Barclays Bank	v	London French
Old Isleworthians	v	London Exiles

October 21 1995 (Week 7)

Bank of England	v	Feltham
Hayes	v	Hammersmith & Fulham
Antlers	v	Old Abbotstonians
London French	v	Old Isleworthians
Thamesians	v	Barclays Bank
Pinner & Grammarians	v	Enfield Ignatians

October 28 1995 (Week 8)

Hammersmith & Fulham	v	Antlers
Feltham	v	Hayes
Enfield Ignatians	v	Bank of England
Barclays Bank	v	Pinner & Grammarians
Old Isleworthians	v	Thamesians
London Exiles	v	London French

November 11 1995 (Week 10)

Bank of England	v	Barclays Bank
Hayes	v	Enfield Ignatians
Antlers	v	Feltham
Old Abbotstonians	v	Hammersmith & Fulham
Thamesians	v	London Exiles
Pinner & Grammarians	v	Old Isleworthians

January 6 1996 (Week 17)

Feltham	v	Old Abbotstonians
Enfield Ignatians	v	Antlers
Barclays Bank	v	Hayes
Old Isleworthians	v	Bank of England
London Exiles	v	Pinner & Grammarians
London French	v	Thamesians

January 13 1996 (Week 18)

Bank of England	v	London Exiles
Hayes	v	Old Isleworthians
Antlers	v	Barclays Bank
Old Abbotstonians	v	Enfield Ignatians
Hammersmith & Fulham	v	Feltham
Pinner & Grammarians	v	London French

February 10 1996 (Week 22)

Enfield Ignatians	v	Hammersmith & Fulham
Barclays Bank	v	Old Abbotstonians
Old Isleworthians	v	Antlers
London Exiles	v	Hayes
London French	v	Bank of England
Thamesians	v	Pinner & Grammarians

February 17 1996 (Week 23)

Bank of England	v	Thamesians
Hayes	v	London French
Antlers	v	London Exiles
Old Abbotstonians	v	Old Isleworthians
Hammersmith & Fulham	v	Barclays Bank
Feltham	v	Enfield Ignatians

February 24 1996 (Week 24)

Barclays Bank	v	Feltham
Old Isleworthians	v	Hammersmith & Fulham
London Exiles	v	Old Abbotstonians
London French	v	Antlers
Thamesians	v	Hayes
Pinner & Grammarians	v	Bank of England

March 30 1996 (Week X7)

Hayes	v	Pinner & Grammarians
Antlers	v	Thamesians
Old Abbotstonians	v	London French
Hammersmith & Fulham	v	London Exiles
Feltham	v	Old Isleworthians
Enfield Ignatians	v	Barclays Bank

MIDDLESEX TWO

ANTLERS RFC
Ground Address: Bushy Park, Teddington, Middlesex.
Tel: 0181 977 4989
Club Secretary: Peter J Woolgar, 114 Elgin Avenue,
Ashford, Middx TW15 1QG. Tel: (H) 01784 259734 Tel:
(W) 01268 544001
Fixtures Secretary: R Bromfield, 104 Station Road,
Hampton, Middx. Tel: (H) 0181 979 5635
Club Colours: Dark blue.
BANK OF ENGLAND RFC
Ground Address: Priory Lane, Roehampton, London
SW15 5JQ. Tel: 0181 876 8417
Club Secretary: Bryan Brown, Bank of England (PSO),
Threadneedle Street, London EC2R 8AH. Tel: (H) 0181
878 3396 Tel: (W) 0171 601 4949
Fixtures Secretary: Bryan Brown, Bank of England
(PSO), Threadneedle Street, London EC2R 8AH. Tel: (H)
0181 878 7790 Tel (W) 0171 209 6182
Club Colours: Blue, gold & white stripes.
BARCLAYS BANK RFC
Ground Address: Park View Road, Ealing, London W5
2JF. Tel: 0181 998 4904
Club Secretary: Mr SC Payne, 289 Basinghall Gardens,
Sutton, Surrey SM2 6AP. Tel: (H) 0181 661 2177 Tel: (W)
0181 946 3091
Fixtures Secretary: D Martin Bevan Jones, 23 Cypress
Avenue, Whitton, Twickenham, Middlesex TW2 7JY. Tel:
(H) 0181 898 4107 Tel (W) 0171 696 2865
Club Colours: Maroon with silver edged gold band.
ENFIELD IGNATIANS RFC
Ground Address: Enfield Playing Fields, Donkey Lane,
Carterhatch Lane, Enfield, Middx. Tel: 0811 363 2877
Club Secretary: Glyn Jones, 45 Halifax Road, Enfield,
Middx EN2 0PR. Tel: (H) 0181 366 3207 Tel: (W) 0181
967 9474
Fixtures Secretary: Peter Tiernan, 19 Hawkwood
Crescent, Chingford, London E4. Tel: (H) 0181 529 8130
Club Colours: Blue & gold.
FELTHAM RFC
Ground Address: Park Road, Hanworth Park, Feltham,
Middlesex, TW13 7EY. Tel: 0181 894 3609
Club Secretary: Simon C Griffiths, 27 Fosse Way. Ealing,
London W13 0BZ. Tel: (H) 0181 997 6153 Tel: (W) 0181
861 1313
Fixtures Secretary: Frank Parslow, 16 Pilgrims Way,
Bisley, Woking, Surrey. Tel: 01486 76525
Club Colours: Light blue, dark blue, gold hoop.
HAMMERSMITH & FULHAM RFC
Ground Address: Hurlingham Park, Hurlingham Road,
London SW6. Tel: 0171 736 5186
Club Secretary: Chris Cuthbertson, 17 Wheatsheaf Wharf,
Wheatsheaf Lane, London SW6 6LS. Tel: (H) 0171 381
5064 Tel: (W) 0171 233 5611
Fixtures Secretary: Mr Lyndon Walters, Flat 1, Adelina
Yard, 13-18 Adelina Grove, London E1 3AD. Tel: (H)
0171 790 1233 Tel (W) 0171 962 8047
Club Colours: Red with white & navy bands.
HAYES RFC
Ground Address: Grosvenor Playing Fields, Kingshill
Avenue, Hayes, Middx UB3 2NF. Tel: 0181 845 4963
Club Secretary: Gary Peacock, 13 Ivy Cottages, Uxbridge
Road, Hillingdon, Middlesex UB10 0PJ. Tel: (H) 01895 232079
Fixtures Secretary: Fred Mundy, 54 Woodrow Avenue,
Hayes, Middlesex UB4 8QL. Tel: (H) 0181 561 5335
Club Colours: Navy blue shirts, white shorts, navy socks.
LONDON EXILES RUFC
Ground Address: Barn Elms Sports Fields, Queen Elizabeth
Walk, Barnes, London SW13 0DG. Tel: 0181 876 7685
Fixtures Secretary: President: Tim Edghill, 72A Lilyville
Road, London W6. Tel: (H) 0171 736 7412 Tel: (W) 0171
413 1313

FINAL TABLE

	P	W	D	L	F	A	Pts
London Nigerians	11	10	1	0	374	67	21
HAC	11	8	2	1	249	91	18
Enfield Ignatians	11	9	0	2	234	134	18
Barclays Bank	11	7	0	4	190	181	14
Hammersmith-Fulham	11	6	0	5	193	182	12
Bank of England	11	5	1	5	171	156	11
Old Abbotstonians	10	4	0	6	181	153	8
Old Isleworthians	11	4	0	7	118	217	8
Thamesians	10	4	0	6	101	202	8
Feltham	11	3	0	8	212	193	6
Hayes	11	3	0	8	114	210	6
Pinner & Grammarian	11	0	0	11	61	406	0

Fixtures Secretary: Tim Edghill, 72A Lilyville Road,
London W6. Tel: (H) 0171 736 7412 Tel (W) 0171 413
1313
Club Colours: Claret, white & navy hoops.
LONDON FRENCH RFC
Ground Address: Barn Elms Playing Fields, Rocks Lane,
Barnes, London SW13.
Club Secretary: Andre P James, 2 Oak End Cottages,
Lower Road, Gerrards Cross, Buckinghamshire SL9 0PY.
Tel: (H) 01753 892108 Tel: (W) 0171 629 8191
Fixtures Secretary: Howard Smith, 28 Hazelbank Court,
Hazelbank Road, Chertsey, Surrey KT16 8PE. Tel: (H)
01932 560680 Tel (W) 0181 667 5377
Club Colours: French blue shirts, white shorts, red socks.
OLD ABBOTSTONIANS RFC
Ground Address: Pole Hill Open Spaces, Raeburn Road,
Hayes, Middlesex. Tel: 0181 845 1452
Club Secretary: Mr Glen Baptista, 2 Denecroft Crescent,
Hillingdon, Middlesex UB10 9HU. Tel: (H) 01895 271100
Tel: (W) 0171 798 7699
Fixtures Secretary: Mr Mark Nettleton, 21 Pinn Close, Cowley,
Uxbridge, Middlesex UB8 3TV. Tel: (H) 01895 440714
Club Colours: Red & blue quarters.
OLD ISLEWORTHIANS RFC
Ground Address: Memorial Ground, Wood Lane,
Isleworth, Middlesex. Tel: 0181 560 7949
Club Secretary: Huw Davies, 230 Whitton Dene,
Isleworth, Middlesex TW7 7LU. Tel: (H) 0181 898 5924
Tel: (W) 0171 315 6023
Fixtures Secretary: Steve Rac, 71 Wills Crescent,
Hounslow, Middlesex TW3 2JE. Tel: (H) 0181 8198 8982
Tel (W) 0181 567 5661
Club Colours: Blue jerseys with horizontal red band &
grey stripe, white shorts, red socks.
PINNER & GRAMMARIANS RFC
Ground Address: Shaftesbury Playing Fields, Grimsdyke
Road, Hatch End, Pinner, Middx. Tel: 0181 428 3136
Club Secretary: David Hiles, 31 Lulworth Close, South
Harrow, Middx HA2 9NR. Tel: (H) 0181 933 6357
Fixtures Secretary: Philip Skelton, 66 St Michael's
Crescent, Pinner, Middx. Tel: (H) 0181 429 4095
Club Colours: Navy with 1' scarlet hoops.
THAMESIANS RFC
Ground Address: Richmond-upon-Thames College,
Egerton Road, Twickenham, Middlesex TW2 7SJ. Tel:
0181 894 3110
Club Secretary: E Burrows, 133 Cranleigh Road, Lower
Feltham, Middlesex TW13 4QA. Tel: (H) 0181 890 7162
Tel: (W) 0181 890 7162
Fixtures Secretary: M Williams, 58 Agbara Road,
Teddington, Middlesex TW11 9PD. Tel: (H) 0181 977 4152
Club Colours: Maroon & green.

LONDON & SOUTH EAST DIVISION

MIDDLESEX THREE
1995-96
FIXTURES

September 23 1995 (Week 4)

Quintin	v	Orleans FP
Old Tottonians	v	Southgate
British Airways	v	UCS Old Boys
London Cornish	v	Northolt

September 30 1995 (Week X1)

Old Grammarians	v	Quintin
UCS Old Boys	v	London Cornish
Southgate	v	British Airways
St Nicholas Old Boys	v	Old Tottonians

October 14 1995 (Week 6)

Quintin	v	Northolt
Orleans FP	v	Old Grammarians
British Airways	v	St Nicholas Old Boys
London Cornish	v	Southgate

October 21 1995 (Week 7)

Northolt	v	Orleans FP
UCS Old Boys	v	Quintin
St Nicholas Old Boys	v	London Cornish
Old Tottonians	v	British Airways

October 28 1995 (Week 8)

Quintin	v	Southgate
Orleans FP	v	UCS Old Boys
Old Grammarians	v	Northolt
London Cornish	v	Old Tottonians

November 11 1995 (Week 10)

UCS Old Boys	v	Old Grammarians
Southgate	v	Orleans FP
St Nicholas Old Boys	v	Quintin
British Airways	v	London Cornish

January 6 1996 (Week 17)

Quintin	v	Old Tottonians
Orleans FP	v	St Nicholas Old Boys
Old Grammarians	v	Southgate
Northolt	v	UCS Old Boys

January 13 1996 (Week 18)

Southgate	v	Northolt
St Nicholas Old Boys	v	Old Grammarians
Old Tottonians	v	Orleans FP
British Airways	v	Quintin

February 10 1996 (Week 22)

Quintin	v	London Cornish
Orleans FP	v	British Airways
Old Grammarians	v	Old Tottonians
Northolt	v	St Nicholas Old Boys
UCS Old Boys	v	Southgate

February 17 1996 (Week 23)

St Nicholas Old Boys	v	UCS Old Boys
Old Tottonians	v	Northolt
British Airways	v	Old Grammarians
London Cornish	v	Orleans FP

February 24 1996 (Week 24)

Old Grammarians	v	London Cornish
Northolt	v	British Airways
UCS Old Boys	v	Old Tottonians
Southgate	v	St Nicholas Old Boys

MIDDLESEX THREE

BRITISH AIRWAYS RFC
Ground Address: Concorde Centre, Crane Lodge Road, off High Street, Cranford, Hounslow, Middx TW6 2JA. Tel: 0181 562 0291
Club Secretary: Carl Irminger, 38 Gwainersbury Lane, Acton, London W3 8EE. Tel: (H) 0181 993 3108 Tel: (W) 0181 562 0970 Fax: 0181 562 0978
Fixtures Secretary: Peter Attard, 38 Hounslow Road, Feltham, Middlesex TW14 9DG. Tel: (H) 0181 751 1605 Tel (W) 01956 511460
Club Colours: Red, blue & white quarters.

LONDON CORNISH RFC
Ground Address: Richardson-Evans Memorial Ground, Roehampton Vale, London SW15. Tel: 0181 788 3638
Club Secretary: Dave Fletcher, 27 Riverbank, Laleham Road, Staines, Middlesex TW18 2QE. Tel: (H) 01784 461927 Tel: (W) 0181 813 9494
Fixtures Secretary: Keith Allardice, 18 Grand Field Court, 19 Park Road, Chiswick, London W4 3EP. Tel: (H) 0181 747 1089
Club Colours: Black/gold hoops.

NORTHOLT RFC
Ground Address: Cayton Green Park, Cayton Road, Greenford, Middlesex UB6 8BJ. Tel: 0181 813 1701
Club Secretary: Colin Nicholl, 43 Columbia Avenue, Ruislip, Middlesex HA4 9SU. Tel: (H) 0181 866 8201 Tel: (W) 0181 975 2209
Fixtures Secretary: Geoff Payne, 16 Brackenbridge Drive, South Ruislip, Middlesex HA4 0NG. Tel: (H) 0181 845 0874 Tel (W) 0171 361 2642
Club Colours: Navy & sky blue hoops, navy shorts, hooped socks.

OLD GRAMMARIANS RFC
Ground Address: Worlds End Lane, Green Dragon Lane, Grange Park, Enfield, Middlesex.
Club Secretary: Brian Calderwood, 17 Birch Crescent, Aylesford, Kent ME20 7QE. Tel: (H) 01622 718350 Tel: (W) 01622 710811
Fixtures Secretary: Mike Holt, 64 Chandos Road, East Finchley, London N2 9AP. Tel: (H) 0181 883 4016
Club Colours: Navy, light blue & red.

OLD TOTTONIANS RFC
Ground Address: Churchfields, Great Cambridge Road, Harrow Drive, Edmonton, London N9. Tel: 0181 364 3099
Club Secretary: Trevor de la Salle, 55 Welsummer Way, Le Motte Chase, Cheshunt, Herts EN8 0UG. Tel: (H) 01992 638492 Tel: (W) 01494 444811
Fixtures Secretary: John Cockrill, 7 Sutherland Way, Cuffley, Herts EN6 6EG. Tel: (H) 01707 872507 Tel (W) 0171 278 7372
Club Colours: Blue & amber hoops.

ORLEANS FP RFC
Ground Address: Orleans Park, off Richard Road, Twickenham. Tel: 0181 892 5743
Club Secretary: Steve Frost, 13 Langham Place, Chiswick W4 2QL. Tel: (H) 0181 747 5026 Tel: (W) 0181 943 5331
Fixtures Secretary: G Todd, 24 Clarendon Drive, Putney, London SW15 1AA. Tel: (H) 0181 789 2191 Tel (W) 0181 398 4101 x3245
Club Colours: Gold & white hooped shirts, white shorts.

SOUTHGATE RFC
Ground Address: Northern Telecom, Oakleigh Road South, New Southgate, London N11 1HB. Tel: 0181 945 2655/2181
Club Secretary: David Hockey, 5 The Vineries, Enfield, Middlesex EN1 3DQ. Tel: (H) 0181 342 0202 Tel: (W) 0171 270 3874
Fixtures Secretary: Simon Stormer, 51 Knightsfield, Welwyn Garden City AL8 7JE. Tel: (H) 01707 324731 Tel (W) 0181 945 3219
Club Colours: Navy blue, light blue & gold hoops.

FINAL TABLE

	P	W	D	L	F	A	Pts
London Exiles	9	8	0	1	333	79	16
London French	9	6	1	2	243	78	13
Old Tottonians	8	5	1	2	116	91	11
UCS Old Boys	9	5	0	4	202	177	10
St Nicholas OB	9	6	0	2	207	86	8*
Orleans FP	9	4	0	5	130	239	8
Southgate	9	3	0	6	114	204	6
London Cornish	9	2	0	6	150	120	4
Northolt	9	3	0	6	97	168	2*
Osterley	8	0	0	8	21	371	-2*

ST NICHOLAS OLD BOYS RFC
Ground Address: c/o Ickenham Cricket Club, Oak Avenue, Ickenham, Middlesex. Tel: 01895 639366
Club Secretary: Mr Michael Lafford, 44 Haydon Drive, Eastcote, Pinner, Middlesex HA5 2PN. Tel: (H) 0181 868 1321 Tel: (W) 0181 756 2647
Fixtures Secretary: Mr Stuart Telfer, 19 Highgrove Way, Ruislip, Middlesex HA4 8EA. Tel: (H) 01895 624199 Tel (W) 0181 246 9771
Club Colours: Red, white & black.

THE QUINTIN RFC
Ground Address: Hartington Road, Chiswick, London W4.
Club Secretary: Nigel Smith, 4 Australia Avenue, Maidenhead, Berks SL6 7DJ. Tel: (H) 01628 75899 Tel: (W) 01628 822166 x5971
Fixtures Secretary: Colin Smith, 34 Oakdean Drive, Surbiton, Surrey KT5 9NH. Tel: (H) 0181 337 9631
Club Colours: Red & green hoops.

UCS OLD BOYS RFC
Ground Address: Ranulf Road, London NW3. Tel: 0181 452 4337
Club Secretary: Paul Gee, 63 Blackhorse Lane, South Mimms EN6 3PS. Tel: (H) 01707 662748 Tel: (W) 0181 340 8055 x2450
Fixtures Secretary: Andrew Wiseman, 37 Connaught Avenue, London E4 7AE. Tel: (H) 0181 529 9460 Tel (W) 01992 788822
Club Colours: Maroon, black & white.

LONDON & SOUTH EAST DIVISION

MIDDLESEX FOUR
1995-96
FIXTURES

October 14 1995 (Week 6)

Meadhurst	v	Royal Hospitals
Great Western Railway	v	Osterley
Kodak	v	Middlesex Hospital

October 21 1995 (Week 7)

Royal Hospitals	v	Great Western Railway
Meadhurst	v	Kodak
Osterley	v	Middlesex Hospital

October 28 1995 (Week 8)

Great Western Railway	v	Meadhurst
Middlesex Hospital	v	Royal Hospitals
Kodak	v	Osterley

February 10 1996 (Week 22)

Royal Hospitals	v	Osterley
Meadhurst	v	Middlesex Hospital
Great Western Railway	v	Kodak

February 17 1996 (Week 23)

Middlesex Hospital	v	Great Western Railway
Osterley	v	Meadhurst
Kodak	v	Royal Hospitals

MIDDLESEX FOUR

KODAK RFC
Ground Address: Kodak Sports Ground, Harrow View, Harrow, Middlesex, HA1 4TY. Tel: 0181 427 2642
Club Secretary: Dr A Jones, 1 The Sonnets, Gadbridge, Hemel Hempstead HP1 3RS. Tel: (H) 01442 868666 Tel: (W) 0181 424 5352
Fixtures Secretary: Bruce Haynes, 17 Exmouth Road, South Ruislip, Middx. Tel: (H) 0181 841 4545 Tel (W) 0181 559 9555
Club Colours: Green & gold.

MEADHURST RFC
Ground Address: Meadhurst Sports & Social Club, Chertsey Road, Sunbury-on-Thames, Middlesex TW16 7LN. Tel: 01932 763500
Club Secretary: Brian Messenger, BP Chemicals, Poplar House, Chertsey Road, Sunbury-on-Thames, Middlesex TW16 7LL. Tel: (H) 01784 251542 Tel: (W) 01932 774054
Fixtures Secretary: Keith Wills, 42 Overdale Road, Ealing, London W5 4TT. Tel: (H) 0181 840 0297 Tel (W) 0181 965 6031
Club Colours: Green.

OSTERLEY RFC
Ground Address: Tentelow Lane, Norwood Green, Southall, Middlesex. Tel: 0181 747 5026
Club Secretary: John Green, 92 Rocksborough Avenue, Isleworth, Middx TW7 5HJ. Tel: (H) 0181 568 5557
Fixtures Secretary: John Green, 92 Rocksborough Avenue, Isleworth, Middx TW7 5HJ. Tel: (H) 0181 568 5557
Club Colours: Black & white hoops.

ROYAL HOSPITALS RUFC
Ground Address: Perry Street, Foxbury, Chislehurst, Kent or Hale End, Wadham Road, Walthamstow, London E17 4LT. Tel: 0181 527 5720/8996
Fixtures Secretary: League contact: A Macquillan, 40 Antill Road, Mile End, London E3 5BP.
Club Colours: Black & white chequers.

THE GREAT WESTERN RAILWAYS RFC
Ground Address: Castle Bar Park, Vallis Way, Argyle Road, West Ealing, London W13 0DD. Tel: 0181 998 7928
Club Secretary: TV Shoey, 32 Croyde Avenue, Greenford, Middlesex UB6 9LS. Tel: (H) 0181 578 8706
Fixtures Secretary: Roy Sullivan, 100 Westcott, Crescent, Hanwell, London W7 1PB. Tel: (H) 0181 575 6074
Club Colours: Cardinal red & black.

UNIVERSITY COLLEGE LONDON MEDICAL SCHOOL RFC
Ground Address: Chislehurst Sports Ground, Perry Street, Chislehurst BR7 6HA. Tel: 0181 467 1744 (home); 0181 467 3859 (pavilion)
Club Secretary: Justin Edwards, 43-49 Huntley Street, Bloomsbury, London WC1E 6DG. Tel: (H) 0171 580 7310
Fixtures Secretary: Nick Rogers, 43-49 Huntley Street, Bloomsbury, London WC1E 6DG.
Club Colours: Navy blue, sky blue, gold, white quarters.

FINAL TABLE

	P	W	D	L	F	A	Pts
Quintin	5	5	0	0	123	34	10
British Airways	7	5	0	2	98	75	10
GWR	7	4	0	3	167	115	8
St George's Hosp'l	5	3	0	2	64	171	6
St Bart's Hospital	4	2	0	2	90	41	4
Kodak	5	2	0	3	121	88	4
Middlesex Hospital	4	0	0	4	41	98	0
Meadhurst	5	0	0	5	24	106	0

LONDON & SOUTH EAST DIVISION

HERTFORDSHIRE ONE
1995-96
FIXTURES

September 23 1995 (Week 4)

Old Ashmoleans	v	Datchworth
QE II Hospital	v	Stevenage Town
Old Standfordians	v	Hatfield
Royston	v	Hitchin
Watford	v	Harpenden

September 30 1995 (Week X1)

Harpenden	v	Old Ashmoleans
Hitchin	v	Watford
Hatfield	v	Royston
Stevenage Town	v	Old Standfordians
Cuffley	v	QE II Hospital

October 14 1995 (Week 6)

Old Ashmoleans	v	Hitchin
Datchworth	v	Harpenden
Old Standfordians	v	Cuffley
Royston	v	Stevenage Town
Watford	v	Hatfield

October 21 1995 (Week 7)

Hitchin	v	Datchworth
Hatfield	v	Old Ashmoleans
Stevenage Town	v	Watford
Cuffley	v	Royston
QE II Hospital	v	Old Standfordians

October 28 1995 (Week 8)

Old Ashmoleans	v	Stevenage Town
Datchworth	v	Hatfield
Harpenden	v	Hitchin
Royston	v	QE II Hospital
Watford	v	Cuffley

November 11 1995 (Week 10)

Hatfield	v	Harpenden
Stevenage Town	v	Datchworth
Cuffley	v	Old Ashmoleans
QE II Hospital	v	Watford
Old Standfordians	v	Royston

January 13 1996 (Week 18)

Old Ashmoleans	v	QE II Hospital
Datchworth	v	Cuffley
Harpenden	v	Stevenage Town
Hitchin	v	Hatfield
Watford	v	Old Standfordians

February 10 1996 (Week 22)

Stevenage Town	v	Hitchin
Cuffley	v	Harpenden
QE II Hospital	v	Datchworth
Old Standfordians	v	Old Ashmoleans
Royston	v	Watford

February 17 1996 (Week 23)

Old Ashmoleans	v	Royston
Datchworth	v	Old Standfordians
Harpenden	v	QE II Hospital
Hitchin	v	Cuffley
Hatfield	v	Stevenage Town

February 24 1996 (Week 24)

Cuffley	v	Hatfield
QE II Hospital	v	Hitchin
Old Standfordians	v	Harpenden
Royston	v	Datchworth
Watford	v	Old Ashmoleans

March 30 1996 (Week X7)

Datchworth	v	Watford
Harpenden	v	Royston
Hitchin	v	Old Standfordians
Hatfield	v	QE II Hospital
Stevenage Town	v	Cuffley

HERTFORDSHIRE

CUFFLEY RFC
Ground Address: Cheshunt School, College Road, Cheshunt, Hertfordshire EN7 9LY. Tel: (Weekdays only) 01992 624375/6
Club Secretary: CA Palmer, 10 Connaught Road, Harpenden, Hertfordshire AL5 4HF. Tel: (H) 01582 768152 Tel: (W) 0171 895 1515
Fixtures Secretary: P Cushing, 6 Montgomery Close, Lutterworth, Leicestershire. Tel: (H) 01455 555 7568 Tel (W) 01582 470605
Club Colours: Navy blue with gold & red hoop.
DATCHWORTH RFC
Ground Address: Datchworth Green, Datchworth, Herts. Tel: 01438 812490
Club Secretary: Mrs LD Wyatt, 7 Hazeldell, Watton-at-Stone, Hertford SG14 3SL. Tel: (H) 01920 830407
Fixtures Secretary: Mr P Nightingale, 11 Gomer Close, The Shires, Codicote, Herts. Tel: (H) 01438 820500
Club Colours: Green shirts & socks, black shorts.
HARPENDEN RFC
Ground Address: Redbourn Lane, Harpenden, Herts AL5 2BA. Tel: 01585 460711
Club Secretary: M Aldous-Ball, 4 Wells Close, Harpenden, Herts AL5 3LQ. Tel: (H) 01582 621037 Tel: (W) 0181 979 9951
Fixtures Secretary: Andy Finch, 3 Doon Court, 46 Luton Road, Harpenden, Herts. Tel: (H) 01582 713797 Tel (W) 01438 7555376
Club Colours: Brown & white quartered shirts.
HATFIELD RFC
Ground Address: Roe Hill Hall, Briars Lane, Roe Hill, Hatfield, Hertfordshire. Tel: 01707 269814
Club Secretary: Miss A Nicholson, 43 Handside Lane, Welwyn Garden City, Hertfordshire AL8 6SH. Tel: (H) 01707 326660
Fixtures Secretary: Graham Waddingham, 2 Sheepwell Cottage, Shepherds Lane, Brookmans Park, Hatfield, Hertfordshire AL9 6NW. Tel: (H) 01707 663659 Tel (W) 01707 666013
Club Colours: Green, white, brown and gold quarters.
HITCHIN RFC
Ground Address: King George V Recreation Ground, Old Hale Way, Hitchin, Herts. Tel: 01462 432679
Club Secretary: Stephen Ward, 73 Millstream Close, Hitchin, Herts SG4 0DB. Tel: (H) 01462 455358
Fixtures Secretary: G Morgan, 209 Cambridge Road, Hitchin, Herts SG4 0JP. Tel: (H) 01462 431781
Club Colours: Maroon shirts, white shorts.
OLD ASHMOLEAN RFC
Ground Address: Ashmole School, Burleigh Gardens, Southgate, N14. Tel: 0181 368 4984 (Sports Hall); 0181 886 3344 (Clubhouse)
Club Secretary: Mr GJ Bull, 60 Ladysmith Road, Enfield EN1 3AA. Tel: (H) 0181 363 5991 Tel: (W) 01831 875071 (Mobile)
Fixtures Secretary: Mr S Stamp, 9 Kenwood House, 74 Wellington Road, Enfield, EN1 2NZ. Tel: (H) 0181 364 3213
Club Colours: Scarlet & emerald hoops.
OLD STANFORDIANS RFC
Ground Address: Old Kents Lane, Standon, Herts.
Club Secretary: Ted Moody, 1 Stable Mews, Hillside Road, St Albans, Herts AL1 3QW. Tel: (H) 01727 834413
Fixtures Secretary: Ted Moody, 1 Stable Mews, Hillside Road, St Albans, Herts AL1 3QW. Tel: (H) 01727 834413
Club Colours: Black with pink hoop.

FINAL TABLE

	P	W	D	L	F	A	Pts
Tring	9	9	0	0	255	51	18
Stevenage	9	7	0	2	155	73	14
Datchworth	9	7	0	2	144	81	12*
Royston	9	5	1	3	176	106	11
Old Stanfordians	9	4	1	4	87	83	9
Old Ashmoleans	9	3	1	5	151	134	7
Hatfield	9	3	0	6	94	210	6
Bacavians	9	4	1	4	144	151	3*
Watford	9	1	0	8	91	216	-2*
QE II Hospital	9	0	0	9	41	233	-2*

QUEEN ELIZABETH II HOSPITAL RFC
Ground Address: Hatfield Hyde Sports Club, King George V Playing Fields, Beehive Lane, Welwyn Garden City, Hertfordshire, AL7 4BP. Tel: 01707 326700
Club Secretary: Steve Murray, 73 Howicks Green, Welwyn Garden City, Herts AL7 4RJ. Tel: (H) 01707 324022 Tel: (W) 01582 400034
Fixtures Secretary: Wayne Gorring, 86 Mount Way, Welwyn Garden City, Herts. Tel: (H) 01707 326 371
Club Colours: Myrtle green & amber.
ROYSTON RFC
Ground Address: Baldock Road, Royston, Herts SG8 5BG. Tel: 01763 243613
Club Secretary: Julie-Ann Singleton, 17 Chilcourt, Royston, Herts SG8 9DD. Tel: (H) 01763 245546
Fixtures Secretary: Godfrey Everett, 24 Clarkes Way, Bassingbourn, Royston SG8 5LT. Tel: (H) 01763 243846
Club Colours: Black & white quarters.
STEVENAGE RUFC
Ground Address: North Road, Old Town, Stevenage, Herts. Tel: 01438 359788
Club Secretary: Richard Stephens, 18 Russell Close, Stevenage, Herts SG2 8PB. Tel: (H) 01438 351971 (Answerphone) Tel: (W) 01438 355751
Fixtures Secretary: Fred McCarthy, 106 Raleigh Crescent, Stevenage, Herts SG2 0ED. Tel: (H) 01438 364641
Club Colours: Black shirts with green & amber hoop or red shirts (as needed).
WATFORD RFC
Ground Address: Knutsford Playing Fields, Radlett Road, Watford, Herts. Tel: 01923 243292
Club Secretary: Mr BA De-Honri, 163 Hagden Lane, Watford, Herts WD1 8LN. Tel: (H) 01923 461675 Tel: (W) 0181 420 9232
Fixtures Secretary: R Wynne, 125 North Approach WD2 9EP. Tel: (H) 01923 678928
Club Colours: Red, white & blue hoops.

LONDON & SOUTH EAST DIVISION

LONDON THREE NORTH EAST 1995-96 FIXTURES

November 11 1995 (Week 10)

Lowestoft & Yarmouth	v	Ipswich
Campion	v	Old Edwardians
Rochford	v	Shelford
West Norfolk	v	Maldon
Braintree	v	Bury St Edmunds
Chelmsford	v	Canvey Island

September 16 1995 (Week 3)

Lowestoft & Yarmouth	v	Campion
Canvey Island	v	Old Edwardians
Bury St Edmunds	v	Shelford
Chingford	v	Maldon
Braintree	v	West Norfolk
Chelmsford	v	Rochford

January 6 1996 (Week 17)

Shelford	v	West Norfolk
Old Edwardians	v	Rochford
Ipswich	v	Campion
Canvey Island	v	Lowestoft & Yarmouth
Bury St Edmunds	v	Chelmsford
Chingford	v	Braintree

September 23 1995 (Week 4)

Rochford	v	Lowestoft & Yarmouth
West Norfolk	v	Chelmsford
Maldon	v	Braintree
Shelford	v	Chingford
Old Edwardians	v	Bury St Edmunds
Ipswich	v	Canvey Island

January 13 1996 (Week 18)

Lowestoft & Yarmouth	v	Bury St Edmunds
Campion	v	Canvey Island
Rochford	v	Ipswich
West Norfolk	v	Old Edwardians
Maldon	v	Shelford
Chelmsford	v	Chingford

September 30 1995 (Week X1)

Lowestoft & Yarmouth	v	West Norfolk
Campion	v	Rochford
Bury St Edmunds	v	Ipswich
Chingford	v	Old Edwardians
Braintree	v	Shelford
Chelmsford	v	Maldon

February 10 1996 (Week 22)

Old Edwardians	v	Maldon
Ipswich	v	West Norfolk
Canvey Island	v	Rochford
Bury St Edmunds	v	Campion
Chingford	v	Lowestoft & Yarmouth
Braintree	v	Chelmsford

October 14 1995 (Week 6)

West Norfolk	v	Campion
Maldon	v	Lowestoft & Yarmouth
Shelford	v	Chelmsford
Old Edwardians	v	Braintree
Ipswich	v	Chingford
Canvey Island	v	Bury St Edmunds

February 17 1996 (Week 23)

Lowestoft & Yarmouth	v	Braintree
Campion	v	Chingford
Rochford	v	Bury St Edmunds
West Norfolk	v	Canvey Island
Maldon	v	Ipswich
Shelford	v	Old Edwardians

October 21 1995 (Week 7)

Lowestoft & Yarmouth	v	Shelford
Campion	v	Maldon
Rochford	v	West Norfolk
Chingford	v	Canvey Island
Braintree	v	Ipswich
Chelmsford	v	Old Edwardians

February 24 1996 (Week 24)

Ipswich	v	Shelford
Canvey Island	v	Maldon
Bury St Edmunds	v	West Norfolk
Chingford	v	Rochford
Braintree	v	Campion
Chelmsford	v	Lowestoft & Yarmouth

October 28 1995 (Week 8)

Maldon	v	Rochford
Shelford	v	Campion
Old Edwardians	v	Lowestoft & Yarmouth
Ipswich	v	Chelmsford
Canvey Island	v	Braintree
Bury St Edmunds	v	Chingford

March 30 1996 (Week X7)

Campion	v	Chelmsford
Rochford	v	Braintree
West Norfolk	v	Chingford
Maldon	v	Bury St Edmunds
Shelford	v	Canvey Island
Old Edwardians	v	Ipswich

LONDON THREE NORTH EAST

BRAINTREE RUFC
Ground Address: The Clubhouse, Robswood, Beckers
Green Road, Braintree, Essex CM7 6PR. Tel: 01376 322282
Club Secretary: Mrs C Wadforth, 8 Chelmer Road,
Braintree, Essex CM7 6PY. Tel: (H) 01376 341642
Fixtures Secretary: Mr S Ross, 12 Kelso Close, Great
Horksley, Colchester, Essex. Tel: (H) 01206 271007
Club Colours: Black & amber quarters.
BURY ST EDMUNDS RUFC
Ground Address: The Haberden, Southgate Green, Bury
St Edmunds, Suffolk. Tel: 01284 753920
Club Secretary: Mr RM Peacock, 31 Plovers Way, Bury
St Edmunds, Suffolk. Tel: (H) 01284 761536 Tel: (W)
01284 754450
Fixtures Secretary: Mrs Carol Palombo, 41 Oakes Road,
Bury St Edmunds, Suffolk. Tel: (H) 01284 761871
Club Colours: Emerald & amber quarters.
CAMPION RFC
Ground Address: Cottons Park, Cottons Approach,
Romford, Essex RM7 7AA. Tel: 01708 753209
Club Secretary: P O'Brien, 68 Lancaster Drive, Elm Park,
Hornchurch, Essex RM12 5ST. Tel: (H) 01708 446980
Fixtures Secretary: Kevin O'Neill, 26 Priests Field,
Ingrave, Brentwood CM13 3QJ. Tel: (H) 01277 811742 Tel
(W) 0181 534 5544
Club Colours: Red & black hoops.
CANVEY ISLAND RUFC
Ground Address: Tewkes Creek, Dovervelt Road, Canvey
Island, Essex. Tel: 01268 681881
Club Secretary: Martin Powell, 7 Chichester Close,
Canvey Island, Essex SS8 0DZ. Tel: (H) 01268 695130
Tel: (W) 0171 418 3270
Fixtures Secretary: Don Maclean, 9 St Luke's Close,
Canvey Island, Essex SS8 9NF. Tel: (H) 01268 694771
Club Colours: Red & blue.
CHELMSFORD RFC
Ground Address: Timsons Lane, Coronation Park,
Springfield, Chelmsford, Essex CM2 6AF. Tel: 01245
261159
Club Secretary: Mr D Triggs, Fir Trees, Riffhams Lane,
Danbury, Essex CM3 4DS. Tel: (H) 01245 226001 Tel:
(W) 01702 202571
Fixtures Secretary: Mr A Bass, 91 Beardsley Drive,
Chelmsford, Essex CM1 5GJ. Tel: (H) 01245 461029 Tel
(W) 01245 702703
Club Colours: Navy blue shirts & shorts.
CHINGFORD RFC
Ground Address: Lea Valley Playing Fields, Waltham
Way, Chingford, London E4 7SR. Tel: (H) 0181 529 4879
Club Secretary: Howard K Hartley, 85 Whitehall Gardens,
Chingford, London E4 6EJ. Tel: (H) 0181 559 4821
Fixtures Secretary: Peter Wilton, 39 College Gardens,
Chingford, London E4 7LN. Tel: (H) 0181 529 2052 Tel
(W) 0181 529 4879
Club Colours: Black jerseys with royal blue & white
hoops.
IPSWICH RUFC
Ground Address: Humber Doucy Lane, Ipswich IP4 3PZ.
Tel: (& Fax) 01473 724072
Club Secretary: Mr Stan Gaskin, 6 Parkside Avenue,
Ipswich, Suffolk IP4 2UL. Tel: (H) 01473 217920 Tel: (W)
01473 343501 Fax: 01473 225120
Fixtures Secretary: Mrs Lisa Greetham, 159 Woodbridge
Road, Ipswich IP4 2PE. Tel: (H) 01473 233731 Tel (W)
01473 724072 (club)
Club Colours: Black shirts with amber hoops.
LOWESTOFT & YARMOUTH RUFC
Ground Address: Gunton Park, Old Lane, off Corton
Long Lane, Corton, Nr Lowestoft. Tel: 01502 730350
Club Secretary: June Nelson, 70 Upper Cliff Road,
Gorleston, Great Yarmouth NR31 6AJ. Tel: (H) 01493

FINAL TABLE

	P	W	L	D	F	A	Pts
Colchester	12	11	0	1	300	102	22
Rochford	12	10	0	2	198	80	20
Ipswich	12	9	0	3	237	115	18
Bury St Edmunds	12	7	0	5	153	160	14
Braintree	12	6	0	6	236	186	12
Old Edwardians	12	4	1	7	163	180	9
Maldon	12	4	1	7	129	166	9
Chelmsford	12	4	1	7	96	177	9
Shelford	12	4	0	8	169	210	8
West Norfolk	12	4	0	8	146	213	8
Campion	12	4	0	8	159	233	8
Basildon	12	4	0	8	109	183	8
Woodbridge	12	5	0	7	133	211	8*

653095 Tel: (W) 01493 656071
Fixtures Secretary: Ken Brickell, 51 McLean Drive,
Kessingland, Nr Lowestoft. Tel: (H) 01502 740036 Tel (W)
01502 740036
Club Colours: Blue & white hoops.
MALDON RUFC
Ground Address: Drapers Farm Sports Club, Drapers
Chase, Heybridge, Maldon, Essex. Tel: 01621 852152
Club Secretary: Mike Beckwith, Oakwood, The Mallows,
Fambridge Road, Maldon, Essex CM9 6BJ. Tel: (H) 01621
857106 Tel: (W) 01702 216570
Fixtures Secretary: N Manning, 57 Larch Walk, Maldon,
Essex CM9 7TS. Tel: (H) 01621 856073
Club Colours: Royal blue & white.
OLD EDWARDIANS RFC
Ground Address: Westlands Playing Fields, London
Road, Romford, Essex. Tel: 01708
Club Secretary: C Hunt, Orchard End, St James Court,
Billericay, Essex. Tel: 01277 626536
Fixtures Secretary: P Griffith, 15 Holme Road,
Hornchurch, Essex. Tel: (H) 01708 450022
Club Colours: Navy blue shirts, white shorts.
ROCHFORD HUNDRED RFC
Ground Address: The Clubhouse, Magnolia Road,
Hawkwell, Rochford, Essex SS4 3AD. Tel: 01702 544021
Club Secretary: R Simon Wakefield, 54 Parklands Drive,
Springfield, Chelmsford, Essex CM1 7SP. Tel: (H) 01245
266158 Tel: (W) 01702 541581
Fixtures Secretary: Mr Michael Tuck, 51 Highfield Road,
Billericay, Essex CM11 2PE. Tel: (H) 01277 655483
Club Colours: Black shirts & shorts.
SHELFORD RUFC
Ground Address: Davey Field, Cambridge Road, Great
Shelford, Cambridge. Tel: 01223 843357
Club Secretary: Lydia Langenheim, 37 Rock Road,
Cambridge CB1 4UG. Tel: (H) 01223 245446 Tel: (W)
01223 314988
Fixtures Secretary: Mike Whibley, Driftway House, 111a
Glebe Road, Cambridge CB1 4TE. Tel: (H) 01223 214070
Club Colours: French grey with cerise band, navy blue
shorts.
WEST NORFOLK RUFC
Ground Address: Gatehouse Lane, North Wootton, King's
Lynn, Norfolk. Tel: 01553 631307
Club Secretary: JA Williams, 1 Courtnell Place,
Springwood, King's Lynn, Norfolk PE30 4TW. Tel: (H)
01553 760986 Tel: (W) 01603 627107
Fixtures Secretary: K Foreman, 1 Caretakers House,
NORCAT, Tennyson Avenue, King's Lynn, Norfolk. Tel:
(H) 01553 764391
Club Colours: French grey with cerise band, navy blue
shorts.

LONDON & SOUTH EAST DIVISION

EASTERN COUNTIES ONE 1995-96 FIXTURES

November 11 1995 (Week 10)

Upminster	v	Newmarket
Ilford Wanderers	v	Wymondham
Holt	v	Basildon
Harwich & Dovercourt	v	Bancroft
Loughton	v	Diss
Saffron Walden	v	Woodbridge

September 16 1995 (Week 3)

Upminster	v	Ilford Wanderers
Woodbridge	v	Wymondham
Diss	v	Basildon
Ely	v	Bancroft
Loughton	v	Harwich & Dovercourt
Saffron Walden	v	Holt

January 6 1996 (Week 17)

Basildon	v	Harwich & Dovercourt
Wymondham	v	Holt
Newmarket	v	Ilford Wanderers
Woodbridge	v	Upminster
Diss	v	Saffron Walden
Ely	v	Loughton

September 23 1995 (Week 4)

Holt	v	Upminster
Harwich & Dovercourt	v	Saffron Walden
Bancroft	v	Loughton
Basildon	v	Ely
Wymondham	v	Diss
Newmarket	v	Woodbridge

January 13 1996 (Week 18)

Upminster	v	Diss
Ilford Wanderers	v	Woodbridge
Holt	v	Newmarket
Harwich & Dovercourt	v	Wymondham
Bancroft	v	Basildon
Saffron Walden	v	Ely

September 30 1995 (Week X1)

Upminster	v	Harwich & Dovercourt
Ilford Wanderers	v	Holt
Diss	v	Newmarket
Ely	v	Wymondham
Loughton	v	Basildon
Saffron Walden	v	Bancroft

February 10 1996 (Week 22)

Wymondham	v	Bancroft
Newmarket	v	Harwich & Dovercourt
Woodbridge	v	Holt
Diss	v	Ilford Wanderers
Ely	v	Upminster
Loughton	v	Saffron Walden

October 14 1995 (Week 6)

Harwich & Dovercourt	v	Ilford Wanderers
Bancroft	v	Upminster
Basildon	v	Saffron Walden
Wymondham	v	Loughton
Newmarket	v	Ely
Woodbridge	v	Diss

February 17 1996 (Week 23)

Upminster	v	Loughton
Ilford Wanderers	v	Ely
Holt	v	Diss
Harwich & Dovercourt	v	Woodbridge
Bancroft	v	Newmarket
Basildon	v	Wymondham

October 21 1995 (Week 7)

Upminster	v	Basildon
Ilford Wanderers	v	Bancroft
Holt	v	Harwich & Dovercourt
Ely	v	Woodbridge
Loughton	v	Newmarket
Saffron Walden	v	Wymondham

February 24 1996 (Week 24)

Newmarket	v	Basildon
Woodbridge	v	Bancroft
Diss	v	Harwich & Dovercourt
Ely	v	Holt
Loughton	v	Ilford Wanderers
Saffron Walden	v	Upminster

October 28 1995 (Week 8)

Bancroft	v	Holt
Basildon	v	Ilford Wanderers
Wymondham	v	Upminster
Newmarket	v	Saffron Walden
Woodbridge	v	Loughton
Diss	v	Ely

March 30 1996 (Week X7)

Ilford Wanderers	v	Saffron Walden
Holt	v	Loughton
Harwich & Dovercourt	v	Ely
Bancroft	v	Diss
Basildon	v	Woodbridge
Wymondham	v	Newmarket

EASTERN COUNTIES ONE

BANCROFT RFC
Ground Address: Buckhurst Way, Buckhurst Hill, Essex IG9 6JD. Tel: 0181 504 0429
Club Secretary: SB Thirsk, 4 Bentley Way, Woodford Green, Essex IG8 0SE. Tel: (H) 0181 504 1468 Tel: (W) 01279 441111
Fixtures Secretary: Ian Fleet, 40 Lordship Park, Stoke Newington, London N16 5UD. Tel: (H) 0181 880 2105
Club Colours: Blue, black, claret & light blue hoops.

BASILDON RFC
Ground Address: Gardiner's Close, Basildon, Essex SS14 3AW. Tel: 01268 533136
Club Secretary: RJ Phillips, 118 Great Spenders, Basildon, Essex SS14 2NT. Tel: (H) 01268 454662 Tel: (W) 01268 282146
Fixtures Secretary: L Hymans, 32 Devons Way, Canvey Island, Essex SS9 9YD. Tel: (H) 01268 693899 Tel (W) 01850 500159
Club Colours: Bottle green with two white hoops.

DISS RFC
Ground Address: Mackenders, Bellrope Lane, Roydon, Diss, Norfolk IP21 3RG. Tel: 01379 642891
Club Secretary: NP Kingsley, c/o Sprans & Kingsley, 16 Broad Street, Bungay, Suffolk NR35 1ON. Tel: (H) 01508 499641 Tel: (W) 01986 892721
Fixtures Secretary: Paul D Mitchell, 19 Denmark Street, Diss, Norfolk IP22 3LG. Tel: (H) 01379 650638 Tel (W) 01508 473219
Club Colours: Royal blue & white.

ELY RUFC
Ground Address: Little Downham Road, Ely, Cambs. Tel: 01353 662363
Club Secretary: Richard Wilding, 12 West End, Ely, Cambs CB6 3BY. Tel: (H) 01353 665963
Fixtures Secretary: Martin Hammond, 5 Common Lane, Southery, Norfold PE38 0PB. Tel: (H) 013666 400
Club Colours: Black & gold hoops.

HARWICH & DOVERCOURT RUFC
Ground Address: Swimming Pool Road, Wick Lane, Dovercourt, Harwich, Essex. Tel: 01255 240225
Club Secretary: Kieran Coyles, 4 Acorn Close, Dovercourt, Harwich, Essex CO12 4XF. Tel: (H) 01255 504432 Tel: (W) 01255 502267
Fixtures Secretary: Barry Male, 28 Mayes Lane, Ramsey, Harwich, Essex CO12 5EJ. Tel: (H) 01255 886165 Tel (W) 01255 502246
Club Colours: Black with one white hoop, black shorts, black socks with white tops.

HOLT RFC
Ground Address: Bridge Road, High Kelling, Holt, Norfolk NR25 6QT. Tel: 01263 712191
Club Secretary: MD Bush, The Warren, Sir Williams Lane, Aylsham, Norwich NR11 6AW. Tel: (H) 01263 732051 Tel: (W) 01603 867355
Fixtures Secretary: J Lockhart, April Cottage, The Rosary, Mulbarton, Norwich NR14 8AL. Tel: (H) 01508 570835 Tel (W) 01603 628251
Club Colours: Black shirts, shorts & socks.

ILFORD WANDERERS RFC
Ground Address: Forest Road, Barkingside, Ilford, Essex. Tel: 0181 500 4622
Club Secretary: Alan Lewis, 161A Albborough Road South, Seven Kings, Ilford, Essex IG3 8HU. Tel: 0181 597 1158 Tel: (W) 0181 594 4894
Fixtures Secretary: Beiron Rees, 161A Aldborough Road South, Seven Kings, Ilford, Essex IG3 8HU. Tel: (H) 0181 597 1158 Tel (W) 0181 592 7861
Club Colours: Red, green & white hoops.

LOUGHTON RFC
Ground Address: Squirrels Lane, Hornbeam Road, Buckhurst Hill, Essex. Tel: 0181 504 0065

FINAL TABLE

	P	W	D	L	F	A	Pts
Lowestoft & Yarm'th	12	11	0	1	424	92	22
Canvey Island	12	9	1	2	286	151	19
Diss	11	8	0	3	255	97	16
Wymondham	12	8	0	4	277	129	16
Ely	12	7	0	5	204	177	14
Saffron Walden	12	5	1	6	183	205	11
Newmarket	12	5	1	6	141	194	11
Bancroft	12	4	1	7	152	173	9
Harwich & Doverct	12	4	1	7	126	236	9
Holt	11	4	0	7	115	218	8
Upminster	12	3	0	9	98	309	6
Ravens	12	3	1	8	125	280	5*
Westcliff	12	2	2	8	100	225	4*

Club Secretary: Anna Coote, Post Office Stores, 1 The Street, Hatfield Peverel, Chelmsford, Essex CM3 2DL. Tel: (H) 01245 380 201
Fixtures Secretary: Brian Westley, 30 The Avenue, St Pauls Cray, Orpington, Kent BR5 3DJ. Tel: (H) 0168 981 9365
Club Colours: White with black hoop between two green hoops.

NEWMARKET RUFC
Ground Address: Scaltback Middle School, Exning Road, Newmarket, Suffolk CB8 0DJ. Tel: 01638 663082
Club Secretary: James W Paxton, 7 Beechwood Close, Exning, Newmarket, Suffolk CB8 7EL. Tel: (H) 01638 577251 Tel: (W) 01638 577251
Fixtures Secretary: John Taylor, 32 High Street, Stetchworth, Newmarket CB8 9TJ. Tel: (H) 01638 507103 Tel (W) 01638 507483
Club Colours: Emerald green & black hoops.

SAFFRON WALDEN RFC
Ground Address: Springate, Henham, Nr Bishop's Stortford, Herts. Tel: 01279 850791
Club Secretary: B Peachey, 2 Gloucester Place, Clare, Suffolk CO10 8QR. Tel: (H) 01787 278464 Tel: (W) 01277 260 600
Fixtures Secretary: M Flood, 30a Elizabeth Road, Bishop's Stortford. Tel: (H) 01279 657772 Tel (W) 01628 771800
Club Colours: Myrtle green jersey.

UPMINSTER RFC
Ground Address: Hall Lane Playing Fields, Hall Lane, Upminster, Essex RM14. Tel: 01708 220320
Club Secretary: M Eve, 142 Cranston Park Avenue, Upminster, Essex RM14 3XJ. Tel: (H) 01708 225383 Tel: (W) 01708 858935
Fixtures Secretary: Shaun Neale, 26 Fern Bank Avenue, Hornchurch, Essex RM12 5RA. Tel: (H) 01708 445423
Club Colours: Yellow & blue hoops.

WOODBRIDGE RUFC
Ground Address: Hatchley Barn, Bromeswell, Woodridge, Suffolk IP12 2PP. Tel: 01394 460630
Club Secretary: Keith J Blow, 14 Cobbold Road, Woodbridge IP12 1HA. Tel: (H) 01394 384642 Tel: (W) 01473 643417
Fixtures Secretary: Mr Ian Rafferty, Larches, 24 Moorfield Road, Woodbridge, Suffolk IP12 4JN. Tel: (H) 01394 382369 Tel (W) 01473 383100
Club Colours: Sky blue.

WYMONDHAM RUFC
Ground Address: Foster Harrison Memorial Ground, Tuttles Lane, Wymondham, Norfolk. Tel: 01953 607332
Club Secretary: M Warren, 67 Hawkes Lane, Bracon Ash, Norfolk NR14 8EW. Tel: (H) 01508 70669 Tel: (W) 01603 616112 Fax: 01603 760538
Fixtures Secretary: K Scott, 101 Dalrymple Way, Weston Road, Norwich NR6 6TR. Tel: (H) 01603 486104 Tel (W) 01603 680821
Club Colours: Red & black hoops.

LONDON & SOUTH EAST DIVISION

EASTERN COUNTIES TWO 1995-96 FIXTURES

November 11 1995 (Week 10)

Met Police Chigwell	v	Wanstead
Fakenham	v	Lakenham-Hewett
Ravens	v	Thames
Southwold	v	Old Bealonians
Old Cooperians	v	Old Palmerians
Cantabrigians	v	Thetford

September 16 1995 (Week 3)

Met Police Chigwell	v	Fakenham
Thetford	v	Lakenham-Hewett
Old Palmerians	v	Thames
Westcliff	v	Old Bealonians
Old Cooperians	v	Southwold
Cantabrigians	v	Ravens

January 6 1996 (Week 17)

Thames	v	Southwold
Lakenham-Hewett	v	Ravens
Wanstead	v	Fakenham
Thetford	v	Met Police Chigwell
Old Palmerians	v	Cantabrigians
Westcliff	v	Old Cooperians

September 23 1995 (Week 4)

Ravens	v	Met Police Chigwell
Southwold	v	Cantabrigians
Old Bealonians	v	Old Cooperians
Thames	v	Westcliff
Lakenham-Hewett	v	Ols Palmerians
Wanstead	v	Thetford

January 13 1996 (Week 18)

Met Police Chigwell	v	Old Palmerians
Fakenham	v	Thetford
Ravens	v	Wanstead
Southwold	v	Lakenham-Hewett
Old Bealonians	v	Thames
Cantabrigians	v	Westcliff

September 30 1995 (Week X1)

Met Police Chigwell	v	Southwold
Fakenham	v	Ravens
Old Palmerians	v	Wanstead
Westcliff	v	Lakenham-Hewett
Old Cooperians	v	Thames
Cantabrigians	v	Old Bealonians

February 10 1996 (Week 22)

Lakenham-Hewett	v	Old Bealonians
Wanstead	v	Southwold
Thetford	v	Ravens
Old Palmerians	v	Fakenham
Westcliff	v	Met Police Chigwell
Old Cooperians	v	Cantabrigians

October 14 1995 (Week 6)

Southwold	v	Fakenham
Old Bealonians	v	Met Police Chigwell
Thames	v	Cantabrigians
Lakenham-Hewett	v	Old Cooperians
Wanstead	v	Westcliff
Thetford	v	Old Palmerians

February 17 1996 (Week 23)

Met Police Chigwell	v	Old Cooperians
Fakenham	v	Westcliff
Ravens	v	Old Palmerians
Southwold	v	Thetford
Old Bealonians	v	Wanstead
Thames	v	Lakenham-Hewett

October 21 1995 (Week 7)

Met Police Chigwell	v	Thames
Fakenham	v	Old Bealonians
Ravens	v	Southwold
Westcliff	v	Thetford
Old Cooperians	v	Wanstead
Cantabrigians	v	Lakenham-Hewett

February 24 1996 (Week 24)

Wanstead	v	Thames
Thetford	v	Old Bealonians
Old Palmerians	v	Southwold
Westcliff	v	Ravens
Old Cooperians	v	Fakenham
Cantabrigians	v	Met Police Chigwell

October 28 1995 (Week 8)

Old Bealonians	v	Ravens
Thames	v	Fakenham
Lakenham-Hewett	v	Met Police Chigwell
Wanstead	v	Cantabrigians
Thetford	v	Old Cooperians
Old Palmerians	v	Westcliff

March 30 1996 (Week X7)

Fakenham	v	Cantabrigians
Ravens	v	Old Cooperians
Southwold	v	Westcliff
Old Bealonians	v	Old Palmerians
Thames	v	Thetford
Lakenham-Hewett	v	Wanstead

EASTERN COUNTIES TWO

CANTABRIGIAN RUFC
Ground Address: Sedley Taylor Road, Cambridge CB2
2PW. Tel: 01223 516061
Club Secretary: Mr R Ladds, 4 Flamsteed Road,
Cambridge CB1 3QU. Tel: (H) 01223 249008 Tel: (W)
01223 553311
Fixtures Secretary: Mr D Gellatly, 78 High Street, West
Wratting, Cambridge CB1 5LU. Tel: (H) 01223 290472
Club Colours: Navy blue & white hoops.

FAKENHAM RUFC
Ground Address: Old Wells Road, Fakenham, Norfolk.
Tel: 01328 851007
Club Secretary: Andrea Summers, 105 Norwich Road,
Fakenham, Norfolk NR21 8JA. Tel: (H) 01328 851272
Fixtures Secretary: Chris Evans, 64 Boyd Avenue,
Toftwood, East Dereham, Norfolk NR19 1ND. Tel: (H)
01362 694537
Club Colours: Light blue & black.

LAKENHAM-HEWETT RFC
Ground Address: Hilltop Sports Centre, Norwich Road,
Swardston, Norwich, Norfolk. Tel: 01508 578826
Club Secretary: Phil Boyce, 2 Branksome Road, Norwich.
Tel: (H) 01603 454208
Fixtures Secretary: Bruce Ridgeway, Rye House, Newton
Street, Newton St Faith, Norwich NR10 3AD. Tel: (H)
01603 897771 Tel (W) 01603 628333 x271
Club Colours: Red shirt, white shorts, red socks.

METROPOLITAN POLICE CHIGWELL RFC
Ground Address: Chigwell Hall, High Road, Chigwell,
Essex. Tel: 0181 500 2755
Club Secretary: Malcolm Barrett, 11 Fairfield Road,
Ongar, Essex CM5 9HJ. Tel: (H) 01277 364206 Tel: (W)
0181 217 2735
Fixtures Secretary: James Harding, 37 Abbey Road,
Hulbridge, Mr Hockley, Essex. Tel (W) 0181 984 5521
Club Colours: Royal blue shirts, black shorts, red socks.

OLD BEALONIANS RFC
Ground Address: Beal High School, off Woodford
Avenue, Ilford, Essex.
Club Secretary: AD Lloyd, 54 Peel Road, South
Woodford, London E18 2LG. Tel: (H) 0181 505 0973 Tel:
(W) 01737 769055
Fixtures Secretary: P Collins, 14A Electric Parade, South
Woodford, London E18 2LY. Tel: (H) 0181 530 6366 Tel
(W) 0181 555 5552
Club Colours: Black shorts, scarlet shirts.

OLD COOPERIANS RUFC
Ground Address: Blake Hall Sports Ground, Blake Hall
Road, Wanstead. Tel: 0181 989 1673
Club Secretary: John C Green, Greenlow House,
Melbourn, Herts SG8 6DG. Tel: (H) 01763 260624 Tel:
(W) 01279 652214
Fixtures Secretary: Mr Dave Russell, 51 Perth Road,
Leyton, London E10. Tel: (H) 0181 539 0794
Club Colours: Dark blue with light blue & gold hoops.

OLD PALMERIANS RUFC
Ground Address: Palmers College, Chadwell Road,
Grays, Essex. Tel: 01375 370121
Club Secretary: Carwyn Owen, 1B Rose Cottage, South
Sitford, Grays, Essex RM20 4ID. Tel: (H) 01375 378668
Fixtures Secretary: John Maclean, 8 Ash Road, Hadleigh,
Benfleet, Essex. Tel: (H) 01702 557423 Tel (W) 01375
853325
Club Colours: Light blue & dark blue hoops.

RAVENS RFC
Ground Address: Ford Sports & Social Club, Aldborough
Road South, Newbury Park, Ilford, Essex.
Club Secretary: Gary Bishop, 34 Bendemeer Road,
Putney, London SW15 1JU. Tel: (H) 0181 788 7962 Tel:
(W) 0171 606 7777
Fixtures Secretary: AC Guest, 57 Shaftesbury Road,

FINAL TABLE							
	P	W	D	L	F	A	Pts
Ilford Wanderers	11	9	0	2	216	52	18
Loughton	11	9	0	2	257	110	16*
Wanstead	11	8	2	1	153	56	16*
Old Palmerians	10	6	1	3	121	109	13
Cantabrigian	11	6	0	5	149	144	12
Thetford	10	5	0	5	137	170	10
Old Cooperians	11	5	0	6	156	222	10
Met Pol Chigwell	11	4	0	7	118	161	8
Old Bealonians	11	4	0	7	127	177	8
Lakenham Hewett	10	3	0	7	101	238	6
Thames	10	2	0	8	114	135	4
East London	11	1	1	9	118	193	4

Forest Gate, London E7 8PD. Tel: (H) 0181 471 7571
Club Colours: Navy blue & gold hoops.

SOUTHWOLD RFC
Ground Address: The Pavilion, The Common, Southwold,
Suffolk.
Club Secretary: Andy Toone, 17 Portsch Close, Carlton
Colville, Lowestoft, Suffolk NR33 8TY. Tel: (H) 01502
515649 Tel: (W) 01502 566321
Fixtures Secretary: John winter, Stream House,
Cheddeston, Halesworth, Suffolk. Tel: (H) 01986 875994
Tel (W) 01986 784234
Club Colours: Black & single old gold chest hoop.

THAMES RFC
Ground Address: St Cedd's Playing Fields, Garrow Lane,
Aveley, Essex.
Club Secretary: David Northfield, 179 Blackshots Lane,
Grays, Essex RM16 2LL. Tel: (H) 01375 371125 Tel: (W)
01268 402239
Fixtures Secretary: Tony Smith, 67 St Michael's Close,
Aveley, Essex. Tel: (H) 01708 868331 Tel (W) 0171 325
1432
Club Colours: Emerald green & black hoops.

THETFORD RFC
Ground Address: Twomile Bottom, Mundford Road,
Thetford, Norfolk IP24 1LY. Tel: 01842 755176
Club Secretary: Peter Candlin, 67 Nunnery Drive,
Thetford, Norfolk IP24 3EP. Tel: (H) 01842 750416 Tel:
(W) 01842 750415
Fixtures Secretary: Bill Smith, 'Casita', Castle Lane,
Thetford, Norfolk. Tel: (H) 01842 766113
Club Colours: Red & white hooped shirts & socks, white
shorts.

WANSTEAD RFC
Club Secretary: Neil Joyce, 21 Grosvenor Road, Leyton,
London E10 6LG. Tel: (H) 0181 556 9125
Fixtures Secretary: Terry Elliot, 18 Highbury Gardens,
Seven Kings, Essex IG3 8AA. Tel: (H) 0181 599 2743
Club Colours: Blue & white hoops.

WESTCLIFF RFC
Ground Address: The Gables, Aviation Way,
Southend-on-Sea, Essex SS2 6UN. Tel: 01702 541499
Club Secretary: Nick J Crowe, 68 Leighton Avenue,
Leigh-on-Sea, Essex SS9 1QA. Tel: (H) 01702 711647 Tel:
(W) 01268 7561111 (Emergency)
Fixtures Secretary: Steve Cray, 99 Fairfield Road,
Eastwood, Leigh-on-Sea, Essex SS9 5RY. Tel: (H) 01702
523977 Tel (W) 01268 540054
Club Colours: Maroon & gold hoops.

485

LONDON & SOUTH EAST DIVISION

EASTERN COUNTIES THREE
1995-96 FIXTURES

November 11 1995 (Week 10)

Broadland	v	East London
Ipswich YMCA	v	Crusaders
Felixstowe	v	Stowmarket
Billericay	v	Thurston
Clacton	v	Sth Woodham Ferrers
Hadleigh	v	Haverhill

September 16 1995 (Week 3)

Broadland	v	Ipswich YMCA
Haverhill	v	Crusaders
Sth Woodham Ferrers	v	Stowmarket
Wisbech	v	Thurston
Clacton	v	Billericay
Hadleigh	v	Felixstowe

January 6 1996 (Week 17)

Stowmarket	v	Billericay
Crusaders	v	Felixstowe
East London	v	Ipswich YMCA
Haverhill	v	Broadland
Sth Woodham Ferrers	v	Hadleigh
Wisbech	v	Clacton

September 23 1995 (Week 4)

Felixstowe	v	Broadland
Billericay	v	Hadleigh
Thurston	v	Clacton
Stowmarket	v	Wisbech
Crusaders	v	Sth Woodham Ferrers
East London	v	Haverhill

January 13 1996 (Week 18)

Broadland	v	Sth Woodham Ferrers
Ipswich YMCA	v	Haverhill
Felixstowe	v	East London
Billericay	v	Crusaders
Thurston	v	Stowmarket
Hadleigh	v	Wisbech

September 30 1995 (Week X1)

Broadland	v	Billericay
Ipswich YMCA	v	Felixstowe
Sth Woodham Ferrers	v	East London
Wisbech	v	Crusaders
Clacton	v	Stowmarket
Hadleigh	v	Thurston

February 10 1996 (Week 22)

Crusaders	v	Thurston
East London	v	Billericay
Haverhill	v	Felixstowe
Sth Woodham Ferrers	v	Ipswich YMCA
Wisbech	v	Broadland
Clacton	v	Hadleigh

October 14 1995 (Week 6)

Billericay	v	Ipswich YMCA
Thurston	v	Broadland
Stowmarket	v	Hadleigh
Crusaders	v	Clacton
East London	v	Wisbech
Haverhill	v	Sth Woodham Ferrers

February 17 1996 (Week 23)

Broadland	v	Clacton
Ipswich YMCA	v	Wisbech
Felixstowe	v	Sth Woodham Ferrers
Billericay	v	Haverhill
Thurston	v	East London
Stowmarket	v	Crusaders

October 21 1995 (Week 7)

Broadland	v	Stowmarket
Ipswich YMCA	v	Thurston
Felixstowe	v	Billericay
Wisbech	v	Haverhill
Clacton	v	East London
Hadleigh	v	Crusaders

February 24 1996 (Week 24)

East London	v	Stowmarket
Haverhill	v	Thurston
Sth Woodham Ferrers	v	Billericay
Wisbech	v	Felixstowe
Clacton	v	Ipswich YMCA
Hadleigh	v	Broadland

October 28 1995 (Week 8)

Thurston	v	Felixstowe
Stowmarket	v	Ipswich YMCA
Crusaders	v	Broadland
East London	v	Hadleigh
Haverhill	v	Clacton
Sth Woodham Ferrers	v	Wisbech

March 30 1996 (Week X7)

Ipswich YMCA	v	Hadleigh
Felixstowe	v	Clacton
Billericay	v	Wisbech
Thurston	v	Soth Woodham Ferrers
Stowmarket	v	Haverhill
Crusaders	v	East London

EASTERN COUNTIES THREE

BILLERICAY RFC
Ground Address: Willowbrook Sports Ground, Stock Road, Stock, Billericay, Essex. Tel: 01277 841442
Club Secretary: GJ Buggle, 96 Norsey View Drive, Billericay, Essex CM12 0QU. Tel: (W) 01375 677777
Fixtures Secretary: M Scoggins, 38 St Mary's Drive, South Benfleet, Essex SS7 1LB. Tel: (H) 01268 751007 Tel (W) 01268 756276
Club Colours: Black jersey with gold hoop, black shorts & black socks with gold top.

BROADLAND RFC
Ground Address: Cobholm Playing Fields, Cobholm, Great Yarmouth, Norfolk NR31 0AZ.
Club Secretary: Miss AJ Blizzard, c/o 44A Southtown Road, Great Yarmouth, Norfolk NR31 0DT. Tel: (H) 01493 667488 Tel: (W) 01603 222874
Fixtures Secretary: Mr D Todd, 22 Rumburgh Road, Lowestoft, Suffolk NR32 4JL. Tel: (H) 01502 512671 Tel (W) 01493 452192
Club Colours: Red, white & blue hoops.

CLACTON RUFC
Ground Address: Clacton Rugby Clubhouse, Recreation Ground, Valley Road, Clacton-on-Sea, Essex CO15 4NA. Tel: 01255 421602
Club Secretary: David Jaffray, 30 Craigfield Avenue, Clacton-on-Sea, Essex CO15 4HS. Tel: (H) 01255 429762 Tel: (W) 01255 429762
Fixtures Secretary: Alan Lee, 81 High Street, Walton-on-Naze, Essex CO14 8AA. Tel: (H) 01255 678793 Tel (W) 01255 678793
Club Colours: Maroon jersey, navy shorts, maroon socks & white tops.

CRUSADERS RUFC
Ground Address: Beck Hythe, Little Melton, Norwich, Norfolk. Tel: 01603 811157
Club Secretary: Mr Tim Holliday, 19 Hobart Close, Wymondham, Norfolk NR18 0EQ. Tel: (H) 01953 601101 Tel: (W) 01603 662496
Fixtures Secretary: Mr Mike Bridgeman, 4 Bensley Road, Norwich, Norfolk NR2 3JS. Tel: (H) 01603 250926
Club Colours: Emerald & gold.

EAST LONDON RFC
Ground Address: Holland Road, West Ham, London, E15 3BP. Tel: 0171 474 6761
Club Secretary: RH James, 43 Bounds Oak Way, Southborough, Tunbridge Wells, Kent, TN4 0TW. Tel: (H) 01892 512798 Tel: (W) 01342 410166
Fixtures Secretary: Tony Stavrinou, 136 Bow Common Lane, London E3. Tel: (H) 0181 980 0938 Tel (W) 0171 739 3951
Club Colours: Maroon & navy hoops.

FELIXSTOWE RUFC
Ground Address: The Clubhouse, Coronation Sports Ground, Mill Lane, Felixstowe, Suffolk IP11 8LN. Tel: 01394 270150
Club Secretary: DA Richardson, 1 Landguard View, Felixstowe, Suffolk IP11 9TL. Tel: (H) 01394 285047 Tel: (W) 01394 670845
Fixtures Secretary: J Clark, 6 Capel Drive, Felixstowe, Suffolk IP11 8FR. Tel: (H) 01394 270974 Tel (W) 01394 673200
Club Colours: Black & white hooped shirts, black shorts/socks.

HADLEIGH RUFC
Ground Address: Layham Road Sports Ground, Hadleigh, Ipswich, Suffolk IP7 5NE. Tel: 01473 824217
Club Secretary: Andrew Hunkin, 7 Yeoman Way, Hadleigh, Ipswich, Suffolk IP7 5HW. Tel: (H) 01473 824448 Tel: (W) 01473 825745
Fixtures Secretary: Alan Murray, Clematis Cottage, Hintlesham, Ipswich, Suffolk IP8 3NH. Tel: (H) 01473 652448 Tel (W) 01473 251608
Club Colours: Maroon, white & amber hoops.

HAVERHILL & DISTRICT RFC
Ground Address: Castle Playing Fields, School Lane, Haverhill, Suffolk. Tel: 01440 702871
Club Secretary: Clive D Farrow, 27 Broad Street, Haverhill, Suffolk CB9 9HD. Tel: (H) 01440 63766 Tel: (W) 01440 711435

FINAL TABLE

	P	W	D	L	F	A	Pts
Fakenham	11	9	0	2	203	93	18
Southwold	12	7	1	4	201	123	15
Ipswich YMCA	12	7	1	4	170	122	15
Sth Woodham Ferrers	12	7	0	5	166	139	14
Hadleigh	11	6	0	5	211	129	12
Stowmarket	11	6	0	5	172	100	12*
Felixstowe	11	6	0	5	124	89	10*
Crusaders	11	5	0	6	139	124	10
Thurston	12	5	0	7	155	202	10
Haverhill	10	5	1	4	135	101	9*
Broadland	12	4	1	7	117	221	9
Beccles	12	4	0	8	169	168	8
Redbridge	11	1	0	10	51	402	2

Fixtures Secretary: Mr A Hope, 2 Hart Close, Arrendene Park, Haverhill, Suffolk CB9 9JP. Tel: (H) 01440 63555 Tel (W) 01440 711241
Club Colours: Maroon & blue checks, black shorts & socks.

IPSWICH YM RUFC
Ground Address: Ipswich YM Sports Ground, The Street, Rushmere, Ipswich, Suffolk. Tel: 01473 713807
Club Secretary: RM Daniels, 85 Western Avenue, Felixstowe, Suffolk IP11 9NT. Tel: (H) 01394 283907 Tel: (W) 01473 543850
Fixtures Secretary: Rob Hullis, 2 Godbold Close, Kesgrave, Ipswich IP5 7SE. Tel: (H) 01473 625027 Tel (W) 01473 622701
Club Colours: Maroon & amber hoops.

SOUTH WOODHAM FERRERS RFC
Ground Address: Saltcoats Park, Ferrers Road, South Woodham Ferrers, Essex. Tel: 01245 320041
Club Secretary: Mrs Susan Williams, 11 Drywoods, South Woodham Ferrers, Essex CM3 5ZG. Tel: (H) 01245 325987
Fixtures Secretary: Mr B Gittos, 12 Hillcrest, South Woodham Ferrers, Essex. Tel: (H) 01245 324603
Club Colours: Black shirts, shorts & socks.

STOWMARKET RUFC
Ground Address: Chilton Fields Sports Club, Chilton Way, Stowmarket, Suffolk. Tel: 01449 613181
Club Secretary: N Pearman, 5 Milden Close, Stowmarket, Suffolk IP14 2RF. Tel: (H) 01449 774250 Tel: (W) 01449 612401
Fixtures Secretary: Miss S Denny, 29 Cardinals Road, Stowmarket, Suffolk. Tel: (H) 01449 673857
Club Colours: Navy blue with white/red/white central band.

THURSTON RUFC
Ground Address: Robinson Field, Ixworth Road, Thurston, Bury St Edmunds, Suffolk. Tel: 01359 232450
Club Secretary: Mrs Janet Connor, Sycamore Cottage, The Street, Botesdale, Suffolk IP22 1BZ. Tel: (H) 01379 898798 Tel: (W) 01379 890409
Fixtures Secretary: Bruce Workmaster, 30 Trinity Mews, Bury St Edmunds, Suffolk. Tel: (H) 01284 702693 Tel (W) 01284 756565
Club Colours: Navy blue, red collar & cuffs.

WISBECH RUFC
Ground Address: Chapel Road, Harecroft Road, Wisbech, Cambridgeshire PE13 4666
Club Secretary: JRC Pallant, 139 Lynn Road, Wisbech, Cambridgeshire PE13 3DH. Tel: (H) 01945 588147 Tel: (W) 01354 54321
Fixtures Secretary: D Dobson, 5 Buckingham Walk, Wisbech, Cambridgeshire PE13 3HL. Tel: (H) 01945 461223
Club Colours: Red shirts, blue shorts.

LONDON & SOUTH EAST DIVISION

EASTERN COUNTIES FOUR
1995-96 FIXTURES

September 16 1995 (Week 3)
Burnham-on-Crouch	v	Witham
Brightlingsea	v	March
Ongar	v	Rayleigh
Sawston	v	Beccles
Mersea Island	v	Dereham

September 23 1995 (Week 4)
Dereham	v	Burnham-on-Crouch
Beccles	v	Mersea Island
Rayleigh	v	Sawston
March	v	Ongar
May & Baker	v	Brightlingsea

September 30 1995 (Week X1)
Burnham-on-Crouch	v	Beccles
Witham	v	Dereham
Brightlingsea	v	Essex Police
Ongar	v	May & Baker
Sawston	v	March
Mersea Island	v	Rayleigh

October 14 1995 (Week 6)
Beccles	v	Witham
Rayleigh	v	Burnham-on-Crouch
March	v	Mersea Island
May & Baker	v	Sawston
Essex Police	v	Ongar

October 21 1995 (Week 7)
Burnham-on-Crouch	v	March
Witham	v	Rayleigh
Dereham	v	Beccles
Sawston	v	Essex Police
Mersea Island	v	May & Baker

October 28 1995 (Week 8)
Rayleigh	v	Dereham
March	v	Witham
May & Baker	v	Burnham-on-Crouch
Essex Police	v	Mersea Island
Brightlingsea	v	Ongar

November 11 1995 (Week 10)
Burnham-on-Crouch	v	Essex Police
Witham	v	May & Baker
Dereham	v	March

Beccles	v	Rayleigh
Sawston	v	Brightlingsea

January 6 1996 (Week 17)
March	v	Beccles
May & Baker	v	Dereham
Essex Police	v	Witham
Brightlingsea	v	Mersea Island
Ongar	v	Sawston

January 13 1996 (Week 18)
Burnham-on-Crouch	v	Brightlingsea
Dereham	v	Essex Police
Beccles	v	May & Baker
Rayleigh	v	March
Mersea Island	v	Ongar

February 10 1996 (Week 22)
May & Baker	v	Rayleigh
Essex Police	v	Beccles
Brightlingsea	v	Witham
Ongar	v	Burnham-on-Crouch
Sawston	v	Mersea Island

February 17 1996 (Week 23)
Burnham-on-Crouch	v	Sawston
Witham	v	Ongar
Dereham	v	Brightlingsea
Rayleigh	v	Essex Police
March	v	May & Baker

February 24 1996 (Week 24)
Essex Police	v	March
Brightlingsea	v	Beccles
Ongar	v	Dereham
Sawston	v	Witham
Mersea Island	v	Burnham-on-Crouch

March 30 1996 (Week X7)
Witham	v	Mersea Island
Dereham	v	Sawston
Beccles	v	Ongar
Rayleigh	v	Brightlingsea
May & Baker	v	Essex Police

EASTERN COUNTIES FOUR

BECCLES RUFC
Ground Address: Beef Meadow, Common Lane, Beccles.
Tel: 01502 712016
Club Secretary: W Wells, Cliff Cottage, Puddingmoor,
Beccles, Suffolk. Tel: (H) 01502 715509
Fixtures Secretary: Miles James, 48 Grove Road, Beccles,
Suffolk. Tel: (H) 01502 716334 Tel (W) Pager 01603
612513
Club Colours: Emerald green & black quarters.
BRIGHTLINGSEA RFC
Ground Address: Strangers Corner, Brightlingsea, Essex.
Tel: 01206 304946
Club Secretary: James McClure, 10 Pertwee Close,
Brightlingsea, Essex CO7 0RT. Tel: (H) 01206 304761 Tel:
(W) 01268 525631
Fixtures Secretary: Trevor Andrews, 1 Tabor Close,
Brightlingsea, Essex CO7 0QS. Tel: (H) 01206 302235
Club Colours: Royal blue with yellow chevron.
BURNHAM-ON-CROUCH RUFC
Ground Address: Dengie Hundred Sports Centre,
Millfields, Station Road, Burnham-on-Crouch, Essex CM0
8HS. Tel: Office: 01621 784633 Bar: 01621 784656
Club Secretary: Mr Warwick H Bridge, 12 Glendale
Road, Burnham-on-Crouch, Essex CM0 8LY. Tel: (H)
01621 783807
Fixtures Secretary: Mr Warwick H Bridge, 12 Glendale
Road, Burnham-on-Crouch, Essex CM0 8LY. Tel: (H)
01621 783807
Club Colours: Navy blue & amber hoops.
DEREHAM RUFC
Ground Address: Moorgate Sports Field, Moorgate,
Dereham, Norfolk. Tel: c/o 01362 691487
Club Secretary: Barbara Endresen, 1 Bayfield Avenue,
Dereham, Norfolk NR19 1PH. Tel: (H) 01362 691487 Tel:
(W) 01362 695353
Fixtures Secretary: Mark Brown, 47 Hillcrest Avenue,
Toftwood, Dereham, Norfolk NR19 1LP. Tel: (H) 01362
698588
Club Colours: Maroon.
MARCH BRAZA RUFC
Ground Address: Braza Sports Pavilion, Elm Road,
March, Cambridgeshire. Tel: 01354 59741
Club Secretary: Andrew D Woollard, 124 West End,
March, Cambridgeshire PE15 8DE. Tel: (H) 01354 58160
Fixtures Secretary: Mr I Woodward, 34b Westfield Road,
Manea, March, Cambridgeshire. Tel: (H) 01354 78445
Club Colours: Maroon/white hoops.
MAY AND BAKER RUFC
Ground Address: Dagenham Road, Dagenham, Essex.
Tel: 0181 919 3156
Club Secretary: Terry Simmons, 105 Albion Road,
Dagenham, Essex RM10 8DE. Tel: (H) 0181 593 2630 Tel:
(W) 0181 919 2579
Fixtures Secretary: Mike Parnell, The Old Post Office,
High Easter, Chelmsford, Essex. Tel: (H) 01245 231302
Club Colours: Black with a single red hoop, black shorts,
red stockings.
MERSEA ISLAND RFC
Ground Address: The Youth Camp, East Road, East
Mersea, Colchester, Essex.
Club Secretary: Tony Eyes, Dormy House, Lower Road,
Peldon, Colchester, Essex CO5 7QR. Tel: (H) 01206
735537 Tel: (W) 01206 735537
Fixtures Secretary: Graham Woods, 24 Church Field,
West Mersea, Essex. Tel: (H) 01206 383525 Tel (W)
01206 383525
Club Colours: Blue/white squares.
ONGAR RFC
Ground Address: Love Lane, Ongar, Essex. Tel: 01277
363838
Club Secretary: N Doubleday, 105 Roundhills, Waltham

FINAL TABLE

	P	W	D	L	F	A	Pts
Billericay	9	8	0	1	216	40	16
Burnham-on-Crouch	10	7	1	2	161	74	13*
Brightlingsea	10	6	0	4	217	129	12
Wisbech	9	6	0	3	160	75	12
Witham	9	5	0	4	150	141	10
May & Baker	10	5	0	5	180	196	10
Ongar	9	4	0	5	104	122	8
Mersea Island	9	3	0	6	108	122	6
Dereham	8	3	0	5	61	205	6
March	9	3	1	5	110	95	5*
Mayfield Old Boys	10	0	0	10	41	309	0

Abbey, Essex EN9 1TF. Tel: (H) 01992 768950 Tel: (W)
01992 788557
Fixtures Secretary: Peter Hodgson, 74 The Paddocks,
Ingatestone, Essex CM4 1AA. Tel: (H) 01277 354404 Tel
(W) 01836 557104
Club Colours: Blue with amber band.
RAYLEIGH WYVERNS RFC
Ground Address: Sir John Fisher Playing Fields, Little
Wheatleys Chase, Rayleigh, Essex.
Club Secretary: SJ Earl, 22 The Fairway, Leigh-on-Sea,
Essex SS9 4QL. Tel: (H) 01702 524111 Tel: (W) 0181 502
1423
Fixtures Secretary: M Sheppard, 19 Mortimer Road,
Rayleigh, Essex. Tel: (H) 01268 781152
Club Colours: Scarlet & emerald quarters, black shorts.
SAWSTON RUFC
Ground Address: Sawston College, New Road, Sawston
CB2 4BP. Tel: 01223 836615
Club Secretary: Paul Clerke, 1 Crossways, Linton,
Cambridge CB1 6NQ. Tel: (H) 01223 891365 Tel: (W)
0181 965 0313
Fixtures Secretary: Philip Mason, 6 Stanstead Road,
Elsenham, Bishop's Stortford, Herts. Tel: (H) 01279
812545
Club Colours: Blue/black.
WITHAM RUFC
Ground Address: Spa Road, Witham, Essex, CM8 2UN.
Tel: 01376 511066
Club Secretary: Heather Turner, 48 Mulberry Gardens,
Witham, Essex, CM8 2PX. Tel: (H) 01376 520866 Tel:
(W) 01284 768911
Fixtures Secretary: Angus Downes, The Old Manse,
Manse Chase, Maldon, Essex CM9 7GA. Tel: (H) 01621
857593 Tel (W) 01277 219262
Club Colours: Brown & white hoops, navy shorts.

LONDON & SOUTH EAST DIVISION

EASTERN COUNTIES
FIVE
1995-96 FIXTURES

February 24 1996 (Week 24)
Essex County Council v Norwich Union
Swaffham v Orwell
Stanford v Dagenham

September 23 1995 (Week 4)
Swaffham v Essex County Council
Stanford v Orwell
Norwich Union v Dagenham

September 30 1995 (Week X1)
Essex County Council v Stanford
Swaffham v Norwich Union
Orwell v Dagenham

October 14 1995 (Week 6)
Stanford v Swaffham
Dagenham v Essex County Council
Norwich Union v Orwell

October 21 1995 (Week 7)
Essex County Council v Orwell
Swaffham v Dagenham
Stanford v Norwich Union

October 28 1995 (Week 8)
Dagenham v Stanford
Orwell v Swaffham
Norwich Union v Essex County Council

November 11 1995 (Week 10)
Essex County Council v Swaffham
Orwell v Stanford
Dagenham v Norwich Union

January 13 1996 (Week 18)
Dagenham v Orwell
Stanford v Essex County Council
Norwich Union v Swaffham

February 10 1996 (Week 22)
Orwell v Norwich Union
Swaffham v Stanford
Essex County Council v Dagenham

February 17 1996 (Week 23)
Dagenham v Swaffham
Norwich Union v Stanford
Orwell v Essex County Council

EASTERN COUNTIES FIVE

DAGENHAM RFC
Ground Address: The Pavilion, Central Park, Rainham Road, North Dagenham, Essex. Tel: 01708 764036
Club Secretary: Mr RJ Moreton, 21 Central Park Avenue, Dagenham, Essex RM10 7DA. Tel: (H) 0181 984 8444 Tel: (W) 01860 821799
Fixtures Secretary: Mr RJ Moreton, 21 Central Park Avenue, Dagenham, Essex RM10 7DA. Tel: (H) 0181 984 8444 Tel (W) 01860 821799
Club Colours: Red & white quarters.

ESSEX COUNTY COUNCIL RFC
Ground Address: Lordship Road, Writtle, Chelmsford (opposite the Agricultural College).
Club Secretary: David Sharp, 67 Clements Green Lane, South Woodham Ferrers, Chelmsford, Essex CM3 5JS. Tel: (H) 01245 323490 Tel: (W) 01268 702101
Fixtures Secretary: Jamie Price, 53 Redmayne Drive, Chelmsford, Essex CM2 9XG. Tel: (H) 01245 237245
Club Colours: Blue & red quarters.

NORWICH UNION RFC
Ground Address: Pinebanks Sports & Leisure Club, White Farm Lane, off Harvey Lane, Norwich, Norfolk. Tel: 01603 33752
Club Secretary: Russell Harris, 9 Highgate Court, Poringland, Norwich, Norfolk NR14 7RS. Tel: (H) 01508 494896 Tel: (W) 01603 622200
Fixtures Secretary: Mark Howell, 165 Christchurch Road, Norwich, Norfolk NR2 3PJ. Tel: (H) 01603 501503 Tel (W) 01603 622200
Club Colours: Green & white quarters.

ORWELL RFC
Ground Address: Ransome's Sports & Social club, Sidegate Avenue, Ipswich, Suffolk.
Club Secretary: Daniel B, 12 Vermont Road, Ipswich, Suffolk IP4 2SR.
Fixtures Secretary: Mr B Kearney, 1 Acer Grove, Belmore Road, Ipswich, Suffolk IP8 5RR. Tel: (H) 01473 684909
Club Colours: Black & red.

STANFORD LE HOPE RFC
Ground Address: Billet Lane Recreation Ground, Billet Lane, Stanford le Hope, Essex. Tel: 01375 640957
Club Secretary: Arlan Roach, 159 Lodge Lane, Grays, Essex RM17 5PS. Tel: (H) 01375 377798 Fax: 01375 378077 Tel: (W) 01860 790093
Fixtures Secretary: Albert E Higgs, 18 Gooderham House, Godman Road, Chadwell St Mary, Tilbury, Essex RM16 4TW. Tel: (H) 01375 841803
Club Colours: Red, white & black hoops.

SWAFFHAM RUFC
Ground Address: North Pickenham Road, Swaffham, Norfolk. Tel: 01760 724829
Club Secretary: Hugh Green, Gemini Cottage, Weasenham St Peter, King's Lynn, Norfolk PE32 2TD. Tel: (H) 01328 838269
Fixtures Secretary: Graham Robinson, 9 Beaumont Place, Norwich, Norfolk NR2 2HH. Tel: (H) 01603 622696
Club Colours: Black/amber stripe.

FINAL TABLE

	P	W	D	L	F	A	Pts
Sawston	6	5	0	1	166	36	10
Rayleigh	6	5	0	1	131	88	10
Swaffham	5	3	0	2	112	85	6
Stanford	6	3	0	3	92	71	4*
Essex County Coun'l	5	2	0	3	49	63	4
Norwich Union	6	1	0	5	73	130	2
Dagenham	6	1	0	5	62	211	2

LONDON & SOUTH EAST DIVISION

LONDON TWO SOUTH
1995-96
FIXTURES

November 11 1995 (Week 10)
Maidstone   v Westcombe Park
Old Reigatian   v Streatham-Croydon
Old Wimbledonians v Old Blues
Thanet Wanderers v Old Juddian
Horsham   v Gravesend
Dorking   v Wimbledon

September 16 1995 (Week 3)
Maidstone   v Old Reigatian
Wimbledon   v Streatham-Croydon
Gravesend   v Old Blues
Brockleians v Old Juddian
Horsham   v Thanet Wanderers
Dorking   v Old Wimbledonians

January 6 1996 (Week 17)
Old Blues   v Thanet Wanderers
Streatham-Croydon v Old Wimbledonians
Westcombe Park   v Old Reigatian
Wimbledon   v Maidstone
Gravesend   v Dorking
Brockleians   v Horsham

September 23 1995 (Week 4)
Old Wimbledonians v Maidstone
Thanet Wanderers   v Dorking
Old Juddian   v Horsham
Old Blues   v Brockleians
Streatham-Croydon v Gravesend
Westcombe Park   v Wimbledon

January 13 1996 (Week 18)
Maidstone   v Gravesend
Old Reigatian   v Wimbledon
Old Wimbledonians v Westcombe Park
Thanet Wanderers v Streatham-Croydon
Old Juddian   v Old Blues
Dorking   v Brockleians

September 30 1995 (Week X1)
Maidstone   v Thanet Wanderers
Old Reigatian v Old Wimbledonians
Gravesend   v Westcombe Park
Brockleians   v Streatham-Croydon
Horsham   v Old Blues
Dorking   v Old Juddian

February 10 1996 (Week 22)
Streatham-Croydon v Old Juddian
Westcombe Park   v Thanet Wanderers
Wimbledon   v Old Wimbledonians
Gravesend   v Old Reigatian
Brockleians   v Maidstone
Horsham   v Dorking

October 14 1995 (Week 6)
Thanet Wanderers v Old Reigatian
Old Juddian   v Maidstone
Old Blues   v Dorking
Streatham-Croydon v Horsham
Westcombe Park   v Brockleians
Wimbledon   v Gravesend

February 17 1996 (Week 23)
Maidstone   v Horsham
Old Reigatian   v Brockleians
Old Wimbledonians v Gravesend
Thanet Wanderers v Wimbledon
Old Juddian   v Westcombe Park
Old Blues   v Streatham-Croydon

October 21 1995 (Week 7)
Maidstone   v Old Blues
Old Reigatian   v Old Juddian
Old Wimbledonians v Thanet Wanderers
Brockleians   v Wimbledon
Horsham   v Westcombe Park
Dorking   v Streatham-Croydon

February 24 1996 (Week 24)
Westcombe Park v Old Blues
Wimbledon   v Old Juddian
Gravesend   v Thanet Wanderers
Brockleians   v Old Wimbledonians
Horsham   v Old Reigatian
Dorking   v Maidstone

October 28 1995 (Week 8)
Old Juddian   v Old Wimbledonians
Old Blues   v Old Reigatian
Streatham-Croydon v Maidstone
Westcombe Park   v Dorking
Wimbledon   v Horsham
Gravesend   v Brockleians

March 30 1996 (Week X7)
Old Reigatian   v Dorking
Old Wimbledonians v Horsham
Thanet Wanderers v Brockleians
Old Juddian   v Gravesend
Old Blues   v Wimbledon
Streatham-Croydon v Westcombe Park

LONDON TWO SOUTH

BROCKLEIANS RFC
Ground Address: Eltham Palace Road, Eltham, London
SE9. Tel: 0181 850 8650
Club Secretary: Gordon Robertson, New Lodge, 37
Holbrook Lane, Chislehurst, Kent BR7 6PE. Tel: (H) 0181
462 1997
Fixtures Secretary: George Wright, 3 Birling Avenue,
Bearsted, Maidstone ME14 4AJ. Tel: (H) 01622 38396
Club Colours: Chocolate, emerald & old gold.
DORKING RFC
Ground Address: Big Field Pavilion, Kiln Lane,
Brackham, Betchworth, Surrey. Tel: 01737 843928
Club Secretary: DC Kingham. Posterns Farm, Henfold
Lane, South Holmwood, Dorking, Surrey RH5 4NX. Tel:
(H) 01306 888184 Tel: (W) 01737 763405
Fixtures Secretary: M Long, 72 Reigate Road, Dorking,
Surrey RH4 1QB. Tel: (H) 01306 883226
Club Colours: Red & white.
GRAVESEND RFC
Ground Address: The Rectory Field, Milton Road,
Gravesend, Kent DA12 2PP. Tel: 01474 534840
Club Secretary: John Moore Esq, 375A Singledell Road,
Gravesend, Kent DA11 7RL. Tel: (H) 01474 362996
Fixtures Secretary: RA Wright, 43 Alanbrooke,
Gravesend, Kent DA12 1NA. Tel: (H) 01474 327303
Club Colours: 4' black & white hoops.
HORSHAM RUFC
Ground Address: Hammer Pond Road, Coolhurst,
Horsham, West Sussex RH13 6PJ. Tel: 01403 265027
Club Secretary: John Speleers, 86 Drake Close, Horsham,
West Sussex RH12 5UD. Tel: (H) 01403 272413 Tel: (W)
01403 272413
Fixtures Secretary: Geoff Curtis, The Bunglaow, Church
Road, Mannings Heath, Horsham, West Sussex RH13 6JE.
Tel: (H) 01403 268262 Tel (W) 01444 458166
Club Colours: Green & white.
MAIDSTONE FC
Ground Address: The William Day Memorial Ground,
The Mote, Willow Way, Maidstone, Kent ME15 7RN. Tel:
01622 754159
Club Secretary: Mr Jim Griffiths, 11 Tichbourne Close,
Maidstone, Kent ME16 0RY. Tel: (H) 01622 681802 Tel:
(W) 01622 710108
Fixtures Secretary: Mr AF Kelleher, 5 Conway Road,
Maidstone, Kent ME16 0HD. Tel: (H) 01622 754872 Tel
(W) 01622 754872
Club Colours: Red, white & black hoops.
OLD BLUES RFC
Ground Address: Arthur Road, Motspur Park, New
Malden, Surrey KT3 6PT. Tel: 0181 336 2566
Club Secretary: Ian Hoskins, 1 Oak Tree Drive, Englefield
Green, Surrey TW20 0NR. Tel: (H) 01784 436707 Tel:
(W) 01784 436707
Fixtures Secretary: Alistair Burns, 127B Sugden Road, London
SW11 6BG. Tel: (H) 0171 350 0846 Tel (W) 0171 636 2625
Club Colours: French navy, cardinal & old gold.
OLD JUDDIAN RFC
Ground Address: & Clubhouse: Tonbridge Sports Ground,
The Slade, Tonbridge, Kent TN9 1HR. Tel: 01732 358548
Club Secretary: Steve Davey, 35 Dowgate Close,
Tonbridge, Kent TN9 2EH. Tel: (H) 01732 357429 Tel:
(W) 01732 866066
Fixtures Secretary: Tony Russell, 28 Whistler Road,
Tonbridge, Kent TN10 4RD. Tel: (H) 01732 355582
Club Colours: Claret & light blue hooped jerseys, navy
blue shorts.
OLD REIGATIAN RFC
Ground Address: Geofrey Knight Field, Park Lane,
Reigate, Surrey RH2 8JX. Tel: 01737 245634
Club Secretary: Mr D Forsyth, Hawthorn House, Pendell
Court, Bletchingley, Surrey RH1 4QJ. Tel: (H) 01833 743

FINAL TABLE						
	P	W	D	L	F	A	Pts
Charlton Park	12	11	1	0	332	125	22
Old Blues	12	9	0	3	229	158	18
Old Wimbledonians	12	7	1	4	271	182	15
Westcombe Park	12	7	1	4	228	177	15
Dorking	12	6	1	5	216	199	13
Thanet Wanderers	12	6	0	6	181	200	12
Gravesend	12	6	0	6	222	267	12
Old Juddians	12	5	0	7	217	189	10
Horsham	12	5	0	7	159	205	10
Old Reigatians	12	4	1	7	119	225	9
Sidcup	12	4	0	8	177	169	8
Old Alleynian	12	4	0	8	167	250	8
Portsmouth	12	2	0	10	165	337	4

654 Tel: (W) 01737 773535
Fixtures Secretary: Keith Ireland, 36 Barrow Green Road,
Oxted, Surrey RH8 0NN. Tel: (H) 01883 712713
Club Colours: Green & blue hoops.
OLD WIMBLEDONIANS RFC
Ground Address: 104 Cottenham Park Road, Raynes
Park, London SW20 0TZ. Tel: 0181 879 0700
Club Secretary: Mrs Margaret Parsons, 'Hawth', Glaziers
Lane, Normandy, Guildford, Surrey GU3 2EA. Tel: (H)
01483 811103 Tel: (W) 0171 257 1827
Fixtures Secretary: Ralph Nolan, 156 Horton Hill, Epsom,
Surrey KT19 8ST. Tel: (H) 01372 727063
Club Colours: Green, maroon & gold hoops.
STREATHAM-CROYDON RUFC
Ground Address: Rosevale, 159 Brigstock Road,
Thornton Heath, Surrey CR7 7JP. Tel: 0181 684 1502
Club Secretary: Ian Stevenson, 18 Crown Woods Way,
Eltham, London SE9 2NN. Tel: (H) 0181 850 9061
Fixtures Secretary: RV Towers, 24 Ernest Grove,
Beckenham, Kent BR3 3JF. Tel: (H) 0181 658 2333 Tel
(W) 0181 698 8911
Club Colours: Maroon shirts, white shorts.
THANET WANDERERS RUFC
Ground Address: St Peters Recreation Ground, Callis
Court Road, Broadstairs, Kent.
Club Secretary: Peter Hawkins, 51 Park Road, Ramsgate,
Kent CT11 9TL. Tel: (H) 01843 593142 Tel: (W) 01843
593142
Fixtures Secretary: Peter Hawkins, 51 Park Road,
Ramsgate, Kent CT11 9TL. Tel: (H) 01843 593142 Tel
(W) 01843 593142
Club Colours: Blue, black & yellow hoops.
WESTCOMBE PARK RFC
Ground Address: Goddington Dene, Goddington Lane,
Orpington, Kent BR6 9SH. Tel: 01689 834902
Club Secretary: Robin Taylor, 24 Pinchbeck Road, Green
Street Green, Orpington, Kent BR6 6DR. Tel: (H) 01689
855052 Tel: (W) 0181 310 9868 Car: 0374 212029
Fixtures Secretary: John Bellinger, The Butry, 32A
Courtyard, Eltham, London SE9 5QE. Tel: (H) 0181 850
7280 Tel (W) 0171 481 5507
Club Colours: Navy with white hoops.
WIMBLEDON RFC
Ground Address: Beverley Meads, Barham Road, Copse
Hill, Wimbledon, London SW20 0ET. Tel: 0181 946 3156
Fax: 0181 543 5377
Club Secretary: David Dixon-Smith, 42 Princes Road,
Wimbledon, London SW19 8RB. Tel: (W) 0181 543 6244
Fax: 0181 543 5377
Fixtures Secretary: Mr Michael Keene, 17 Auriol Park
Road, Worcester Park, Surrey KT4 7DP. Tel: (H) 0181 337
6036 Tel (W) 0171 261 3255
Club Colours: Maroon & Cambridge blue.

LONDON & SOUTH EAST DIVISION

LONDON THREE
SOUTH EAST
1995-96 FIXTURES

November 11 1995 (Week 10)

Brighton	v	Heathfield & Waldron
Uckfield	v	Sidcup
Lewes	v	Beckenham
Park House	v	Sevenoaks
Haywards Heath	v	Canterbury
Worthing	v	Old Beccehamians

September 16 1995 (Week 3)

Brighton	v	Uckfield
Old Beccehamians	v	Sidcup
Canterbury	v	Beckenham
Chichester	v	Sevenoaks
Haywards Heath	v	Park House
Worthing	v	Lewes

January 6 1996 (Week 17)

Beckenham	v	Park House
Sidcup	v	Lewes
Heathfield & Waldron	v	Uckfield
Old Beccehamians	v	Brighton
Canterbury	v	Worthing
Chichester	v	Haywards Heath

September 23 1995 (Week 4)

Lewes	v	Brighton
Park House	v	Worthing
Sevenoaks	v	Haywards Heath
Beckenham	v	Chichester
Sidcup	v	Canterbury
Heathfield & Waldron	v	Old Beccehamians

January 13 1996 (Week 18)

Brighton	v	Canterbury
Uckfield	v	Old Beccehamians
Lewes	v	Heathfield & Waldron
Park House	v	Sidcup
Sevenoaks	v	Beckenham
Worthing	v	Chichester

September 30 1995 (Week X1)

Brighton	v	Park House
Uckfield	v	Lewes
Canterbury	v	Heathfield & Waldron
Chichester	v	Sidcup
Haywards Heath	v	Beckenham
Worthing	v	Sevenoaks

February 10 1996 (Week 22)

Sidcup	v	Sevenoaks
Heathfield & Waldron	v	Park House
Old Beccehamians	v	Lewes
Canterbury	v	Uckfield
Chichester	v	Brighton
Haywards Heath	v	Worthing

October 14 1995 (Week 6)

Park House	v	Uckfield
Sevenoaks	v	Brighton
Beckenham	v	Worthing
Sidcup	v	Haywards Heath
Heathfield & Waldron	v	Chichester
Old Beccehamians	v	Canterbury

February 17 1996 (Week 23)

Brighton	v	Haywards Heath
Uckfield	v	Chichester
Lewes	v	Canterbury
Park House	v	Old Beccehamians
Sevenoaks	v	Heathfield & Waldron
Beckenham	v	Sidcup

October 21 1995 (Week 7)

Brighton	v	Beckenham
Uckfield	v	Sevenoaks
Lewes	v	Park House
Chichester	v	Old Beccehamians
Haywards Heath	v	Heathfield & Waldron
Worthing	v	Sidcup

February 24 1996 (Week 24)

Heathfield & Waldron	v	Beckenham
Old Beccehamians	v	Sevenoaks
Canterbury	v	Park House
Chichester	v	Lewes
Haywards Heath	v	Uckfield
Worthing	v	Brighton

October 28 1995 (Week 8)

Sevenoaks	v	Lewes
Beckenham	v	Uckfield
Sidcup	v	Brighton
Heathfield & Waldron	v	Worthing
Old Beccehamians	v	Haywards Heath
Canterbury	v	Chichester

March 30 1996 (Week X7)

Uckfield	v	Worthing
Lewes	v	Haywards Heath
Park House	v	Chichester
Sevenoaks	v	Canterbury
Beckenham	v	Old Beccehamians
Sidcup	v	Heathfield & Waldron

LONDON THREE SOUTH EAST

BECKENHAM RFC
Ground Address: Balmoral Avenue, Elmers End, Beckenham, Kent BR3 3RD. Tel: 0181 650 7176
Club Secretary: Martin Parker, 34 The Fairway, Bickley, Kent BR1 2JY. Tel: (W) 0181 776 7272
Fixtures Secretary: John Arger, 15 Thatcher Road, Staplehurst, Kent TN12 0ND. Tel: (H) 01580 891550
Club Colours: Royal blue & old gold hoops.
BRIGHTON FC
Ground Address: Waterhall Playing Fields, Waterhall Road, Mill Road, Patchem, Brighton, Sussex, BN1 8YR. Tel: 01273 562729
Club Secretary: Miss Colette Duggan, 42 Woodland Drive, Hove BN3 6DL. Tel: (H) 01273 885407 Tel: (W) 01403 250277
Fixtures Secretary: Ray Greenwood, 11 Lyminster Ave, Brighton, BN1 8JL. Tel: (H) 01273 502898
Club Colours: Royal blue shirts, blue shorts, red socks.
CANTERBURY RFC
Ground Address: The Pavilion, Merton Lane (North), Nackington, Canterbury, Kent. Tel: 01227 768958
Club Secretary: TDO Hall, Whiteacre Farmhouse, Whiteacre Lane, Waltham, Canterbury, Kent CT4 5SR. Tel: (H) 01227 700344 Tel: (W) 01227 768155
Fixtures Secretary: D Creed, 47c The Street, Boughton, Faversham, Kent. Tel: (H) 01227 750747 Tel (W) 01227 766161
Club Colours: Black & amber hoops.
CHICHESTER RFC
Ground Address: Oaklands Park, Wellington Road, Chichester, West Sussex. Tel: 01243 779820
Club Secretary: Simon Hill, St Ronans, 8 Clayton Road, Selsey, West Sussex. Tel: (H) 01243 603598 Tel: (W) 01243 781000
Fixtures Secretary: Mike French, 16 Third Avenue, Denvilles, Hampshire. Tel: (H) 01705 482382
Club Colours: Dark blue & light blue hoops.
HAYWARDS HEATH RFC
Ground Address: The Clubhouse, Whitemans Green, Cuckfield, Haywards Heath, West Sussex. Tel: 01444 413950
Club Secretary: MK Cook, 'Tinkers', Summerhill Lane, Haywards Heath, West Sussex RH16 1RL. Tel: (H) 01444 452327 Tel: (W) 0171 753 1972
Fixtures Secretary: Ian Beckett, 94 Sunnywood Drive, Haywards Heath, West Sussex. Tel: (H) 01444 412576
Club Colours: Red & black quarters.
HEATHFIELD & WALDRON RFC
Ground Address: Hardy Roberts Playing Fields, Cross in Hand, Heathfield, East Sussex. Tel: (H) 01435 868747
Club Secretary: Peter R Mercer, Mapsedge, Cross in Hand, Heathfield, East Sussex TN21 0TA. Tel: (H) 01435 863396 Tel: (H) 01424 775999
Fixtures Secretary: Philip Bell, 3 Highams Cottages, Salehurst, Nr Robertsbridge, East Sussex TN32 5PS. Tel: (H) 01580 880887 Tel (W) 01580 860103
Club Colours: Green & white quarters. **LEWES RFC**
Ground Address: Stanley Turner Sports Ground, Kingston Road, Lewes, East Sussex BN7 3NB. Tel: 01273 473732
Club Secretary: AH Powell, 29 Cradle Hill Road, Seaford, East Sussex BN25 3JA. Tel: (H) 01323 893094
Fixtures Secretary: K Gordon, 'Lynstead', Coopers Green, Buxted, East Sussex TN22 4AT. Tel: (H) 01825 732440
Club Colours: Blue & white hoops.
OLD BECCEHAMIAN RFC
Ground Address: Sparrows Den, Corkscrew Hill, West Wickham, Kent BR4 9BB. Tel: 0181 777 8105
Club Secretary: Alan Pitt, 12 Manor Road, West Wickham, Kent. Tel: 0181 777 6307
Fixtures Secretary: Clive Putner, 12 Manor Road, West

FINAL TABLE

	P	W	D	L	F	A	Pts
Brockleians	12	12	0	0	282	118	24
Beckenham	12	10	0	2	300	100	20
Worthing	12	9	1	2	262	126	19
Canterbury	12	9	0	3	217	126	18
Park House	12	7	0	5	167	146	14
Lewes	12	5	1	6	183	145	11
Old Beccehamian	12	5	0	7	177	140	10
Chichester	12	5	0	7	196	206	10
Haywards Heath	12	5	0	7	183	214	10
Brighton	12	4	0	8	179	197	8
Heathfield-Waldron	12	3	0	9	156	324	4*
East Grinstead	12	1	1	10	151	303	3
Erith	12	1	1	10	86	394	3

Wickham, Kent. Tel: (H) 0181 777 6307
Club Colours: Black, white & maroon hoops.
PARK HOUSE FC
Ground Address: Barnet Wood Road (south side), Hayes, Kent. Tel: 0181 462 7318
Club Secretary: Robert D Elves, 47 Ramillies Road, Sidcup, Kent DA15 9JA. Tel: (H) 0181 304 9170 Tel: (W) 01474 853731
Fixtures Secretary: Alan Appleton, 69 Colyers Lane, Erith, Kent DA8 3NG. Tel: (H) 01322 341538 Tel (W) 0171 353 8836
Club Colours: Black & red shirts, black shorts, red socks.
SEVENOAKS RFC
Ground Address: Knole Paddock, Plymouth Drive, Sevenoaks, Kent TN13 3RP. Tel: 01732 452027
Club Secretary: John Maslin, 198 Chesterfield Drive, Sevenoaks, Kent TN13 2EH. Tel: (H) 01732 460910 Tel: (W) 0171 528 1888
Fixtures Secretary: Howard Pearl, Nearly Corner, Heaverham, Sevenoaks, Kent TN15 6NQ. Tel: (H) 01732 763431 Tel (W) 0171 240 7171
Club Colours: Gold & navy hoops.
SIDCUP RFC
Ground Address: Crescent Farm, Sydney Road, Sidcup, Kent DA14 6RA. Tel: 0181 300 2336
Club Secretary: Allan Jones, 53 Goodwin Drive, Sidcup, Kent DA14 4NX. Tel: (H) 0181 302 2382 Tel: (W) 0181 302 2382
Fixtures Secretary: Malcolm J Leamon, 43 Glenhouse Road, Eltham, London SE9 1JH. Tel: (H) 0181 859 5598 Tel (W) 0171 305 2024
Club Colours: White.
UCKFIELD RFC
Ground Address: Hempstead Playing Fields, Manor Park, Uckfield, Sussex. Tel: 01825 768956
Club Secretary: Jerry Miller, 8 Streele View, Uckfield, Sussex TN22 1UG. Tel: (H) 01825 767861 Tel: (W) 01892 503143
Fixtures Secretary: Mrs Maureen Poole, 'Pentlands', 9 Keld Avenue, Uckfield, Sussex TN22 5BN. Tel: (H) 01825 761151
Club Colours: Amber & purple & white stripes.
WORTHING RFC
Ground Address: The Rugby Park, Roundstone Lane, Angmering, West Sussex. Tel: 01903 784706
Club Secretary: CFH Packwood, 15 Anscombe Close, Worthing, West Sussex BN11 5EW. Tel: (H) 01903 505250 Tel: (W) 01903 238273
Fixtures Secretary: Paul Hughes, 74 Lanfranc Road, Worthing, West Sussex. Tel: (H) 01903 209053 Tel (W) 01732 361500
Club Colours: Blue, gold & chocolate hoops.

LONDON & SOUTH EAST DIVISION

KENT ONE
1995-96
FIXTURES

November 11 1995 (Week 10)

Tunbridge Wells	v	Gillingham Anchorians
Ashford	v	Old Elthamians
Dartfordians	v	Bromley
Dover	v	Sheppey
Medway	v	Erith
Old Shootershillians	v	Met Police Hayes

September 16 1995 (Week 3)

Tunbridge Wells	v	Ashford
Met Police Herts	v	Old Elthamians
Erith	v	Bromley
Old Dunstonians	v	Sheppey
Medway	v	Dover
Old Shootershillians	v	Dartfordians

January 6 1996 (Week 17)

Bromley	v	Dover
Old Elthamians	v	Dartfordians
Gillingham Anchorians	v	Ashford
Met Police Hayes	v	Tunbridge Wells
Erith	v	Old Shootershillians
Old Dunstonians	v	Medway

September 23 1995 (Week 4)

Dartfordians	v	Tunbridge Wells
Dover	v	Old Shootershillians
Sheppey	v	Medway
Bromley	v	Old Dunstonians
Old Elthamians	v	Erith
Gillingham Anchorians	v	Met Police Hayes

January 13 1996 (Week 18)

Tunbridge Wells	v	Erith
Ashford	v	Met Police Hayes
Dartfordians	v	Gillingham Anchorians
Dover	v	Old Elthamians
Sheppey	v	Bromley
Old Shootershillians	v	Old Dunstonians

September 30 1995 (Week X1)

Tunbridge Wells	v	Dover
Ashford	v	Dartfordians
Erith	v	Gillingham Anchorians
Old Dunstonians	v	Old Elthamians
Medway	v	Bromley
Old Shootershillians	v	Sheppey

February 10 1996 (Week 22)

Old Elthamians	v	Sheppey
Gillingham Anchorians	v	Dover
Met Police Hayes	v	Dartfordians
Erith	v	Ashford
Old Dunstonians	v	Tunbridge Wells
Medway	v	Old Shooterhillians

October 14 1995 (Week 6)

Dover	v	Ashford
Sheppey	v	Tunbridge Wells
Bromley	v	Old Shootershillians
Old Elthamians	v	Medway
Gillingham Anchorians	v	Old Dunstonians
Met Police Hayes	v	Erith

February 17 1996 (Week 23)

Tunbridge Wells	v	Medway
Ashford	v	Old Dunstonians
Dartfordians	v	Erith
Dover	v	Met Police Hayes
Sheppey	v	Gillingham Anchorians
Bromley	v	Old Elthamians

October 21 1995 (Week 7)

Tunbridge Wells	v	Bromley
Ashford	v	Sheppey
Dartfordians	v	Dover
Old Dunstonians	v	Met Police Hayes
Medway	v	Gillingham Anchorians
Old Shootershillians	v	Old Elthamians

February 24 1996 (Week 24)

Gillingham Anchorians	v	Bromley
Met Police Hayes	v	Sheepey
Erith	v	Dover
Old Dunstonians	v	Dartfordians
Medway	v	Ashford
Old Shootershillians	v	Tunbridge Wells

October 28 1995 (Week 8)

Sheppey	v	Dartfordians
Bromley	v	Ashford
Old Elthamians	v	Tunbridge Wells
Gillingham Anchorians	v	Old Shootershillians
Met Police Hayes	v	Medway
Erith	v	Old Dunstonians

March 30 1996 (Week X7)

Ashford	v	Old Shootershillians
Dartfordians	v	Medway
Dover	v	Old Dunstonians
Sheppey	v	Erith
Bromley	v	Met Police Hayes
Old Elthamians	v	Gillingham Anchorians

KENT ONE

ASHFORD (KENT) RFC
Ground Address: Kinneys Field, Bybrook Ground,
Canterbury Road, Bybrook, Ashford, Kent. Tel: 01233
640905
Club Secretary: Peter Humphreys, Withershane Green
Farmhouse, Wye, Nr Ashford, Kent TN25 5DL. Tel: (H)
01233 813263 Tel: (W) 0181 700 2201
Fixtures Secretary: Colin Yalden, 23 Weavers Way,
Ashford, Kent TN23 2DY. Tel: (H) 01233 640905
Club Colours: Red, gold & black hoops.
BROMLEY RFC
Ground Address: Barnet Wood Road, Hayes, Kent. Tel:
0181 462 3430
Club Secretary: Alec Lauder, 32 Turnpike Drive, Pratts
Bottom, Orpington, Kent BR6 7SJ. Tel: (H) 01689 855004
Tel: (W) 01322 343239
Fixtures Secretary: Alex Mackintosh, 1 Gundulph Road,
Bromley, Kent. Tel: (H) 0181 460 8049 Tel (W) 0181 460
8049
Club Colours: Black jerseys, amber hoops, black shorts.
DARTFORDIANS RUFC
Ground Address: Bourne Road, Bexley, Kent. Tel: 01322
669817
Club Secretary: Jack Morris, 7 Irving Way, Swanley, Kent
BR8 7EP. Tel: (H) 01322 669817
Fixtures Secretary: D Rapley, 11 Felhampton Road, New
Eltham, London SE9. Tel: (H) 0181 857 6198
Club Colours: Maroon & old gold shirts, navy shorts.
DOVER RFC
Ground Address: Crabble Athletic Ground, Crabble Road,
River, Dover, Kent. Tel: 01304 210296
Club Secretary: JD Thomas, Karma, Minnis Lane, River,
Dover, Kent CT17 0PT. Tel: (H) 01304 822169
Fixtures Secretary: R Dixon, 2 Roman Way, St Margaret's
at Cliffe, Nr Dover, Kent. Tel: (H) 01304 852776
Club Colours: Light & dark blue hoops.
ERITH RFC
Ground Address: Northumberland Heath Playing Fields,
Sussex Road, Northumberland Heath, Erith, Kent. Tel:
01322 432295
Club Secretary: RW Shepherd, 24 Lishley Park, Erith,
Kent DA8 3DN. Tel: (H) 01322 341073 Tel: (W) 0181 785
7082
Fixtures Secretary: Mr S Button, 26 Pilgrims View,
Greenhithe, Kent DA9 9QB. Tel: (H) 01322 387689
Club Colours: Light & dark blue hoops.
GILLINGHAM ANCHORIANS RFC
Ground Address: Watling Street Playing Fields, off
Darland Avenue, Gillingham, Kent. Tel: 01634 851495
Club Secretary: John Jennings, 49 Marshall Road,
Gillingham, Kent ME8 0AW. Tel: (H) 01634 233431
Fixtures Secretary: Neil Cripps, 2 Derwent Way,
Rainham, Gillingham, Kent ME8 0BX. Tel: (H) 01634
378140 Tel (W) 01322 336060
Club Colours: Purple, black & white hoops, black shorts.
MEDWAY RFC
Ground Address: Priestfields Recreation Ground,
Rochester, Kent ME1 3AD. Tel: 01634 847737
Club Secretary: Andy Green, 18a City Way, Rochester,
Kent ME1 2AB. Tel: (H) 01634 818428
Fixtures Secretary: Jim Hillier, 9 Oxford Road,
Gillingham, Kent ME7 4BP. Tel: (H) 01634 572440 Tel
(W) 01322 391747
Club Colours: Scarlet & gold hoops, navy blue shorts.
METROPOLITAN POLICE HAYES RFC
Ground Address: Metropolitan Police, The Warren Sports
Club, Croydon Road, Hayes, Kent BR2 0BN. Tel: 0181
462 1266
Club Secretary: Mr Chris McHale, 18 Elm Road,
Warlingham, Surrey CR6 9NB. Tel: (H) 01883 625058
Fixtures Secretary: Mr George Strachan, 244 Pickhurst

FINAL TABLE

	P	W	D	L	F	A	Pts
Sevenoaks	12	12	0	0	503	116	24
Tunbridge Wells	12	11	0	1	332	106	22
Dartfordians	12	9	0	3	201	183	18
Met Police Hayes	12	7	0	5	192	151	14
Sheppey	12	6	1	5	209	145	13
Bromley	12	5	0	7	251	201	10
Old Dunstonians	12	5	0	7	181	169	10
O Shootershillians	12	5	0	7	195	186	10
Medway	12	5	2	5	194	214	10*
Gillingham Anchor	12	4	2	6	153	212	10
Old Elthamians	12	3	1	8	181	344	7
Betteshanger	12	3	0	9	146	324	6
Thames Polytechnic	12	0	0	12	65	452	0

Lane, West Wickham, Kent BR4 0HN. Tel: (H) 0181 462
7996
Club Colours: Blue & maroon quarters, black shorts, blue
& maroon hooped socks.
OLD DUNSTONIAN RFC
Ground Address: St Dunstan's Lane, Langley Park,
Beckenham, Kent BR3 3SS. Tel: 0181 650 1779
Club Secretary: MA Rogers, Aboyne, Pickhurst Lane,
West Wickham, Kent BR4 0HN. Tel: (H) 0181 462 3064
Tel: (W) 0171 379 7383
Fixtures Secretary: PW France, 5 The Mead, West
Wickham, Kent BR4 0BA. Tel: (H) 0181 776 2335 Tel (W)
0171 396 6002
Club Colours: Navy & white.
OLD ELTHAMIANS RFC
Ground Address: Foxbury Avenue, Perry Street,
Chislehurst, Kent. BR7 6HA. Tel: (H) 0181 467 1296
Club Secretary: Mr Ian McKinnon, 25 The Gardens,
Beckenham, Kent BR3 2PH. Tel: (H) 0181 650 1936
Fixtures Secretary: Mr David Shaw, 22 Abbotts Green,
Addington, Croydon. Tel: (H) 0181 656 8973 Tel (W) 0181
686 5555
Club Colours: Old gold & blue hoops.
OLD SHOOTERSHILLIANS RFC
Ground Address: Entrance between 123 & 125 Mayday
Gardens, Kidbrooke, London SE3 8NP. Tel: 0181 856 1511
Club Secretary: Kevin Bailey, 15 Grace Avenue,
Allington, Nr Maidstone, Kent ME16 0BS. Tel: (H) 01622
675930 Mobile: 0589 216801 Tel: (W) 01206 767763 Fax:
01206 549123
Fixtures Secretary: I Trevett, 28 Reventlow Road, New
Eltham, London SE9 2DJ. Tel: (H) 0181 859 0746 Tel (W)
0171 514 4551
Club Colours: Blue, green, red & yellow.
SHEPPEY FC
Ground Address: Lower Road, Minster, Sheerness, Kent.
Tel: 01795 872082
Club Secretary: Mrs Linda Neal, 16 New Road, Minster,
Sheerness, Kent ME12 3PX. Tel: (H) 01795 873983 Tel:
(W) 01634 830000 x3196/3383
Fixtures Secretary: Mr Gerry Lawson, 435 Minster Road,
Minster, Sheerness, Kent ME12 3NS. Tel: (H) 01795
875120 Tel (W) 01795 660756
Club Colours: White with single red hoop.
TUNBRIDGE WELLS RFC
Ground Address: St Marks, Frant Road, Tunbridge Wells,
Kent. Tel: 01892 522748
Club Secretary: Andy Hill, 18 Lime Hill Road, Tunbridge
Wells, Kent. Tel: (H) 01892 548114
Fixtures Secretary: Sue Kench, 63 Frant Road, Tunbridge
Wells, Kent. Tel: (H) 01892 533397
Club Colours: Royal blue & white hoops, white shorts,
royal blue socks.

LONDON & SOUTH EAST DIVISION

KENT TWO
1995-96
FIXTURES

September 16 1995 (Week 3)
Nat West Bank v Cranbrook
Old Williamsonians v Sittingbourne
Whitstable v Betteshanger
Old Gravesendians v Snowdown CW
Vigo v Greenwich Academicals
Folkestone v Deal Wanderers

September 23 1995 (Week 4)
Deal Wanderers v Nat West Bank
Greenwich Academicals v Folkestone
Snowdown CW v Vigo
Betteshanger v Old Gravesendians
Sittingbourne v Whitstable
Lordswood v Old Williamsonians

September 30 1995 (Week X1)
Nat West Bank v Greenwich Academicals
Cranbrook v Deal Wanderers
Whitstable v Lordswood
Old Gravesendians v Sittingbourne
Vigo v Betteshanger
Folkestone v Snowdown CW

October 14 1995 (Week 6)
Greenwich Academicals v Cranbrook
Snowdown CW v Nat West Bank
Betteshanger v Folkestone
Sittingbourne v Vigo
Lordswood v Old Gravesendians
Old Williamsonians v Whitstable

October 21 1995 (Week 7)
Nat West Bank v Betteshanger
Cranbrook v Snowdown CW
Deal Wanderers v Greenwich Academicals
Old Gravesendians v Old Williamsonians
Vigo v Lordswood
Folkestone v Sittingbourne

October 28 1995 (Week 8)
Snowdown CW v Deal Wanderers
Betteshanger v Cranbrook
Sittingbourne v Nat West Bank
Lordswood v Folkestone
Old Williamsonians v Vigo
Whitstable v Old Gravesendians

November 11 1995 (Week 10)
Nat West Bank v Lordswood
Cranbrook v Sittingbourne
Deal Wanderers v Betteshanger
Greenwich Academicals v Snowdown CW
Vigo v Whitstable
Folkestone v Old Williamsonians

January 6 1996 (Week 17)
Betteshanger v Greenwich Academicals
Sittingbourne v Deal Wanderers
Lordswood v Cranbrook
Old Williamsonians v Nat West Bank
Whitstable v Folkestone
Old Gravesendians v Vigo

January 13 1996 (Week 18)
Nat West Bank v Whitstable
Cranbrook v Old Williamsonians
Deal Wanderers v Lordswood
Greenwich Academicals v Sittingbourne
Snowdown CW v Betteshanger
Folkestone v Old Gravesendians

February 10 1996 (Week 22)
Sittingbourne v Snowdown CW
Lordswood v Greenwich Academicals
Old Williamsonians v Deal Wanderers
Whitstable v Cranbrook
Old Gravesendians v Nat West Bank
Vigo v Folkestone

February 17 1996 (Week 23)
Nat West Bank v Vigo
Cranbrook v Old Gravesendians
Deal Wanderers v Whitstable
Greenwich Academicals v Old Williamsonians
Snowdown CW v Lordswood
Betteshanger v Sittingbourne

February 24 1996 (Week 24)
Lordswood v Betteshanger
Old Williamsonians v Snowdown CW
Whitstable v Greenwich Academicals
Old Gravesendians v Deal Wanderers
Vigo v Cranbrook
Folkestone v Nat West Bank

March 30 1996 (Week X7)
Cranbrook v Folkestone
Deal Wanderers v Vigo
Greenwich Academicals v Old Gravesendians
Snowdown CW v Whitstable
Betteshanger v Old Williamsonians
Sittingbourne v Lordswood

KENT TWO

BETTESHANGER CW RFC
Ground Address: Welfare Ground, Cavell Square, Deal,
Kent. **Clubhouse:** Welfare Club (First floor), Cowdray
Square, Deal, Kent. Tel: 01304 365090
Club Secretary: Simon Rickatson, 40 Mongeham Road,
Great Mongeham, Deal, Kent CT14 9PQ. Tel: (H) 01304
361178 Tel: (W) 01233 616031
Fixtures Secretary: Bob Pinnick, 65 Courtenay Road,
Dunkirk, Faversham, Kent ME13 9LH. Tel: (H) 01227
750530 Tel (W) 01843 822686
Club Colours: Red & white hoops.

CRANBROOK RFC
Ground Address: Tomlin Ground, Angley Road,
Staplehurst, Kent TN17 3LB. Tel: 01580 712777
Club Secretary: David Davies, Beeches, Station Road,
Staplehurst, Kent TN12 0QG. Tel: (H) 01580 891448 Tel:
(W) 01580 891448
Fixtures Secretary: John Hemmings, Wilsley Oast,
Wilsley Green, Angley Road, Cranbrook TN17 2LB. Tel:
(H) 01580 713141 Tel (W) 01732 742042
Club Colours: Magenta & white.

DEAL WANDERERS RFC
Ground Address: Clubhouse, Western Road, Deal, Kent.
Tel: 01304 365892
Fixtures Secretary: Mr R Dorling, 13 Halsatt Road, Deal,
Kent CT14 9ED. Tel: (H) 01304 373112
Club Colours: Blue & amber.

FOLKESTONE RFC
Ground Address: New Burlington Field, Bargrove,
Newington, Folkestone, Kent. Tel: 01303 266887
Club Secretary: BG Keating, Carbery, Church Hill, Hythe,
Kent CT21 5DW. Tel: (H) 01303 264604 Tel (W) 01303 850206
Fixtures Secretary: Mr J Richards, 18 Oast Meadow,
Willesborough, Ashford, Kent TN24 0AS. Tel: (H) 01233
660162 Tel (W) 01233 644095
Club Colours: Emerald green with white hoops.

GREENWICH ACADEMICALS RFC
Ground Address: Sparrows Farm Centre, University of
Greenwich, Sparrows Lane, New Eltham, London SE9
2BU. Tel: 0181 859 2921
Club Secretary: John Baker, 31 Willow Avenue, Swanley,
Kent BR8 8AT. Tel: (H) 01322 614513
Fixtures Secretary: G 'Dusty' Miller, 85 Earlshall Road,
London SE9 1PP. Tel: (H) 0181 850 2794 Tel (W) 0181
850 2794
Club Colours: Green with gold & red bands.

LORDSWOOD RUFC
Ground Address: Lordswood Sports & Social Club, North
Dane Way, Lordswood, Chatham, Kent ME5 8YE. Tel: 01634
669138
Club Secretary: Hugh Thomas, 97 Ballens Road,
Lordswood, Chatham, Kent ME5 8PD. Tel: (H) 01634
867045 Tel: (W) 01634 271511
Fixtures Secretary: Mr Peter O'Neill, 28 Wittersham
Close, Lordswood, Chatham, Kent ME5 7NA. Tel: (H)
01634 201006 Tel (W) 01634 687166 x2048
Club Colours: Amber/black irregular hoops.

NATIONAL WESTMINSTER BANK RFC
Ground Address: Copers Cope Road, Lower Sydenham,
Beckenham, Kent BR3 1NZ. Tel: 0181 650 9217
Club Secretary: CJ Longhurst, 8 Lydia Cottages,
Wrotham Road, Gravesend, Kent DA11 0QE. Tel: (H)
01474 333955 Tel: (W) 0171 491 4500
Fixtures Secretary: GWC Teale, 17 Queensway, Coney
Hall, West Wickham, Kent BR4 9EP. Tel: (H) 0181 462
9288 Tel (W) 0171 398 8540
Club Colours: Dark & light blue hoops.

OLD GRAVESENDIANS RFC
Ground Address: Fleetway Sports Ground, Bronte View,
Parrock Road, Gravesend, Kent DA12 1PX. Tel: 01474
365503

FINAL TABLE

	P	W	D	L	F	A	Pts
Ashford	12	10	0	2	248	75	20
Dover	12	10	0	2	249	130	20
Cranbrook	12	9	1	2	282	97	19
Old Gravesendians	12	7	1	4	267	206	15
Folkestone	12	6	1	5	212	151	13
Snowdown CW	12	6	0	6	149	173	12
Whitstable	12	6	0	6	159	197	12
Vigo	12	5	1	6	151	153	11
Nat West Bank	12	5	0	7	179	168	10
Sittingbourne	12	2	2	8	101	175	6
Deal	12	4	1	7	183	206	5*
New Ash Green	12	2	0	10	128	322	4
Midland Bank	12	2	1	9	119	365	3*

Club Secretary: Kevin Whittington, 86 Cheyne Walk,
Meopham, Kent DA13 0PG. Tel: (H) 01474 812638 Tel:
(W) 0171 214 9123
Fixtures Secretary: Peter Green, 10 Sycamore Close,
Gravesend,Kent DA12 2TJ. Tel: (H) 01474 352090
Club Colours: Light blue & dark blue hoops.

OLD WILLIAMSONIAN RFC
Ground Address: Maidstone Road, Rochester, Kent. Tel:
01634 842883
Club Secretary: Andy I Campbell, Fernside, 85 Seal
Hollow Road, Sevenoaks, Kent TN13 3SA. Tel: (H) 01732
453623 Tel: (W) 0171 283 3434
Fixtures Secretary: Dean Painter, 82A Marshall Road,
Wigmore, Gillingham, Kent. Tel: (H) 01634 269892
Club Colours: Navy blue with single gold hoop.

SITTINGBOURNE RUFC
Ground Address: Gore Court Cricket Club, The Grove,
Key Street, Sittingbourne, Kent ME10 1YT. Tel: 01795
423813
Club Secretary: SD Smith, 34 Crouch Hill Court, Lower
Halstow, Sittingbourne, Kent, ME9 7EJ. Tel: (H) 01795
843356 Tel: (W) 01795 843356
Fixtures Secretary: J Regan, 13 Heather Close,
Sittingbourne, Kent ME10 4TJ. Tel: (H) 01795 434356 Tel
(W) 01795 434356
Club Colours: Gold & blue hoops.

SNOWDOWN COLLIERY WELFARE RFC
Ground Address: Snowdown Colliery Welfare, Aylesham,
Canterbury, Kent. Tel: 01304 840278
Club Secretary: EJ Sullivan, 4 Burgess Road, Aylesham,
Canterbury, Kent CT3 3AU. Tel: (H) 01304 840052
Fixtures Secretary: Alan Booth, 91 Milner Crescent,
Aylesham, Canterbury, Kent. Tel: (H) 01304 840619
Club Colours: Red & blue hoops.

VIGO RFC
Ground Address: Swanswood Field, Harvel Road, Harvel,
Kent. Tel: 01732 823830
Club Secretary: Mr N Simpson, Pitfield House, Meopham
Green, Meopham, Kent DA13 0PZ. Tel: (H) 01474 812407
Tel: (W) 0181 854 1331
Fixtures Secretary: John Taylor, Sandon, Burnt House
Lane, Hawley, Dartford, Kent. Tel: (H) 01322 227363 Tel
(W) 0171 488 0733 x318
Club Colours: Red shirt, black shorts.

WHITSTABLE RFC
Ground Address: Whitstable Waterfront Club, Beach
Walk, Whitstable, Kent. Tel: 01227 265500
Club Secretary: Colin James, 71 Swalecliffe Court Drive,
Whitstable, Kent CT5 2NF. Tel: (H) 01227 793031
Fixtures Secretary: Roger Dengate, 70 Regent Street,
Whitstable, Kent CT5 1JQ. Tel: (H) 01227 264604 Tel (W)
01304 812501
Club Colours: Blue & white hoops.

LONDON & SOUTH EAST DIVISION

KENT THREE
1995-96
FIXTURES

February 10 1996 (Week 22)
Citizens v Midland Bank
Orpington v STC Footscray
Aylesford v Tonbridge
Bexley v Old Olavians
Darenth Valley v New Ash Green

February 17 1996 (Week 23)
Tonbridge v Bexley
STC Footscray v Aylesford
Midland Bank v Orpington
Darenth Valley v Citizens
Old Olavians v New Ash Green

September 23 1995 (Week 4)
Citizens v Orpington
STC Footscray v Old Olavians
Midland Bank v Bexley
Darenth Valley v Aylesford
New Ash Green v Tonbridge

February 24 1996 (Week 24)
Citizens v New Ash Green
Orpington v Darenth Valley
Aylesford v Midland Bank
Bexley v STC Footscray
Old Olavians v Tonbridge

September 30 1995 (Week X1)
Aylesford v Citizens
Tonbridge v STC Footscray
Old Olavians v Midland Bank
Bexley v Darenth Valley
New Ash Green v Orpington

October 14 1995 (Week 6)
Citizens v Bexley
Orpington v Aylesford
STC Footscray v New Ash Green
Darenth Valley v Old Olavians
Midland Bank v Tonbridge

October 21 1995 (Week 7)
Bexley v Orpington
Old Olavians v Citizens
Tonbridge v Darenth Valley
Aylesford v New Ash Green
STC Footscray v Midland Bank

October 28 1995 (Week 8)
Citizens v Tonbridge
Orpington v Old Olavians
Aylesford v Bexley
New Ash Green v Midland Bank
Darenth Valley v STC Footscray

November 11 1995 (Week 10)
Old Olavians v Aylesford
Tonbridge v Orpington
STC Footscray v Citizens
Midland Bank v Darenth Valley
New Ash Green v Bexley

KENT THREE

AYLESFORD RFC
Ground Address: Adj. Ferry Field, Hall Road, Aylesford,
Kent. Tel: Cobdown Sports & Social Club Clubhouse
01622 716824
Club Secretary: Kevin D Burbidge, 77 Holborough Road,
Snodland, Kent ME6 5PA. Tel: (H) 01634 242147 Tel: (W)
01474 337571
Fixtures Secretary: David Enston, 47 Hornbeam Close,
Larkfield, Aylesford, Kent ME20 6LZ. Tel: (H) 01732
842666
Club Colours: Red shirts, black shorts, red socks.

BEXLEY RFC
Ground Address: Hall Place Park, Bourne Road, Bexley,
Kent.
Club Secretary: Peter Butler, 194 Claremont Road,
Hextable, Kent BR8 7QU. Tel: (H) 01322 664389
Fixtures Secretary: James Butler, 39 Baldwyns Road,
Bexley, Kent. Tel: (H) 01322 522693
Club Colours: Royal blue & white hooped shirts, blue
shorts, blue socks with white tops.

CITIZENS RFC
Ground Address: UCL Athletic Ground, Perry Street,
Chislehurst, Kent BR7 6HA. Tel: 0181 467 3859
Club Secretary: CR Southgate, Sunny Bank, Kingsland,
Leominster, Herefordshire HR6 9SE. Tel: (H) 01568
708010 Tel: (W) 01568 708050
Fixtures Secretary: RJ Mannell, 281 Green Lane, London
SE9 3TB. Tel: (H) 0181 857 3057
Club Colours: Black with maroon & white hoops.

DARENTH VALLEY RFC
Ground Address: Leigh City Technical College, Green
Road, Dartford, Kent DA1 1QE. Tel: 01322 290801
Club Secretary: Amanda Robertson, Pilgrims Rest, Priory
Lane, Eynsford, Kent DA4 0AY. Tel: (H) 01322 864215
Tel: (W) 0171 437 0549
Fixtures Secretary: Stuart Sullivan, 34 Egerton Avenue,
Hextable, Kent BR8 7LQ. Tel: (H) 01322 667218
Club Colours: White V on black.

FOOTS CRAY RUFC
Ground Address: 239A Foots Cray Road, New Eltham,
London SE2 2EL.
Club Secretary: Stephen Roberts, 279 Burnt Oak Lane,
Sidcup, Kent DA15 8LR. Tel: 0181 302 7141 Tel: (W)
01753 679253
Fixtures Secretary: Tony Codd, 74 Felthampton Road,
New Eltham, London SE9 3NX. Tel: (H) 0181 857 6040
Club Colours: Blue & gold hoops.

MIDLAND BANK RFC
Ground Address: Lennard Road, Beckenham, Kent. Tel:
0181 778 7784
Club Secretary: C Rouse, 59 Crantock Road, London SE6.
Tel: (H) 0181 698 4327 Tel: (W) 0171 260 4239
Fixtures Secretary: JRD Hayhow, Five Trees, 36
Holbrook Lane, Chislehurst, Kent BR7 6PF. Tel: (H) 0181
467 3314 Tel (W) 0171 623 9333
Club Colours: Green shirts, blue shorts.

NEW ASH GREEN RFC
Ground Address: Punch Croft, New Ash Green, Kent.
Tel: 01474 874660
Club Secretary: Keith Milner, 32 Lambardes, New Ash
Green, Kent, DA3 9HX. Tel: (H) 01474 874531 Tel: (W)
0171 202 3566 Mobile: 0585 661245
Fixtures Secretary: Paul Martin, 11 Chapel Wood, New
Ash Green, Kent DA3 8RA. Tel: (H) 01474 874513
Club Colours: Dark green & black quarters, black shorts.

FINAL TABLE

	P	W	D	L	F	A	Pts
Lordswood	9	8	0	1	249	174	16
Old Williamsonians	9	7	1	1	133	75	15
Tonbridge	9	6	2	1	285	51	14
Bexley	9	6	0	3	189	93	12
Darenth Valley	9	4	0	5	186	114	8
Old Olavians	9	4	0	5	129	137	8
Linton (Aylesford)	9	3	2	4	79	105	8
Citizens	9	3	0	6	97	178	6
Greenwich	9	1	1	7	55	264	3
Lloyds Bank	9	0	0	9	19	330	0

OLD OLAVIANS RUFC
Ground Address: (Rear of) St Olave's School,
Goddington Lane, Orpington, Kent. Tel: 01689 830744
Club Secretary: GJ Cox, 69 Glendower Crescent,
Orpington, Kent BR6 OUP. Tel: (H) 01689 821939 Tel:
(W) 0181 508 5555
Fixtures Secretary: A MacNamara, 10 Franks Wood
Avenue, Petts Wood, Kent. Tel: (H) 01689 822522 Tel (W)
0171 377 1444
Club Colours: Purple/black/white hoops.

ORPINGTON RFC
Ground Address: Hoblingwell Wood, Leesons Way, St
Pauls Cray, Orpington, Kent BR5 2QB. Tel: 01689 823913
Club Secretary: Ken Hall, The Lodge, ORFC, Leesons
Way, St Pauls Cray, Orpington, Kent BR5 2QB. Tel: (H)
01689 896262 Tel: (W) 01689 823913
Fixtures Secretary: Les Whittingham, 246 Bexley Road,
Eltham, London SE9 2PJ. Tel: (H) 0181 850 8004 (after
2pm)
Club Colours: Black & amber hoops.

TONBRIDGE RFC
Ground Address: The Clubhouse, Avebury Avenue,
Tonbridge, Kent.
Club Secretary: David Metcalf, Greenacre, 51 East Street,
Tonbridge, Kent. Tel: (H) 01732 357558
Fixtures Secretary: David Carver, 50 Pennington Place,
Southborough, Tunbridge Wells, Kent. Tel: (H) 01892
543736
Club Colours: Chocolate & old gold hoops.

LONDON & SOUTH EAST DIVISION

KENT FOUR
1995-96
FIXTURES

February 24 1996 (Week 24)
Edenbridge v Lloyds Bank
Faversham v Greenwich
Canterbury Exiles v Westerham

September 23 1995 (Week 4)
Faversham v Edenbridge
Canterbury Exiles v Greenwich
Lloyds Bank v Westerham

September 30 1995 (Week X1)
Edenbridge v Canterbury Exiles
Faversham v Lloyds Bank
Greenwich v Westerham

October 14 1995 (Week 6)
Canterbury Exiles v Faversham
Westerham v Edenbridge
Lloyds Bank v Greenwich

October 21 1995 (Week 7)
Edenbridge v Greenwich
Faversham v Westerham
Canterbury Exiles v Lloyds Bank

October 28 1995 (Week 8)
Westerham v Canterbury Exiles
Greenwich v Faversham
Lloyds Bank v Edenbridge

November 11 1995 (Week 10)
Edenbridge v Faversham
Greenwich v Canterbury Exiles
Westerham v Lloyds Bank

January 13 1996 (Week 18)
Westerham v Greenwich
Canterbury Exiles v Edenbridge
Lloyds Bank v Faversham

February 10 1996 (Week 22)
Greenwich v Lloyds Bank
Faversham v Canterbury Exiles
Edenbridge v Westerham

February 17 1996 (Week 23)
Westerham v Faversham
Lloyds Bank v Canterbury Exiles
Greenwich v Edenbridge

KENT FOUR

CANTERBURY EXILES RFC
Ground Address: 'The Pound', Stodmarsh Road, Stodmarsh, Nr Canterbury, Kent.
Club Secretary: Stephen Giles, Red Tiles, Beauchamps Lane, Nonington, Dover, Kent CT15 4EZ. Tel: (H) 01304 840622 Tel: (W) 01304 616191
Fixtures Secretary: Mr T Allan, The Two Sawyers, 58 Ivy Lane, Canterbury, Kent. Tel: (H) 01227 765419 Tel (W) 01622 750131
Club Colours: Red & yellow hoops.

EDENBRIDGE RFC
Ground Address: The Recreation Ground, Lingfield Road, Edenbridge, Kent. Tel: 01732 862435
Club Secretary: Stan Peacock, 15 Hitchen Hatch Lane, Sevenoaks, Kent TN13 3AU. Tel: (H) 01732 456957 Tel: (W) 0171 204 6165
Fixtures Secretary: Hugh Field, 5 Orchard Close, Edenbridge, Kent TN8 5EU. Tel: (H) 01732 865973 Tel (W) 0181 663 6565
Club Colours: Black & amber hoops.

FAVERSHAM RUFC
Ground Address: Faversham Recreation Ground Lodge, Faversham, Kent ME13 8HA. Tel: 01795 530651
Club Secretary: Pat Rowan, 14 Abbey Street, Faversham, Kent ME13 7BE. Tel: (H) 01795 530651
Fixtures Secretary: Pat Rowan, 14 Abbey Street, Faversham, Kent ME13 7BE. Tel: (H) 01795 530651
Club Colours: Sky blue & white squares.

GREENWICH RFC
Ground Address: The Pavilion, Old Mill Road, Plumstead, London, SE18. Tel: 0181 854 8637
Club Secretary: Tony Smith, 41 Ashden Drive, Dartford, Kent, DA1 3L2. Tel: (H) 01322 222832
Fixtures Secretary: S Oelman, 26 Isla Road, Plumstead, London SE18 3AA. Tel: (H) 0181 854 7780
Club Colours: Red & black quarters, black shorts.

LLOYDS BANK RFC
Ground Address: Lloyds Bank Sports Club, Copers Cope Road, Beckenham, Kent. Tel: 0181 658 3818
Club Secretary: Bob Brazier, 2 Crushes Close, Hutton, Brentwood, Essex CM13 1PB. Tel: (H) 01277 213626 Tel: (W) 01277 227272
Fixtures Secretary: Alan Stow, 4 Silkham Road, Oxted, Surrey RH8 0NP. Tel: (H) 01883 717565
Club Colours: White shirts with 2 narrow black hoops & 1 broad magenta hoop.

WESTERHAM RFC
Ground Address: Costells Meadow, Westerham, Kent. Tel: 01959 561106
Club Secretary: Andy Richman, 290 The Grove, Biggin Hill, Kent TN16 3TA. Tel: (H) 01959 575597
Fixtures Secretary: Jeremy Bailiss, 10 Havelock Hall, 70A Havelock Road, Croydon CR0 6QP. Tel: (H) 0181 662 0622
Club Colours: Black & white quarters.

FINAL TABLE

	P	W	D	L	F	A	Pts
Orpington	8	6	0	2	158	68	12
STC Footscray	8	5	1	2	76	50	11
Faversham	8	3	1	4	71	78	7
Edenbridge	7	2	2	3	49	96	6
Westerham	7	1	0	6	39	101	2

LONDON & SOUTH EAST DIVISION

SUSSEX ONE
1995-96
FIXTURES

November 11 1995 (Week 10)
Seaford	v	Eastbourne
Pulborough	v	Old Brightonians
East Grinstead	v	Bognor
Hastings & Bexhill	v	Burgess Hill
Hove	v	Hellingly
Sun Alliance Horsham	v	Crawley

September 16 1995 (Week 3)
Seaford	v	Pulborough
Crawley	v	Old Brightonians
Hellingly	v	Bognor
BA Wingspan	v	Burgess Hill
Hove	v	Hastings & Bexhill
Sun Alliance Horsham	v	East Grinstead

January 6 1996 (Week 17)
Bognor	v	Hastings & Bexhill
Old Brightonians	v	East Grinstead
Eastbourne	v	Pulborough
Crawley	v	Seaford
Hellingly	v	Sun Alliance Horsham
BA Wingspan	v	Hove

September 23 1995 (Week 4)
East Grinstead	v	Seaford
Hastings & Bexhill	v	Sun Alliance Horsham
Burgess Hill	v	Hove
Bognor	v	BA Wingspan
Old Brightonians	v	Hellingly
Eastbourne	v	Crawley

January 13 1996 (Week 18)
Seaford	v	Hellingly
Pulborough	v	Crawley
East Grinstead	v	Eastbourne
Hastings & Bexhill	v	Old Brightonians
Burgess Hill	v	Bognor
Sun Alliance Horsham	v	BA Wingspan

September 30 1995 (Week X1)
Seaford	v	Hastings & Bexhill
Pulborough	v	East Grinstead
Hellingly	v	Eastbourne
BA Wingspan	v	Old Brightonians
Hove	v	Bognor
Sun Alliance Horsham	v	Burgess Hill

February 10 1996 (Week 22)
Old Brightonians	v	Burgess Hill
Eastbourne	v	Hastings & Bexhill
Crawley	v	East Grinstead
Hellingly	v	Pulborough
BA Wingspan	v	Seaford
Hove	v	Sun Alliance Horsham

October 14 1995 (Week 6)
Hastings & Bexhill	v	Pulborough
Burgess Hill	v	Seaford
Bognor	v	Sun Alliance Horsham
Old Brightonians	v	Hove
Eastbourne	v	BA Wingspan
Crawley	v	Hellingly

February 17 1996 (Week 23)
Seaford	v	Hove
Pulborough	v	BA Wingspan
East Grinstead	v	Hellingly
Hastings & Bexhill	v	Crawley
Burgess Hill	v	Eastbourne
Bognor	v	Old Brightonians

October 21 1995 (Week 7)
Seaford	v	Bognor
Pulborough	v	Burgess Hill
East Grinstead	v	Hastings & Bexhill
BA Wingspan	v	Crawley
Hove	v	Eastbourne
Sun Alliance Horsham	v	Old Brightonians

February 24 1996 (Week 24)
Eastbourne	v	Bognor
Crawley	v	Burgess Hill
Hellingly	v	Hastings & Bexhill
BA Wingspan	v	East Grinstead
Hove	v	Pulborough
Sun Alliance Horsham	v	Seaford

October 28 1995 (Week 8)
Burgess Hill	v	East Grinstead
Bognor	v	Pulborough
Old Brightonians	v	Seaford
Eastbourne	v	Sun Alliance Horsham
Crawley	v	Hove
Hellingly	v	BA Wingspan

March 30 1996 (Week X7)
Pulborough	v	Sun Alliance Horsham
East Grinstead	v	Hove
Hastings & Bexhill	v	BA Wingspan
Burgess Hill	v	Hellingly
Bognor	v	Crawley
Old Brightonians	v	Eastbourne

SUSSEX ONE

BOGNOR RFC
Ground Address: The Clubhouse, Hampshire Avenue, Bognor Regis, West Sussex PO21 5JY. Tel: 01243 824000
Club Secretary: Steve Emmett, 'Chimneys', Bilsham Road, Yapton, Nr Bognor Regis, West Sussex BN18 0JU. Tel: (H) 01243 554022 Tel: (W) 01903 884663 Fax: 01903 883693
Fixtures Secretary: Dean Dewey, 39 Carlton Avenue, Rose Green, Bognor Regis, West Sussex. Tel: (H) 01243 266185
Club Colours: Purple/green/white hoops, black shorts, green socks.

BRITISH AIRWAYS (WINGSPAN) RUFC
Ground Address: Bewbush Leisure Centre, Breezehurst Drive, Bewbush, Crawley, Sussex. Tel: 01293 546477
Club Secretary: Harry Townsend, 6 Manor Road, East Grinstead, Sussex RH19 1LR. Tel: (H) 01342 322508 Tel: (W) 01342 322508
Fixtures Secretary: Harry Townsend, 6 Manor Road, East Grinstead, Sussex RH19 1LR. Tel: (H) 01342 322508 Tel (W) 01342 322508
Club Colours: Red, white & blue.

BURGESS HILL RFC
Ground Address: Poveys Close, Burgess Hill, West Sussex RH15 9TA. Tel: 01444 232221
Club Secretary: MJ Bushell, 4 Kirdford Close, Burgess Hill, West Sussex RH15 0BN. Tel: (H) 01444 246795
Fixtures Secretary: KJ Hollingdale, 10 Park Road, Burgess Hill, West Sussex RH15 8ET. Tel: (H) 01444 241078 Tel (W) 01444 247494
Club Colours: Black.

CRAWLEY RFC
Ground Address: Willoughby Field, 1 Field Avenue, Crawley, Sussex. Tel: 01293 533995
Club Secretary: Ray Lloyd, 105 Gales Drive, Three Bridges, Crawley, Sussex, RH10 1QD. Tel: (H) 01293 536664 Tel: (W) 0171 865 5723
Fixtures Secretary: Tony Smith, 57 Spring Plat, Pound Hill, Crawlwy, Sussex. Tel: (H) 01293 546751 Tel (W) 01293 523515
Club Colours: Maroon & blue.

EAST GRINSTEAD RFC
Ground Address: Saint Hill Ground, Saint Hill Road, Saint Hill, East Grinstead, West Sussex. Tel: 01342 322338
Club Secretary: AM Kirk, 50 Shelley Road, East Grinstead, West Sussex RH19 1SY. Tel: (H) 01342 328975 Tel: (W) 01342 328975
Fixtures Secretary: RP Russell, 1 Rose Cottages, Plaistow Street, Lingfield, Surrey RH7 6AU. Tel: (H) 01342 834648 Tel (W) 0181 668 8859
Club Colours: Blue shirts with a broad white hoop.

EASTBOURNE RFC
Ground Address: Park Avenue, Hampden Park, Eastbourne, East Sussex BN22 9QN. Tel: 01323 503076
Club Secretary: Hugh T Graham, 17A Pashley Road, Eastbourne, East Sussex BN20 8DU. Tel: (H) 01323 646600 Tel: (W) 01323 430003
Fixtures Secretary: Mark Westlake, 3 The Gate Lodge, Letheren Place, Eastbourne, East Sussex BN21 1HL. Tel: (H) 01323 410786 Tel (W) 01273 606766 x33852
Club Colours: Navy blue & gold quarters.

HASTINGS & BEXHILL RFC
Ground Address: William Parker School Site, Park Avenue, Hastings, East Sussex. Tel: 01424 444255
Club Secretary: L Morgan, 10 Delaware Road, St Leonards-on-Sea, East Sussex. Tel: (H) 01424 855040
Fixtures Secretary: P Knight, 15 Salisbury Road, Bexhill-on-Sea, East Sussex. Tel: (H) 01424 731379
Club Colours: Blue & white hoops.

HELLINGLY RFC
Ground Address: Hellingly Sports Club, Horsebridge, Nr

FINAL TABLE

	P	W	D	L	F	A	Pts
Uckfield	12	11	0	1	309	87	22
Seaford	12	10	0	2	218	144	20
Hastings & Bexhill	12	9	0	3	331	92	18
Crawley	12	8	0	4	270	109	16
Burgess Hill	12	6	1	5	166	202	13
Bognor	11	6	0	5	193	125	11
Hove	11	6	0	5	222	172	12
Old Brightonians	12	5	0	7	167	268	10
Sun Alliance H'sham	12	4	0	8	130	202	8
Pulborough	12	4	0	8	135	262	8
Eastbourne	12	3	2	7	164	342	8
Crowborough	12	3	1	8	151	184	7
Ditchling	12	0	0	5	64	331	0

Hailsham, East Sussex.
Club Secretary: Ross Hollister, 17 Sycamore Drive, Hailsham, East Sussex BN27 3TT. Tel: (H) 01323 840756
Fixtures Secretary: Phil Townshend, 34 Oaktree Way, Hailsham, East Sussex BN27 1JJ. Tel: (H) 01323 844923
Club Colours: Amber & black.

HOVE RFC
Ground Address: Hove Park, Goldstone Crescent, Hove, East Sussex. Tel: 01273 505103
Club Secretary: G & L Gordon, 9 Albany Towers, 6 St Catherine's Terrace, Hove, East Sussex BN3 2RQ. Tel: (H) 01273 726081 Tel: (W) 0171 412 4377
Fixtures Secretary: Mike Richardson, 6 Wayside, Westdene, Brighton, East Sussex BN1 5HL. Tel: (H) 01273 500512 Tel (W) 0181 644 4388
Club Colours: Maroon & sky blue hoops.

OLD BRIGHTONIAN RFC
Ground Address: c/o Brighton Rugby Football Club, The Club House, Waterhall, Mill Road, Patcham, Brighton, Sussex BN1 8ZD. Tel: 01273 562729
Club Secretary: CD Loadsman, 20 Meadow Close, Hove, East Sussex BN3 2QQ. Tel: (H) 01273 552988 Tel: (W) 01273 735207
Fixtures Secretary: FPR Rumney, 17 Benett Drive, Hove, East Sussex BN3 6PL. Tel: (H) 01273 504981
Club Colours: Light blue, magenta & navy hoops.

PULBOROUGH RFC
Ground Address: Sports & Social Club, Rectory Lane, Pulborough, West Sussex. Tel: 01798 873020
Club Secretary: C Brazier, 20 St Nicholas Place, Emerald Quay, Harbour Way, Shoreham, West Sussex. Tel: (W) 01798 812345 Fax: 01798 812306
Fixtures Secretary: Michael Ford, 14 Ravenscroft, Storrington, West Sussex RH20 1EH. Tel: (H) 01903 745697
Club Colours: Black & white hoops.

SEAFORD RFC
Ground Address: Salts Recreation Ground, The Esplanade, Seaford, Sussex. Tel: 01323 892355
Club Secretary: EA Pugh, Shottery, 19 Chyngton Road, Seaford, Sussex BN25 4HL. Tel: (H) 0q323 892020
Fixtures Secretary: R Ungoed, 5 The Ridgeway, Seaford, Sussex. Tel: (H) 0q323 893688
Club Colours: Scarlet shirts, navy shorts.

SUN ALLIANCE HORSHAM RFC
Ground Address: North Heath Lane, Horsham, West Sussex RH12 4PJ. Tel: 01403 253814
Club Secretary: BR Lewis Esq, 2 Wain End, Horsham, West Sussex RH12 5TQ. Tel: (H) 01403 266267
Fixtures Secretary: S West Esq, 31 Redford Avenue, Horsham, West Sussex RH12 2HW. Tel: (H) 01403 269838 Tel (W) 01403 232323 x4285
Club Colours: Yellow & blue.

505

LONDON & SOUTH EAST DIVISION

SUSSEX TWO
1995-96
FIXTURES

February 24 1996 (Week 24)
Ditchling   v   Crowborough
Rye   v   St Francis
Shoreham   v   Newick

September 23 1995 (Week 4)
Rye   v   Ditchling
Shoreham   v   St Francis
Crowborough   v   Newick

September 30 1995 (Week X1)
Ditchling   v   Shoreham
Rye   v   Crowborough
St Francis   v   Newick

October 14 1995 (Week 6)
Shoreham   v   Rye
Newick   v   Ditchling
Crowborough   v   St Francis

October 21 1995 (Week 7)
Ditchling   v   St Francis
Rye   v   Newick
Shoreham   v   Crowborough

October 28 1995 (Week 8)
Newick   v   Shoreham
St Francis   v   Rye
Crowborough   v   Ditchling

November 11 1995 (Week 10)
Ditchling   v   Rye
St Francis   v   Shoreham
Newick   v   Crowborough

January 13 1996 (Week 18)
Newick   v   St Francis
Shoreham   v   Ditchling
Crowborough   v   Rye

February 10 1996 (Week 22)
St Francis   v   Crowborough
Rye   v   Shoreham
Ditchling   v   Newick

February 17 1996 (Week 23)
Newick   v   Rye
Crowborough   v   Shoreham
St Francis   v   Ditchling

SUSSEX TWO

CROWBOROUGH RFC
Ground Address: Steel Cross, Crowborough, East Sussex.
Tel: 01892 654832
Club Secretary: Gavin Tyler, 109 Fermor Way,
Crowborough, East Sussex TN6 3BH. Tel: (H) 01892
665153 Tel: (W) 01892 515121
Fixtures Secretary: John Gibb, 42 Belvedere Gardens,
Crowborough, East Sussex TN6 2LS. Tel: (H) 01892
667984
Club Colours: Cherry with white stripes.

DITCHLING
Ground Address: The Playing Fields, Lewes Road,
Ditchling, East Sussex. Tel: 01273 843423
Club Secretary: Justin Wallden, 10 Station Road, Burgess
Hill, West Sussex RH15 9DQ. Tel: (H) 01444 239347 Tel:
(W) 01444 235664
Fixtures Secretary: Vernon Atkinson, 19 Wolstonbury
Court, Burgess Hill, West Sussex RH15 9DP. Tel: (H)
01444 233249 Tel (W) 0181 681 5500
Club Colours: Bottle green shirts, white shorts, green
socks.

NEWICK RFC
Ground Address: The Crown Inn, Church Road, Newick,
East Sussex. Tel: 01825 723293
Club Secretary: Jane Alexander, 18 Allington Road,
Newick, East Sussex, BN8 4NA. Tel: (H) 01825 722383
Tel: (W) 01825 722383
Fixtures Secretary: Martin Barling, Cairn Cottage, 41
Western Road, Newick, Sussex 8NB 4NX. Tel: (H) 01825
724054 Tel (W) 0181 686 9717
Club Colours: Dark blue & maroon hoops.

RYE RFC
Ground Address: New Road, Rye, East Sussex. Tel:
01797 224867
Club Secretary: J Bowen, 15 Southundercliff, Rye, East
Sussex TN31 7HN. Tel: (H) 01797 226597 Tel: (W) 01850
598358
Fixtures Secretary: W Sherwood, 5 Pottingfield Road,
Rye, East Sussex. Tel: (H) 01797 226714
Club Colours: Red & white quarters, black shorts.

SHOREHAM RFC
Ground Address: Kings Manor School, Kingston Lane,
Southwick, Sussex.
Club Secretary: Mr RF Beal, 20 St Giles Close,
Shoreham-by-Sea, Sussex BN43 6GR. Tel: (H) 01273
884827 Tel: (W) 01273 624242
Fixtures Secretary: Mrs SM Beal, 20 St Giles Close,
Shoreham-by-Sea, Sussex BN43 6GR. Tel: (H) 01273
884827
Club Colours: Bottle green & amber quarters.

ST FRANCIS RFC
Ground Address: Broadfield Playing Fields, Broadfield,
Crawley, Sussex. Tel: Club House, Goffs Park, Crawley
01253 533071
Club Secretary: I Mitchell, 9 Tangmer Road, Ifield,
Crawley, West Sussex. Tel: (H) 01293 516108 Tel: (W)
0171 240 7222
Fixtures Secretary: Vince McGahan, 24 Cobbles
Crescent, Northgate, Crawley, West Sussex. Tel: (H) 01293
547194 Tel (W) 01293 503278
Club Colours: Black with blue & white hoops.

FINAL TABLE

	P	W	D	L	F	A	Pts
BA Wingspan	10	10	0	0	387	63	20
Hellingly	10	7	0	3	223	103	14
St Francis	10	5	1	4	230	192	11
Newick	10	2	1	7	58	152	8
Sussex Police	10	2	1	7	64	243	5
Plumpton	10	1	0	9	53	262	2

LONDON & SOUTH EAST DIVISION

SUSSEX THREE
1995-96
FIXTURES

February 24 1996 (Week 24)
Plumpton   v   Robertsbridge
Sussex Police   v   Midhurst
Arun   v   Barns Green

September 23 1995 (Week 4)
Sussex Police   v   Plumpton
Arun   v   Midhurst
Robertsbridge   v   Barns Green

September 30 1995 (Week X1)
Plumpton   v   Arun
Sussex Police   v   Robertsbridge
Midhurst   v   Barns Green

October 14 1995 (Week 6)
Arun   v   Sussex Police
Barns Green   v   Plumpton
Robertsbridge   v   Midhurst

October 21 1995 (Week 7)
Plumpton   v   Midhurst
Sussex Police   v   Barns Green
Arun   v   Robertsbridge

October 28 1995 (Week 8)
Barns Green   v   Arun
Midhurst   v   Sussex Police
Robertsbridge   v   Plumpton

November 11 1995 (Week 10)
Plumpton   v   Sussex Police
Midhurst   v   Arun
Barns Green   v   Robertsbridge

January 13 1996 (Week 18)
Barns Green   v   Midhurst
Arun   v   Plumpton
Robertsbridge   v   Sussex Police

February 10 1996 (Week 22)
Midhurst   v   Robertsbridge
Sussex Police   v   Arun
Plumpton   v   Barns Green

February 17 1996 (Week 23)
Barns Green   v   Sussex Police
Robertsbridge   v   Arun
Midhurst   v   Plumpton

SUSSEX THREE

ARUN RUFC
Ground Address: The Littlehampton School, Hill Road, Littlehampton, West Sus sex. Tel: 01903 713217
Club Secretary: NA Cousins, 16 Trinity Way, Littlehampton, West sussex BN17 5SS. Tel: (H) 01903 713756 Tel: (W) 01403 792853 Mobile: 0836 372312
Fixtures Secretary: P Best, 9 St Mary's Close, Littlehampton, West Sussex. Tel: (H) 01903 723969 Tel (W) 01903 723969
Club Colours: Red, navy & white quarters.

BARNS GREEN RFC
Ground Address: Christ's Hospital School, Horsham, West Sussex.
Club Secretary: Miss Sue Blanchard, 42 Finians Field, Barns Green, West sussex RH13 7PW. Tel: (H) 01403 731652
Fixtures Secretary: Mr PA Bailey, 5 Trout Lane, Barns Green, West Sussex RH13 7QD. Tel: (H) 01403 730068 Tel (W) 0181 667 5504
Club Colours: Gold & green quarters.

MIDHURST RFC
Ground Address: The Ruins, Cowdray Park, Midhurst, West Sussex. Tel: 01730 816658
Club Secretary: Simon Flint, Broadoak, Chichester Road, Midhurst, West Sussex GU29 9PF. Tel: (H) 01730 816465 Tel: (W) 0181 390 1144
Fixtures Secretary: Simon Fay, 5 Bennett Terrace, Bepton Road, Midhurst, West Sussex. Tel: (H) 01730 813357
Club Colours: Amber with a blue hoop.

PLUMPTON RFC
Ground Address: The Racecourse, Plumpton, East Sussex.
Club Secretary: Mr C Woodward, 2 Monks Way, Lewes, East Sussex BN7 2EX. Tel: (H) 01273 476219 Tel: (W) 01273 526110
Fixtures Secretary: Mr Graham Glendenning, 57 Carlyle Avenue, Brighton BN2 4DR. Tel: (H) 01273 620585
Club Colours: Maroon & gold.

ROBERTSBRIDGE RUFC
Ground Address: Robertsbridge Community College, Knelle Rd, Robertsbridge, East Sussex TN32 5EA. Tel: 01580 880360 (school hours only). Fax/Ans: 01580 882120
Club Secretary: Grant Vincent, Upper Maisonette, 120 Braybrooke Road, Hastings, East Sussex TN34 1TG. Tel: (H) 01424 438984 Tel: (W) 01424 853481 x23
Fixtures Secretary: Gareth Stoten, Snepes, Northbridge Street, Robertsbridge, East Sussex TN32 5NY. Tel: (H) 01580 880174 Tel (W) 0181 905 1661 x6020 Mob:0374 431988
Club Colours: Purple with single white hoop.

SUSSEX POLICE RFC
Ground Address: Brighton Rugby Football Club, Waterhall Ground, Brighton, Sussex BN1 8YR. Tel: 01273 562729
Club Secretary: P Johnson, Police Station, Kingsham Road, Chichester, Sussex PO19 2AD. Tel: (H) 01243 825408 Tel: (W) 01243 536733 x20252
Fixtures Secretary: C Gale, Police Station, Brighton, Sussex. Tel: (H) 01444 458482 Tel (W) 01273 206340
Club Colours: Blue & gold quarters.

FINAL TABLE

	P	W	D	L	F	A	Pts
Rye	8	6	2	0	125	82	14
Shoreham	8	4	0	4	110	78	8
Arun	8	4	0	4	79	91	8
Midhurst	8	2	2	4	92	98	6
Robertsbridge	8	2	0	6	68	125	4

LONDON & SOUTH EAST DIVISION

LONDON THREE
SOUTH WEST
1995-96 FIXTURES

November 11 1995 (Week 10)
Gosport	v	Alton
Warlingham	v	Old Walcountians
Guy's Hospital	v	Portsmouth
Old Emanuel	v	Cranleigh
Purley	v	Jersey
Old Guildfordians	v	Old Alleynian

September 16 1995 (Week 3)
Gosport	v	Warlingham
Old Alleynian	v	Old Walcountians
Jersey	v	Portsmouth
Old Whitgiftians	v	Cranleigh
Purley	v	Old Emanuel
Old Guildfordians	v	Guy's Hospital

January 6 1996 (Week 17)
Portsmouth	v	Old Emanuel
Old Walcountians	v	Guy's Hospital
Alton	v	Warlingham
Old Alleynian	v	Gosport
Jersey	v	Old Guildfordians
Old Whitgiftians	v	Purley

September 23 1995 (Week 4)
Guy's Hospital	v	Gosport
Old Emanuel	v	Old Guildfordians
Cranleigh	v	Purley
Portsmouth	v	Old Whitgiftians
Old Walcountians	v	Jersey
Alton	v	Old Alleynian

January 13 1996 (Week 18)
Gosport	v	Jersey
Warlingham	v	Old Alleynian
Guy's Hospital	v	Alton
Old Emanuel	v	Old Walcountians
Cranleigh	v	Portsmouth
Old Guildfordians	v	Old Whitgiftians

September 30 1995 (Week X1)
Gosport	v	Old Emanuel
Warlingham	v	Guy's Hospital
Jersey	v	Alton
Old Whitgiftians	v	Old Walcountians
Purley	v	Portsmouth
Old Guildfordians	v	Cranleigh

February 10 1996 (Week 22)
Old Walcountians	v	Cranleigh
Alton	v	Old Emanuel
Old Alleynian	v	Guy's Hospital
Jersey	v	Warlingham
Old Whitgiftians	v	Gosport
Purley	v	Old Guildfordians

October 14 1995 (Week 6)
Old Emanuel	v	Warlingham
Cranleigh	v	Gosport
Portsmouth	v	Old Guildfordians
Old Walcountians	v	Purley
Alton	v	Old Whitgiftians
Old Alleynian	v	Jersey

February 17 1996 (Week 23)
Gosport	v	Purley
Warlingham	v	Old Whitgiftians
Guy's Hospital	v	Jersey
Old Emanuel	v	Old Alleynian
Cranleigh	v	Alton
Portsmouth	v	Old Walcountians

October 21 1995 (Week 7)
Gosport	v	Portsmouth
Warlingham	v	Cranleigh
Guy's Hospital	v	Old Emanuel
Old Whitgiftians	v	Old Alleynian
Purley	v	Alton
Old Guildfordians	v	Old Walcountians

February 24 1996 (Week 24)
Alton	v	Portsmouth
Old Alleynian	v	Cranleigh
Jersey	v	Old Emanuel
Old Whitgiftians	v	Guy's Hospital
Purley	v	Warlingham
Old Guildfordians	v	Gosport

October 28 1995 (Week 8)
Cranleigh	v	Guy's Hospital
Portsmouth	v	Warlingham
Old Walcountians	v	Gosport
Alton	v	Old Guildfordians
Old Alleynian	v	Purley
Jersey	v	Old Whitgiftians

March 30 1996 (Week X7)
Warlingham	v	Old Guildfordians
Guy's Hospital	v	Purley
Old Emanuel	v	Old Whitgiftians
Cranleigh	v	Jersey
Portsmouth	v	Old Alleynian
Old Walcountians	v	Alton

LONDON THREE SOUTH WEST

ALTON RFC
Ground Address: Anstey Park, Anstey Lane, Alton, Hampshire GU34 2RL. Tel: 01420 82076
Club Secretary: Jerry Pugh, 8 Silver Birch Close, Liss, Hampshire, GU34 2SB. Tel: (H) 01730 895248 Tel: (W) 01730 894638
Fixtures Secretary: Martin Simpson, 10 Gauvain Close, Alton, Hants, GU34 2SB. Tel: (H) 01420 86880
Club Colours: Red shirts, black shorts.

CRANLEIGH RFC
Ground Address: Wildwood Lane, off A281 near Alfold, Cranleigh, Surrey. Tel: 01483 275843
Club Secretary: Stuart R Pope, Lyndhurst House, Birtley Rise, Bramley, Nr Guildford, Surrey GU5 0HZ. Tel: 01483 893140 Tel: (W) 01483 893140 Fax: 01483 894275
Fixtures Secretary: Mr Derek Coward, 2 Dover Court, Cranleigh, Surrey GU6 7EZ. Tel: (H) 01483 271247 Tel (W) 01483 275248
Club Colours: Shirts - Red & navy quarters, shorts - navy.

GOSPORT & FAREHAM RFC
Ground Address: Gosport Park, Dolphin Crescent, Gosport, Hampshire PO12 2HE. Tel: 01705 353235
Club Secretary: Mrs Susan Pazdzierski, 18 Palmerston Avenue, Fareham, Hants PO16 7DP. Tel: (H) 01329 232173
Fixtures Secretary: Mr Peter Tomlinson, 18 Freemantle Road, Gosport PO12 4RD. Tel: (H) 01705 589661
Club Colours: Royal blue & old gold.

GUY'S HOSPITAL RFC
Ground Address: Honor Oak Park, London SE23 1NW. Tel: 0181 690 1612
Club Secretary: Samy Darwish, 16 Claylands Road, Oval, London SE8 1NZ. Tel: (H) 0171 820 9373
Fixtures Secretary: Ben Chalercombe, 176 Trafalgar Street, Walworth, London SE17 2TP. Tel: (H) 0171 701 2339
Club Colours: Blue & gold hoops.

JERSEY RFC
Ground Address: Rue des Landes, St Peter, Jersey, Channel Islands JE3 7BG. Tel: 01534 499929
Club Secretary: Michael T Vibert, 'Santa Maria', Victoria Street, St Saviour, Jersey JE2 7QG. Tel: (H) 01534 33483 Tel: (W) 01534 33365
Fixtures Secretary: R Lapidus Esq, Channel Hotels & Leisure Ltd, PO Box 306, St Helier, Channel Islands JE2 8WZ. Tel (W) 01534 619600
Club Colours: Red shirts, white shorts.

OLD ALLEYNIAN FC
Ground Address: Dulwich Common, Dulwich, London SE21 7HA. Tel: 0181 693 2402
Club Secretary: RA (Joe) Crow, 13 Gable Court, Lawrie Park Avenue, London SE26 6HR. Tel: (H) 0181 778 2868
Fixtures Secretary: Alastair N Capon, 29 Cranmore Road, Chislehurst, Kent BR7 6EP. Tel: (H) 0181 289 8387
Club Colours: Dark blue, light blue & black hoops.

OLD EMANUEL RFC
Ground Address: Blagdon House, Blagdon Lane, New Malden, Surrey KT3 4PU. Tel: 0181 942 3857
Club Secretary: Ian Blair, 28 Hunters Road, Chessington, Surrey KT9 1RU. Tel: (H) 0181 397 1272 Tel: (W) 0171 872 3349
Fixtures Secretary: JA Monkhouse, 26 Oriental Road, Woking, Surrey GU22 7AH. Tel: (H) 01483 727816
Club Colours: White.

OLD GUILDFORDIANS RFC
Ground Address: Stoke Park, London Road, Guildford, Surrey. Tel: 01483 300752
Club Secretary: DJ Pym, Flat 3, 4 Guildown Road, Guildford, Surrey GU2 5EN. Tel: (H) 01483 69953 Tel: (W) 01483 403534
Fixtures Secretary: JP Allen, Hillmount, 9 Llanaway Road, Farncombe, Godalming, Surrey GU7 3EB. Tel: (H)

FINAL TABLE

	P	W	D	L	F	A	Pts
Wimbledon	11	11	0	0	255	64	22
Alton	11	9	0	2	263	97	18
Old Emanuel	11	6	0	5	196	174	12
Gosport	11	6	0	5	171	152	12
Warlingham	11	6	0	5	145	201	12
Cranleigh	11	5	1	5	138	149	11
Purley	11	5	0	6	164	161	10
Old Guildfordians	11	4	1	6	151	200	9
Guy's Hospital	11	4	0	7	181	195	8
Old Walcountians	11	4	0	7	137	209	8
Southampton	11	2	1	8	130	224	5
Eastleigh	11	2	0	9	106	211	4

01483 421249 Tel (W) 0171 480 2353
Club Colours: Green with narrow red & white hoops, green shorts, red socks.

OLD WALCOUNTIANS RFC
Ground Address: Clockhouse, Carshalton Road, Woodmansterne, Banstead, Surrey SM7 3HU. Tel: 01737 354348
Club Secretary: Richard A Tait, 60 Taylor Road, Wallington, Surrey SM6 0AX. Tel: (H) 0181 669 8689 Tel: (W) 0181 688 9243
Fixtures Secretary: Robert McDowell, 56 Hillside Gardens, Wallington, Surrey SM6 9MY. Tel: (H) 0181 669 6801
Club Colours: Black, blue, yellow.

OLD WHITGIFTIAN RFC
Ground Address: Croham Manor Road, South Croydon, Surrey, CR2 7BG. Tel: 0181 688 3248
Club Secretary: Geoff Austin, 97 Clifton Road, Kingston-upon-Thames, Surrey KT2 6PL. Tel: (H) 0181 549 3757 Tel: (W) 0171 926 5400
Fixtures Secretary: Geoff Austin, 97 Clifton Road, Kingston-upon-Thames, Surrey KT2 6PL. Tel: (H) 0181 549 3757 Tel (W) 0171 926 5400
Club Colours: Red, black & blue hooped shirts, white shorts.

PORTSMOUTH RFC
Ground Address: Rugby Camp, Norway Road, Hilsea, Portsmouth PO3 5HR. Tel: 01705 660610
Club Secretary: Ian Henderson, Flat 1, 22 High Street, Old Portsmouth, PO1 2LR. Tel: (H) 0705 876185 Tel: (W) 01329 288644
Fixtures Secretary: Maurice Twells, York Cottage, 1 Chalkridge Road, Cosham, Portsmouth PO6 2BE. Tel: (H) 01243 389350 Tel (W) 01705 370660
Club Colours: Black with single white & gold hoop.

PURLEY RFC
Ground Address: Parson's Pightle, Old Coulsdon, Surrey CR3 1EE. Tel: 01737 553042
Club Secretary: Simon Witham, 119 Hillside Road, Whyteleafe, Surrey. Tel: (H) 01883 624029 Tel: (W) 0171 247 4466 x2208
Fixtures Secretary: Martin Bazley, 88 The Waldrons, Croydon, Surrey CR0 4HB. Tel: (H) 0181 680 9978 Tel (W) 0171 377 6852
Club Colours: Black & white hoops, black shorts.

WARLINGHAM RFC
Ground Address: Limpsfield Road, Hamsey Green, Warlingham, Surrey CR6 9RB. Tel: 01883 622825
Club Secretary: Chris Cave, 57 Ridge Langley, Sanderstead, South Croydon, Surrey CR2 0AP. Tel: (H) 0181 651 0742 Tel: (W) 0171 826 8789
Fixtures Secretary: Paul Fettes, 63 Mitchley Hill, Sanderstead, South Croydon, Surrey. Tel: (H) 0181 657 7628
Club Colours: Royal blue & white hoops, navy shorts.

LONDON & SOUTH EAST DIVISION

HAMPSHIRE ONE
1995-96
FIXTURES

September 16 1995 (Week 3)
Fordingbridge v Guernsey
Trojans v Farnborough
Petersfield v Southampton
Tottonians v Eastleigh
Andover v Esso
US Portsmouth v Millbrook

September 23 1995 (Week 4)
Millbrook v Fordingbridge
Esso v US Portsmouth
Eastleigh v Andover
Southampton v Tottonians
Farnborough v Petersfield
Winchester v Trojans

September 30 1995 (Week X1)
Fordingbridge v Esso
Guernsey v Millbrook
Petersfield v Winchester
Tottonians v Farnborough
Andover v Southampton
US Portsmouth v Eastleigh

October 14 1995 (Week 6)
Esso v Guernsey
Eastleigh v Fordingbridge
Southampton v US Portsmouth
Farnborough v Andover
Winchester v Tottonians
Trojans v Petersfield

October 21 1995 (Week 7)
Fordingbridge v Southampton
Guernsey v Eastleigh
Millbrook v Esso
Tottonians v Trojans
Andover v Winchester
US Portsmouth v Farnborough

October 28 1995 (Week 8)
Eastleigh v Millbrook
Southampton v Guernsey
Farnborough v Fordingbridge
Winchester v US Portsmouth
Trojans v Andover
Petersfield v Tottonians

November 11 1995 (Week 10)
Fordingbridge v Winchester
Guernsey v Farnborough
Millbrook v Southampton
Esso v Eastleigh
Andover v Petersfield
US Portsmouth v Trojans

January 6 1996 (Week 17)
Southampton v Esso
Farnborough v Millbrook
Winchester v Guernsey
Trojans v Fordingbridge
Petersfield v US Portsmouth
Tottonians v Andover

January 13 1996 (Week 18)
Fordingbridge v Petersfield
Guernsey v Trojans
Millbrook v Winchester
Esso v Farnborough
Eastleigh v Southampton
US Portsmouth v Tottonians

February 10 1996 (Week 22)
Farnborough v Eastleigh
Winchester v Esso
Trojans v Millbrook
Petersfield v Guernsey
Tottonians v Fordingbridge
Andover v US Portsmouth

February 17 1996 (Week 23)
Fordingbridge v Andover
Guernsey v Tottonians
Millbrook v Petersfield
Esso v Trojans
Eastleigh v Winchester
Southampton v Farnborough

February 24 1996 (Week 24)
Winchester v Southampton
Trojans v Eastleigh
Petersfield v Esso
Tottonians v Millbrook
Andover v Guernsey
US Portsmouth v Fordingbridge

March 30 1996 (Week X7)
Guernsey v US Portsmouth
Millbrook v Andover
Esso v Tottonians
Eastleigh v Petersfield
Southampton v Trojans
Farnborough v Winchester

512

HAMPSHIRE ONE

ANDOVER RFC
Ground Address: The Goodship Ground, Foxcotte Park, Hatherden Road, Charlton, Andover, Hants SP11 0HN. Tel: 01264 339518
Club Secretary: WAJ Kent, Croye Lodge, 3 The Avenue, Andover, Hants SP10 3EL. Tel: (H) 01264 324963 Tel: (W) Ans 01264 336593 Fax 01264 336594
Fixtures Secretary: RJ Smith, 17 Longstock Close, Andover, Hants SP10 3UN. Tel: (H) 01264 359491 Tel (W) 01264 332299. Fax 01264 334737
Club Colours: Black shirts, shorts, socks.

EASTLEIGH RFC
Ground Address: Bishopstoke Playing Fields, Bishopstoke Road, Eastleigh, Hants. Tel: 01703 641312
Club Secretary: Bryan Michael Booth, Redlynch, 72 Station Road, Netley Abbey, Southampton, Hants SO31 5AF. Tel: (H) 01703 452718 Tel: (W) 01256 51658
Fixtures Secretary: John Sneezum, Bursledon Lodge, Salterns Lane, Old Bursledon, Southampton SO3 8OH. Tel: (H) 01703 402286 Tel (W) 01703 616941
Club Colours: Black/red/amber hoops.

ESSO (FAWLEY) RFC
Ground Address: Long Lane, Holbury, Hants. Tel: 01703 893750
Club Secretary: Alan McElevey, 32 Butts Ash Avenue, Hythe, Southampton SO45 3RE. Tel: (H) 01703 840201 Tel: (W) 01703 895400
Fixtures Secretary: Jeff Plumley, 4 Roseberry Avenue, Hythe, Southampton. Tel: (H) 01703 848539
Club Colours: Scarlet shirts & socks, blue shorts.

FARNBOROUGH RFC
Ground Address: Tilebarn Close, Cove, Farnborough, Hampshire GU14 8LS. Tel: 01252 542750
Club Secretary: Paul L Davies, 7 Woodcut road, Wrecclesham, Farnham, Surrey GU10 4QF. Tel: (H) 01252 716088 Tel: (W) 01252 342266
Fixtures Secretary: Barry Mackay, 43 The Grove, Farnborough, Hampshire GU14 6QS. Tel: (H) 01252 512363
Club Colours: Light & dark blue hoops.

FORDINGBRIDGE RFC
Ground Address: Recreation Ground, Fordingbridge, Hampshire. Tel: 01425 652047
Club Secretary: SCJ Godden, 157 Station Road, Fordingbridge, Hants SP6 1DF. Tel: (H) 01425 654069
Fixtures Secretary: J Trim, Trees, Fryern Court Road, Fordingbridge, Hants SP6 1NG. Tel: (H) 01425 655156 Tel (W) 01425 652254
Club Colours: Sky blue.

GUERNSEY RUFC
Ground Address: Footes Lane, St Peter Port, Guernsey. Tel: 01481 54590
Club Secretary: BJ Mildon, PO Box 181, St Peter Port, Guernsey. Tel: (H) 01481 65493 Tel: (W) 01481 715055
Fixtures Secretary: Alun Jenkins, PO Box 181, St Peter Port, Guernsey. Tel: (H) 01481 36125
Club Colours: Green & white.

MILLBROOK RFC
Ground Address: Lordshill Outdoor Recreation Centre, Redbridge Lane, Lordshill, Southampton. Tel: 01703 739759
Club Secretary: Mrs J Ings, 27 Gemini Close, Lordshill, Southampton SO16 8BG. Tel: (H) 01703 345559
Fixtures Secretary: Mr Wayne Renwick, 15 Kestrel Close, Bishop's Waltham, Southampton. Tel: (H) 01489 892231
Club Colours: Red & green hoops.

PETERSFIELD RFC
Ground Address: Penns Place, Petersfield, Hants GU32. Tel: 01730 264588
Club Secretary: Peter J Williamson, 20 Bridge Meadows, Liss, Hants GU33 7JY. Tel: (H) 01730 894542 Tel: (W)

FINAL TABLE

	P	W	D	L	F	A	Pts
Jersey	12	12	0	0	401	89	24
US Portsmouth	12	11	0	1	374	70	22
Winchester	12	8	0	4	328	156	16
Millbrook	11	7	0	4	373	156	14
Petersfield	12	7	1	4	203	219	13*
Trojans	12	5	0	7	141	242	10
Esso	11	4	1	6	177	177	9
Tottonians	12	4	0	8	203	209	8
Guernsey	9	4	0	5	143	150	8
Farnborough	12	4	1	7	161	228	7*
Sandown & Shanklin	11	1	0	10	78	372	2
New Milton	12	0	1	11	97	493	1
Isle of Wight	12	6	0	6	184	202	-4*

01256 841919
Fixtures Secretary: Hayden Smith, 44 Moggs Mead, Petersfield, Hants GU31 4NX. Tel: (H) 01730 261776
Club Colours: Red with white hoops.

SOUTHAMPTON RFC
Ground Address: Lower Brownhill Road, Millbrook, Southampton, Hants. Tel: 01703 737777
Club Secretary: Paul Raine, 7 Beattie Rise, Hedge End, Southampton SO30 2RF. Tel: (H) 01489 788460 Tel: (W) 01489 575420
Fixtures Secretary: George Materna, 29 Netley Firs Road, Hedge End, Southampton, Hants SO30 4AY. Tel: (H) 01489 786704 Tel (W) 01489 886611
Club Colours: Red & white hoops.

TOTTONIANS RFC
Ground Address: Totton College, Water Lane, Totton, Hants.
Club Secretary: Mr A Hamilton, 17 Betteridge Drive, Rownhams, Southampton, Hants. Tel: (H) 01374 112677
Fixtures Secretary: Mr S Anderson, 16 Buckland Gardens, Calmore, Southampton. Tel: (H) 01703 865691
Club Colours: Green/black/white hoops.

TROJANS FC
Ground Address: Stoneham Park, Stoneham Lane, Eastleigh, Hants SO50 9HT. Tel: 01703 612400/613068
Club Secretary: JWJ Mist, Westbury House, 14 Bellevue Road, Southampton SO15 2AY. Tel: (H) 01703 583450 Tel: (W) 01703 332844
Fixtures Secretary: CG Holt, The Chase, 338 Hill Lane, Southampton SO15 7PH. Tel (W) 01703 330993
Club Colours: Blue with narrow red hoops.

UNITED SERVICES PORTSMOUTH RFC
Ground Address: Burnaby Road, Portsmouth, Hants. Tel: 01705 825394
Club Secretary: John Collins, 4 Neelands Grove, Paulsgrove, Portsmouth, Hants PO6 4QL. Tel: (H) 01705 380859 Tel: (W) 01705 333579
Fixtures Secretary: Colin Bostock, 31 Collins Road, Southsea, Portsmouth, Hants PO4 9NY. Tel: (H) 01705 864737
Club Colours: Blue & red hoops, navy blue shorts.

WINCHESTER RFC
Ground Address: St Bartholomews Playing Fields, off Nuns Road, Winchester, Hants SO23 7EF. Tel: 01962 867021 Fax: 01962 867045
Club Secretary: David Allam, 20 Chawton Close, Harestock, Winchester, Hants SO22 6HY. Tel: (H) 01962 882658 Tel: (W) 01962 867021
Fixtures Secretary: James Jermain, 7 Pack Road, Winchester, Hants SO22 6AA. Tel: (H) 01962 852589 Tel (W) 0171 261 6580
Club Colours: Black & amber.

LONDON & SOUTH EAST DIVISION

HAMPSHIRE TWO
1995-96
FIXTURES

September 16 1995 (Week 3)
Sandown & Shanklin   v   Fareham Heathens
Romsey   v   Isle of Wight
Fleet   v   Ventnor

September 23 1995 (Week 4)
Isle of Wight   v   Sandown & Shanklin
New Milton   v   Fleet
Ventnor   v   Romsey

September 30 1995 (Week X1)
Sandown & Shanklin   v   Ventnor
Fareham Heathens   v   Isle of Wight
Romsey   v   New Milton

October 14 1995 (Week 6)
Ventnor   v   Fareham Heathens
New Milton   v   Sandown & Shanklin
Fleet   v   Romsey

October 21 1995 (Week 7)
Sandown & Shanklin   v   Fleet
Fareham Heathens   v   New Milton
Isle of Wight   v   Ventnor

October 28 1995 (Week 8)
New Milton   v   Isle of Wight
Fleet   v   Fareham Heathens
Romsey   v   Sandown & Shanklin

November 11 1995 (Week 10)
Fareham Heathens   v   Romsey
Isle of Wight   v   Fleet
Ventnor   v   New Milton

January 6 1996 (Week 17)
Fareham Heathens   v   Sandown & Shanklin
Isle of Wight   v   Romsey
Ventnor   v   Fleet

January 13 1996 (Week 18)
Sandown & Shanklin   v   Isle of Wight
Fleet   v   New Milton
Romsey   v   Ventnor

February 10 1996 (Week 22)
Ventnor   v   Sandown & Shanklin
Isle of Wight   v   Fareham Heathens
New Milton   v   Romsey

February 17 1996 (Week 23)
Fareham Heathens   v   Ventnor
Sandown & Shanklin   v   New Milton
Romsey   v   Fleet

February 24 1996 (Week 24)
Fleet   v   Sandown & Shanklin
New Milton   v   Fareham Heathens
Ventnor   v   Isle of Wight

March 30 1996 (Week X7)
Isle of Wight   v   New Milton
Fareham Heathens   v   Fleet
Sandown & Shanklin   v   Romsey

April 13 1996 (Week 30)
Romsey   v   Fareham Heathens
Fleet   v   Isle of Wight
New Milton   v   Ventnor

HAMPSHIRE TWO

FAREHAM HEATHENS RFC
Ground Address: Cams Alders Recreation Ground, Highfield Avenue, Fareham, Hampshire. Tel: 01329 221793
Club Secretary: CR Townsend, 9 Daisy Lane, Locksheath, Southampton SO31 6RA. Tel: (H) 01489 574945 Tel: (W) 01489 574945
Fixtures Secretary: Mr CEH Turner, 4 Walberton Avenue, Cosham, Portsmouth, Hampshire PO6 2JH. Tel: (H) 01705 370139 Tel (W) 01705 370139
Club Colours: Red & black quarters.

FLEET RUFC
Ground Address: Wavel Cody School, Lynchford Road, Farnborough, Hants GU14.
Club Secretary: Merrik Knight, 31 Osborne Road, Farnborough, Hants GU14 6AE. Tel: (H) 01252 518798 Tel: (W) 0181 563 4945
Fixtures Secretary: David Cave, 110 Peabody Road, Farnborough, Hants GU14 6DZ. Tel: (H) 01252 524646
Club Colours: Royal blue & scarlet.

ISLE OF WIGHT RFC
Ground Address: The Clubhouse, Wootton Recreation Ground, Footways, Wootton, Isle of Wight PO33 4NQ. Tel: 01983 883240
Club Secretary: Miss Tracy Allen, 19 Victoria Grove, East Cowes, Isle of Wight PO32 6DJ. Tel: (H) 01983 280549 Tel: (W) 01983 403766
Fixtures Secretary: Mr David Metcalfe, 2 Bristol Terrace, Blackbridge Road, Freshwater, Isle of Wight PO40 9QW. Tel: (H) 01983 755339
Club Colours: Navy blue, narrow gold hoops.

NEW MILTON RFC
Ground Address: Ashley Sports Ground, Ashley, New Milton, Hants. Tel: 01425 610401
Club Secretary: NE Hanmer, Walsingham, Andrew Lane, Ashley, New Milton, Hants BH25 5QD. Tel: (H) 01425 612613 Tel: (W) 01590 682495
Fixtures Secretary: J Jupe, 9 Molyneaux Road, Ashley, New Milton, Hants. Tel: (H) 01425 612184
Club Colours: Green & white quarters.

ROMSEY RUFC
Ground Address: Romsey Sports Centre, Southampton Road, Romsey, Hants. Tel: 01794 515103
Club Secretary: Andrew R Mott, 3 South Close, Romsey, Hampshire SO51 7UP. Tel: (H) 01794 515295 Tel: (W) 01725 512777
Fixtures Secretary: Andrew R Mott, 3 South Close, Romsey, Hampshire SO51 7UP. Tel: (H) 01794 515295 Tel (W) 01725 512777
Club Colours: Blue with gold hoops.

SANDOWN & SHANKLIN RUFC
Ground Address: The Clubhouse, The Fairway, Sandown, IOW PO36 9ES. Tel: 01983 404707
Club Secretary: Brian Smith, 3 Carter Street, Sandown, IOW PO36 8BL. Tel: (H) 01983 403298
Fixtures Secretary: Colin Bond, c/o The Warden's Chalet, Sandown Bay Holiday Centre, Yaverland, Sandown IOW. Tel: (H) 01983 406129
Club Colours: Navy blue & white close hooped shirts, navy blue shorts & socks.

VENTNOR RFC
Ground Address: Watcombe Bottom, Whitwell Road, Upper Ventnor, IOW. Tel: 01983 854155
Club Secretary: Mr Ian Agnew, No. 3 Wingates Cottages, Crocker Lane, Niton, IOW PO38 2NU. Tel: (H) 01983 730197 Tel: (W) 01983 822811
Fixtures Secretary: Marvin Champion, The Homestead, Monkton Street, Ryde, Isle of Wight PO33 2BZ. Tel: (H) 01983 566896 Tel (W) 01705 876061
Club Colours: Navy blue with white hoop.

FINAL TABLE

	P	W	D	L	F	A	Pts
Andover	12	12	0	0	373	57	22*
Fordingbridge	12	7	0	5	186	151	14
Ventnor	12	7	0	5	195	142	12*
Fareham Heathens	12	6	0	6	179	213	10*
Romsey	12	5	0	7	171	197	8*
AC Delco	12	4	0	8	133	288	6*
Overton	12	1	0	11	84	273	2

LONDON & SOUTH EAST DIVISION

HAMPSHIRE THREE
1995-96
FIXTURES

September 16 1995 (Week 3)
Basingstoke Wombats v AC Delco
Ellingham v Waterlooville
Nomads v Alresford

September 23 1995 (Week 4)
Waterlooville v Basingstoke Wombats
Overton v Nomads
Alresford v Ellingham

September 30 1995 (Week X1)
Basingstoke Wombats v Alresford
AC Delco v Waterlooville
Ellingham v Overton

October 14 1995 (Week 6)
Alresford v AC Delco
Overton v Basingstoke Wombats
Nomads v Ellingham

October 21 1995 (Week 7)
Basingstoke Wombats v Nomads
AC Delco v Overton
Waterlooville v Alresford

October 28 1995 (Week 8)
Overton v Waterlooville
Nomads v AC Delco
Ellingham v Basingstoke Wombats

November 11 1995 (Week 10)
AC Delco v Ellingham
Waterlooville v Nomads
Alresford v Overton

January 6 1996 (Week 17)
AC Delco v Basingstoke Wombats
Waterlooville v Ellingham
Alresford v Nomads

January 13 1996 (Week 18)
Basingstoke Wombats v Waterlooville
Nomads v Overton
Ellingham v Alresford

February 10 1996 (Week 22)
Alresford v Basingstoke Wombats
Waterlooville v AC Delco
Overton v Ellingham

February 17 1996 (Week 23)
AC Delco v Alresford
Basingstoke Wombats v Overton
Ellingham v Nomads

February 24 1996 (Week 24)
Nomads v Basingstoke Wombats
Overton v AC Delco
Alresford v Waterlooville

March 30 1996 (Week X7)
Waterlooville v Overton
AC Delco v Nomads
Basingstoke Wombats v Ellingham

April 13 (Week 30)
Ellingham v AC Delco
Nomads v Waterlooville
Overton v Alresford

HAMPSHIRE THREE

AC DELCO RFC
Ground Address: AC Delco (Southampton) Sports &
Social Club, Sports Ground, Stoneham Lane, Eastleigh,
Southampton, Hants. Tel: 01703 613334
Club Secretary: Simon Fitzjohn, 104 Alma Road,
Portswood, Southampton, Hants SO14 6UW. Tel: (H)
01703 324061
Fixtures Secretary: Richard Legge, 145 Chalvington
Road, Chandlers Ford, Southampton SO53 3EL. Tel: (H)
01703 261830
Club Colours: Navy blue & red squares.
ALRESFORD RFC
Ground Address: Bighton, Nr Alresford, Hants. Changing
room at Perins School, Alresford.
Club Secretary: Jason Rees, c/o Horse & Groom, Broad
Street, Alresford, Hants SO24 9HQ. Tel: (H) 01962 734007
Fixtures Secretary: Robin Howard, The Horse & Groom,
Broad Street, Alresford, Hants SO24 9HQ. Tel: (H) 01962
734809
Club Colours: Green, black & gold hoops.
BASINGSTOKE WOMBATS RFC
Ground Address: Hockey Club, Down Grange, Pack
Lane, Basingstoke.
Club Secretary: Dave Thurston, 3 Musket Copse, Old
Basing, Basingstoke, Hampshire RG24 7NQ. Tel: (H)
01256 462672 Tel: (W) 01256 818110
Fixtures Secretary: Martin Rawlings, The Feather Hotel,
5-7 Wote Street, Basingstoke. Tel: (H) 01256 473309
Club Colours: Red, green, yellow & blue quarters.
ELLINGHAM & RINGWOOD RFC
Ground Address: Picket Post, Ringwood, Hants. Tel:
01425 476668
Club Secretary: Douglas Middleton, 56 Eastfield Lane,
Ringwood, Hants, BH24 1UP. Tel: (H) 01425 475521 Tel:
(W) 01202 893000
Fixtures Secretary: Philip Lambert, 44 Waterloo Way,
Ringwood, Hants. Tel: (H) 01425 476643
Club Colours: Blue & amber.
NOMADS RFC
Ground Address: Farlington Sports Ground, Eastern
Road, Portsmouth, Hants.
Club Secretary: Mr K Walker, 130 Portchester Road,
Fareham, Hants PO16 8QP. Tel: (H) 01329 237584
Fixtures Secretary: Mr A Bold, 49 Primrose Way, Locks
Heath, Southampton, Hants SO31 6WW. Tel: (H) 01489
579044 Tel (W) 01705 669832
Club Colours: Scarlet & black irregular hoops.
OVERTON RUFC
Ground Address: Town Meadow, High Street, Overton,
Basingstoke, Hants (on B3400).
Club Secretary: Colin Gordon, 6 Waltham Court,
Overton, Hampshire RG25 3NY. Tel: (W) 01264 334477
Fixtures Secretary: Alec Coles, 15 Rochford Road,
Basingstoke, Hants RG21 7TQ. Tel: (H) 01256 462827
Club Colours: Royal blue.
WATERLOOVILLE RFC
Ground Address: Rowlands Avenue, Waterlooville,
Hants.
Club Secretary: Ray Mowatt, 9 Holst Way, Waterlooville,
Hants PO7 5SJ. Tel: (H) 01705 269275
Fixtures Secretary: Mark Hibberd, 4 Orchard Grove,
Cowplain, Waterlooville, Hants PO8 8TP. Tel: (H) 01705
264422 Tel (W) 01705 219224
Club Colours: Sky blue & red halves.

FINAL TABLE

	P	W	D	L	F	A	Pts
Fleet	9	7	0	2	183	69	12*
Nomads	9	6	0	3	121	79	12
Alresford	9	6	0	3	159	89	10*
Basingstoke Wombats	7	4	0	3	97	81	8
Waterlooville	8	2	0	6	66	145	2*
Ellingham	10	1	0	9	47	210	2

LONDON & SOUTH EAST DIVISION

SURREY ONE
1995-96
FIXTURES

November 11 1995 (Week 10)
Kingston v Old Cranleighans
Barnes v Effingham
Old Caterhamians v KCS Old Boys
Shirley Wanderers v Woking
Old Reedonians v University Vandals
Farnham v Chobham

September 16 1995 (Week 3)
Kingston v Barnes
Chobham v Effingham
University Vandals v KCS Old Boys
John Fisher Old Boys v Woking
Old Reedonians v Shirley Wanderers
Farnham v Old Caterhamians

January 6 1996 (Week 17)
KCS Old Boys v Shirley Wanderers
Effingham v Old Caterhamians
Old Cranleighans v Barnes
Chobham v Kingston
Univeristy Vandals v Farnham
John Fisher Old Boys v Old Reedonians

September 23 1995 (Week 4)
Old Caterhamians v Kingston
Shirley Wanderers v Farnham
Woking v Old Reedonians
KCS Old Boys v John Fisher Old Boys
Effingham v University Vandals
Old Cranleighans v Chobham

January 13 1996 (Week 18)
Kingston v Univeristy Vandals
Barnes v Chobham
Old Caterhamians v Old Cranleighans
Shirley Wanderers v Effingham
Woking v KCS Old Boys
Farnham v John Fisher Old Boys

September 30 1995 (Week X1)
Kingston v Shirley Wanderers
Barnes v Old Caterhamians
University Vandals v Old Cranleighans
John Fisher Old Boys v Effingham
Old Reedonians v KCS Old Boys
Farnham v Woking

February 10 1996 (Week 22)
Effingham v Woking
Old Cranleighans v Shirley Wanderers
Chobham v Old Caterhamians
Univeristy Vandals v Barnes
John Fisher Old Boys v Kingston
Old Reedonians v Farnham

October 14 1995 (Week 6)
Shirley Wanderers v Barnes
Woking v Kingston
KCS Old Boys v Farnham
Effingham v Old Reedonians
Old Cranleighans v John Fisher Old Boys
Chobham v Univeristy Vandals

February 17 1996 (Week 23)
Kingston v Old Reedonians
Barnes v John Fisher Old Boys
Old Caterhamians v Univeristy Vandals
Shirley Wanderers v Chobham
Woking v Old Cranleighans
KCS Old Boys v Effingham

October 21 1995 (Week 7)
Kingston v KCS Old Boys
Barnes v Woking
Old Caterhamians v Shirley Wanderers
John Fisher Old Boys v Chobham
Old Reedonians v Old Cranleighans
Farnham v Effingham

February 24 1996 (Week 24)
Old Cranleighans v KCS Old Boys
Chobham v Woking
University Vandals v Shirley Wanderers
John Fisher Old Boys v Old Caterhamians
Old Reedonians v Barnes
Farnham v Kingston

October 28 1995 (Week 8)
Woking v Old Caterhamians
KCS Old Boys v Barnes
Effingham v Kingston
Old Cranleighans v Farnham
Chobham v Old Reedonians
University Vandals v John Fisher Old Boys

March 30 1996 (Week X7)
Barnes v Farnham
Old Caterhamians v Old Reedonians
Shirley Wanderers v John Fisher Old Boys
Woking v University Vandals
KCS Old Boys v Chobham
Effingham v Old Cranleighans

518

SURREY ONE

BARNES RFC
Ground Address: Barn Elms, Queen Elizabeth Walk, Barnes, London SW15 0DG. Tel: 0181 876 7685
Club Secretary: Mr Paul Kirby, 53 Stanhope Gardens, London SW7 5RF. Tel: (H) 0171 373 0120 Tel: (W) 0171 602 5678
Fixtures Secretary: Gary Scroby, 39E Earlsfield Road, London SW18. Tel: (H) 0181 877 9538 Tel (W) 0171 279 4119
Club Colours: Green & gold shirts, green shorts.

CHOBHAM RFC
Ground Address: Fowlers Wells, Windsor Road, Chobham, Surrey GU24 8NA. Tel: 01276 858616
Club Secretary: A Thomas, Hazel Cottage, Viggory Lane, Horsell, Woking, Surrey GU21 4XH. Tel: (H) 01483 720810 Tel: (W) 01483 761036
Fixtures Secretary: Wallace Hooper, 8 Fowlers Mead, Chobham, Woking, Surrey GU24 8LF. Tel: (H) 01276 858661
Club Colours: Scarlet & gold hoops on dark blue jersey.

EFFINGHAM RFC
Ground Address: King George V Playing Fields, Browns Lane, Effingham, Surrey. Tel: 01372 458845
Club Secretary: Mike Wheeler, 34 Oakfields, Broadacres, Guildford, Surrey GU3 3AU. Tel: (H) 01483 36022
Fixtures Secretary: Ed Newton, 42 Milney Road, Kingston, Surrey KT1 2AU. Tel: (H) 0181 549 8213 Tel (W) 0171 738 1122
Club Colours: Green & amber hoops, black shorts.

FARNHAM RUFC
Ground Address: Westfield Lane, Wrecclesham, Farnham, Surrey GU10 4QP. Tel: 01252 721138
Club Secretary: Derek R Wall, 22 Hope Lane, Farnham, Surrey GU9 0HZ. Tel: (H) 01252 710476
Fixtures Secretary: JF Robertson, Akora, 98 Shoreham Road, Farnham, Surrey GU9 8SE. Tel: (H) 01252 712387 Tel (W) 01344 850414
Club Colours: Black & white 2' hooped shirts, black shorts, black socks with white tops.

JOHN FISHER OLD BOYS RFC
Ground Address: 198 Limpsfield Road, Hamsey Green, Warlingham, Surrey. Tel: 01883 625149
Club Secretary: Chris Mallows, 14 Braemer Avenue, South Croydon, Surrey CR2 0QY. Tel: (H) 0181 660 4756 Tel: (W) 01737 768511
Fixtures Secretary: Chris Doyle, 157 Sandy Lane, South Wallington, Surrey SM6 9NP. Tel: (H) 0181 647 3601 Tel (W) 0171 710 8000
Club Colours: Blue, gold & white hoops.

KCS OLD BOYS RFC
Ground Address: Arthur Road, Motspur Park, New Malden, London KT3 6LX. Tel: 0181 336 2512
Club Secretary: Noel M Crockford, 78 Claygate Lane, Hinchley Wood, Surrey KT10 0BJ. Tel: (H) 0181 398 7474 Tel: (W) 0181 398 6499
Fixtures Secretary: Andy Todd, 5 Wendover Drive, New Malden, Surrey KT3 5RN. Tel: (H) 0181 942 0048 Tel (W) 0181 395 3808
Club Colours: Red, blue & old gold hoops.

KINGSTON RFC
Ground Address: King Edward Sports Ground, Hook Road, Chessington, Surrey KT9 1PL. Tel: 0181 397 8385
Club Secretary: Nick Deere, 8 Rowan Court, Queens Road, Kingston, Surrey KT2 7TR. Tel: (H) 0181 541 3923 Tel: (W) 0181 456 5917
Fixtures Secretary: K Walker, 3 Woodcote Side, Epsom, Surrey KT18 7HB. Tel: (H) 01372 741791
Club Colours: Maroon & white hoops.

OLD CATERHAMIAN RFC
Ground Address: Park Avenue, Caterham, Surrey CR3 6AH. Tel: 01883 347919
Club Secretary: Peter Smith, Three Chimneys, Gravelly Hill, Caterham, Surrey CR3 6ES. Tel: (H) 01883 347919

FINAL TABLE

	P	W	D	L	F	A	Pts
Old Whitgiftians	12	11	1	0	283	111	23
Barnes	12	8	1	3	243	150	17
Effingham	12	8	0	4	115	104	16
Old Reedonians	12	7	2	3	124	134	16
Old Cranleighans	12	6	1	5	126	129	13
John Fisher OB	12	6	1	5	126	103	11*
University Vandals	12	5	1	6	164	182	11
Chobham	12	5	1	6	137	175	11
Kingston	12	6	0	6	147	150	10*
Shirley Wanderers	12	5	0	7	116	125	10
Farnham	12	4	0	8	140	179	8
Old Rutlishians	12	2	1	9	133	219	5
Raynes Park	12	0	1	11	80	173	1

Tel: (W) 01883 347919
Fixtures Secretary: Mark Rowland, 12 Park Road, Smallfield, Nr Horley, Surrey RH6 9RZ. Tel: (H) 01342 842115 Tel (W) 01737 775160
Club Colours: Black, amber, silver & mauve, black shorts.

OLD CRANLEIGHAN RFC
Ground Address: Old Portsmouth Road, Thames Ditton, Surrey KT7 0HB. Tel: 0181 398 3092
Club Secretary: Mark Lubbock, 52 Sarsfeld Road, London SW12 8HN. Tel: (H) 0181 672 1310 Tel: (W) 0171 638 1111
Fixtures Secretary: Tony Price, 32 Beverley Road, New Malden, Surrey KT3 4AW. Tel: (H) 0181 949 1194 Tel (W) 0181 533 7588
Club Colours: Blue, white & gold hoops.

OLD REEDONIANS RFC
Ground Address: North Avenue, Whiteley Village, off Burwood Road, Walton-on-Thames, Surrey. Tel: 01932 849616
Club Secretary: Mr JB Rogers, 8 Model Cottages, East Sheen, London SW14 7PH. Tel: (H) 0181 876 1512
Fixtures Secretary: Mr A Procter, 4 Friston Street, Fulham, London SW6 3AT. Tel: (H) 0171 731 3791 Tel (W) 0181 974 6150
Club Colours: Dark blue, light blue, red & white hoops.

SHIRLEY WANDERERS RUFC
Ground Address: Kent Gate, Addington Road, West Wickham, Kent. Tel: 0181 777 5298
Club Secretary: Martin Stone, 251 Quentin Court, Regency Walk, Shirley, Croydon, Surrey. Tel: (H) 0181 777 6712
Fixtures Secretary: Geoff Jeffcoat, 96 Woodland Way, West Wickham, Kent BR4 9LT. Tel: (H) 0181 777 5174 Tel (W) 0181 761 3000
Club Colours: All white.

UNIVERSITY VANDALS RFC
Ground Address: Brownacres, The Towing Path, Walton-on-Thames, Surrey. Tel: 01932 227659
Club Secretary: A Williams, 7 Clarence Close, Walton-on-Thames, Surrey KT12 5JX. Tel: (H) 01932 229727 Tel: (W) 0171 259 6633
Fixtures Secretary: CJ Cockrean, 94 Albany Road, Hersham, Surrey. Tel: (H) 01932 226837
Club Colours: Black, purple & emerald green.

WOKING RFC
Ground Address: Byfleet Recreation Ground, Stream Close, off Rectory Lane, Byfleet, Surrey.
Club Secretary: Sean Elder, Corner House, 64 Chertsey Road, Byfleet, Surrey. Tel: (H) 01932 343003 Tel: (W) 0181 547 2250
Fixtures Secretary: Mr Ian Vousden, 142 Blackmore Crescent, Sheerwater, Woking, Surrey GU21 5NY. Tel: (H) 01483 715715 Tel (W) Mobile: 0374 624753
Club Colours: Blue & gold hoops, black shorts, blue socks.

LONDON & SOUTH EAST DIVISION

SURREY TWO
1995-96
FIXTURES

September 16 1995 (Week 3)

Wandsworthians v Old Suttonians
Mitcham v Old Rutlishians
Chipstead v Law Society
Battersea Ironsides v Merton
Bec Old Boys v Cobham
Raynes Park v Old Haileyburians

September 23 1995 (Week 4)

Old Haileyburians v Wandsworthians
Cobham v Raynes Park
Merton v Bec Old Boys
Law Society v Battersea Ironsides
Old Rutlishians v Chipstead
Old Tiffinians v Mitcham

September 30 1995 (Week X1)

Wandsworthians v Cobham
Old Suttonians v Old Haileyburians
Chipstead v Old Tiffinians
Battersea Ironsides v Old Rutlishians
Bec Old Boys v Law Society
Raynes Park v Merton

October 14 1995 (Week 6)

Cobham v Old Suttonians
Merton v Wandsworthians
Law Society v Raynes Park
Old Rutlishians v Bec Old Boys
Old Tiffinians v Battersea Ironsides
Mitcham v Chipstead

October 21 1995 (Week 7)

Wandsworthians v Law Society
Old Suttonians v Merton
Old Haileyburians v Cobham
Battersea Ironsides v Mitcham
Bec Old Boys v Old Tiffinians
Raynes Park v Old Rutlishians

October 28 1995 (Week 8)

Merton v Old Haileyburians
Law Society v Old Suttonians
Old Rutlishians v Wandsworthians
Old Tiffinians v Raynes Park
Mitcham v Bec Old Boys
Chipstead v Battersea Ironsides

November 11 1995 (Week 10)

Wandsworthians v Old Tiffinians
Old Suttonians v Old Rutlishians
Old Haileyburians v Law Society
Cobham v Merton
Bec Old Boys v Chipstead
Raynes Park v Mitcham

January 6 1996 (Week 17)

Law Society v Cobham
Old Rutlishians v Old Haileyburians
Old Tiffinians v Old Suttonians
Mitcham v Wandsworthians
Chipstead v Raynes Park
Battersea Ironsides v Bec Old Boys

January 13 1996 (Week 18)

Wandsworthians v Chipstead
Old Suttonians v Mitcham
Old Haileyburians v Old Tiffinians
Cobham v Old Rutlishians
Merton v Law Society
Raynes Park v Battersea Ironsides

February 10 1996 (Week 22)

Old Rutlishians v Merton
Old Tiffinians v Cobham
Mitcham v Old Haileyburians
Chipstead v Old Suttonians
Battersea Ironsides v Wandsworthians
Bec Old Boys v Raynes Park

February 17 1996 (Week 23)

Wandsworthians v Bec Old Boys
Old Suttonians v Battersea Ironsides
Old Haileyburians v Chipstead
Cobham v Mitcham
Merton v Old Tiffinians
Law Society v Old Rutlishians

February 24 1996 (Week 24)

Old Tiffinians v Law Society
Mitcham v Merton
Chipstead v Cobham
Battersea Ironsides v Old Haileyburians
Bec Old Boys v Old Suttonians
Raynes Park v Wandsworthians

March 30 1996 (Week X7)

Old Suttonians v Raynes Park
Old Haileyburians v Bec Old Boys
Cobham v Battersea Ironsides
Merton v Chipstead
Law Society v Mitcham
Old Rutlishians v Old Tiffinians

SURREY TWO

BATTERSEA IRONSIDES RFC
Ground Address: Battersea Ironsides Sports & Social Club, Openview, Earlsfield, London SW17. Tel: 0181 879 9913
Club Secretary: Martin Paul Tanner, 1 Woodland Way, Morden, Surrey SM4 4DS. Tel: (H) 0181 540 5784
Fixtures Secretary: Trefor Jenkins, 3 Harold Way, London SE19. Tel: (H) 0181 653 6615
Club Colours: Green & white.

BEC OLD BOYS RFC
Ground Address: Sutton Manor Sports & Social Ground, Northey Avenue, Cheam, Surrey. Tel: 0181 642 3423
Club Secretary: Austin Copp, 19 Edgeley Road, Clapham, London, SW4 6EH. Tel: (H) 0171 738 8725 Tel: (W) 0171 357 6323
Fixtures Secretary: Rick Mayhew, 11 Willowhayne Gardens, Worcester Park, Surrey KT4 8TH. Tel: (H) 0181 335 4038
Club Colours: Blue, old gold & white hoops.

CHIPSTEAD RFC
Ground Address: Chipstead Meads, High Road, Chipstead, Surrey. Tel: 01737 553035
Club Secretary: AD Malyon, 4 Hillside Road, East Ewell, Epsom, Surrey KT17 3EH. Tel: (H) 0181 393 3578 Tel: (W) 0181 680 1017
Fixtures Secretary: A Carr, 53 Woodplace Lane, Coulsdon, Surrey CR5 1NE. Tel: (H) 01737 551919
Club Colours: Blue & gold hoops.

COBHAM RFC
Ground Address: Old Surbitonians Memorial Ground, Fairmile Lane, Cobham, Surrey. Tel: 01932 863245
Club Secretary: IJ Johnson, 209 Portsmouth Road, Cobham, Surrey KT11 1JR. Tel: (H) 01932 862694 Tel: (W) 0181 942 1033
Fixtures Secretary: IJ Johnson, 209 Portsmouth Road, Cobham, Surrey KT11 1JR. Tel: (H) 01932 862694 Tel (W) 0181 942 1033
Club Colours: Blue, maroon & gold quarters.

LAW SOCIETY RFC
Ground Address: c/o Old Wimbledonians Cricket Club, Clayton Road, Hook, Surrey. Tel: 0181 397 1962
Club Secretary: NB Cannon, Flat 5, 25 Belsize Park, London, NW3 4DU. Tel: (H) 0171 431 3210 Tel: (W) 0171 832 7304
Fixtures Secretary: John Smith, 55 Turney Road, Dulwich, London SE21 7JB. Tel: (H) 0171 733 8828 Tel (W) 0171 727 0581
Club Colours: Black jersey with single maroon & white hoops, black shorts.

MERTON RFC
Ground Address: Morden Recreation Ground, Middleton Road, Morden, Surrey. Tel: 0181 646 5192
Club Secretary: R Smith, SCCS, Charrington Street, London NW1 1RG. Tel: (H) 0171 622 3729 Tel: (W) 0171 387 0126
Fixtures Secretary: A Yorke, 31 Lyndon Gardens, Totteridge road, High Wycombe HP13 7QJ.
Club Colours: Gold/white/black quadrants.

MITCHAM RUFC
Ground Address: Rosehill Recreation Ground, Rosehill, Sutton, Surrey.
Club Secretary: Dave Starling, 28 Poole Road, West Ewell, Surrey. Tel: (H) 0181 394 2672 Tel: (W) 0171 926 3995
Fixtures Secretary: Tony Antoniou, 62 Melrose Avenue, London SW16. Tel: (H) 0181 679 5644 Tel (W) 0171 525 3316
Club Colours: Lavender & green.

OLD HAILEYBURIANS RFC
Ground Address: 27 Ruxley Lane, Kingston Road, Ewell. Tel: 0181 393 3901
Club Secretary: RJ Sheen, 29 Kenilworth Ave, Wimbledon SW19 7LN. Tel: (H) 0181 879 7851 Tel: (W) 071 782 0990

FINAL TABLE

	P	W	D	L	F	A	Pts
Old Caterhamians	12	11	0	1	334	114	22
Woking	11	10	1	0	361	76	21
Chipstead	12	9	1	2	216	167	19
Old Tiffinians	12	8	0	4	206	194	16
Bec Old Boys	10	6	0	4	146	112	12
Merton	10	5	0	5	111	101	10
Cobham	10	5	0	5	126	121	10
Mitcham	12	4	1	7	142	152	9
Wandsworthians	11	4	1	6	117	192	9
Law Society	12	3	1	8	164	273	7
Old Haileyburians	12	3	0	9	219	273	6
London Fire Brigade	12	2	1	9	102	202	3*
Reigate & Redhill	12	1	0	11	81	348	0*

Fixtures Secretary: Peter Blackmore, 31 Maidenhead Street, Hertford, Herts. Tel: (H) 01763 84 8636 Tel (W) 01992 553900
Club Colours: Magenta and white hoops.

OLD RUTLISHIANS RFC
Ground Address: The Clubhouse, Old Rutlishians Association, Poplar Road, Merton Park, London SW19 3JS. Tel: 0181 542 3678
Club Secretary: WH Griffin, 68 Love Lane, Morden, Surrey SM4 6LP. Tel: (H) 0181 395 1875
Fixtures Secretary: Ian Baxter, 17 The Green, Morden, Surrey SM4 4HJ. Tel: (H) 0181 540 3429
Club Colours: Gold, azure, silver & black.

OLD SUTTONIANS RFC
Ground Address: Walch Pavilion, Priest Hill, Banstead Road, Ewell, Surrey. Tel: 0181 393 7427
Club Secretary: Mr SJ Udall, 16 Kingsdown Road, Cheam, Sutton, Surrey SM3 8NY. Tel: (H) 0181 644 7259 Tel: (W) 01992 560330
Fixtures Secretary: Mr I Connell, 43 Grove Road, Sutton, Surrey SM1 2DF. Tel: (H) 0181 642 8915 Tel (W) 0171 223 3458
Club Colours: Red, white & black hoops.

OLD TIFFINIAN RFC
Ground Address: Grist Memorial Ground, Summer Road, off Hampton Court Way, East Molesey, Surrey. Tel: 0181 398 1391
Club Secretary: BA Bench, 12 Angas Court, Pine Grove, Weybridge, Surrey. Tel: (H) 01932 842533 Tel: (W) 0181 549 9222
Fixtures Secretary: RG Kirkwood, 63 Shaftesbury Way, Strawberry Hill, Twickenham, Middlesex TW2 5RW. Tel: (H) 0181 898 1767
Club Colours: Violet, white & navy blue.

RAYNES PARK RFC
Ground Address: Taunton Avenue, Raynes Park, London SW20.
Club Secretary: Russell Price, 101 Belmont Avenue, New Malden, Surrey KT3 6QE. Tel: (H) 0181 949 2448 Tel: (W) 0171 976 7199
Fixtures Secretary: Russell Price, 101 Belmont Avenue, New Malden, Surrey KT3 6QE. Tel: (H) 0181 949 2448 Tel (W) 0171 976 7199
Club Colours: Blue with gold circlet, blue shorts.

WANDSWORTHIANS RFC
Ground Address: Kings College Sports Ground, Windsor Road, New Malden, Surrey KT3 5HA. Tel: 0181 942 0495
Club Secretary: Ian Maclean, 45 More Lane, Esher, Surrey. Tel: (H) 01372 463121
Fixtures Secretary: Gary Kirkwood, 53 Leominster Road, Morden, Surrey SM4 6HY. Tel: (H) 0181 640 0263 Tel (W) 0181 665 3756
Club Colours: Maroon, white & gold hoops.

LONDON & SOUTH EAST DIVISION

SURREY THREE
1995-96
FIXTURES

September 23 1995 (Week 4)

Old Johnians	v	Old Wellingtonians
Carshalton	v	Old Bevonians
London Media	v	Reigate & Redhill
London Fire Brigade	v	Lightwater
Egham	v	Kew Occasionals
Croydon	v	Old Freemans

September 30 1995 (Week X1)

Kew Occasionals	v	Old Johnians
Lightwater	v	Egham
Reigate & Redhill	v	London Fire Brigade
Old Bevonians	v	London Media
Croydon	v	Carshalton
Old Freemans	v	Old Wellingtonians

October 14 1995 (Week 6)

Old Johnians	v	Lightwater
Old Wellingtonians	v	Kew Occasionals
London Media	v	Croydon
London Fire Brigade	v	Old Bevonians
Egham	v	Reigate & Redhill
Carshalton	v	Old Freemans

October 21 1995 (Week 7)

Lightwater	v	Old Wellingtonians
Reigate & Redhill	v	Old Johnians
Old Bevonians	v	Egham
Croydon	v	London Fire Brigade
Carshalton	v	London Media
Old Freemans	v	Kew Occasionals

October 28 1995 (Week 8)

Old Johnians	v	Old Bevonians
Old Wellingtonians	v	Reigate & Redhill
Kew Occasionals	v	Lightwater
London Fire Brigade	v	Carshalton
Egham	v	Croydon
London Media	v	Old Freemans

November 11 1995 (Week 10)

Reigate & Redhill	v	Kew Occasionals
Old Bevonians	v	Old Wellingtonians
Croydon	v	Old Johnians
Carshalton	v	Egham
London Media	v	London Fire Brigade
Old Freemans	v	Lightwater

January 6 1996 (Week 17)

Old Johnians	v	Carshalton
Old Wellingtonians	v	Croydon
Kew Occasionals	v	Old Bevonians
Lightwater	v	Reigate & Redhill
Egham	v	London Media
London Fire Brigade	v	Old Freemans

January 13 1996 (Week 18)

Old Bevonians	v	Lightwater
Croydon	v	Kew Occasionals
Carshalton	v	Old Wellingtonians
London Media	v	Old Johnians
London Fire Brigade	v	Egham
Old Freemans	v	Reigate & Redhill

February 10 1996 (Week 22)

Old Johnians	v	London Fire Brigade
Old Wellingtonians	v	London Media
Kew Occasionals	v	Carshalton
Lightwater	v	Croydon
Reigate & Redhill	v	Old Bevonians
Egham	v	Old Freemans

February 17 1996 (Week 23)

Croydon	v	Reigate & Redhill
Carshalton	v	Lightwater
London Media	v	Kew Occasionals
London Fire Brigade	v	Old Wellingtonians
Egham	v	Old Johnians
Old Freemans	v	Old Bevonians

February 24 1996 (Week 24)

Old Johnians	v	Old Freemans
Old Wellingtonians	v	Egham
Kew Occasionals	v	London Fire Brigade
Lightwater	v	London Media
Reigate & Redhill	v	Carshalton
Old Bevonians	v	Croydon

SURREY THREE

CARSHALTON RFC
Ground Address: Poulter Park, Bishopsford Road, Mitcham, Surrey. Tel: 0181 648 3755
Club Secretary: P Davison, 204 Hillcross Avenue, Morden, Surrey SM4 4ET. Tel: (H) 0181 540 1495
Fixtures Secretary: DJ Turner, 49 Chelsam Road, Clapham, London SW14 6NN. Tel: (H) 0171 627 4778 Tel (W) 0171 926 9449
Club Colours: All black.

CROYDON RFC
Ground Address: Layhams Road (junction with King Henry's Drive), Keston, Bromley, Kent. Tel: 01959 573409
Club Secretary: Trevor Davies, 62 Coulsdon Road, Coulsdon, Surrey CR5 2LB. Tel: (H) 0181 668 4864 Tel: (W) 0171 233 0288
Fixtures Secretary: R Goodwin, 298 Grange Road, Upper Norwood, London SE19 3DF. Tel: (H) 0181 653 8919 Tel (W) 0181 777 8040
Club Colours: Black, magenta & white.

EGHAM RFC
Ground Address: Strodes College, High Street, Egham, Surrey TW20.
Club Secretary: AG Codling, Brookside, 18 Vicarage Avenue, Egham, Surrey TW20 8NW. Tel: (H) 01784 434139 Tel: (W) 01784 434139
Fixtures Secretary: P Garrett, 61 Denham Road, Egham, Surrey TW20 9DF. Tel: (H) 01784 477151
Club Colours: Royal blue with gold band round chest.

KEW OCCASIONALS
Ground Address: Westminster University Sports Ground, Cavendish Road, (off Hartington Road), Chiswick, London W4 3UH. Tel: 0181 994 1554
Club Secretary: Mrs LS Rule, 68 Rosebury Road, London SW6 2NG. Tel: (H) 0171 736 8469 Tel: (W) 0171 736 8469
Fixtures Secretary: Mrs LS Rule, 68 Rosebury Road, London SW6 2NG. Tel: (H) 0171 736 8469 Tel (W) 0171 736 8469
Club Colours: Pink shirts, blue shorts.

LIGHTWATER RFC
Ground Address: The Sports Centre, The Avenue, Lightwater, Surrey, GU18 5RQ. Tel: 01276 472664
Club Secretary: Anthony Sharp, 65 Cedar Close, Bagshot, Surrey, GU19 5AB. Tel: (H) 01276 472994 Tel: (W) 01483 729661
Fixtures Secretary: Dave Forsaith, 21 Benjamin Walk, Yateley, Camberley, Surrey GU17 7YP. Tel: (H) 01252 871400
Club Colours: Green & white quarters, black shorts.

LONDON FIRE BRIGADE RFC
Ground Address: LFCDA Welfare Fund Sports Ground, Banstead Road, Ewell, Surrey. Tel: 0181 394 1946/994 3819
Club Secretary: Mrs J Brunning, 20 Middle Way, Norbury, London, SW16 4HN. Tel: (H) 0181 715 9812 Tel: (W) 0181 764 5100
Fixtures Secretary: C Rowsome, 23 Stayton Road, Sutton, Surrey SM1 1QY. Tel: (H) 0181 644 2134
Club Colours: Flame, amber, charcoal.

LONDON MEDIA RUFC
Ground Address: Battersea Park, Albert Bridge Road Entrance, Battersea, London.
Club Secretary: NT Field, Flat 4, 43 Gleneagle Road, Streatham, London SW16 6AY. Tel: (H) 0181 769 2242 Tel: (W) 0171 278 2656
Fixtures Secretary: Mike Jefferies, 64A Rossendale Road, Dulwich, London SE21 8DP. Tel: (H) 0181 761 2346 Tel (W) 0171 831 2981
Club Colours: Black & white quarters.

FINAL TABLE

	P	W	D	L	F	A	Pts
Old Suttonians	10	9	0	1	217	65	18
Battersea Ironsides	10	8	1	1	169	53	17
Egham	10	6	1	3	113	123	13
Old Freemans	10	5	1	4	155	95	11
Old Bevonians	10	4	2	4	123	133	10
London Media	10	4	1	5	152	148	9
Old Pelhamians	10	4	1	5	123	157	9
Old Johnians	9	3	0	6	95	156	6
Croydon	10	3	0	7	83	172	6
Lightwater	9	2	1	6	95	157	5
Haslemere	10	2	0	8	98	164	4

OLD BEVONIANS RFC
Ground Address: Ballard Coombe, Robin Hood Way, Kingston Vale, London SW15 3QX. Tel: 0181 942 2907
Club Secretary: Mr Ian James Cecil, 53 Orme Road, Kingston upon Thames, Surrey KT1 3SD. Tel: (H) 0181 942 0152 Tel: (W) 0171 621 9353
Fixtures Secretary: Mr Alex Kerr, 427 West Barnes Lane, New Malden, Surrey KT3 6PA. Tel: (H) 0181 949 2009 Tel (W) 0181 751 1242
Club Colours: Black, amber & green hoops.

OLD FREEMEN'S RFC
Ground Address: Old Freemen's Memorial Clubhouse, City of London Freemen's School, Ashtead Park, Ashtead, Surrey KT21 1ET. Tel: 01372 274158
Club Secretary: JG Wild, Beeches, Ermyn Way, Leatherhead, Surrey KT22 8TW. Tel: (H) 01372 276085 Tel: (W) 01483 729661
Fixtures Secretary: MJ Bailey, 123 Overdale, Ashtead, Surrey KT21 8PZ. Tel: (H) 01372 278505 Tel (W) 0181 642 3419/5685
Club Colours: Blue with maroon & gold hoops, dark blue shorts.

OLD JOHNIAN RFC
Ground Address: Oaken Lane, Hinchley Wood, Surrey. Tel: 0181 398 0535
Club Secretary: Mike Stuttard, 22 Cedarville Gardens, London SW16 3DA. Tel: (H) 0181 764 4052 Tel: (W) 0181 764 0401
Fixtures Secretary: David Robinson. Tel: (H) 0243 538019 Tel (W) 0243 770523
Club Colours: Bottle green & white hoops.

OLD WELLINGTONIAN RFC
Ground Address: 27 Ruxley Lane, Kingston Road, Ewell, Surrey. Tel: 0181 393 3901
Club Secretary: Stuart Layzell, 20 Sangora Road, London SW11 1RL. Tel: (H) 0171 207 0273 Tel: (W) 0171 213 1145
Fixtures Secretary: N Prichard, 86A Iffley Road, London W6 0PF. Tel: (H) 0181 748 4002 Tel (W) 0181 748 4058
Club Colours: Yellow, light blue, orange, black.

REIGATE & REDHILL RFC
Ground Address: Eric Hodgkins Memorial Ground, Colley Lane, Reigate, Surrey RH2 9JL. Tel: 01737 221110
Club Secretary: Clive Harrington, 15 Arlington Court, Oakfield Drive, Reigate, Surrey RH2 9NU. Tel: (H) 01737 224403 Tel: (W) 0181 666 0201
Fixtures Secretary: Steve Wagstaff, 45 Middlefield, Langshott, Horley, Surrey RH6 9XP. Tel: (H) 01293 820 450
Club Colours: Dark blue.

LONDON & SOUTH EAST DIVISION

SURREY FOUR
1995-96
FIXTURES

September 23 1995 (Week 4)
Racal Decca	v	Worth
Haslemere	v	St George's Hospital
Surrey Police	v	Oxted
Royal Holloway College	v	Surrey University
Kings College Hospital	v	Economicals
Charing Cross Hospital	v	Old Epsomians

September 30 1995 (Week X1)
Racal Decca	v	Haslemere
Surrey University	v	Kings College Hospital
Oxted	v	Royal Holloway College
Old Epsomians	v	Surrey Police
Charing Cross Hospital	v	St George's Hospital
Economicals	v	Worth

October 14 1995 (Week 6)
Haslemere	v	Economicals
St George's Hospital	v	Racal Decca
Royal Holloway College	v	Old Epsomians
Kings College Hospital	v	Oxted
Surrey Police	v	Charing Cross Hospital
Worth	v	Surrey University

October 21 1995 (Week 7)
Economicals	v	St George's Hospital
Surrey University	v	Haslemere
Old Epsomians	v	Kings College Hospital
Surrey Police	v	Royal Holloway College
Worth	v	Oxted
Charing Cross Hospital	v	Racal Decca

October 28 1995 (Week 8)
Haslemere	v	Oxted
St George's Hospital	v	Surrey University
Racal Decca	v	Economicals
Kings College Hospital	v	Surrey Police
Charing Cross Hospital	v	Royal Holloway College
Worth	v	Old Epsomians

November 11 1995 (Week 10)
Surrey University	v	Racal Decca
Oxted	v	St George's Hospital
Old Epsomians	v	Haslemere
Royal Holloway College	v	Kings College Hospital
Surrey Police	v	Worth
Economicals	v	Charing Cross Hospital

January 6 1996 (Week 17)
Haslemere	v	Surrey Police
St George's Hospital	v	Old Epsomians
Racal Decca	v	Oxted
Economicals	v	Surrey University
Royal Holloway College	v	Worth
Kings College Hospital	v	Charing Cross Hospital

January 13 1996 (Week 18)
Oxted	v	Economicals
Old Epsomians	v	Racal Decca
Surrey Police	v	St George's Hospital
Royal Holloway College	v	Haslemere
Surrey University	v	Charing Cross Hospital
Kings College Hospital	v	Worth

February 10 1996 (Week 22)
Haslemere	v	Kings College Hospital
St George's Hospital	v	Royal Holloway College
Racal Decca	v	Surrey Police
Economicals	v	Old Epsomians
Surrey University	v	Oxted
Worth	v	Charing Cross Hospital

February 17 1996 (Week 23)
Old Epsomians	v	Surrey University
Surrey Police	v	Economicals
Royal Holloway College	v	Racal Decca
Kings College Hospital	v	St George's Hospital
Worth	v	Haslemere
Oxted	v	Charing Cross Hospital

February 24 1996 (Week 24)
Oxted	v	Old Epsomians
Racal Decca	v	Kings College Hospital
Economicals	v	Royal Holloway College
Surrey University	v	Surrey Police
St George's Hospital	v	Worth
Charing Cross Hospital	v	Haslemere

SURREY FOUR

CHARING CROSS AND WESTMINSTER MEDICAL SCHOOL RFC
Ground Address: Mr T Ralston, Groundsman, Charing Cross & Westminster Medical School Sports Grounds, Stoke Road, Stoke D'Abernon, Mr Cobham, Surrey.
Club Secretary: Patrick Clarke, 126 St Dunstan's Road, Hammersmith, London W6 8RA. Tel: (H) 0181 741 2509 Tel: (W) 0181 846 1234 (Students Union)
Fixtures Secretary: Paul Theruchellam, Charing Cross & Westminster Medical School, The Reynolds Building, St Dunstan's Road, Hammersmith, London W6. Tel (W) 0181 846 1234 (Students Union)
Club Colours: Red, blue, gold stripes.
ECONOMICALS RUFC
Ground Address: LSE Sports Ground, Windsor Avenue, New Malden, Surrey. Tel: 0181 942 1229
Club Secretary: Steve Bowen, 97 Salehurst Road, Crofton Park, London SE4 1AR. Tel: (H) 0181 690 5393 Tel: (W) 0181 486 1234
Fixtures Secretary: Steve Bowen, 97 Salehurst Road, Crofton Park, London SE4 1AR. Tel: (H) 0181 690 5393 Tel (W) 0181 486 1234
Club Colours: Green & white hoops.
HASLEMERE RFC
Ground Address: The Pavilion, Woolmer Hill Sports Ground, Woolmer Hill, Haslemere, Surrey GU27 1QA. Tel: 01428 643072
Club Secretary: Colin Andrews, Combedene, Portsmouth Road, Hindhead, Surrey GU26 6TQ. Tel: (H) 01428 604511 Tel: (W) 0171 340 0015
Fixtures Secretary: Joe Riley, 4 New Mills Cottages, Critchmere Lane, Haslemere, Surrey GU27 3RA. Tel: (H) 01428 652869 Tel (W) 01483 68889
Club Colours: Light blue & white broad hoops.
KINGS COLLEGE HOSPITAL RFC
Ground Address: Griffin Sports Ground, 12 Dulwich Village, Dulwich, London SE21 7AL. Tel: 0181 693 6900/2330
Club Secretary: Mr Nick McGrath, c/o Mr J Garnett, Kings College Hospital Medical School, Guild of Students, Bessemer Road, London SE5 9PJ. Tel: 0171 737 4000 (11am-3pm)
Fixtures Secretary: Mr Di Con, Kings College Hospital Rugby Football Club, Kings College Hospital Medical School, Bessemer Road, London SE5 9PJ.
Club Colours: Maroon, light blue, dark blue hoops.
OLD EPSOMIANS RFC
Club Secretary: D Collins, 80 Selsdon Road, South Croydon, Surrey CR2 6PF. Tel: (W) 0181 760 1144
Fixtures Secretary: S Schlaefli, 40 Broadhurst Gardens, Reigate, Surrey RG2 8AW.
Club Colours: Blue shirts, white shorts, blue socks.
OXTED RFC
Ground Address: Holland Field, Holland Road, Hurst Green, Oxted, Surrey. Tel: 01883 717468
Club Secretary: David Wood, 32A Queens Mansions, Brighton Road, South Croydon, Surrey CR2 6AL. Tel: (H) 0181 688 2935 Tel: (W) 0181 680 9581
Fixtures Secretary: Gary Allen, Flat 4, 138 Woodside Green, South Norwood, London SE25 5EW. Tel: (H) 0181 656 4702 Tel (W) 0171 269 7155
Club Colours: Blue with red hoop, red stockings.
RACAL DECCA RFC
Ground Address: Racal Decca Sports & Social Club, Kingston Road, Tolworth KT5 9NU. Tel: 0181 337 0519
Club Secretary: Mike Stevens, 18 Egerton Road, New Malden, Surrey KT3 4AP. Tel: (H) 0181 949 3643 Tel: (W) 01252 382960
Fixtures Secretary: Mike Stevens, 18 Egerton Road, New Malden, Surrey KT3 4AP. Tel: (H) 0181 949 3643 Tel (W) 01252 382960

FINAL TABLE

	P	W	D	L	F	A	Pts
Kew Occasionals	8	8	0	0	322	59	16
Old Wellingtonians	8	7	0	1	283	72	14
Kings Coll Hospital	8	5	0	3	144	129	10
Surrey University	7	4	1	2	84	99	9
Economicals	7	4	0	3	81	77	8
Royal Holloway Coll	7	3	0	4	201	162	6
Oxted	9	2	1	6	85	166	5
Surrey Police	8	2	1	5	78	208	5
Racal-Decca	8	1	1	6	88	182	3
Old Epsomians	8	1	0	7	35	247	2

Club Colours: Blue & white hoops.
ROYAL HOLLOWAY COLLEGE UNIVERSITY OF LONDON RFC
Ground Address: 'Nobles', Royal Holloway College University of London, Englefield Green, Egham, Surrey TW20 0EX.
Club Secretary: F Atekpe, Students Union, RHUL, Egham Hill, Egham, Surrey.
Fixtures Secretary: M Lloyd Davies, Students Union, Royal Holloway College University of London, Egham Hill, Egham, Surrey TW20 0EX. Tel: (H) 01784 435035
Club Colours: Purple & green.
ST GEORGE'S HOSPITAL MEDICAL SCHOOL RFC
Ground Address: St George's Hospital Sports Ground, Stoke Road, Cobham, Surrey. Tel: 01932 864341
Club Secretary: D Wallace, Canmer Terrace, Tooting, London SW17 0RE. Tel: (H) 0181 542 8894
Fixtures Secretary: D Wallace, Canmer Terrace, Tooting, London SW17 0RE. Tel: (H) 0181 542 8894
SURREY POLICE RFC
Ground Address: Police HQ, Mount Browne, Sandy Lane, Guildford GU1 3HG. Tel: 01483 571212
Club Secretary: SP Burrows, 4 Junewood Close, Woodham, New Haw, Addlestone, Surrey KT15 3PX. Tel: (H) 01932 344607 Tel: (W) 01483 482757
Fixtures Secretary: AP Brown, 49 Kingston Rise, New Haw, Addlestone, Surrey. Tel: (H) 01932 349874 Tel (W) 01932 845544 x5360
Club Colours: Black top with red V, black shorts.
UNIVERSITY OF SURREY RFC
Ground Address: Varsity Centre Sports Pavilion, Egerton, Guildford, Surrey. Tel: 01483 259393 x9242
Club Secretary: M Cusack, SURFC, c/o Students Union, University of Surrey, Guildford, Surrey GU2 5XH. Tel: (H) 01483 259981
Fixtures Secretary: S De Wint, c/o Students Union, Univsersity of Surrey, Guildford, Surrey GU2 5XH. Tel: (H) 01483 259981
Club Colours: Black with blue, red & gold hoops.
WORTH OLD BOYS' SOCIETY RFC
Ground Address: c/o Old Haileyburians, 27 Ruxley Lane, Ewell, Surrey. Tel: 0181 393 3901
Club Secretary: Mark Madsen, 129 Stormont Rad, London SW11. Tel: (H) 0171 228 7072 Tel: (W) 0171 629 8863
Fixtures Secretary: Sean Taylor, 17 Leconfield Avenue, London SW13 0LD. Tel: (H) 0181 878 9065 Tel (W) 0171 488 4000
Club Colours: Purple/orange/black hoops.

SOUTH WEST DIVISION

ADMINISTRATIVE RULES

1. MATCH RESULTS REPORTING INSTRUCTIONS

ALL LEAGUES

(i) Home Clubs will telephone the First Eleven Sports Agency on (01734) 311244 as soon as possible after the end of each game and certainly before 6.00pm, with the Match Result.

(ii) Both Clubs in each game will complete a Match Result Card, listing the team and replacements in block letters, with initials and the Match Result. The card must be signed by the Match Referee and posted, first class, to the First Eleven Sports Agency, by first post Monday latest.

2. NOTIFICATION OF RESULTS

Club Secretaries are responsible for their Club's compliance with the rules for notification of results. Failure to telephone and card-in the match result and team and replacements list, within the time limits laid down, will incur a fine for each offence of £15.00. Offending Clubs will be notified of fines imposed, failure to pay within 28 days will result in the offending Club being deducted two Competition points. Any outstanding fines at the end of the Season can result in the South West Division requesting the RFU to expel the offending club from the leagues.

3. POSTPONED AND ABANDONED GAMES

Club Secretaries of Clubs with Home matches must, in the event of a postponement or abandonment of any League match, immediately inform the First Eleven Sports Agency on 01734 311244 and their appropriate League Secretary. In the case of a game which is called off prior to kick off it is not necessary to complete a match card.

4. RESCHEDULED MATCHES

A match postponed or abandoned under Regulation 11 (a) or (b) or a match not played on the appointed day for reasons acceptable to the Organising Committee SHALL be played on the NEXT AVAILABLE Saturday.

A Saturday is deemed to be "available" UNLESS one of the following conditions applies:

(a) Either club has, on that day, a scheduled Courage League match.

(b) Either club has, on that day, a Pilkington Cup or Shield match.

(c) Either club has, on that weekend, a match in a Competition under the authority of their constituent body BUT NOT a Merit Table match.

(d) Either club has a demand on one or more of their effectively registered players to play in a representative match under the authority of the RFU, their Division of their Constituent Body on that Day.

(e) In addition, the South West Division Organising Committee, whose decision is final, may – at its absolute discretion and usually at the start of a season – declare a specific Saturday "unavailable" where it falls on or close to a public holiday or where it is considered inappropriate to play for other particular reasons.

Clubs must also notify the Agency and the League Secretary within SEVEN days of the date of the re-arranged fixture.

5. PLAYER REGISTRATION FORMS

All Player Registration Forms must, on completion, be forwarded to: The Registrar, PO Box 11, Reading RG6 3DT. Faxed registrations will not be accepted.

All enquiries regarding player registrations must be made to the Registrar by post or fax (No. 01734 757764) except on Wednesday evenings prior to league matches when a registration clinic is available between 8.00 and 10.00pm. The telephone number of the Clinic is 01734 311244.

6. CLUBS JOINING LEAGUES

All Clubs wishing to join the Courage Leagues should ensure that their membership of the Rugby Football Union has been accepted by 14th April to qualify for entry in the following Season.

7. CHANGE OF CLUB'S NAME

(i) Any proposals to change the name of a Club must be notified to the Co-ordinating Secretary before 1st May for inclusion in the Season commencing the September following.

(ii) Any Clubs proposing a merger should note the regulation in respect of Club mergers contained in the Rugby Football Union's Handbook.

8. GENERAL ENQUIRIES

Apart from registration of players, see pararaph 5, and the telephoning of results, paragraph 1, a clubs first point of contact over interpretation of the playing regulations or other matters involving the Courage Clubs Championship should be directed in the first instance to the club's League Secretary.

SOUTH WEST DIVISION

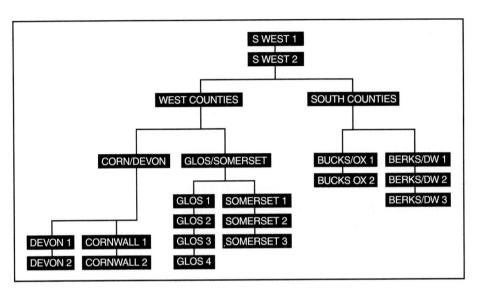

OFFICIALS 1995-96

CHAIRMAN, League Sub-Committee
Dr. C.V. Phillips, "Barlowena", Alexandra Road, Illogan, Cornwall TR16 4EN (H/Fax) 01209 842660 (B) 01209 714866 (B/Fax) 01209 716977
LEAGUES CO-ORDINATING SECRETARY
Mike Gee, "Suhaili", 7 Hellesvean Close, St Ives, Cornwall TR26 2HQ (H & Fax) 01736 797777
LEAGUE SECRETARIES
South West One & South West Two Jack D. Wooldridge, 16 Grange Drive, Durleigh, Bridgwater, Somerset, TA6 7LL (H/Fax) 01278 422009
Western Counties Mike Gee, "Suhaili", 7 Hellesvean Close, St Ives, Cornwall, TR26 2HQ (H/Fax) 01736 797777
Southern Counties Trevor Palm, 13 Dolesford Road, Aylesbury, Bucks (H) 01296 81847 (B) 01753 533223 (Fax) 01753 693724
Cornwall/Devon Bert Barber, 86 Dolcoath Road, Camborne, Cornwall TR14 8RP (H/Fax) 01209 710593 (B) 01752 665951
Devon One Geoff Simpson, 108 Pattison Drive, Mainstone, Plymouth PL6 8RU (H) 01752 707432 (B) 01752 563001 (Fax) 01752 564647
Devon Two Gillian Hoggins, The Old Forge, North Street, North Tawton, Devon EX20 2DE (H) 01837 82516

Cornwall One & Two Beverley Davis, 8 Penrose Road, Helston, Cornwall TR13 8TP (H/Fax) 01326 563744 (B) 01209 215620
Gloucestershire/Somerset, Somerset One Bill Bishop, "Hellvellyn", 1 Wiltshire Place, Kingswood, Bristol, Avon BS15 4XA.(H) 0117 957 5729 (B) 0117 935 2017 (Fax) 0117 940 1290
Somerset Two & Three Clive MacDonald, 8 Sycamore Drive, Crewkerne, Somerset, TA18 7BT (H/Fax) 01460 76136.
Gloucestershire One & Two Alan Townsend, St Kelelm, 2 Kencourt Close, Kenilworth Avenue, Gloucester GL2 0QL (H/Fax) 01452 522721 (B) 01452 300180
Gloucestershire Three & Four Cyril Ravenhill, 18 Merevale Road, Longlevens, Gloucester GL2 0QY (H/Fax) 01452 304317
Berk/Dorset & Wilts One, Two & Three Tony Bott, Kew House, Anchor Road, Calne, Wilts SN11 8DI (H & Fax) 01249 821448 (Mobile) 0860 448328
Bucks/Oxon One & Two Brian Flanders, Old Cross House, Coscote, Didcot, Oxon OX11 0NP (H) 01235 816523
COMMITTEE MEMBERS
Tony Boyer, 11 Christopher Court, Boundary Road, Newbury, Berks RG14 7PQ (H) 01635 40574
Bob Morrison, First Eleven Sports Agency, PO Box 11, Reading RG6 3DT (H) 01734 311244 (Fax) 01734 757764

SOUTH WEST DIVISION
FEATURED CLUBS

KEYNSHAM

KEYNSHAM, after missing promotion to the Western Counties League for two consecutive seasons, finally won the Gloucestershire and Somerset League on points differential from Whitehall – each club lost two of their dozen matches – and achieved their objective, even though it took them right to the wire and a local derby against Old Redcliffians before the title was theirs. It was an annus mirabilis for them in many ways as they also reached the final of the Somerset Cup to a dropped-goal by local rivals Weston Hornets and won the Bath Combination Cup and look forward to making a realistic challenge for further promotion, which with the inspiration of captain Mark Westcott and good support from such fine players as Ian Waker, Mike Pells, Russell Thompson and Steve Capon among others
should by no way be beyond them.

They have excellent facilities at their neat Crown Fields ground in Keynsham and are a very friendly outfit. Their backroom staff is superb and the back-up will make sure that one good season will not be the end of their successes. Last season they were a thorn in the flesh of several higher rated clubs – particularly in the County Cup. Watch for big things from them this coming season.

SWINDON

SWINDON by winning the Berkshire, Dorset and Wilts One find themselves in the Southern Counties League and they are determined to climb further and prove that the best clubs in the South West are not all from the Gloucestershire area and points West and their excellent form in winning their league with a perfect record from 12 matches and an astonishing 356-80 points differential would strongly suggest that after two near misses for promotion they have built a side strong enough to maintain a challenge for even better things.

If they do so they will be able to point to the shrewd move made by their committee in appointing Lloyd Morgan as Director of Coaching after his superb work as an England Under 21 coaching panelist) and Martin Popowicz as captain of the first team for a fourth consecutive season.

Swindon is a sleeping giant and a good rugby side is badly needed, so something special is needed from the present representatives which was founde3d as long ago as 1895, although a club called Swindon Rovers had been in existence even longer. In the next 100 years they plan to achieve big things and let no-one bet against that happening.

Swindon RFC

SOUTH WEST CHAMPIONS ROLL OF HONOUR 1994/95

South West 1
Cheltenham
South West 2
Matson
Western Counties
Launceston
Southern Counties
Dorchester
Cornwall & Devon
Paignton
Gloucester & Somerset
Keynsham
Cornwall 1
St Austell
Cornwall 2
Redruth Albany
Devon 1
Old Plymothian
Devon 2
Totnes
Somerset 1
Wellington

Somerset 2
Imperial
Somerset 3
Avonvale
Gloucestershire 1
Cleve
Gloucestershire 2
Tredworth
Gloucestershire 3
Cainscross
Gloucestershire 4
Gloucestershire Police
Berks, Dorset & Wilts 1
Swindon
Berks, Dorset & Wilts 2
Bournemouth University
Berks, Dorset & Wilts 3
Portcastrians
Bucks & Oxon 1
Chinnor
Bucks & Oxon 2
Wheatley

Keynsham

SOUTH WEST DIVISION

November 11 1995 (Week 10)

Bridgwater	v	Taunton
Brixham	v	Barnstaple
Cinderford	v	Salisbury
Gloucester OB	v	St Ives
Matson	v	Maidenhead
Sherborne	v	Newbury

September 16 1995 (Week 3)

Gloucester OB	v	Brixham
Maidenhead	v	Salisbury
Matson	v	Bridgwater
Newbury	v	Barnstaple
Sherborne	v	Cinderford
Torquay	v	Taunton

January 6 1996 (Week 17)

Barnstaple	v	Cinderford
Maidenhead	v	Sherborne
Newbury	v	Gloucester OB
Salisbury	v	Bridgwater
St Ives	v	Brixham
Torquay	v	Matson

September 23 1995 (Week 4)

Barnstaple	v	Maidenhead
Bridgwater	v	Sherborne
Cinderford	v	Gloucester OB
Salisbury	v	Torquay
St Ives	v	Newbury
Taunton	v	Matson

January 13 1996 (Week 18)

Bridgwater	v	Barnstaple
Brixham	v	Newbury
Cinderford	v	St Ives
Gloucester OB	v	Maidenhead
Sherborne	v	Torquay
Taunton	v	Salisbury

September 30 1995 (Week X1)

Brixham	v	Cinderford
Gloucester OB	v	Bridgwater
Maidenhead	v	St Ives
Matson	v	Salisbury
Sherborne	v	Taunton
Torquay	v	Barnstaple

February 10 1996 (Week 22)

Barnstaple	v	Taunton
Maidenhead	v	Brixham
Matson	v	Sherborne
Newbury	v	Cinderford
St Ives	v	Bridgwater
Torquay	v	Gloucester OB

October 14 1995 (Week 6)

Barnstaple	v	Matson
Bridgwater	v	Brixham
Newbury	v	Maidenhead
Salisbury	v	Sherborne
St Ives	v	Torquay
Taunton	v	Gloucester OB

February 17 1996 (Week 23)

Bridgwater	v	Newbury
Brixham	v	Torquay
Cinderford	v	Maidenhead
Gloucester OB	v	Matson
Salisbury	v	Barnstaple
Taunton	v	St Ives

October 21 1995 (Week 7)

Brixham	v	Taunton
Cinderford	v	Bridgwater
Gloucester OB	v	Salisbury
Matson	v	St Ives
Sherborne	v	Barnstaple
Torquay	v	Newbury

February 24 1996 (Week 24)

Maidenhead	v	Bridgwater
Matson	v	Brixham
Newbury	v	Taunton
Sherborne	v	Gloucester OB
St Ives	v	Salisbury
Torquay	v	Cinderford

October 28 1995 (Week 8)

Barnstaple	v	Gloucester OB
Maidenhead	v	Torquay
Newbury	v	Matson
Salisbury	v	Brixham
St Ives	v	Sherborne
Taunton	v	Cinderford

March 30 1996 (Week X7)

Barnstaple	v	St Ives
Bridgwater	v	Torquay
Brixham	v	Sherborne
Cinderford	v	Matson
Salisbury	v	Newbury
Taunton	v	Maidenhead

SOUTH WEST ONE

BARNSTAPLE RFC
Ground Address: Pottington Road, Barnstaple, North Devon EX31 1DZ. Tel: 01271 45627
Club Secretary: RM Pettifer, Baileys Cottage, Lake, Barnstaple EX31 3HU. Tel: (H) 01271 73475
Fixtures Secretary: M Hughes, Dale House, 15 Meadowside, Ashford, Barnstaple EX31 4BS. Tel: (H) 01271 43547
Club Colours: Red shirts, white shorts.
BRIDGWATER & ALBION RFC
Ground Address: College Way, Bath Road, Bridgwater, Somerset TA6 4TZ. Tel: 01278 423900
Club Secretary: Anthony Pomeroy, Hafod-y-gân, Newton Road, North Petherton, Somerset TA6 6SN. Tel: (H) 01278 662181 Tel: (W) 01278 455631
Fixtures Secretary: Ralph Sealey, 12 Capes Close, Bridgwater, Somerset. Tel: (H) 01278 444757
Club Colours: Red, black & amber.
BRIXHAM RFC
Ground Address: Astley Park, Higher Ranscombe Road, Brixham. Tel: 01803 882162
Club Secretary: Bob Houston, 'St Cloud', Cliff Park Road, Brixham, South Devon TQ4 6NS. Tel: (H) 01803 550427 Tel: (W) -1752 224141
Fixtures Secretary: Danny Irvine, 1 Great Rea Road, Brixham, South Devon TQ5 9SW. Tel: (H) 01803 882219
Club Colours: Black with 6' white band.
CINDERFORD RFC
Ground Address: Recreation Ground, Dockham Road, Cinderford, Glos GL14 2AQ. Tel: 01594 822673
Club Secretary: Mrs M Beavis, 5 Abbots Road, Cinderford, Glos GL14 3BN. Tel: (H) 01594 823779
Fixtures Secretary: Mr J Gazzard, 1 Wedgewood Crescent, Cinderford, Glos. Tel: (H) 01594 822333
Club Colours: Red, black & amber.
GLOUCESTER OLD BOYS' RFC
Ground Address: Horton Road, Gloucester GL1 3PX. Tel: 01452 302390
Club Secretary: Dylan Green, 47 Lanham Gardens, Quedgley, Gloucester GL2 6 ME. Tel: (H) 01452 723229
Fixtures Secretary: C Read, 21 Meadowgate, Longlevens, Gloucester GL2 0PW. Tel: (H) 01452 306491 Tel (W) 01452 424418
Club Colours: Claret, gold & navy hoops.
MAIDENHEAD RUFC
Ground Address: Braywick Park, Braywick Road, Maidenhead, Berkshire SL6 1BN. Tel: 01628 35452/29663
Club Secretary: Richard M Brown, 49 Barnard Road, Maidenhead, Berkshire SL6 4NP. Tel: (H) 01628 70586 Tel: (W) 01628 53308
Fixtures Secretary: Mr AG Cowen, 31 Furze Platt Road, Maidenhead, Berkshire SL6 7NE. Tel: (H) 01628 29237 Tel (W) 01865 792336
Club Colours: Magenta, violet & black.
MATSON RFC
Ground Address: Redwell Road, Matson, Gloucester GL4 9JG. Tel: 01452 528963
Club Secretary: Gilbert Locke, 39 Oxmoor, Abbeydale, Gloucester GL4 9XW. Tel: (H) 01452 419587 Tel: (W) 01452 712802
Fixtures Secretary: Les Pearce, 92 Matson Avenue, Matson, Gloucester. Tel: (H) 01452 311547
Club Colours: Black shirts, white shorts.
NEWBURY RFC
Ground Address: Pinchington Lane, Newbury, Berkshire RG14 7HB. Tel: 01635 40103
Club Secretary: Mr LA Sugden, Brook Cottage, Boxford, Newbury, Berkshire. Tel: (H) 01488 608607 Tel: (W) 01635 46881
Fixtures Secretary: Richard Little, 27 Lipscombe Close, Hermitage, Newbury, Berkshire. Tel: (H) 01635 200304

FINAL TABLE

	P	W	D	L	F	A	Pts
Cheltenham	12	11	1	0	275	112	21*
Newbury	12	9	1	2	376	113	19
Barnstaple	12	9	0	3	224	115	18
Gloucester Old Boys	12	9	0	3	222	147	18
Brixham	12	5	2	5	177	180	12
St Ives	12	7	0	5	151	170	12*
Maidenhead	12	5	1	6	198	159	11
Salisbury	12	4	1	7	183	296	9
Cinderford	12	3	2	7	141	178	8
Torquay Athletic	12	3	1	8	134	244	7
Sherborne	12	4	0	8	168	257	6*
Taunton	12	2	1	9	193	285	5
Stroud	12	2	0	10	136	324	4

Club Colours: Light blue & dark blue.
SALISBURY RFC
Ground Address: Castle Road, Salisbury SP1 3SA. Tel: 01722 325317
Fixtures Secretary: RH Rowland, 1 Lode Hill, Downton, Wilts SP5 3PW. Tel: (H) 01725 512064 Tel (W) 0171 734 8697
Club Colours: Green & white.
SHERBORNE RFC
Ground Address: The Terraces, Sherborne, Dorset DT9 5NS. Tel: 01935 812478
Club Secretary: Mr N Rawles, 17 Kings Road, Sherborne, Dorset DT9 4HU. Tel: (H) 01935 814108
Fixtures Secretary: Mrs Val Rushton, 2 Sackmore Green, Sturminster Newton, Marnhull, Dorset DT10 1PW. Tel: (H) 01258 820195
Club Colours: Black shirts, black shorts.
ST IVES RFC
Ground Address: Alexandra Road, St Ives, Cornwall. Tel: 01736 795346
Club Secretary: Carol Bell, Trerice, Clodgy View, St Ives, Cornwall TR26 1JG. Tel: (H) 01736 717472
Fixtures Secretary: M Gee, 'Suhaila', 7 Hellesvane Close, St Ives, Cornwall TR6 7HQ. Tel: (H) 01736 797169
Club Colours: Navy blue & white.
TAUNTON RFC
Ground Address: Priory Park, Priory Bridge Road, Taunton, Somerset TA1 1QB. Tel: 01823 275670
Club Secretary: Peter Hancock, 21 Kirke Grove, Taunton, Somerset TA2 8SB. Tel: (H) 01823 277982
Fixtures Secretary: Rodney Reed, 22 Barrow Drive, Taunton, Somerset. Tel: (H) 01823 276354 Tel (W) 01823 337900 x3375
Club Colours: Crimson, black & white hoops.
TORQUAY ATHLETIC RFC
Ground Address: Recreation Ground, Sea Front, Torquay, Devon. Tel: 01803 293842
Club Secretary: Robin Foster, Garden Flat, Seacrest. Roundham Crescent, Paignton, Torquay, TQ4 6DF. Tel: (H) 01803 529985 Tel: (W) 01803 655002
Fixtures Secretary: Dave Thompson, 44 Bidwell Brook Drive, Churston, Paignton, Devon. Tel: (H) 01803 845115 Tel (W) 01803 858271
Club Colours: Black and white.

SOUTH WEST DIVISION

SOUTH WEST TWO
1995-96
FIXTURES

November 11 1995 (Week 10)

Aylesbury	v	Clevedon
Bournemouth	v	Stroud
Combe Down	v	Banbury
Dorchester	v	Launceston
Old Patesians	v	Oxford
Swanage & Wareham	v	Penryn

September 16 1995 (Week 3)

Aylesbury	v	Bournemouth
Gordon League	v	Banbury
Old Patesians	v	Dorchester
Oxford	v	Stroud
Penryn	v	Launceston
Swanage & Wareham	v	Combe Down

January 6 1996 (Week 17)

Clevedon	v	Bournemouth
Gordon League	v	Swanage & Wareham
Launceston	v	Combe Down
Oxford	v	Aylesbury
Penryn	v	Old Patesians
Stroud	v	Dorchester

September 23 1995 (Week 4)

Banbury	v	Swanage & Wareham
Clevedon	v	Oxford
Combe Down	v	Old Patesians
Dorchester	v	Aylesbury
Launceston	v	Gordon League
Stroud	v	Penryn

January 13 1996 (Week 18)

Aylesbury	v	Penryn
Banbury	v	Launceston
Bournemouth	v	Oxford
Combe Down	v	Stroud
Dorchester	v	Clevedon
Old Patesians	v	Gordon League

September 30 1995 (Week X1)

Aylesbury	v	Combe Down
Bournemouth	v	Dorchester
Gordon League	v	Stroud
Old Patesians	v	Banbury
Penryn	v	Clevedon
Swanage & Wareham	v	Launceston

February 10 1996 (Week 22)

Clevedon	v	Combe Down
Gordon League	v	Aylesbury
Oxford	v	Dorchester
Penryn	v	Bournemouth
Stroud	v	Banbury
Swanage & Wareham	v	Old Patesians

October 14 1995 (Week 6)

Banbury	v	Aylesbury
Clevedon	v	Gordon League
Combe down	v	Bournemouth
Launceston	v	Old Patesians
Oxford	v	Penryn
Stroud	v	Swanage & Wareham

February 17 1996 (Week 23)

Aylesbury	v	Swanage & Wareham
Banbury	v	Clevedon
Bournemouth	v	Gordon League
Combe Down	v	Oxford
Dorchester	v	Penryn
Launceston	v	Stroud

October 21 1995 (Week 7)

Aylesbury	v	Launceston
Bournemouth	v	Banbury
Dorchester	v	Combe Down
Gordon League	v	Oxford
Old Patesians	v	Stroud
Swanage & Wareham	v	Clevedon

February 24 1996 (Week 24)

Clevedon	v	Launceston
Gordon League	v	Dorchester
Old Patesians	v	Aylesbury
Oxford	v	Banbury
Penryn	v	Combe Down
Swanage & Wareham	v	Bournemouth

October 28 1995 (Week 8)

Banbury	v	Dorchester
Clevedon	v	Old Patesians
Launceston	v	Bournemouth
Oxford	v	Swanage & Wareham
Penryn	v	Gordon League
Stroud	v	Aylesbury

March 30 1996 (Week X7)

Banbury	v	Penryn
Bournemouth	v	Old Patesians
Combe Down	v	Gordon League
Dorchester	v	Swanage & Wareham
Launceston	v	Oxford
Stroud	v	Clevedon

SOUTH WEST TWO

AYLESBURY RFC
Ground Address: Ostler's Field, Brook End, Weston Turville, Aylesbury, Buckinghamshire HP22 5RN. Tel: 01296 612556
Club Secretary: Graham N Roberts, 11 Langdon Avenue, Aylesbury, Bucks HP21 9UL. Tel: (H) 01296 85695
Fixtures Secretary: Mr JP Williams, 11 Little Mollards, Wingrave, Aylesbury, Bucks. Tel: (H) 01296 688249
Club Colours: Magenta & black.

BANBURY RUFC
Ground Address: Oxford Road, Bodicote, Banbury, Oxon. Tel: 01295 263862
Club Secretary: M Thomas, 24 Poplars Road, Chacombe, Banbury, Oxon OX17 2JY. Tel: (H) 01295 711582 Tel: (W) 01295 267511
Fixtures Secretary: R Croft, 1 Daisy Hill Farm Cottage, Duns Tew, Oxford OX6 4JS. Tel: (H) 01869 347124 Tel (W) 01869 347124
Club Colours: Navy blue & white hoops.

BOURNEMOUTH RFC
Ground Address: Bournemouth Sports Club, Chapel Gate, Bast Parley, Christchurch, Dorset BH23 6BD. Tel: 01202 581933
Club Secretary: Mike Wilkes, 581 Christchurch Road, Bournemouth, Dorset BH1 4BU. Tel: (H) 01202 395168 Tel: (W) 01202 302345
Fixtures Secretary: Ian Mure, 17 Barn Road, Broadstone, Dorset BH18 8NH. Tel: (H) 01202 696331
Club Colours: Sable & Or (black with small gold hoops on shirts).

CLEVEDON RFC
Ground Address: Coleridge Vale Playing Fields, Southey Road, Clevedon, Avon BS21 6PF. Tel: 01275 877772
Club Secretary: RG Legge, 2 Kingston Avenue, Clevedon, Avon BS21 6DS. Tel: (H) 01275 874624 Tel: (W) 0117 9291031 x2995
Fixtures Secretary: J Evans, 79 Kenn Road, Clevedon, Avon BS21 6HE. Tel: (H) 01275 871443
Club Colours: Royal blue & gold hoops.

COMBE DOWN RFC
Ground Address: Holly's Corner, North Road, Combe Down, Bath. Tel: 01225 832075
Club Secretary: N Williams, 2 Abbey View Gardens, Widcombe, Bath BA2 6DQ. Tel: (H) 01225 312405 Tel: (W) 01225 444222 x3124
Fixtures Secretary: W Bailey, 2 Warbler Close, Trowbridge, Wilts. Tel: (H) 01225 760217
Club Colours: Black & amber.

DORCHESTER RFC
Ground Address: Coburg Road, Dorchester, Dorset. Tel: 01305 265692
Club Secretary: Mr Graham Aspley, 5 Nappers Court, Charles Street, Dorchester, Dorset DT1 1EE. Tel: (H) 01305 814802 Tel: (W) 01305 269944
Fixtures Secretary: Tony Foot, 25 Cromwell Road, Dorchester, Dorset DT1 2DN. Tel: (H) 01305 250137 Tel (W) 01305 262123
Club Colours: Green & white hoops.

GORDON LEAGUE RFC
Ground Address: Hempsted Lane, Hempsted, Gloucester GL2 6NF. Tel: 01452 303434
Club Secretary: Mr W R King, 361 Innsworth Lane, Churchdown, Gloucester GL3 1EY. Tel: (H) 01452 856787 Tel: (W) 01452 371371 x2656
Fixtures Secretary: Mr R Hancock, Willow Lawn, Hempsted, Gloucester. Tel: (H) 01452 523556 Tel (W) 01452 526631
Club Colours: White with red sash.

LAUNCESTON RFC
Ground Address: The New Club House, Polson, Launceston, Cornwall. Tel: 01566 773406

	P	W	D	L	F	A	Pts
FINAL TABLE							
Matson	12	10	1	1	279	130	21
Bridgwater	12	10	0	2	238	127	20
Gordon League	12	8	1	3	173	131	17
Clevedon	12	8	0	4	266	168	16
Old Patesians	12	7	0	5	288	167	12*
Combe Down	12	6	0	6	202	208	12
Bournemouth	12	5	1	6	166	163	12
Oxford	12	5	0	7	157	237	10
Swanage	12	4	1	7	212	288	9
Aylesbury	12	4	0	8	143	186	8
Banbury	12	4	0	8	170	289	8
Penryn	12	3	0	9	181	295	4*
Marlow	12	2	0	10	156	242	2*

Club Secretary: Mr Ralph BW Wilkinson, St Dominick House, The Walk, Launceston, Cornwall PL15 8BP. Tel: (H) 01566 772433
Fixtures Secretary: Mr W Gladwell, 5 Hendra, Tor View, Five Lanes, Altarnun, Nr Launceston, Cornwall. Tel: (H) 01566 86964
Club Colours: Black.

OLD PATESIANS RFC
Ground Address: Everest Road, Leckhampton, Cheltenham, Gloucestershire. Tel: 01242 524633
Club Secretary: PJ McMurray, Avon, Victoria Terrace, Cheltenham, Gloucestershire GL52 6BN. Tel: (H) 01242 570947 Tel: (W) 01242 515881
Fixtures Secretary: S Cohen, Rosslyn, Moorend Grove, Leckhampton, Cheltenham, Gloucestershire GL53 0EX. Tel: (H) 01242 520873 Tel (W) 01242 221221 x281
Club Colours: Magenta, blue & white hoops.

OXFORD RFC
Ground Address: North Hinksey Village, Oxford. Tel: 01865 243984
Club Secretary: RL Martin, Pantiles, 22 Didcot Road, Long Wittenham, Oxon OX14 4PZ. Tel: (H) 01865 407528
Fixtures Secretary: R Mountford, 28 Crecy Walk, Woodstock, Oxon OX7 1US. Tel: (H) 01993 812389
Club Colours: Black/green/silver hoops.

PENRYN RFC
Ground Address: The Memorial Ground, Kernick Road, Penryn, Cornwall TR10 8QP. Tel: 01326 372239
Club Secretary: Mrs MSD O'Neill, 80 Bohelland Road, Penryn, Cornwall TR10 8DY. Tel: (H) 01326 373283
Club Colours: Black & red hoops.

STROUD RFC
Ground Address: Fromehall Park, Stroud, Glos GL5 3HS. Tel: 01453 763019
Club Secretary: Dennis Little, Lower Court, Selsley Road, Woodchester, Stroud, Glos GL5 5PH. Tel: (H) 01453 872800 Fax: 01453 872383
Fixtures Secretary: Russell Hillier, Marijon, Pagan Hill Lane, Stroud, Glos GL5 4AW. Tel: (H) 01453 764381
Club Colours: Blue & white hoops.

SWANAGE & WAREHAM RFC
Ground Address: Bestwall, Wareham, Dorset BH20 4AY. Tel: 01929 552224
Club Secretary: Kevin Large, 20 Gannetts Park, Swanage, Dorset. Tel: (H) 01929 426523 Tel: (W) 01929 425818
Fixtures Secretary: John M Hopkins, Sospan, Greenclose Lane, Leigh, Wimborne, Dorset BH21 9AL. Tel: (H) 01202 886804
Club Colours: Maroon shirts, white shorts, maroon hose.

SOUTH WEST DIVISION

WESTERN COUNTIES 1995-96 FIXTURES

September 16 1995 (Week 3)
Dings Crusaders   v   Crediton
Keynsham   v   Bristol
Paignton   v   Okehampton
Spartans   v   Devonport Services
Tiverton   v   Old Culverhaysians

September 23 1995 (Week 4)
Crediton   v   Keynsham
Drybrook   v   Dings Crusaders
Okehampton   v   Tiverton
Old Culverhaysians   v   Spartans
Penzance-Newlyn   v   Paignton

September 30 1995 (Week X1)
Bideford   v   Crediton
Dings Crusaders   v   Devonport Services
Keynsham   v   Drybrook
Spartans   v   Okehampton
Tiverton   v   Penzance-Newlyn

October 14 1995 (Week 6)
Devonport Services   v   Keynsham
Drybrook   v   Bideford
Old Culverhaysians   v   Dings Crusaders
Paignton   v   Tiverton
Penzance-Newlyn   v   Spartans

October 21 1995 (Week 7)
Bideford   v   Devonport Services
Crediton   v   Drybrook
Dings Crusaders   v   Okehampton
Keynsham   v   Old Culverhaysians
Spartans   v   Paignton

October 28 1995 (Week 8)
Devonport Services   v   Crediton
Okehampton   v   Keynsham
Old Culverhaysians   v   Bideford
Penzance-Newlyn   v   Dings Crusaders
Tiverton   v   Spartans

November 11 1995 (Week 10)
Bideford   v   Okehampton
Crediton   v   Old Culverhaysians
Dings Crusaders   v   Paignton
Drybrook   v   Devonport Services
Keynsham   v   Penzance-Newlyn

January 6 1996 (Week 17)
Okehampton   v   Crediton
Old Culverhaysians   v   Drybrook
Paignton   v   Keynsham
Penzance-Newlyn   v   Bideford
Tiverton   v   Dings Crusaders

January 13 1996 (Week 18)
Bideford   v   Paignton
Crediton   v   Penzance-Newlyn
Devonport Services   v   Old Culverhaysians
Dings Crusaders   v   Spartans
Drybrook   v   Okehampton
Keynsham   v   Tiverton

February 10 1996 (Week 22)
Okehampton   v   Devonport Services
Paignton   v   Crediton
Penzance-Newlyn   v   Drybrook
Spartans   v   Keynsham
Tiverton   v   Bideford

February 17 1996 (Week 23)
Bideford   v   Spartans
Crediton   v   Tiverton
Devonport Services   v   Penzance-Newlyn
Drybrook   v   Paignton
Old Culverhaysians   v   Okehampton

February 24 1996 (Week 24)
Dings Crusaders   v   Keynsham
Paignton   v   Devonport Services
Penzance-Newlyn   v   Old Culverhaysians
Spartans   v   Crediton
Tiverton   v   Drybrook

March 30 1996 (Week X7)
Bideford   v   Dings Crusaders
Devonport Services   v   Tiverton
Drybrook   v   Spartans
Okehampton   v   Penzance-Newlyn
Old Culverhaysians   v   Paignton

WESTERN COUNTIES

BIDEFORD RFC
Ground Address: King George's Field, Bank End, Bideford, Devon. Tel: 01237 474049
Club Secretary: Bernard A Ridd, The Firs, Glen Gardens, Bideford, Devon EX39 3PH. Tel: (H) 01237 475180 Tel: (W) 01237 475180
Fixtures Secretary: B Cork, 4 Park Lane, Bideford, Devon. Tel: (H) 01237 479841 Tel (W) 0237 479841
Club Colours: Red & white hooped jerseys, white shorts, red socks.

CREDITON RFC
Ground Address: Exhibition Road, Crediton, Devon EX17 1BY. Tel: 01363 772784
Club Secretary: Mr Philip H Gibbings, 80 Greenway, Crediton, Devon EX17 3LP. Tel: (H) 01363 774820 Tel: (W) 01363 774820
Fixtures Secretary: Captain KS Pitt RN (Ret'd), Tannery Farm, Bow, Devon EX17 6JP. Tel: (H) 01363 82230 Tel (W) 01363 82230
Club Colours: Black & amber.

DEVONPORT SERVICES RFC
Ground Address: The Rectory, Second Avenue, Devonport, Plymouth PL1 5QE. Tel: 01752 501559
Club Secretary: Lt Cdr M A Waythe, Field Gun Office, HMS Drake, HM Naval Base, Plymouth. Tel: (H) 01752 848802 Tel: (W) 01752 555483
Fixtures Secretary: Lr Cdr R Wiltcher, Staff of Flag Officer Plymouth, Mount Wise, Devonport, Plymouth. Tel: (H) 01752 481589 Tel (W) 01752 501425
Club Colours: Navy blue shirts & shorts, red socks.

DINGS CRUSADERS RFC
Ground Address: Shaftesbury Crusader, Landseer Avenue, Lockleaze, Bristol BS7. Tel: 0117 969 1367
Club Secretary: Gerry Williams, 22 Crowther Road, Horfield, Bristol BS7 9NS. Tel: (H) 0117 951 6059 Tel: (W) 0117 943 6205
Fixtures Secretary: Terry Webb, 50 Monks Park Avenue, Horfield, Bristol BS7 0UH. Tel: (H) 0117 983 0273
Club Colours: Royal blue & black.

DRYBROOK RFC
Ground Address: The Mannings, High Street, Drybrook, Glos. Tel: 01594 542594
Club Secretary: Glyn Tingle, Southview, Hazel Hill, Drybrook, Glos GL17 9HH. Tel: (H) 01594 543294 Tel: (W) 01594 542769
Fixtures Secretary: Derek Trigg, Lyveden, Ruardean Hill, Drybrook, Glos. Tel: (H) 01594 542258
Club Colours: Green with black on white band.

KEYNSHAM RFC
Ground Address: Keynsham RFC, Crown Field, Bristol Road, Keynsham, Bristol BS18 2BE. Tel: 0117 987 2520
Club Secretary: Dermot Courtier, 15 Montague Road, Saltford, Bristol BS18 3LA. Tel: (H) 01225 873522 Tel: (W) 0171 320 7405
Fixtures Secretary: John Holliday, 38 Fourth Avenue, Filton, Bristol BS7 0RW. Tel: (H) 0117 969 1821
Club Colours: Amber & black.

OKEHAMPTON RFC
Ground Address: Oaklands Park, Okehampton, Devon. Tel: 01837 52508
Club Secretary: Ted Cann, 11 Exeter Road, Okehampton, Devon EX20 1NN. Tel: (H) 01837 52759
Fixtures Secretary: David Dixon, Mistlebank, Ramsley Lane, South Zeal, Nr Okehampton, Devon. Tel: (H) 01837 840818
Club Colours: Maroon & amber hoops.

FINAL TABLE

	P	W	D	L	F	A	Pts
Launceston	12	12	0	0	438	90	24
Devonport Services	12	9	1	2	272	111	19
Dings Crusaders	12	9	0	3	335	124	18
Pemzance & Newlyn	12	8	0	4	287	160	16
Spartons	12	9	0	3	253	152	16*
Okehampton	12	7	0	5	172	168	14
Old Culverhaysians	12	5	0	7	167	226	10
Tiverton	12	4	1	7	143	232	9
Crediton	12	3	2	7	141	205	8
Drybrook	12	3	1	8	136	391	7
Bideford	12	3	0	9	118	238	6
Devon-Cornwall Pol	12	3	0	9	104	313	6
Avonmouth	12	0	1	11	91	247	1

OLD CULVERHAYSIANS RFC
Ground Address: The Glasshouse, Bradford Road, Bath, Avon. Clubhouse: Old Fosse Road, Odd down, Bath. Tel: 01225 832081
Club Secretary: Mike Harding, 6 Gages Close, Kingswood, Bristol BS15 2UH. Tel: (H) 0117 947 5862 Tel: (W) 01453 835431
Fixtures Secretary: Bob Toghill, The Parsonage, The Street, Farrington Gurney, Bristol BS18 5UB. Tel: (H) 01761 453553
Club Colours: All black.

PAIGNTON RFC
Ground Address: Queens Park, Queens Road, Paignton, Devon. Tel: 01803 557715
Club Secretary: Ray Squires, 67 Brantwood Drive, Paignton TQ4 5HY. Tel: (H) 01803 554360
Fixtures Secretary: Gary Moate, 12 Knapp Park Road, Paignton, Devon TQ4 7LA. Tel: (H) 01803 555655 Tel (W) 01392 50822
Club Colours: Red & white hoops.

PENZANCE & NEWLYN RFC
Ground Address: Westholme, Alexandra Road, Penzance, Cornwall TR18 4LY. Tel: 01736 64227
Club Secretary: AR Blewett, 17 Church Street, Newlyn, Penzance, Cornwall TR18 5JY. Tel: (H) 01736 62562
Fixtures Secretary: A Edwards, Chy Kembro, Boslandew Hill, Paul, Penzance, Cornwall TR19 6UD. Tel: (H) 01736 731042 Tel (W) 01736 331166
Club Colours: Black, white & red.

SPARTANS RFC
Ground Address: Archdeacon Meadow (at rear of Cattle Market), Gloucester. Tel: 01452 410552
Club Secretary: Phil Minns, 8 Sebert Street, Kingsholm, Gloucester GL1 3BP. Tel: (H) 01452 500122
Fixtures Secretary: Mr Paul Smith, 162 Coney Hill Road, Gloucester. Tel: (H) 01452 533027
Club Colours: Red shirt, black shorts, red socks.

TIVERTON RFC
Ground Address: Coronation Field, Bolham Road, Tiverton, Devon EX16 6SG. Tel: 01884 252271
Club Secretary: David Baker, Millhouse, Burn, Silverton, Exeter, Devon. Tel: (H) 01884 855548 Tel: (W) 01884 256412
Fixtures Secretary: Raymond Takel, 90 Westexe South, Tiverton, Devon. Tel: (H) 01884 257526
Club Colours: Light & dark blue.

SOUTH WEST DIVISION

CORNWALL & DEVON 1995-96 FIXTURES

September 16 1995 (Week 3)

Exmouth	v	Ivybridge
Honiton	v	OPM
Saltash	v	Veor
Sidmouth	v	Truro
St Austell	v	Plymouth CS
Teignmouth	v	South Molton

September 23 1995 (Week 4)

Hayle	v	Exmouth
Ivybridge	v	Sidmouth
Plymouth CS	v	Honiton
South Molton	v	Saltash
Truro	v	Teignmouth
Veor	v	St Austell

September 30 1995 (Week X1)

Honiton	v	Veor
OPM	v	Plymouth CS
Saltash	v	Truro
Sidmouth	v	Hayle
St Austell	v	South Molton
Teignmouth	v	Ivybridge

October 14 1995 (Week 6)

Exmouth	v	Sidmouth
Hayle	v	Teignmouth
Ivybridge	v	Saltash
South Molton	v	Honiton
Truro	v	St Austell
Veor	v	OPM

October 21 1995 (Week 7)

Honiton	v	Truro
OPM	v	South Molton
Plymouth CS	v	Veor
Saltash	v	Hayle
St Austell	v	Ivybridge
Teignmouth	v	Exmouth

October 28 1995 (Week 8)

Exmouth	v	Saltash
Hayle	v	St Austell
Ivybridge	v	Honiton
Sidmouth	v	Teignmouth
South Molton	v	Plymouth CS
Truro	v	OPM

November 11 1995 (Week 10)

Honiton	v	Hayle
OPM	v	Ivybridge
Plymouth CS	v	Truro
Saltash	v	Sidmouth
St Austell	v	Exmouth
Veor	v	South Molton

January 6 1996 (Week 17)

Exmouth	v	Honiton
Hayle	v	OPM
Ivybridge	v	Plymouth CS
Sidmouth	v	St Austell
Teignmouth	v	Saltash
Truro	v	Veor

January 13 1996 (Week 18)

Honiton	v	Sidmouth
OPM	v	Exmouth
Plymouth CS	v	Hayle
South Molton	v	Truro
St Austell	v	Teignmouth
Veor	v	Ivybridge

February 10 1996 (Week 22)

Exmouth	v	Plymouth CS
Hayle	v	Veor
Ivybridge	v	South Molton
Saltash	v	St Austell
Sidmouth	v	OPM
Teignmouth	v	Honiton

February 17 1996 (Week 23)

Honiton	v	Saltash
OPM	v	Teignmouth
Plymouth CS	v	Sidmouth
South Molton	v	Hayle
Truro	v	Ivybridge
Veor	v	Exmouth

February 24 1996 (Week 24)

Exmouth	v	South Molton
Hayle	v	Truro
Saltash	v	OPM
Sidmouth	v	Veor
St Austell	v	Honiton
Teignmouth	v	Plymouth CS

March 30 1996 (Week X7)

Ivybridge	v	Hayle
OPM	v	St Austell
Plymouth CS	v	Saltash
South Molton	v	Sidmouth
Truro	v	Exmouth
Veor	v	Teignmouth

CORNWALL & DEVON

EXMOUTH RFC
Ground Address: Imperial Recreation Ground, Royal Avenue, Exmouth, Devon EX8 1DG. Tel: 01395 263665
Club Secretary: Asst. Sec. Mrs Janet McCarthy, 7 Dorchester Way, Exmouth, Devon EX8 5QE. Tel: (H) 01395 276901 Tel: (W) 01395 445581
Fixtures Secretary: Mr R Nye, 22 Broadfields Road, Heavitree, Exeter, Devon. Tel: (H) 01392 435608 Tel (W) 01823 433933
Club Colours: Heliotrope & white hoops.

HAYLE RFC
Ground Address: Memorial Park, Marsh Lane, Hayle, Cornwall TR27 4PS. Tel: 01736 753320
Club Secretary: TC Mungles, 5 Eglishayle Road, Hayle, Cornwall TR27 4EL. Tel: (H) 01736 752987 Tel: (W) 01209 612780
Fixtures Secretary: Mike Gee, 'Suhaili', 7 Hellesvean Close, St Ives, Cornwall TR26 2HQ. Tel: (H) 01736 797168
Club Colours: Green, black & white.

HONITON RFC
Ground Address: Allhallows Playing Fields, Northcote Lane, Honiton, Devon. Tel: 01404 41239
Club Secretary: Mr Dave Todd, Omega, Sidmouth Road, Honiton, Devon EX14 8BE. Tel: (H) 01404 41608
Fixtures Secretary: Mr Jeremy Rice, 5 Park Road, Exeter, Devon. Tel: (H) 01392 423575
Club Colours: Red, black & amber hoops.

IVYBRIDGE RFC
Ground Address: Cross-in-Hand, Exeter Road, Ivybridge, Devon. Tel: 01752 894392
Club Secretary: John Naylor, Trem-y-wawr, Crescent Road, Ivybridge, Devon PL21 0BP. Tel: (H) 01752 892412 Tel: (W) 01752 892516
Fixtures Secretary: Gary Aldridge, 99 Cleeve Drive, Ivybridge PL21 0JP. Tel: (H) 01752 893773 Tel (W) 01752 402623
Club Colours: Green, black & white.

OLD PLYMOTHIANS & MANNAMEADIANS RFC
Ground Address: Bickleigh Down, Bickleigh Lane, Roborough, Plymouth.
Club Secretary: E J Bolster, 22 Carlton Close, Lower Compton, Plymouth, PL3 6JS. Tel: (H) 01752 223908 Tel: (W) 01752 673626
Fixtures Secretary: Simon Matthews, 14 Trevians Road, Eggbuckland, Plymouth. Tel: (H) 01752 780114 Tel (W) 01392 382457
Club Colours: Claret & blue quarters.

PLYMOUTH CIVIL SERVICE RFC
Ground Address: Civil Service Sports Club, Beacon Down, Plymouth PL2 3NA. Tel: 01752 702303
Club Secretary: Danny R Avery, 25 Weston Mill Hill, Weston Mill, Plymouth PL5 2AR. Tel: (H) 01752 365890 Tel: (W) 01752 554586
Fixtures Secretary: Stewart Brown, 35 Knapps Close, Elburton, Plymouth PL9 8UX. Tel: (H) 01752 492216 Tel (W) 01752 557258
Club Colours: Red/white hoops, black shorts.

SALTASH RFC
Ground Address: Moorlands Lane, Burraton, Saltash, Cornwall. Tel: 01752 847227
Club Secretary: Mr DR Jenkins, Windward, St Ann's Chapel, Gunnislake, Cornwall PL18 9HQ. Tel: (H) 01822 832785
Fixtures Secretary: Mr J Westaway, 16 Orchard Close, Tideford, Cornwall. Tel: (H) 01752 881727
Club Colours: Black, gold & red hoops.

SIDMOUTH RFC
Ground Address: Blackmore Ground, Heydon's Lane, Sidmouth, Devon. Tel: 01395 516816
Club Secretary: Brian Showell, 3 Connaught Close,

FINAL TABLE							
	P	W	D	L	F	A	Pts
Paignton	12	11	0	1	216	111	22
Sidmouth	12	8	0	4	244	153	16
Exmouth	12	8	0	4	225	157	16
Hayle	12	6	2	4	174	143	14
Truro	12	6	2	4	148	154	14
Saltash	12	6	1	5	156	140	13
Honiton	12	6	0	6	171	227	12
Ivybridge	12	8	1	3	190	123	11*
Teignmouth	12	6	0	6	245	173	10*
South Molton	12	4	0	8	179	185	8
Veor	12	4	0	8	176	245	4
Plymouth Civil Serv	12	3	0	10	144	289	4
Newquay Hornets	12	0	0	12	114	282	-2*

Sidmouth, Devon EX10 8TU. Tel: (H) 01395 512055
Fixtures Secretary: T O'Brien, 2 Rivulet Cottages, Sidford, Sidmouth, Devon. Tel: (H) 01395 577403
Club Colours: Green jerseys, white shorts.

SOUTH MOLTON RFC
Ground Address: Pathfields, Station Road, South Molton, Devon EX36 3LH. Tel: 01769 572024
Club Secretary: Mrs Anne White, 8 Duke Street, South Molton, Devon EX36 3AL. Tel: (H) 01769 573741 Tel: (W) 01769 573204 Fax: 01769 573200
Fixtures Secretary: Mr Denis Cronk, Old Rectory, Rose Ash, South Molton, Devon. Tel: (H) 01769 550402
Club Colours: Black.

ST AUSTELL RFC
Ground Address: Tregorrick Lane, St Austell, Cornwall PL26 7AG. Tel: 01726 76300
Club Secretary: Brian Perkins, 28 Duporth Bay, St Austell, Cornwall PL26 6AF. Tel: (H) 01726 67772 Tel: (W) 01726 76300
Fixtures Secretary: Howard Roberts, Trethevy Farm, Par, Cornwall PL24 2SA. Tel: (H) 01726 812065 Tel (W) 01726 76300
Club Colours: Red & white hoops.

TEIGNMOUTH RFC
Ground Address: Bitton Park Sports Ground, Bitton Park Road, Teignmouth, Devon TQ14 9DR. Tel: 01626 774714
Club Secretary: Mr Robert Loveridge, 59 Second Avenue, Teignmouth, Devon TQ14 9DN. Tel: (H) 01626 775891 Tel: (W) 01626 774556
Club Colours: Red, white & black hoops.

TRURO RFC
Ground Address: St Clements Hill, Truro, Cornwall TR1 1NY. Tel: 01872 74750
Club Secretary: Philip A Rowe, 36 Chirgwin Road, Truro, Cornwall TR1 1TT. Tel: (H) 01872 71915 Tel: (W) 01872 224202
Fixtures Secretary: Philip Lear, 5 Carclew Street, Truro, Cornwall TR1 2DY. Tel: (H) 01872 260741
Club Colours: Blue & amber quarters.

VEOR RFC
Ground Address: Wheal Gerry, Cliff View Road, Camborne, Cornwall.
Club Secretary: Bert Barber JP, 86 Dolcoath Road, Camborne, Cornwall TR14 8RP. Tel: (H) & Fax: 01209 710593 Tel: (W) 01752 665951
Fixtures Secretary: Paul Pascoe, 18 Condurrow Road, Beacon, Camborne, Cornwall. Tel: (H) 01209 716535 Tel (W) 01872 74282
Club Colours: Amber shirts, black shorts.

SOUTH WEST DIVISION

DEVON ONE
1995-96
FIXTURES

September 16 1995 (Week 3)
Dartmouth	v	Exeter Saracens
Newton Abbot	v	Totnes
Old Public Oaks	v	Cullompton
Salcombe	v	Old Technicians
Tavistock	v	Ilfracombe
Withycombe	v	Kingsbridge

September 23 1995 (Week 4)
Cullompton	v	Withycombe
Ilfracombe	v	Dartmouth
Kingsbridge	v	Tavistock
Old Technicians	v	Old Public Oaks
Topsham	v	Newton Abbot
Totnes	v	Salcombe

September 30 1995 (Week X1)
Dartmouth	v	Kingsbridge
Exeter Saracens	v	Ilfracombe
Old Public Oaks	v	Totnes
Salcombe	v	Topsham
Tavistock	v	Cullompton
Withycombe	v	Old Technicians

October 14 1995 (Week 6)
Cullompton	v	Dartmouth
Kingsbridge	v	Exeter Saracens
Newton Bbot	v	Salcombe
Old Technicians	v	Tavistock
Topsham	v	Old Public Oaks
Totnes	v	Withycombe

October 21 1995 (Week 7)
Dartmouth	v	Old Technicians
Exeter Saracens	v	Cullompton
Ilfracombe	v	Kingsbridge
Old Public Oaks	v	Newton Abbot
Tavistock	v	Totnes
Withycombe	v	Topsham

October 28 1995 (Week 8)
Cullompton	v	Ilfracombe
Newton Abbot	v	Withycombe
Old Technicians	v	Exeter Saracens
Salcombe	v	Old Public Oaks
Topsham	v	Tavistock
Totnes	v	Dartmouth

November 11 1995 (Week 10)
Dartmouth	v	Topsham
Exeter Saracens	v	Totnes
Ilfracombe	v	Old Technicians
Kingsbridge	v	Cullompton
Tavistock	v	Newton Abbot
Withycombe	v	Salcombe

January 6 1996 (Week 17)
Newton Abbot	v	Dartmouth
Old Public Oaks	v	Withycombe
Old Technicians	v	Kingsbridge
Salcombe	v	Tavistock
Topsham	v	Exeter Saracens
Totnes	v	Ilfracombe

January 13 1996 (Week 18)
Cullompton	v	Old Technicians
Dartmouth	v	Salcombe
Exeter Saracens	v	Newton Abbot
Ilfracombe	v	Topsham
Kingsbridge	v	Totnes
Tavistock	v	Old Public Oaks

February 10 1996 (Week 22)
Newton Abbot	v	Ilfracombe
Old Public Oaks	v	Dartmouth
Salcombe	v	Exeter Saracens
Topsham	v	Kingsbridge
Totnes	v	Cullompton
Withycombe	v	Tavistock

February 17 1996 (Week 23)
Cullompton	v	Topsham
Dartmouth	v	Withycombe
Exeter Saracens	v	Old Public Oaks
Ilfracombe	v	Salcombe
Kingsbridge	v	Newton Abbot
Old Technicians	v	Totnes

February 24 1996 (Week 24)
Newton Abbot	v	Cullompton
Old Public Oaks	v	Ilfracombe
Salcombe	v	Kingsbridge
Tavistock	v	Dartmouth
Topsham	v	Old Technicians
Withycombe	v	Exeter Saracens

March 30 1996 (Week X7)
Cullompton	v	Salcombe
Exeter Saracens	v	Tavistock
Ilfracombe	v	Withycombe
Kingsbridge	v	Old Public Oaks
Old Technicians	v	Newton Abbot
Totnes	v	Topsham

DEVON ONE

CULLOMPTON RFC
Ground Address: Stafford Park, Knowle Lane, Cullompton, Devon EX15 1PZ. Tel: 01884 32480
Club Secretary: Nigel Nichols, 91 Bilbie Close, Cullompton, Devon EX15 1LG. Tel: (H) 01884 38365 Tel: (W) 01884 840458
Fixtures Secretary: Derek Keeling, 7 Andrew Allen Road, Rockwell Green, Wellington, Somerset TA21 9DY. Tel: (H) 01823 660199
Club Colours: Scarlet & black hoops.

DARTMOUTH RFC
Ground Address: Roseville Pavilion, Roseville Street, Dartmouth, Devon TQ6 9QH. Tel: 01803 833994
Club Secretary: TE Atkins, Flat 1, 81 Victoria Road, Dartmouth, Devon TQ6 9QX. Tel: (H) 01803 833433
Fixtures Secretary: SR Atkins, 125 Victoria Road, Dartmouth, Devon TQ6 9DY. Tel: (H) 01803 832281
Club Colours: Red & green hoops.

EXETER SARACENS RFC
Ground Address: Exhibition Field, Summer Lane, Whipton, Exeter, Devon. Tel: 01392 462651
Club Secretary: Peter Blackmore, 1 Vieux Close, Behind Hayes, Otterton, Budleigh Salterton, Devon EX9 7JT. Tel: (H) 01395 567777 Tel: (W) 01395 264373
Fixtures Secretary: Andrew Kift, 126 Whipton Lane, Exeter, Devon EX1 3DL. Tel: (H) 01392 77976
Club Colours: Red shirts, black shorts.

ILFRACOMBE RFC
Ground Address: Brimlands, Hillsborough Road, Ilfracombe, Devon. Tel: 01271 864249
Club Secretary: c/o Brimlands, Hillsborough Road, Ilfracombe, Devon.
Fixtures Secretary: Stuart Swanson, 5 Church Cottages, Swimbridge, North Devon. Tel: (H) 01271 830514
Club Colours: Blue & white hoops.

KINGSBRIDGE RFC
Ground Address: High House, Kingsbridge, Devon TQ7 1JL. Tel: 01548 852051
Club Secretary: Martin Newman, 'Fourwinds', 46 Saffron Park, Kingsbridge, Devon TQ7 1RL. Tel: (H) 01548 853976 Tel: (W) 01548 853101 x11
Fixtures Secretary: Arthur Ball, 7 Riverview Place, Kingsbridge, Devon. Tel: (H) 01548 852182
Club Colours: Blue & white.

NEWTON ABBOT RFC
Ground Address: Rackenhayes, Kingsteignton Road, Newton Abbot, Devon. Tel: 01626 54150
Club Secretary: Mrs Deborah Aggett, 42 Powderham Road, Newton Abbot, Devon TQ12 1EZ. Tel: (H) 01626 68855 Tel: (W) 01626 61101
Fixtures Secretary: Keith Maclean, 121 Exeter Road, Kingsteignton, Newton Abbot, Devon TQ12 3NA. Tel: (H) 01626 51493
Club Colours: All white.

OLD PUBLIC OAKS RFC
Ground Address: King George V Playing Fields, Elburton, Plymouth. Tel: 01752 252039
Club Secretary: GH Mathews, 25 Colwill Road, Mainstone Estate, PLymouth PL6 8RP. Tel: (H) 01752 707363 Tel: (W) 01752 663231
Fixtures Secretary: N Jordan, 112A Underwood Road, Plympton, Plymouth PL7 3TA. Tel: (H) 01752 330455 Tel (W) 01752 663231
Club Colours: Green/gold hoops.

OLD TECHNICIANS RFC
Ground Address: Weston Mill Oak Villa, Ferndale Road, Weston Mill, Plymouth, Devon. Tel: 01752 363352
Club Secretary: Mr TR Ozanne, 109 Townshend Avenue, Keynsham, Plymouth PL2 1PB. Tel: (H) 01752 606696 Tel: (W) 01752 553834
Fixtures Secretary: Mr M Putt, 139 Truro Drive, Badgers

FINAL TABLE

	P	W	D	L	F	A	Pts
Old Plymothians	12	11	0	1	314	86	22
Newton Abbot	12	11	0	1	295	84	22
Kingsbridge	12	10	0	2	281	128	20
Old Public Oaks	12	8	0	4	155	161	16
Withycombe	12	6	0	6	160	165	12
Ilfracombe	12	6	1	5	214	117	11*
Old Technicians	12	6	1	5	216	128	11*
Tavistock	12	7	0	5	244	169	10*
Topsham	12	5	0	7	208	254	8*
Salcombe	12	3	1	8	71	244	7
Exeter Saracens	12	2	1	9	96	195	5
Dartmouth	12	1	0	11	104	306	2
Prince Rock	12	0	0	12	71	392	0

Wood, Tamerton Foliot, Plymouth, Devon. Tel: (H) 01752 790256
Club Colours: Black with white circlet.

SALCOMBE RFC
Ground Address: Twomgades, Camperdown Road, Salcombe TQ8 8AX. Tel: 01548 842639
Club Secretary: GS Jacobs, Cornerways, Bonaventure Road, Salcombe, Devon TQ8 8BG. Tel: (H) 01548 842521
Fixtures Secretary: B Wotton, Bingley, Onslow Road, Salcombe, Devon. Tel: (H) 01548 843824
Club Colours: Red & white.

TAVISTOCK RFC
Ground Address: Sandy Park, Trelawney Road, Tavistock, Devon PL19 0JL. Tel: 01822 618275
Club Secretary: Trevor Masters, St Peters, 10 Uplands, Tavistock, Devon PL19 8ET. Tel: (H) 01822 614323 Tel: (W) 01752 701188
Fixtures Secretary: Mr CJ Sutton, 121 Plymouth Road, Tavistock, Devon PL19 9DT. Tel: (H) 01822 615829
Club Colours: Black with red hoops.

TOPSHAM RFC
Ground Address: Bonfire Field, Topsham, Devon. Tel: 01392 873651
Club Secretary: David Burdick, 21 Victoria Road, Topsham, Devon EX3 0EU. Tel: (H) 01392 873065 Tel: (W) 01392 52666
Fixtures Secretary: Paul Pirongs, The Dutch House, The Strand, Topsham, Devon. Tel: (H) 01392 877347 Tel (W) 01626 52655
Club Colours: Light & dark blue hoops.

TOTNES RFC
Ground Address: The Clubhouse, Borough Park, Totnes, Devon TQ9 5XX. Tel: 01803 867796
Club Secretary: Miss J Pantry, 50 Punchards Down, Follaton, Totnes, Devon TQ9 5FC. Tel: (H) 01803 864581 Tel: (W) 01803 866560
Fixtures Secretary: Roger Lang, 42 The Carrions, Totnes, Devon TQ9 5SX. Tel: (H) 01803 864516
Club Colours: Royal blue & white.

WITHYCOMBE RFC
Ground Address: Raleigh Park, Hulham Road, Withycombe, Exmouth, Devon EX8 3HS. Tel: 01395 266762
Club Secretary: Mr M Norman, 2 Claremont Lane, Exmouth EX8 2LE. Tel: (H) 01395 270644
Fixtures Secretary: Peter Cozens, 2 Meadow Street, Exmouth, Devon EX8 1LH. Tel: (H) 01395 269970
Club Colours: Emerald green & black hoops.

SOUTH WEST DIVISION

DEVON TWO
1995-96
FIXTURES

September 16 1995 (Week 3)

Axminster	v	Plymouth Argaum
Bovey Tracey	v	Prince Rock
Jesters	v	Plympton Victoria
St Columba	v	Plymstock
Tamar Saracens	v	Plymouth YMCA
Torrington	v	North Tawton

September 30 1995 (Week X1)

Axminster	v	St Columba
North Tawton	v	Bovey Tracey
Plymouth Argaum	v	Prince Rock
Plymouth YMCA	v	Torrington
Plympton Victoria	v	Tamar Saracens
Plymstock	v	Jesters

October 14 1995 (Week 6)

Bovey Tracey	v	Plymouth YMCA
Jesters	v	Axminster
Prince Rock	v	North Tawton
St Columba	v	Plymouth Argaum
Tamar Saracens	v	Plymstock
Torrington	v	Plympton Victoria

October 28 1995 (Week 8)

Axminster	v	Tamar Saracens
Plymouth Argaum	v	North Tawton
Plymouth YMCA	v	Prince Rock
Plympton Victoria	v	Bovey Tracey
Plymstock	v	Torrington
St Columba	v	Jesters

November 11 1995 (Week 10)

Bovey Tracey	v	Plymstock
Jesters	v	Plymouth Argaum
North Tawton	v	Plymouth YMCA
Prince Rock	v	Plympton Victoria
Tamar Saracens	v	St Columba
Torrington	v	Axminster

January 6 1996 (Week 17)

Axminster	v	Bovey Tracey
Jesters	v	Tamar Saracens
Plymouth Argaum	v	Plymouth YMCA
Plympton Victoria	v	North Tawton
Plymstock	v	Prince Rock
St Columba	v	Torrington

January 13 1996 (Week 18)

Bovey Tracey	v	St Columba
North Tawton	v	Plymstock
Plymouth YMCA	v	Plympton Victoria
Prince Rock	v	Axminster
Tamar Saracens	v	Plymouth Argaum
Torrington	v	Jesters

February 10 1996 (Week 22)

Axminster	v	North Tawton
Jesters	v	Bovey Tracey
Plymouth Argaum	v	Plympton Victoria
Plymstock	v	Plymouth YMCA
St Columba	v	Prince Rock
Tamar Saracens	v	Torrington

February 17 1996 (Week 23)

Bovey Tracey	v	Tamar Saracens
North Tawton	v	St Columba
Plymouth YMCA	v	Axminster
Plympton Victoria	v	Plymstock
Prince Rock	v	Jesters
Torrington	v	Plymouth Argaum

February 24 1996 (Week 24)

Axminster	v	Plympton Victoria
Jesters	v	North Tawton
Plymouth Argaum	v	Plymstock
St Columba	v	Plymouth YMCA
Tamar Saracens	v	Prince Rock
Torrington	v	Bovey Tracey

March 30 1996 (Week X7)

Bovey Tracey	v	Plymouth Argaum
North Tawton	v	Tamar Saracens
Plymouth YMCA	v	Jesters
Plympton Victoria	v	St Columba
Plymstock	v	Axminster
Prince Rock	v	Torrington

DEVON TWO

AXMINSTER RUFC
Ground Address: Gammons Hill, Kilmington, Axminster, Devon.
Club Secretary: Alan Beer, 8 Athelstan Close, Axminster, Devon. Tel: (H) 01297 34144
Fixtures Secretary: Nigel Powell, 6 Fairfield Close, Axminster, Devon EX13 5LP. Tel: (H) 01297 34938
Club Colours: Red & royal blue.

BOVEY TRACEY RUFC
Ground Address: Bullands, Monks Way, Bovey Tracey, Devon.
Club Secretary: Carolyn Leigh, 34 East Street, Bovey Tracey, Devon TQ13 9EJ. Tel: (H) 01626 834432
Fixtures Secretary: MJ Dyke, Revelstoke, Mazy Street, Bovey Tracey, Devon TQ13 9HQ. Tel: (H) 01626 834337
Club Colours: Navy & white.

JESTERS RFC
Ground Address: Marsh Meadows, Lower Leigham, Plym Valley, Plymouth, Devon.
Club Secretary: Debbie Hancock, 8 Abbots Road, Peverell, Plymouth PL3 4PB. Tel: (H) 01752 260321
Fixtures Secretary: Paul Bronn, 16 Dartington Walk, Leigham, Plymouth. Tel: (H) 01752 771019
Club Colours: Red, white, gold & black quarters.

NORTH TAWTON RFC
Ground Address: The Butts, Barton Street, North Tawton, Devon.
Club Secretary: Mrs Gillian Mary Hoggins, The Old Forge, 33 North Street, North Tawton, Devon EX20 2DE. Tel: (H) 01837 82516
Fixtures Secretary: Mr Colin Sharp, 74 Fore Street, North Tawton, Devon EX20 2ED. Tel: (H) 01837 82869
Club Colours: Black & amber.

PLYMOUTH ARGAUM RFC
Ground Address: The Clubhouse, Blackeven Hill, Bickleigh Down Road, Roborough, Plymouth, Devon. Tel: 01752 772156
Club Secretary: JL Davey, 3 Hazeldene Close, Lee Mill, Ivybridge, Devon PL21 9EL. Tel: (H) 01752 894453 Tel: (W) 01752 663600
Fixtures Secretary: I Roberts, 31 Grasmere Close, Derriford, Plymouth PL6 5HE. Tel: (H) 01752 779163
Club Colours: Green, black & white.

PLYMOUTH YMCA RFC
Ground Address: Suttons Field, John Kitto Community College, Burrington Way, Honicknowle, Plymouth. Tel: 01752 268169
Club Secretary: Mr Jim Mather, 126 Pike Road, Efford, Plymouth. Tel: (H) 01752 563820
Fixtures Secretary: Mr John Pritchard, 2 Delaware Court, Delaware Road, Drakewalls, Gunnislake, Cornwall. Tel: (H) 01822 833371
Club Colours: Red with black & white hoops.

PLYMPTON VICTORIA RFC
Ground Address: King George V Playing Fields, Elburton, Plymstock, Plymouth, Devon.
Club Secretary: GB Knight, 62 The Mead, Plympton, Plymouth, Devon PL7 4HT. Tel: (H) 01752 342888
Fixtures Secretary: P Evans, 9 Brookingfield Close, Underwood, Plympton, Plymouth, Devon. Tel: (H) 01752 340025
Club Colours: Red & white hoops.

PLYMSTOCK RFC
Ground Address: New club being built.
Club Secretary: Nigel Passmore, Orchard Close, Watergate, Wembury PL9 0LE. Tel: (H) 01752 862656
Fixtures Secretary: Paul Vewel, 10 Marsh Close, Longbridge, Plymouth, Devon. Tel: (H) 01752 673532 Tel: (W) 01752 402 063
Club Colours: Blue.

FINAL TABLE							
	P	W	D	L	F	A	Pts
Totnes	11	9	0	2	373	90	18
Cullompton	11	9	0	2	247	81	18
Tamar Saracens	11	9	0	2	204	74	18
Jesters	11	7	1	3	129	105	13*
Plymstock	11	6	1	4	174	136	11*
Torrington	11	6	0	5	378	157	10*
Plymouth Argaum	11	6	0	5	197	152	10*
St Columba	11	4	0	7	181	194	6*
North Tawton	11	3	0	9	143	268	6
Axminster	11	3	1	7	72	287	3*
Plymouth Victoria	11	1	1	9	79	342	3
Plymouth YMCA	11	1	0	10	71	354	-2*

PRINCE ROCK RFC
Ground Address: Seaton Barracks or King George V Playing Fields, Elburton, Plymouth.
Club Secretary: Gary Darragh, 1B Clifton Street, Greenbank, Plymouth. Tel: (H) 01752 233513
Fixtures Secretary: Les Fowdon, 1 Hayes Road, Oreston, Plymstock, Plymouth. Tel: (H) 01752 405018
Club Colours: Amber shirts, white shorts.

ST COLUMBA TORPOINT RFC
Ground Address: Defiance Field, Torpoint, Cornwall.
Club Secretary: Peter Charles Summers, 112 Rochford Crescent, Ernesettle, Plymouth, Devon PL5 2QD. Tel: (H) 01752 362785 Tel: (W) 01752 552115
Fixtures Secretary: Peter Charles Summers, 112 Rochford Crescent, Ernesettle, Plymouth, Devon PL5 2QD. Tel: (H) 01752 362785 Tel: (W) 01752 552115
Club Colours: Scarlet & thin royal blue hoops.

TAMAR SARACENS RFC
Ground Address: Parkway Sports Club, Ernesettle Lane, Ernesettle, Plymouth, Devon. Tel: 01752 344639
Club Secretary: K McDermottroe, 8 Pinewood Close, Plympton, Plymouth, Devon PL7 3DW. Tel: (H) 01752 344639 Tel: (W) 01752 364341
Fixtures Secretary: J Bentley, 29 Dunster Close, Plympton, Plymouth PL7 3FN. Tel: (H) 01752 345020 Tel (W) 01752 364341
Club Colours: Black with red, green & white hoops.

TORRINGTON RFC
Ground Address: Donnacroft Fields, Hatchmoor Road, Torrington, North Devon.
Club Secretary: Darren Nudds, 27 Holwill Drive, Tarka Hill, Torrington, North Devon. Tel: (H) 01805 624899
Fixtures Secretary: David Glover, Haye Down, Little Torrington, Torrington, North Devon. Tel: (H) 01805 624566
Club Colours: Green, black & white hoops.

SOUTH WEST DIVISION

CORNWALL ONE 1995-96 FIXTURES

September 16 1995 (Week 3)
Helston	v	St Day
Newquay Hornets	v	Bude
St Agnes	v	Falmouth
Stithians	v	Redruth Albany
Wadebridge	v	Liskeard-Looe

September 30 1995 (Week X1)
Falmouth	v	Wadebridge
Liskeard-Looe	v	Newquay Hornets
Perranporth	v	Helston
Redruth Albany	v	St Agnes
St Day	v	Stithians

October 14 1995 (Week 6)
Bude	v	Liskeard-Looe
Newquay Hornets	v	Falmouth
St Agnes	v	St Day
Stithians	v	Perranporth
Wadebridge	v	Redruth Albany

October 28 1995 (Week 8)
Falmouth	v	Bude
Helston	v	Stithians
Perranporth	v	St Agnes
Redruth Albany	v	Newquay Hornets
St Day	v	Wadebridge

November 11 1995 (Week 10)
Bude	v	Redruth Albany
Liskeard-Looe	v	Falmouth
Newquay Hornets	v	St Day
St Agnes	v	Helston
Wadebridge	v	Perranporth

January 6 1996 (Week 17)
Helston	v	Wadebridge
Perranporth	v	Newquay Hornets
Redruth Albany	v	Liskeard-Looe
St Day	v	Bude
Stithians	v	St Agnes

January 13 1996 (Week 18)
Bude	v	Perranporth
Falmouth	v	Redruth Albany
Liskeard-Looe	v	St Day
Newquay Hornets	v	Helston
Wadebridge	v	Stithians

February 10 1996 (Week 22)
Helston	v	Bude
Perranporth	v	Liskeard-Looe
St Agnes	v	Wadebridge
St Day	v	Falmouth
Stithians	v	Newquay Hornets

February 17 1996 (Week 23)
Bude	v	Stithians
Falmouth	v	Perranporth
Liskeard-Looe	v	Helston
Newquay Hornets	v	St Agnes
Redruth Albany	v	St Day

February 24 1996 (Week 24)
Helston	v	Falmouth
Perranporth	v	Redruth Albany
St Agnes	v	Bude
Stithians	v	Liskeard-Looe
Wadebridge	v	Newquay Hornets

March 30 1996 (Week X7)
Bude	v	Wadebridge
Falmouth	v	Stithians
Liskeard-Looe	v	St Agnes
Redruth Albany	v	Helston
St Day	v	Perranporth

CORNWALL ONE

BUDE RFC
Ground Address: Bencoolen Meadow (off Kings Hill), Bude, Cornwall EX23 8QG. Tel: 01288 354795
Club Secretary: Mr FB Sykes, 65 Kings Hill, Bude EX23 8QL. Tel: (H) 01288 354210
Fixtures Secretary: Mr JA Boundy, Linhays, Buttsbeare Cross, Bridgerule, Holsworthy, Devon EX22 7HB. Tel: (H) 01288 381296 Tel (W) 01288 353766
Club Colours: Maroon & sky blue hoops.

FALMOUTH RFC
Ground Address: Dracaena Avenue, Falmouth, Cornwall. Tel: 01326 311304
Club Secretary: JK Dryden, 15 Pengarth Road, Falmouth, Cornwall TR11 2TY. Tel: (H) 01126 316644 Tel: (W) 01126 311644
Fixtures Secretary: GV Wilkes, 17 Rose Valley, Three Milestones, Truro, Cornwall TR1. Tel: (H) 01872 77249 Tel (W) 01872 222111
Club Colours: Black & white.

HELSTON RFC
Ground Address: King George V Playing Fields, Cloogey Lane, Helston, Cornwall. Tel: 01326 573423
Club Secretary: Mrs Bev Davis, 8 Penrose Road, Helston, Cornwall TR13 8TP. Tel: (H) & Fax: 01326 563744 Tel: (W) 01209 215620
Fixtures Secretary: Mrs Bev Davis, 8 Penrose Road, Helston, Cornwall TR13 8TP. Tel: (H) & Fax: 01326 563744 Tel (W) 01209 215620
Club Colours: Navy & white hoops.

LISKEARD-LOOE RFC
Ground Address: Lux Park, Liskeard, Cornwall. Tel: 01579 342665
Club Secretary: Geoff Collings, Little Polscoe, Lostwithiel, Cornwall PL22 0HS. Tel: (H) 01208 873201
Fixtures Secretary: Geoff Collings, Little Polscoe, Lostwithiel, Cornwall PL22 0HS. Tel: (H) 01208 873201
Club Colours: Red & black 4' hoops.

NEWQUAY HORNETS RFC
Ground Address: Newquay Sports Centre, Tretherras, Newquay, Cornwall. Tel: 01637 875533
Club Secretary: Russell Edwards, 17 St Thomas Road, Newquay, Cornwall TR7 1RS. Tel: (H) 01637 871479 Tel: (W) 01637 871479
Fixtures Secretary: Reg Roberts, 18 St Anne's Road, Newquay, Cornwall. Tel: (H) 01637 874568
Club Colours: Green & white.

PERRANPORTH RFC
Ground Address: Ponsmere Valley, Perranporth, Cornwall. Tel: 01872 572016
Club Secretary: Mr Nik Lewis, Cornerways, Perranwell Road, Goonhavern, Nr Truro, Cornwall TR4 9JL. Tel: (H) 01872 571217
Fixtures Secretary: R Trevail, Treskyber, Rose, Goonhavern, Cornwall. Tel: (H) 01872 573547
Club Colours: Green & gold.

REDRUTH ALBANY RFC
Ground Address: Trewirgie Hill, Redruth, Cornwall TR15 2PP. Tel: 01209 216945
Club Secretary: Mr CS Polkinghorne, 44 Trenoweth Estate, North Country, Redruth, Cornwall TR16 4AQ. Tel: (H) 01209 213147
Fixtures Secretary: Mr I M Wills, 16 Strawberry Fields, Pennance Road, Lanner, Redruth TR16 5TO. Tel: (H) 01209 215349
Club Colours: Royal blue, white shorts.

ST AGNES RFC
Ground Address: Enys Parc, Trevannance Road,St Agnes, Cornwall. Tel: 01872 553673
Club Secretary: Mr Tim Barnes, c/o T & JB Produce Ltd, Stanley Way, Cardrew Industrial Estate, Redruth, Cornwall TR15 1SP. Tel: (H) 01209 890218 Tel: (W) 01209 314477

FINAL TABLE

	P	W	D	L	F	A	Pts
St Austell	10	10	0	0	321	111	20
Liskeard-Looe	10	9	0	1	225	99	18
Bude	10	7	0	3	286	73	14
Falmouth	10	6	0	4	260	137	12
St Agnes	10	5	0	5	177	190	10
Helston	10	6	0	4	193	141	8*
Perranport	10	3	0	7	133	243	6
Stithians	10	2	0	8	152	239	4
Wadebridge	10	3	0	7	95	204	4*
Bodmin	10	3	0	7	73	271	4*
Illogan Park	10	1	0	9	65	272	2

Fixtures Secretary: Mr Bob Howard, Wheal Friendly Chalets, Roughwood, Rocky Lane, St Agnes, Cornwall. Tel: (H) 01872 553160
Club Colours: Red background, black hoops.

ST DAY RFC
Ground Address: The Playing Field, St Day, Redruth, Cornwall.
Club Secretary: PC Newcombe, 21 Martinvale Parc, Mount Ambrose, Redruth, Cornwall TR15 1SD. Tel: (H) 01209 212834 Tel: (W) 01872 76477
Fixtures Secretary: T Dunstan, 29 Scorrier Street, St Day, Redruth, Cornwall. Tel: (H) 01209 821729
Club Colours: White with red band.

STITHIANS RFC
Ground Address: Stithians Playing Field, Stithians.
Club Secretary: TJ Knight, 6 Chainwalk Drive, Kenwyn, Truro, Cornwall TR1 3ST. Tel: (H) 01872 70849 Tel: (W) 01872 76116
Fixtures Secretary: C Burley, 54 Collins Parc, Stithians, Truro, Cornwall. Tel: (H) 01209 860148 Tel (W) 01209 860555
Club Colours: Maroon.

WADEBRIDGE CAMELS RFC
Ground Address: Molesworth Field, Egloshayle, Wadebridge, Cornwall.
Club Secretary: Mark Richards, Perlees Farm, St Breock, Wadebridge, Cornwall PL27 7HU. Tel: (H) 01208 812848 Tel: (W) 01726 860308
Fixtures Secretary: Chris Taylor, Penhale Farm, St Breock, Wadebridge, Cornwall. Tel: (H) 01208 813919
Club Colours: Chocolate & gold.

SOUTH WEST DIVISION

CORNWALL TWO
1995-96
FIXTURES

September 16 1995 (Week 3)

Camborne School of Mines	v	Lankelly
Illogan Park	v	St Just
Roseland	v	Bodmin

September 30 1995 (Week X1)

Bodmin	v	Illogan Park
Lankelly	v	St Just
Roseland	v	Camborne School of Mines

October 14 1995 (Week 6)

Camborne School of Mines	v	Bodmin
Illogan Park	v	Lankelly
St Just	v	Roseland

October 28 1995 (Week 8)

Bodmin	v	St Just
Illogan Park	v	Camborne School of Mines
Lankelly	v	Roseland

November 11 1995 (Week 10)

Bodmin	v	Lankelly
Roseland	v	Illogan Park
St Just	v	Camborne School of Mines

January 6 1996 (Week 17)

Bodmin	v	Roseland
Lankelly	v	Camborne School of Mines
St Just	v	Illogan Park

February 10 1996 (Week 22)

Camborne School of Mines	v	Roseland
Illogan Park	v	Bodmin
St Just	v	Lankelly

February 17 1996 (Week 23)

Bodmin	v	Camborne School of Mines
Lankelly	v	Illogan Park
Roseland	v	St Just

February 24 1996 (Week 24)

Camborne School of Mines	v	Illogan Park
Roseland	v	Lankelly
St Just	v	Bodmin

March 30 1996 (Week X7)

Camborne School of Mines	v	St Just
Illogan Park	v	Roseland
Lankelly	v	Bodmin

CORNWALL TWO

BODMIN RFC
Ground Address: Cliffden Park, Carminnon Cross,
Bodmin, Cornwall. Tel: 01208 74629
Club Secretary: Mr Alan Cornish, 11 Springwell View,
Love Lane, Bodmin, Cornwall PL31 2QP. Tel: (H) 01208
75519 Tel: (W) 01208 79128 x218
Fixtures Secretary: Mr Alan Rowe, 6 Treburdon Drive,
Roche, St Austell, Cornwall PL26 8RB. Tel: (H) 01726
890670
Club Colours: Light blue with blue hoop.

CAMBORNE SCHOOL OF MINES RFC
Ground Address: The Memorial Ground, Boundervean
Lane, Penponds, Camborne, Cornwall. Tel: 01209 612959
Clubhouse: 01209 711935
Club Secretary: Dr CV Phillips, Barlowena, Alexandra
Road, Illogan, Redruth, Cornwall TR16 4EN. Tel: (H)
01209 842660 Tel: (W) 01209 714866
Fixtures Secretary: S Atkinson Esq, Camborne School of
Mines, Trevenson, Redruth, Cornwall TR15 3SE. Tel: (H)
01209 613037 Tel (W) 01209 714866
Club Colours: Navy/gold/silver hoops.

ILLOGAN PARK RFC
Ground Address: The Club Room, New Inn Park Bottom,
Illogan, Redruth, Cornwall. Tel: 01209 218785
Club Secretary: Mr GR Tonkins, 20 Lower Pengegon,
Camborne, Cornwall. Tel: (H) 01209 712395 Tel: (W)
01209 218785
Fixtures Secretary: RJ McLellan, 59 Tregundy Road,
Perranporth, Cornwall TR6 0EP. Tel: (H) 01872 572696
Tel (W) 01209 712712
Club Colours: Yellow & black.

LANKELLY-FOWEY RFC
Ground Address: Lankelly Farm, Lankelly Lane, Fowey,
Cornwall. Tel: 01726 833350
Club Secretary: D Taylor, Fourturnings Bungalow,
Fourturnings Garage, Fowey, Cornwall. Tel: (H) 01726
832565 Tel: (W) 01726 832428
Fixtures Secretary: RL Sainsbury, 21 Wood Lane,
Tywardreath, Par, Cornwall PL24 2PS. Tel: (H) 01726
814035 Tel (W) 01726 860101
Club Colours: Blue & white hoops, black shorts.

ROSELAND RFC
Ground Address: Philleigh, Truro, Cornwall. Tel: 01872
580254
Club Secretary: CR Thomas, Parton Vrane, Gerrans,
Portscatho, Truro, Cornwall TR2 5ET. Tel: (H) 01872
580495 Tel: (W) 01872 580885
Fixtures Secretary: CJ Trerice, Omega, West End,
Blackwater, Truro, Cornwall TR4 8EX. Tel: (H) 01872
560248
Club Colours: Navy & scarlet.

ST JUST RFC
Ground Address: St Just RFC, Tregeseal, St Just,
Penzance, Cornwall TR19 7PF. Tel: 01736 788593
Club Secretary: R Bassett, St Just RFC, Tregeseal, St Just,
Penzance, Cornwall TR19 7PF. Tel: (H) 01736 62311 Tel:
(W) 01736 62341
Fixtures Secretary: P Whiteman, Ashmore Cottage,
Nanquidno, Kellynack, St Just, Penzance, Cornwall. Tel:
(H) 01736 788150
Club Colours: Black.

FINAL TABLE

	P	W	D	L	F	A	Pts
Redruth Albany	10	10	0	0	502	49	20
St Day	10	6	0	4	133	181	12
Camborne S of Mines	10	5	1	4	270	172	11
St Just	10	5	0	5	198	172	10
Roseland	10	2	1	7	140	308	5
Lankelly Fowey	10	1	0	9	62	423	2

SOUTH WEST DIVISION

GLOUCESTER/SOMERSET 1995-96 FIXTURES

November 11 1995 (Week 10)
Avonmouth v Cleve
Bristol Harlequins v Hornets
Cirencester v Wellington
St Mary's OB v Oldfield OB
Stow-on-the-Wold v North Bristol
Thornbury v Old Redcliffians

September 16 1995 (Week 3)
Cirencester v Bristol Harlequins
Old Redcliffians v Hornets
Oldfield OB v Cleve
St Mary's OB v Stow-on-the-Wold
Thornbury v Avonmouth
Whitehall v North Bristol

January 6 1996 (Week 17)
Cleve v Stow-on-the-Wold
Hornets v Avonmouth
Old Redcliffians v Cirencester
Oldfield OB v Thornbury
Wellington v Bristol Harlequins
Whitehall v St Mary's OB

September 23 1995 (Week 4)
Avonmouth v Cirencester
Cleve v Whitehall
Hornets v Oldfield OB
North Bristol v St Mary's OB
Stow-on-the-Wold v Thornbury
Wellington v Old Redcliffians

January 13 1996 (Week 18)
Avonmouth v Wellington
Bristol Harlequins v Old Redcliffians
Cirencester v Oldfield OB
North Bristol v Cleve
Stow-on-the-Wold v Hornets
Thornbury v Whitehall

September 30 1995 (Week X1)
Bristol Harlequins v Avonmouth
Cirencester v Stow-on-the-Wold
Oldfield OB v Wellington
St Mary's OB v Cleve
Thornbury v North Bristol
Whitehall v Hornets

February 10 1996 (Week 22)
Hornets v North Bristol
Old Redcliffians v Avonmouth
Oldfield OB v Bristol Harlequins
St Mary's OB v Thornbury
Wellington v Stow-on-the-Wold
Whitehall v Cirencester

October 14 1995 (Week 6)
Cleve v Thornbury
Hornets v St Mary's OB
North Bristol v Cirencester
Old Redcliffians v Oldfield OB
Stow-on-the-Wold v Bristol Harlequins
Wellington v Whitehall

February 17 1996 (Week 23)
Avonmouth v Oldfield OB
Bristol Harlequins v Whitehall
Cirencester v St Mary's OB
Cleve v Hornets
North Bristol v Wellington
Stow-on-the-Wold v Old Redcliffians

October 21 1995 (Week 7)
Avonmouth v Stow-on-the-Wold
Bristol Harlequins v North Bristol
Cirencester v Cleve
St Mary's OB v Wellington
Thornbury v Hornets
Whitehall v Old Redcliffians

February 24 1996 (Week 24)
Old Redcliffians v North Bristol
Oldfield OB v Stow-on-the-Wold
St Mary's OB v Bristol Harlequins
Thornbury v Cirencester
Wellington v Cleve
Whitehall v Avonmouth

October 28 1995 (Week 8)
Cleve v Bristol Harlequins
Hornets v Cirencester
North Bristol v Avonmouth
Old Redcliffians v St Mary's OB
Oldfield OB v Whitehall
Wellington v Thornbury

March 30 1996 (Week X7)
Avonmouth v St Mary's OB
Bristol Harlequins v Thornbury
Cleve v Old Redcliffians
Hornets v Wellington
North Bristol v Oldfield OB
Stow-on-the-Wold v Whitehall

GLOUCESTERSHIRE & SOMERSET

AVONMOUTH OLD BOYS RFC
Ground Address: Barracks Lane, Shirehampton, Bristol.
Tel: 0117 982 9093
Club Secretary: IK McNab, 48 Nibley Road,
Shirehampton, Bristol, Avon BS11 9XR.
Fixtures Secretary: A Woodruff, 69 Prior Road,
Shirehampton, Bristol. Tel: (H) 0117 983 3066 Tel (W)
0117 983 936 2173
Club Colours: Black with red chest band.
BRISTOL HARLEQUINS RFC
Ground Address: Valhalla, Broomhill Road, Brislington,
Bristol BS4. Tel: 0117 972 1650
Club Secretary: Mr P Broome, 1 Ketch Road, Lower
Knowle, Bristol. Tel: (H) 0117 940 7929 Tel: (W) 0117
972 1261
Fixtures Secretary: Mr E Morrison, 4 Lowbourne,
Whitchurch, Bristol. Tel: (H) 01275 832580
Club Colours: Blue, black & white hoops.
CIRENCESTER RFC
Ground Address: The Whiteway, Cirencester, Glos. Tel:
01285 654434
Club Secretary: Richard H Evans, 66 Rose Way,
Cirencester, Glos GL7 1PS. Tel: (H) 01285 640954 Tel:
(W) 01285 720593
Fixtures Secretary: John Lawrence, 'Timberley',
Winstone, Cirencester, Glos GL7 7JU. Tel: (H) 01285
821435
Club Colours: Red & black hoops, black shorts.
CLEVE RFC
Ground Address: Bromley Heath Road, Downend, Bristol
BS16 6HY. Tel: 0117 961 1079
Club Secretary: Pocock, 44 Spring Hill, Kingswood,
Bristol BS15 1XT. Tel: (H) 0117 961 1079
Fixtures Secretary: Mr LA Millard, 177 Lodge Causeway,
Fishponds, Bristol BS16 3QE. Tel: (H) 0117 965 6673
Club Colours: Maroon.
HORNETS RFC
Ground Address: Hutton Moor Road,
Weston-super-Mare, Avon BS22 8LY. Tel: 01934 621433
Club Secretary: Tony Wilson, 29 Grove Road, Milton,
Weston-super-Mare, Avon BS22 8EY. Tel: (H) 01934
415240
Fixtures Secretary: Paul Davidson, 27 Chesham Road
South, Weston-super-Mare, Avon. Tel: (H) 01934 414112
Club Colours: Black & amber.
NORTH BRISTOL RFC
Ground Address: Oaklands, Gloucester Road,
Almondsbury, Bristol BS12 4AG. Tel: 01454 612740
Club Secretary: CH Hill, 7 Keinton Walk, Henbury,
Bristol BS10 7EE. Tel: (H) 0117 950 8123
Fixtures Secretary: D Kettlewell, 227 Gloucester Road,
Patchway, Bristol BS12 5AD. Tel: (H) 01454 613418
Club Colours: Royal blue & scarlet hoops.
OLD REDCLIFFIANS RFC
Ground Address: Stockwood Lane, Brislington, Bristol.
Tel: 0117 977 8501
Club Secretary: Richard Yandell, 11 Imperial Walk,
Knowle, Bristol BS14 9AD. Tel: (H) 0117 977 7657 Tel:
(W) 0117 987 3636
Fixtures Secretary: Russell Yandell, 5 High Street,
Portbury, Nr Bristol. Tel: (H) 0117 937 3444 Tel (W) 0117
983 6077
Club Colours: Red & black hoops.
OLDFIELD OLD BOYS RFC
Ground Address: Shaft Road, Combe Down, Bath. Tel:
01225 834135
Club Secretary: Steve Godwin, 12 Lime Grove Gardens,
Bath, Avon BA2 4HE. Tel: (H) 01225 318612 Tel: (W)
01258 451441
Fixtures Secretary: Gary Lynch, 30 Bloomfield Park,
Bath. Tel: (H) 01225 33823

FINAL TABLE

	P	W	D	L	F	A	Pts
Keynsham	12	10	0	2	344	140	20
Whitehall	12	10	0	2	252	164	20
Hornets	12	9	1	2	213	146	19
St Mary's Old Boys	12	9	0	3	251	153	18
Stow-on-the-Wold	12	6	0	6	209	160	12
Thornbury	12	5	1	6	226	218	11
Oldfield Old Boys	12	6	0	6	203	181	10*
Bristol Harlequins	12	5	0	7	180	211	10
North Bristol	12	5	0	7	171	258	10
Cirencester	12	4	0	8	178	217	8
Old Redcliffians	12	3	1	8	92	192	7
Wiveliscombe	12	3	0	9	183	306	6
Midsomer Norton	12	1	1	10	127	283	3

Club Colours: Maroon & gold.
ST MARY'S OLD BOYS RFC
Ground Address: Trench Lane, Winterbourne, Bristol.
Tel: 0117 01454 250489
Club Secretary: Mrs L Collins, 18 Belmont Road, St
Andrews, Bristol BS6 5AS. Tel: (H) 0117 924 9879
Fixtures Secretary: Mr W Hopkins, 66 Down Road,
Aveston, Nr Bristol BS12 2JR. Tel: (H) 0117 0145 419571
Club Colours: Emerald green & black.
STOW-ON-THE-WOLD & DISTRICT RFC
Ground Address: Oddington Road, Stow-on-the-Wold,
Glos. Tel: 01451 830887
Club Secretary: N Drury, Aston House, Broadwell,
Moreton-in-Marsh, Glos GL56 0TJ. Tel: (H) 01451 830961
Tel: (W) 01608 650428
Fixtures Secretary: B Proctor, 33 Cleevemont, Evesham
Road, Cheltenham, Glos. Tel: (H) 01242 234199
Club Colours: Black & white hoops.
THORNBURY RFC
Ground Address: Cooper's Farm, Lower Morton,
Thornbury. Tel: 01454 412096
Club Secretary: HR Bowker, 2 Brunksea Road, Filton
Park, Bristol BS7 0SE. Tel: (H) 0117 969 8744
Fixtures Secretary: MJ Carling, 57 Ashgrove, Thornbury,
Bristol BS12 1BH. Tel: (H) 01454 885353
Club Colours: Black & amber hoops.
WELLINGTON RFC
Ground Address: The Athletic Ground, Corams Lane,
Wellington, Somerset TA21 8LL. Tel: 01823 663758
Club Secretary: BK Colman, Meadowside, Mantle Street,
Wellington, Somerset TA21 8BG. Tel: (H) 01823 663307
Tel: (W) 01823 333451 x5121
Fixtures Secretary: GR Vickery, 7 Seymour Street,
Wellington, Somerset. Tel: (H) 01823 664695 Tel (W)
01823 335166
Club Colours: Red & black.
WHITEHALL RFC
Ground Address: Speedwell Playing Fields, Foundry
Lane, Speedwell, Bristol (No correspondence to ground
address). Tel: 0117 965 9636
Club Secretary: Tim Hickey, 47 Berkeley Road,
Fishponds, Bristol BS16 3NA. Tel: (H) 0117 965 7305
Fixtures Secretary: Alec Ferguson, 8 Stoneleigh Road,
Knowle, Bristol BS4 2RT. Tel: (H) 0117 977 2898
Club Colours: Myrtle & gold.

SOUTH WEST DIVISION

GLOUCESTERSHIRE ONE 1995-96 FIXTURES

November 11 1995 (Week 10)

Barton Hill	v	Bristol Saracens
Bream	v	Tredworth
Coney Hill	v	Longlevens
Frampton Cotterell	v	Cheltenham North
Old Cryptians	v	Brockworth
Old Richians	v	Hucclecote

September 16 1995 (Week 3)

Bream	v	Barton Hill
Brockworth	v	Longlevens
Hucclecote	v	Bristol Saracens
Old Cryptians	v	Frampton Cotterell
Old Richians	v	Coney Hill
Widden OB	v	Cheltenham North

September 23 1995 (Week 4)

Bristol Saracens	v	Brockworth
Cheltenham North	v	Old Cryptians
Coney Hill	v	Bream
Frampton Cotterell	v	Old Richians
Longlevens	v	Widden OB
Tredworth	v	Hucclecote

September 30 1995 (Week X1)

Barton Hill	v	Coney Hill
Bream	v	Frampton Cotterell
Brockworth	v	Tredworth
Old Cryptians	v	Longlevens
Old Richians	v	Cheltenham North
Widden OB	v	Bristol Saracens

October 14 1995 (Week 6)

Bristol Saracens	v	Old Cryptians
Cheltenham North	v	Bream
Frampton Cotterell	v	Barton Hill
Hucclecote	v	Brockworth
Longlevens	v	Old Richians
Tredworth	v	Widden OB

October 21 1995 (Week 7)

Barton Hill	v	Cheltenham North
Bream	v	Longlevens
Coney Hill	v	Frampton Cotterell
Old Cryptians	v	Tredworth
Old Richians	v	Bristol Saracens
Widden OB	v	Hucclecote

October 28 1995 (Week 8)

Bristol Saracens	v	Bream
Brockworth	v	Widden OB
Cheltenham North	v	Coney Hill
Hucclecote	v	Old Cryptians
Longlevens	v	Barton Hill
Tredworth	v	Old Richians

January 6 1996 (Week 17)

Bristol Saracens	v	Coney Hill
Brockworth	v	Old Richians
Hucclecote	v	Bream
Longlevens	v	Frampton Cotterell
Tredworth	v	Barton Hill
Widden OB	v	Old Cryptians

January 13 1996 (Week 18)

Barton Hill	v	Hucclecote
Bream	v	Brockworth
Cheltenham North	v	Longlevens
Coney Hill	v	Tredworth
Frampton Cotterell	v	Bristol Saracens
Old Richians	v	Widden OB

February 10 1996 (Week 22)

Bristol Saracens	v	Cheltenham North
Brockworth	v	Barton Hill
Hucclecote	v	Coney Hill
Old Cryptians	v	Old Richians
Tredworth	v	Frampton Cotterell
Widden OB	v	Bream

February 17 1996 (Week 23)

Barton Hill	v	Widden OB
Bream	v	Old Cryptians
Cheltenham North	v	Tredworth
Coney Hill	v	Brockworth
Frampton Cotterell	v	Hucclecote
Longlevens	v	Bristol Saracens

February 24 1996 (Week 24)

Brockworth	v	Frampton Cotterell
Hucclecote	v	Cheltenham North
Old Cryptians	v	Barton Hill
Old Richians	v	Bream
Tredworth	v	Longlevens
Widden OB	v	Coney Hill

March 30 1996 (Week X7)

Barton Hill	v	Old Richians
Bristol Saracens	v	Tredworth
Cheltenham North	v	Brockworth
Coney Hill	v	Old Cryptians
Frampton Cotterell	v	Widden OB
Longlevens	v	Hucclecote

GLOUCESTERSHIRE ONE

BARTON HILL OLD BOYS RUFC
Ground Address: Duncombe Lane, Speedwell, Bristol.
Tel: 0117 987 2895
Club Secretary: Keith Strickland, 18 The Close,
Soundwell, Bristol BS16 4PH. Tel: (H) 0117 965 7614 Tel:
(W) 0117 982 5145
Fixtures Secretary: Paul Uppington, 18 Eaton Close,
Fishponds, Bristol. Tel: (H) 0117 965 0340
Club Colours: White shirts with cherry red band, black
collar & cuffs.
BREAM RFC
Ground Address: High Street, Bream, Nr Lydney, Glos
GL15 6JG. Tel: 01594 562320
Club Secretary: John Grail, 31 Highbury Road, Bream, Nr
Lydney, Glos GL15 6EF. Tel: (H) 01594 562737 Tel: (W)
01594 562320
Fixtures Secretary: G Byett, Woodside View, Blakney
Hill, Nr Lydney, Glos, GL15 4BT. Tel: (H) 01594 517203
Club Colours: Red & black.
BRISTOL SARACENS RFC
Ground Address: Station Road, Cribbs Causeway,
Henbury, Bristol. Tel: 0117 950 0037
Club Secretary: AE Swash, 6 Downs Road,
Westbury-on-Trym, Bristol BS9 3TX. Tel: (H) 0117 962
9047 Tel: (W) 01626 832283
Fixtures Secretary: CJ Matthews, 6 Wellington Drive,
Henleaze, Bristol BS9 4SR. Tel: (H) 0117 924 3696 Tel
(W) 01454 419008
Club Colours: Myrtle green & white hooped shirts, black
shorts.
BROCKWORTH RFC
Ground Address: Mill Lane, Brockworth, Gloucester. Tel:
01452 862556
Club Secretary: RJ Cassidy, 90 Boverton Drive,
Brockworth, Glos GL3 4BS. Tel: (H) 01452 862621 Tel:
(W) 01452 413531
Fixtures Secretary: Mr P Hickey, 63 Falfield Road,
Tuffley, Gloucester GL4 0ND. Tel: (H) 01452 308819
Club Colours: Black with white V.
CHELTENHAM NORTH RFC
Ground Address: Stoke Orchard Road, Bishop's Cleeve,
Cheltenham. Tel: 01242 675968
Club Secretary: Andrew Page, Baytrees, 3 Chargrove
Lane, Up Hatherley, Cheltenham GL51 5LP. Tel: (H)
01242 510932 Tel: (W) 01242 523580
Fixtures Secretary: P Shand, 103 Brooklyn Road, St
Mark's, Cheltenham. Tel: (H) 01242 693130
Club Colours: Black & red.
CONEY HILL RFC
Ground Address: Metz Way, Barnwood, Gloucester. Tel:
01452 306239
Club Secretary: DC Veale, 13 Stanway Road, Coney Hill,
Gloucester GL4 7RE. Tel: (H) 01452 306510
Fixtures Secretary: D Carter, 55 Paygrove Lane,
Longlevens, Gloucester GL2 0BA. Tel: (H) 01452 500424
Club Colours: Amber, black & white hoops.
FRAMPTON COTTERELL RFC
Ground Address: Crossbow House Community
Association, School Road, Frampton Cotterell, Bristol. Tel:
01454 772947
Club Secretary: Mrs Sue Soper, 58 Lower Chapel Lane,
Frampton Cotterell, Bristol BS17 2RH. Tel: (H) 01454
772095 Tel: (W) 01454 322422
Fixtures Secretary: Mr Simon Brooks, 5 Breeches Gate,
Bradley Stoke, Bristol. Tel: (H) 0117 969 7760
Club Colours: Green, black & gold.
HUCCLECOTE OLD BOYS RFC
Club Secretary: John E Ring, 9 Conway Road,
Hucclecote, Gloucester GL3 3PD. Tel: (H) 01452 618920
Fixtures Secretary: Colin Bevan, 2 Watermead Cottages,
Green Street, Brockworth, Glos GL3 4RR. Tel: (H) 01452

FINAL TABLE

	P	W	D	L	F	A	Pts
Cleve	12	11	1	0	314	112	21*
Longlevens	12	7	1	4	173	163	15
Barton Hill	12	7	0	5	217	157	14
Old Cryptians	12	7	0	5	206	173	14
Cheltenham North	12	6	0	6	241	200	12
Frampton Cotterell	12	7	0	5	226	233	12*
Hucclecote Old Boys	12	5	2	5	163	170	12
Old Richians	12	6	0	6	232	207	10*
Brockworth	12	6	0	6	228	224	10*
Bream	12	5	1	6	221	177	9*
Widden Old Boys	12	4	1	7	137	175	9
Coney Hill	12	3	0	9	143	279	6
Painswick	12	1	0	11	115	346	2

863689
Club Colours: Amber & black.
LONGLEVENS RFC
Ground Address: Longford Lane, Longlevens, Gloucester.
Tel: 01452 306880
Club Secretary: Colin F Dunford, 66 Estcourt Road,
Gloucester GL1 3LG. Tel: (H) 01452 306880 Tel: (W)
01452 411656
Fixtures Secretary: Mark J Dunford, 22 Hayes Court,
Longford, Gloucester. Tel: (H) 01452 311750 Tel (W)
01242 221221
Club Colours: Red.
OLD CRYPTIANS RFC
Ground Address: Memorial Ground, Tuffley Avenue,
Gloucester GL1 5NS. Tel: 01452 520052
Club Secretary: Gordon Hill, 244 Stroud Road, Gloucester
GL4 0AU. Tel: (H) 01452 521651 Tel: (W) 01454 260681
x337
Fixtures Secretary: Derek Howell, 255C Stroud Road,
Gloucester. Tel: (H) 01452 414010 Tel (W) 01452 425611
Club Colours: Maroon, gold & navy blue.
OLD RICHIANS RFC
Ground Address: Sandyleaze, Longlevens, Gloucester
GL2 0PU. Tel: 01452 524649
Club Secretary: Paul Toleman, 4 Upper Rea, Hempsted,
Gloucester GL2 6LR. Tel: (H) 01452 422274 Tel: (W)
01452 416138
Fixtures Secretary: Mark Carter, 58 Sandyleaze,
Longlevens, Gloucester. Tel: (H) 01452 531456 Tel (W)
01452 531456
Club Colours: Royal blue & gold hoops.
TREDWORTH RUFC
Ground Address: The Lannet, King Edwards Avenue,
Gloucester. Tel: 01452 308939
Club Secretary: Howard Kenneth Speck, Salem, 1
Ashcroft Close, St Leonards Park, Gloucester GL4 9JX.
Tel: (H) 01452 302699
Fixtures Secretary: R Williams, 16 Highworth Road,
Tredworth, Gloucester. Tel: (H) 01452 411338
Club Colours: Green & black.
WIDDEN OLD BOYS RFC
Ground Address: Memorial Ground, Tuffley Avenue,
Gloucester. Tel: 01452 304080
Club Secretary: Mr Chris Hinde, 32 Millfields,
Hucclecote, Gloucester. Tel: (H) 01452 814104
Fixtures Secretary: Mr Mike Taylor, 285 Tuffley Lane,
Tuffley, Gloucester. Tel: (H) 01452 413480
Club Colours: Myrtle green.

SOUTH WEST DIVISION

GLOUCESTERSHIRE TWO
1995-96
FIXTURES

November 11 1995 (Week 10)

Ashley Down OB	v	Bristol Telephone Area
Bishopston	v	Cotham Park
Broad Plain	v	Cheltenham Saracens
Cainscross	v	Cheltenham Civil Ser
Old Centralians	v	Old Bristolians
Tetbury	v	Chosen Hill

September 16 1995 (Week 3)

Ashley Down OB	v	Bishopston
Chosen Hill	v	Cotham Park
Old Bristolians	v	Cheltenham Saracens
Old Centralians	v	Cainscross
Painswick	v	Cheltenham Civil Ser
Tetbury	v	Broad Plain

September 23 1995 (Week 4)

Bristol Telephone Area	v	Chosen Hill
Broad Plain	v	Ashley Down OB
Cainscross	v	Tetbury
Cheltenham Civil Ser	v	Old Centralians
Cheltenham Saracens	v	Painswick
Cotham Park	v	Old Bristolians

September 30 1995 (Week X1)

Ashley Down OB	v	Cainscross
Bishopston	v	Broad Plain
Old Bristolians	v	Bristol Telephone Area
Old Centralians	v	Cheltenham Saracens
Painswick	v	Cotham Park
Tetbury	v	Cheltenham Civil Ser

October 14 1995 (Week 6)

Bristol Telephone Area	v	Painswick
Cainscross	v	Bishopston
Cheltenham Civil Ser	v	Ashley Down OB
Cheltenham Saracens	v	Tetbury
Chosen Hill	v	Old Bristolians
Cotham Park	v	Old Centralians

October 21 1995 (Week 7)

Ashley Down OB	v	Cheltenham Saracens
Bishopston	v	Cheltenham Civil Ser
Broad Plain	v	Cainscross
Old Centralians	v	Bristol Telephone Area
Painswick	v	Chosen Hill
Tetbury	v	Cotham Park

October 28 1995 (Week 8)

Bristol Telephone Area	v	Tetbury
Cheltenham Civil Ser	v	Broad Plain
Cheltenham Saracens	v	Bishopston
Chosen Hill	v	Old Centralians
Cotham Park	v	Ashley Down OB
Old Bristolians	v	Painswick

January 6 1996 (Week 17)

Bristol Telephone Area	v	Bishopston
Cheltenham Saracens	v	Cainscross
Chosen Hill	v	Ashley Down OB
Cotham Park	v	Broad Plain
Old Bristolians	v	Tetbury
Painswick	v	Old Centralians

January 13 1996 (Week 18)

Ashley Down OB	v	Old Bristolians
Bishopston	v	Chosen Hill
Broad Plain	v	Bristol Telephone Area
Cainscross	v	Cotham Park
Cheltenham Civil Ser	v	Cheltenham Saracens
Tetbury	v	Painswick

February 10 1996 (Week 22)

Bristol Telephone Area	v	Cainscross
Chosen Hill	v	Broad Plain
Cotham Park	v	Cheltenham Civil Ser
Old Bristolians	v	Bishopston
Old Centralians	v	Tetbury
Painswick	v	Ashley Down OB

February 17 1996 (Week 23)

Ashley Down OB	v	Old Centralians
Bishopston	v	Painswick
Broad Plain	v	Old Bristolians
Cainscross	v	Chosen Hill
Cheltenham Civil Ser	v	Bristol Telephone Area
Cheltenham Saracens	v	Cotham Park

February 24 1996 (Week 24)

Bristol Telephone Area	v	Cheltenham Saracens
Chosen Hill	v	Cheltenham Civil Ser
Old Bristolians	v	Cainscross
Old Centralians	v	Bishopston
Painswick	v	Broad Plain
Tetbury	v	Ashley Down OB

March 30 1996 (Week X7)

Bishopston	v	Tetbury
Broad Plain	v	Old Centralians
Cainscross	v	Painswick
Cheltenham Civil Ser	v	Old Bristolians
Cheltenham Saracens	v	Chosen Hill
Cotham Park	v	Bristol Telephone Area

GLOUCESTERSHIRE TWO

ASHLEY DOWN OLD BOYS RFC
Ground Address: Bonnington Walk Playing Fields,
Lockleaze, Bristol. Tel: 0117 931 2642
Club Secretary: MJ Delderfield, 1 Charlton Gardens,
Brentry, Bristol BS10 6LU. Tel: (H) 0117 950 4360 Tel:
(W) 01452 653826
Fixtures Secretary: R Johnson, 46 Kendal Road, Horfield,
Bristol BS7 0DU. Tel: (H) 011 969 1581
Club Colours: White with purple hoop.

BISHOPSTON RFC
Ground Address: Bonnington Walk, Lockleaze, Bristol.
Tel: 0117 969 1916
Club Secretary: DGJ Hockley, 21 Pinewood Close,
Westbury-on-Trym, Bristol BS9 4AJ. Tel: (H) 0117 962
3509 Tel: (W) 0117 929 1031 x2391
Fixtures Secretary: Stuart Brain, 9 Chewton Close,
Fishponds, Bristol BS16 3SR. Tel: (H) 0117 958 5560
Club Colours: Red with black hoop edged in centenary
gold.

BRISTOL TELEPHONE AREA RFC
Ground Address: BTRA Sports Ground, Stockwood Lane,
Stockwood, Bristol BS14. Tel: 01272 891776
Club Secretary: Mike Cross, 21 Grangeville Close,
Longwell Green, Bristol BS15 6YA. Tel: (H) 0117 932
5146 Tel: (W) 0117 951 9912
Fixtures Secretary: Bernie Nicholls, 58 Durville Road,
Headley Park, Bristol. Tel: (H) 0117 964 7400
Club Colours: Blue with red & white V neck.

BROAD PLAIN RFC
Ground Address: Hartcliffe School, Bishport Avenue,
Hartcliffe, Bristol. Tel: 0117 964 9757
Club Secretary: Don Collins, 77 Lake Road, Henleaze,
Bristol BS10 5JE. Tel: (H) 0117 962 2094 Tel: (W) 0117
924 8051
Fixtures Secretary: John Daveridge, 115 Ravenshill Road,
Knowle, Bristol BS3 5BT. Tel: (H) 0117 977 1823
Club Colours: Blue, maroon & gold hoops.

CAINSCROSS RFC
Ground Address: Victory Park, Ebley, Stroud, Glos. Tel:
01453 766707
Club Secretary: WR Tocknell, Pendaleon House, Selsley
Road, North Woodchester, Stroud, Glos GL5 5PH. Tel: (H)
01453 872333 Tel: (W) 01453 762773
Fixtures Secretary: D Roberts, 41 Boakes Drive, Bristol
Road, Stonehouse, Glos. Tel: (H) 01453 824694
Club Colours: Amber & blue.

CHELTENHAM CIVIL SERVICE RFC
Ground Address: Civil Service Sports Ground,
Tewkesbury Road, Uckington, Cheltenham, Glos. Tel:
01242 680847
Club Secretary: Brian Didlick, 15 Stoneville Street,
Cheltenham, Glos GL51 8PH. Tel: (H) 01242 519285
Fixtures Secretary: Julie Mortlock, 88 Arle Road,
Cheltenham, Glos. Tel: (H) 01242 582945
Club Colours: Navy blue.

CHELTENHAM SARACENS RFC
Ground Address: King George V Playing Fields,
Brooklyn Road, Cheltenham, Glos.
Club Secretary: Colin Wheeler, Bredon School, Pull
Court, Bushley, Nr Tewkesbury, Glos GL20 6AH. Tel: (H)
01684 294119 Tel: (W) 01684 293156
Fixtures Secretary: DS Garside, 1 Solway Road,
Springbank, Cheltenham, Glos GL51 0LY. Tel: (H) 01242
515177
Club Colours: Blue with gold circlet.

CHOSEN HILL FORMER PUPILS RFC
Ground Address: Brookfield Road, Churchdown,
Gloucester GL3 2PL. Tel: 01452 712384
Club Secretary: Colin Yeates, 14 Drews Court,
Churchdown, Gloucester GL3 2LD. Tel: (H) 01452 712427
Tel: (W) 01242 230881

FINAL TABLE

	P	W	D	L	F	A	Pts
Tredworth	12	9	0	3	219	158	18
Bristol Saracens	12	8	1	3	243	110	17
Cheltenham Civil S	12	8	1	3	162	137	17
Cheltenham Saracens	12	9	0	3	218	129	16*
Ashley Down O Boys	12	8	0	4	217	148	16
Saintsbridge	12	7	0	5	161	130	14
Bishopston	12	5	0	7	162	170	10
Old Bristolians	12	5	0	7	186	214	10
Bristol Telephones	12	5	0	7	123	171	10
Tetbury	12	5	2	5	154	216	10*
Cotham Park	12	3	0	9	100	157	6
Chosen Hill	12	3	0	9	147	207	4*
Kingswood	12	1	0	11	118	263	0*

Fixtures Secretary: Ian Yeates, 98 Melville Road,
Churchdown, Gloucester GL3 2RG. Tel: (H) 01452 531502
Tel (W) 01242 527511
Club Colours: Myrtle green & white.

COTHAM PARK RFC
Ground Address: Beggar Bush Lane, Failand, Bristol. Tel:
01275 392501
Club Secretary: Frank Nesbitt, 94 Kenn Road, Clevedon,
Avon BS21 6EX. Tel: (H) 01275 342334
Fixtures Secretary: Mike Gill, 8 Holmwood, Bristol BS9
3EB. Tel: (H) 0117 950 0361 Tel (W) 0117 930 6200
Club Colours: Black & white.

OLD BRISTOLIANS RFC
Ground Address: Memorial Playing Field, Longwood
Lane, Failand, Bristol. Tel: 01275 392137
Club Secretary: Mr S Williams (St John), 7 Old Sneed
Avenue, Stoke Bishop, Bristol BS9 1SD. Tel: (H) 0117 968
5136 Tel: (W) 0117 929 5077
Fixtures Secretary: Mr D Furze (Don), 103 Manor Road,
Keynsham, Bristol BS18 1SF. Tel: (H) 0117 986 5222 Tel
(W) 0117 979 7687
Club Colours: Maroon, amber & green.

OLD CENTRALIANS RFC
Ground Address: Saintbridge Sports Centre, Painswick
Road, Gloucester GL4 9QX. Tel: 01452 303768
Club Secretary: PK Fritchley, 195 Seymour Road,
Gloucester GL1 5HR. Tel: (H) 01452 418427 Tel: (W)
0585 788508
Fixtures Secretary: Mr A Stephenson, 10 Brookside
Villas, Coronation Grove, Barnwood, Gloucester GL2 0SS.
Tel: (H) 01452 531793
Club Colours: Navy blue, royal blue & gold.

PAINSWICK RFC
Ground Address: Broadham Fields, Stroud Road,
Painswick, Nr Stroud, Glos. Tel: 01452 813861
Club Secretary: ATC Morgan, Pipers Edge, Cheltenham
Road, Painswick, Nr Stroud, Glos GL6 6SJ. Tel: (H) 01452
814202 Tel: (W) 01452 521267 Fax: 01452 300184
Fixtures Secretary: I Hogg, 77 Fieldcourt Gardens,
Quedgeley, Gloucester. Tel: (H) 01452 728310
Club Colours: Cherry & white hoops.

TETBURY RFC
Ground Address: Recreation Ground, Hampton Street,
Tetbury, Glos. Tel: 01666 505052
Club Secretary: WR Eastling, The Cottage, Highfield
Farm, Tetbury, Glos GL8 8SD. Tel: (H) 01666 504949 Tel:
(W) 0860 224274
Fixtures Secretary: Ray McCarthy, 98 Longtree Close,
Tetbury, Glos. Tel: (H) 01666 502724
Club Colours: Black with amber collar & cuffs.

SOUTH WEST DIVISION

GLOUCESTERSHIRE THREE 1995-96 FIXTURES

September 16 1995 (Week 3)
Chipping Sodbury	v	Old Colstonians
Kingswood	v	Glos Police
Old Elizabethans	v	Tewkesbury
Smiths Industries	v	Dursley
Southmead	v	Aretians
Westbury-on-Severn	v	Bristol Aero

September 23 1995 (Week 4)
Aretians	v	Kingswood
Bristol Aero	v	Smiths Industries
Dursley	v	Chipping Sodbury
Gloucester Civil Ser	v	Old Elizabethans
Glos Police	v	Westbury-on-Severn
Tewkesbury	v	Southmead

September 30 1995 (Week X1)
Chipping Sodbury	v	Bristol Aero
Kingswood	v	Tewkesbury
Old Colstonians	v	Dursley
Smiths Industries	v	Glos Police
Southmead	v	Gloucester Civil Ser
Westbury-on-Severn	v	Aretians

October 14 1995 (Week 6)
Aretians	v	Smiths Industries
Bristol Aero	v	Old Colstonians
Gloucester Civil Ser	v	Kingswood
Glos Police	v	Chipping Sodbury
Old Elizabethans	v	Southmead
Tewkesbury	v	Westbury-on-Severn

October 21 1995 (Week 7)
Chipping Sodbury	v	Aretians
Dursley	v	Bristol Aero
Kingswood	v	Old Elizabethans
Old Colstonians	v	Glos Police
Smiths Industries	v	Tewkesbury
Westbury-on-Severn	v	Gloucester Civil Ser

October 28 1995 (Week 8)
Aretians	v	Old Colstonians
Gloucester Civil Ser	v	Smiths Industries
Glos Police	v	Dursley
Old Elizabethans	v	Westbury-on-Severn
Southmead	v	Kingswood
Tewkesbury	v	Chipping Sodbury

November 11 1995 (Week 10)
Bristol Aero	v	Glos Police
Chipping Sodbury	v	Gloucester Civil Ser
Dursley	v	Aretians
Old Colstonians	v	Tewkesbury
Smiths Industries	v	Old Elizabethans
Westbury-on-Severn	v	Southmead

January 6 1996 (Week 17)
Aretians	v	Bristol Aero
Gloucester Civil Ser	v	Old Colstonians
Kingswood	v	Westbury-on-Severn
Old Elizabethans	v	Chipping Sodbury
Southmead	v	Smiths Industries
Tewkesbury	v	Dursley

January 13 1996 (Week 18)
Bristol Aero	v	Tewkesbury
Chipping Sodbury	v	Southmead
Dursley	v	Gloucester Civil Ser
Glos Police	v	Aretians
Old Colstonians	v	Old Elizabethans
Smiths Industries	v	Kingswood

February 10 1996 (Week 22)
Gloucester Civil Ser	v	Bristol Aero
Kingswood	v	Chipping Sodbury
Old Elizabethans	v	Dursley
Southmead	v	Old Colstonians
Tewkesbury	v	Glos Police
Westbury-on-Severn	v	Smiths Industries

February 17 1996 (Week 23)
Aretians	v	Tewkesbury
Bristol Aero	v	Old Elizabethans
Chipping Sodbury	v	Westbury-on-Severn
Dursley	v	Southmead
Glos Police	v	Gloucester Civil Ser
Old Colstonians	v	Kingswood

February 24 1996 (Week 24)
Gloucester Civil Ser	v	Aretians
Kingswood	v	Dursley
Old Elizabethans	v	Glos Police
Smiths Industries	v	Chipping Sodbury
Southmead	v	Bristol Aero
Westbury-on-Severn	v	Old Colstonians

March 30 1996 (Week X7)
Aretians	v	Old Elizabethans
Bristol Aero	v	Kingswood
Dursley	v	Westbury-on-Severn
Glos Police	v	Southmead
Old Colstonians	v	Smiths Industries
Tewkesbury	v	Gloucester Civil Ser

GLOUCESTERSHIRE THREE

ARETIANS RFC
Ground Address: The Clubhouse, Station Road, Little Stoke, Bristol BS12 6HW. Tel: 01454 888069
Club Secretary: Andy Vaughan, 42 Elm Close, Little Stoke, Bristol BS12 6RQ. Tel: (H) 0117 975 6513 Tel: (W) 0117 955 7767
Fixtures Secretary: Andy Williams, 145 Finch Road, Chipping Sodbury, Bristol BS17 6JB. Tel: (H) 01454 886179 Tel (W) 0117 979 7187
Club Colours: Black.

BRISTOL AEROPLANE CO RFC
Ground Address: Bristol Aerospace Welfare Association Sports Ground, 589 Southmead Road, Filton, Bristol BS12 7DG. Tel: 0117 979 8066
Club Secretary: Neil Elliott, 4 The Bluebells, Bradley Stoke, Bristol BS12 8BE. Tel: (H) 0117 969 3714 Tel: (W) 0117 979 5399
Fixtures Secretary: Roy Williams, 90 Cock Road, Kingswood, Bristol BS15 2SL. Tel: 0117 967 8600 Tel (W) 0117 956 8775
Club Colours: Red, white & blue hoops.

CHIPPING SODBURY RFC
Ground Address: The Ridings, Wickwar Road, Chipping Sodbury, Bristol. Tel: 01454 312852
Club Secretary: Mark Kirkham, 27 Sutherland Avenue, Yate, Bristol BS17 5UE. Tel: (H) 01454 324496 Tel: (W) Mobile: 0973 203184
Fixtures Secretary: Mr Tony Windsor, The Bungalow, King Edmund School, Sunbridge Park Road, Yate, Bristol. Tel: (H) 01454 315959
Club Colours: Black.

DURSLEY RFC
Ground Address: Hounds Green, Stinchcombe, Dursley, Glos. Tel: 01453 543693
Club Secretary: Simon Bilous, 8 Ferney, Dursley, Glos GL11 5AB. Tel: (H) 01453 545493 Tel: (W) 0117 965 5261
Fixtures Secretary: Steve Tocknell, 57 Shutehay Drive, Cam, Dursley, Glos GL11 5UU. Tel: (H) 01453 544236
Club Colours: Maroon with amber hoop.

GLOUCESTER CIVIL SERVICE TIGERS RFC
Ground Address: GSSSA, Estcourt Road, Gloucester GL1 3LG. Tel: 01452 528317
Club Secretary: David M Oliver, 60 Larkhay Road, Hucclecote, Gloucester GL3 3NB. Tel: (H) 01452 613418
Fixtures Secretary: Barrie Humphries, 283 Bristol Road, Quedgeley, Gloucester GL2 6QP. Tel: (H) 01452 728024
Club Colours: Red & blue hoops.

GLOUCESTERSHIRE CONSTABULARY RFC
Ground Address: c/o Dowty Sports & Social Club, Down Hatherly Lane, Staverton, Glos. Tel: 01452 712223
Club Secretary: Alex Drummond, The Orchard, Green Lane, Churchdown, Glos. Tel: (H) 01452 712709 Tel: (W) 01242 276453
Fixtures Secretary: Peter Haines, Savanah, Church Road, Cainscross, Stroud, Glos GL5 4JE. Tel: (H) 01453 765003 Tel (W) 01242 276427
Club Colours: All black.

KINGSWOOD RFC
Ground Address: Church Avenue Playing Field, London Road, Warmley, Kingswood, Nr Bristol. Tel: 0117 967 5001
Club Secretary: Roger Clease, 166 Mounthill Road, Kingswood, Bristol BS15 2SX. Tel: (H) 0117 975 0890
Fixtures Secretary: Nick Long, 119 Woodland Way, Kingswood, Avon BS15 1PY. Tel: (H) 0117 960 8804
Club Colours: Sky blue/chocolate brown.

OLD COLSTONIANS RFC
Ground Address: New Road, Stoke Gifford, Bristol. Tel: 0117 969 0009
Club Secretary: David C Parker, 37 Ratcliffe Drive, Stoke Gifford, Bristol BS12 6TX. Tel: (H) 0117 969 7438 Tel:

FINAL TABLE

	P	W	D	L	F	A	Pts
Cainscross	12	12	0	0	304	94	22*
Broad Plain	12	10	0	2	229	110	18*
Southmead	12	9	0	3	254	160	18
Smiths (Industries)	12	8	0	4	245	176	16
Aretians	12	8	0	4	154	140	16
Chipping Sodbury	12	6	0	6	222	157	12
Westbury-on-Severn	12	6	0	6	171	156	12
Tewkesbury	12	5	0	7	131	159	10
Dursley	12	5	0	7	168	197	10
Old Colstonians	12	3	0	9	125	264	6
Gloucester Civil S	12	3	0	9	130	205	4*
Old Elizabethans	12	2	0	10	102	271	2*
Michinhampton	12	1	0	11	112	258	0*

(W) 01275 555434
Fixtures Secretary: Dr Bill Burrows, The Firs, Westend, Wickwar, Wotton-under-Edge, Glos. Tel: (H) 01454 294357 Tel (W) 01454 842214
Club Colours: Black, blue & gold hoops.

OLD ELIZABETHANS RFC
Ground Address: Severn Road, Hallen, Bristol. Tel: 0117 959 1072
Club Secretary: David Langdon, 13 Gloucester Street, Wotton-under-Edge, Glos GL12 7DN. Tel: (H) 01453 845349 Tel: (W) 0117 966 8431
Fixtures Secretary: Philip Cheek, 38 Durdham Park, Redland, Bristol BS6 6XB. Tel: (H) 0117 973 4109 Tel (W) 0117 982 1000
Club Colours: Old gold, white & blue hoops.

SMITHS INDUSTRIES RFC
Ground Address: The Newlands, Evesham Road, Bishops Cleeve, Cheltenham, Glos. Tel: 01242 672752
Club Secretary: Gerald Owen, 79 Station Road, Bishops Cleeve, Cheltenham, Glos. Tel: (H) 01242 676345 Tel: (W) 01242 673333
Fixtures Secretary: Robert Etchells, 179 Broadoak Way, Hatherley, Cheltenham, Glos. Tel: (H) 01242 528921 Tel (W) 01684 290243
Club Colours: Royal blue & white.

SOUTHMEAD RFC
Ground Address: Greenway Centre, Doncaster Road, Southmead, Bristol. Tel: 0117 959 3060
Club Secretary: Mike Haddon, 20 Braydon Avenue, Little Stoke, Bristol BS12 6EH. Tel: (H) 01454 614019
Fixtures Secretary: Mike Haddon, 20 Braydon Avenue, Little Stoke, Bristol BS12 6EH. Tel: (H) 01454 614019
Club Colours: Blue shirts with emerald green hoops.

TEWKESBURY RFC
Ground Address: The Moats, Lankett Lane, Tewkesbury, Glos. Tel: 01684 275266 (changing rooms); 01684 294364 (clubhouse)
Club Secretary: The Secretary, c/o Tewkesbury RFC, The Moats, Lankett Lane, Tewkesbury, Glos.
Fixtures Secretary: Mr Paul Cole, 7 East Street, Tewkesbury, Glos. Tel: (H) 01684 295932
Club Colours: Black & amber hoops or quarters.

WESTBURY-ON-SEVERN RFC
Ground Address: Parish Grounds, Westbury-on-Severn, Glos. Tel: 01452 760359
Club Secretary: Phil Bleathman, The Hollies, Elton, Westbury-on-Severn, Glos GL14 1JJ. Tel: (H) 01452 760751 Tel: (W) 01452 760751 & 0831 184474
Fixtures Secretary: Tony Osborne, 42 Baynham Road, Mitchledean, Glos GL17 0JR. Tel: (H) 01594 542613 Tel (W) 01452 760209
Club Colours: Royal blue & white hoops.

SOUTH WEST DIVISION

GLOUCESTERSHIRE FOUR
1995-96 FIXTURES

September 16 1995 (Week 3)
Minchinhampton v Dowty
Tudorville v Pilning
Wotton-under-Edge v Newent

September 23 1995 (Week 4)
Dowty v Gloucester All Blues
Pilning v Newent
Tudorville v Minchinhampton

September 30 1995 (Week X1)
Gloucester All Blues v Tudorville
Minchinhampton v Newent
Pilning v Wotton-under-Edge

October 14 1995 (Week 6)
Newent v Dowty
Pilning v Minchinhampton
Wotton-under-Edge v Gloucester All Blues

October 21 1995 (Week 7)
Dowty v Pilning
Minchinhampton v Gloucester All Blues
Tudorville v Newent

October 28 1995 (Week 8)
Gloucester All Blues v Dowty
Pilning v Tudorville
Wotton-under-Edge v Minchinhampton

November 11 1995 (Week 10)
Dowty v Wotton-under-Edge
Newent v Pilning
Tudorville v Gloucester All Blues

December 30 1995 (Week X4)
Minchinhampton v Pilning
Newent v Tudorville
Wotton-under-Edge v Dowty

January 6 1996 (Week 17)
Dowty v Minchinhampton
Gloucester All Blues v Newent
Wotton-under-Edge v Tudorville

January 13 1996 (Week 18)
Minchinhampton v Tudorville
Newent v Wotton-under-Edge
Pilning v Gloucester All Blues

February 10 1996 (Week 22)
Gloucester All Blues v Minchinhampton
Tudorville v Dowty
Wotton-under-Edge v Pilning

February 17 1996 (Week 23)
Gloucester All Blues v Wotton-under-Edge
Newent v Minchinhampton
Pilning v Dowty

February 24 1996 (Week 24)
Dowty v Tudorville
Minchinhampton v Wotton-under-Edge
Newent v Gloucester All Blues

March 30 1996 (Week X7)
Dowty v Newent
Gloucester All Blues v Pilning
Tudorville v Wotton-under-Edge

GLOUCESTERSHIRE FOUR

DOWTY RFC
Ground Address: Dowty Sports and Social Society, Staverton Division, Down Hatherley Lane, Gloucester GL2 9QD. Tel: 01452 714567
Club Secretary: Mrs G Blackwell, 6 Kaybourne Crescent, Churchdown, Gloucester GL3 2HL. Tel: (H) 01425 859388
Fixtures Secretary: Mr R Newton, 109 Oldbury Orchard, Churchdown, Gloucester GL3 2NX. Tel: (H) 01452 857046 Tel (W) 01452 335367
Club Colours: Blue & white hoops.

GLOUCESTER ALL BLUES RFC
Ground Address: The Oxleaze, Westgate Street, Gloucester. Tel: 01452 306984
Club Secretary: Mr GR Selwyn, Millbank, Chessgrove Lane, Longhope, Gloucester GL17 0LE. Tel: (H) 01452 831215 Tel: (W) 01452 529553
Fixtures Secretary: Mr M Heath, 35 Dimore Close, Hardwicke, Gloucester GL2 6QQ. Tel: (H) 01452 728159
Club Colours: Dark blue shirts, shorts & socks.

MINCHINHAMPTON RFC
Ground Address: Minchinhampton Sports & Social Club, Tobacconist Road, Minchinhampton, Glos. Tel: 01453 882636
Club Secretary: Robert Edmonds, Woodlands Cottage, 205 Slad Road, Stroud, Glos. Tel: (H) 01453 766662 Tel: (W) 01452 308989
Fixtures Secretary: Pete Weaving, 14 Langtoft Road, Stroud, Glos. Tel: (H) 01453 755561
Club Colours: Green/black/white hoops, black shorts.

NEWENT RFC
Ground Address: The Recreation Ground, Watery Lane, Newent, Glos.
Club Secretary: Keri Evans, 303 Foley Road, Newent, Glos GL18 1ST. Tel: (H) 01531 822328
Fixtures Secretary: Mr Alun Hunt, 'Sunlight', Old Pike, Staunton, Glos GL19 3QN. Tel: (H) 01452 840636
Club Colours: Green & gold.

PILNING RFC
Ground Address: The Pitch, Beach Road, Severn Beach, Bristol. Tel: 01454 633549
Club Secretary: Andy Holmes, 4 Westfield Way, Bradley Stoke, Bristol BS12 0EN. Tel: (H) 01454 201256 Tel: (W) 01761 416034
Fixtures Secretary: Mr M O'Brien, 19 Prospect Road, Severn Beach, Bristol BS12. Tel: (H) 01454 633768
Club Colours: Blue & white hoops.

TUDORVILLE RFC
Ground Address: John Kyrle High School, Ross-on-Wye, Herefordshire.
Club Secretary: Paul Hayward, 6 Wallford road, Ross-on-Wye, Herefordshire. Tel: (H) 01989 565095 Tel: (W) 01989 566888
Fixtures Secretary: Stuart Baldwin, Noah's Arc, Chapel Road, Ross-on-Wye, Herefordshire. Tel: (H) 01989 563060
Club Colours: Black & red quarters.

WOTTON FC
Ground Address: New Road Ground, Wotton-under-Edge, Glos.
Club Secretary: CR Baker, 13 Bradley Street, Wotton-under-Edge, Glos GL12 7AP. Tel: (H) 01453 842455
Fixtures Secretary: R Flippence, 22 Bearlands, Wotton-under-Edge, Glos GL12 7SF. Tel: (H) 01453 844958
Club Colours: 4' black & 1' gold hoops.

FINAL TABLE

	P	W	D	L	F	A	Pts
Gloucestershire Pol	12	11	0	1	333	62	22
Bristol Aerospace	12	8	1	3	204	82	17
Gloucester All Blue	12	7	0	5	159	143	14
Pilning	12	6	2	4	130	138	12*
Newent	12	3	0	9	111	195	6
Dowty	12	5	1	6	103	136	5*
Wotton-under-Edge	12	0	0	12	45	329	-2

SOUTH WEST DIVISION

SOMERSET ONE
1995-96
FIXTURES

September 16 1995 (Week 3)
Frome	v	Chard
Old Sulians	v	Imperial
Stothert & Pitt	v	Tor
Walcot OB	v	St Bernadette
Wiveliscombe	v	Gordano
Yatton	v	Minehead

September 23 1995 (Week 4)
Gordano	v	Frome
Imperial	v	Wiveliscombe
Midsomer Norton	v	Walcot OB
Minehead	v	Old Sulians
St Bernadette	v	Stothert & Pitt
Tor	v	Yatton

September 30 1995 (Week X1)
Chard	v	Gordano
Frome	v	Imperial
Old Sulians	v	Tor
Stothert & Pitt	v	Midsomer Norton
Wiveliscombe	v	Minehead
Yatton	v	St Bernadette

October 14 1995 (Week 6)
Imperial	v	Chard
Midsomer Norton	v	Yatton
Minehead	v	Frome
St Bernadette	v	Old Sulians
Tor	v	Wiveliscombe
Walcot OB	v	Stothert & Pitt

October 21 1995 (Week 7)
Chard	v	Minehead
Frome	v	Tor
Gordano	v	Imperial
Old Sulians	v	Midsomer Norton
Wiveliscombe	v	St Bernadette
Yatton	v	Walcot OB

October 28 1995 (Week 8)
Midsomer Norton	v	Wiveliscombe
Minehead	v	Gordano
St Bernadette	v	Frome
Stothert & Pitt	v	Yatton
Tor	v	Chard
Walcot OB	v	Old Sulians

November 11 1995 (Week 10)
Chard	v	St Bernadette
Frome	v	Midsomer Norton
Gordano	v	Tor
Imperial	v	Minehead
Old Sulians	v	Stothert & Pitt
Wiveliscombe	v	Walcot OB

January 6 1996 (Week 17)
Midsomer Norton	v	Chard
St Bernadette	v	Gordano
Stothert & Pitt	v	Wiveliscombe
Tor	v	Imperial
Walcot OB	v	Frome
Yatton	v	Old Sulians

January 13 1996 (Week 18)
Chard	v	Walcot OB
Frome	v	Stothert & Pitt
Gordano	v	Midsomer Norton
Imperial	v	St Bernadette
Minehead	v	Tor
Wiveliscombe	v	Yatton

February 10 1996 (Week 22)
Midsomer Norton	v	Imperial
Old Sulians	v	Wiveliscombe
St Bernadette	v	Minehead
Stothert & Pitt	v	Chard
Walcot OB	v	Gordano
Yatton	v	Frome

February 17 1996 (Week 23)
Chard	v	Yatton
Frome	v	Old Sulians
Gordano	v	Stothert & Pitt
Imperial	v	Walcot OB
Minehead	v	Midsomer Norton
Tor	v	St Bernadette

February 24 1996 (Week 24)
Midsomer Norton	v	Tor
Old Sulians	v	Chard
Stothert & Pitt	v	Imperial
Walcot OB	v	Minehead
Wiveliscombe	v	Frome
Yatton	v	Gordano

March 30 1996 (Week X7)
Chard	v	Wiveliscombe
Gordano	v	Old Sulians
Imperial	v	Yatton
Minehead	v	Stothert & Pitt
St Bernadette	v	Midsomer Norton
Tor	v	Walcot OB

SOMERSET ONE

CHARD RFC
Ground Address: The Park, Essex Close, Chard,
Somerset. Tel: 01460 62495
Club Secretary: Mr NJ Urch, 2 South View, Listers Hill,
Ilminster, Somerset TA19 0EJ. Tel: (H) 01460 57864 Tel:
(W) 01935 702913 Fax: 01935 704168
Fixtures Secretary: Mr M Berry, 8 Ashcroft, Chard,
Somerset. Tel: (H) 01460 65481 Tel (W) 01460 53221
Club Colours: Black, red & gold.

FROME RFC
Ground Address: Gypsy Lane, Frome, Somerset BA11
2NA. Tel: 01373 462506
Club Secretary: PF Holdaway, 4 Market Place, Nunney,
Nr Frome, Somerset BA11 4LY. Tel: (H) 01373 836821
Tel: (W) 01373 465651
Fixtures Secretary: RJ Griffiths, 33 Innox Hill, Frome,
Somerset BA11 2LN. Tel: (H) 01373 462537 Tel (W)
01985 213595
Club Colours: Red, white & black hoops.

GORDANO RFC
Ground Address: The National Stadium, Caswell Lane,
Portbury, Nr Bristol BS20 9UY. Tel: 01275 373486
Club Secretary: A Moore, 135 Kellaway Avenue,
Henleaze, Bristol BS6 7YF. Tel: (H) 0117 975 4438 Tel:
(W) 0117 950 7777 x193
Fixtures Secretary: A Stanton, 7 Halswell Road,
Clevedon, Nr Bristol, Avon. Tel: (H) 01275 877103
Club Colours: Red & black shirts, black shorts.

IMPERIAL RFC
Ground Address: West Town Lane, Knowle, Bristol BS14
9EA. Tel: 01275 546000
Club Secretary: Stuart Eld, 43 Avonleigh Road,
Bedminster, Bristol BS3 3HS. Tel: (H) 0117 963 1688
Fixtures Secretary: Jason Gardiner, 42 Airport Road,
Hengrove, Bristol BS14 9TA. Tel: (H) 0117 987 7638
Club Colours: Myrtle & amber.

MIDSOMER NORTON RFC
Ground Address: Norton Down Playing Fields, Stratton
on the Fosse, Somerset BA3 4RW. Tel: 01761 412827
Club Secretary: John Presley, 73 Welton Grove,
Midsomer Norton, Bath, Avon BA3 2TT. Tel: (H) 01761
416089 Tel: (W) 01749 682267
Fixtures Secretary: Brian Willcox, Fossil Place, Chicks
Lane, Ston Easton, Somerset BA3 4BY. Tel: (H) 01761
241477
Club Colours: Scarlet shirts & socks, black shorts.

MINEHEAD BARBARIANS RFC
Ground Address: Tom Stewart Field, Ellicombe,
Minehead TA24 6TR. Tel: 01643 707155/705662
Club Secretary: Malcolm Parslow, Ladbrook, The
Holloway, Minehead TA24 5PB. Tel: (H) 01643 702101
Fixtures Secretary: Terry Mote, 17 Grove Road, Blue
Anchor, Minehead TA24. Tel: (H) 01643 707155
(Clubhouse - evenings)
Club Colours: Black & white hoops.

OLD SULIANS RFC
Ground Address: Lansdown Road, Bath, Avon BA1 9BH.
Tel: 01225 310201
Club Secretary: Terry Haines, 24 Rockliffe Avenue, Bath,
Avon BA2 6QP. Tel: (H) 01225 465107 Tel (W) 0117 979
7540
Fixtures Secretary: Tony Slee, 8 Heathfield Close,
Weston, Bath, Avon BA1 4NW. Tel: (H) 01225 317256
Club Colours: Blue with red dash.

ST BERNADETTE'S OLD BOYS RFC
Ground Address: Bamfield, Hengrove Park, Whitchurch,
Bristol.
Club Secretary: Barry Taylor, 39 Woodleigh Gardens,
Whitchurch, Bristol BS14 9JA. Tel: (H) 01275 831880
Fixtures Secretary: Brian Murphy, 4 Rookery Way,
Whitchurch, Bristol BS14 0AF. Tel: (H) 01275 837702

FINAL TABLE

	P	W	D	L	F	A	Pts
Wellington	12	12	0	0	332	127	24
Walcot Old Boys	12	9	0	3	203	126	18
Yatton	12	9	0	3	181	157	16*
Chard	12	8	0	4	162	166	16
Tor	12	6	1	5	213	161	13
Old Sulians	12	6	0	6	166	189	12
St Bernadette's OB	12	5	0	7	157	177	10
Gordano	12	5	0	7	182	221	10
Minehead Barbarians	12	5	0	7	150	275	10
Frome	12	5	1	6	253	182	9*
Wells	12	3	0	9	165	197	6
North Petherton	12	2	0	10	136	192	4
Yeovil	12	2	0	10	121	251	2*

Club Colours: Green & blue.

STOTHERT & PITT RFC
Ground Address: (a) Adamsfield, Corston, Bath (b)
Newtonfield, Lower Bristol Road, Bath. Tel: (a) 01225
874802 (b) 01225 425569
Club Secretary: RV Garraway, 2 Westfield Park South,
Lower Weston, Bath BA1 3HT. Tel: (H) 01225 316863
Fixtures Secretary: JP Burcombe, 199 Whiteway Road,
Southdown, Bath BA2 2RG. Tel: (H) 01225 425909
Club Colours: Blue, black & amber.

THE TOR RFC
Ground Address: Lowerside Park, Lowerside Lane,
Glastonbury, Somerset BA6 9AE. Tel: 01458 831360
(Players); 01458 832236 (Bar)
Club Secretary: Mr Malcolm R Dykes, 1 The Lovells,
Lubborn Lane, Baltonsborough, Glastonbury, Somerset
BA6 8QP. Tel: (H) 01458 50498 Tel: (W) 01935 402215
Fixtures Secretary: Mr Keith Elver, 170 Strode Road,
Street, Somerset. Tel: (H) 01458 447284 Tel (W) 01749
673199
Club Colours: Maroon.

WALCOT OLD BOYS RFC
Ground Address: Albort Field, Lansdown, Bath. Tel:
01225 330199
Club Secretary: K Jones, 14 Canterbury Road, Oldfield
Park, Bath BA2 3LG. Tel: (H) 01225 427045 Tel: (W)
01245 712051
Fixtures Secretary: Mr B Richman, 14 Primrose Hill,
Weston, Bath BA1 3UT. Tel: (H) 01225 422989
Club Colours: Blue & white hoops.

WIVELISCOMBE RFC
Ground Address: Recreation Ground, West Road,
Wiveliscombe, Taunton, Somerset TA4. Tel: 01984 623897
Club Secretary: Alan Weaver, 21 Mount Street, Bishop's
Lydeard, Taunton, Somerset TA4 3AN. Tel: (H) 01823
433632
Fixtures Secretary: C Mann, 'Lockyers', Fore Street,
Milverton, Taunton, Somerset TA4 1JU. Tel: (H) 01823
400673
Club Colours: Blue with red sash.

YATTON RFC
Ground Address: North End, Yatton, Avon BS19. Tel:
01934 832085
Club Secretary: John Crabtree, 11 Old Park Road,
Clevedon, Avon BS21 7JH. Tel: (H) 01275 876954 Tel:
(W) 0117 943 2399
Fixtures Secretary: Chris Bates, 17 Yew Tree Park,
Congresbury, Avon BS19 5ER. Tel: (H) 01934 838642 Tel
(W) 01453 813110
Club Colours: Amber & black.

SOUTH WEST DIVISION

SOMERSET TWO 1995-96 FIXTURES

November 11 1995 (Week 10)

Avon	v	Crewkerne
Avonvale	v	Wells
Blagdon	v	Old Ashtonians
Chew Valley OB	v	Bath Saracens
Nailsea & Backwell	v	North Petherton
Yeovil	v	Bath Old Edwardians

September 16 1995 (Week 3)

Avonvale	v	Nailsea & Backwell
Bath Old Edwardians	v	North Petherton
Blagdon	v	Chew Valley OB
Old Ashtonians	v	Crewkerne
Winscombe	v	Bath Saracens
Yeovil	v	Avon

January 6 1996 (Week 17)

Bath Old Edwardians	v	Avonvale
Crewkerne	v	Chew Valley OB
North Petherton	v	Avon
Old Ashtonians	v	Yeovil
Wells	v	Nailsea & Backwell
Winscombe	v	Blagdon

September 23 1995 (Week 4)

Avon	v	Avonvale
Bath Saracens	v	Blagdon
Chew Valley OB	v	Yeovil
Crewkerne	v	Winscombe
North Petherton	v	Old Ashtonians
Wells	v	Bath Old Edwardians

January 13 1996 (Week 18)

Avon	v	Wells
Avonvale	v	Old Ashtonians
Bath Saracens	v	Crewkerne
Chew Valley OB	v	North Petherton
Nailsea & Backwell	v	Bath Old Edwardians
Yeovil	v	Winscombe

September 30 1995 (Week X1)

Avonvale	v	Chew Valley OB
Blagdon	v	Crewkerne
Nailsea & Backwell	v	Avon
Old Ashtonians	v	Wells
Winscombe	v	North Petherton
Yeovil	v	Bath Saracens

February 10 1996 (Week 22)

Bath Old Edwardians	v	Avon
Blagdon	v	Yeovil
North Petherton	v	Bath Saracens
Old Ashtonians	v	Nailsea & Backwell
Wells	v	Chew Valley OB
Winscombe	v	Avonvale

October 14 1995 (Week 6)

Bath Old Edwardians	v	Old Ashtonians
Bath Saracens	v	Avonvale
Chew Valley OB	v	Nailsea & Backwell
Crewkerne	v	Yeovil
North Petherton	v	Blagdon
Wells	v	Winscombe

February 17 1996 (Week 23)

Avon	v	Old Ashtonians
Avonvale	v	Blagdon
Bath Saracens	v	Wells
Chew Valley OB	v	Bath Old Edwardians
Crewkerne	v	North Petherton
Nailsea & Backwell	v	Winscombe

October 21 1995 (Week 7)

Avon	v	Chew Valley OB
Avonvale	v	Crewkerne
Blagdon	v	Wells
Nailsea & Backwell	v	Bath Saracens
Winscombe	v	Bath Old Edwardians
Yeovil	v	North Petherton

February 24 1996 (Week 24)

Bath Old Edwardians	v	Bath Saracens
Blagdon	v	Nailsea & Backwell
Old Ashtonians	v	Chew Valley OB
Wells	v	Crewkerne
Winscombe	v	Avon
Yeovil	v	Avonvale

October 28 1995 (Week 8)

Bath Old Edwardians	v	Blagdon
Bath Saracens	v	Avon
Crewkerne	v	Nailsea & Backwell
North Petherton	v	Avonvale
Old Ashtonians	v	Winscombe
Wells	v	Yeovil

March 30 1996 (Week X7)

Avon	v	Blagdon
Bath Saracens	v	Old Ashtonians
Chew Valley OB	v	Winscombe
Crewkerne	v	Bath Old Edwardians
North Petherton	v	Wells
Nailsea & Backwell	v	Yeovil

SOMERSET TWO

AVON RFC
Ground Address: Hicks Field, London Road, Batheaston, Bath. Tel: 01225 852446
Club Secretary: D Loader, 34 West Avenue, Oldfield Park, Bath, Avon, BA2 3QD. Tel: (H) 01225 316864 Tel: (W) 01225 331116
Fixtures Secretary: D Waters, 10 Stepney Walk, Whitehall, Bristol. Tel: (H) 0117 9350 847
Club Colours: Black & amber hoops.
AVONVALE RFC
Ground Address: Bathford Playing Fields, Bathford, Bath, Avon. Tel: 01225 858295
Club Secretary: Martin Bath, 30 Forrester Green, Colerne, Nr Chippenham, Wiltshire SN14 8EB. Tel: (H) 01225 742396 Tel: (W) 01831 600314
Fixtures Secretary: Steve Vowles, 72 Locksbrook Road, Lower Weston, Bath BA1 3ES. Tel: (H) 01225 333852 Tel (W) 01225 766451
Club Colours: Navy blue & white.
BATH OLD EDWARDIANS RFC
Ground Address: Kes Sportsfield, Bathampton, Bath. Tel: 01225 462354
Club Secretary: Jonathan Miles, The Close, Gloucester Road, Upper Swainswick, Bath. Tel: (H) 01225 859341 Tel: (W) 01225 443336 Fax: 443337
Fixtures Secretary: Rory O'Connell, Riverside Cottage, Swineford, Bristol BS15 6LW. Tel: (H) 01272 325932 Tel (W) 01275 340343
Club Colours: Gold, maroon & navy hoops.
BATH SARACENS RFC
Ground Address: Civil Service Sports Ground, Claverton Down, Bath, Avon. Tel: 01225 832403
Club Secretary: Mr Neil Pirie, Poolemead Road, Twerton, Bath, Avon BA2 1QP. Tel: (H) 01225 314521 Tel: (W) 01225 882975
Fixtures Secretary: Mr Rob Lawrence, 91 Englishcombe Lane, Bath, Avon. Tel: (H) 01225 427356 Tel (W) 01225 462039ba
Club Colours: Blue with red & gold hoops.
BLAGDON RFC
Ground Address: The Mead, Blagdon, Nr Bristol. Tel: 01761 463196
Club Secretary: Andy McKeown, 4 Prospect Cottages, High Street, Winford, Nr Bristol BS18 8EQ. Tel: (H) 01275 472439 Tel: (W) 0117 964 4809
Fixtures Secretary: Mark Ryan, Flat 9, Old Rectory, Pilgrims Way, Chew Stoke, Bristol BS18 8TX. Tel: (H) 01275 333778 Tel (W) 01272 264662
Club Colours: Green.
CHEW VALLEY OLD BOYS RFC
Ground Address: The Lobbingtons, Chew Lane, Chew Stoke, Nr Bristol BS18.
Club Secretary: Tim Weatherley, 10 Malago Walk, The Ridings, Bishopsworth, Bristol BS13 8NZ. Tel: (H) 0117 9783216
Fixtures Secretary: Bob Martin, 66 Meadowside Drive, Whitchurch, Bristol. Tel: (H) 01275 832547
Club Colours: Green & white hoops.
CREWKERNE RFC
Ground Address: Henhayes, Main Car Park, South Street, Crewkerne, Somerset.
Club Secretary: RG Physick, 4 Henley View, Crewkerne, Somerset TA18 8JD. Tel: (H) 01460 75482 Tel: (W) 01935 75181
Fixtures Secretary: D Holley, Shorlands, Back Lane, North Perrott, Crewkerne, Somerset TA18 7SP. Tel: (H) 0460 76449
Club Colours: Red & black hoops.
NAILSEA & BACKWELL RFC
Ground Address: North Street, Nailsea, Bristol. Tel: 01275 810818

FINAL TABLE	P	W	D	L	F	A	Pts
Imperial	12	10	0	2	299	120	20
Stothert & Pitt	12	9	0	3	271	145	18
Chew Valley	12	9	0	3	209	108	18
Winscombe	12	9	0	3	214	102	16*
Blagdon	12	6	1	5	189	119	11*
Chew Valley	12	9	0	3	209	108	18
Crewkerne	12	6	0	6	194	144	12
Old Ashtonians	12	6	0	6	172	159	10*
Avon	12	6	0	6	155	190	10*
Backwell	12	5	0	7	157	208	10
Bath Old Edwardians	12	4	1	7	133	212	9
St Brendan's OB	12	3	0	9	147	233	6
Westlands	12	1	1	10	90	231	3

Club Secretary: A Nelson, 51 Westway, Nailsea, Bristol BS19 1EF. Tel: (H) 01275 851340
Fixtures Secretary: C Down, 52 Coombe Road, Nailsea, Bristol BS19 2HS. Tel: (H) 01275 858025
Club Colours: Black.
NORTH PETHERTON RFC
Ground Address: Beggars Brook, North Petherton, Somerset. Tel: 10278 663028
Club Secretary: Mrs J Goddard, Brookfield, 6 Schoolfields, North Petherton, Nr Bridgwater, Somerset. Tel: (H) 01278 663512
Fixtures Secretary: Mr Malcolm House, 2 Hardings Close, North Petherton, Nr Bridgwater, Somerset. Tel: (H) 01278 663118
Club Colours: Black & white hoops.
OLD ASHTONIANS RFC
Ground Address: Ashton Park School, Blackmoors Lane, Bower Ashton, Bristol. Tel: c/o 0117 9877796
Club Secretary: Mr Ian Reed, 261/3 Hotwells Road, Hotwells, Bristol BS8 4SF. Tel: (H) 0117 987 7796 Tel: (W) 0117 987 7796
Fixtures Secretary: Mr Tony Excel, 18 Perrycroft Road, Bishopsworth, Bristol 3. Tel: (H) 0117 964 2352
Club Colours: Blue shirts with white, green & yellow band, black shorts, yellow socks.
WELLS RFC
Ground Address: Charter Way, (off The Portway), Wells, Somerset BA5 2FB. Tel: 01749 672823
Club Secretary: Mr AC Cox, 10 Mount Pleasant Avenue, Well,s somerset BA5 2JQ. Tel: (H) 01749 673407
Fixtures Secretary: Mrs C Sullivan, 3 Bignall Rand Close, Wells, Somerset BA5 2EE. Tel: (H) 01749 679248
Club Colours: Black & white hoops.
WINSCOMBE RFC
Ground Address: Longfield Recreation Ground, Winscombe, Avon. Tel: 01934 842720
Club Secretary: Alun George, 3 Landseer Close, Worle, Weston-super-Mare, Avon BS22 9NL. Tel: (H) 01934 518270
Fixtures Secretary: Adrian Ellis, 20 Wimblestone Road, Winscombe, Avon. Tel: (H) 01934 843087 Tel (W) 0117 982 3564
Club Colours: Black with white band.
YEOVIL RFC
Ground Address: Johnson Park, Yeovil, Somerset BA21 3NY. Tel: 01935 74433
Club Secretary: Mr Andrew Gillett, 7 Shelley Close, Abbey Manor Park, Yeovil, Somerset BA21 3TX. Tel: (H) 01935 410413 Tel: (W) 01935 456297
Fixtures Secretary: Mr Damian Teale, Plot 3, Higher Hurcot Farm, Hurcot, Somerton, Somerset TA11 6AA. Tel: (H) 01458 273199
Club Colours: Blue & yellow hoops.

SOUTH WEST DIVISION

SOMERSET THREE
1995-96
FIXTURES

September 16 1995 (Week 3)

Cheddar Valley	v	Aller
Martock	v	British Gas
Morganians	v	Burnham-on-Sea
St Brendan's	v	Castle Cary
Westlands	v	Wincanton

September 23 1995 (Week 4)

Aller	v	Morganians
British Gas	v	Westlands
Burnham-on-Sea	v	Martock
Castle Cary	v	Cheddar Valley
Wincanton	v	St Brendan's

September 30 1995 (Week X1)

Castle Cary	v	Aller
Cheddar Valley	v	Wincanton
Martock	v	Morganians
St Brendan's	v	British Gas
Westlands	v	Burnham-on-Sea

October 14 1995 (Week 6)

Aller	v	Martock
British Gas	v	Cheddar Valley
Burnham-on-Sea	v	St Brendan's
Morganians	v	Westlands
Wincanton	v	Castle Cary

October 21 1995 (Week 7)

Castle Cary	v	British Gas
Cheddar Valley	v	Burnham-on-Sea
St Brendan's	v	Morganians
Westlands	v	Martock
Wincanton	v	Aller

October 28 1995 (Week 8)

Aller	v	Westlands
British Gas	v	Wincanton
Burnham-on-Sea	v	Castle Cary
Martock	v	St Brendan's
Morganians	v	Cheddar Valley

November 11 1995 (Week 10)

Aller	v	British Gas
Castle Cary	v	Morganians
Cheddar Valley	v	Martock
St Brendan's	v	Westlands
Wincanton	v	Burnham-on-Sea

November 18 1995 (Week 11)

Burnham-on-Sea	v	British Gas
Martock	v	Castle Cary
Morganians	v	Wincanton
St Brendan's	v	Aller
Westlands	v	Cheddar Valley

December 2 1995 (Week 13)

Aller	v	Burnham-on-Sea

British Gas	v	Morganians
Castle Cary	v	Westlands
Cheddar Valley	v	St Brendan's
Wincanton	v	Martock

December 16 1995 (Week 15)

Aller	v	Cheddar Valley
British Gas	v	Martock
Burnham-on-Sea	v	Morganians
Castle Cary	v	St Brendan's
Wincanton	v	Westlands

December 30 1995 (Week X4)

Cheddar Valley	v	Castle Cary
Martock	v	Burnham-on-Sea
Morganians	v	Aller
St Brendan's	v	Wincanton
Westlands	v	British Gas

January 6 1996 (Week 17)

Aller	v	Castle Cary
British Gas	v	St Brendan's
Burnham-on-Sea	v	Westlands
Morganians	v	Martock
Wincanton	v	Cheddar Valley

January 13 1996 (Week 18)

Castle Cary	v	Wincanton
Cheddar Valley	v	British Gas
Martock	v	Aller
St Brendan's	v	Burnham-on-Sea
Westlands	v	Morganians

February 10 1996 (Week 22)

Aller	v	Wincanton
British Gas	v	Castle Cary
Burnham-on-Sea	v	Cheddar Valley
Martock	v	Westlands
Morganians	v	St Brendan's

February 17 1996 (Week 23)

Castle Cary	v	Burnham-on-Sea
Cheddar Valley	v	Morganians
St Brendan's	v	Martock
Westlands	v	Aller
Wincanton	v	British Gas

February 24 1996 (Week 24)

British Gas	v	Aller
Burnham-on-Sea	v	Wincanton
Martock	v	Cheddar Valley
Morganians	v	Castle Cary
Westlands	v	St Brendan's

March 9 1996 (Week 26)

Aller	v	St Brendan's
British Gas	v	Burnham-on-Sea
Castle Cary	v	Martock
Cheddar Valley	v	Westlands
Wincanton	v	Morganians

March 30 1996 (Week X7)

Burnham-on-Sea	v	Aller
Martock	v	Wincanton
Morganians	v	British Gas
St Brendan's	v	Cheddar Valley
Westlands	v	Castle Cary

SOMERSET THREE

ALLER RFC
Ground Address: Westfield, Curry Rivel, Somerset. Tel: 01458 252687
Club Secretary: Mark Roddie, The Annexe, Heron House, North Street, Langport, Somerset TA10 9RQ. Tel: (H) 01458 253599 Tel: (W) 01458 273740
Fixtures Secretary: Mark Roddie, The Annexe, Heron House, North Street, Langport, Somerset TA10 9RQ. Tel: (H) 01458 253599 Tel (W) 01458 273740
Club Colours: Red & green hooped shirts, black shorts.
BRITISH GAS (BRISTOL) RFC
Ground Address: 'The Beeches', Broomhill Road, Brislington, Bristol 4.
Club Secretary: Richard Alan Griffin, 28 Whitchurch Road, Bishopsworth, Bristol BS13 7RT. Tel: (H) 0117 964 5373
Fixtures Secretary: Les Brunyee, 31 Maynard Road, Hartcliffe, Bristol 3. Tel: (H) 0117 964 0074
Club Colours: Blue & white hoops.
BURNHAM-ON-SEA RFC
Ground Address: BASC Clubhouse, Stoddens Road, Burnham-on-Sea, Somerset TA8 2DE. Tel: 01278 788355
Club Secretary: Mr DE Baxter, 4 Ashcombe House, 188 Berrow Road, Burnham-on-Sea, Somerset TA8 2JE. Tel: (H) 01278 781323 Tel: (W) 01278 435496
Fixtures Secretary: Mr G Berry, 86 Burnham Road, Highbridge, Somerset. Tel: (H) 01278 786456
Club Colours: Blue and white hoops.
CASTLE CARY RFC
Ground Address: Brookhouse Park, Sutton, Castle Cary, Somerset. Tel: 01963 351178
Club Secretary: Mr A J Bailey, 2 Enfield Terrace, Weymouth Road, Evercreech, Somerset, BA4 6JE. Tel: (H) 0749 830268
Fixtures Secretary: Mr C Watts, 15 Woodford Green, Ansford, Castle Cary, Somerset. Tel: (H) 01963 350162
Club Colours: Red & black hoops.
CHEDDAR VALLEY RFC
Ground Address: Sharpham Road, Cheddar, Somerset. Tel: 01934 743623
Club Secretary: Andrew Pilgrim, 28 Gough Place, Cheddar, Somerset. Tel: (H) 01934 744511 Tel: (W) 01934 744511
Fixtures Secretary: Derek Buxton, Hillingdon, Cliff Street, Cheddar, Somerset. Tel: (H) 01934 742050
Club Colours: Scarlet & sky blue hoops.
MARTOCK RFC
Ground Address: Martock Recreation Ground, Stoke Road, Martock, Somerset. Tel: Nag's Head) 01935 823432
Club Secretary: Philip Jackson, Church Lodge Cottage, Church Street, Martock, Somerset, TA12 6JL. Tel: (H) 01935 823514
Fixtures Secretary: John Hole, The Nag's Head, East Street, Martock, Somerset TA12 6NF. Tel: (H) 01935 823432 Tel (W) 01935 823432
Club Colours: Green & black quarters.
MORGANIANS RFC
Ground Address: Chedzoy Lane, Bridgwater, Somerset. Tel: 01278 423434
Club Secretary: P Culverwell, 23 Adscombe Avenue, Bridgwater, Somerset TA6 4NH. Tel: (H) 01278 457168
Fixtures Secretary: Gordon Clark, 34 Plum Tree Close, Bridgwater, Somerset TA6 4XG. Tel: (H) 01278 452721
Club Colours: Navy blue with red & gold hoops.
ST BRENDAN'S OLD BOYS RFC
Ground Address: Combination Ground, Northway, Filton, Bristol BS12 7QG. Tel: 0117 969 2793
Club Secretary: Richard A Kolanko, 91 Church Road, Horfield, Bristol BS7 8SD. Tel: (H) 0117 924 1390 Tel: (W) 0117 966 6861
Fixtures Secretary: Frank Probert, 9 St Aldwyn's Close,

FINAL TABLE							
	P	W	D	L	F	A	Pts
Avondale	16	15	0	1	725	103	30
Bath Saracens	16	14	1	1	646	119	27*
Burnham-on-Sea	16	10	0	6	315	207	20
Castle Cary	16	7	2	7	227	218	16
Morganians	16	7	2	6	199	291	16
British Gas	16	8	0	8	318	235	12*
Wincanton	16	4	0	12	179	411	8
Aller	16	3	1	12	133	531	7
Martock	16	1	0	15	82	709	2

Monks Park, Bristol BS7 0UQ. Tel: (H) 0117 969 4779
Club Colours: Old gold & maroon.
WESTLANDS RFC
Ground Address: Yeovil Recreation Centre, Yeovil, Somerset. Tel: 01935 411121
Club Secretary: Guy Williams, 41 The Avenue, Yeovil, Somerset BA21 4BN. Tel: (H) 01935 32647 Tel: (W) 01935 642211
Fixtures Secretary: Martin Jakes, 36 Lower Odcombe, Yeovil, Somerset BA22 8TX. Tel: (H) 01935 862564 Tel (W) 01935 702939
Club Colours: Maroon & sky blue quarters.
WINCANTON RUFC
Ground Address: Lattiford, Wincanton (farmer's field).
Club Secretary: Mr Martin Clarke, 52 Lyde Road, Yeovil, Somerset. Tel: (H) 01935 71716
Fixtures Secretary: Mr Richard Lund, 29 Verrington Park Road, Wincanton, Somerset. Tel: (H) 01963 32008
Club Colours: Black & amber.

SOUTH WEST DIVISION

SOUTHERN COUNTIES 1995-96 FIXTURES

November 11 1995 (Week 10)
Abbey v Devizes
Bicester v Marlow
Bletchley v Amersham & Chiltern
Chippenham v Wimborne
Olney v Chinnor
Swindon v Windsor

September 16 1995 (Week 3)
Abbey v Bicester
Bracknell v Chinnor
Chippenham v Olney
Swindon v Bletchley
Wimborne v Amersham & Chiltern
Windsor v Marlow

January 6 1996 (Week 17)
Amersham & Chiltern v Olney
Bracknell v Chippenham
Devizes v Bicester
Marlow v Bletchley
Wimborne v Swindon
Windsor v Abbey

September 23 1995 (Week 4)
Amersham & Chiltern v Bracknell
Bletchley v Abbey
Chinnor v Chippenham
Devizes v Windsor
Marlow v Wimborne
Olney v Swindon

January 13 1996 (Week 18)
Abbey v Wimborne
Bicester v Windsor
Bletchley v Devizes
Chinnor v Amersham & Chiltern
Olney v Marlow
Swindon v Bracknell

September 30 1995 (Week X1)
Abbey v Olney
Bicester v Bletchley
Bracknell v Marlow
Chippenham v Amersham & Chiltern
Swindon v Chinnor
Wimborne v Devizes

February 10 1996 (Week 22)
Bracknell v Abbey
Chippenham v Swindon
Devizes v Olney
Marlow v Chinnor
Wimborne v Bicester
Windsor v Bletchley

October 14 1995 (Week 6)
Amersham & Chiltern v Swindon
Chinnor v Abbey
Devizes v Bracknell
Marlow v Chippenham
Olney v Bicester
Windsor v Wimborne

February 17 1996 (Week 23)
Abbey v Chippenham
Amersham & Chiltern v Marlow
Bicester v Bracknell
Bletchley v Wimborne
Chinnor v Devizes
Olney v Windsor

October 21 1995 (Week 7)
Abbey v Amersham & Chiltern
Bicester v Chinnor
Bletchley v Olney
Bracknell v Windsor
Chippenham v Devizes
Swindon v Marlow

February 24 1996 (Week 24)
Bracknell v Bletchley
Chippenham v Bicester
Devizes v Amersham & Chiltern
Swindon v Abbey
Wimborne v Olney
Windsor v Chinnor

October 28 1995 (Week 8)
Amersham & Chiltern v Bicester
Chinnor v Bletchley
Devizes v Swindon
Marlow v Abbey
Wimborne v Bracknell
Windsor v Chippenham

March 30 1996 (Week X7)
Amersham & Chiltern v Windsor
Bicester v Swindon
Bletchley v Chippenham
Chinnor v Wimborne
Marlow v Devizes
Olney v Bracknell

SOUTHERN COUNTIES

ABBEY RFC
Ground Address: Rosehill, Peppard Road, Emmer Green, Reading, Berkshire. Tel: 0134 722881
Club Secretary: Mrs M Lee, Cotswold, Behoes Lane, Woodcote, Nr Reading, Berks. Tel: (H) 01491 680102
Fixtures Secretary: Mrs M Lee, Cotswold, Behoes Lane, Woodcote, Nr Reading, Berks. Tel: (H) 01491 680102
Club Colours: Navy blue with green & white hoops.

AMERSHAM & CHILTERN RFC
Ground Address: Ash Grove, Weedon Lane, Amersham, Bucks HP6 5QU. Tel: 01494 725161
Club Secretary: Ian McKenzie, 17 Highover Park, Amersham, Bucks HP7 0BN. Tel: (H) 01494 431966
Fixtures Secretary: Roger Cook, 120 Chestnut Lane, Amersham, Bucks HP6 6DZ. Tel: (H) 01494 433144
Club Colours: Claret & white.

BICESTER RUFC
Ground Address: Oxford Road, Bicester, Oxon OX6 8AB. Tel: 01869 241000
Club Secretary: Bernard Evans, 3 Hethe Road, Cottisford, Nr Brackley, Northants NN13 5SR. Tel: (H) 01280 847250 Tel: (W) 01296 432091
Fixtures Secretary: George Davies, 166 Barry Avenue, Bicester, Oxon OX6 8WP. Tel: (H) 01869 241993 Tel (W) 01869 241993
Club Colours: Red, amber & brown hoops, navy blue shorts, red socks.

BLETCHLEY RUFC
Ground Address: Manor Fields, Bletchley, Milton Keynes. Tel: 01908 372298
Club Secretary: Robin Bowen-Williams, 130 Water Eaton Road, Bletchley, Milton Keynes MK2 3AJ. Tel: (H) 01908 378120 Tel: (W) 01908 376614
Fixtures Secretary: Jon Austin, 17 Statham Place, Oldbrook, Milton Keynes. Tel: (H) 01908 608326 Tel (W) 0171 918 5242
Club Colours: Burgundy & white.

BRACKNELL RFC
Ground Address: Lily Hill Park, Lily Hill Road, Bracknell, Berks RG12 2UG. Tel: 01344 424013
Club Secretary: PJ Denham, 57 Ling Wood, Bracknell, Berks RG12 7PZ. Tel: (H) 01344 55400
Fixtures Secretary: Mr E Brown, 57 Chesterblade Lane, Bracknell, Berks. Tel: (H) 01344 412041
Club Colours: Green, gold & black, black shorts & socks.

CHINNOR RFC
Ground Address: Kingsey Road, Thame, Oxon. Tel: 01844 213735
Club Secretary: Jon Durrant, 17a Worminghall Road, Oakley, Aylesbury, Bucks HP18 9QU. Tel: (H) 01844 238030 Tel: (W) 01494 881393
Fixtures Secretary: Kevin Robinson, The Limes, 31 Oxford Road, Thame, Oxon OX9 2AJ. Tel: (H) 01844 217900 Tel (W) 01844 213822
Club Colours: Black & white hoops.

CHIPPENHAM RFC
Ground Address: Allington Field, Frogwell, Chippenham, Wiltshire SN14 0YZ. Tel: 01249 446997
Club Secretary: John Wilding, 8 Foscote Cottages, Grittleton, Chippenham, Wiltshire SN14 6AD. Tel: (H) 01249 782611 Tel: (W) 01793 522688
Fixtures Secretary: Adie Lloyd, 27 Lords Mead, Chippenham, Wiltshire. Tel: (H) 01249 656793
Club Colours: Black & white hoops.

DEVIZES RFC
Ground Address: Chivers Ground Sports Club, London Road, Devizes, Wilts. Tel: 01380 723763
Club Secretary: Paul Rumbold, Belmont, Potterne Road, Devizes, Wilts SN10 5DB. Tel: (H) 01380 724497 Tel: (W) 01672 517237 Fax: 01672 517312
Fixtures Secretary: Chris Combe, Roundway Hill Farm,

FINAL TABLE	P	W	D	L	F	A	Pts
Dorchester	12	10	1	1	257	119	21
Bracknell	12	10	0	2	365	80	20
Chippenham	12	9	0	3	229	156	18
Olney	12	8	0	4	229	164	16
Bicester	12	9	1	2	248	149	15*
Amersham & Chiltern	12	7	0	5	238	154	14
Devizes	12	5	0	7	138	215	10
Wimborne	12	4	0	8	126	186	8
Bletchley	12	4	0	8	158	253	8
Abbey	12	3	1	8	178	228	7
Windsor	12	3	1	8	158	251	7
Oxford Marathon	12	3	0	9	126	275	6
Slough	12	1	0	11	92	313	2

Devizes, Wilts. Tel: (H) 01380 722928 Fax: 01380 727412
Club Colours: Shirt with black & broad white hoop, white shorts.

MARLOW RUFC
Ground Address: Riverwoods Drive, Marlow, Bucks SL6 1QU. Tel: Office: 01628 483911 Clubhouse: 01628 477054
Club Secretary: Graham Cutts, 6 Eastern Dene, Hazlemere, Bucks HP15 7BT. Tel: (H) 01494 711391 Tel: (W) 01494 431717
Fixtures Secretary: Graham Cutts, 6 Eastern Dene, Hazlemere, Bucks HP15 7BT. Tel: (H) 01494 711391 Tel (W) 01494 431717
Club Colours: Black & white hoops, black shorts.

OLNEY RFC
Ground Address: Recreation Ground, East Street, Olney, Bucks. Tel: 01234 712880
Club Secretary: Stuart Parkin, West View Farm, Olney, Bucks MK46 5EX. Tel: (H) 01234 713165 Tel: (W) 01234 711792
Fixtures Secretary: Bob Taylor, 2 Chaseport Close, Ravenstone, Bucks MK46 5AG. Tel: (H) 01908 551244 Tel (W) 0831 462021
Club Colours: Cerise & French grey.

SWINDON RFC
Ground Address: New Pavilion, Greenbridge Road, Swindon, Wiltshire. Tel: 01793 521148
Club Secretary: Kevin Logan, 40 Nindum Road, Coleview, Swindon, Wilts. Tel: (H) 01793 831398 Tel: (W) 01793 504791
Fixtures Secretary: Nick Jenkins, 20 Smitanbrook, Covingham, Swindon, Wilts. Tel: (H) 01793 693329 Tel (W) 01793 538464
Club Colours: Royal blue & amber shirts.

WIMBORNE RFC
Ground Address: Leigh Park, Wimborne, Dorset. Tel: 01202 882602
Club Secretary: Graham Reeves, 37 Leigh Gardens, Wimborne, Dorset BH21 2ES. Tel: (H) 01202 889526 Tel: (W) 0171 222 8161
Fixtures Secretary: Michael Moysey, 42 Lacey Drive, Wimborne, Dorset. Tel: (H) 01202 841478
Club Colours: Black shirts, black shorts, black socks with white tops.

WINDSOR RFC
Ground Address: Home Park, Datchet Road, Windsor, Berks. Tel: 01753 868391
Club Secretary: Mr Leone, 35 Bell View, Windsor, Berks SL4 4ET. Tel: (H) 01753 863713 Tel: (W) 0181 848 8881
Fixtures Secretary: Alan Davies, 46 Buckland Avenue, Slough SL3 7PH. Tel: (H) 01753 536642 Tel (W) 01831 297141
Club Colours: Black, green, gold & maroon quarters.

SOUTH WEST DIVISION

November 11 1995 (Week 10)

Beaconsfield	v	Milton Keynes
Chesham	v	Slough
Chipping Norton	v	Grove
Oxford Old Boys	v	Buckingham
Oxford Marathon	v	Phoenix
Wheatley	v	Witney

September 16 1995 (Week 3)

Beaconsfield	v	Chipping Norton
Chesham	v	Oxford Old Boys
Pennanians	v	Buckingham
Slough	v	Phoenix
Wheatley	v	Oxford Marathon
Witney	v	Grove

January 6 1996 (Week 17)

Grove	v	Oxford Marathon
Milton Keynes	v	Chipping Norton
Pennanians	v	Chesham
Phoenix	v	Oxford Old Boys
Slough	v	Wheatley
Witney	v	Beaconsfield

September 23 1995 (Week 4)

Buckingham	v	Chesham
Grove	v	Slough
Milton Keynes	v	Witney
Oxford Old Boys	v	Wheatley
Oxford Marathon	v	Beaconsfield
Phoenix	v	Pennanians

January 13 1996 (Week 18)

Beaconsfield	v	Slough
Buckingham	v	Phoenix
Chipping Norton	v	Witney
Oxford Old Boys	v	Grove
Oxford Marathon	v	Milton Keynes
Wheatley	v	Pennanians

September 30 1995 (Week X1)

Beaconsfield	v	Oxford Old Boys
Chesham	v	Phoenix
Chipping Norton	v	Oxford Marathon
Pennanians	v	Grove
Slough	v	Milton Keynes
Wheatley	v	Buckingham

February 10 1996 (Week 22)

Chesham	v	Wheatley
Grove	v	Buckingham
Milton Keynes	v	Oxford Old Boys
Pennanians	v	Beaconsfield
Slough	v	Chipping Norton
Witney	v	Oxford Marathon

October 14 1995 (Week 6)

Buckingham	v	Beaconsfield
Grove	v	Chesham
Milton Keynes	v	Pennanians
Oxford Old Boys	v	Chipping Norton
Phoenix	v	Wheatley
Witney	v	Slough

February 17 1996 (Week 23)

Beaconsfield	v	Chesham
Buckingham	v	Milton Keynes
Chipping Norton	v	Pennanians
Oxford Old Boys	v	Witney
Oxford Marathon	v	Slough
Phoenix	v	Grove

October 21 1995 (Week 7)

Beaconsfield	v	Phoenix
Chesham	v	Milton Keynes
Chipping Norton	v	Buckingham
Oxford Marathon	v	Oxford Old Boys
Pennanians	v	Witney
Wheatley	v	Grove

February 24 1996 (Week 24)

Chesham	v	Chipping Norton
Milton Keynes	v	Phoenix
Pennanians	v	Oxford Marathon
Slough	v	Oxford Old Boys
Wheatley	v	Beaconsfield
Witney	v	Buckingham

October 28 1995 (Week 8)

Buckingham	v	Oxford Marathon
Grove	v	Beaconsfield
Milton Keynes	v	Wheatley
Phoenix	v	Chipping Norton
Slough	v	Pennanians
Witney	v	Chesham

March 30 1996 (Week X7)

Buckingham	v	Slough
Chipping Norton	v	Wheatley
Grove	v	Milton Keynes
Oxford Old Boys	v	Pennanians
Oxford Marathon	v	Chesham
Phoenix	v	Witney

BUCKS & OXON ONE

BEACONSFIELD RFC
Ground Address: Oak Lodge Meadow, Windsor End, Beaconsfield, Bucks. Tel: 01494 673783
Club Secretary: Phil Raw, Edgemoor, Britwell Salome, Oxon OX9 5LF. Tel: (H) 01491 612090
Fixtures Secretary: David White, 9 The Closes, Haddenham, Aylesbury, Bucks HP17 8JN. Tel: (H) 01844 291716 Tel (W) 01494 675432
Club Colours: Green & gold hoops.
BUCKINGHAM RUFC
Ground Address: Floyd Field, Moreton Road, Maids Moreton, Buckingham, Bucks MK18 1RF. Tel: 01280 815474
Club Secretary: Finlay M Gemmell, 22 Elmfields Gate, Winslow, Bucks MK18 3JG. Tel: (H) 01296 714640 Tel: (W) 01628 893772
Fixtures Secretary: FAW Smith, 10 Mare Leys, Linden Village, Buckingham. Tel: (H) 01280 815634
Club Colours: Green & white hoops, black shorts.
CHESHAM RUFC
Ground Address: Chesham Moor, bois Moor Road, Chesham. Tel: Ground: 01494 783068; Clubhouse: 01494 783635
Club Secretary: MM Hogg, 37 Lye Green Road, Chesham, Bucks HP5 3LS. Tel: (H) 01494 771576 Tel: (W) 01494 791656
Fixtures Secretary: Dick King, 75 Darvell Drive, Chesham HP5 2QN. Tel: (H) 01494 786056 Tel (W) 0181 868 2674
Club Colours: Claret & blue hoops.
CHIPPING NORTON RUFC
Ground Address: Graystone, Burford Road, Chipping Norton, Oxon. Tel: 01608 643968
Club Secretary: T King, 4 Lewis Road, Chipping Norton, Oxon OX7. Tel: (H) 01608 643097
Fixtures Secretary: A Cripps, 4 Portland Place, Chipping Norton, Oxon OX7 5AG. Tel: (H) 01608 641182 Tel (W) 01608 643911
Club Colours: Red & black hoops.
GROVE RFC
Ground Address: Grove Recreation Ground, Cane Lane, Grove, Wantage, Oxon. Tel: 01235 762750
Club Secretary: Mr Robert Teasdale, Garden Cottage, Denchworth, Wantage, Oxon OX12 0DX. Tel: (H) 01235 868390 Tel: (W) 01235 778674
Fixtures Secretary: John Sevier, 34 Kingfishers, Grove, Oxon. Tel: (H) 01235 763172
Club Colours: Red, white & blue hooped jerseys, white shorts, red socks.
MILTON KEYNES RUFC
Ground Address: Field Lane, Greenleys, Wolverton, Milton Keynes, Bucks. Tel: 01908 313858
Club Secretary: Mr Peter Hemingway, 6 Malvern Drive, Hilltop, Stony Stratford, Milton Keynes MK11 2AE. Tel: (H) 01908 564931 Tel: (W) 0181 863 5611 x2474
Fixtures Secretary: Mr V Wilcox, 8 Caxton Road, Wolverton, Milton Keynes. Tel: (H) 01908 313083
Club Colours: Black shirt with single white chest band, black shorts & socks.
OXFORD MARATHON RFC
Ground Address: Horspath Road Recreation Ground, Horspath, Cowley, Oxford. Tel: 01865 775765
Club Secretary: AWG Barson, 97 Oxford Road, Garsington, Oxford OX44 9AB. Tel: (H) 01865 361540
Fixtures Secretary: Graham Neal, 28 Evenlode Drive, Berinsfield, Oxford. Tel: (H) 01865 340652
Club Colours: Dark blue & amber hoops.
OXFORD OLD BOYS RFC
Ground Address: Marston Ferry Road, Summertown, Oxford, Oxon. Tel: 01865 52813
Club Secretary: Mrs A Collcutt, 24 Templar Close,

FINAL TABLE

	P	W	D	L	F	A	Pts
Chinnor	12	12	0	0	437	106	24
Oxford Old Boys	12	8	0	4	342	186	16
Phoenix	12	8	0	4	154	178	16
Witney	12	7	0	5	217	157	14
Buckingham	12	6	0	6	207	199	12
Grove	12	6	0	6	194	227	12
Chesham	12	6	1	5	133	184	11*
Beaconsfield	12	5	0	7	224	213	10
Milton Keynes	12	5	2	5	148	150	10*
Pennanians	12	5	0	7	175	208	10
Drifters	12	4	0	8	162	203	8
Littlemore	12	3	1	8	149	210	7
Abingdon	12	1	0	11	143	464	2

Wheatley, Oxon. Tel: (H) 01865 873110
Fixtures Secretary: Mr Terry Whitelow, 41 Church Hill Road, Cowley, Oxford. Tel: (H) 01865 716381
Club Colours: Maroon & white hoops, navy blue shorts, red socks.
PENNANIANS RUFC
Ground Address: Farnham Park, Farnham Royal, Bucks. Tel: 01753 646252
Club Secretary: Martin James, 47 Pearl Gardens, Cippenham, Slough, Berkshire SL1 2YX. Tel: (H) 01753 734910 Tel: (W) 01628 413042
Fixtures Secretary: Richard Kearney, 14 Churchfields Mews, Wexham, Slough, Berks. Tel: (H) 01753 824155
Club Colours: Black shirts with 3 white hoops, black shorts & socks.
PHOENIX RC
Ground Address: The Sports Ground, Institute Road, Taplow, Bucks. Tel: 01628 664319
Club Secretary: Andrew Underwood, Crossways, 2 Hag Hill Lane, Taplow, Bucks SL6 0LR. Tel: (H) 01628 669818
Fixtures Secretary: Mr Russell Dixon, 3 Merlin Clove, Winfield Row, Berks RG12 6TQ. Tel: (H) 01344 886633 Tel (W) 01753 554500
Club Colours: Red & black quarters, black shorts.
SLOUGH RFC
Ground Address: Tamblyn Fields, Upton Court Park, Slough, Berkshire SL3 7LT. Tel: 01753 522107
Club Secretary: Malcolm Carter, 65 Wavell Road, Maidenhead, Berkshire SL6 5AB. Tel: (H) 01628 25640 Tel: (W) & Fax: 01628 779060
Fixtures Secretary: Clive Blackman, 11 Coleridge Crescent, Colnbrook, Bucks SL3 0PY. Tel: (H) 01753 684403
Club Colours: Bottle green jerseys with a 6' white hoop.
WHEATLEY RUFC
Ground Address: Playing Fields, Holton, Nr Wheatley, Oxon. Tel: 01865 873476
Club Secretary: Mrs Elaine Murray, The Mead, 56 Clifden Road, Worminghall, Bucks HP18 9JP. Tel: (H) 01844 338940 Tel: (W) 01865 774611
Fixtures Secretary: Mr Bryn Davies, 13 Pelham Road, Thame, Oxon OX9 3WH. Tel: (H) 01844 261615
Club Colours: Purple, white& black bands, black shorts.
WITNEY RFC
Ground Address: The Clubhouse, Hailey Road, Witney, Oxon OX8 5UH. Tel: 01993 771043 Fax: 01993 779985
Club Secretary: Chris Birks, 112 Colwell Drive, Witney, Oxon OX8 7NH. Tel: (H) 01993 778341 Fax: 01993 779985
Fixtures Secretary: Pete Holliday, 88 Blakes Avenue, Witney, Oxon. Tel: (H) 01993 705327
Club Colours: Black hoops on sky blue.

SOUTH WEST DIVISION

September 16 1995 (Week 3)
Cholsey	v	Littlemore
Drifters	v	Abingdon
Gosford	v	Didcot
Winslow	v	Harwell

September 23 1995 (Week 4)
Cholsey	v	Drifters
Didcot	v	Harwell
Gosford	v	Abingdon
Littlemore	v	Winslow

September 30 1995 (Week X1)
Abingdon	v	Didcot
Cholsey	v	Winslow
Drifters	v	Gosford
Harwell	v	Littlemore

October 14 1995 (Week 6)
Abingdon	v	Cholsey
Didcot	v	Winslow
Gosford	v	Harwell
Littlemore	v	Drifters

October 21 1995 (Week 7)
Drifters	v	Didcot
Harwell	v	Cholsey
Littlemore	v	Abingdon
Winslow	v	Gosford

October 28 1995 (Week 8)
Cholsey	v	Gosford
Didcot	v	Littlemore
Harwell	v	Abingdon
Winslow	v	Drifters

November 11 1995 (Week 10)
Abingdon	v	Winslow
Didcot	v	Cholsey
Drifters	v	Harwell
Gosford	v	Littlemore

December 30 1995 (Week 16)
Abingdon	v	Drifters
Didcot	v	Gosford
Harwell	v	Winslow
Littlemore	v	Cholsey

January 6 1996 (Week 17)
Abingdon	v	Gosford
Drifters	v	Cholsey
Harwell	v	Didcot
Winslow	v	Littlemore

January 13 1996 (Week 18)
Didcot	v	Abingdon
Gosford	v	Drifters
Littlemore	v	Harwell
Winslow	v	Cholsey

February 10 1996 (Week 22)
Cholsey	v	Abingdon
Drifters	v	Littlemore
Harwell	v	Gosford
Winslow	v	Didcot

February 17 1996 (Week 23)
Abingdon	v	Littlemore
Cholsey	v	Harwell
Didcot	v	Drifters
Gosford	v	Winslow

February 24 1996 (Week 24)
Abingdon	v	Harwell
Drifters	v	Winslow
Gosford	v	Cholsey
Littlemore	v	Didcot

March 30 1996 (Week X7)
Cholsey	v	Didcot
Harwell	v	Drifters
Littlemore	v	Gosford
Winslow	v	Abingdon

BUCKS & OXON TWO

ABINGDON RFC
Ground Address: Southern Sports Park, Lambrick Way, Abingdon, Oxon, OX14 5TJ. Tel: 01235 553810
Club Secretary: Dr Anton Lavers, 8 Champs Close, Abingdon, Oxon, OX14 2NB. Tel: (H) 01235 526448 Tel: (W) 01865 483489
Fixtures Secretary: Chris Thomas, 63 Farm Road, Abingdon, Oxon OX14 1NE. Tel: (H) 01235 528730
Club Colours: Green & gold hooped shirts, black shorts, green socks.

CHOLSEY RFC
Ground Address: Hithercroft Road, Wallingford, Oxon. Tel: 01491 835044
Club Secretary: GA Thompson, 13 The Murren, Wallingford, Oxon OX10 9DZ. Tel: (H) 01491 836910 Tel: (W) 0171 245 6262
Fixtures Secretary: M Porter, 3 Starlings Drive, Tilehurst, Reading, Berks RG3 5ST. Tel: (H) 01734 410946 Tel (W) 01734 393939
Club Colours: Amber & black.

DIDCOT RUFC
Ground Address: Edmonds Park, Park Road, Didcot.
Club Secretary: Mrs Jane Llewellyn, 54 Loyd Road, Didcot, Oxon OX11 8JT. Tel: (H) 01235 813634
Fixtures Secretary: Andrew Hawkins, 9 Welland Avenue, Didcot, Oxon OX11 7QN. Tel: (H) 01235 819227 Tel (W) 0831 716026 (Mobile)
Club Colours: Red & white hoops, white shorts.

DRIFTERS RFC
Ground Address: Farnham Common Sports Club, One Pin Lane, Farnham Common, Bucks. Tel: 01753 644190
Club Secretary: Patrick Spellman, 44 Iverdale Close, Iver, Bucks, SL0 9RL. Tel: (H) 01753 654153
Fixtures Secretary: Dave Hancock, 19 Thurston Road, Slough SL1 3SW. Tel: (H) 01753 576512
Club Colours: Black & magenta.

GOSFORD ALL BLACKS RFC
Ground Address: Langford Lane, Kidlington, Oxon. Tel: 01865 373994
Club Secretary: Dr Steve Butcher, 16 The Paddocks, Yarnton, Kidlington, Oxon. Tel: (H) 01865 373106 Tel: (W) 01865 844019
Fixtures Secretary: Mark Busby, 83 Ravenscroft, Langford Village, Bicester, Oxon. Tel: (H) 01869 248186
Club Colours: Black.

HARWELL RUFC
Ground Address: Central Sports Field, Aere Harwell, Didcot, Oxon.
Club Secretary: C Bartlett, 66 Upthorps Drive, Wantage, Oxon OX12 7DG. Tel: (H) 01235 767596
Fixtures Secretary: Jenny Bosley, 55 West Lockinge, Wantage, Oxon OX12 8QE. Tel: (H) 01235 833688
Club Colours: Navy blue, light blue & white hoops.

LITTLEMORE RFC
Ground Address: Peers School, Sandy Lane West, Littlemore, Oxon OX4 5JY. Tel: 01865 715776
Club Secretary: CD Bowler, 40 South Avenue, Kidlington, Oxford OX5 1DQ. Tel: (H) 01865 375279 Tel: (W) 01865 392236
Fixtures Secretary: F Hardie, 40 Cardinal Close, Littlemore, Oxford OX43UE. Tel: (H) 01865 774061
Club Colours: White shirts & shorts, royal blue socks.

WINSLOW RUFC
Ground Address: The Winslow Centre, Park Road, Winslow, Buckingham, MK18.
Club Secretary: Duncan Wigley, 18 Offas Lane, Winslow, Bucks MK18 3JS. Tel: (H) 01296 713136
Fixtures Secretary: Mr S Spoors, 99 High Street, Winslow, Bucks MK18. Tel: (H) 01296 714694 Tel (W) 01525 851616
Club Colours: Blue & gold hoops.

FINAL TABLE

	P	W	D	L	F	A	Pts
Wheatley	14	11	1	2	463	74	23
Chipping Norton	14	12	0	2	320	89	22*
Didcot	14	8	2	4	117	213	18
Gosford All Blacks	14	8	1	5	215	169	15*
Thames Valley Pol	14	5	1	8	112	140	11
Winslow	14	5	1	8	127	285	11
Cholsey	14	3	0	11	97	311	4*
Harwell	14	1	0	13	92	322	2

SOUTH WEST DIVISION

BERKS, DORSET & WILTS ONE 1995-96 FIXTURES

September 16 1995 (Week 3)
Corsham	v	North Dorset
Lytchett Minster	v	Redingensians
Marlborough	v	Blandford
Supermarine	v	Bridport
Weymouth	v	Thatcham
Wootton Bassett	v	Aldermaston

September 23 1995 (Week 4)
Aldermaston	v	Marlborough
Bridport	v	Lytchett Minster
Melksham	v	Corsham
North Dorset	v	Weymouth
Redingensians	v	Wootton Bassett
Thatcham	v	Supermarine

September 30 1995 (Week X1)
Blandford	v	Aldermaston
Lytchett Minster	v	Thatcham
Marlborough	v	Redingensians
Supermarine	v	North Dorset
Weymouth	v	Melksham
Wootton Bassett	v	Bridport

October 14 1995 (Week 6)
Bridport	v	Marlborough
Corsham	v	Weymouth
Melksham	v	Supermarine
North Dorset	v	Lytchett Minster
Redingensians	v	Blandford
Thatcham	v	Wootton Bassett

October 21 1995 (Week 7)
Aldermaston	v	Redingensians
Blandford	v	Bridport
Lytchett Minster	v	Melksham
Marlborough	v	Thatcham
Supermarine	v	Corsham
Wootton Bassett	v	North Dorset

October 28 1995 (Week 8)
Bridport	v	Aldermaston
Corsham	v	Lytchett Minster
Melksham	v	Wootton Bassett
North Dorset	v	Marlborough
Thatcham	v	Blandford
Weymouth	v	Supermarine

November 11 1995 (Week 10)
Aldermaston	v	Thatcham
Blandford	v	North Dorset
Lytchett Minster	v	Weymouth
Marlborough	v	Melksham
Redingensians	v	Bridport
Wootton Bassett	v	Corsham

January 6 1996 (Week 17)
Corsham	v	Marlborough
Melksham	v	Blandford
North Dorset	v	Aldermaston
Supermarine	v	Lytchett Minster
Thatcham	v	Redingensians
Weymouth	v	Wootton Bassett

January 13 1996 (Week 18)
Aldermaston	v	Melksham
Blandford	v	Corsham
Bridport	v	Thatcham
Marlborough	v	Weymouth
Redingensians	v	North Dorset
Wootton Bassett	v	Supermarine

February 10 1996 (Week 22)
Corsham	v	Aldermaston
Lytchett Minster	v	Wootton Bassett
Melksham	v	Redingensians
North Dorset	v	Bridport
Supermarine	v	Marlborough
Weymouth	v	Blandford

February 17 1996 (Week 23)
Aldermaston	v	Weymouth
Blandford	v	Supermarine
Bridport	v	Melksham
Marlborough	v	Lytchett Minster
Redingensians	v	Corsham
Thatcham	v	North Dorset

February 24 1996 (Week 24)
Corsham	v	Bridport
Lytchett Minster	v	Blandford
Melksham	v	Thatcham
Supermarine	v	Aldermaston
Weymouth	v	Redingensians
Wootton Bassett	v	Marlborough

March 30 1996 (Week X7)
Aldermaston	v	Lytchett Minster
Blandford	v	Wootton Bassett
Bridport	v	Weymouth
North Dorset	v	Melksham
Redingensians	v	Supermarine
Thatcham	v	Corsham

BERKS, DORSET & WILTS ONE

ALDERMASTON RFC
Ground Address: c/o Aldermaston Recreation Society, Aldermaston, Reading, Berks RG7 4PR. Tel: 01734 817233
Club Secretary: K Jones, 13 Stratfield Road, Basingstoke, Hants RG21 5RS. Tel: (H) 01256 811175 Tel: (W) 01734 826750
Fixtures Secretary: P Bugess, 6 Longs Court, Whitchurch, Hants RG28 6BU. Tel: (H) 01256 895024 Tel (W) 01252 332398; (Mobile) 0378 669834
Club Colours: Red shirts, black shorts.

BLANDFORD RFC
Ground Address: Larksmead, Blandford. Clubhouse: 53A East Street, Blandford, Dorset. Tel: 01258 450665
Club Secretary: Mr G Rowley, 17 Ramsbury Court, Blandford Forum. Dorset DT11 7UL. Tel: (H) 01258 451909
Fixtures Secretary: Dave Stringer, 21 Damory Street, Blandford, Dorset DT11 7EU. Tel: (H) 01258 456954 Tel (W) 01258 453698
Club Colours: Gold & brown with red & white hoop.

BRIDPORT RFC
Ground Address: Bridport Leisure Centre, Skilling Hill Road, Bridport, Dorset DT6 3LN. Tel: 01308 422464
Club Secretary: Richard Salt, 21 South Street, Bridport, Dorset DT6 3NR. Tel: (H) 01308 458347 Tel: (W) 01308 422236 Fax: 10308 427772
Fixtures Secretary: John Greig, 94 West Bay Road, Bridport, Dorset DT6 4AX. Tel: (H) 01308 456692 Tel (W) 01308 424600
Club Colours: Dark blue.

CORSHAM RFC
Ground Address: Lacock Road, Corsham, Wilts SN13 9QG. Tel: 01249 701064
Club Secretary: John G Wiltshire, 84 Springfield Close, Rudloe, Corsham, Wilts SN13 0JR. Tel: (H) 01225 810800
Fixtures Secretary: Richard Slade, 46 Paul Street, Corsham, Wilts. Tel: (H) 01249 712683
Club Colours: Red & white quarters.

LYTCHETT MINSTER RUFC
Ground Address: South Manor Drive, Lytchett Minster, Poole, Dorset.
Club Secretary: DH Smurthwaite, Staddlestones, Cheselbourne, Dorchester, Dorset DT2 7NJ. Tel: (H) 01258 837796 Tel: (W) 01202 622413
Fixtures Secretary: M Hobson, Broomheyes, Beacon Hill, Poole, Dorset. Tel: (H) 01202 623287
Club Colours: Red & blue hoops, white shorts.

MARLBOROUGH RUFC
Ground Address: The Common, Marlborough, Wilts.
Club Secretary: Joyce Adams, 10 Ailesbury Way, Burbage, Marlborough, Wilts. Tel: (H) 01672 810718
Fixtures Secretary: Alec Thomas, 2 Dando Drive, Barton Park, Marlborough, Wilts. Tel: (H) 01672 512296
Club Colours: Black & amber hoops, black shorts.

MELKSHAM (AVON) RFC
Ground Address: Avon Sports & Social Club, Melksham House, Market Place, Melksham, Wilts. Tel: 01225 703265
Club Secretary: Mr AC Butcher, 37 Locking Close, Bowerhill, Melksham, Wilts SN12 6XZ. Tel: (H) 01225 707426 Tel: (W) 01225 703325
Fixtures Secretary: Miss V Jones, 27 Blackmore Road, Melksham, Wilts. Tel: (H) 01225 705936
Club Colours: Blue & sky blue.

NORTH DORSET RFC
Ground Address: Slaughtergate, Longbury Hill Lane, Gillingham, Dorset SP8 5SY. Tel: 01747 822748
Club Secretary: Paul Phillips, 3 Buttercup Close, Wyke, Gillingham, Dorset SP8 4XB. Tel: (H) 01747 825271 Tel: (W) 01373 831800
Fixtures Secretary: Clive Drake, Folly's End, Wyke Street, Gillingham, Dorset SP8 4NA. Tel: (H) 01747 825856
Club Colours: Green & navy.

FINAL TABLE						
	P	W	D	L	F	A	Pts
Swindon	12	12	0	0	356	80	24
Melksham	12	9	1	2	241	151	19
Marlborough	12	8	1	3	256	165	17
Wootton Bassett	12	8	0	4	343	137	16
Redingensians	12	6	1	5	254	185	13
Aldermaston	12	3	3	6	88	135	9
Thatcham	12	4	1	7	149	227	9
Corsham	12	4	1	7	124	206	9
Weymouth	12	4	1	7	149	263	9
Blandford	12	4	1	7	131	252	9
Supermarine	12	4	0	8	143	282	8
Lytchett Minster	12	3	1	8	135	282	7
Swindon College	12	3	1	8	165	269	5*

REDINGENSIANS RFC
Ground Address: Old Bath Road, Sonning, Berks. Tel: 01734 695259
Club Secretary: JH Cook, 95 Century Court, Grove End Road, London NW8 9LD. Tel: (H) 0171 289 1887 Tel: (W) 0171 444 8178
Fixtures Secretary: JM Taylor, 3 The Cedars, Tilehurst, Reading RG3 6JW. Tel: (H) 01734 411444 Tel (W) 01734 393093
Club Colours: Dark blue, light blue & white hoops.

SUPERMARINE RFC
Ground Address: Supermarine Sports & Social Club, Highworth Road, South Marston, Nr Swindon, Wilts. Tel: 01793 824828
Club Secretary: Mr Geoff Bath, 2 Folly Drive, Highworth, Wilts SN6 7JR. Tel: (H) 01793 861619 Tel: (W) 01793 513111
Fixtures Secretary: Ian Frizzle, 277 Windrush, Highworth, Swindon, Wilts. Tel: (H) 01793 763135
Club Colours: Light/dark blue.

THATCHAM RFC
Ground Address: Kennet School, Stoney Lane, Thatcham, Berkshire. Tel: 01635 862121 (School); 01635 871112 (Sports Centre)
Club Secretary: Mr R B Morris, 182 Bath Road, Thatcham, Berkshire RG18 3HJ. Tel: (H) 01635 866303 Tel: (W) 01734 817474
Fixtures Secretary: Mr R Moore, 26 New Wokingham Road, Crowthorne, Berks RG45 6JJ. Tel: (H) 01344 776857 Tel (W) 01932 859433
Club Colours: Red & navy blue quarters.

WEYMOUTH RFC
Ground Address: Monmouth Avenue, Weymouth, Dorset DT3 5HZ. Tel: 01305 77889
Club Secretary: Mrs Glenda Llewellyn, 2 Goulds Hill Close, Upwey, Weymouth DT3 4LG. Tel: (H) 01305 812415
Fixtures Secretary: Mr RE Foyle, 12 Powys Close, Dorchester DT1 2RG. Tel: (H) 01305 266144 Tel (W) 01305 251888 x2846
Club Colours: Light blue & navy blue hoop.

WOOTTON BASSETT RFC
Ground Address: Rylands Field, Stoneover Lane, Wootton Bassett, Swindon, Wiltshire SN4 8LS. Tel: 01793 851425
Club Secretary: Colin Applegate, 26 Briars Close, Wootton Bassett, Swindon, Wiltshire SN4 7HX. Tel: (H) 01793 850436 Tel: (W) 01793 496464
Fixtures Secretary: Jim Brierley, 25 Broad Town Road, Broad Town, Wootton Bassett, Swindon, Wiltshire SN4 7RB. Tel: (H) 01793 731780
Club Colours: Black.

SOUTH WEST DIVISION

BERKS, DORSET & WILTS TWO 1995-96 FIXTURES

September 16 1995 (Week 3)

Bournemouth Uni	v	Berks Shire Hall
Calne	v	Oakmedians
Pewsey Vale	v	Swindon College OB
Puddletown	v	Portcastrians
Trowbridge	v	Bradford-on-Avon
Westbury	v	Tadley

September 23 1995 (Week 4)

Bradford-on-Avon	v	Bournemouth Uni
Oakmedians	v	Pewsey Vale
Portcastrians	v	Trowbridge
Swindon College OB	v	Puddletown
Tadley	v	Calne
Warminster	v	Westbury

September 30 1995 (Week X1)

Berks Shire Hall	v	Bradford-on-Avon
Bournemouth Uni	v	Portcastrians
Calne	v	Warminster
Pewsey Vale	v	Tadley
Puddletown	v	Oakmedians
Trowbridge	v	Swindon College OB

October 14 1995 (Week 6)

Oakmedians	v	Trowbridge
Portcastrians	v	Berks Shire Hall
Swindon College OB	v	Bournemouth Uni
Tadley	v	Puddletown
Warminster	v	Pewsey Vale
Westbury	v	Calne

October 21 1995 (Week 7)

Berks Shire Hall	v	Swindon College OB
Bournemouth Uni	v	Oakmedians
Bradford-on-Avon	v	Portcastrians
Pewsey Vale	v	Westbury
Puddletown	v	Warminster
Trowbridge	v	Tadley

October 28 1995 (Week 8)

Calne	v	Pewsey Vale
Oakmedians	v	Berks Shire Hall
Swindon College OB	v	Bradford-on-Avon
Tadley	v	Bournemouth Uni
Warminster	v	Trowbridge
Westbury	v	Puddletown

November 11 1995 (Week 10)

Berks Shire Hall	v	Tadley
Bournemouth Uni	v	Warminster
Bradford-on-Avon	v	Oakmedians
Portcastrians	v	Swindon College OB
Puddletown	v	Calne
Trowbridge	v	Westbury

January 6 1996 (Week 17)

Calne	v	Trowbridge
Oakmedians	v	Portcastrians
Pewsey Vale	v	Puddletown
Tadley	v	Bradford-on-Avon
Warminster	v	Berks Shire Hall
Westbury	v	Bournemouth Uni

January 13 1996 (Week 18)

Berks Shire Hall	v	Westbury
Bournemouth Uni	v	Calne
Bradford-on-Avon	v	Warminster
Portcastrians	v	Tadley
Swindon College OB	v	Oakmedians
Trowbridge	v	Pewsey Vale

February 10 1996 (Week 22)

Calne	v	Berks Shire Hall
Pewsey Vale	v	Bournemouth Uni
Puddletown	v	Trowbridge
Tadley	v	Swindon College OB
Warminster	v	Portcastrians
Westbury	v	Bradford-on-Avon

February 17 1996 (Week 23)

Berks Shire Hall	v	Pewsey Vale
Bournemouth Uni	v	Puddletown
Bradford-on-Avon	v	Calne
Oakmedians	v	Tadley
Portcastrians	v	Westbury
Swindon College OB	v	Warminster

February 24 1996 (Week 24)

Calne	v	Portcastrians
Pewsey Vale	v	Bradford-on-Avon
Puddletown	v	Berks Shire Hall
Trowbridge	v	Bournemouth Uni
Warminster	v	Oakmedians
Westbury	v	Swindon College OB

March 30 1996 (Week X7)

Berks Shire Hall	v	Trowbridge
Bradford-on-Avon	v	Puddletown
Oakmedians	v	Westbury
Portcastrians	v	Pewsey Vale
Swindon College OB	v	Calne
Tadley	v	Warminster

BERKS, DORSET & WILTS TWO

BERKSHIRE SHIRE HALL RUFC
Ground Address: Royal County of Berkshire Sports &
Social Club, Sonning Lane, Sonning, Nr Reading, Berks.
Tel: 01734 691340
Club Secretary: Dave Norris, 74 Caldbeck Drive,
Woodley, Reading, Berks RG5 4JX. Tel: (H) 01734
696439 Tel: (W) 01344 713851
Fixtures Secretary: Steve Bentley, The John Barleycorn
Inn, Goring-on-Thames RG8 9DP. Tel (W) 01491 872509
Club Colours: Blue & yellow hoops.

BOURNEMOUTH UNIVERSITY RFC
Ground Address: White Farm, Slades Farm, Ensbury
Park, Bournemouth, Dorset. Tel: 01202 595012
Club Secretary: Miss Alison J Eaton, Sports Dept,
Bournemouth University, Poole House, Talbot Campus,
Fern Barrow, Poole, Dorset, BH12 5BB. Tel: (H) 01202
530176 Tel: (W) 01202 595012
Fixtures Secretary: Mr Dai Dower, Sports Dept,
Bournemouth University, Poole House, Talbot Campus, Fern
Barrow, Poole, Dorset, BH12 5BB. Tel: (W) 01202 595012
Club Colours: Royal blue/navy & two white hoops.

BRADFORD ON AVON RFC
Ground Address: St Laurence School, Bradford on Avon,
Wilts.
Club Secretary: Nicholas Cordel, Summerleaze, Northend,
Batheaston, Bath, Avon BA1 8ES. Tel: (H) 01380 860230
Tel: (W) 01225 858551
Fixtures Secretary: Andrew Gerrish, 14 Huntington
Street, Bradford on Avon, Wilts. Tel: (H) 01225 864165
Club Colours: Red & black.

CALNE RFC
Ground Address: The Recreation Ground, Anchor Road,
Calne, Wilts SN11 8JX. Tel: 01249 812206
Club Secretary: Mr Steve Gill, 1 Heddington Wick,
Heddington, Calne, Wilts SN11 0PB. Tel: (H) 01380
850909
Fixtures Secretary: Mr Mark Otridge, 3 Marden Way,
Calne SN11 8LP. Tel: (H) 01249 821593
Club Colours: Blue/white/red.

OAKMEDIANS RFC
Ground Address: Cricket Pavilion, Merick Park,
Bournemouth BH2 6LJ. Tel: 01202 789497
Club Secretary: Amanda Sclater, 77 Latimer Road,
Winton, Bournemouth BH9 1JZ. Tel: (H) 01202 524357
Fixtures Secretary: Mrs J Phillips, 47 Headswell Avenue,
Bournemouth BH10 6JX. Tel: (H) 01202 525311
Club Colours: Royal blue & white hoops.

PEWSEY VALE RFC
Ground Address: Pewsey Vale School, Wilcot Road,
Pewsey, Wiltshire. Tel: 01672 562218
Club Secretary: David Aroskin, 20A Rawlins Road,
Pewsey, Wiltshire SN9 5EB. Tel: (H) 01672 562218 Tel:
(W) 01672 562218
Fixtures Secretary: Mr Viv Philips, 8 Miller Close,
Chirton, Devizes, Wiltshire SN10 39. Tel: (H) 01380
840516 Tel (W) 01980 675371
Club Colours: Red, white, royal blue, black quartered
shirts.

PORTCASTRIAN RFC
Ground Address: Iford Lane Playing Fields, Iford Lane,
Southbourne, Bournemouth. Tel: 01202 424565
Club Secretary: Mr Graeme Willard, 54 Ensbury Park
Road, Moordown, Bournemouth BH9 2SJ. Tel: (H) 01202
524472
Fixtures Secretary: Mr Paul Smith, 34 Masterson Close,
Christchurch, Dorset. Tel: (H) 01202 490353 Tel (W)
01202 484626
Club Colours: Blue, yellow & red hoops.

PUDDLETOWN RFC
Ground Address: Greenfields, Piddlehinton, Dorchester,
Dorset DT2 7VA. Tel: 01305 848808

FINAL TABLE

	P	W	D	L	F	A	Pts
Bournemouth Univ	12	11	0	1	453	139	22
North Dorset	12	9	0	3	412	120	18
Bradford-on-Avon	12	9	0	3	192	144	18
Bridport	12	8	0	4	284	158	16
Calne	12	7	1	4	220	83	15
Berkshire Shire H	12	7	0	5	156	210	14
Trowbridge	12	6	0	6	240	193	12
Westbury	12	5	0	7	177	214	10
Pewsey Vale	12	3	1	8	136	313	7
Oakmedians	12	6	0	6	229	140	6*
Warminster	12	3	0	9	139	280	6
Puddletown	12	3	0	9	110	335	6
Poole	12	0	0	12	71	489	-6*

Club Secretary: Mr L Rickard, 74 St George's Road,
Dorchester, Dorset DT1 1LE. Tel: (H) 01305 266189 Tel:
(W) 01305 203395
Fixtures Secretary: Philip Smeeth, 21 London Close,
Piddlehinton, Dorchester, Dorset DT2 7TQ. Tel: (H) 01300
348310
Club Colours: Red shirts, black shorts, red/white socks.

SWINDON COLLEGE OLD BOYS RFC
Ground Address: Croft Sports Centre, Marlborough Lane,
Swindon.
Club Secretary: Mr T Davis, 15 Sandown Lane, Swindon,
Wilts SN3 1QD. Tel: (H) 01793 73444 Tel: (W) 01488
73444
Fixtures Secretary: Mr P Tyler, 12 Tower View,
Faringdon, Oxfordshire SN7 7UN. Tel: (H) 01367 242386
Club Colours: Red & black quarters.

TADLEY RFC
Ground Address: Red Lane, Aldermaston, Reading,
Berks. Tel: 01734 700072
Club Secretary: RW Mears, 22 Winchfield Gardens,
Tadley, Hants RG26 3TX. Tel: (H) 01734 811648
Fixtures Secretary: RW Mears, 22 Winchfield Gardens,
Tadley, Hants RG26 3TX. Tel: (H) 01734 811648
Club Colours: Black with amber hoop.

TROWBRIDGE RFC
Ground Address: Green Lane, Ashton Park, Trowbridge,
Wilts. BA14 7DH. Tel: 01225 761389
Club Secretary: Bryn Parfitt, 60 Paxcroft Way,
Trowbridge, Wilts. BA14 7DJ. Tel: (H) 01225 764753
Fixtures Secretary: Bill Chidlow, 1 Ashmead,
Trowbridge, Wilts BA14 0PA. Tel: (H) 01225 761874
Club Colours: Dark blue/light blue/gold.

WARMINSTER RFC
Ground Address: Warminster Cricket Club, The Pavilion,
Sambourne Road, Warminster, Wiltshire. Tel: 01985
219039
Club Secretary: Mr SD Pick, Blackthorn Cottage, 95
Portway, Warminster, Wiltshire BA12 0AA. Tel: (H)
01985 847756
Fixtures Secretary: Mr S Evans, Flat 3, The Maltings,
Market Place, Warminster, Wilts BA12 9AW. Tel: (H)
01985 212750
Club Colours: Royal blue/gold hoop shirt, blue shorts &
socks.

WESTBURY RFC
Ground Address: Leighton Sports Ground, Wellhead
Lane, Westbury, Wiltshire. Tel: 01373 826438
Club Secretary: Mr Philip Osborne, 1 Nightingale Drive,
Westbury, Wiltshire BA13 3XY. Tel: (H) 01373 827951
Fixtures Secretary: Mr Mark Knott, Slate Cottage, 80
Fore Street, Warminster, Wilts. Tel: (H) 01985 215054 Tel
(W) 01985 215054
Club Colours: Green & black hoops.

SOUTH WEST DIVISION

BERKS, DORSET & WILTS THREE 1995-96 FIXTURES

September 16 1995 (Week 3)
Dorset Police   v   Christchurch
Hungerford   v   Colerne
Poole   v   Minety

September 23 1995 (Week 4)
Colerne   v   Cricklade
Minety   v   Christchurch
Poole   v   Hungerford

September 30 1995 (Week X1)
Cricklade   v   Poole
Hungerford   v   Christchurch
Minety   v   Dorset Police

October 14 1995 (Week 6)
Christchurch   v   Colerne
Dorset Police   v   Cricklade
Minety   v   Hungerford

October 21 1995 (Week 7)
Colerne   v   Minety
Hungerford   v   Cricklade
Poole   v   Christchurch

October 28 1995 (Week 8)
Cricklade   v   Colerne
Dorset Police   v   Hungerford
Minety   v   Poole

November 11 1995 (Week 10)
Christchurch   v   Minety
Colerne   v   Dorset Police
Poole   v   Cricklade

December 30 1995 (Week 16)
Christchurch   v   Poole
Dorset Police   v   Colerne
Hungerford   v   Minety

January 6 1996 (Week 17)
Colerne   v   Hungerford
Cricklade   v   Christchurch
Dorset Police   v   Poole

January 13 1996 (Week 18)
Christchurch   v   Dorset Police
Hugerford   v   Poole
Minety   v   Cricklade

February 10 1996 (Week 22)
Cricklade   v   Hungerford
Dorset Police   v   Minety
Poole   v   Colerne

February 17 1996 (Week 23)
Christchurch   v   Hungerford
Cricklade   v   Dorset Police
Minety   v   Colerne

February 24 1996 (Week 24)
Christchurch   v   Cricklade
Colerne   v   Poole
Hungerford   v   Dorset Police

March 30 1996 (Week X7)
Colerne   v   Christchurch
Cricklade   v   Minety
Poole   v   Dorset Police

BERKS, DORSET & WILTS THREE

CHRISTCHURCH RFC
Ground Address: Grange Road, Somerford, Christchurch, Dorset BH23 4JE. Tel: 01202 404279
Club Secretary: Nigel Kennett, c/o Siemens Plessey Systems, Grange Road, Somerford, Christchurch, Dorset BH23 4JE. Tel: (W) 01202 404898
Fixtures Secretary: Andy Jolley, 35 Russell Drive, Mudeford, Christchurch, Dorset. Tel: (H) 01202 481482 Tel (W) 01202 407800
Club Colours: Blue & white hoops, black shorts, blue socks.**COLERNE RFC**
Ground Address: Higgins Field, Bath Road, Colerne, Wilts SN14 8AT. Tel: 01225 742835
Club Secretary: Karen Sayers, Daubeneys Stable Cottage, High St, Colerne, Wilts, SN14 8DB. Tel: (H) 01225 744355
Fixtures Secretary: Dave Stirling, 1 Grocyn Close, Colerne, Wilts SN14 8DZ. Tel: (H) 01225 742007
Club Colours: Black.
CRICKLADE RFC
Ground Address: Hatchets, Cricklade, Wilts.
Club Secretary: Mrs Irene W Ross, Vale Hotel, High Street, Cricklade, Wilts BN6 6AY. Tel: (H) 01793 750223
Fixtures Secretary: Vaughan Jelley, 43 North Meadow Road, Cricklade SN6 6LT. Tel: (H) 01793 751045
Club Colours: Red & green quarters.
DORSET POLICE RFC
Ground Address: Dorset Police HQ, Winfrith, Nr Dorchester, Dorset. Tel: 01929 462727 x3797
Club Secretary: Phil Morgan Haye, 17 Halstock Crescent, Canford Heath, Poole, Dorset BH17 9BD. Tel: (H) 01202 697987 Tel: (W) 01929 462727 x3797
Fixtures Secretary: Chris Jenkins, CID Office, Bournemouth Police Station, Madeira Road, Bournemouth, Dorset. Tel: (H) 01202 222115
Club Colours: Black & green hoops.
HUNGERFORD RFC
Ground Address: The Cricket Club, Hungerford Common, Hungerford, Berks. Tel: 01488 682663
Club Secretary: Nigel Peter Smith, Flat 3C, 3 Bridge Street, Hungerford RG17 0EH. Tel: (H) 01488 681359 Tel: (W) 01635 46254
Fixtures Secretary: Peter Goodwin, 42 Grange Court, Boundary Road, Newbury, Berks. Tel: (H) 01635 45887 Tel (W) 01635 48222
Club Colours: Claret & porter.
MINETY RFC
Ground Address: The Playing Fields, Silver Street, Minety, Wiltshire. Tel: 01666 860802
Club Secretary: Mr Kevin Vancil, 12 Essex Walk, Walcot, Swindon, Wiltshire SN3 3EY. Tel: (H) 01793 525898 Tel: (W) 01793 574574 x4945
Fixtures Secretary: Mr Markturner, 11 Cantors Way, Minety, Wiltshire SN16 9QZ. Tel: (H) 01666 860680
Club Colours: Green & purple hoops.
POOLE RFC
Ground Address: Turlin Moor, Blandford Road, Hamworthy, Poole, Dorset.
Club Secretary: R Knight, 58 Wareham Road, Lytchett Matravers, Dorset BH16 6DS. Tel: (H) 01202 622288 Tel: (W) 01305 251414
Fixtures Secretary: G Allsopp, 15 Guest Avenue, Poole, Dorset BH16 6DS. Tel: (H) 01202 733908
Club Colours: Blue & amber.

FINAL TABLE

	P	W	D	L	F	A	Pts
Portcastrians	14	12	0	2	246	89	24
Tadley	14	11	0	3	347	94	22
Dorset Police	14	11	0	3	236	90	22
Minety	14	6	1	7	167	186	13
Colerne	14	6	0	8	249	222	10*
Christchurch	14	4	1	9	217	226	9
Hungerford	14	4	0	10	122	273	8
Cricklade	14	0	2	12	35	439	2

England captain Will Carling shows his strength for Harlequins as he hands off Leicester's Smith watched by John Lilly & Jez Harris

Photo: Joe McCabe

STATISTICAL REVIEW OF THE BRITISH RUGBY UNION SEASON 1994-95

WORLD CUP 1995

WORLD CUP QUALIFYING – 1994-95
American Zone

United States 22 Argentina 28   Saturday, May 28th. Long Beach, California.
Argentina 16 United Staes 11   Monday, June 20th. In Buenos Aires.
Argentina qualify to play in Pool 'B' of the World Cup finals against England, Western Samoa and one from Italy, Romania and Wales.

African Zone

Final Qualifying Pool (in Casablanca)

Wednesday, June 15th	Morocco 17 Cote d'Ivoire 9	Namibia 25 Zimbabwe 20
Friday, June 17th	Cote d'Ivoire 13 Namibia 12	Morocco 9 Zimbabwe 21
Sunday, June 19th	Cote d'Ivoire 13 Zimbabwe 12	Morocco 16 Namibia 16

Cote d'Ivoire qualify for Rugby World Cup Finals Pool 'D' and meet France, Scotland and Tonga in South Africa.

FINAL TABLE						
	P	W	D	L	F	A	Pts
Cote d'Ivoire	3	2	0	1	35	41	7
Namibia	3	1	1	1	53	49	6
Morocco	3	1	1	1	42	46	6
Zimbabwe	3	1	0	2	53	47	5

SEEDING MATCHES

Saturday, 17th September 1994   **In Bucharest**

ROMANIA 9   WALES 16

Penalty-goals: Nichetean (3)   Try: I Evans
                                    Penalty-goals: N Jenkins (3)
                                    Conversion: N Jenkins
                  H.T. 6-10

Saturday, 1st October 1994   **In Catania**

ITALY 24   ROMANIA 6

Penalty-goals: Dominguez (6)   Penalty-goals: Nichetean (2)
                  H.T. 9-6

Wednesday, 12th October 1994   **At Cardiff Arms Park**

WALES 29   ITALY 19

Try: N Davies   Try: Francescato.
Dropped-goal: N Jenkins   Penalty-goals: Dominguez (4)
Penalty-goals: N Jenkins (7)   Conversion: Dominguez
                  H.T. 15-10.

FINAL TABLE						
	P	W	L	F	A	Pts
Wales	2	2	0	45	28	6
Italy	2	1	1	43	35	4
Romania	2	0	2	15	40	2

ASIAN QUALIFYING TOURNAMENT
22nd to 29th October 1994. In Kuala Lumpur, Malaysia (Stadium Cheras)

Saturday, 22nd October

Pool 'A': Malaysia 23 Sri Lanka 18

Pool 'A': Japan 56 Taiwan 5

Sunday, 23rd October

Pool 'B': South Korea 28 Hong Kong 17

Pool 'B': Thailand 69 Singapore 5

Monday, 24th October

Pool 'A': Japan 67 Sri Lanka 3

Pool 'A': Taiwan 23 Malaysia 15

Tuesday, 25th October 1994

Pool 'B': Hong Kong 93 Thailand 0

Pool 'B': South Korea 90 Singapore 3

Wednesday, 26th October 1994

Pool 'A': Japan 97 Malaysia 9

Pool 'A': Taiwan 25 Sri Lanka 9

Thursday, 27th October 1994

Pool 'B': Hong Kong 164 Singapore 13

Pool 'B': South Korea 65 Thailand 13

FINAL – Saturday, 29th October 1994.
JAPAN 26   SOUTH KOREA 11

POOL 'A'	P	W	L	F	A	Pts
Japan	3	3	0	220	17	9
Taiwan	3	2	1	53	80	7
Malaysia	3	2	1	47	138	5
Sri Lanka	3	0	3	30	115	3

POOL 'B'	P	W	L	F	A	Pts
South Korea	3	3	0	183	33	9
Hong Kong	3	2	1	274	41	7
Thailand	3	1	2	82	163	5
Singapore	3	0	3	21	323	3

FINAL ROUNDS – SOUTH AFRICA

POOL A

Thursday, 25th May 1995

At Newlands, Cape Town

SOUTH AFRICA 27   AUSTRALIA 18

Tries: Hendriks (1), Stransky
Dropped-goal: Stransky
Penalty-goals: Stransky (4)
Conversion: Stransky

Tries: Lynagh (1), Kearns (1)
Penalty-goals: Lynagh (2)
Conversion: Lynagh

H.T. 14-13

SOUTH AFRICA (Transvaal unless stated): A Joubert (Natal); J Small (Natal), J Mulder, H le Roux, P Hendriks; J Stransky (Western Province), J van der Westhuizen (Northern Transvaal); P du Randt (Orange Free State), J Dalton, B Swart, F Pienaar (captain), M Andrews (Natal), H Strydom, R Kruger (Northern Transvaal), R Straeuli. Replacement: G Pagel (Western Province) for Swart 68 minutes. New cap: Pagel.

AUSTRALIA (Queensland unless stated): M Pini; D Campese (New South Wales), J Little, D Herbert, D Smith; M Lynagh (captain), G Gregan (Australian Capital Territory); D Crowley, P Kearns (New South Wales), E McvKenzie (New South Wales), W Ofahengaue (New South Wales), R McCall, J Eales, D Wilson, T Gavin (New South Wales). No new caps.

Referee: D Bevan, Wales.

Friday, 26th May 1995 In Port Elizabeth

CANADA 34   ROMANIA 3

Tries: Snow (1), Charron (1), McKenzie (1)   Penalty-goal: Nichitean
Dropped-goal: Rees
Penalty-goals: Rees (4)
Conversions: Rees (2)

H.T. 11-3

CANADA (British Columbia unless stated): S Tewart; W Stanley, C Stewart (Western Province), D Lougheed (Ontario); G Rees (Newport)(captain), J Graf; E Evans, M Cardinal, R Snow, A Charron (Ontario), G Ennis, M James, I Gordon, C McKenzie. No new caps.

ROMANIA: G Solomie (Timisoara); I Colceriu (Steaua Bucharest), N Racean (Cluj University), R Gontineac (Cluj University), I Rotaru (Dinamo Bucharest); N Nichitean (Cluj University), D Neaga (Dinamo Bucharest); G Leonte (Vienne), I Negreci (CFR Constanta), G Vlad (Grivita Rosie), T Oroian (Steaua Bucharest), S Ciorascu (Auch)(captain), C Cojocariu (Bayonne), A Gealapu (Steaua Bucharest), O Siusariuc (Dinamo Bucharest). Replacements: V Flutur (Cluj University) for Neaga 52 minutes, I Ivankciuc (Stinta Petrosani) for Nichitean 65 minutes. No new caps.

Referee: C Hawke, New Zealand.

Tuesday, 30th May 1995 In Cape Town

SOUTH AFRICA 21   ROMANIA 8

Tries: Richter (2)   Try: Guranescu
Penalty-goals: Johnson (3)   Penalty-goal: Ivanciuc
Conversion: Johnson

H.T. 8-0

SOUTH AFRICA (Transvaal unless stade): G Johnson; J Small (Natal), C Scholtz, B Venter (Orange Free State), P Hendriks; H le Roux, J Roux; G Pagel (Western Province), C Rossouw, M Hurter (Northern Transvaal), R Kruger (Northern Transvaal), K Wiese, K Otto (Northern Transvaal), R Brink (Western Province), A Richter (Northern Transvaal)(captain). Temporary replacement: J Stransky (Western Province) for Venter 32 to 36 minutes. New caps: Hurter, Otto, Brink.

ROMANIA: V Brici (Farul Constanta); L Colceriu (Steaua Bucharest), N Racean (Cluj University), R Gontineac (Cluj University), G Solomie (Timisoara); I Ivanciuc (Stinta Petrosani), V Flutur (Cluj University); G Leonte (Vienne), I Negreci (CFR Constanta), G Vlad (Grivita Rosie), A Guranescu (Dinamo Bucharest), S Ciorascu (Dinamo Bucharest), C Cojocariu (Bayonne), A Gealapu (Steaua Bucharest), T Brinza (Cluj University)(captain). Replacement: V Tufa (Dinamo Bucharest) for Negreci 62 minutes. No new caps.

Referee: K McCartney, Scotland.

Wednesday, 31st May 1995 In Port Elizabeth

AUSTRALIA 27   CANADA 11

Tries: Tabua (1), Roff (1)   Try: Charron
Lynagh (1)   Penalty-goals: Rees (2)
Penalty-goals: Lynagh (3),
Conversions: Lynagh (2)

H.T. 20-6

AUSTRALIA (New South Wales unless stated): M Burke; D Campese, J Little (Queensland), T Horan (Queensland), J Roff (Australian Capital Territory); M Lynagh (Queensland), P Slattery (Queensland); A Daly, P Kearns, M Hartill, V Ofahengaue, W Waugh, J Eales (Queensland), I Tabua (Queensland), T Gavin. Replacements: E McKenzie for Hartill 55 minutes, M Foley (Queensland) for Kearns 70 minutes, G Gregan (Australian Capital Territory) for Slattery 80 minutes. New caps: Roff, Foley.

CANADA (British Columbia unless stated): S Stewart; W Stanley, C Stewart (Western Province), S Gray, D Lougheed (Ontario); G Rees (Newport)(captain), J Graf; E Evans, K Svoboda (Ontario), R Snow, G Mackinnon, M James, G Rowlands, J Hutchinson, A Charron (Ontario). Replacement: G Ennis for Rowlands 70 minutes. No new caps.

Referee: P Robin, France.

AUSTRALIA 42   ROMANIA 3

Tries: Roff (2), Foley (1), Burke (1), Smith (1),   Dropped-goal: Ivanciuc
Wilson (1)
Conversions: Eales (4), Burke (2)

H.T. 14-3

AUSTRALIA (Queensland unless stated): M Burke (New South Wales); D Smith, D Herbert, T Horan, J Roff (Australian Capital Territory); S Bowen (New South Wales), G Gregan (Australian Capital Territory); A Daly (New South Wales), M Foley, E McKenzie (New South Wales), I Tabua, R McCall (captain), J Eales, D Wilson, T Gavin (New South Wales). Replacement: P Slattery for Gregan 72 minutes. Temporary replacements: D Manu (New South Wales) for Wilson 28-35 minutes, M Pini for Herbert 28-36 minutes. New caps: Foley, Manu.

ROMANIA: V Brici (Farul Constanta); L Colceriu (Steaua Bucharest), N Racean (Cluj University), R Gontineac (Cluj University), G Solomie (Timisoara); I Ivanciuc (Stinta Petrosani), V Flutur (Cluj University); G Leonte (Vienne), I Negreci (CFR Constanta), G Vlad (Grivita Rosie), A Guranescu (Dinamo Bucharest), S Ciorascu (Auch), C Cojocariu (Bayonne), A Gealupu (Steaua Bucharest), T Brinza (Cluj University)(captain). Replacements: A Lungu (Castres Olymique) for Gontineac 56 minutes, V Tufa (Dinamo Bucharest) for Negreci 32 minutes. No new caps.

Referee: N Saito, Japan.

SOUTH AFRICA 20   CANADA 0

Tries: Richter (2)
Penalty-goals: Stransky (2)
Conversions: Stransky (2)

H.T. 17-0

SOUTH AFRICA (Transvaal unless stated); A Joubert (Natal); G Johnson, C Scholtz, B Venter (Orange Free State), P Hendriks; J Stransky (Western Province), J Roux; G Pagel (Western Province), J Dalton, M Hurter (Northern Transvaal), J Pienaar (captain), K Wiese, H Strydom, R Brink (Western Province), A Richter (Northern Transvaal). Replacements: J van der Westhuizen (Northern Transvaal) for Johnson 19 mins, H le Roux for Stransky 60 minutes, K Otto (Northern Transvaal) for Strydom 72 minutes. No new caps. Sent-off: Dalton 70 minutes.

CANADA (British Columbia unless stated): S Stewart; W Stanley, C Stewart (Western Province), S Gray, D Lougheed (Ontario); G Rees (Newport)(captain), J Graf; E Evans, M Cardinal, R Snow, I Gordon, G Ennis, A Charron (Ontario), G Mackinnon, C McKenzie. Replacements: J Hutchinson for Ennis 65 minutes, C Michaluk for McKenzie 79 minutes. New cap: Michaluk. Sent-off: Rees, Snow 70 minutes.

Referee: D McHugh, Ireland.

NB: This was the first recognised full scale international match in which three players have been sent off. Gareth Rees, Canada's captain, was also the first outside half to be dismissed in an international match. Rees, Snow and Dalton were all banned for 30 days, while South African wing Pieter Hendriks was cited later for foul play and suspended for 90 days with Canadian fullback Scott Stewart, who could justly be blamed for starting the fracas, also being cited and banned for 60 days.

RESULTS

South Africa 27   Australia 18   Canada 34   Romania 3
South Africa   21 Romania 8   Australia 27   Canada 11
Australia 42   Romania 3   South Africa 20   Canada 0

	FINAL TABLE					
	P	W	L	F	A	Pts
South Africa	3	3	0	68	26	9
Australia	3	2	1	87	41	7
Canada	3	1	2	45	50	5
Romania	3	0	3	14	97	3

POOL B

Saturday, 27th May 1995 — In East London

ITALY 18 WESTERN SAMOA 42

Tries: Marcello Cuttitta (1)
Vaccari (1)
Penalty-goals: Dominguez (2)
Conversion: Dominguez

Tries: Lima (2), Harder (2),
Tatupu (1), Kellett (1)
Penalty-goals: Kellett (2)
Conversions: Kellett (2)

H.T. 11-12

ITALY (Milan unless stated): P Vaccari; M Ravazzolo (Calvisano), I Francescato (Treviso), M Bonomi, Marcello Cuttitta; D Dominguez, A Troncon; Massimo Cuttitta (captain), C Orlandi (Piacenza), F Properzi Curti, O Arancio (Catania), R Favaro (Treviso), P Pedroni, J Gardner (Roma), C Checchinato (Rovigo). No new caps.

WESTERN SAMOA: M Umaga (Wellington); B Lima (Marist), T Vaega (Moataa), T Fa'amasino (Vaimoso), G Harder (Auckland); D Kellett (Counties), T Nu'ualiti'itia (Auckland/Waikemata); M Mika (Otago), T Leisamaivao (Moataa), P Fatialofa (Manurewa)(captain), S Vaifale (Marist), L Falaniko (Marist), D Williams (Colomiers), J Paramore (Manurewa), S Tatupu (Ponsonby). Replacement: P Leavasa (Apia) for Falaniko 57 minutes. New caps: Umaga, Harder, Mika, Falaniko, Williams, Leavasa.

Referee: J Dume, France.

Saturday, 27th May 1995 — In Durban

ARGENTINA 18 ENGLAND 24

Tries: Noriega (1), Arbizu (1)
Penalty-goal: Arbizu
Conversion: Arbizu

Dropped-goals: Andrew (2)
Penalty-goals: Andrew (6)

H.T. 0-12

ARGENTINA: E Jurado (Jockey, Rosario); M Teran (Tucuman), D Cuesta Silva (Alumni), S Salvat (Alumni)(captain), D Albanase (San Isidro); L Arbizu (Belgrano AT), R Crexell (Jockey, Rosario); M Corral (San Isidro), F Mendez (Mendoza), P Noriega (Hindu), R Martin (San Isidro), P Sporleder (La Plata), G Llanes (Curupayti), C Viel (Newman), J Santamarina (Tucuman). Replacement: S Irasoqui (Palermo Bajo) for Viel 71 minutes. No new caps.

ENGLAND: M Catt (Bath); T Underwood (Leicester), W Carling (Harlequins)(captain), J Guscott (Bath), R Underwood (Leicester/RAF); R Andrew (Wasps), D Morris (Orrell); J Leonard (Harlequins), B Moore (Harlequins), V Ubogu (Bath), T Rodber (Northampton/Army), M Johnson (Leicester), M Bayfield (Northampton), B Clarke (Bath), S Ojomoh (Bath). Replacement: P de Glanville (Bath) for Carling 78 minutes. Temporary replacement: N Back (Leicester) for Ojomoh 34-36 minutes, 50-53 minutes. No new caps.

Referee: J Fleming, Scotland.

Tuesday, 30th May 1995 — In East London

ARGENTINA 26 WESTERN SAMOA 32

Tries: Crexell (1), penalty try
Penalty-goals: Cilley (4)
Conversions: Cilley (2)

Tries: Harder (1), Leaupepe (1)
Lam (1)
Penalty-goals: Kellett (5)
Conversion: Kellett

H.T. 16-10

ARGENTINA: E Jurado (Jockey Club); D Cuesta Silva (San Isidro), L Arbizu (Belgrano AT), S Salvat (Alumni)(captain), M Teran (Tucuman); J Cilley (San Isidro), R Crexell (Jockey, Rosario); M Corral (San Isidro), F Mendez (Mendoza), P Noriega (Hindu), R Martin (San Isidro), G Llanes (La Plata), P Sporleder (Curupayti), C Viel (Newman), J Santamarina (Tucuman). No new caps.

WESTERN SAMOA: M Umaga (Wellington); B Lima (Marist), T Vaega (Moataa), T Fa'amisino (Vaimoso), G Harder (Auckland); D Kellett (Counties), T Nu'ualiti'itia (Auckland/Waitemata); M Mika (Otago), T Leiasamaivao (Moataa), G Latu (Vaimoso), S Tatupu (Ponsonby), P Leavasa (Apia), L Falaniko (Marist), J Paramore (Manurewa), P Lam (Marist)(captain). Replacements: P Fatialofa (Auckland) for Latu 40 minutes, G Leaupepe (Papakura/Counties) for Harder 51 minutes, F Sini (Marist) for Kellett 79 minutes. New caps: Leaupepe, Sini.

Referee: D Bishop, New Zealand.

ENGLAND 27   ITALY 20

Tries: T Underwood (1)
R Underwood (1)
Penalty-goals: Andrew (5)
Conversion: Andrew

Tries: Vaccari (1), Massimo
Cuttitta (1)
Penalty-goals: Dominguez (2)
Conversions: Dominguez (2)

H.T. 16-10

ENGLAND: M Catt (Bath); T Underwood (Leicester), P de Glanville (Bath), J Guscott (Bath), R Underwood (Leicester/RAF); R Andrew (Wasps)(captain), K Bracken (Bristol); G Rowntree (Leicester), B Moore (Harlequins), J Leonard (Harlequins), T Rodber (Northampton/Army), M Johnson (Leicester), M Bayfield (Northampton), N Back (Leicester), B Clarke (Bath). No new caps.

ITALY (Milan unless stated): L Troiani (L'Aquila); P Vaccari, I Francescato (Treviso), S Bordon (Rovigo), M Gerosa (Piacenza); D Dominguez, A Troncon; Massimo Cuttitta (captain), C Orlandi (Piacenza), F Properzi Curti, A Sgorlon (San Dona), P Pedroni, M Giacheri (Treviso), O Arancio (Catania), J Gardner (Roma). No new caps.
Referee: S Hilditch, Ireland.

ARGENTINA 25   ITALY 31

Tries: Martin (1), Corral (1), Cilley (1), penalty try.
Penalty-goal: Cilley
Conversion: Cilley

Tries: Vaccari (1), Gerosa (1), Dominguez (1)
Penalty-goals: Dominguez (4)
Conversions: Dominguez (2)

H.T. 12-12

ARGENTINA: E Jurado (Jockey, Rosario); D Cuesta Silva (San Isidro), S Salvat (Alumni)(captain), L Arbizu (Belgrano AT), M Teran (Tucuman); J Cilley (San Isidro), R Crexell (Jockey, Rosario); M Corral (San Isidro), F Mendez (Mendoza), P Noriega (Hindu), R Martin (San Isidro), G Llanes (La Plata), P Sporleder (Curupayti), C Viel (Newman), J Santamarina (Tucuman). No new caps.

ITALY: L Troiani (L'Aquila); P Vaccari (Milan), I Francescato (Treviso), S Bordon (Rovigo), M Gerosa (Piacenza); D Dominguez (Milan), A Troncon (Milan); Massimo Cuttitta (Milan)(captain), C Orlandi (Piacenza), F Properzi Curti (Milan), A Sgorlon (San Dona), P Pedroni (Milan), M Giacheri (Treviso), O Arancio (Catania), J Gardner (Roma). No new caps.

ENGLAND 44   WESTERN SAMOA 22

Tries: R Underwood (2), Catt (1) penalty try
Dropped-goal: Catt
Penalty-goals: Callard (5)
Conversions: Callard (3)

Tries: Fata Sini (2), Umaga (1)
Penalty-goal: Fa'amasino
Conversions: Fa'amisino (2)

H.T. 21-0

ENGLAND: J Callard (Bath); I Hunter (Northampton), W Carling (Harlequins)(captain), P de Glanville (Bath), R Underwood (Leicester/RAF); M Catt (Bath), D Morris (Orrell); G Rowntree (Leicester), G Dawe (Bath), V Ubogu (Bath), S Ojomoh (Bath), M Johnson (Leicester), R West (Gloucester), N Back (Leicester), D Richards (Leicester). Replacements: J Mallett (Bath) for Rowntree 25 minutes, T Rodber (Northampton) for Back 27 minutes, D Hopley (Wasps) for Carling 71 minutes, B Moore (Harlequins) for Richards 75 minutes. Temporary replacements: K Bracken (Bristol) for Richards 72 minutes, B Moore (Harlequins) for Rodber 72-76 minutes. New caps: West, Mallett, Hopley.

WESTERN SAMOA: M Umaga (Wellington); B Lima (Marist), T Vaega (Moataa), T Fa'amasino (Vaimoso), G Leaupepe (Papakura); E Puleitu (Auckland Institute), T Nu'uali'itia (Auckland/Waitemata); M Mika (Otago), T Leiasamavao (Moataa), G Latu (Vaimoso), P Leavasa (Apia), D Williams (Colomiers), L Falaniko (Marist), M Iupeli (Marist), P Lam (Marist)(captain). Replacements: S Tatupu (Ponsonby) for Leavasa 31 minutes, F Sini (Marist) for Puleitu 41 minutes, S Lemanea (Scopa) for Tatupu 68 minutes, P Fatialofa (Auckland) for Latu 74 minutes. New caps: Puleitu, Sini.
Referee: P Robin, France.

FINAL TABLE	P	W	L	F	A	Pts
England	3	3	0	95	60	9
Western Samoa	3	2	1	96	88	7
Italy	3	1	2	69	94	5
Argentina	3	0	3	69	87	3

POOL C

In Bloemfontein

JAPAN 10 WALES 57

Tries: Oto (2)

Tries: G Thomas (3), I Evans (2),
Moore (1), Taylor (1)
Penalty-goals: N Jenkins (4)
Conversions: N Jenkins (5)

H.T. 0-36

JAPAN: T Matsuda (Toshiba Fuchu); L Oto (Daita Bunka University), A Yoshida (Isotan), Y Motoki (Kobe Steel), T Masuho (Kobe Steel); S Hirao (Kobe Steel), M Horikoshi (Steel); O Ota (NEC), M Kunda (Toshiba Fuchu)(captain), K Takahashi (Toyota), H Kajihara (Kataunuma), Y Sakuraba (Nippon Steel), B Ferguson (Hino Motor), Sinali Latu (Sanyo Electric), Sione Latu (Daito Bunka University). No new caps.
WALES (Cardiff unless stated): A Clement (Swansea); I Evans (Llanelli), M Hall (captain), N Jenkins (Pontypridd), G Thomas (Bridgend); A Davies, A Moore; M Griffiths, G Jenkins (Swansea), J Davies (Neath), S Davies (Swansea0, D Jones, G Llewellyn (Neath), H Taylor, E Lewis. Replacements: D Evans (Treorchy) for A Davies 59 minutes, S Roy for D Jones 71 minutes. New caps: G Thomas, Moore, Roy.
Referee: E Sklar, Argentina.

Saturday, 27th May 1995 **At Ellis Park, Johannesburg**

IRELAND 19 NEW ZEALAND 43

Tries: Halpin (1), McBride (1), Corkery (1)
Conversions: Elwood (2)

Tries: Lomu (2), Bunce (1), Kronfeld (1), Osborne (1)
Penalty-goals: Mehrtens (4)
Conversions: Mehrtens (3)

H.T. 12-20

IRELAND: J Staples (Harlequins); R Wallace (Garryowen), B Mullin (Blackrock College), J Bell (Ballymena), S Geoghegan (Bath); E Elwood (Lansdowne), M Bradley (Cork Constitution); N Popplewell (Wasps), T Kingston (Dolphin)(captain), G Halpin (London Irish), D Corkery (Cork Constitution), N Francis (Old Belvedere), G Fulcher (Cork Constitution), D McBride (Malone), P Johns (Dungannon). Replacement: M Field (Malone) 37 for Staples. Temporary replacement: M Field (Malone) for Bell 13-32 minutes. No new caps.
NEW ZEALAND: G Osborne (North Harbour); J Wilson (Otago), F Bunce (North Harbour), W Little (North Harbour), J Lomu (Counties); A Mehrtens (Canterbury), G Bachop (Canterbury); C Dowd (Auckland), S Fitzpatrick (Auckland)(captain), O Brown (Auckland), J Joseph (Otago), I Jones (North Harbour), B Larsen (North Harbour), M Brewer (Canterbury), J Kronfeld (Otago). Replacements: M Ellis (Otago) for Wilson 33 minutes, K Schuler (North Harbour) for Brewer 77 minutes. Temporary replacement: N Hewitt (Hawke's Bay) for Fitzpatrick 56-61 minutes. New cap: Hewitt.
Referee: W Erickson, Australia.

Wednesday, 31st May 1995 **In Bloemfontein**

IRELAND 50 JAPAN 28

Tries: Corkery (1), Francis (1), Geoghegan (1),
Halvey (1), Hogan (1), penalty-tries (2)
Penalty-goal: Burke
Conversions: Burke (6)

Tries: Sinali Latu (1),
Izawa (1), Hirao (1), Takura (1)
Conversions: Y Yoshida (4)

H.T. 19-14

IRELAND: C O'Shea Lansdowne); R Wallace (Garryowen), B Mullin (Blackrock College), M Field (Malone), S Geoghegan (Bath); P Burke (Cork Constitution), N Hogan (Terenure College); N Popplewell (Wasps)(captain), K Wood (Garryowen), P Wallace (Blackrock College), D Corkery (Cork Constitution), D Tweed (Ballymena), N Francis (Old Belvedere), E Halvey (Shannon), P Johns (Dungannon). Replacements: T Kingston (Dolphin) for Wood 8 minutes, A Foley (Shannon) for Tweed 74 minutes. New cap: P Wallace.
JAPAN: T Matsuda (Toshiba Fuchu); L Oto (Daio Bunka University), A Yoshiba (Kobe Steel), Y Motoki (Kobe Steel), Y Yoshida (Isotan); S Hirao (Kobe Steel), M Horokishi (Steel); M Takura (Mitsubishi Motor), M Kunda (Toshiba Fuchu)(captain), O Ota (NEC), Sione Latu (Daito Bunka University), Y Sakuraba (Nippon Steel), B Ferguson (Hino Motor), H Kajihara (Katsunuma), Sinali Latu (Sanyo Elecric). Replacement: K Izawa (Daito Bunku University) for Sione Latu 8 minutes. New cap: A Yoshida.
Referee: S Neethling, South Africa.

NEW ZEALAND 34　WALES 9
Tries: Bunce (1), Ellis (1), Kronfeld (1)　　　Dropped-goal: N Jenkins
Dropped-goal: Mehrtens (2)　　　　　　　　　Penalty-goals: N Jenkins
Penalty-goals: Mehrtens (4)
Conversions: Mehrtens (2)

H.T. 20-6

NEW ZEALAND: G Osborne (North Harbour); M Ellis (Otago), F Bunce (North Harbour), W Little (Counties), J Lomu (Counties); A Mehrtens (Canterbury), G Bachop (Canterbury); O Brown (Auckland), S Fitzpatrick (Auckland)(captain), C Dowd (Auckland), J Joseph (Otago), I Jones (North Harbour), B Larsen (North Harbour), J Kronfeld (Otago), M Brewer (Canterbury). Replacement: E Rush (North Harbour) for Lomu 62 minutes. New cap: Rush.

WALES: A Clement (Swansea); I Evans (Llanelli), M Hall (Cardiff)(captain), G Thomas (Bridgend), W Proctor (Llanelli); N Jenkins (Pontypridd), R Jones (Swansea); R Evans (Llanelli), J Humphries (Cardiff), J Davies (Neath), M Bennett (Cardiff), D Jones (Cardiff), G Prosser (Pontypridd), G Llewellyn (Neath), H Taylor (Cardiff). New caps: Humphries, Prosser, Bennett.

Referee: E Morrison, England.

JAPAN 17　NEW ZEALAND 145
Tries: Kajihara (2),　　　　　　　　Tries: Ellis (6), Wilson (3), Rush (3), R Brooke (2)
Penalty-goal: Hirose (3)　　　　　　Osborne (2), Loe (1), Ieremiah (1), Culhane (1)
Conversions: Hirose (2)　　　　　　Dowd (1), Henderson (1)
　　　　　　　　　　　　　　　　　Conversions: Culhane (20)

H.T. 3-84

JAPAN: T Matsuda (Toshiba Fuchu); L Oto (Daito Bunka University), A Yoshida (Kobe Steel), Y Motoki (Kobe Steel), Y Yoshida (Isotan); K Hirose (Kyoto Sangyo University), W Murata (Toshiba Fuchu); O Ota (NEC), M Kunda (Toshiba Fuchu)(captain), K Takahashi (Toyota), H Kajihara (Kataunuma), B Ferguson (Hino Motor), Y Sakuraba (Nippon Steel), Sinali Latu (Sanyo Electric), K Izawa (Daito Burha University). Replacement: T Akatsuka (Meiji University) for Sinali Latu 55 minutes. New cap: Murata.

NEW ZEALAND: G Osborne (North Harbour); J Wilson (Otago), M Ellis (Otago), A Ieremiah (Wellington), E Rush (North Harbour); S Culhane (Southland), A Strachan (North Harbour); C Dowd (Auckland), N Hewitt (Hawke's Bay), R Loe (Canterbury), K Schuler (North Harbour), R Brooke (Auckland), B Larsen (North Harbour), P Henderson (Otago)(captain), Z Brooke (Auckland). Replacement: J Joseph (Otago) for Larsen 15 minutes. New cap: Culhane.

Referee: G Gadjovich, Canada.

NB: New Zealand's score was a World Cup record for both its total and margin of victory. Simon Culhane, on his New Zealand debut, broke Gavin Hastings' individual record for a World Cup match with 45 points – one try and 20 conversions.

IRELAND 24　WALES 23
Tries: Popplewell (1)　　　　　　　Tries: Humphries (1), Taylor McBride (1), Halvey (1)
Penalty-goal: Elwood　　　　　　　Dropped-goal: A Davies
Conversions: Elwood (3)　　　　　　Penalty-goals: N Jenkins (2)
　　　　　　　　　　　　　　　　　Conversions: N Jenkins (2)

H.T. 14-6

IRELAND: C O'Shea (Lansdowne); R Wallace (Garryowen), B Mullin (Blackrock College), J Bell (Ballymena), S Geoghegan (Bath); E Elwood (Lansdowne), N Hogan (Terenure College); N Popplewell (Wasps), T Kingston (Dolphin)(captain), G Halpin (London Irish), D McBride (Malone), G Fulcher (Cork Constitution), N Francis (Old Belvedere), D Corkery (Cork Constitution), P Johns (Dungannon). Replacement: E Halvey (Shannon) for McBride 64 minutes. No new caps.

WALES (Cardiff unless stated): T Clement (Swansea); I Evans (Llanelli), M Hall (captain), N Jenkins (Pontypridd), G Thomas (Bridgend); A Davies, R Jones (Swansea); M Griffiths, J Humphries, J Davies (Neath), S Davies (Swansea), G Llewellyn (Neath), D Jones, H Taylor, E Lewis. No new caps.

Referee: I Rogers, South Africa.

RESULTS

Japan 10   Wales 57   Ireland 19   New Zealand 42
Ireland 50   Japan 28   New Zealand   34 Wales 9
Japan 17   New Zealand 145   Ireland 24   Wales 23

| FINAL TABLE | | | | | |
	P	W	L	F	A	Pts
New Zealand	3	3	0	222	45	9
Ireland	3	2	1	93	94	7
Wales	3	1	2	89	68	5
Japan	3	0	3	55	252	3

POOL D

Friday, 26th May 1995   **At Rustenburg**

COTE D'IVOIRE 0   SCOTLAND 89

Tries: G Hastings (4), Walton (2), Logan (2), Chalmers (1),
Stanger (1), Burnell (1), Wright (1), Shiel (1)
Penalty-goals: G Hastings (2)
Conversions: G Hastings (9)

H.T. 0-34

COTE D'IVOIRE: V Kouassi (Burotic); P Bouazo (Burotic), J Sathicq (CASG), L Niakoiu (Niort), C N'Gbala (Cahors); A Dali (Clamart)(captain), F Dupont (ASPAA); A Bley (ASPAA), E Angoran (Rodez), T Djehi (Miliau), A Kone (Soustons), G Bado (Cognac), P Pere (ACBB Paris), I Lassissi (Burotic), D Sanako (Biarritz). Replacements: A Camara (ASPAA) for Dali 30 minutes, M Brito (Biscarosse) for N'Gbala 40 minutes, A Okou (Poitiers) for Bado 70 minutes. New caps: Dupont, Kone, Pere.

SCOTLAND: G Hastings (Watsonians)(captain); C Joiner (Melrose), A Stanger (Hawick), G Shiel (Melrose), K Logan (Stirling County); C Chalmers (Melrose), B Redpath (Melrose); P Burnell (London Scottish), K McKenzie (Stirling County), P Wright (Boroughmuir), P Walton (Northampton), G Weir (Melrose), S Campbell (Dundee High School FP), I Smith (Gloucester), R Wainwright (Newcastle Gosforth). No new caps.

Referee: F Vito, Western Samoa.

NB: Scotland's 89 point score and Gavin Hastings' haul of 44 individual points were a World Cup record and an individual international match highest total respectively.

Friday, 27th May 1995   **In Pretoria**

FRANCE 38   TONGA 10

Tries: Lacroix (2), Hueber (1), Saint-Andre (1)   Try: Va'enuku
Dropped-goal: Delaigue   Penalty-goal: Tu'ipolutu
Penalty-goals: Lacroix (3)   Conversion: Tu'ipolutu
Conversions: Lacroix (3)

H.T. 6-0.

FRANCE: J-L Sadourny (Colomiers); E N'Tamack (Toulouse), T Lacroix (Dax), P Sella (Agen), P Saint-Andre (Montferrand (captain); Y Delaigue (Toulon), A Hueber (Toulon); P Gallart (Beziers), J-M Gonzales (Bayonne), L Armary (Lourdes), M Cecillon (Bourgoin), O Brouzet (Grenoble), O Merle (Montferrand), A Benazzi (Agen), P Benetton (Agen). Replacement: L Cabannes (Racing Club) for Cecillon 58 minutes. No new caps.

TONGA: S Tu'ipolutu (Manly); A Taufa (Wellington Harlequins), U Va'enuku (Toloa Old Boys), P Latu (Vaheloto), T Va'enuku (Police); E Vunipola (Toa-Ko-Ma'afu), M Vunipola (Toa-Ko-Ma'afu); S Fe'ao (Queensland), F Masila (Kolomotu'a), T Fukofuka (Grammar Old Boys), F Mahoni (Fasi/Ma'ufanga), W Lose (North Harbour), F Mali (Australian Capital Territory), I Fenukitau (Australian Capital Territory), M Otai (Kia-Toa)(captain). Replacements: F Vunipola (Toa-Ko-Ma'afu) for Masila 9 minutes, I Afeaki (Australian Capital Territory) for Mafi 76 minutes. Sent off: Mahoni 68 minutes.

Referee: S Lander, England.

NB: The Tongan flanker Mahoni was suspended for 30 days for being sent off – the first dismissal of the tournament.

FRANCE 54   COTE D'IVOIRE 18

Tries: Lacroix (2), Accoceberry (1), Benazzi (1)
Costes (1), Saint-Andre (1), Techoueyres (1), Viars (1)
Penalty-goals: Lacroix (2)
Conversions: Deylaud (2), Lacroix (2)

Tries: Camara (1), Soulama (1)
Penalty-goals: Kouassi(2)
Conversion: Kouassi

H.T. 28-3

FRANCE: S Viars (Brive); P Saint-Andre (Montferrand)(captain), F Mesnel (Racing Club), T Lacroix (Dax), W Techoueyres (SBUC); Y Delaigue (Toulon), G Accoceberry (Begles-Bordeaux); L Benezech (Racing Club), M de Rougemont (Toulon), C Califano (Toulouse), A Costes (Montferrand), O Brouzet (Grenoble), O Roumat (Dax), L Cabannes (Racing Club), A Benazzi (Agen). Replacements: C Deylaud (Toulouse) for Delaigue 40 minutes, P Benetton (Agen) for Benazzi 71 minutes.

COTE D'IVOIRE: J Sathicq (CASG)(captain); A Soulama (Burotic), T Kouame (ASPAA), L Niakou (Niort), M Brito (Biscarosse); A Camara (ASPAA), F Dupont (Nimes); J-P Ezoua (ASPAA), A Niamien (Bouaka), T Djehi (Miliau), P Pere (ACBB Paris), B Aka (Burotic), D Sanoko (Biarritz), A Okou (Poitiers), I Lassissi (Burotic). Replacements: E Bley (ASPAA) for Aka 46 minutes, A Kone (Soustons) for Sanoko 55 minutes, E Angoran (Rodez) for Djehi 74 minutes. No new caps.

Referee: H Moon Soo, South Korea.

Tuesday, 30th May 1995

SCOTLAND 41   TONGA 5

Tries: Peters (1), G Hastings (1)
S Hastings (1)
Penalty-goals: G Hastings (8)
Conversion: G Hastings

Try: Fenukitau

SCOTLAND: G Hastings (Watsonians)(captain); C Joiner (Melrose), S Hastings (Watsonians), I Jardine (Stirling County), K Logan (Stirling County); C Chalmers (Melrose), D Patterson (West Hartlepool); D Hilton (Bath), K Milne (Heriot's FP), P Wright (Boroughmuir), R Wainwright (West Hartlepool), D Cronin (Bourges), G Weir (Melrose), I Morrison (London Scottish), E Peters (Bath). Replacement: P Burnell (London Scottish) for Wright 76 minutes. No new caps.

TONGA: S Tu'ipolutu (Manly); A Taufa (Wellington Harlequins), U Va'enuku (Toloa Old Boys), P Latu (Vaheloto), T Va'enuku (Police); E Vunipola (Toa-Ko-Ma'afu), M Vunipola (Toa-Ko-Ma'afu); S Fe'ao (Queensland), T Vunipola (Toa-Ko-Ma'afu), T.Fukofuka (Grammar Old Boys), I Afeaki (Wellington), W Lose (North Harbour), P Latukefu (Canberra Royals), I Fenukitau (Australian Capital Territory), M Otai (Kia-Toa). Replacement: N Tufui (Kolomutu'a) for M Vunipola 56 minutes.

Referee: B Leask, Australia.

Saturday, 3rd June 1995

COTE D'IVOIRE 11   TONGA 29

Try: Okou
Penalty-goals: Dali (2)

Tries: Latukefo (1), Otai (1),
Tu'ipolutu (1), penalty try.
Penalty-goal: Tu'ipolutu
Conversions: Tu'ipolutu (3)

H.T. 0-24

COTE D'IVOIRE: V Kouassi (Burotic); A Soulama (Burotic), J Sathicq (CASG)(captain), L Niakou (Niort), M Brito (Biscarosse); A Camara (ASPAA), F Dupont (Nimes); E Bley (ASPAA), E Angoran (Rodez), J Djehi (Miliau), P Pere (ACBB Paris), G Bado (Cognac), S Kone (Burotic), A Okou (Poitiers), I Lassisi (Burotic). replacements: T Kouame (ASPAA) for Brito 3 minutes, A Dali (Clamart) for Camara 39 minutes, D Sanoko (Biarritz) 40 minutes. No new caps.

TONGA: S Tu'ipolutu (Manly); P Latu (Vaheloto), S Mafile'o (-), U Va'entuku Toloa Old Boys), T Va'entuku (Police); E Vunipola (Toa-Ko-Mafu), N Tufui (Kolomutu'a); T Fukofuka (Grammar Old Boys), F Vunipola (Toa-Ko-Maafu), E Talakai (Auckland), W Lose (North Harbour), P Latukefu (Australian Capital Territory), F Mafi (Australian Capital Territory), I Afeaki (Wellington), M Otai (Kia-Toa)(captain). Replacements: T Iutua (Police) for Fukofuka 51 minutes, F Fakaongo (-) for Lose 64 minutes, T Isitolo (Kolofo'ou) for Va'entuku 67 minutes. New caps: Mafile'o, Fakaongo.

Referee: D Reordan, United States.

FRANCE 22   SCOTLAND 19

Try: N'Tamack   Try: Wainwright
Penalty-goals: Lacroix (5)   Penalty-goals: G Hastings (4)
Conversion: Lacroix   Conversion: G Hastings

H.T. 3-13

FRANCE: J-L Sadourny (Colomiers); E N'Tamack (Toulouse), P Sella (Agen), T Lacroix (Dax), P Saint-Andre (Montferrand)(captain); C Deylaud (Toulouse), G Accoceberry (Begles-Bordeaux); L Benezech (Racing Club), J-M Gonzales (Bayonne), C Califano (Toulouse), A Benazzi (Agen), O Merle (Montferrand), O Roumat (Dax), L Cabannes (Racing Club), P Benetton (Agen). Replacements: M Cecillon (Bourgoin) for Benetton 19 minutes, A Hueber (Toulon) for Accoceberry 32 minutes. No new caps.

SCOTLAND: G Hastings (Watsonians)(captain); C Joiner (Melrose), S Hastings (Watsonians), G Shiel (Melrose), K Logan (Stirling County); C Chalmers (Melrose), B Redpath (Melrose); D Hilton (Bath), K Milne (Heriot's FP), P Wright (Boroughmuir), R Wainwright (West Hartlepool), D Cronin (Bourges), G Weir (Melrose), I Morrison (London Scottish), E Peters (Bath). Replacements: I Jardine (Stirling County) for Shiel 45 minutes, P Burnell (London Scottish) for Wright 77 minutes. Temporary replacement: I Jardine (Stirling County) for Shiel 21-40 minutes.

Referee: W Erickson, Australia.

RESULTS

Scotland 89   Cote d'Ivoire 0   France 38   Tonga 10
France 54   Cote d'Ivoire 18   Scotland 41   Tonga 5
Cote d'Ivoire 11   Tonga 29   France 22   Scotland 19

| | FINAL TABLE | | | | | |
	P	W	L	F	A	Pts
France	3	3	0	114	47	9
Scotland	3	2	1	149	27	7
Tonga	3	1	2	44	90	5
Cote d'Ivoire	3	0	3	29	172	3

QUARTER-FINALS

FRANCE 36   IRELAND 12

Tries: Saint-Andre (1), N'Tamack   Penalty-goals: Elwood (4)
Penalty-goals: Lacroix (6)
Conversion: Lacroix

H.T. 12-12

FRANCE: J-L Sadourny (Colomiers); E N'Tamack (Toulouse), P Sella (Agen), T Lacroix (Dax), P Saint-Andre (Montferrand)(captain); C Deylaud (Toulouse), A Hueber (Toulon); L Armary (Lourdes), J-M Gonzalez (Bayonne), C Califano (Toulouse), A Benazzi (Agen), O Merle (Montferrand), O Roumat (Dax), L Cabannes (Racing Club), M Cecillon (Bourgoin). No new caps.

IRELAND: C O'Shea (Lansdowne); D O'Mahony (University College Dublin), B Mullin (Blackrock College), J Bell (Ballymena), S Geoghegan (Bath); E Elwood (Lansdowne), N Hogan (Terenure College); N Popplewell (Wasps), T Kingston (Dolphin)(captain), G Halpin (London Irish), D Corkery (Cork Constitution), G Fulcher (Cork Constitution), N Francis (Old Belvedere), D McBride (Malone), P Johns (Dungannon). Replacement: Halvey (Shannon) for Fulcher 60 minutes. No new caps.

Referee: E Morrison, England.

SOUTH AFRICA 42   WESTERN SAMOA 14

Tries: Williams (4), Rossouw (1), Andrews (1)   Tries: Nu'uali'tia (1), Tatupu (1)
Penalty-goals: Johnson (2)   Conversions: Fa'amisino (2)
Conversions: Johnson (3)

H.T. 23-0

586

SOUTH AFRICA (Transvaal unless stated): A Joubert (Natal); G Johnson, J Mulder, C Scholtz, C Williams (Western Province); H le Roux, J van der Westhuizen (Northern Transvaal); J du Randt (Orange Free State), C Rossouw, B Swart, F Pienaar (captain), K Wiese, M Andrews (Natal), R Kruger (Northern Transvaal), R Straeuli. Replacements: B Venter (Orange Free State) for Joubert 18 minutes, A Richter (Northern Transvaal) for Kruger 48 minutes, K Otto (Northern Transvaal) for Andrews 60 minutes, N Drotske (Orange Free State) for Wiese 76 minutes. No new caps.

WESTERN SAMOA: M Umaga (Wellington); B Lima (Marist), T Vaega (Counties), T Fa'amisino (Vaimoso), G Harder (Auckland); F Sini (Marist), T Nu'ualitia (Auckland); M Mika (Otago), T Leiasamaivao (Wellington), G Latu (Vaimoso), S Tatupu (Ponsonby), L Falaniko (Marist), S Lemamea (SCOPA), J Paramore (Manurewa), P Lam (Marist)(captain). Replacements: F Tuilagi (Marist) for Harter 45 minutes, P Fatalofa (Manurewa) for Latu 65 minutes, S Vifale (Marist) for Tatupu 72 minutes. No new caps.

Referee: J Fleming, Scotland.

Sunday, 11th June 1995 **In Cape Town**

AUSTRALIA 22 ENGLAND 25

Try: Smith	Try: T Underwood
Penalty-goals: Lynagh (5)	Dropped-goal: Andrew
Conversion: Lynagh	Penalty-goals: Andrew (5)
	Conversion: Andrew

H.T. 3-13

AUSTRALIA (Queensland unless stated): M Burke (New South Wales); D Campese (New South Wales), J Little, T Horan, D Smith; M Lynagh (captain), G Gregan (Australian Capital Territory); D Crowley, P Kearns (New South Wales), E McKenzie (New South Wales), W Ofahengaue (New South Wales), R McCall, J Eales, D Wilson, T Gavin (New South Wales). No new caps.

ENGLAND: M Catt (Bath); T Underwood (Leicester), W Carling (Harlequins)(captain), J Guscott (Bath), R Underwood (Leicester/RAF); R Andrew (Wasps), D Morris (Orrell); J Leonard (Harlequins), B Moore (Harlequins), V Ubogu (Bath), T Rodber (Northampton/Army), M Johnson (Leicester), M Bayfield (Northampton), B Clarke (Bath), D Richards (Leicester). Temporary replacement: S Ojomoh (Bath) for Richards 2 minutes and 30-40 minutes. No new caps.

Referee: D Bishop, New Zealand.

Sunday, 11th June 1995 **In Pretoria**

NEW ZEALAND 48 SCOTLAND 30

Tries: Little (2), Lomu (1), Mehrtens (1)	Tries: Weir (2), S.Hastings (1)
Bunce (1), Fitzpatrick (1)	Penalty-goals: G Hastings (3)
Penalty-goals: Mehrtens (2)	Conversions: G Hastings (3)
Conversions: Mehrtens (6)	

H.T. 17-9

NEW ZEALAND: J Wilson (Otago); M Ellis (Otago), F Bunce (North Harbour), W Little (North Harbour), J Lomu (Counties); A Mehrtens (Canterbury), G Bachop (Canterbury); R Loe (Canterbury), S Fitzpatrick (Auckland)(captain), O Brown (Auckland), J Joseph (Otago), I Jones (North Harbour), R Brooke (Auckland), J Kronfeld (Otago), Z Brooke (Auckland). No new caps.

SCOTLAND: G Hastings (Watsonians)(captain); C Joiner (Melrose), S Hastings (Watsonians), G Shiel (Melrose), K Logan (Stirling County); C Chalmers (Melrose), B Redpath (Melrose); D Hilton (Bath), K Milne (Heriot's FP), P Wright (Boroughmuir), R Wainwright (West Hartlepool), D Cronin (Bourges), G Weir (Melrose), I Morrison (London Scottish), E Peters (Bath). Replacements: I Jardine (Stirling County) for Chalmers 41 minutes, S Campbell (Dundee High School FP) for Cronin 63 minutes. No new caps.

Referee: D Bevan, Wales.

SEMI-FINALS

Saturday, 17th June 1995 **In Durban**

SOUTH AFRICA 19 FRANCE 15

Try: Kruger	Penalty-goals: Lacroix (5)
Penalty-goals: Stransky (4)	
Conversion: Stransky	

H.T. 10-6

SOUTH AFRICA (Transvaal unless stated): A Joubert (Natal); J Small (Natal), J Mulder, H le Roux, C Williams (Western Province); J Stransky (Western Province), J van der Westhuizen (Northern Transvaal); P du Randt (Orange Free State), C Rossouw, B Swart, F Pienaar (captain), K Weise, H Strydom, R Kruger (Northern Transvaal), M Andrews (Natal). Replacement: J Roux for van der Westhuizen 52 minutes. No new caps.

FRANCE: J-L Sadourny (Colomiers); E N'Tamack (Toulouse), P Sella (Agen), T Lacroix (Dax), P Saint-Andre (Montferrand)(captain); C Deylaud (Toulouse), F Galthie (Colomiers); L Armary (Lourdes), J-M Gonzalez (Bayonne), C Califano (Toulouse), A Benazzi (Agen), O Merle (Montferrand), O Roumat (Dax), L Cabannes (Racing Club), M Cecillon (Bourgoin). No new caps.

Referee: D Bevan, Wales.

Sunday, 18th June 1995   **In Cape Town**

ENGLAND 29   NEW ZEALAND 45

Tries: R Underwood (2), Carling (2)	Tries: Lomu (4), Kronfeld (1), Bachop (1)
Penalty-goal: Andrew	Dropped-goals: Z Brooke (1), Mehrtens (1)
Conversions: Andrew (3)	Penalty-goal: Mehrtens
	Conversions: Mehrtens (3)

H.T. 3-25

ENGLAND: M Catt (Bath); T Underwood (Leicester), W Carling (Harlequins)(captain), J Guscott (Bath), R Underwood (Leicester/RAF); R Andrew (Wasps), D Morris (Orrell); J Leonard (Harlequins), B Moore (Harlequins), V Ubogu (Bath), T Rodber (Northampton/Army), M Johnson (Leicester), M Bayfield (Northampton), B Clarke (Bath), D Richards (Leicester). No new caps.

NEW ZEALAND: G Osborne (North Harbour); J Wilson (Otago), F Bunce (North Harbour), W Little (North Harbour), J Lomu (Counties); A Mehrtens (Canterbury), G Bachop (Canterbury); C Dowd (Auckland), S Fitzpatrick (Auckland)(captain), O Brown (Auckland), M Brewer (Canterbury), I Jones (North Harbour), R Brooke (Auckland), J Kronfeld (Otago), Z Brooke (Auckland). Replacement: B Larsen (North Harbour) for Z Brooke 63 minutes. No new caps.

Referee: S Hilditch, Ireland.

NB 1: Andrew Mehrtens reached 100 points in international matches in only his fifth test for New Zealand – a new record beating that of Grant Fox (NZ) in six tests.

NB 2: England in gaining their highest points total against New Zealand also conceded their largest deficit in any international. They lost to the same opposition in 1985 by 42-15.

NB 3: Zinzan Brooke's dropped-goal was the first by a forward in the history of New Zealand rugby. The French flanker Jean Prat landed five for France in his international career. The last by a British forward was by Peter Kininmonth for Scotland against Wales at Murrayfield in 1951.

NB 4: Rory Underwood's two tries took his overall World Cup finals total to 11 (a new record) and his England record total to 47.

RESULTS

South Africa   19 France 15
England 29   New Zealand 45

THIRD/FOURTH PLACE MATCH

Thursday, 22nd June 1995   **In Pretoria**

ENGLAND 9   FRANCE 19

Penalty-goals: Andrew (3)	Tries: Roumat (1), N'Tamack (1)
	Penalty-goals: Lacroix (3)

H.T. 3-3

ENGLAND: M Catt (Bath); I Hunter (Northampton), W Carling (Harlequins)(captain), J Guscott (Bath), R Underwood (Leicester/RAF); R Andrew (Wasps), D Morris (Orrell); J Leonard (Harlequins), B Moore (Harlequins), V Ubogu (Bath), T Rodber (Northampton/Army), M Johnson (Leicester), M Bayfield (Northampton), B Clarke (Bath), S Ojomuh (Bath). No new caps.

FRANCE: J-L Sadourny (Colomiers); E N'Tamack (Toulouse), P Sella (Agen), T Lacroix (Dax), P Saint-Andre (Montferrand)(captain); F Mesnel (Racing Club), F Galthie (Colomiers); L Benezech (Racing Club), J-M Gonzalez (Bayonne), C Califano (Toulouse), A Benazzi (Agen), O Merle (Montferrand), O Roumat (Dax), L Cabannes (Racing Club), A Cigagna (Toulouse). Temporary replacement: O Brouzet (Grenoble) for Merle 35-39 minutes. New cap: Cigagna.

Referee: D Bishop, New Zealand.

Saturday, 24th June 1995   **At Ellis Park, Johannesburg**

SOUTH AFRICA 15 NEW ZEALAND 12
(after extra time)

Dropped-goals: Stransky (2)   Dropped-goal: Mehrtens
Penalty-goals: Stransky (3)   Penalty-goals: Mehrtens (2)
H.T. 9-6. Full time: 9-9. 90 minutes: 12-12.

SOUTH AFRICA (Transvaal unless stated): A Joubert (Natal); J Small (Natal), J Mulder, H le Roux, C Williams (Western Province); J Stransky (Western Province), J van der Westhuizen (Northern Transvaal); J du Randt (Orange Free State), C Rossouw, B Swart, F Pienaar (captain), K Wiese, J Strydom, R Kruger (Northern Transvaal), M Andrews (Natal). Replacements: G Pagel (Western Province) for Swart 69 minutes, R Straeuli for Andrews 90 minutes, B Venter (Orange Free State) for Small 97 minutes. No new caps.

NEW ZEALAND: G Osborne (North Harbour); J Wilson (Otago), F Bunce (North Harbour), W Little (North Harbour), J Lomu (Counties); A Mehrtens (Canterbury), G Bachop (Canterbury); G Dowd (Auckland), S Fitzpatrick (Auckland)(captain), O Brown (Auckland), M Brewer (Canterbury), I Jones (North Harbour), R Brooke (Auckland), J Kronfeld (Otago), Z Brooke (Auckland). Replacements: J Joseph (Otago) for Brewer 41 minutes, M Ellis (Otago) for Wilson 56 minutes, R Loe (Canterbury) for Dowd 84 minutes. Temporary replacement: A Strachan (North Harbour) for Bachop 67-73 minutes. No new caps.

Referee: E Morrison, England.

THIS was a great occasion, which helped to demonstrate that South Africa is united, and the thanks for that go to President Nelson Mandela and the home skipper Francois Pienaar, who both wore Springbok No. 6 jerseys for the match, the former to show where his sympathies lay with the intention
successfully to provide inspiration and the latter as his team's charismatic and diplomatic captain – one of the best in the game on both counts and a superb player into the bargain.

The All Blacks were firm favourites to win a game in which defences were to dominate with the man of the tournament Jonah Lomu kept quiet thanks to the combined efforts of James Small and Joost van der Westhuizen aided by excellent covering from others.

There were a few occasions when tries almost came with the South Africans probably scoring tries twice in the first half through the strength of their forwards; referee Ed Morrison was unlucky enough on both occasions to have positioned himself on the other side of the scrums in question, but who could fault him for making wrong guesses? No fair critic!

Jonah Lomu was clear once in the second half but a forward pass was called by Mr Morrison probably correctly and that was the state of affairs also in the first period of extra time when the admirable Stransky over-ran a pass from James Small. Those incidents apart try opportunities were few.

So the scoring came from the boots of two players and South Africa's Joel Stransky with three penalties and two dropped-goals, the second the match winner early in the second period of extra- time, was the more successful with Andrew Mehrtens landing only two penalties and a single dropped-goal from four attempts. Two of the latter were fairly easy and an effort near the end of proper time might have won the tournament for New Zealand.

There may have been no tries but bravery was a quality which was never missing and the game was littered with instances of heroism, so much so that to single out anyone would be invidious, so we should restrict selection to Stransky for his cool play overall under pressure, flanker Reuben Kruger, skipper Francois Peinaar and scrum-half Joost van der Westhuizen – all from the winners. Had they lost this choice might have been different as New Zealand in patches showed why they were the competition's most attractive team

Justice was probably done by the result, but it was close.

Since others have stuck their necks out in making selections of World Cup teams from performances in the tournament may we suggest the following:

A Joubert (South Africa); E N'Tamack (France), J Mulder (South Africa), W Little (New Zealand), J Lomu (New Zealand); J Stransky (South Africa), J van der Westhuizen (South Africa); J du Randt (South Africa), P Kearns (Australia), P Noriega (Argentina), F Pienaar (South Africa)(captain), I Jones (New Zealand), J Eales (Australia), R Kruger (South Africa), Z Brooke (New Zealand). Replacements: G Osborne (New Zealand), H le Roux (South Africa), G Bachop (New Zealand), L Benezech (France), F Mendez (Argentina), A Benazzi (France). Referee: D Bevan, Wales. Touch judges: E Morrison, England; D Bishop, New Zealand.

Player of the Tournament: J Lomu (New Zealand).

In making our selection we have been guided by form in the event itself along with consistency – single virtuoso performances take second place behind consistency – and naturally players who have played in the best and winning sides take precedence. Thus, South Africa and New Zealand, the two best teams, have the best representation with England, who were lucky to finish as high as fourth, draw a blank with Dewi Morris, probably the event's third placed scrum-half, the only member of their party who on a basis of consistency really merited consideration. Rob Andrew did well in his first three outings and kept England in the competition virtually on his own, but his luck eventually ran out and others over all did better.

Of the other British Isles countries Ireland's Jonathan Bell, Nick Popplewell and David Corkery came into serious contention as did Scotland's Gavin Hastings, Craig Chalmers, Doddie Weir and Rob Wainwright. The fact that Chalmers was singled out by the All Blacks for special treatment proved that they must have rated him very highly. No Welsh player did anything to deserve anything more than a passing thought.

Western Samoa also produced players worthy of consideration, but their form when they faced class opposition was moderate – sometimes violent – and there were better players in the tournament than their top players, but among the unfancied countries they were the best.

WORLD CUP RECORDS

Most points in a single competition:
G Fox (New Zealand – 1987) 126
T Lacroix (France – 1995) 112
G Hastings (Scotland – 1995) 104

Most tries:
M Ellis (New Zealand – 1995) 7
J Lomu (New Zealand – 1995) 7
(new World Cup records)

Most conversions:
G Fox (New Zealand – 1987) 30
D Culhane (N Zealand – 1995, 20*
M Lynagh (Australia – 1987, 20
* All scored in one match – his debut against Japan

Most penalty-goals:
T Lacroix (France – 1995) 26
G Fox (New Zealand – 1987) 21
R Andrew (England – 1995) 20

Most dropped-goals:
(all managed three)
A Mehrtens (New Zeraland – 1995)
J Stransky (Soutjh Africa – 1995)
R Andrew (England – 1995)
J Davies (Wales – 1987)

Most individual points in one match:
S Culhane (New Zealand v Japan 1995) 45
G Hastings (Scotland v Cote d'Ivoire 1995) 44
G Hastings (Scotland v Tonga 1995) 31

Most team points in one match:
New Zealand v Japan 1995, 145
Scotland v Cote d'Ivoire (1995) 89
New Zealand v Fiji (1987) 74
New Zealand v Italy (1987) 70
France v Zimbabwe (1987) 70

Most team tries in one match:
New Zealand v Japan (1987) 21
Scotland v Cote d'Ivoire (1987) 13
France v Zimbabwe (1987) 13

Most individual tries in one match:
M Ellis New Zealand v Japan 1995 6
(there have been six instances of players scoring four in a match with two in the latest tournament by C Williams (South Africa against Western Samoa) and J Lomu (New Zealand against England).

Leading aggregate points scorer (all World Cups):
G Hastings (Scotland – 1987, '91, 95) 227
Leading try scorer (all World Cups):
R Underwood (England – 1987, '91, '93) 11

Most penalty-goals in one match):
T Lacroix (France v Ireland 1995) 8

Most conversions (all World Cups):
G Hastings (Scotland – 1987, '91, '95) 39

Most dropped-goals (all World Cups):
R Andrew (England 1987, '91, '95) 5

FIVE NATIONS

FRANCE 21   WALES 9

Tries: N'Tamack (1), Saint-Andre (1)   Penalty-goals: N Jenkins (3)
Penalty-goals: Lacroix (3)
Conversion: Lacroix

H.T. 15-6.

FRANCE: J-L Sadourny (Colomiers); E N'Tamach (Toulouse), P Sella (Agen), T Lacroix (Dax), P Saint-Andre (Montferrand)(captain); C Deylaud (Toulouse), G Accoceberry (Begles-Bordeaux); L Benezech (Racing Club), J-M Gonzalez (Bayonne), C Califano (Toulouse), A Benazzi (Agen), O Merle (Montferrand), O Roumat (Dax), L Cabannes (Racing Club), P Benetton (Agen). No new caps.

WALES: A Clement (Swansea); S Hill (Cardiff), M Hall (Cardiff), M Taylor (Pontypool), N Walker (Cardiff); N Jenkins (Pontypridd), R Jones (Swansea); R Evans (Llanelli), G Jenkins (Swansea), J Davies (Neath), H Taylor (Cardiff), D Jones (Cardiff), G Llewellyn (Neath), R Collins (Pontypridd), P Davies (Llanelli). Replacements: M Griffiths (Cardiff) for R Evans 7 minutes, M Back (Bridgend) for Hill 31 minutes. New cap: Back.

Referee: J Pearson, England.

IRELAND 8   ENGLAND 20

Try: Foley   Tries: Carling (1), Clarke (1), T Underwood (1)
Penalty-goal: Burke   Penalty-goal: Andrew
Conversion: Andrew

H.T. 3-12

IRELAND: C O'Shea (Lansdowne); S Geoghegan (Bath), B Mullin (Blackrock College)(captain), P Danaher (Garryowen), N Woods (Blackrock College); P Burke (Cork Constitution), N Hogan (Terenure College); N Popplewell (Wasps), K Wood (Garryowen), P Clohessy (Young Munster), A Foley (Shannon), M Galwey (Shannon), N Francis (Old Belvedere), D Corkery (Cork Constitution), P Johns (Dungannon). Replacement: G Fulcher (Cork Constitution) for Francis 44 minutes. New caps: Burke and Hogan.

ENGLAND: M Catt (Bath), T Underwood (Leicester), W Carling (Harlequins)(captain), J Guscott (Bath), R Underwood (Leicester/RAF); R Andrew (Wasps), K Bracken (Bristol); J Leonard (Harlequins), B Moore (Harlequins), V Ubogu (Bath), T Rodber (Northampton/Army), M Johnson (Leicester), M Bayfield (Northampton), B Clarke (Bath), D Richards (Leicester). No new caps. Yellow card: Clarke.

Referee: P Thomas, France.

ENGLAND 31   FRANCE 10

Tries: T Underwood (2), Guscott (1)   Try: Viars
Penalty-goals: Andrew (4)   Penalty-goal: Lacroix
Conversions: Andrew (2)   Conversion: Lacroix

H.T. 13-3.

ENGLAND: M Catt (Bath); T Underwood (Leicester), W Carling (Harlequins)(captain), J Guscott (Bath), R Underwood (Leicester/RAF); R Andrew (Wasps), K Bracken (Bristol); J Leonard (Harlequins), B Moore (Harlequins), V Ubogu (Bath), T Rodber (Northampton/Army), M Johnson (Leicester), M Bayfield (Northampton), B Clarke (Bath), D Richards (Leicester). No new caps.

FRANCE: J-L Sadourny (Colomiers); P Bernat-Salles (Pau), P Sella (Agen), T Lacroix (Dax), P Saint-Andre (Montferrand)(captain); C Deylaud (Toulouse), G Accoceberry (Begles-Bordeaux); L Benezech (Racing Club), J-M Gonzalez (Bayonne), C Califano (Toulouse), A Benazzi (Agen), O Brouzet (Grenoble), O Roumat (Dax), L Cabannes (Racing Club), P Benetton (Agen). Replacements: L Seigne (Brive) for Benezech 23 minutes, S Viars (Grenoble) for Sadourny 37 minutes. Temporary replacement: M de Rougemont (Toulon) for Gonzalez 6-7 minutes. New cap: De Rougemont.

Referee: K McCartney, Scotland.

SCOTLAND 26   IRELAND 13

Tries: Joiner (1), Cronin (1)
Penalty-goals: Hastings (4)
Conversions: Hastings (2)

Tries: Mullin (1), Bell (1)
Penalty-goal: Burke

H.T. 9-8.

SCOTLAND: G Hastings (Watsonians)(captain); C Joiner (Melrose), I Jardine (Stirling County), G Townsend (Gala), K Logan (Stirling County); C Chalmers (Melrose), B Redpath (Melrose); D Hilton (Bath), K Milne (Heriot's FP), P Wright (Boroughmuir), R Wainwright (West Hartlepool), D Cronin (Bourges), A Campbell (Dundee High School FP), I Morrison (London Scottish), E Peters (Bath). No new caps.

IRELAND: C O'Shea (Lansdowne); S Geoghegan (Bath), B Mullin (Blackrock College), P Danaher (Garryowen), J Bell (Ballymena); P Burke (Cork Constitution), M Bradley (Cork Constitution)(captain); N Popplewell (Wasps), K Wood (Garryowen), P Clohessy (Young Munster), A Foley (Shannon), P Johns (Dungannon), G Fulcher (Cork Constitution), D McBride (Malone), B Cronin (Garryowen). No new caps.

Referee: D Bevan, Wales.

Saturday, 18th February 1995   **At Parc des Princes, Paris**

FRANCE 21   SCOTLAND 23

Tries: Saint-Andre (2), Sadourny (1)
Dropped-goal: Deylaud
Penalty-goal: Lacroix

Tries: Townsend (1), Hastings (1)
Penalty-goals: Hastings (3)
Conversions: Hastings (2)

H.T. 5-13

FRANCE: J-L Sadourny (Colomiers); P Bernat-Salles (Pau), P Sella (Agen), T Lacroix (Dax), P Saint-Andre (Montferrand)(captain); C Deylaud (Toulouse), G Accoceberry (Begles-Bordeaux); L Seigne (Brive), J-M Gonzalez (Bayonne), C Califano (Toulouse), A Benazzi (Agen), O Brouzet (Grenoble), O Roumat (Dax), L Cabannes (Racing Club), P Benetton (Agen). No new caps.

SCOTLAND: G Hastings (Watsonians)(captain); C Joiner (Melrose), I Jardine (Stirling County), K Logan (Stirling County); C Chalmers (Melrose), B Redpath (Melrose); D Hilton (Bath), K Milne (Heriot's FP), P Wright (Boroughmuir), R Wainwright (West Hartlepool), D Cronin (Bourges), A Campbell (Dundee High School FP), I Morrison (London Scottish), E Peters (Bath). Replacement: G Weir (Melrose) for Cronin 41 minutes.

Referee: D McHugh, Ireland.

At Cardiff Arms Park

WALES 9   ENGLAND 23

Penalty-goals: N Jenkins (3)

Tries: R Underwood (2), Ubogu (1)
Penalty-goals: Andrew (2)
Conversion: Andrew

H.T. 3-10

WALES: A Clement (Swansea); I Evans (Llanelli)(captain), M Taylor (Pontypool), N Davies (Llanelli), N Walker (Cardiff); N Jenkins (Pontypridd), Robert Jones (Swansea); M Griffiths (Cardiff), G Jenkins (Swansea), J Davies (Neath), H Taylor (Cardiff), Gareth Llewellyn (Neath), D Jones (Cardiff), R Collins (Pontypridd), E Lewis (Cardiff). Replacements: M Back (Bridgend) for Clement 10 minutes, R Moon (Llanelli) for Walker 46 minutes, H Williams-Jones (Llanelli) for H Taylor 65 minutes. No new caps. Sent-off: J Davies 62 minutes.

ENGLAND: M Catt (Bath); T Underwood (Leicester), W Carling (Harlequins)(captain), J Guscott (Bath), R Underwood (Leicester/RAF); R Andrew (Wasps), K Bracken (Bristol); J Leonard (Harlequins), B Moore (Harlequins) V Ubogu (Bath), T Rodber (Northampton/Army), M Johnson (Leicester), M Bayfield (Northampton), B Clarke (Bath), D Richards (Leicester).

No new caps.

Referee: D Mene, France.

NB: John Davies, the Wales tighthead prop, was the first player to be shown a red card in an international match.

IRELAND 7　FRANCE 25

Try: Geoghegan
Conversion: Elwood

Tries: Delaigue (1), Cecillon (1),
N'Tamack (1), Saint-Andre (1)
Penalty-Goal: N'Tamack
Conversion: N'Tamack

H.T. 0-3

IRELAND: J Staples (Harlequins); S Geoghegan (Bath), B Mullin (Blackrock College), P Danaher (Garryowen), N Woods (Blackrock College); E Elwood (Lansdowne), M Bradley (Cork Constitution)(captain); N Popplewell (Wasps), T Kingston (Dolphin), P Clohessy (Young Munster), E Halvey (Shannon), G Fulcher (Cork Constitution), D Tweed (Ballymena), D McBride (Malone), A Foley (Shannon). Replacement: M Field (Malone) for Mullin 40 minutes. New caps: Halvey, Tweed.

FRANCE: J-L Sadourny (Colomiers); E N'Tamach (Toulouse), P Sella (Agen), F Mesnel (Racing Club), P Saint-Andre (Montferrand)(captain); Y Delaigue (Toulon), G Accoceberry (Begles-Bordeaux); L Armary (Lourdes), J-M Gonzalez (Bayonne), C Califano (Toulouse), A Benazzi (Agen), O Brouzet (Grenoble), O Merle (Montferrand), P Benetton (Agen), M Cecillon (Bourgoin). Replacement: P Gallart (Beziers) for Armary 56-59 minutes (temporary) and 66 minutes. No new caps.

Referee: C Thomas, Wales.

David Tweed (Ballymena) was at 35 the oldest player to make his debut for Ireland.

At Murrayfield

SCOTLAND 26　WALES 13

Tries: Peters (1), Hilton (1)
Penalty-goals: G Hastings (4)
Conversions: G Hastings (2)

Try: Robert Jones
Penalty-goals: N Jenkins (2)
Conversion: N Jenkins

H.T. 20-7.

SCOTLAND: G Hastings (Watsonians)(captain); C Joiner (Melrose), S Hastings (Watsonians), G Townsend (Gala), K Logan (Stirling County); C Chalmers (Melrose), B Redpath (Melrose); D Hilton (Bath), K Milne (Heriot's FP), P Wright (Boroughmuir), R Wainwright (West Hartlepool), G Weir (Melrose), A Campbell (Dundee High School FP), I Morrison (London Scottish), E Peters (Bath). No new caps.

WALES: M Back (Bridgend); I Evans (Llanelli)(captain), N Davies (Llanelli), M Hall (Cardiff), W Proctor (Llanelli); N Jenkins (Pontypridd), Robert Jones (Swansea); M Griffiths (Cardiff), G Jenkins (Swansea), S John (Llanelli), H Taylor (Cardiff), Gareth Llewellyn (Neath), D Jones (Cardiff), R Collins (Pontypridd), E Lewis (Cardiff). New cap: John.

Referee: S Lander, England.

Saturday, 18th March 1995　　　　　　　　　　　　　　　　　**At Twickenham**

ENGLAND 24　SCOTLAND 12

Dropped-goal: Andrew
Penalty-goals: Andrew (7)

Dropped-goals: Chalmers (2)
Penalty-goals: G Hastings (2)

H.T. 12-6.

ENGLAND: M Catt (Bath); T Underwood (Leicester), W Carling (Harlequins)(captain), J Guscott (Bath), R Underwood (Leicester/RAF); R Andrew (Wasps), K Bracken (Bristol); J Leonard (Harlequins), B Moore (Harlequins), V Ubogu (Bath), T Rodber (Northampton/Army), M Johnson (Leicester), M Bayfield (Northampton), B Clarke (Bath), D Richards (Leicester). Replacement: S Ojomoh (Bath) for Richards 51 minutes. Temporary replacements: D Morris (Orrell) for Bracken 18-23 minutes, G Rowntree (Leicester) for Leonard 65-78 minutes. New cap: Rowntree.

SCOTLAND: G Hastings (Watsonians)(captain); C Joiner (Melrose), S Hastings (Watsonians), G Townsend (Gala), K Logan (Stirling County); C Chalmers (Melrose), B Redpath (Melrose); D Hilton (Bath), K Milne (Heriot's FP), P Wright (Boroughmuir), R Wainwright (West Hartlepool), G Weir (Melrose), A Campbell (Dundee High School FP), I Morrison (London Scottish), E Peters (Bath). Replacment: J Manson (Dundee High School FP) for Hilton 45 minutes. New cap: Manson.

Referee: B Stirling, Ireland.

NB: This was England's third Grand Slam in five seasons.

WALES 12   IRELAND 16

Penalty-goals: N Jenkins (4)

Try: Mullin
Dropped-goal: Burke
Penalty-goal: Burke
Conversion: Burke

H.T. 6-13

WALES: M Back (Bridgend); I Evans (Llanelli)(captain), N   Davies (Llanelli), M Hall (Cardiff), W Proctor (Llanelli); N Jenkins (Pontypridd), Robert Jones (Swansea); M Griffiths (Cardiff), G Jenkins (Swansea), S John (Llanelli), A Gibbs (Newbridge), Gareth Llewellyn (Neath), P Davies (Llanelli), R Collins (Pontypridd), E Lewis (Cardiff). New cap: Gibbs.

IRELAND: J Staples (Harlequins); R Wallace (Garryowen), B   Mullin (Blackrock College), P Danaher (Garryowen), S Geoghegan (Bath); E Elwood (Lansdowne), N Hogan (Terenure College); N Popplewell (Wasps), T Kingston (Dolphin)(captain), P Clohessy (Young Munster), A Foley (Shannon), G Fulcher (Cork Constitution), D Tweed (Ballymena), E Halvey (Shannon), P Johns (Dungannon). Replacement: P Burke (Cork Constitution) for Elwood 18 minutes. New cap: Halvey.

Referee: R Megson, Scotland.

NB: This was the second time Wales have been whitewashed in their whole history.

FINAL TABLE

	P	W	L	F	A	Pts
England	4	4	0	98	39	8
Scotland	4	3	1	87	71	6
France	4	2	2	77	70	4
Ireland	4	1	3	44	83	2
Wales	4	0	4	43	86	0

OTHER INTERNATIONALS

AUSTRALIA 20   NEW ZEALAND 16

Tries: Little (1), Kearns (1)
Penalty-goals: Knox (2)
Conversions: Knox (2)

Try: Howarth
Penalty-goals: Howarth (3)
Conversion: Howarth

H.T. 17-6.

AUSTRALIA: M Pini (Queensland); D Campese (New South Wales), J Little (Queensland), P Howard (Queensland), D Smith (Queensland); D Knox (New South Wales), G Gregan (Australian Capital Territory); A Daly (New South Wales), P Kearns (New South Wales)(captain), E McKenzie (New South Wales), W Ofahengaue (New South Wales), G Morgan (Queensland), J Eales (Queensland), D Wilson (Queensland), T Gavin (New South Wales). Replacement: D Junee (New South Wales) for Pini 69 minutes. No new caps.

NEW ZEALAND: S Howarth (Auckland); J Wilson (Otago), F Bunce (North Harbour), W Little (North Harbour), J Timu (Otago); S Bachop (Otago), G Bachop (Canterbury); R Loe (Canterbury), S Fitzpatrick (Auckland)(captain), O Brown (Auckland), M Brewer (Canterbury), M Cooksley (Counties), I Jones (North Auckland), M Jones (Auckland), Z Brooke (Auckland). Temporary replacement: B Larsen (North Harbour) for Brooke 35 to 38 minutes. No new caps.

Referee: E Morrison, England.

UNDER 21 INTERNATIONAL

IRELAND 12   ENGLAND 8

Penalty-goals: Mason (4)

Try: Naylor

H.T. 6-5. Penalty-goal: Stimpson

IRELAND: S Mason (Newcastle Gosforth); M Dillon (Lansdowne), J Bell (Ballymena), D Blewitt (Queen's University, Belfast), R Kearns (Blackrock College); F Campion (St Mary's College), R Saverimutto (Waterloo); W O'Kelly (Lansdowne), J Blaney (Terenure College), C Boyd (Currie), A Foley (Shannon), K Spicer (University College, Dublin)(captain), J Davidson (Dungannon), K Dawson (Bangor), C McEntee (Greystones).

ENGLAND: T Stimpson (West Hartlepool); A Healey (Orrell), M Denney (Wasps), J Keyter (Harlequins), J Naylor (Orrell); S Howard (Blackheath), A Gomersall (Wasps); M Volland (Northampton), G McCarthy (Bath), N Webber (Moseley), P Scrivener (Wasps), G Archer (Newcastle Gosforth), R Metcalfe (Newcastle Gosforth), K Yates (Wakefield), M Corry (Newcastle Gosforth)(captain).

Referee: D Davies, Wales.

WALES 20   ROMANIA 8

Tries: G Thomas (1), M Thomas (1), Horgan (1)
Penalty-goal: Griffiths
Conversion: Griffitha

Try: I Ionel
Penalty-goal: Valentin

H.T. 5-0.

WALES: J Thomas (Cardiff Institute); G Thomas (Bridgend), J Hewlett (Cardiff), G Jones (Bridgend), C Moir (Northampton); L Griffiths (Swansea), P Horgan (Aberavon); C Loader (Swansea)(captain), M Thomas (Swansea), S John (Llanelli), C Billen (Pontypool), S Martin (Cardiff Institute), S Johnson, (Llanelli), R Morris (Neath), P Beard (Cardiff). Replacement: J Strange (Llanelli) for Griffiths 76 minutes.

ROMANIA: M Valentin; T Dorin, V Mihai, F Radu, R Ionel; H Vasile, A Iulian; B Cristian, B Eduard, A Mihai, T Adrian (captain), M Adrian, D Marius, S Florin, I Ionel. Replacements: P Constantin for Radu 24 minutes, M Razvan for Eduard 48 minutes.

Referee: J Pearson, England.

'A' INTERNATIONAL

Saturday, 7th January 1995   At McDiarmid Park, Perth
SCOTLAND 'A' 18   ITALY 16

Tries: Peters (1), Redpath (1)   Try: Troiani
Penalty-goals: Shepherd (1), Glasgow (1)   Penalty-goals: Dominguez (3)
Conversion: Glasgow   Conversion: Dominguez

H.T. 8-3.

SCOTLAND 'A': R Shepherd (Edinburgh Academicals); C Joiner (Melrose), I Jardine (Stirling County), R Eriksson (London Scottish), C Glasgow (Heriot's FP); D Hodge (Watsonians), B Redpath (Melrose); D Hilton (Bath), K McKenzie (Stirling County)(captain), P Wright (Boroughmuir), F Wallace (Glasgow High/Kelvinside), D Cronin (Bourges), S Campbell (Dundee High School FP), E Peters (Bath), I Smith (Gloucester).

ITALY: L Troiani; M Ravazzolo, I Francescato, S Bonomi, Marcello Cuttitta; D Dominguez, A Troncon; Massimo Cuttitta (captain), C Orlandi, F Properzi-Curti, O Arancio, R Favaro, M Giacheri, A Sgorlon, D Scaglia. Replacement: J Gardner for Sgorlon 60 mins.

Referee: G Black, Ireland.

At Donnybrook, Dublin
IRELAND 20   ENGLAND 21

Tries: David O'Mahony (1), Mulcahy (1)   Tries: Diprose (1), Back (1)
Penalty-goals: McGowan (2)   Dropped-goal: Grayson
Conversions: McGowan (2)   Penalty-goals: Grayson (2)
                                            Conversion: Grayson

H.T. 10-8.

IRELAND: J Staples (Harlequins); R Wallace (Garryowen), M McCall (Bangor), M Field (Malone), Daragh O'Mahony (University College, Dublin); A McGowan (Blackrock College), David O'Mahony (Cork Constitution); J Fitzgerald (Young Munster), W Mulcahy (Skerries), P Wallace (Blackrock College), E Halvey (Shannon), D Tweed (Ballymena), R Costello (Garryowen), D McBride (Malone)(captain), B Cronin (Garryowen).

ENGLAND: A Tunningley (Saracens); D Hopley (Wasps), S Potter (Leicester), N Greenstock (Wasps), J Sleightholme (Bath); P Grayson (Northampton), S Bates (Wasps)(captain); R Hardwick (Coventry), M Regan (Bristol), J Mallett (Bath), L Dallaglio (Wasps), G Archer (Newcastle Gosforth), S Shaw (Bristol), N Back (Leicester), A Diprose (Saracens).

Referee: N Lasaga, France.

At Hughenden, Glasgow
SCOTLAND 9   FRANCE 13

Penalty-goals: Laing (3)   Try: Hallinger
                                            Penalty-goals: Bellot (2)
                                            Conversion: Bellot

H.T. 6-0

SCOTLAND: R Shepherd (Edinburgh Academicalas); H Gilmour (Heriot's FP), S Hastings (Watsonians), R Eriksson (London Scottish), C Dalgleish (Gala); S Laing (Instonians), G Burns (Stewart's- Melville FGP); J Manson (Dundee High School FP), J Hay (Hawick), D Herrington (Dundee High School FP), F Wallace (Glasgow High/Kelvinside), R Scott (London Scottish), J Richardson (Edinburgh Academicals)(captain), I Smith (Gloucester), S Reid (Boroughmuir).

FRANCE: O Campan (Agen); D Venditi (Bourgoin), P Carbonneau (Toulouse), T Castaignede (Toulouse), P Bernat-Salles (Pau); B Bellot (Graulhet), A Hueber (Toulon)(captain); E Menieu (Montferrand), F Landreau (Grenoble), P Gallart (Beziers), N Hallinger (Colomiers), O Brouzet (Grenoble), A Berthozat (Begles-Bordeaux), S Dispagne (Narbonne), A Costes (Montferrand). Replacement: S Loubsens (Begles-Bordeaux) for Bernat-Salles 39 minutes.

Referee: G Gadjovich, Canada.

SPECIAL INTERNATIONAL

Saturday, 21st January 1995   **At Murrayfield**

SCOTLAND 22   CANADA 6

Try: Cronin   Penalty-goals: Rees (2)
Penalty-goals: Hastings (5)
Conversion: Hastings

H.T. 12-6.

SCOTLAND: G Hastings (Watsonians)(captain); C Joiner (Melrose), I Jardine (Stirling County), G Townsend (Gala), K Logan (Stirling County); C Chalmers (Melrose), B Redpath (Melrose); D Hilton (Bath), K Milne (Heriot's FP), P Wright (Boroughmuir), R Wainwright (Newcastle Gosforth), D Cronin (Bath), A Campbell (Dundee High School FP), I Morrison (London Scottish), E Peters (Bath). New caps: Hilton, Campbell, Peters.

CANADA (British Columbia unless stated): S Stewart; W Stanley, C Stewart (Western Province/Rovigo), S Gray, R Toews; G Rees (Oxford University/Newport)(captain), J Graf; E Evans, M Cardinal, D Jackart, I Gordon, M James, K Whitley (Alberta), G MacKinnon, C McKenzie. Replacement: J Hutchinson for Whitley 38 minutes. New Cap. Whitley.

Referee: C Thomas, Wales.

UNDER 21 INTERNATIONAL

Friday, 3rd February 1995   **At Myreside, Edinburgh**

SCOTLAND 22   IRELAND 24

Try: Dalgleish   Tries: Dillon (1), penalty try
Penalty-goals: Easson (5)   Dropped-goal: Campion
Conversion: Easson   Penalty-goals: Campion (3)
                                  Conversions: Campion (2)

H.T. 16-8

SCOTLAND: P Flockhart (Stewart's-Melville FP); H R Gilmour (Heriot's FP), R Brown (Melrose), M McGrandles (Stirling County), C Dalgleish (Gala); B Easson (Boroughmuir), A Featherstone (Morgan Academy FP); M McCluskie (Edinbury Academicals), G Bulloch (West of Scotland), B Stewart (Edinburgh Academicals), S Grimes (Edinburgh University), I Elliot (Hawick), P Jennings (Boroughmuir), D Clark (Stewart's-Melville FP), G Dall (Heriot's FP)(captain). Replacement: D Cunningham (Boroughmuir) for Bulloch 33 minutes. Temporary replacement: D Massey (Currie) for Cunningham 64-70 minutes.

IRELAND: S Mason (Newcastle-Gosforth); M Dillon (Lansdowne), A Thompson (Shannon), D Blewitt (Queen's University, Belfast), R Kearns (Blackrock College); F Campion (St Mary's College), R Saverimutto (Waterloo); J Hickey (Shannon), J Blaney (Terenure College), C Boyd (Currie), S Patterson (Dungannon), K Spicer (University College, Dublin)(captain), J Davidson (Dungannon), K Dawson (Bangor), C McEntee (Greystones).

Referee: J Wallis, England.

'A' INTERNATIONAL

Friday, 3rd February 1995   At Leicester

ENGLAND 29   FRANCE 9

Tries: Regan (1), Sleightholme (1)   Penalty-goals: Charvet (3)
Dropped-goals: Harris (2)
Penalty-goals: Harris (3)
Conversions: Harris (2)

H.T. 17-3

ENGLAND: P Hull (Bristol); D Hopley (Wasps), S Potter (Leicester), N Greenstock ((Wasps), J Sleightholme ((Bath); J Harris (Leicester), S Bates (Wasps)(captain); R Hardwick (Coventry), M Regan (Bristol) D Garforth (Leicester), L Dallaglio (Wasps), G Archer (Newcastle Gosforth), S Shaw (Bristol), N Back (Leicester), Diprose (Saracens).
Replacements: H Thorneycroft (Northampton) for Hopley 62 minutes, C Clark (Bath) for Garforth 76 minutes.
FRANCE: O Campan (Agen); W Techoueyres (SBUC), P Carbonneau (Toulouse), S Loubsens (Mont-de-Marsan), R Arbo (Perpignan); D Charvet (Racing Club), A Hueber (Toulon); E Menieu (Montferrand), F Landreau (Grenoble), P Gallart (Beziers), A Costes (Montferrand), A Berthozat (Begles), C Deslandes (Racing Club), S Dispagne (Narbonne), L Loppy (Toulon). Sent-off: Menieu 76 minutes.
Referee: A Lewis, Ireland.

At Myreside, Edinburgh

SCOTLAND 24   IRELAND 18

Tries: Stanger (2)   Tries: Wallace (1), McCall (1)
Penalty-goals: Laing (4)   Dropped-goal: McGowan
Conversion: Laing   Penalty-goal: McGowan
Conversion: Malone

H.T. 9-8

SCOTLAND: R Shepherd (Edinburgh Academicals); H Gilmour (Heriot's FP), A Stanger (Hawick), S Hastings (Watsonians), D Stark (Boroughmuir); S Laing (Instonians), G Burns (Stewart's-Melville FP); I Manson (Dundee High School FP), M Scott (Orrell), S Paul (Heriot's FP), F Wallace (Glasgow High/Kelvinside), J Richardson (Edinburgh Academicals)(captain), R Scott (London Scottish), I Smith (Gloucester), S Reid (Boroughmuir).
IRELAND: P Murray (Shannon); R Wallace (Garryowen), L Boyle (Harlequins), M McCall (Bangor)(captain), D O'Mahony (University College, Dublin); A McGowan (Blackrock College), D O'Mahony (Cork Constitution); J Fitzgerald (Young Munster), B Mulcahy (Skerries), P Wallace (Blackrock College), E Halvey (Shannon), D Tweed (Ballymena), R Costello (Garryowen), D Corkery (Cork Constitution), R Wilson (Instonians). Replacements: N Malone (Leicester) for Boyle 48 minutes, C Clarke (Lansdowne) for McGowan 56 minutes.
Referee: B Campsall, England.

UNDER 21 INTERNATIONAL

Friday, 17th February 1995   At Evry (near Paris)

FRANCE 35   SCOTLAND 12

Tries: Barrague (2), Giordani (1)   Penalty-goals: Easson (4)
Azam (1), Castaignede (1)
Penlty-goals: Castaignede (2)
Conversions: Castaignede (2)

H.T. 13-9

FRANCE: N Nadau (PUC); W Olombel (Beziers), T Lombard (Racing Club), R Paillat (Brive), P Giordani (Dax); T Castaignede (Toulouse), S Bonnet (Brive)(captain); P Collazo (Begles-Bordeaux), O Azam (Tarbes),

L Dehez (Montferrand), S Besten (Biarritz), S Chinarro (Perpignan), M Macurdy (Racing Club), M Barrague (Begles-Bordeaux), L Mallid (Grenoble). Replacement: G Bastide (Brive) for Olombel 77 minutes.

SCOTLAND: P Flockhart (Stewart's-Melville FP); H Gilmour (Heriot's FP), R Brown (Melrose), M McGrandles (Stirling County), C Murray (Hawick); B Easson (Boroughmuir), J Weston (Watsonians); M McCluskie (Edinburgh Academicals), N Dickson (Boroughmuir), L Graham (Boroughmuir), T McVie (Edinburgh Academicals), G Perrett (West of Scotland), P Jennings (Boroughmuir), D Clark (Stewart's-Melville FP), G Dall (Heriot's FP)(captain).

Referee: H Rohr, Germany.

'A' INTERNATIONAL

Sunday, 19th February 1995   **At Kingsholm, Gloucester**

ENGLAND 33   ITALY 9

Tries: Thorneycroft (1), Bates(1)   Penalty-goals: Troiani (3)
Sleightholme (1), Hill (1)
Penalty-goals: Harris (3)
Conversions: Harris (2)

H.T. 28-3.

ENGLAND: P Hull (Bristol/RAF); J Sleightholme (Bath), N Greenstock (Wasps), S Potter (Leicester), H Thorneycroft (Northampton); J Harris (Leicester), S Bates (Wasps)(captain); R Hardwick (Coventry), R Cockerill (Leicester), D Garforth (Leicester), L Dallaglio (Wasps), G Archer (Newcastle Gosforth), S Shaw (Bristol), R Hill (Saracens), A Diprose (Saracens). Replacement: C Wilkins (Wasps) for Shaw 63 minutes. Temporary replacement: C Clark (Bath) for Garforth 21-22 minutes.

ITALY: J Pertile (Roma); S Crotti (Milan), S Bordon (Rovigo), M Piovene (L'Aquila), F Mazzariol (Treviso); L Troiani (L'Aquila)(captain), G Faltiba (Sandona); G Grespan (Treviso), G de Carli (Roma), A Castellina (L'Aquila), M Capuzzoni (Milan), R Cassina (Casela), M Giacheri (treviso), A Sgorlon (Sandona), D Scaglia (Tarvisum). Replacement: G Cicono (L'Aquila) for Scaglia 72 minutes.

Referee: D Gillet, France.

UNDER 21 INTERNATIONAL

Friday, 3rd March 1995   **At Inverleith, (Edinburgh)**

SCOTLAND 15   WALES 9

Penalty-goals: Hodge (5)   Dropped-goal: A Thomas
     Penalty-goals: A Thomas (2)

H.T. 6-6

SCOTLAND: P Flockhart (Stewart's-Melville FP); H Gilmour (Heriot's FP), M McGrandles (Stirling County), C Murray (Hawick), C Morley (Bath); D Hodge (Watsonians), E Weston (Watsonians); M McCluskie (Edinburgh Academicals), G Bulloch (West of Scotland), B Stewart (Edinburgh Academicals), T McVie (Edinburgh Academicals), I Elliot (Hawick), P Jennings (Boroughmuir), G Dall (Heriot's FP)(captain), D Clark (Stewart's-Melville FP). Replacements: S Grimes (Edinburgh University) for Clark 38 minutes, I Leighton (Melrose) for Murray 75 minutes.

WALES: M Evans (Cardiff IHE); O Thomas (Cardiff), R Jones (Neath), G Thomas (Bridgend), C Moir (Northampton); A Thomas (Neath), J Hewlett (Cardiff); C Loader (Swansea)(captain), M Thomas (Swansea), L Manning (Bridgend), A Quinnell (Llanelli), C Billen (Pontypool), S Ford (Aberavon), P Beard (Cardiff), A Moore (Swansea). Replacements: P Horgan (Aberavon) for Hewlett 43 minutes, C Stephens (Maesteg) for Moore 56-58 minutes (temporary) and 80 minutes.

Referee: A Watson, Ireland.

NB: This was Scotland's first win at Under 21 level since 1986 when Italy were beaten.

WALES 16 IRELAND 9

Tries: G Thomas (1), Jones (1) Penalty-goals: Begley (3)
Penalty-goals: A Thomas (2)

H.T. 13-6

WALES: M Evans (Cardiff IHE); O Thomas (Cardiff), R Jones (Neath), G Thomas (Bridgend), C Moir (Northampton); A Thomas (Neath), J Hewlett (Cardiff); C Loader (Swansea)(captain), M Thomas (Swansea), L Manning (Bridgend), C Quinnell (Llanelli), C Billen (Pontypool), S Ford (Aberavon), P Beard (Cardiff), A Moore (Swansea). Replacements: J Savastano (Cardiff) for Quinnell 62 minutes, D Morris (Neath) for Manning 77 minutes.

IRELAND: B Begley (Old Crescent); M Dillon (Lansdowne), A Thompson (Shannon), D Blewitt (Queen's University, Belfast), D Hickey (Shannon); F Campion (St Mary's College), C McGuinness (St Mary's College); W O'Kelly (Lansdowne), J Blaney (Terenure College), C Boyd (Currie), K Spicer (University College, Dublin)(captain), J Davidson (Dungannon), M O'Kelly (St Mary's College), K Dawson (Bangor), E Miller (Old Wesley). Replacement: T Brennan for M O'Kelly 65 minutes.

Referee: J Bacigalupo, Scotland.

'A' INTERNATIONAL

Friday, 17th March 1995 Pontypridd

WALES 30 IRELAND 19

Tries: Williams (2), Taylor (1), Thomas (1) Tries: Wilson (1),
Penalty-goals: Evans (2) Daragh O'Mahony (1)
Conversions: Evans (2) Penalty-goals: O'Shea (3)

H.T. 18-5

WALES: J Thomas (Cardiff Institute); D Manley (Pontypridd), M Taylor (Pontypool), D Edwards (Leicester), S Hill (Cardiff); D Evans (Treorchy), P John (Pontypridd)(captain); A Dibble (Treorchy), J Humphreys (Cardiff), L Mustoe (Cardiff), C Wyatt (Neath), G Prosser (Pontypridd), A Copsey (Llanelli), M Bennett (Cardiff), O Williams (Cardiff).

IRELAND: C O'Shea (Lansdowne); Daragh O'Mahony (University College, Dublin), L Boyle (Harlequins), M McCall (Bangor)(captain), N Woods (Blackrock College); A McGowan (Blckrock College), David O'Mahony (Cork Constitution); J Fitzgerald (Young Munster), B Mulcahy (Skerries), P Wallace (Blackrock College), S Rooney (Lansdowne), M Galwey (Shannon), N Francis (Old Belvedere), L Toland (Old Crescent), R Wilson (Instonians).

Referee: E Morrison, England.

'A' REPRESENTATIVE MATCH

Saturday, 18th March 1995 In Durban

NATAL 33 ENGLAND 'A' 25

Tries: Allan (1), Small (1) Tries: Hunter (1), Potter (1)
Dropped-goal: Honiball Dropped-goal: Grayson
Penalty-goals: Honiball (6) Penalty-goals: Grayson (4)
Conversion: Honiball

H.T. 16-17

NATAL: H Reece-Edwards; C van der Westhuizen, D Muir, P Muller, J Small; H Honiball, K Putt; R Kempson, J Allan, A Garvey, W Bartmann (captain), M Andrews, S Atherton, D Kriese, G Teichmann. Replacements: J

Thompson for Muller 51 minutes, W van Heerden for Kriese 64 minutes.
ENGLAND 'A': P Hull (Bristol); I Hunter (Northampton), S Potter (Leicester), D Hopley (Wasps), J Sleightholme (Bath); P Grayson (Northampton), M Dawson (Northampton), R Hardwick (Coventry), M Regan (Bristol), D Garforth (Leicester), J Hall (Bath)(captain), G Archer (Newcastle Gosforth), R West (Gloucester), N Back (Leicester), A Diprose (Saracens).
Referee: J Neethling, Boland.

SPECIAL INTERNATIONAL

Saturday, 8th April 1995   In Bucharest

ROMANIA 15   FRANCE 24

Dropped-goals: Nichitean (3)
Penalty-goals: Nichitean (2)

Tries: Sadourny (1), penalty try
Penalty-goals: Lacroix (4)
Conversion: Lacroix

H.T. 12-6

ROMANIA: V Brici (Farul Constanta); L Colceriu (Steaua Bucharest), N Racean (Cluj University), R Gontineac (Cluj University), G Solomie (Timosoara University); N Nichitean (Cluj University), D Neaga (Dinamo Bucharest); G Leonte (Vienne), V Tufa (Dinamo Bucharest), L Costea (Steaua Bucharest), T Oroian (Steaua Bucharest), C Ciorascu (Auch), C Cojocariu (Bayonne), A Gealapu (Steaua Bucharest), T Brinza (Cluj University)(captain).

In Suva

FIJI 10   CANADA 22

Try: Sorovaki
Dropped-goal: Turueva
Conversion: Sorovaki

Tries: C Stewart (1), Rees (1), Evans (1)
Penalty-goal: Rees
Conversions: Rees (2)

UNDER 21 INTERNATIONAL

Saturday, 15th April 1995   At Bridgehaugh, Stirling

SCOTLAND 36   ITALY 15

Tries: Morley (2), Dall (1)
McVie (1)
Penalty-goals: Hodge (4)
Conversions: Hodge (2)

Tries: Marchetti (2)
Dropped-goal: Pilat
Conversion: Pilat

SCOTLAND: P Flockhart (Stewart's-Melville FP); H Gilmour (Heriot's FP), M McGrandles (Stirling County), C Murray (Hawick) C Morley (Bath); D Hodge (Watsonians), A Featherstone (Morgan Academy FP); M McCluskie (Edinburgh Academicals), G Bulloch (West of Scotland), B Stewart (Edinburgh Academicals), S Grimes (Edinburgh University), I Elliot (Hawick), P Jennings (Boroughmuir), G Dall (Heriot's FP)(captain), T McVie (Edinburgh Academicals).
ITALY: A Pavin (Paese); L Gorla (Sandrio), A Lomasto (Partenope), T Visentin (Treviso), V Marrano (Roma); C Pilat (Bologna), L Martin (Padova); F Guidetti (Parma), A Comperti (L'Aquila), S Saviozzi (Livorno), F Piovan (Padova0, A Gritti (Bologna0, F Gumiero (San Dona), R Rampazzo (Padova), D Bezzati (Padova). Replacements: R Marchetti (Padova) for Marrano 52 minutes, G Mazzi (Roma) for Martin 54 minutes.
Referee: H Lewis, Wales.

SPECIAL INTERNATIONAL

SCOTLAND 49   ROMANIA 16

Tries: Stanger (2), G Hastings (1), Shiel (1),
Peters (1), Joiner (1), Logan (1)
Penalty-goals: G Hastings (2)
Conversions: G Hastings (4)

Try: Racean
Penalty-goals: Nichitean (3)
Conversion: Nichitean (1)

H.T. 19-6.

SCOTLAND: G Hastings (Watsonians)(captain); C Joiner (Melrose), A Stanger (Hawick), G Shiel (Melrose), K Logan (Stirling County); C Chalmers (Melrose), B Redpath (Melrose); D Hilton (Bath), K McKenzie (Stirling County), P Wright (Boroughmuir), R Wainwright (West Hartlepool), G Weir (Melrose), S Campbell (Dundee High School FP), I Morrison (London Scottish), E Peters (Bath). Replacement: S Hastings (Watsonians) for G Hastings 78 minutes. No new caps.

ROMANIA: V Brici(Farul Constanta); R Cioca (Dinamo Bucharest), R Racean (Cluj University), R Gontineac (Cluj University), G Solomie (Timosoara University); N Nichitean (Cluj University), D Neaga (Dinamo Bucharest); G Leonte (Vienne), V Tufa (Dinamo Bucharest), L Costea (Steaua Bucharest), T Oroian (Steua Bucharest),S Ciorascu (Auch), C Cojocariu (Bayonne), A Gealapu (Steaua Bucharest), T Brinza (Cluj University)(captain). Replacement: C Draguceanu (Steaua Bucharest) for Gealapu 53 minutes. No New caps.
Referee: N Lasaga, France.

JAPAN 25   ROMANIA 30

JAPAN 34   ROMANIA 21

ITALY 22   IRELAND 12

Try: Vaccari
Dropped-goal Dominguez
Penalty-goals; Dominguez (4)
Conversion: Dominguez

Penalty-goals: Burke (4)

H.T. 9-12

ITALY (Milan unless stated): P Vaccari; M Ravazzolo (Calvisano), I Francescato, M Bonomi, Marcello Cuttita; D Dominguez, A Troncon; Massimo Cuttitta (Captain), C Orlandi (Piacenza), F Properzi Curti, O Arancio (Catania), R Favaro (Treviso), C Giacheri (Treviso), J Gardner (Roma), P Pedroni.

UNDER-21 INTERNATIONAL

ITALY 6   ENGLAND 22

Tries: Jones (1), Anderson (1)
Penalty-goals: Ufton (4)

ENGLAND UNDER-21: J Ufton (Wasps); S Jones (West Hartlepool), J Shepherd (Morley), M Denney (Bristol), E Anderson (Moseley); S Binns (Leicester), M Chudleigh (Bristol); M Volland (Northampton), N McCarthy (Bath), W Green (Wasps), G Seely (Northampton), J Stow (Morley), S Hart (Leicester), A Pountney (Northampton), P Scrivener (Wasps)(captain). Replacements: A Blyth (Tynedale), S Howard (Blackheath), S Benton (Morley), P Shadbolt (Blackheath), S Kneale (West Hartlepool), N Webber (Moseley), R Poll (Moseley).
SCORERS: Tries: Jones (1), Anderson (1). Pens: Ufton (4).

CIS COUNTY CHAMPIONSHIP

NORTHERN GROUP

1ST MATCHES (Tuesday, 15th November 1994)
Cheshire 3   Lancashire 16
Cumbria 15   Northumberland 10
Durham 5   Yorkshire 13

2ND MATCHES (Saturday, 19th November 1994)
Cheshire 10   Cumbria 6
Lancashire 43   Durham 8
Northumberland 30   Yorkshire 14

3RD MATCHES (Saturday, 26th November 1994)
Cheshire 17   Northumberland 19
Cumbria 6   Durham 5
Yorkshire 27   Lancashire 27

4TH MATCHES (Saturday, 3rd December 1994)
Cumbria 24   Lancashire 17
Northumberland 11   Durham 3
Yorkshire 49   Cheshire 19

5TH MATCHES (Saturday, 10th December 1994)
Durham 5   Cheshire 6
Lancashire 8   Northumberland 17
Yorkshire 25   Cumbria 18

FINALS TABLES

	P	W	D	L	F	A	Pts
Northumberland	5	4	0	1	87	57	8
Yorkshire	5	3	1	1	128	99	7
Cumbria	5	3	0	2	69	67	6
Lancashire	5	2	1	2	111	79	5
Cheshire	5	2	0	3	55	95	4
Durham	5	0	0	5	26	79	0

Northumberland qualify for National semi-finals

MIDLANDS GROUP
GROUP 'A'

Leicestershire 13   North Midlands 14
Staffordshire 12   Leicestershire 15
North Midlands 17   Staffordshire 25

FINALS TABLES

	P	W	D	L	F	A	Pts
Staffordshire	2	1	0	1	37	32	2
Leicestershire	2	1	0	1	28	26	2
North Midlands	2	1	0	1	31	38	2

GROUP 'B'

Warwickshire 70   East Midlands 3
East Midlands 29   Notts., Lincs. & Derbys 31
Notts., Lincs. & Derbys 8   Warwickshire 42

FINALS TABLES

	P	W	D	L	F	A	Pts
Warwickshire	2	1	0	1	112	11	4
Notts.,Lincs,Derbys	2	1	0	1	39	71	2
East Midlands	2	0	0	2	32	101	0

Semi-finals (Saturday, 3rd December 1994)
Staffordshire 18   Notts., Lincs. & Derbys 8
Warwickshire 21   Leicestershire 8

Final (Saturday, 10th December 1994. At Coventry)
Warwickshire 30   Staffordshire 3
(Warwickshire qualify for National semi-finals)

SOUTHERN GROUP
POOL 1

FIRST MATCH (Saturday, 19th November 1994)
Surrey 42   Hertfordshire 7

SECOND MATCH (Saturday, 26th November 1994)
Hertfordshire 18   Somerset 14

THIRD MATCH (Saturday, 3rd December 1994)
Somerset 27   Surrey 20

FINALS TABLES

	P	W	D	L	F	A	Pts
Surrey	2	1	0	1	62	34	2
Somerset	2	1	0	1	41	38	2
Hertfordshire	2	1	0	1	25	56	2

Surrey qualify for Group semi-finals.

POOL 2
FIRST MATCHES
Buckinghamshire 16   Sussex 18
Gloucestershire 25   Devon 12

SECOND MATCHES
Devon 16   Sussex 13
Gloucestershire 44   Buckinghamshire 13

THIRD MATCHES
Buckinghamshire 3   Devon 3
Sussex 19   Gloucestershire 42

FINALS TABLES

	P	W	D	L	F	A	Pts
Gloucestershire	3	3	0	0	108	44	6
Devon	3	1	1	1	31	41	3
Sussex	3	1	0	2	50	74	2
Buckinghamshire	3	0	1	2	32	62	1

Gloucestershire qualify for Group semi-finals.

FIRST MATCHES
Hampshire 40   Oxfordshire 15
Kent 49 Eastern   Counties 32
SECOND MATCHES
Hampshire 20   Kent 24
Oxfordshire 19   Eastern Counties 37
THIRD MATCHES
Eastern Counties 18   Hampshire 21
Kent 62   Oxfordshire 0

FINALS TABLES	P	W	D	L	F	A	Pts
Kent	3	3	0	0	135	52	6
Hampshire	3	2	0	1	81	57	4
Eastern Counties	3	1	0	2	89	89	2
Oxfordshire	3	0	0	3	34	141	0

Kent qualify for Group semi-finals

FIRST MATCHES
Cornwall 16   Middlesex 17
Dorset & Wiltshire 13   Berkshire 28
SECOND MATCHES
Cornwall 39   Dorset & Wiltshire 15
Middlesex 13   Berkshire 18
THIRD MATCHES
Berkshire 22   Cornwall 11
Dorset & Wiltshire 6   Middlesex 58

FINALS TABLES	P	W	D	L	F	A	Pts
Berkshire	3	3	0	0	68	37	6
Middlesex	3	2	0	1	88	40	4
Cornwall	3	1	0	2	66	54	2
Dorset & Wilts	3	0	0	3	34	125	0

Berkshire qualify for Group semi-finals

Quarter-finals (Saturday, 28th January 1995. At Reading)
Berkshire 25   Kent 12
(Sunday, 5th February. At Cheltenham)
Gloucestershire 23   Surrey 6

SEMI-FINALS

Saturday, 11th March 1995   At Tynedale

NORTHUMBERLAND 14   GLOUCESTERSHIRE 13

Tries: Wilkinson (2)   Try: D Morgan
Conversions: Johnson (2)   Penalty-goals: Smith (2)
                                        Conversion: Smith

H.T. 7-10

NORTHUMBERLAND: A Blyth (Tynedale); G Ward (Novocastrians), R Wilkinson (Newcastle Gosforth), I Chandler (Newcastle Gosforth), D Rees (Sale); D Johnson (Blaydon), S Clayton-Hibbert (Tynedale); R Parker (Tynedale), E Parker (Tynedale)(captain), D Clark (Morpeth), N Frankland (Newcastle Gosforth), K Westgarth (West Hartlepool), R Metcalfe (Newcastle Gosforth), R Hoole (Edinburgh Academicals), D Guthrie (Blaydon). Temporary replacement: M Carr (Percy Park) for Wilkinson 51-56 minutes.

GLOUCESTERSHIRE: T Smith (Gloucester); D John (Bristol), A Williams (Bristol), I Morgan (Gloucester), D Morgan (Cheltenham); M Hamlin (Gloucester)(captain), J Davis (Lydney); G Williams (Lydney), N Nelmes (Lydney), S Baldwin (Gloucester Old Boys), R Fowke (Gloucester), T Clink (Cheltenham), R Blake (Clifton), A Stanley (Gloucester), I Patten (Bristol).

Referee: B Campsall, Yorkshire.

At Rugby

WARWICKSHIRE 31   BERKSHIRE 5

Tries: Smallwood (1), Revan (1)   Try: Hart
Watson (1), Ruddlesdin (1)
Penalty-goals: Quantrill (3)
Conversion: Quantrill

H.T. 18-0

WARWICKSHIRE (Rugby unless stated); J Quantrill; A Smallwood (Nottingham), A Gillooly, M Palmer, D Watson: M Gallagher (Nottingham), M Warr (Sale); G Tregilgas (Coventry)(captain), D Addleton (Coventry), T Revan, A Ruddlesdin (Long Buckby), S Smith, P Bowman, M Ellis (Kenilworth), S Carter (Coventry).

BERKSHIRE (Reading unless stated); S Smith; M Richmond, S Kearns (captain), L Fanning, St J Ford (Maidenhead); S Rogers, C Phillips; A Greene (Maidenhead), R Kelham (London Irish), N Collins (Harlequins), M Hart (Maidenhead), M Atherton, D Pratt, I Armstrong, C Hutson.

Referee: D Reordon, United States.

Saturday, 22nd April 1995   At Twickenham

NORTHUMBERLAND 9   WARWICKSHIRE 15

Penalty-goals: Johnson (3)   Penalty-goals: Quantrill (5)

H.T. 6-9.

NORTHUMBERLAND: M Old (Tynedale); G Ward (Novocastrians), R Wilkinson (Newcastle Gosforth), I Chandler (Newcastle Gosforth), D Rees (Sale); D Johnson (Blaydon), S Clayton-Hibbott (Tynedale); R Parker (Tynedale)(captain), E Parker (Tynedale), D Clark (Morpeth), R Hoole (Edinburgh Academicals), K Westgarth (West Hartlepool), R Metcalfe (Newcastle Gosforth), N Frankland (Newcastle Gosforth), D Guthrie (Blaydon).

WARWICKSHIRE (Rugby unless stated): J Quantrill; A Smallwood (Nottingham), A Gillooly, M Palmer, D Watson; M Gallagher (Nottingham), M Warr (Sale); G Tregilgas (Coventry), D Addleton (Coventry), T revan, D Oram, S Smith, P Bowman, M Ellis (Kenilworth), S Carter (Coventry).

Referee: M Bayliss, Gloucestershire.

CIS DIVISIONAL CHAMPIONSHIP

1st Matches. Saturday, 19th November 1994   **At Bristol**

SOUTH WEST 18   LONDON 23

Tries: Hill (2)   Tries: Bates (10, Dallaglio (1)
Penalty-goals: Tainton (2)   Penalty-goals: Gregory (3)
Conversion: Tainton   Conversions: Gregory (2)

H.T. 15-10

SOUTH WEST (Bristol unless stated): A Lumsden (Bath); N Beal (Northampton), M Denney, S Morris (Gloucester), P Holford (Gloucester); M Tainton, R Kitchin (Harlequins)(captain); C Clark (Bath), M Regan, D Hinkins, R Armstrong, D Sims (Gloucester), A Blackmore, D Eves, R Hill (Saracens).

LONDON (Wasps unless stated): A Tunningley (Saracens); J Keyter (Harlequins), N Greenstock, G Childs, D O'Leary (Harlequins); G Gregory, S Bates (captain); D Molloy, G Botterman (Saracens), I Dunston, C Wilkins, A Diprose (Saracens), S Shaw (Bristol), L Dallaglio, D Ryan.

Referee: S Piercy, Yorkshire.

                                           At Otley

NORTH 10   MIDLANDS 12

Try: Vyvyan   Penalty-goals: Angell (4)
Penalty-goal: Greenwood
Conversion: Scully

H.T. 3-9

NORTH: W Greenwood (Harlequins); J Sleightholme (Bath), P Johnson (Orrell), S Ravenscroft (Saracens), A Healey (Orrell); N Ryan (Waterloo), D Scully (Wakefield)(captain); P Smith (Sale), S Mitchell (West Hartlepool), A Smith (Sale), C Vyvyan (Sale), D Baldwin (Sale), J Fowler (Sale), P Manley (Orrell), M Watson (West Hartlepool).

MIDLANDS (Leicester unless stated): M Mapletoft (Gloucester); S Hackney, S Potter, D Edwards, H Thorneycroft (Northampton); R Angell (Coventry), A Kardooni; R Hardwick (Coventry), R Cockerill, D Garforth, I Skingsley (Bedford), J Phillips (Northampton), R West (Gloucester), G Rees (Nottingham)(captain), C Tarbuck.

Referee: J Bacigalupo, Scotland.

2nd Matches. Saturday, 26th November 1994   **At Sudbury (Wasps RFC)**

LONDON 38   NORTH 16

Tries: Sheasby (3), Roiser (1), Gregory (1)   Try: Baldwin
Penalty-goals: Gregory (3)   Penalty-goals: Greenwood (2), Scully (1)
Conversions: Gregory (2)   Conversion: Greenwood

H.T. 11-16.

LONDON (Wasps unless stated): A Tunningley (Saracens); S Roiser, N Greenstock, G Childs, D O'Leary (Harlequins); G Gregory, S Bates (captain); D Molloy, G Botterman (Saracens), I Dunston, A Diprose (Saracens), M Greenwood, S Shaw (Bristol), L Dallaglio, C Sheasby (Harlequins).

NORTH: W Greenwood (Harlequins); J Sleightholme (Bath), P Johnson (Orrell), S Ravenscroft (Saracens), A Healey (Orrell); N Ryan (Waterloo), D Scully (Wakefield)(captain); P Smith (Sale), S Mitchell (West Hartlepool), A Smith (Sale), C Vyvyan (Sale), D Baldwin (Sale), J Fowler (Sale), P Manley (Orrell), M Watson (West Hartlepool). Replacement: A Brown (West Hartlepool) for Manley 49 minutes.
Referee: B Stirling, Ireland.

At Leicester

MIDLANDS 43 SOUTH WEST 23

Tries: Potter (1), Hackney (1)
Tarbuck (1), Skingsley (1), Hardwick (1)
Penalty-goals: Harris (4)
Conversions: Harris (3)

Tries: Eves (2)
Penalty-goals: Dix (3)
Conversions: Dix (2)

H.T. 25-13.

MIDLANDS (Leicester unless stated): R Angell (Coventry); S Hackney, S Potter, D Edwards, H Thorneycroft (Northampton); J Harris, A Kardooni; R Hardwick (Coventry), R Cockerill, D Garforth, I Skingsley (Bedford), R West (Gloucester), J Phillips (Northampton), G Rees (Nottingham)(captain), C Tarbuck. Replacement: D Bishop (Rugby) for Kardooni 72 minutes.
SOUTH WEST: L Anson (Narberth); M Beal (Northampton), M Denney (Bristol), S Morris (Gloucester), P Holford (Gloucester); R Dix (Cambridge University), R Kitchin (Harlequins)(captain); D Crompton (Bath), J Hawker (Gloucester), D Hinkins (Bristol), R Hill (Saracens), D Sims (Gloucester), C Yandell (Narberth), D Eves (Bristol), I Patten (Bristol). Replacements: A Turner (Exeter) for Anson 52 minutes, M Olsen (Bath) for Beal 75 minutes.
Referee: S Lander, Liverpool.

3rd Matches. Saturday, 3rd December 1994   **At Sudbury (Wasps RFC)**

LONDON 15 MIDLANDS 17

Penalty-goals: Greenwood (5)

Tries: Thorneycroft (2)
Penalty-goal: Angell
Conversions: Angell (2)

H.T. 3-10

LONDON (Wasps unless stated): A Tunningley (Saracens); S Roiser, H Davies, G Childs, D O'Leary (Harlequins); G Gregory, S Bates (captain); D Molloy, G Botterman (Saracens), I Dunston, A Diprose (Saracens), M Greenwood, D Ryan, C Wilkins, C Sheasby (Harlequins). Replacement: A Snow (Harlequins) for Ryan 12 minutes.
MIDLANDS (Leicester unless stated): W Kilford; S Hackney, S Potter, D Edwards, H Thorneycroft (Northampton); R Angell (Coventry), A Kardooni; R Hardwick (Coventry), R Cockerill, D Garforth, I Skingsley (Bedford), R West (Gloucester), J Phillips (Northampton), G Rees (Nottingham)(captain), C Tarbuck.
Referee: W Erickson, Australia.

At Brooklands (Sale)

NORTH 33 SOUTH WEST 26

Tries: Naylor (1), Johnson (1)
Greenwood (1), Fowler (1), Watson (1)
Penalty-goals: Scully (2)
Conversion: Scully

Tries: Hill (3),
Holford (1)
Conversions: Dix (2),
Belshaw (1)

H.T. 25-12

NORTH: W Greenwood (Harlequins); J Naylor (Orrell), A Northey (Waterloo), P Johnson (Orrell), A Healey (Orrell); N Ryan (Waterloo), D Scully (Wakefield)(captain), P Winstanley (Orrell), G French (Bath), P Manley (Orrell), A Smith (Sale), D Baldwin (Sale), J Fowler (Sale), A Brown (West Hartlepool), M Watson (West Hartlepool).
SOUTH WEST: P Belshaw (Reading); P Holford (Gloucester), S Morris (Gloucester), M Denney (Bristol), A Adebayo (Bath); R Dix (Cambridge University), R Kitchin (Harlequins)(captain); C Clark (Bath), J Hawker (Gloucester), D Crompton (Bath), P Glanville (Gloucester), D Sims (Gloucester), C Yandell (Narberth), R Hill (Saracens), R White (Loughborough University). Replacement: A Turner (Exeter) for Morris 57 minutes.
Referee: P Robin, France.

FINALS TABLES						
	P	W	D	L	F	A	Pts
Midlands	3	3	0	0	72	48	6
London	3	2	0	1	76	51	4
North	3	1	0	2	59	76	2
South West	3	0	0	3	67	99	0

SUN ALLIANCE COLTS CHAMPIONSHIP

FINAL

At Twickenham

DURHAM 10   SURREY 18

Try: Chesters

Penalty-goal: Benson

Conversion: Benson

Tries: Chapman (2), Evans (1)

Penalty-goal: Washington

H.T. 3-10.

DURHAM (Durham City unless stated): J Benson; I Chesters (Westoe), M Shaw (West Hartlepool), M Duncan (Blaydon), M Wood (Newcastle University); B Cosbie-Ross, B Stevenson; A Robson, R Horton (Middlesbrough), J Ryan (Bishop Auckland), C Archer, R Mangles (Bishop Auckland), M Farren (Darlington), J Roberts (captain), G Tinkler (Newcastle University). Replacements: I Potter (Stockton) for Robson 60 minutes, S Watson (Gateshead Fell) for Archer 66 minutes, L Jones for Chesters 69 minutes.

SURREY: C Catling (Exeter University); D Charles (London Irish), D Mellor (Sutton & Epsom), S Power (Harlequins), D Chapman (Esher); T Washington (Richmond), M Percival (Harlequins)(captain); J Kozinsky (Harlequins), G Chuter (Old Midwhitgiftians), M Fitzgerald (Durham University), M Curtis (Sutton & Epsom), R Evans (Richmond), K Cox (Loughborough Students), R Marsh (Bristol University), S Mathieson (Sutton & Epsom). Referee: A Spreadbury, Somerset.

Quarter-finals

Devon 5   Durham 6

Gloucestershire 19   Surrey 27

Yorkshire 24   North Midlands 17

(played on Saturday, 19th November).

Kent 3   East Midlands 6

(played on Sunday, 20th November).

Semi-finals

Durham 33   East Midlands 5

Yorkshire 11   Surrey 21

(played on Sunday, 4th December

at Castlecroft, Wolverhampton).

UNDER 21 COUNTY CHAMPIONSHIP

Semi-finals

Middlesex 9   Yorkshire 13

(Saturday, 11th March 1995. Old Merchant Taylors, Croxley Green)

Buckinghamshire 21   Warwickshire 18

(Sunday, 12th March 1995. At Aylesbury)

FINAL

Saturday, 22nd April 1995   At Twickenham

BUCKINGHAMSHIRE   6 YORKSHIRE 20

Penalty-goals: Williams (2)

Tries: Massey (1), Yates (1), Benton (1)

Penalty-goal: Massey

Conversion: Massey

H.T. 3-12

BUCKINGHAMSHIRE (Wasps unless stated): S Gaster (High Wycombe); J Wyatt, A Hamid (Clifton), G Williams (Narberth), M Dene; A Toone (Terenure College), B Ayres; M Tutt (Buckingham), W Davis (Trinity College), K Line (Northampton), A Mortimore (Bedford), M Moss, D Hoyte, A Little, C Eke.

YORKSHIRE (Morley unless stated): P Massey; C Barnes, A Burnham (Plymouth Albion), J Shepherd, C Reed (Harrogate); S Binns (Leicester), S Benton; C Baldwin (Otley), S Kneale (West Hartlepool), A Reid (Otley), K Yates (Wakefield), A Ludiman (Harrogate), J Stow, B Wade, J Ions (Wakefield). Referee: J Coulson, Durham.

INTER SERVICES CHAMPIONSHIP

Saturday, 1st April   1995. At Twickenham
ROYAL NAVY 34   ARMY 17

Tries: Fletcher (1), Powell (1), Burns (1), White (1)   Tries: Graham (1), Sanger (1)
Livingstone (1)   Dropped-goal: Sibson   Penalty-goal: Hammond (1)
Penalty-goals: Coulton (2)   Conversions: Hammond (2)

H.T. 13-3

ROYAL NAVY: S/Lt J Coulton (RNAS Culdrose); Mne C White (RM Deal), L/S D Sibson (HMS London), Surg Lt B Powell (GCRM), Mne (Musn) S Brown (RM Deal); PO I Fletcher (HMS Repulse), Cpl P Livingstone (RM Stonehouse); LWEM S Burns (HMS Collingwood), Cpl M Wooltorton (45 CDORM), WEM R Parkes (HMS Drake), Cpl R Armstrong (CTCRM), LRO G Harrison (HMS Warrior), L/Cpl D Cross (RM Stonehouse), Lt C Palmer (HMS Warrior)(captain), C/Sgt M Reece (CTCRM). Temporary replacement: S/Lt M Jarrett (HMS Dryad) 35-38 for Sibson.

ARMY: Lt R Abernethy (RGR); Lt H Graham (RHA), Capt A Glasgow (RE), Capt A Deans (AGC), Lt B Johnson (R Signals); Sgt D Hammond (REME), Capt S Pinder (DWR); L Cpl M Stewart (PWRR), Capt J Brammer (RE)(captain), Sgt J Fowers (RHA), Cpl P Curtis (R Signals), Sig G Archer (R Signals), Spr R Hunter (RE), Capt G Knight (DWR), Sgt C Rushworth (REME). Replacement: Cpl A Sanger (RE) for Deans 70 minutes.

Referee: J Pearson, Durham Society.

Wednesday, 12th April 1995   At Twickenham
ARMY 28   ROYAL AIR FORCE 26

Tries: Deans (1), Johnson (1), Dahinten (1),   Tries: Williams (1), Hull (1)
Knight (1)   Penalty-goals: Abernethy (2)   Penalty-goals: Worrall (4)
Conversion: Abernethy   Conversions: Worrall (2)

H.T. 10-17

ARMY: Lt R Abernethy (RGR); Cpl S Bartliff (R Sigs), Capt A Glasgow (RE), Capt A Deans (AGC), Lt B Johnson (R Sigs); 2 Lt P Knowles (RRF), Capt S Pinder (DWR); L Cpl M Stewart (PWRR), Capt J Brammar (RE), Sgt J Fowers (RHA), Spr R Hunter (RE), Lt D Dahinton (RHA), Sig G Archer (R Sigs), Capt G Knight (DWR), Sgt C Rushworth (REME).

ROYAL AIR FORCE: Sgt S Lazenby (Cosford); Fl Lt R Underwood (Finningley), SAC G Sharp (Rudloe Manor), Cpl S Roke (Wittering), SAC S Crossland (Innsworth); Cpl P Hull (Innsworth), Sgt S Worrall (Cottesmore)(captain); C/T D Robson (Odiham), Sqn Ldr R Miller (Wyton), Cpl A Billet (St Athan), Fl Lt D Williams (Locking), SAC P Taylor (Northolt), Sgt B Richardson (CIO Bradford), Fl Lt D Watkins (Locking), Fl Lt C Moore (Lyneham). Replacement: Cpl S Carbutt (Linton-on-Ouse) for Miller 41 minutes. Temporary replacements: Fl Lt J Dearing (Halton) for Billet 46-62 minutes, Fl Lt R Burn (Lossiemouth) for Robson 47-52 minutes.

Referee: S.Lander, Liverpool Society.

Wednesday, 26th April 1995   At Twickenham
ROYAL NAVY 43   ROYAL AIR FORCE 19

Tries: White (1), Powell (1), Harrison (1), Sibson (1)   Try: Watkins
Armstrong (1)   Livingstone (1) penalty try   Penalty-goals: Lazenby (4)
Conversions: Coulton (4)   Conversion: Lazenby (1)

H.T. 24-16

ROYAL NAVY: S/Lt J Coulton (RNAS Culdrose); Mne C White (RM Deal), L/S D Sibson (HMS London), Surg Lt B Powell (CTCRM), Mne S Brown (RM Deal); PO I Fletcher (HMS Repulse), Col P Livingstone (RM Stonehouse); Capt W Dunham (RM), Cpl J Wooltorton (45 CDORM), PO E Cowie (RNAS Culdrose), Cpl R Armstrong (CTCRM), LRO G Harrison (HMS Warrior), L/Cpl D Cross (RM Stonehouse), Lt C Palmer (HMS Warrior)(captain), C/Sgt M Reece (CTCRM). Replacement: S/Lt M Jarrett (HMS Dryad) for Powell 55 minutes.

ROYAL AIR FORCE: Cpl P Hull (Innsworth); SAC G Sharp (Rudloe Manor), Sgt S Lazenby (Cosford), Cpl S Roke (Wittering), SAC S Crossland (Innsworth); Cpl N James (Locking), Sgt S Worrall (Cottesmore)(captain); C/T D Robson (Odiham), Sqn/Ldr R Miller (Wyton), Cpl A Billett (St Athan), Flt/Lt D Williams (Locking), Flt/Lt R Burn (Lossiemouth), Sgt B Richardson (CIO Bradford), Flt/Lt D Watkins (Locking), Flt/Lt C Moore (Lyneham). Replacement: Sgt R Wadmore (Brize Norton) for Worrall 76 minutes.

Referee: J Wallis, Somerset.

PILKINGTON CUP

ROUND ONE

Alton 9 v Lydney 28
Aylesbury 10 v High Wycombe 38
Camborne 23 v Colfeians 15
Ealing 7 v Basingstoke 26
Esher 11 v Bridgwater & Albion 0
Henley 10 v Sudbury 6
Hereford 14 v Nuneaton 6
Launceston 38 v Banbury 3
Lichfield 20 v Stockton 12
London Welsh 20 v Gloucester Old Boys 15
Loughborough Students 11 v Winnington Park 43
Maidenhead 3 v Horsham 0
North Walsham 27 v Okehampton 3
Old Albanians 3 v Barking 22
Old Coventrians 6 v Camp Hill 13
Preston Grasshoppers 31 v Stockwood Park 3
Ruislip 28 v Ipswich 3
Sandal 18 v Wigton 3
Scunthorpe 27 v Kendal 21
Sheffield 11 v Birmingham & Solihull 5
Sherborne 16 v Tabard 26
Southend 8 v Metropolitan Police 20
Stourbridge 15 v New Brighton 10 20
Tynedale 35 v Barkers' Butts 210
Walsall 56 v Stafford 0
West Park 38 v Old Crosleyans 5
Weston-super-Mare 19 v Berry Hill 3
Wharfedale 20 v Stoke-on-Trent 11
Result of the Round:
Scunthorpe 27 v Kendal 21
Saturday, 10th September 1994

ROUND THREE

Basingstoke 29 v Clifton 26
Lydney 16 v Reading 6
Blackheath 31 v Redruth 0
Havant 13 v Richmond 15
High Wycombe 22 v Tabard 36
Launceston 7 v Exeter 30
Tynedale 16 v Rugby Lions 23
Camp Hill 6 v Sandal 17
West Park 14 v Bedford 40
Aspatria 14 v Scunthorpe 9
Harrogate 22 v Lichfield 14
Rotherham 33 v Wharfedale 30
Result of the Round:
Basingstoke 29 v Clifton 26
Saturday, 5th November 1994

ROUND TWO

Askeans 12 v Redruth 19
Lydney 17 v Esher 15
Metropolitan Police 10 v Havant 16
Rosslyn Park 12 v Blackheath 24
Ruislip 19 v Clifton 20
Henley 5 v Launceston 27
Basingstoke 13 v Plymouth Albion 10
Reading 26 v Barking 15
Tabard 13 v Weston-super-Mare 5
Maidenhead 14 v High Wycombe 18
North Walsham 7 v Exeter 32
Richmond 47 v Camborne 22
West Park 20 v Broughton Park 0
Sandal 23 v Winnington Park 10
Tynedale 29 v Otley 28
Stourbridge 17 v Bedford 35
Camp Hill 15 v Liverpool St Helens 10
Aspatria 23 v Leeds 0
Lichfield 24 v Preston Grasshoppers 12
Harrogate 46 v Sheffield 10
Rugby 23 v London Welsh 10
Morley 11 v Rotherham 15
Scunthorpe 17 v Hereford 16
Wharfedale 32 v Walsall 16
Result of the Round and match of the round:
Tynedale 29 v Otley 28
Saturday, 8th October 1994

ROUND FOUR

Aspatria 32 v Bedford 6
Basingstoke 3 v London Irish 18
Bristol 41 v Nottingham 10
Coventry 7 v Fylde 45
Exeter 9 v Rugby Lions 7
Harlequins 9 v Saracens 5
Leicester 56 v Blackheath 11
London Scottish 6 v Bath 31
Moseley 6 v Northampton 16
Newcastle Gosforth 12 v Wasps 58
Orrell 28 v West Hartlepool 7
Rotherham 19 v Waterloo 21
Sale 33 v Harrogate 0
Sandal 5 v Lydney 17
Wakefield 19 v Gloucester 9
Sunday, 18th December 1994
Richmond 24 v Tabard 16
Result of the Round:
Wakefield 19 v Gloucester 9
Saturday, 17th December 1994

ROUND FIVE

Bristol 8   v   Leicester 16
Exeter 18   v   Aspatria 6
London Irish 15   v   Harlequins 40
Lydney 10   v   Wakefield 23
Northampton 27   v   Richmond 6
Orrell 19   v   Bath 25
Sale 55   v   Fylde 13
Waterloo 13   v   Wasps 54
Saturday, 28th January 1995

QUARTER FINALS

Bath 26   v   Northampton 6
Exeter 0   v   Wasps 31
Harlequins 13   v   Wakefield 8
Sale 12   v   Leicester 14
Saturday, 25th February 1995

SEMI-FINALS

Saturday, 1st April 1995   **At Stoop Memorial Ground**

HARLEQUINS 13   BATH 31

Tries: Staples (1)
Challinor (1)
Penalty-goal: Staples

Tries: Swift (2), de Glanville (1)
Dropped-goal: Catt
Penalty-goals: Callard (3)
Conversions: Callard (2)

H.T. 8-13

HARLEQUINS: J Staples; P Mensah, W Carling, W Greenwood, S Bromley; D Pears, R Kitchin; J Leonard, B Moore (captain), A Mullins, M Watson, A Snow, P Thresher, R Jenkins, C Sheasby. Replacement: P Challinor for Staples 70 minutes.

BATH: J Callard; A Swift, P de Glanville, J Guscott, J Sleightholme; M Catt, I Sanders; K Yates, G Adams, J Mallett, S Ojomoh, M Haag, N Redman, J Hall (captain), B Clarke. Replacement: R Butland for Catt 65 minutes.

Referee: B Campsall, Yorkshire.

     At Welford Road, Leicester

LEICESTER 22   WASPS 25

Try: R Underwood
Penalty-goals: Liley (5)
Conversion: Liley

Try: D Hopley
Dropped-goals: Andrew (3)
Penalty-goals: Andrew (3)
Conversion: Andrew

H.T. 6-19

LEICESTER: J Liley; T Underwood, D Edwards, S Potter, R Underwood; J Harris, A Kardooni; G Rowntree, R Cockerill, D Garforth, J Wells (captain), M Johnson, M Poole, N Back, C Tarbuck.

WASPS: J Ufton; P Hopley, D Hopley, G Childs, S Roiser; R Andrew, S Bates; N Popplewell, K Dunn, I Dunston, L Dallaglio, M Greenwood, N Hadley, M White, D Ryan (captain).

Referee: S Lander, Liverpool.

FINAL

Saturday, 6th May 1995   **At Twickenham**

BATH 36   WASPS 16

Tries: Haag (2), Clarke (1)
Swift (1), Callard (1)
Penalty-goal: Callard
Conversions: Calllard (4)

Tries: Dunston (1), D Hopley (1)
Penalty-goals: Andrew (2)

H.T. 19-11

BATH: J Callard; A Swift, P de Glanville (captain), J Guscott, A Adebayo; R Butland, I Sanders; K Yates, G Dawe, V Ubogu, S Ojomoh, M Haag, N Redman, A Robinson, B Clarke. Replacement: J Mallett for Ubogu 73 minutes.

WASPS: J Ufton; P Hopley, D Hopley, G Childs, N Greenstock; R Andrew, S Bates; D Molloy, K Dunn, I Dunston, L Dallaglio, M Greenwood, N Hadley, M White, D Ryan (captain).

Referee: J Pearson, RFU.

PILKINGTON SHIELD

Round Five

London
Ilford Wanderers 11   Tring 0
St Albans 11   HAC 6
Old Bevonians 13   Ventnor 16
Darenth Valley 6   Whitstable 12
Wisbech 19   Stowmarket 12

Midlands
Rushden & Higham 16 Birmingham CS 6
Bromyard 10 Oakham 9
Bedford Queens 14 Erdington 6

North
Huddersfield YMCA 14 Winlaton Vulcans 3
Wibsey 22 Ponteland 0
Blackpool 9 South Shiels 17
Wallasey 32 Marple 5

South West
Beaconsfield 20 Burntwood 6
Tredworth 15 Cainscross 8
Kingsbridge 17 Crewkerne 7
Buckingham 24 Bristol Saracens 19

(Matches played on Saturday, 17th December 1994).

Round Six

North
Bromyard 0 North Shields 11
Rushden & Higham 8 Buckingham 0
Wallasey 19 Bedford Queens 33
(played on Saturday, 11th February 1995)
Wibsey 12 Hudersfield YMCA 8
(played on Saturday, 18th February 1995)

South
Ilford Wanderers 16 Beaconsfield 11
Kingsbridge 23 Ventnor 3
St Albans 15 Whitstable 5
Tredworth 5 Wisbech 0
(Matches played on Saturday, 28th January 1995)

Quarter-finals

North & Midlands
Rushden & Higham 3 Bedford Queens 14
Wibsey 6 North Shields 15

London & South West
Ilford Wanderers 11 St Albans 30
Tredworth 3 Kingsbridge 6
(Matches played on Saturday, 25th February 1995)

SEMI-FINALS

Saturday, 1st April 1995   **At Memorial Ground, Bristol**

BEDFORD QUEENS 21
KINGSBRIDGE 16

Tries: McMillan (1), Clarke (1)   Try: Davies
Dropped-goal: Twigden   Penalty-goals: Bowles (3)
Penalty-goals: Moffat (2)   Conversion: Bowles
Conversion: Moffat

H.T. 21-10

BEDFORD QUEENS: A Moffat; K McMillin, J Kitchener, D Twigden, J Smith; D Fale (captain), J Cunningham; J Matthews, D Stapleton, I Mortimer, S Lousada, A Radnor, S Pearce-Roberts, R Millard, T Clarke. Replacement: A Foley for Pearce-Roberts 60 minutes.
KINGSBRIDGE: A Davies; R Masters, C Massey, P Jackson, T Kingdom; C Bowles (captain), D Mercer; A Toms, J Putt, M Partridge, S Jarvis, A Ball, J Haddy, S Ellis, N Harvey.
Referee: M Bayliss, Gloucester.

                               At Harrogate

NORTH SHIELDS 8   ST ALBANS 21

Try: Tubman   Tries: Morete (1), Cox (1),
Penalty-goal: Crombie   Dickinson (1)
                         Penalty-goals: King (2)

H.T. 8-3

NORTH SHIELDS: G Crombie; I Tubman, J Hall, S Turnbull, B Fenwick; T Rendles, G Duff; S Sansom, B Hope, J Burton, F Taylor, P Scott, T Gallon, M Allott, S Hansen (captain).
ST ALBANS: N Lister; D Falvey, D Morete, G Cox, J Dickinson; A King, T Andrews (captain); M Millar, R Hume, D Batchelor, W Pearson, A Smith, R Doggett, D Stanford, J Sayers.
Referee: D Hudson, Manchester.

611

BEDFORD QUEENS 11   ST ALBANS 10

Try: Clarke
Dropped-goal: Moffat
Penalty-goal: Stapleton

Try: Dickinson
Penalty-goal: King
Conversion: King

H.T. 5-0

BEDFORD QUEENS: A Moffat; K McMillin, J Kitchener, D Twigden, J Smith; D Fale (captain), J Cunningham; J Matthews, D Stapleton, I Mortimer, R Millard, A Radnor, S Pearce-Roberts, T Dean, T Clarke. Replacement: C Holloway for Smith 62 minutes.

ST ALBANS: N Lister; D Falvey, D Morete, W Cox, J Dickinson; A King, T Andrews (captain); M Millar, R Hume, D Batchelor, D Patrick, A Smith, R Doggett, D Stanford, J Sayers.

Referee: B Campsall, Yorkshire.

BARBARIANS 1994-95

RESULTS

Sat, Sept 3rd 1994	Bath	Bath	L 18-23
Tue, Sept 4th 1994	French Barbarians	Paris	L 18-35
Tue, Oct 4th 1994	Newport	Newport	W 54-45
Tue, Oct 18th 1994	Swansea	Swansea	L 17-39
Sat, Dec 3rd 1994	SOUTH AFRICA	Dublin	W 23-15
Tue, Dec 27th 1994	Leicester	Leicester	L 18-31
Wed, Mar 8th 1995	East Midlands	Northampton	W 56-19
Sat, Apr 15th 1995	Cardiff	Cardiff	L 33-75

Summary: Played 8, won 3, lost 5, points for 237, against 282.

SCOTLAND

McEWAN'S NATIONAL LEAGUES
(Divisions One & Two Final Tables)

DIVISION ONE

	P	W	D	L	F	A	Pts
Stirling County	13	11	1	1	234	162	23
Watsonians	13	9	0	4	298	212	18
Edinburgh Acacies	13	7	2	4	216	141	16
Hawick	13	7	2	4	215	199	16
Heriot's FP	13	7	1	5	299	197	15
Boroughmuir	13	7	1	5	325	226	15
Gala	13	7	1	5	226	245	15
Melrose	13	7	0	6	308	261	14
Glasgow High/Kelvin	13	6	1	6	228	183	13
Jed-Forest	13	6	0	7	221	256	12
West of Scotland	13	5	0	8	166	233	10
Dundee HS FP	13	3	1	9	200	266	7
Currie	13	3	0	10	186	280	6
Stewart's-Melville	13	1	0	12	158	321	2

DIVISION TWO

	P	W	D	L	F	A	Pts
Kelso	13	11	0	2	318	159	22
Selkirk	13	10	2	1	338	184	22
Kirkcaldy	13	8	1	4	271	230	17
Biggar	13	7	2	4	180	173	16
Preston Lodge	13	7	1	5	269	211	15
Glasgow Academicals	13	7	0	6	299	239	14
Peebles	13	7	0	6	175	204	14
Musselburgh	13	6	1	6	253	223	13
Grangemouth	13	6	0	7	223	246	12
Corstorphine	13	5	1	7	180	214	11
Edinburgh Wands	13	5	0	8	208	261	10
Wigtownshire	13	3	0	10	173	267	6
Gordonians	13	3	0	10	145	300	6
Haddington	13	2	0	11	178	275	4

DIVISION THREE

	P	W	D	L	F	A	Pts
Ayr	13	12	0	1	464	126	24
Kilmarnock	13	11	0	2	449	162	22
Clarkston	13	10	1	2	261	120	21
Langholm	13	9	0	4	204	152	18
Hillhead/Jordanhill	13	8	0	5	240	147	16
Dunfermline	13	7	0	6	237	261	14
Dumfries	13	6	1	6	209	293	13
Trinity Academicals	13	6	0	7	233	272	12
Portobello FP	13	6	0	7	151	270	12
Stewartry	13	5	0	8	164	201	10
Edinburgh Univ	13	4	0	9	206	252	8
Royal High	13	3	1	9	145	358	7
East Kilbride	13	1	1	11	191	318	3
Hutcheson's/Aloy	13	1	0	12	151	373	2

DIVISION FOUR

	P	W	D	L	F	A	Pts
Glenrothes	13	12	0	1	317	99	24
Duns	13	10	1	2	316	166	21
Livingstone	13	10	1	2	266	174	21
Aberdeen GSFP	13	8	0	5	452	144	16
Ardrossan Accies	13	8	0	5	177	157	16
Cambuslang	13	7	0	6	165	148	14
Perthshire	13	6	1	6	163	184	13
St Boswells	13	6	0	7	145	188	12
Howe of Fife	13	5	1	7	178	208	11
Dalziel High Sch FP	13	5	0	7	152	211	10
Highland	13	4	0	9	193	254	8
North Berwick	13	3	1	9	101	319	7
Alloa	13	2	0	10	116	239	4
Morgan Academy FP	13	1	1	11	124	313	3

DIVISION FIVE (top seven places)

	P	W	D	L	F	A	Pts
Berwick	13	10	1	2	380	141	21
Allan Glen's	13	9	0	4	254	135	18
Cartha Queen's Park	13	9	0	4	259	195	18
Linlithgow	13	8	1	4	259	154	17
Leith Academicals	13	8	0	5	233	199	16
Cumbernauld	13	7	1	5	186	163	15
Madras College FP	13	7	0	6	157	216	14

DIVISION SIX (top seven places)

	P	W	D	L	F	A	Pts
Annan	13	11	1	1	505	114	23
Waysiders/Drumpel	13	11	0	2	283	124	22
Dunbar	13	8	2	3	181	141	18
Forrester FP	13	8	0	5	193	165	16
Aberdeenshire	13	7	0	6	268	162	14
Lenzie	13	7	0	6	288	240	14
Greenock Wands	13	6	2	5	195	255	

DIVISION SEVEN (top six places),

	P	W	D	L	F	A	Pts
Garnock	12	12	0	0	425	47	24
Whitecraigs	13	10	0	3	273	146	20
Cumnock	13	9	1	3	262	153	19
Lochaber	11	8	1	2	228	94	17
Walkerburn	13	8	0	5	250	137	16
Holy Cross	12	8	0	4	207	161	16

NB: Lochaber's matches against Garnock and Holy Cross were not played.

613

McEWAN'S INTER-DISTRICT CHAMPIONSHIP

Saturday, 3rd December 1994

Glasgow 25   North Midlands 19
(at Hughenden)

South of Scotland 9   Scottish Exiles 25
(at Murrayfield)

Saturday, 10th December 1994

North & Midlands 11   Edinburgh 11
(Duffus Park, Cuper)

Scottish Exiles 34   Glasgow 13
(Murrayfield)

Wednesday, 14th December 1994

South of Scotland 19   Edinburgh 19
(Jedburgh)

Saturday, 17th December 1994

Edinburgh 16   Glasgow 13
(Myreside, Edinburgh)

North & Midlands 26   South of Scotland 7
(Rubislaw, Aberdeen)

Wednesday, 21st December 1994

Scottish Exiles 41   North & Midlands 13
(Murrayfield)

Friday, 23rd December 1994

Edinburgh 16   Scottish Exiles 19
(Murrayfield)

Saturday, 24th December 1994

Glasgow 11   South of Scotland 26
(Bridgehaugh, Stirling)

FINAL TABLE							
	P	W	D	L	F	A	Pts
Scottish Exiles	4	4	0	0	119	51	8
Edinburgh	4	1	2	1	62	62	4
North & Midlands	4	1	1	2	69	84	3
South of Scotland	4	1	1	2	61	81	3
Glasgow	4	1	0	3	62	95	2

TennantTennants Midland Cup Final:
Glenrothes 5   Kirkcaldy 21

WALES – HEINEKEN LEAGUES

FINAL TABLES 1994-95

DIVISION 1

	P	W	D	L	F	A	Pts
Cardiff	22	18	0	4	672	269	36
Pontypridd	22	17	0	5	555	255	34
Treorchy	22	13	0	9	479	312	26
Neath	22	12	2	8	379	398	26
Bridgend	22	12	1	9	518	451	25
Swansea	22	12	0	10	475	400	24
Llanelli	22	10	0	12	459	409	18*
Newport	22	9	0	13	366	433	18
Newbridge	22	8	0	14	302	452	16
Abertillery	22	8	0	14	349	604	16
Dunvant	22	7	1	14	333	542	15
Pontypool	22	4	0	18	293	655	8

* Two points deducted
Champions: Cardiff
Relegated: Dunvant & Pontypool

DIVISION 2

	P	W	D	L	F	A	Pts
Aberavon	22	17	0	5	506	263	34
Ebbw Vale	22	16	1	5	447	283	33
Abercynon	22	16	1	5	380	260	33
S Wales Police	22	12	2	8	413	357	26
Bonymaen	22	11	1	10	370	312	23
Maesteg	22	10	1	11	365	388	21
Tenby United	22	10	0	12	290	374	20
Llandovery	22	9	0	13	313	363	18
Llanharan	22	9	0	13	316	319	18
Cross Keys	22	8	0	14	292	438	16
Narberth	22	6	2	14	299	446	14
Penarth	22	4	0	18	289	477	8

Promoted: Aberavon (champions) & Ebbw Vale
Relegated: Narberth & Penarth

DIVISION 3

	P	W	D	L	F	A	Pts
Ystradgynlais	22	19	0	3	411	192	38
Caerphilly	22	18	1	3	424	210	37
Tredegar	22	14	0	8	375	339	28
Mountain Ash	22	13	1	8	372	253	27
Builth Wells	22	11	0	11	297	300	22
Blaina	22	10	2	10	248	252	22
Kenfig Hill	22	10	0	12	384	360	20
Blackwood	22	9	2	11	268	291	20
Glamorgan Wand	22	9	0	13	293	356	18
Tondu	22	7	1	14	304	316	15
Aberavon Quins	22	6	2	14	196	357	14
Pontypool Utd	22	1	1	20	238	584	3

Promoted: Ystradgynlais (champions) & Caerphilly
Relegated: Aberavon Quins & Pontypool United

DIVISION 4

	P	W	D	L	F	A	Pts
Cardiff Inst	22	18	0	4	447	256	36
Pyle	22	16	1	5	443	246	33
Whitland	22	14	0	8	379	249	28
Carmarthen Qns	22	13	0	9	414	373	26
Glynneath	22	11	1	10	305	274	23
St Peter's	22	10	0	12	326	301	20
Tumble	22	9	1	12	318	351	19
Rhymney	22	9	0	13	275	376	18
Vardre	22	8	0	14	208	385	16
Llantrisant	22	8	0	14	256	354	16
Oakdale	22	7	1	14	270	366	15
Kidwelly	22	7	0	15	250	360	14
Vardre	21	7	0	14	181	372	14

Promoted: Cardiff Institute (champions) & Pyle
Relegated: Oakdale & Kidwelly

DIVISION 5

	P	W	D	L	F	A	Pts
Rumney	22	19	1	2	583	148	39
Merthyr	22	16	1	5	538	266	33
Seven Sisters	22	12	1	9	334	255	25
Hendy	22	11	1	10	322	457	23
Abercarn	22	10	3	9	306	357	23
Tonmawr	22	11	1	10	263	262	23
Cardiff Quins	22	11	0	11	342	281	22
Felinfoel	22	10	1	11	340	383	21
Garndiffaith	22	10	1	11	318	293	21
Cardigan	22	9	3	10	301	329	21
Pwllheli	22	4	0	18	162	382	8
Wrexham	22	2	1	19	185	581	5

Promoted: Rumney (champions) & Merthyr
Relegated to regional Sixth Divisions: Cardigan,
Pwllheli & Wrexham
Promoted to Division Five: Abergavenny (Division
Six East), Ystrad Rhondda (Division Six Central) &
Pontyberem (Division Six West)

WALES – SWALEC CUP

1st Round

Abercrave 41	v	Maesteg Quins 0
Aberystwyth 22	v	Tonna 11
Alltwen 17	v	Nantymoel 40
Ammanford 11	v	Nantyffyllon 8
Barry 18	v	Bynas Powys 11
BP Llandarcy 3	v	Llandeilo 53
Bridgend Athletic 26	v	Cefn Cribbwr 16
Bridgend Sports 10	v	Tonyrefail 42
British Steel PT 42	v	Glais 7
Bro Ffestiniog 28	v	Loughor 29
Brynamman 14	v	Llanishen 11

Brynmawr beat Gwent College (scratched)

Bynea 20	v	Bryncoch 0
Caernarvon 3	v	Birchgrove 53
Caldicott 18	v	Pembroke Dock Quins 5
Carmarthen College 0	v	Pentyrch 84
Cefn Coed 27	v	Crumlin 26
Cwmgors 11	v	Rhiwbina 14
Cwmllynfell 31	v	Aberystwyth Uni 20
Deri 15	v	Porthcawl 29
Dolgellau 24	v	Trimsaran 11
Fishguard 8	v	Bargoed 27
Fleur de Lys 16	v	Senghenydd 15
Glyncoch 42	v	Cardiff Medicals 14
Hartridge HS OB 13	v	Carmarthen Athletic 0
Hirwaun 31	v	Beddau 0
Laugharne 35	v	Haverfordwest 15
Llandaff North 18	v	Amman United 29
Llandudno 5	v	Llandaff 8
Llanelli Wanderers 0	v	Trinant 13
Llangennech 8	v	Pontyberem 10
Llantwit Fardre 25	v	Talywain 6
Mold 48	v	Cwmbran 0
Monmouth 6	v	Tylorstown 11
Morriston 46	v	Briton Ferry 6
Mumbles 33	v	Burry Port 25
Nantyglo 14	v	Penygroes 35
Nelson 105	v	Bangor NC 0
Newcastle Emlyn 3	v	Machen 14
New Dock 37	v	Cwmgwrach 21
Newport HS OB 18	v	Blaengarw 12
Newport Sr 32	v	Usk 0
Neyland 37	v	Pontarddulais 10
Ogmore Vale 0	v	Rhydyfelin 59
Old Penarthians 20	v	Cylfynnydd 13
Pembroke 26	v	Crynant 0
Penclawdd 7	v	Taff's Well 6
Pill Harriers 35	v	Llanhilleth 10
Pontardawe 4	v	Neath Athletic 45
Resolven 12	v	Waunarlwydd 8
Rhyl & District 73	v	Swansea Uplands 5
Risca 18	v	Hoel-y-Cyw 0
Ruthin 31	v	Bangor 13
Skewen 9	v	Bedwas 8
St David's 3	v	Aberaman 51

St Joseph's OB beat Bangor University (scratched)

Swansea Uni 5	v	Denbigh 5

(aet - away team wins)

Taibach 50	v	Tredegar Iron 7
Treherbert 34	v	Gowerton 5
Tycroes 25	v	Abercwmboi 3
Wattstown 22	v	Newtown 17
Welshpool 3	v	Ystrad Rhondda 38
Ynysddu 3	v	Penygriag 39
Ystalyfera 78	v	Furnace United 0

(Played on Saturday 17th September 1994)
Result of the Round:

Hartridge HS OB 13	v	Carmarthen Athletic 0

2nd Round

Aberavon GS 20	v	Denbigh 10
Abercarn 27	v	Pembroke 10
Aberystwyth 13	v	Skewen 3
Bargoed 24	v	Blaenau Gwent 3
Barry 13	v	Brynmawr 24
Birchgrove 8	v	Abergavenny 10
Bridgend Athletic 9	v	Garndiffaith 15
Cardiff Harlequins 3	v	Old Illtyduans 18
Cardiff University 9	v	Aberamman 31
Chepstow 0	v	Hartridge HS OB 10
Colwyn Bay 13	v	Fleur de Lys 19
Cwmavon 5	v	Trebanos 12
Cwmllynfell 37	v	Gilfach Goch 11
Dolgellau 0	v	Morriston 10
Glycoch 12	v	Porthcawl 6
Hirwaun 11	v	Rhiwbina 0
Lampeter College 3	v	Risca 24
Lampeter Town 6	v	St Joseph's FP 5
Laugharne 0	v	Ammanford 26
Llandaff 11	v	Abercrave 21
Llandeilo 31	v	Loughor 3
Llangwm 5	v	Ystrad Rhondda 19
Llandybydder 15	v	Pentyrch 17
Machen 5	v	Amman United 6
Merthyr 14	v	Rumney 13
Milford Haven 3	v	Pontycymmer 22
Mold 22	v	Wrexham 6
Nantymoel 10	v	Seven Sisters 38
Nelson 24	v	Newport Saracens 3
New Dock Stars 51	v	Brecon 0
Newport HS OB 18	v	Hendy 27
Old Penarthians 35	v	Llantwit Major 8
Pencoed 7	v	Neath Athletic 15
Penygraig 74	v	Gorseinon 3
Pill Harriers 22	v	Caldicott 14
Pontyates 0	v	Tylorstown 20
Pontyclun 0	v	Llantwit Fardre 32
Pwllheli 41	v	Blaenavon 12
Resolven 22	v	Cowbridge 16
Rhydyfelin 20	v	Croesyceiliog 23
Rhyl 29	v	Trinant 6
RTB 8	v	Ynysybwl 10
Ruthin 27	v	Bynea 20
St Joseph's 0	v	Llandybie 19
Tonmawr 15	v	Cefn Coed 9
Tonyrefail 40	v	Penclawdd 12
Tredegar Ironsides 17	v	Brynamman 10
Treherbert 23	v	Pontyberem 11
Tycroes 3	v	Neyland 17
Wattstown 17	v	Penygroes 5
Ystalyfera 15	v	Cefneithin 12

(Played on Saturday 22nd October 1994)

Mumbles 3	v	Cardigan 21

(Played on Tuesday 8th November 1994)
Result of the Round:

Cardiff Harlequins 3	v	Old Illtydians 18

3rd Round

Aberavon 17	v	Rhymney 9
Aberavon Green Stars 11	v	Oakdale 6
Abergavenny 17	v	Blaina 20
Blackwood 5	v	Brynmawr 3
Cardiff Institute 47	v	Tredegar 0
Cardigan 7	v	Nelson 19
Carmarthen Quins 43	v	Wattstown 0
Croesyceiliog 0	v	Glamorgan Wanderers 27
Garndiffaith 15	v	Fleur de Lys 16
Glynneath 12	v	Pontycymmer 3

616

Hartridge HS OB 31	v	Ybysbwl 10
Hendy 6	v	Abercrave 13
Hirwaun 0	v	Gilfach Goch 3
Llandybie 3	v	Llantwit Fardre 8
Merthyr 48	v	Pill Harriers 8
Mountain Ash 8	v	Llandeilo 7
Neyland 22	v	Ystalefera 13
Old Penarthians 26	v	New Dock Stars 18
Pentyrch 8	v	Risca 3
Penygraig 25	v	Treherbert 11
Pwllheli 21	v	Pontypool United 13
Pyle 30	v	Tredegar Ironsides 0
Resolven 12	v	Mold 0
Rhyl 11	v	Llantrisant 10
Ruthin 29	v	Kidwelly 9
Seven Sisters 25	v	Resolven 12
St Peter's 9	v	Bargoed 10
Tondu 31	v	Neath Athletic 0
Tonmawr 0	v	Builth Wells 5
Tylorstown 16	v	Lampeter 10
Vardre 15	v	Tumble 13
Whitland 28	v	Ammanford 13
Ystrad Rhondda 28	v	Abercarn 3

(Played on Saturday 19th November 1994)
Result of the Round:

St Peter's 9	v	Bargoed 10
Amman 17	v	Tonyrefail 29
Glyncoch 3	v	Morriston 20

(Played on Saturday 3rd December 1994)

Aberystwyth 8	v	Old Illtydians 14
Caerphilly 27	v	Trebanos 5

(Played on Saturday. 10th December 1994)

4th Round

Aberavon Green Stars 15	v	Tenby United 27
Aberavon Quins 17	v	Tonyrefail 23
Abercrave 6	v	Aberavon 21
Abertillery 6	v	Abercynon 29
Blackwood 23	v	Glamorgan Wanderers 3
Blaina 0	v	Bonymain 21
Bridgend 80	v	Cross Keys 5
Cardiff 63	v	Merthyr 8
Cardiff Institute 32	v	Llandovery 3
Carmarthen Quins 18	v	South Wales Police 32
Glynneath 26	v	Vardre United 0
Hartridge HS OB 12	v	Old Illtydians 14
Llanelli 51	v	Caerphilly 0
Maesteg 9	v	Ebbw Vale 14
Maesteg Celtic 35	v	Penygraig 10
Morriston 21	v	Gilfach Goch 8
Narberth 10	v	Mountain Ash 15
Neath 79	v	Aberamman 12
Nelson 5	v	Fleur de Lys 0
Newbridge 25	v	Treorchy 20
Neyland 8	v	Dunvant 32
Penarthians 24	v	Bargoed 11
Pentyrch 7	v	Whitland 25
Pontypridd 56	v	Newport 0
Pyle 29	v	Tylorstown 8
Resolven 6	v	Pontypool 13
Rhyl 14	v	Llantwit Fardre 3

Ruthin 7	v	Builth Wells 30
Seven Sisters 14	v	Ystradgynlais 6
Swansea 22	v	Llanharan 12
Tondu 40	v	Pwellheli 9
Ystrad Rhondda 19	v	Penarth 8

Played on Saturday 17th December 1994
Result of the Round:

Abertillery 6	v	Abercynon 29

5th Round

Builth Wells 10	v	Bonymaen 0
Dunvant 28	v	Tonyrefail 7
Glynneath 0	v	Llanelli 27
Morriston 13	v	Neath 40
Nelson 0	v	Newbridge 20
Penygraig 13	v	Rhyl 10
Pontypridd 69	v	Pontypool 12
Pyle 7	v	Cardiff 36
Swansea 58	v	Abercynon 22
Tondy 5	v	Cardiff Institute 22
Ystrad Rhondda 0	v	Bridgend 39

(five matches postponed)
Played on Saturday 28th January 1995

Ebbw Vale 11	v	Old Illtydians 14
Seven Sisters 13	v	Blackwood 15
South West Police 3	v	Old Penarthians 20

(two matches still unplayed)
Played on Saturday 4th February 1995

Tenby United 3	v	Aberavon 6
Whitland 14	v	Mountain Ash 14

(Mountain Ash advance as away team)
Played on Saturday 25th February 1995
Results of the Round:

Ebbw Vale 11	v	Old Illtydians 14
South Wales Police 3	v	Old Penarthians 20

6th Round

Aberavon 21	v	Cardiff Institute 15
Blackwood 6	v	Newbridge 14
Bridgend 25	v	Penygraig 10
Builth Wells 13	v	Mountain Ash 18
Llanelli 29	v	Dunvant 8
Neath 20	v	Swansea 22
Old Penarthians 9	v	Cardiff 45
Pontypridd 66	v	Old Illtydians 0

Quarter-finals

Cardiff 72	v	Aberavon 3
Llanelli 18	v	Bridgend 11
Newbridge 11	v	Swansea 19
Pontypridd 76	v	Mountain Ash 3

(Matches played on Saturday 8th April 1995)

Semi-finals

Cardiff 9	v	Swansea 16

(after extra time at Llanelli)

Llanelli 14	v	Pontypridd 20

(at Cardiff)
(played on Saturday 22nd April 1995)

FINAL

Saturday, 6th May 1995   At Cardiff Arms Park.

PONTYPRIDD 12   SWANSEA 17

Tries: Manley (2)   Tries: Appleyard (1), Stuart (1), Davies (1)
Conversion: N Jenkins   Penalty-goal: Williams
     Conversions: Williams (2)
H.T. 7-0

IRELAND

INSURANCE CORPORATION LEAGUE

DIVISION ONE

	P	W	D	L	F	A	Pts
Shannon	10	10	0	0	162	160	20
Blackrock College	10	7	0	3	228	135	14
St Mary's College	10	7	0	3	151	137	14
Garryowen	10	6	0	4	160	113	12
Cork Constitution	10	6	0	4	148	129	12
Old Wesley	10	5	0	5	131	171	10
Lansdowne	10	3	1	6	150	225	7
Instonians	10	3	0	7	111	160	6
Young Munster	10	3	0	7	115	153	6
Sunday's Well	10	2	1	7	119	165	5
Dungannon	10	2	0	8	114	141	4

Champions: Shannon.
Relegated: Sunday's Well & Dungannon.

Leading Scorers:

	T	DG	P	C	Pts
K Smith (Garryowen)	2	0	24	6	94
A McGowan (Blackrock C)	1	1	18	18	93
P Burke (Cork Con)	1	1	22	5	84
A Thompson (Shannon)	3	0	16	5	73

DIVISION TWO

	P	W	D	L	F	A	Pts
Old Belvedere	10	8	0	2	149	120	16
Ballymena	10	7	1	2	191	122	15
Wanderers	10	6	1	3	151	133	13
Terenure College	10	6	0	4	187	171	12
Malone	10	5	0	5	143	139	10
Old Crescent	10	4	1	5	179	173	9
Greystones	10	4	1	5	173	194	9
Bective Rangers	8	4	0	4	126	93	8
Univ College Dublin	10	2	2	6	141	157	6
Dolphin	9	3	0	6	85	127	6
Bangor	9	1	0	8	83	161	2

Promoted: Old Belvedere (champions) & Ballymena.
Relegated: University College Dublin & Bangor.

Leading Scorers:

	T	DG	P	C	Pts
B Begley (Old Crescent)	2	1	31	9	114
D McAleese (Ballymena)	0	1	21	10	86
R Murphy (Greystones)	2	1	20	6	85

DIVISION THREE

	P	W	D	L	F	A	Pts
North of Ireland FC	11	9	0	2	210	135	18
Clontarf	11	8	0	3	187	126	16
Highfield	11	7	0	4	172	147	14
City of Derry	11	6	1	4	140	117	13
Buccaneers	11	6	0	5	179	142	12
De La Salle/Pal'stn	11	5	1	5	135	125	11
Monkstown	11	5	1	5	138	137	11
Waterpark	11	5	0	6	160	183	10
Galwegians	11	4	1	6	121	128	9
Univ College Cork	11	3	3	5	129	141	9
Corinthians	11	3	1	7	116	174	7
Ballina	11	1	0	10	115	247	2

Promoted: North of Ireland FC (champions) & Clontarf.
Relegated: Corinthians & Ballina.

Leading Scorers:

	T	DG	P	C	Pts
B Moran (Waterpark)	0	7	25	2	100
G O'Dowd (Buccaneers)	0	6	23	5	97
N Lamont (NIFC)	0	0	21	10	83

DIVISION FOUR

	P	W	D	L	F	A	Pts
Bohemians	10	9	0	1	213	92	18
Skerries	10	8	1	1	254	74	17
Portadown	10	8	1	1	166	92	17
Dublin University	10	7	2	1	329	108	16
Queens University	10	5	1	4	183	163	11
CIYMS	10	4	0	6	145	134	8
Ards	10	3	1	6	90	143	7
Collegians	10	2	1	7	110	207	5
City of Armagh	10	2	1	7	112	246	5
Sligo	10	2	0	8	95	196	4
Univ College Galway	10	0	2	8	60	302	2

Promoted: Bohemians (champions) & Skerries.

Leading Scorers:

	T	DG	P	C	Pts
B Style (Queens Univ)	4	2	15	6	83
O Moran (Bohemians)	0	0	24	4	80
C Morgan (Dublin Univ)	0	3	9	21	78

IRISH INTER-PROVINCIAL CHAMPIONSHIP

Saturday, 12th November 1994
Connacht 9   Irish Exiles 35   (Galway)
Munster 17   Ulster 16   (Musgrave Park, Cork)
Saturday, 19th November 1994
Ulster 20   Connacht 6   (Belfast)
Leinster 20   Irish Exiles 18   (Dublin)
Saturday, 26th November 1994
Connacht 20   Leinster 19   (Galway)
Irish Exiles 8   Munster 46   (Sunbury)

Saturday, 10th December 1994
Irish Exiles 16   Ulster 42   (Sale)
Leinster 14   Munster 36   (Donnybrook, Dublin)
Saturday, 17th December 1994
Munster 60   Connacht 20   (Limerick)
Ulster 6   Leinster 12   (Ravenhill, Belfast)

FINAL TABLE

	P	W	D	L	F	A	Pts
Munster	4	4	0	0	159	58	8
Ulster	4	2	0	2	84	51	4
Leinster	4	2	0	2	65	80	4
Irish Exiles	4	1	0	3	77	117	2
Connacht	4	1	0	3	55	134	2

SMITHWICK'S BOSTON FLOODLIT CUP – Final
Dungannon 10   Instonians 3

UNIVERSITY MATCHES

UNDER 21 MATCH

Tuesday, 6th December 1994   At Stoop Memorial Ground, Twickenham

OXFORD UNIVERSITY 19   CAMBRIDGE UNIVERSITY 21

Tries: Dargie (2), Djaba (1)   Tries: Penalty-try, Clark (1)

Conversions: Dargie (2)   Penalty-goals: Lippett (3)

     Conversion: Lippett

H.T. 12-13

OXFORD UNIVERSITY UNDER 21: M Dumbell (Brasenose); M Djaba (Pembroke), J Wyatt (Pembroke), J Cameron (St Peter's), J Tilley (Pembroke); J Dargie (Brasenose)(captain), N Street (Worcester); H Slack (St Hugh's), N Hockley (Worcester), N Sharp (Brasenose), J Bevan (St John's), C Smith (Keble), M Fanning (Exeter), J Britton (New College), M Hutchinson (Keble).

CAMBRIDGE UNIVERSITY UNDER 21: A Janisch (Trinity); S Lippett (Corpus Christi), J Hurst (Homerton), D Clark (Fitzwilliam)(captain), M Cooksley (Emanuel); O Clayton (Magdalene), S Young (Pembroke); N Studer (St John's), R Sugden (St Catherine's), N Holgate (Robinson), J Hammill (Trinity), D Sommers (Gonville & Caius), C Courtney (St John's), M Holmes (Peterhouse), R Earnshaw (St John's).

Referee: R Rees, London Society.

UNIVERSITY MATCH

Tuesday, 6th December 1994   At Twickenham

OXFORD UNIVERSITY 21   CAMBRIDGE UNIVERSITY 26

Tries: Rees (1), Martin (1)   Tries: Reynolds (2), Harrison (1)

Dropped-goal: Rees   Dropped-goals: McCarthy (2)

Penalty-goals: Rees (2)   Penalty-goal: McCarthy

Conversion: Rees   Conversion: McCarthy

H.T. 6-8

OXFORD UNIVERSITY (Keble unless stated): * M Joy (Marling School, Stroud); I Gray (Royal Belfast Academical Institute/St Catherine's); S Bromley (Cardinal Langley HS), M Nolan (Tonbridge/Pembroke), T Howe (Bambridge Academy); * G Rees (St Michael's University School, BC, Canada & Harrow), M Kirsten (Diocesan College, Cape Town); A Bryce (Glenalmond), * D Henderson (Glenalmond)(captain), S Thompson (Durham/St Cross), * N Martin (King Edward's, Birmingham), P Coveney (Clongowes Wood College/New College), * J Daniell (Wanganui Collegiate School, NZ & Eton/St Catherine's), G Allison (St Paul's/Templeton), R Yeabsley (Haberdasher's, Aske's). Replacement: N Marval (Queen Elizabeth's, Bristol/St Catherine's) for Bromley 64 minutes.

CAMBRIDGE UNIVERSITY: * A Dalwood (St Alban's School/St Edmund's); N Walne (Caerleon CS/St Catherine's), G Harrison (Ermysted's GS, Skipton/Christ's), * A Palfrey (St Cyres CS/Hughes Hall), A Reynolds (Christ's College, Brecon/Homerton); M McCarthy (Mount St Mary's, Sheffield/Hughes Hall), R Davies (Gresham's/Downing); L Mooney (St Boniface, Plymouth/Hughes Hall), I Mackenzie (Brentwood County HS/Homerton), M Cox (St Columba's, Dublin/Hughes Hall), A Metcalfe (Sedbergh/Homerton), A Meadows (Sedbergh/St Edmund's), R Bramley (Queen Elizabeth GS, Wakefield/St Edmund's), * N Richardson (King's School, Worcester/St Edmund's)(captain), E Rollitt (St Paul's/Magdalene). Replacments: A Spencer (Priestly VIth Form College/St John's) for Harrison 57 minutes, R Dix (Millfield/Homerton) 80 for Palfrey.

* Denotes Old Blue (both teams).

Referee: S Hildith, Ireland.

(Colleges only recorded against players)

OXFORD UNIVERSITY (Keble unless stated): *M Joy; I Gray (St Catherine's), S Bromley, M Nolan (Pembroke), T Howe; *G Rees, M Kirsten; A Bryce, *D Henderson (captain), S Thompson (St Cross), *N Martin, P Coveney (New College), *J Daniell (St Catherine's), G Allison (Templeton), R Yeabsley. Replacement: N Marval (St Catherine's) for Bromley 64 minutes.

CAMBRIDGE UNIVERSITY: *A Dalwood (St Edmund's); N Walne (St Catherine's), G Harrison (Christ's), *A Palfrey (Hughes Hall), A Reynolds (Homerton); M McCarthy (Hughes Hall), R Davies (Downing); L Mooney (Hughes Hall), I Mackenzie (Homerton), M Cox (Hughes Hall), A Metcalfe (Homerton), *A Meadows (St Edmund's), R Bramley (St Edmund's), *N Richardson (St Edmund's)(captain), E Rollitt (Magdalene). Replacements: A Spencer (St John's) 57 for Harrison, R Dix (Homerton) 80 for Palfrey.

Referee: S Hilditch, Ireland.

BRITISH UNIVERSITIES CHAMPIONSHIP

Last sixteen

Aberdeen 20   Durham 33
Manchester Metropolitan 10   Keele 3
Northumbria 11   Sheffield Hallam 7
Loughborough 41   Birmingham 12
Swansea 41   West Sussex 11
Essex 13   Brighton 31
Bath 5   West London Institute 29
St Mary's College 0   Exeter 26

Quarter-finals

Durham 11   Manchester Metroploitan 3
Northumbria 10   Loughborough 36
Swansea 39   Brighton 10
West London Institute 46   Exeter 10

Semi-finals

Durham 17   Swansea 29
(Wednesday, 8th March 1995 in Nottingham)
Loughborough 12   West London Institute 27
(Thursday, 9th March 1995 at Grange Road, Cambridge)

FINAL

Wednesday, 22nd March 1995   At Twickenham

SWANSEA 30   WEST LONDON INSTITUTE 31

Tries: Williams (1), Hughes (1), Griffiths (1)	Try: Kemp
Beard (1) Dropped-goal: Hughes	Dropped-goal: Lee
Penalty-goal: Davies	Penalty-goals: Lee (7)
Conversions: Davies (2)	Conversion: Lee

H.T. 17-3

SWANSEA UNIVERSITY: N Ferns (Haberdashers', Monmouth); G Williams (Monmouth), D Hughes (King's School, Worcester), D Fitzgerald (Trinity), A Harris (Bishopston CS); L Davies (Bishopston CS), S Powell (RGS Worcester); A Lewis (Christ College, Brecon), D Robins (Kingswinford), A Collins (King Edward's, Bath), A Little (Aylesbury GS), R Heal (Millfield), C Yandell (Worle CS), P Beard (Monmouth), R Griffiths (YSGL Gyfun Llanhari)(captain). Replacement: B Martin (St Brendan's VIth Form College) for Little 79 minutes.

WEST LONDON INSTITUTE OF HIGHER EDUCATION: R Hennessy (Oatlands College, Dublin); A Clarke (St Edward's, Oxford), M Kemp (Coopers Company & Coburn), S Thompson (Warwick), R Francis (Walton HS); A Lee (Chigwell), A Down (Marlwood); E Cripps (Guildford), S Rodgers (The Leys)(captain), I Peel (Wharfedale GS), C Clements (Slough GS), D Ruffell (Chosen Hill), D Zaltzman (Campion), R Hill (Bishop Wordswoth GS), N Jones (Bridgend Boys).

Referee: D Reordan, United States.

HOSPITALS CUP

1st Round

St Bartholomew's 19 St George's 17
University College-Middlesex lost to Guy's

2nd Round

Guy's 6   St Mary's 11
St Thomas's lost to The London
St Bartholomew's 8   Charing Cross-Westminster 28
Royal Free 3   King's College 0

Semi-finals

(Wednesday, 1st March 1995)
St Mary's 19   The London 12
(At Old Deer Park)
Royal Free 12 Charing Cross-Westminster 25

FINAL

Wednesday. 15th March 1995   Old Deer Park

CHARING CROSS-WESTMINSTER 6   ST MARY'S 3

Penalty-goals: Rowe (2)   Penalty-goal: Richards

H.T. 3-0

CHARING CROSS-WESTMINSTER: A Redman; A Sinclair, G O'Driscoll (captain), M Hutton, P Clark; D Clift, E Rowe; H Noble, A Dalrymple, F Banks, D Griffiths, J Waite, M Jeffery, J Hickey, R Walker.

ST MARY'S: D Abrams; I Ugboma, W Jackson, A Morgan, J Platt; S Berry, P Sauve; A Evans, N Wood, N Hunt, P Toozs-Hobson, B Odunuga, M Tremelling (captain), C Langrish, A Sankey. replacement: A Richards for Berry 60 minutes.

Referee: R Preston.

DAILY MAIL SCHOOLS DAY

UNDER 15 FINAL
DULWICH COLLEGE 37   BRISTOL GS 0

Tries: Brewer (3), Sheridan (1), West (1), Dawson (1)
Penalty-goal: West
Conversions: West (2)

DULWICH COLLEGE: N West; D Brewer, T Dux (captain), C King, F Reynolds; N Martin, N Anderson; J Dawson, R Innes, B Graham, M Graham, J Nurse, J Onwubalili, A Thompson, A Sheridan. Replacements: J Franklin, M Woolsey, J Abraham, E Hutton-Mills, H Stewart, L Nargi, N White.

BRISTOL GS: N Raine; L Davies, S Peacock, A Dallimore, A Lockyer; S Marsden, R Blake (captain); P Shepherd, P Jennings, P Bailey, C Robinson, J Davidson, R Morse, S Boorman, C Cavill. Replacements: R Barnes, L Phelan, M Pendrill, R Parker, T Sillence, J Singh, P Jansen.

Referee: J Wallis, Somerset.

UNDER 18 FINAL
COLSTON'S 23   QEGS WAKEFIELD 0

Tries: James (2), Millet (1)
Dropped-goal: Samuel
Penalty-goal: Samuel
Conversion: Samuel

COLSTON'S: M Pitt; M James, J Ewens, P Whitaker (captain), J Pritchard; G Samuel, C Taylor; P Stevenson, J Clark, R Mathieson, M Button, C Chambers, M Jones, N Millet, R Bryan. Replacements: R Pellow, B Tarasuik, P Mackenzie, S Paris, M Haskins, B Hudson, S Williams.

QUEEN ELIZABETH GRAMMAR SCHOOL WAKEFIELD: A Appleyard; E Hadojicharitou, R Field, S Manson, A Phillips; L Cholewa, A Birkby; K Stead, S Pievey, R Jeavons, G Yates, B Annable, M Cusack, I Hird, R Wade (captain). Replacements: N Perigo, M Tindall, A Ahmad, A Nicholas, B Salmons, R Wheatley, M Hemingway.

Referee: S Lander, Liverpool.

UNDER 18 GROUP INTERNATIONAL
ENGLAND 19   SCOTLAND 14

Try: Worsley	Try: Outlaw
Penalty-goals: Cook (4)	Penalty-goals: Mallinson (3)
Conversion: Cook	

Half-time: 9-14

ENGLAND: P Sampson (Woodhouse Grove); N Booth (Lytham HS), C Pawson (Skinner's), K Sorrell (Campion School), J Cook (Millfield); J Hursy (Stonyhurst), M Wood (Harrogate GS); M Worsley (St Ambrose College), R Protherough (King's, Worcester), C Cano (Thomas Alleyne), J Cockle (Prior Park College), A Bell (Colston's), W Fuller (Wallington GS), M Cornish (Ivybridge College), G Wappett (Bradford GS)(captain).

SCOTLAND: S Moffat (Edinburgh Academy); J Craig (St Aloysius College), A Bulloch (Hutchesons' GS), J Mayer (Merchiston Castle), D Mallinson (George Watson's College); G Ross (Georeg Heriot's School), S Hannah (Merchiston Castle)(captain); P Fitzgerald (Dollar Academy), M Landale (Loretto), G Hoyle (Stewart's-Melville College), A Gladstone (Gordonstoun), J White (Cults Academy), A Barnes (Stewart's-Melville College), N Outlaw (Loretto), A Dall (George Heriot's School).

Referee: J Cole, Ireland.

COUNTY CUPS

NORTH

Cheshire:	Macclesfield 29	Winnington Park 18
Cumbria:	Netherhall 9	Kendal 12
Durham:	Stockton 19	Horden 0
Lancashire:	Fylde 15	Manchester 11
Northumberland:	Northern 6	Tynedale 3
Westmorland:	Windermere 13	Millom 24*
Yorkshire:	Harrogate 3	Rotherham 39

MIDLANDS

Bedfordshire:	Leighton Buzzard 9	Stockwood Park 6*
East Midlands:	Leighton Buzzard 15	Stockwood Park 0
Leicestershire:	Loughborough Students 23	Syston 13 (aet)
North Midlands:	Stourbridge 49	Selly Oak 19
Nottinghamshire:	West Bridgford 7	Nottingham Casuals 18*
Notts., Lincs. & Derbys:	Mansfield 14	Scunthorpe 21
Shropshire:	Newport 34	Telford 13*
Staffordshire:	Walsall 27	Stafford 8
Warwickshire:	Broad Street 15	Kenilworth 3

SOUTH WEST

Berkshire:	Reading 30	Abbey 3
Buckinghamshire:	High Wycombe 22	Olney 10
Cornwall:	Redruth 26	Launceston 20
Devon:	Brixham 3	Exeter 22
Dorset & Wiltshire:	Bournemouth 13	Dorchester 8
Gloucestershire:	Gloucester Old Boys 13	Matson 6
Oxfordshire:	Henley 28	Oxford 0
Somerset:	Hornets 14	Keynsham 12

LONDON

Eastern Counties:	Harlow 24	North Walsham 12
Essex:	Barking 14	Harlow 12*
Essex President's Cup:	Billericay 10	May & Baker 7*
Hampshire:	Portsmouth 16	Basingstoke 16
	(after extra-time. Basingstoke win as away team)	
Hertfordshire:	Tabard 40	Letchworth 11
Kent:	Westcombe Park 25	Thanet Wanderers 17
Middlesex:	Ruislip 17	Grasshoppers 10
North West Middlesex:	Ruislip 23	Old Gaytonians 23*
	(after extra time - away team wins)	
Surrey:	Old Blues 0	Camberley 34
Sussex:	Lewes 29	Worthing 18

* Do not qualify for Pilkington Cup

SEVENS

WORTHINGTON WELSH SEVENS
Saturday, 13th August 1994. In Cardiff.
Quarter-finals
Cross Keys 0   Bath 47
Llanelli 7   Bridgend 43
Newport 7   Cardiff 42
Treorchy (Rhondda) 19   Maesteg 5.
Semi-finals:
Bath 26   Bridgend 14
Cradiff 24   Treorchy (Rhondda) 7
FINAL
BATH 42   CARDIFF 5

TOULON
SEMI-FINALS
Argentina 24   France 12
Western Samoa 15   Tonga 5.
THIRD PLACE
Tonga 40   France 14
FINAL
ARGENTINA 27   WESTERN SAMOA 7

CATHAY PACIFIC-HONG KONG BANK SEVENS
25th & 26th March 1995. In Hong Kong.
CUP Quarter-finals:
New Zealand 26   South Africa 0
Western Samoa 28   Tonga 5
Fiji 47   Namibia 0
Australia 26   England 0
Semi-finals:
New Zealand 26   Western Samoa 0
Fiji 35   Australia 5
FINAL
NEW ZEALAND 35   FIJI 17

SCHOOLS SEVENS
Christ College Brecon Sevens
Semi-finals:
Christ College Brecon 5   King's Taunton 12
Solihull 0   Millfield 34
FINAL
Millfield 31   King's Taunton 17
Marches (Hereford) Sevens
Semi-finals:
Hawthorn High School 40   Llandovery 7
Rossall 7   Monmouth 14
FINAL
Hawthorn High School 31   Monmouth 5

JAPAN SEVENS
(Saturday, 15th April 1995. In Tokyo)
FINAL
FIJI 47   NEW ZEALAND 26

LONDON FLOODLIT SEVENS
Wednesday, 3rd May 1995. At Rosslyn Park,
Roehampton.
FINAL
BLACKHEATH 36
WEST LONDON INSTITUTE 29

JED-FORES
FINAL
GALA 22   KELSO 28

MIDDLESEX SEVENS
Saturday, 13th May 1995. At Twickenham.
6th Round:
Orrell 17   Blackheath 27
Wasps 31   Gloucester 10
Leicester 40   West Sussex Institute 12
Nortahmpton 14   Selkirk 17
Ithuba (South Africa) 31   Haywards Heath 7
Harlequins 19   London Scottish 14
Bristol 28   Reading 7
Rosslyn Park 17   Bath 14
Quarter-finals:
Blackheath 19   Wasps 12
Leicester 31   Selkirk 7
Ithuba (South Africa) 28   Harlequins 7
Bristol 14   Rosslyn Park 24
Semi-finals:
Blackheath 5   Leicester 21
Ithuba (South Africa) 24   Rosslyn Park 14
FINAL
LEICESTER 38   ITHUBA (SOUTH AFRICA) 19
Finalists squads: Leicester: O Wingham, C Tarbuck,
N Richardson, C Johnson, J Liley (captain), A
McAdam, R Robinson, T Reynolds, J Hamilton.
Ithuba (South Africa): S Langenhoven, K Januarie, N
Witbool, D Neetling, P Booyesen, J Visser, I Oktober
(captain), W Louw, R Leukes, G Scholtz.

PLATE
1st Round:
Orrell 26   Gloucester 12
West Sussex Institute 12   Northampton 26
Haywards Heath 14   London Scottish 24
Reading 12   Bath 5
Semi-finals:
Orrell 19MNorthampton 0
London Scottish 7   Reading 21
FINAL
ORRELL 15   READING 12

SUPER TEN TOURNAMENT

Pool 'A'

Saturday, 4th March 1995
Transvaal 21   New South Wales 18 (Johannesburg)
Western Province 21   Otago 33 (Cape Town)
Friday, 10th March 1995
New South Wales 31   Otago 16 (Sydney)
Saturday, 11th March 1995
Transvaal 17   North Harbour 14 (Johannesburg)
Saturday, 18th March 1995
North Harbour 6   New South Wales 6 (Auckland)
Western Province 15   Transvaal 13 (Cape Town)
Saturday, 25th March 1995
Otago 35   North Harbour 12 (Dunedin)
New South Wales 23   Western Province 21
(Sydney)
Saturday, 1st April 1995
Canterbury 35   Orange Free State 42
(Christchurch)
Otago 18   Transvaal 27 (Dunedin)

Pool 'B'

Friday, 3rd March 1995
Queensland 24   Canterbury 6 (Brisbane)
Saturday, 4th March 1995
Orange Free State 21   Auckland 15 (Bloemfontein)
Saturday, 11th March 1995
Orange Free State 15   Tonga 12 (Bloemfontein)
Queensland 31   Auckland 15 (Brisbane)
Friday, 17th March 1995
Auckland 27   Canterbury 22 (Auckland)
Queensland 32   Tonga 20 (Brisbane)
Friday, 24th March 1995
Queensland 29   Orange Free State 7 (Brisbane)
Saturday, 25th March 1995
Canterbury 75   Tonga 5 (Christchurch)
Friday, 31st March 1995
Auckland 37   Tonga 25 (Auckland)
Saturday, 1st April 1995
North Harbour 37   Western Province 42 (Auckland)

FINAL TABLE POOL 'A'

	P	W	D	L	F	A	Pts
Transvaal	4	3	0	1	78	65	13
New South Wales	4	2	1	1	78	64	11
Western Province	4	2	0	2	99	106	9
Otago	4	2	0	2	102	91	8
North Harbour	4	0	1	3	69	100	4

FINAL TABLE POOL 'B'

	P	W	D	L	F	A	Pts
Queensland	4	4	0	0	116	48	16
Orange Free State	4	3	0	1	85	81	12
Auckland	4	2	0	2	94	99	9
Canterbury	4	1	0	3	138	98	7
Tonga	4	0	0	4	62	159	1

FINAL

Saturday, 8th April 1995   In Johannesburg

TRANSVAAL 16   QUEENSLAND 30

Try: Roux
Dropped-goals: de Beer (3)
Conversion: de Beer

Tries: Connors (1), Johnstone (1),
Little (1), Herbert (1)
Dropped-goal: Kahl
Penalty-goal: Eales
Conversion: Eales (2)

ROMANIA TOUR TO ENGLAND

NOVEMBER 1994

Saturday, 5th November	Oxford University	Oxford	L 16-26
Tuesday, 8th November	Cambridge University	Cambridge	W 27-18
Saturday, 12th November	ENGLAND	Twickenham	L 3-54

Summary: Played 3, won 1, lost 2, points for 46, against 98.

Saturday, 5th November 1994   **At Iffley Road Oxford**

OXFORD UNIVERSITY 26   ROMANIA 16

Tries: Joy (1), Nolan (1)
Dropped-goal: Rees
Penalty-goals: Rees (3),
Conversions: Rees (2)

Try: Oroian
Penalty-goals: Ivanciuc (2),
Colceriu (1)
Conversion: Ivanciuc

H.T. 16-13

OXFORD UNIVERSITY: M Joy; I Gray, S Bromley, M Nolan, T Howe; G Rees, M Kirsten; A Bryce, D Henderson (captain), S Thompson, G Allison, P Coveney, J Daniell, N Martin, R Yeabsley.
ROMANIA: V Brici; L Colceriu, G Solomie, S Tofan, R Cioca; I Ivanciuc, V Flutur; G Vlad, C Gheorghe, C Stan, T Oroian, C Cojocariu, C Branescu, A Gealapu, C Draguceanu.
Con: Ivanciuc. Half-time: 16-13.
Referee: N Lasaga, France.

Tuesday, 8th November 1994   **At Grange Road, Cambridge**

CAMBRIDGE UNIVERSITY 18   ROMANIA 27

Penalty-goals: Richards (6)

Tries: Negreci (1), Gealapu (1), Brinza (1)
Dropped-goal: Ivanciuc
Penalty-goals: Ivanciuc (3)

H.T. 15-16

CAMBRIDGE UNIVERSITY: S Phillips; A Richards, A Palfrey, S Cottrell (captain), J Reynolds; A Kennedy, J Davies; L Mooney, I Mackenzie, M Cox, A Metcalfe, R Bramley, A Meadows, H Jones, E Rollitt. Temporary replacement: G Fury for Rollitt 2-11 minutes.
ROMANIA: V Brici; L Colceriu, G Solomie, S Tofan, R Cioca; I Ivanciuc, D Neaga; G Vlad, I Negreci, F Marioara, A Guranescu, T Oroain, C Branescu, A Gealapu, T Brinza (captain). Replacements: C Cojocariu for Oroian 29 minutes, S Tranca for Colceriu 40 minutes, C Draguceanu for Gurunuscu 69 minutes.
Referee: C Muir, Langholm.

Saturday, 12th November 1994   **At Twickenham**

ENGLAND 54   ROMANIA 3

Tries: T Underwood (2), Carling (1)
Rodber (1), R Underwood (1), penalty try
Penalty-goals: Andrew (4)
Conversions: Andrew (6)

Penalty-goal: Ivanciuc

H.T. 26-3.

ENGLAND: P Hull (Bristol/RAF); T Underwood (Leicester), W Carling (Harlequins)(captain), J Guscott (Bath), R Underwood (Leicester/RAF); R Andrew (Wasps), D Morris (Orrell); J Leonard (Harlequins), B Moore (Harlequins), V Ubogu (Bath), T Rodber (Northampton/Army), M Johnson (Leicester), M Bayfield (Northampton), S Ojomoh (Bath), B Clarke (Bath). No new caps.
ROMANIA: V Brici (Farul Constanta); G Solomie (Timisoara University), M Vioreanu (Timisoara University), S Tofan (Dinamo Bucharest), R Cioca (Dinamo Bucharest); I Ivanciuc (CSM Suceava), D Neaga (Dinamo Bucharest); L Costea (Steaua Bucharets), I Negreci (CFR Constanta), G Vlad (Dinamo Bucharest), T Oroian (Steaua Bucharest), C Cojocariu (Bayonne), C Branescu (Farul Constanta), A Gealapu (Steaua Bucharest), T Brinza (Cluj University)(captain). Replacements: C Draguceanu (Steaua Bucharest) for Oroian 50 minutes, F Marioara (Dinamo Bucharest) for Coastea 52 minutes, C Gheorghe (Grivita Bucharets) for Negreci 67 minutes, A Gurunescu (Steaua Bucharest) for Branescu 78 minutes. New caps: Vioreanu, Costea, Negreci, Marioara.
Referee: S Neethling, South Africa.

ROMANIA 'A' IN ENGLAND
FEBRUARY 1995

Tue, 14th Feb	Midlands 'A',	Moseley	W 26-23
Fri, 17th Feb	England Emerging West Players	Hartlepool	L 14-97

Summary: Played 2, won 1, lost 1, points for 40, against 120.

Tuesday, 14th February 1995   **At The Reddings, Moseley**

MIDLANDS 'A' 23   ROMANIA 'A' 26

Tries: Cassell (1) penalty try

Penalty-goals: Kerr (3)

Conversions: Stent (1)

Kerr (1)

Tries: Nedelcu (1), Ruxanda (1), Stanca (1)

Penalty-goals: Apjoc (3)

Conversion: Apjoc

H.T. 23-14

MIDLANDS 'A': A Quantrill (Rugby); E Subbiani (Bedford), A Kerr (Moseley), P Flood (Rosslyn Park), A Smallwood (Nottingham); I Stent (Nottingham), G Becconsall (Moseley); M Freer (Nottingham), D West (Nottingham)(captain), W Bullock (Gloucester), M Bradley (Nottingham), J Hyde (Coventry), R Field (Leicester), D Grewcock (Coventry), J Cassell (Northampton). Replacements: B Whetstone (Bedford) for Stent 20 minutes, M Warr (Sale) for Becconsall 55 minutes.

ROMANIA 'A': V Maftei; R Gontineac, M Nedelcu, M Stan, I Rotaru; E Apjoc, V Flutur (captain); L Costea, G Cilinca, L Rotaru, I ruxanda, A Stanca, M Dragomir, N Marin, F Scafariu. Replacements: V Tufa for Cilinca 46 minutes, R Fugigi for Nedelcu 65 minutes, G Voicu for Costea 65 minutes.

Referee: B Campsall, Yorkshire.

Friday, 17th February 1995   **At West Hartlepool**
ENGLAND EMERGING PLAYERS 97   ROMANIA 'A' 14
Tries: Hackney (5), Greenwood(3)

Beal (2), Grayson (1)

Childs (1), Adams (1),

Mensah (1), Haag (1)

Conversions: Grayson (11)

Tries: Stan (1), Fugigi (1)

Conversions: Apjok (2)

H.T. 50-7

ENGLAND EMERGING PLAYERS: W Greenwood (Harleequins); N Beal (Northampton), G Childs (Wasps), P Mensah (Harlequins), S Hackney (Leicester); P Grayson (Northampton), R Kitchin (Harlequins); D Molloy (Wasps), G Adams (Bath), D Hinkins (Bristol), R Jenkins (Harlequins), M Haag (Bath), R West (Gloucester), D Eves (Bristol)(captain), C Sheasby (Harlequins).

ROMANIA 'A': C Patrichi; G Voicu, M Stan, R Fugigi, E Florea; E Apjok, V Flutur (captain); C Constantin, V Tufu, G Voicu, F Scafariu, N Branescu, A Stanca, I Ruxanda, N Marin.

Referee: E Murray, Scotland.

WOMEN'S RUGBY

Women's Final
Wednesday, 22nd March 1995   **At Twickenham**
Loughbrough University 53   De Montford Bedford 11

Vladivar Cup Final
Sunday, 9th April 1995   **At Stoop Memorial Ground, Twickenham**
Richmond 27   Wasps 0

SOUTH AFRICA TOUR TO WALES, SCOTLAND & IRELAND

OCTOBER TO DECEMBER 1994

Sat, 22nd October	Cardiff	Cardiff	W 11- 6
Wed, 26th October	Wales 'A'	Newport	W 25-13
Sat, 29th October	Llanelli	Llanelli	W 30-12
Wed, 2nd November	Neath	Neath	W 16-13
Sat, 5th November	Swansea	Swansea	W 78- 7
Wed, 9th November	Scotland 'A'	Melrose	L 15-17
Sat, 12th November	Scottish Districts	Glasgow (Old Anniesland)	W 33- 6
Tue, 15th November	Scottish Select	Aberdeen	W 35-10
Sat, 19th November	SCOTLAND	Murrayfield	W 34-10
Tue, 22nd November	Pontypridd	Pontypridd	W 9- 3
Sat, 26th November	WALES	Cardiff Arms Park	W 20-12
Tue, 29th November	Combined Irish	Belfast Provinces	W 54-19
Sat, 3rd December	BARBARIANS	Dublin	L 15-23

Summary: Played 13, won 11, lost 2, points for 375, against 141.

APPEARANCES

NB1 + Denotes appearance as a replacement.
NB2 Figures in brackets show international appearances.
NB3 * Denotes replacement during tour.

BACKS: A Joubert (Natal) 7+1 (2); C Badenhorst (Orange Free State) 3; B Venter (Orange Free State) 5; P Muller (Natal) 7(2); C Williams (Western Province) 7(2); J Stransky (Natal) 7+2; J van der Westhuizen (Northern Transvaal) 7(2); G Johnson (Transvaal) 7+1; J Olivier (Northern Transvaal) 5; J Mulder (Transvaal) 6(2); M Linee (Western Province) 4; P Hendriks (Transvaal) 6(2); H le Roux (Transvaal) 6(2); K Putt (Natal) 6; * JF van der Westhuizen (Natal) 4; * H Muller (Orange Free State) 3; * J Classens 1.

FORWARDS: B Swart (Transvaal) 6; U Schmidt (Transvaal) 7(2); I Hattingh (Transvaal) 7; M Andrews (Natal) 7(2); H Hattingh (Northern Transvaal) 4; R Kruger (Northern Transvaal) 7(2); R Straeuli (Transvaal) 7+1(2); G Teichmann (Natal) 7+1; J du Randt (Orange Free State) 7(2); J Dalton (Transvaal) 6; T Laubscher (Western Province) 6(2); J Wiese (Transvaal) 6; P Schutte (Transvaal) 6(2); E van der Bergh (Eastern Province) 7; F Pienaar (Transvaal)(captain); C Strauss (Western Province) 5; * K Otto (Northern Transvaal) 3.

SCORERS: (All Matches): A Joubert (6 tries, 3 pens, 18 cons) 75 pts; G Johnson (3 tries, 12 pens, 10 cons) 71 pts; R Straeuli (5 tries) 25pts; J van der Westhuizen (5 tries) 25pts; J Stransky (3 tries, 3 pens) 24pts; H le Roux (1 try, 3 pens. 3 cons) 20 pts; U Schmidt 3 tries) 15pts; R Kruger (3 tries) 15pts; C Williams (3 tries) 15pts; P Muller (3 tries) 15pts; K Otto (3 tries) 15 pts; I Hattingh (2 tries) 10pts; P Hendriks (2 tries) 10pts; K Putt (1 try) 5pts; M Linee (1 try) 5 pts; E van der Bergh (1 try) 5pts; F Pienaar (1 try) 5pts; C Strauss (1 try) 5pts; B Venter (1 try) 5pts; H Hattingh (1 try) 5pts; J Mulder (1 try) 5pts.

(Internationals): A Joubert (1 try, 1 pen, 3 cons) 14pts; J van der Westhuizen (2 tries) 10pts; C Williams (2 tries) 10pts; R Straeuli (2 tries) 10pts; P Muller (1 try) 5pts; H le Roux (1 pen, 1 con) 5pts.

Saturday, 22nd October 1994 **At Cardiff Arms Park**

CARDIFF 6   SOUTH AFRICA 11

Penalty-goals: Davies (1)
John (1)

Try: Van der Westhuizen
Penalty-goals: Stransky (2)

H.T. 6-0

CARDIFF: C John; S Ford, M Hall (captain), C Laity, N Walker; A Davies, A Moore; M Griffiths, J Humphreys, L Mustoe, H Taylor, S Roy, D Jones, O Williams, E Lewis. Temporary replacement: A Booth for Moore 34-40 minutes.

SOUTH AFRICA: A Joubert; C Badenhorst, B Venter, P Muller, C Williams; J Stransky, J van der Westhuizen; B Swart, U Schmidt, I Hattingh, R Kruger, M Andrews, H Hattingh, R Straeuli, G Teichmann.

Referee: J Fleming, Scotland.

WALES 'A' 13   SOUTH AFRICA 25

Try: Walker
Penalty-goals: A Davies (2)
Conversion: A Davies

Tries: Putt (1), Linee (1),
Straeuli (1)
Penalty-goals: Le Roux (2)
Conversions: Le Roux (2)

H.T. 10-3

WALES 'A': M Back (Bridgend); D Manley (Pontypridd), S Lewis (Pontypridd), M Taylor (Pontypool), N Walker (Cardiff); A Davies (Cardiff), P John (Pontypridd)(captain); I Buckett (Swansea), B Williams (Neath), L Mustoe (Cardiff), S Davies (Swansea), P Arnold (Swansea), D Jones (Cardiff), R Appleyard (Swansea), S Williams (Neath). Replacement: M Griffiths (Cardiff) for Mustoe 66 minutes.

SOUTH AFRICA: G Johnson; J Olivier, J Mulder, M Linee, P Hendriks; H le Roux, K Putt; J du Randt, J Dalton, T Laubscher, R Kruger, J Weise, P Schutte, E van der Bergh, R Straeuli (captain). Replacement: G Teichmann for Kruger 56 minutes.

Referee: A Spreadbury, England.

LLANELLI 12   SOUTH AFRICA 30

Tries: Wintle (1)
Proctor (1)
Conversion: Stephens
Conversions: Joubert (2)

Tries: Stransky (1), van der Bergh
(1), Joubert (1), Pienaar (1)
Penalty-goals: Stransky (1), Joubert (1)

H.T. 7-23

LANELLI: I Jones; W Proctor, N Boobyer, N Davies, M Wintle; C Stephens, R Moon (captain); R Evans, R McBryde, S John, P Jones, P Davies, A Copsey, M Perego, J Williams. Replacements: J Strange for Stephens 68 minutes, H Harries for Proctor 77 minutes.

SOUTH AFRICA: A Joubert; C Badenhorst, B Venter, J Mulder, C Williams; J Stransky, J van der Westhuizen; B Swart, U Schmidt, I Hattingh, F Pienaar (captain), M Andrews, H Hattingh, E van der Bergh, G Teichmann. Replacement: T Laubscher for Swart 40 minutes.

Referee: D McHugh, Ireland.

NEATH 13   SOUTH AFRICA 16

Try: Jones
Penalty-goals: Thomas (2)
Conversion: Thomas (1)

Try: Strauss
Penalty-goals: Johnson (2), Joubert
Conversion: Joubert.

H.T. 10-6

NEATH: P Thorburn; H Higgs, J Bird, H Woodland, L Davies; A Thomas, Rhodri Jones; Brian Williams, Barry Williams, J Davies, A Kembery, Gareth Llewellyn (captain), C Wyatt, C Scott, S Williams.

SOUTH AFRICA: G Johnson; C Badenhorst, P Muller, B Venter, J Olivier; J Stransky, K Putt; P du Randt, J Dalton, I Hattingh, G Teichmann, J Wiese, H Hattingh, E van der Bergh, C Strauss (captain). Replacement: A Joubert for Badenhorst 21 minutes.

Referee: R Megson, Scotland.

SWANSEA 7   SOUTH AFRICA 78

Try: Simon Davies
Conversion: Williams

Tries: Joubert (4), Hendriks (2), Schmidt (1),
le Roux (1), Kruger (1), Straeuli (1),
van der Westhuizen (1), Williams (1)
Conversions: Joubert (9)

H.T. 7-12

SWANSEA: A Clement (captain); Simon Davies, R Boobyer, D Weatherley, S Marshall; A Williams, Robert Jones; I Buckett, G Jenkins, K Colclough, A Reynolds, P Arnold, R Moriarty, R Appleyard, I Davies. Replacements: M Evans for Moriarty 55 minutes, Stuart Davies for Appleyard 63 minutes.
SOUTH AFRICA: A Joubert; P Hendriks, J Mulder, P Muller, C Williams; H le Roux, J van der Westhuizen; P du Randt, U Schmidt, T Laubscher, F Pienaar (captain), M Andrews, P Schutte, R Kruger, R Straeuli. Referee: S Hilditch, Ireland.

SCOTLAND 'A' 17   SOUTH AFRICA 15

Try: Wallace
Dropped-goals: Hodge (2)
Penalty-goals: Shepherd

Tries: Venter (1), H Hattingh (1)
Penalty-goal: Johnson
Conversion: Johnson (2)

H.T. 8-8.

SCOTLAND 'A': R Shepherd (Edinburgh Academicals); C Joiner (Melrose), S Nichol (Selkirk), I Jardine (Stirling County), C Glasgow (Heriot's FP); D Hodge (Watsonians), B Redpath (Melrose); D Hilton (Bath), K McKenzie (Stirling County)(captain), P Wright (Boroughmuir), F Wallace (Glasgow High/Kelvinside), D Cronin (Bourges), S Campbell (Dundee High School FP), I Smith (Gloucester), R Wainwright (West Hartlepool). Temporary replacement: B Robertson (Stirling County) for Wright 58-60 minutes.
SOUTH AFRICA: G Johnson; J Olivier, M Linee, B Venter, C van der Westhuizen; J Stransky, K Putt; I Hattingh, J Dalton, B Swart, G Teichmann, J Wiese, H Hattingh, E van der Bergh, C Strauss (captain). Referee: P Thomas, France.

SCOTTISH DISTRICTS 6   SOUTH AFRICA 33

Penalty-goals: McKenzie (2)

Tries: Muller (2), van der Westhuizen (1),Straeuli (1) Kruger (1)
Conversions: Joubert (3), Johnson (1)

H.T. 6-12

SCOTTISH DISTRICTS: N Mardon (Boroughmuir); H Gilmour (Heriot's FP), A McRobbie (Heriot's FP), S Lineen (Boroughmuir)(captain), J Kerr (Watsonians); M McKenzie (Stirling County), G Burns (Stewart's-Melville FP); G Wilson (Boroughmuir), G Ellis (Currie), B Robertson (Stirling County), B Ward (Currie), A Watt (Glasgow High/Kelvinside), S Munro (Glasgow High/Kelvinside), G McKay (Stirling County) S Reid (Boroughmuir).
SOUTH AFRICA: A Joubert; P Hendriks, P Muller, B Venter, C Williams; H le Roux, J van der Westhuizen; P du Randt, U Schmidt, T Laubscher, F Pienaar (captain), M Andrews, P Schutte, R Kruger, R Straeuli. Replacements: G Johnson for Joubert 60 minutes, J Stransky for Venter 74 minutes. Referee: C Thomas, Wales.

SCOTTISH SELECT XV 10   SOUTH AFRICA 35

Try: Oliver
Penalty-goal: Welsh
Conversion: Welsh

Tries: Otto (1), Johnson (1),
I Hattingh (1)
Penalty-goals: Johnson (6)
Conversion: Johnson

H.T. 3-22.

SCOTTISH SELECT XV: M Dods (Gala); G Sharp (Bristol), F Harrold (London Scottish), R Eriksson (London Scottish), M Appleson (Sale); S Welsh (Hawick), G Oliver (Hawick)(captain); J Manson (Dundee High School FP), M Scott (Dunfermline), D Herrington (Dundee High School FP), D Turnbull (Hawick), R Brown (Melrose) R Scott (London Scottish), R Kirkpatrick (Jed-Forest), E Peters (Bath). Replacement: B Renwick (Hawick) for Turnbull 43 minutes.

SOUTH AFRICA: G Johnson; C van der Westhuizen, H Muller, M Linee, J Olivier; J Stransky, K Putt; Hattingh, J Dalton, B Swart, G Teichmann, J Wiese, K Otto, E van der Bergh, C Strauss (captain).

Referee: G Simmonds, Wales.

SCOTLAND 10   SOUTH AFRICA 34

Try: Stanger
Penalty-goal: G Hastings
Conversion: G Hastings

Tries: J Van der Westhuizen (2)
Williams (1), Straeuli (1),
Mulder (1)
Penalty-goal: Joubert
Conversions: Joubert (3)

H.T. 0-8

SCOTLAND: G Hastings (Watsonians)(captain); A Stanger (Hawick), S Hastings (Watsonians), G Shiel (Melrose), K Logan (Stirling County); C Chalmers (Melrose), D Patterson (West Hartlepool); A Sharp (Bristol), K Milne (Heriot's FP), P Burnell (London Scottish), D McIvor (Edinburgh Academicals), J Richardson (Edinburgh Acaedmicals), A Reed (Bath), I Morrison (London Scottish), G Weir (Melrose). New caps: Patterson, Richardson.

SOUTH AFRICA (Transvaal unless stated): A Joubert (Natal); P Hendriks, P Muller (Natal), C Mulder, C Williams (Western Province); H le Roux, J van der Westhuizen (Northern Transvaal); J du Randt (Orange Free State), U Schmidt, T Laubscher (Western Province), F Pienaar (captain), M Andrews (Natal), P Schutte, R Kruger (Northern Transvaal), R Straeuli.

New cap: Schutte.

Referee: O Doyle, Ireland.

PONTYPRIDD 3   SOUTH AFRICA 9

Penalty-goal: Cormack

Penalty-goals: Johnson (3)

H.T. 3-3

PONTYPRIDD: G Jones; D Manley, J Lewis, S Lewis, O Robbins; C Cormack, Paul John; N Bezani (captain), Phil John A Metcalfe, M Spiller, G Prosser, M Rowley, M Lloyd, P Thomas. Replacement: C Jones for J Lewis 72 minutes.

SOUTH AFRICA: G Johnson; J Olivier, H Muller, M Linee, C van der Westhuizen; J Stransky, K Putt; Swart, J Dalton, I Hattingh, G Teichmann, J Wiese, K Otto, E van der Bergh, C Strauss (captain).

Referee: B Campsall, Yorkshire.

WALES 12   SOUTH AFRICA 20

Penalty-goals: N Jenkins (4)   Tries: Straeuli (1), Joubert (1), Williams (1)
                                                       Penalty-goal: Le Roux
                                                       Conversion: Le Roux

H.T. 6-10

WALES: A Clement (Swansea); W Proctor (Llanelli), M Hall (Cardiff), M Taylor (Pontypool), S Hill (Cardiff); N Jenkins (Pontypridd), R Moon (Llanelli); R Evans (Llanelli), G Jenkins (Swansea) J Davies (Neath), H Taylor (Cardiff), D Jones (Cardiff), Gareth Llewellyn (Neath)(captain), R Collins (Pontypridd), E Lewis (Cardiff). Temporary replacement: R McBryde (Swansea) for G Jenkins 32-38 minutes. New caps: M Taylor, D Jones.

SOUTH AFRICA (Transvaal unless stated): A Joubert (Natal); P Hendriks, P Muller (Natal), J Mulder, C Williams (Western Province); H le Roux, J van der Westhuizen (Northern Transvaal); J du Randt (Orange Free State), U Schmidt, T Laubscher (Western Province), J Pienaar, M Andrews (Natal), P Schutte, R Kruger (Northern Transvaal), R Straeuli. No new caps.

Referee: D Mene, France.

COMBINED IRISH PROVINCES 19   SOUTH AFRICA 54

Tries: Bell (1), Fitzgerald (1)   Tries: Stransky (2), Otto (2)
Penalty- goals: McGowan (3)   Schmidt (2), I Hattingh (1), Johnson (1)
                                               Conversions: Johnson (7)

COMBINED IRISH PROVINCES: J Bell (Ballymena); P Gavin (Old Belvedere), P Danaher (Garryown), M Field (Malone), R Wallace (Garryowen); A McGowan (Blackrock College), A Rolland (Blackrock College); J Fitzgerald (Young Munster), T Kingston (Dolphin)(captain), G Halpin (London Irish), E Halvey (Shannon), M Galwey (Shannon), N Francis (Old Belvedere), D Corkery (Cork Constitution), S McKinty (Bangor).

SOUTH AFRICA: G Johnson; P Hendriks, H Muller, J Classens, C van der Westhuizen; J Stransky, K Putt; I Hattingh, U Schmidt, T Laubscher, G Teichmann, K Otto, P Schutte, E van der Bergh, R Straeuli (captain).

Referee: R Yemen, Wales.

BARBARIANS 23   SOUTH AFRICA 15

Tries: Saint-Andre (1)   Tries: Kruger (1), Muller (1),
Geoghegan (1)   Johnson (1)
Dropped-goal: Chalmers
Penalty-goals: Callard (2)
Conversions: Callard (2)

H.T. 10-5

BARBARIANS: J Callard (Bath); P Saint-Andre (Montferrand), M Hall (Cardiff0, S Hastings (Watsonians), S Geoghegan (Bath); C Chalmers (Melrose), R Jones (Swansea)(captain); N Popplewell (Wasps), K Wood (Garryown), P Clohessy (Young Munster), A Charron (Ottawa Irish/Ontario), I Jones (North Auckland), S Shaw (Bristol), N Back (Leicester), R Wainwright (West Hartlepool). Replacements: G Manson-Bishop (Newport) for Charron 28 minutes, P Howard (Queensland University) for Hastings 47 minutes.

SOUTH AFRICA (Transvaal unless stated): A Joubert (Natal); G Johnson, P Muller (Natal), J Mulder (Orange Free State), C Williams (Western Province); H le Roux, J van der Westhuizen (Northern Transvaal); P du Randt (Orange Free State), J Dalton, B Swart, F Pienaar (captain), J Wiese, M Andrews (Natal), R Kruger (Northern Transvaal), C Strauss (Western Province). Replacments: J Stransky (Western Province) for Williams 22 minutes, R Straeuli for Pienaar 78 minutes.

Referee: D Bevan, Wales.

ENGLAND 'A' IN AUSTRALIA – MAY & JUNE 1995

SOUTH AUSTRALIA 9   ENGLAND 'A' 66   In Adelaide

Penalty-goals: Elliott (3)

Tries: Eves (2), Naylor (2) Sleightholme (1)
Gomarsall (1), Crompton (1), Hull (1), Sims (1) PT
Penalty-goals: Grayson (2)
Conversions: Grayson (5)

H.T. 6-32

ENGLAND 'A': P Hull (captain); J Naylor, P Mensah, W Greenwood, J Sleightholme; P Grayson, A Gomarsall; R Hardwick, G Adams, D Crompton, R Jenkins, D Sims, J Fowler, D Eves, A Diprose. Replacement: R Hill for Jenkins 60 minutes.
Referee: K O'Halloran, ARU.

VICTORIA 19   ENGLAND 'A' 76   In Melbourne

Tries: Goodman (2), Strauss (1)
Conversions: Goodman (2)

Tries: Dawson (3), Hackney (2), Hill (1), Holford (1)
Regan (1), Sheasby (1), Yates (1), penalty tries (2)
Conversions: Pears (5), Stimpson (3)

QUEENSLAND 20   ENGLAND 'A' 15

Tries: Kahl (1), Murray (1)
Penalty-goals: Kahl (1), Mandrusiak (1)
Conversions: Kahl (1), Mandrusiak (1)

Penalty-goals: Pears (5)

H.T. 3-9

ENGLAND 'A': P Hull (Bristol/RAF)(captain); J Naylor (Orrell), S Potter (Leicester), P Mensah (Harlequins), J Sleightholme (Bath); D Pears (Harlequins), M Dawson (Northampton); R Hardwick (Coventry), M Regan (Bristol), D Garforth (Leicester), R Corry (Newcastle Gosforth), G Archer (Bristol), J Fowler (Sale), R Jenkins (Harlequins), A Diprose (Saracens).

AUSTRALIAN UNIVERSITIES 32   ENGLAND 'A' 30   In Sydney

Tries: Hill (2), Harrison (1)
Penalty-goals: Madz (2), Hull (1), Metcalfe (1)
Conversions: Madz (3)

Tries: Gomarsall (1), Howard (1), Hackney (1)
Penalty-goals: Grayson (2)
Conversions: Grayson (2)

NEW SOUTH WALES COUNTRY 28   ENGLAND 'A' 23   In Newcastle

Tries: Friss (1), McQueen (1)
Penalty-goals: Eddy (3)
Conversions: Eddy (2)

Tries: Eves (1), Holford (1), Tonkin (1), Yates (1)
Penalty-goals: Grayson (2)
Conversion: Grayson

AUSTRALIA XV 19   ENGLAND 'A' 27   In Brisbane

Tries: Kelaher (1), Murdoch (1)
Dropped-goal: Kelaher
Penalty-goals: Kelaher (2), Hull (1)

Tries: Naylor (1), Mensah (1)
Dropped-goal: Grayson
Penalty-goals: Grayson (3),
Conversion: Grayson

ENGLAND 'A': P Hull (Bristol/RAF)(captain); J Naylor (Orrell), S Potter (Leicester), P Mensah (Harlequins), J Sleightholme (Bath); P Grayson (Northampton), R Kitchin (Harlequins); R Hardwick (Coventry), M Regan (Bristol), D Garforth (Leicester), C Sheasby (Harlequins), J Fowler (Sale), D Sims (Gloucester), R Jenkins (Harlequins), A Diprose (Saracens).

FIJI 59   ENGLAND 25   In Suva

Tries: Masirewa (2), Sorovaki (2)
Rasila (1), Rauluni (1), Savai (1)
Conversions: Turuva (6), Waqa (1)

Tries: Sheasby (2), Jenkins Bari (1), Little (1)
Penalty-goals: Grayson (2)
Conversions: Hull (2)

H.T. 24-6

OTHER ENGLISH REPRESENTATIVE MATCHES

Saturday, 3rd December 1994   At Devonport
COMBINED SERVICES 21   CANADA 20

Tries: Sharp (1), Brammar (1)   Tries: McKenzie (1), Gordon (1)
Penalty-goals: Worrall (3)   Penalty-goals: Ross (2)
Conversions: Ross (2)   Conversion: Worrall

H.T. 13-6

COMBINED SERVICES (Royal Air Force unless stated): S Lazenby; S Bartliff (Army), G Sharp, D Sibson (Royal Navy), S Crossland; E Rayner, S Worrall (captain); B Williams, J Brammer (Army), H Fowers (Army), G Harrison (Royal Navy), D Dahinton (Army), D Williams, I Dixon (Royal Navy), R Armstrong (Royal Marines).

Tuesday, 6th December 1994   In Bath
EMERGING ENGLAND 34   CANADA 6

Tries: Greenstock (2), Sleight-holme (1), Childs (1)   Penalty-goals: Ross (2)
Penalty-goals: Gregory (2)
Conversions: Gregory (4)

H.T. 7-6

EMERGING ENGLAND: W Greenwood (Harlequins); J Sleightholme (Bath), G Childs (Wasps), N Greenstock (Wasps), H Thorneycroft (Northampton); G Gregory (Wasps), R Kitchen (Harlequins); R Hardwick (Coventry), G Adams (Bath), D Hinkins (Bristol), A Diprose (Saracens), G Archer (Newcastle Gosforth), R West (Gloucester), D Eves (Bristol)(captain), R Hill (Saracens).

Saturday, 10th December 1994   At Twickenham
ENGLAND 60   CANADA 19

Tries: R Underwood (2), Catt (2)   Tries: Lougheed (2),
T Underwood (1), Bracken (1)   Evans (1)
Penalty-goals: Andrew (6)   Conversions: Rees (2)
Conversions: Andrew (6)

H.T.15-0

ENGLAND: P Hull (Bristol/RAF); T Underwood (Leicester), W Carling (Harlequins)(captain), J Guscott (Bath), R Underwood (Leicester/RAF); R Andrew (Wasps), K Bracken (Bristol); J Leonard (Harlequins), B Moore (Harlequins), V Ubogu (Bath), T Rodber (Northampton/Army), M Johnson (Leicester), M Bayfield (Northampton), B Clarke (Bath), D Richards (Leicester). Replacements: M Catt (Bath) for Hull 26 minutes, P de Glanville (Bath) for T Underwood 64 minutes. No new caps.

Wednesday, 8th March 1995   In Bristol
EMERGING ENGLAND 3   NORTHERN TRANSVAAL 19
Penalty-goal: Gregory   Try: Kruger
                                Penalty-goals: Van As (4)
                                Conversion: Van As

H.T. 3-16

EMERGING ENGLAND: T Stimpson (West Hartlepool); S Hackney (Leicester), N Beal (Northampton), G Stocks (Sale), P Holford (Gloucester); G Gregory (Wasps), A Gommersall (Wasps); D Molloy (Wasps), G Adams (Bath), D Crompton (Bath), R Jenkins (Harlequins), M Haag (Bath), J Fowler (Sale), D Eves (Bristol)(captain), C Sheasby (Harlequins).

EDITOR'S NOTE

We have been much more ambitious this season as our statistics present more and more fascinating facts and figures for leagues and individual clubs.

However, you will see there are some gaps, so should you know individual club details that we haven't unearthed please write to Steve McCormack c/o the publishers.

It should also be noted that the views and opinions published in this Directory are not necessarily those of the Rugby Union, Courage or Michael Humphreys Partners.

We have tried to include clues for readers to find clubs who have changed their names and hopefully this increased indices will help!

Once again may we thank all the club officials who have sent in such comprehensive information and some excellent photos with captions.

However, those who didn't bother are sadly letting their own club supporters down as a depleted section upsets them most. We are determined to improve the club coverage every year, but we can only do this with club officials' help and of course the sales of books at clubs which bring in the revenue to enable us to enlarge The Directory.

With our thanks again.

Tony Williams

STOP PRESS

New Secretarys:

HARTLEPOOL ROVERS FC: N-N2
Phil Mitchell
McArdle, Cardwell & Mitchell Solicitors
Victoria Road
Hartlepool
TS26 8DJ
Tel: (W) 01429 866542

DITCHLING RUFC: L-Sx2
HON. SEC.:
Julian Wallden
NEW **Tel: 01273 890675**

WESTERHAM RFC: L-KENT4
A Richman
Tygoch
17A Victoria Gardens
Biggin Hill
Kent
TN16 5DH
Tel: (H) 01959 575597

LEAGUE
STRUCTURE
&
CLUB INDEX

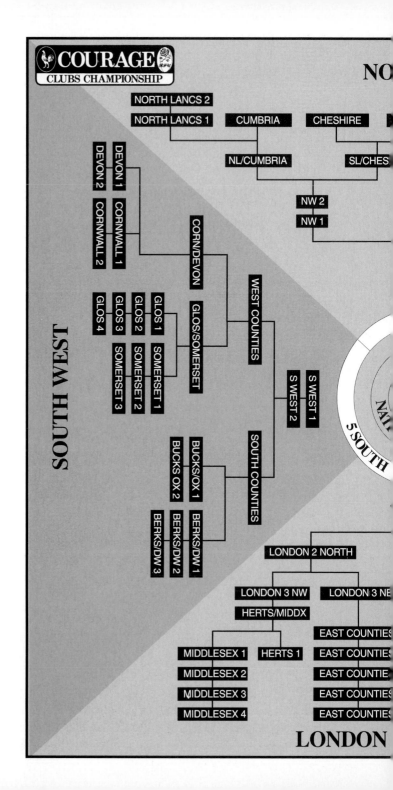

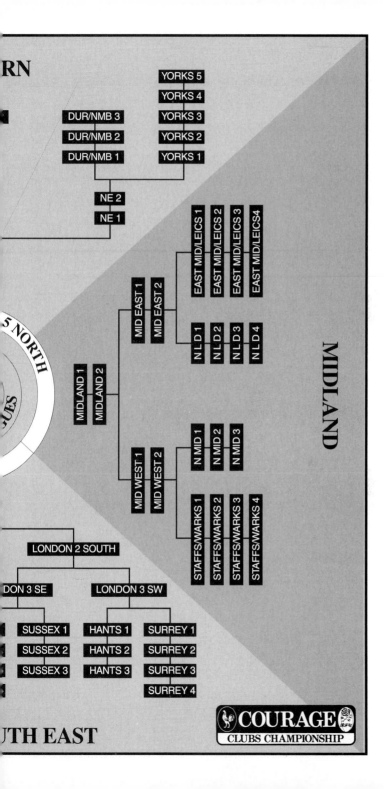

The very sad and sudden death of Richard Langhorn last December shocked the rugby world.
Richard who was 29, suffered a heart attack after an operation on his back.
Peter Winterbottom has set up a trust fund the proceeds of which to provide sporting opportunities for underpriviledged children.
Any contributions can be sent to:-

"The Richard Langhorn Trust"
c/o Peter Winterbottom
Harlequin F.C.
Stoop Memorial Ground
Cranford Way
Twickenham
Middlesex   TW27 5Q

Thank you
Joe McCabe

CLUB INDEX

CLUB INDEX

CLUB INDEX

CLUB INDEX

CLUB INDEX

CLUB INDEX

CLUB INDEX

CLUB INDEX

CLUB INDEX

CLUB INDEX

SERVICES DIRECTORY
FOR
RUGBY UNION CLUBS

In future issues of The Courage Rugby Union Clubs Directory we will be including a section in which companies who provide services to Rugby Union Clubs will be able to advertise their products and skills. As every club strives to improve its facilities and its ability to raise funds these services will be vital.

List of Services

Race Nights
Healthcare Organisations
Cabaret Nights
Agents for Guest Speakers
Insurance Companies
Free Phone Lines
Book Clubs
Pool Tables
Dart Boards
Training Aids
Goal Posts
Rugby Boots
Pre-Match Entertainments
Electrical Equipment
Showers
Flooring
Indoor Ceilings
Grass Seed
Turfing
Burglar Alarms
Fire Alarms
Double Glazing
Drinking Glasses
Crisps/Peanuts
Security Lights
Touchline Flags
Sports Injuries Clinics
Vending Machines
White-Liners for Pitches
Video Games (by Mail etc)
Glass Glazing Designers
TV & Cable Companies

Protective Padding
Club Houses
Large Stands
Small Stands
Suppliers Floodlights
Tarmac Suppliers
Advertising Boards
Signwriters
Fund Raisers
Lottery Organisers
Fruit Machines
Paint Suppliers
Programme Compilers
Programme Printers
Sports Drink Suppliers
Shower Installers
Architects
Brewers
Cigarette M/C Suppliers
Metal Badges
Scarfs
Rosettes
Cutlery & Plates
Cardboard Cups & Plates
Stationery Suppliers
Tannoy Systems
Injury Supports
Agencies – Sponsorship
Mail-Shot Companies
Tactics' Aids (Tactixboard)
Compost & Fertiliser Cos
Commercial Radio Stations

Medical Supplies
Kit Supplies
Rugby Balls
Programme Clubs
Trophies
Computers for Administration
Software for Administration
Coach Companies
Hotel Groups
All Weather Facilities
Tour Operators
Photographers
Rugby Publications
Minibar Suppliers
Ground Surrounds
Pitch Surrounds
Portable Seating
Seats for Stands
Club Ties
Club Blazers
Blazer Badges
Track Suits
Fast Food Supplies
Gifts for Club Shops
Ground Maintenance
Video Services
Sports Rubs & Medication
Stopwatches
Marking Liquids
D-Icers
Leisure Clothing Manufacturers

To book your half page advertisement (similar to those on the next two pages) please contact – The Advertising Executive at Tony Williams Publications, FREEPOST, Taunton, TA3 6BR or make contact through the telephone on 01823 490080 or Fax 01823 490281.

Rotherham captain Kevin Plant proudly hoists the Yorkshire Cup having beaten Harrogate 39-6 in the Final at Kirkstall.

This is the first time Rotherham have won the Yorkshire Cup, and was a fitting conclusion to their most successful season – becoming Courage League Four Champions, and winning promotion.

Also in the picture are (right) Derek Bradburn President of Yorkshire RFU, and (left) flanker Craig West and RAF scrum-half Steve Worrall.   *Photo: Gordon Bunney*

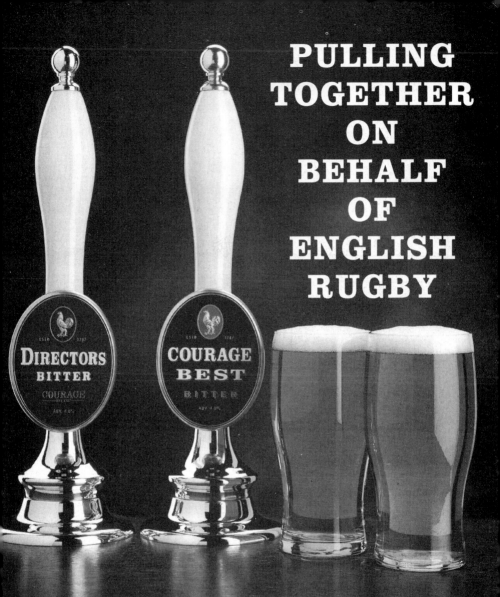

PULLING TOGETHER ON BEHALF OF ENGLISH RUGBY

Proud Sponsors of The Courage Clubs Championship and the England Squad

Kevin Oliphant makes a West Hartlepool mark but waits anxiously for the onslaught.

Photo: Joe McCabe

Make sure you Order your copy
of
THE COURAGE CLUBS CHAMPIONSHIP
OFFICIAL
RUGBY UNION
CLUB DIRECTORY 1996-97

Any orders received for the 1996-97 edition before 1st August, 1996, with a coupon from the corner of this page attached, will be honoured at this years price of £13.99.

Mail orders received in this way will also be sent post and package free and will be posted in the first week of September, 1996.

Please send your orders to: Football Directories, FREEPOST, Taunton, TA3 6LE – with cheques made payable to Tony Williams Publications.

Thank you.

Courage
Rugby
Directory
1996-97

The Perfect Present for a Rugby Enthusiast

In every Rugby Union Club (even those who only turn out one team) there will be at least ten rugby enthusiasts amongst their players, parents, girlfriends, wives, supporters, administrators, social members and local referees who will derive hours of enjoyment from the Courage Club Directory.

As you will see from the discounts listed below.

An order of 10 books only costs £70 and if you sell them at £13.99 they would make you £69.90 profit (£139.90-£70.00).

Many clubs are now raffling a Directory at home Courage League games and only 14 x 50p tickets have to be sold before a profit is made. A full bar before or after the game should make a club between £20.00-£70.00 from each raffle.

If the Directory is shown by the raffle ticket sellers and it is announced (in the programme and over the loud speaker) that the book is available on sale (in the shop/behind the bar etc.) for those who do not win the raffle, then the books will sell out very quickly.

DISCOUNT PRICES

For orders of 1 to 2 copies £13.99 each   For orders of between 6-9 copies £9.99 each
For orders of 3-5 copies £11.99 each   For orders of 10 and over £7.00 each
Please send cheques made out to **Tony Williams Publications**
to Football Directories, FREEPOST, Taunton, TA3 6LE

Orders can also be made over the telephone by credit card or by sending in your credit card number, its expiry date and your name and address.

For this Directory to continue to expand and for us to be able to give more space to clubs in the four Regional Divisions, as well as the National leagues we must make sure more people know about the book.

All orders will help us develop the Directory in the future.

Thank you

Tony Williams
Publisher/Editor